Ecology and Management
of the
WOOD DUCK

Supplementing this book is a companion volume, *The Unique Wood Duck*, by Richard E. McCabe, produced by the Wildlife Management Institute and published by Stackpole Books. *The Unique Wood Duck* is a 136-page, full-color "field trip" with Frank Bellrose and wildlife photographer Scott Nielsen. Copies of this companion book are available for $24.95 each from Stackpole Books, 5067 Ritter Road, Mechanicsburg, Pennsylvania 17055 or call 1-800-732-3669.

Ecology and Management of the

WOOD DUCK

by
Frank C. Bellrose and Daniel J. Holm

Artwork by
Francis E. Sweet

Technical editors
Glen C. Sanderson, Richard E. McCabe, and Audrey Hodgins

A WILDLIFE MANAGEMENT INSTITUTE BOOK
produced and published in cooperation with the
Illinois Natural History Survey

Published by Stackpole Books, Mechanicsburg, Pennsylvania
1994

The *WILDLIFE MANAGEMENT INSTITUTE* is a private, nonprofit, scientific and educational organization based in Washington, D.C. The Institute's sole objective, since its founding in 1911, has been to help advance restoration and proper management of North America's natural resources, especially wildlife. As a part of the Institute's program, scientific information generated through research and management experiences is consolidated, published, and used to improve understanding and to strengthen decision-making and resource management. *Ecology and Management of the Wood Duck* is one of more than twenty-five wildlife books produced by WMI, including the award-winning *Ducks, Geese and Swans of North America, Big Game of North America, Mule and Black-tailed Deer of North America, Elk of North America, White-tailed Deer, Ecology and Management of the Mourning Dove,* and *The Unique Wood Duck*. For additional information about the Institute, its programs and publications, write to: Wildlife Management Institute, Suite 801, 1101 Fourteenth Street, N.W., Washington, D.C. 20005.

Copyright © 1994 by the **Wildlife Management Institute**

Published by STACKPOLE BOOKS
5067 Ritter Road
Mechanicsburg, Pennsylvania 17055

Design and layout by REM/WMI

Printed in the U.S.A.

10 9 8 7 6 5 4 3 2 1

First edition

Library of Congress Cataloging-in-Publication Data

Bellrose, Frank Chapman, 1916–
    Ecology and management of the wood duck / by Frank C. Bellrose and
Daniel J. Holm ; artwork by Francis E. Sweet. – 1st ed.
       p.   cm.
    "A Wildlife Management Institute book."
    Includes bibliographical references and index.
    ISBN 0-8117-0605-2
    1. Wood duck–North America. 2. Waterfowl management–North
America. I. Holm, Daniel J. II. Wildlife Management Institute.
III. Title.
QL696.A52B45   1994
598.4'1–dc20   93-30746
                                                          CIP

This book is dedicated to Arthur S. Hawkins, U.S. Fish and Wildlife Service (retired), for a lifetime of devoted contribution to better waterfowl management.

Foreword

The science of wildlife ecology is more than research. It also is more than on-the-ground management and fieldwork. And it is more than politics and administration. At its best, wildlife ecology is a carefully orchestrated blend of all three. At its heart are individuals who, by inclination, training, and experience, are motivated to perpetuate the natural rhythms, order, and beauty of the environment. They are individuals of dedication, sacrifice, and inspiration, for whom wildlife ecology and a cleaner, greener landscape are not merely the toil of vocation but compelling, personal avocations. Two such individuals are Frank C. Bellrose and Daniel J. Holm. So, too, are the gentlemen who share in the fashioning of this ternary Foreword. They are friends and colleagues. All are retired from distinguished and influential professional careers as wildlife biologists. One was principally a manager, one primarily a researcher, and one primarily an administrator. None is retired from the science of wildlife ecology.

Arthur S. Hawkins

If ducks could hold a contest to decide which human was their greatest benefactor during the past half century, Frank Bellrose most likely would win. Frank deserves such tribute for many reasons, particularly his relentless quest to preserve and enhance waterfowl habitat. Through his writings, speeches, testimony at hearings, and persuasiveness, Frank has spread the message from coast to coast about the critical relationship between ducks and their habitat. No one in the wildlife management profession or anyone else concerned about ducks is better known or more highly respected than Frank Bellrose.

Early in his career, Frank observed that ducks by the hundreds died horribly from lead poisoning after picking up spent shot while feeding in heavily hunted marshes. He resolved to do something about this sad situation. It took years of research and salesmanship before he and coworkers could convince the authorities and industry that lead poisoning was a preventable waste. Present legislation, which requires U.S. waterfowl hunters to use nontoxic shot, confirms that his insight and persistence finally paid off.

Always fascinated by when, where, how, and why ducks migrated, and dissatisfied with the limitations of banding data, Frank pioneered in the use of high-tech methods to gain further insight into the mysteries of waterfowl migration.

Perhaps his greatest single accomplishment was publication of *Ducks, Geese and Swans of North America*, second and third editions, regarded by many as the definitive reference on the identification, distribution, abundance, and habits of waterfowl. But for all Frank's other interests, one species—the wood duck—held center stage throughout his career. This book is the culmination of that lifelong fascination.

Frank's boyhood environment was conducive to the career he later followed. He grew up in Ottawa, a town along the Illinois River, one of North America's foremost duck migration routes. With its combination of rich bottomland lakes adjacent to wooded uplands, the Illinois River Valley was a prime nesting area for wood ducks. It was a great place to live for someone interested in birds, as Frank was, and he made good use of his background.

The Illinois River was undergoing drastic changes when Frank arrived on the scene. Early in this century, a diversion canal from Lake Michigan was used to flush Chicago's sewage down the river. Later, levees were built and drainage systems installed along the river to convert many bottomland lakes into agricultural cropland. Dam building along the river changed the pattern of flooding and drying out so important in maintaining the richness of the bottomlands for wildlife. Frank saw these things happening firsthand. He has spent his entire career trying to understand the consequences of these changes and seeking measures to compensate for them. His many publications show that his efforts have been highly successful.

One late summer in 1934, while paddling his canoe on the filling Starved Rock Pool created by a new dam on the Illinois River near Ottawa, Frank had his first close experience with wood ducks. Thirty to 40 woodies, in various stages of eclipse plumage, were swimming about along the banks and among shoreline emergents. Where these attractive birds had come from and why they were there at that time were questions Frank couldn't answer. The happenstance encounter was the beginning of his special love affair with woodies and the genesis of a careerlong probe of the many mysteries of this fascinating species.

Frank's formal training in scientific methods came during the period 1934–1937, at the University of Illinois under the guidance of S. Charles Kendeigh and Victor E. Shelford, pioneers in a comparatively new discipline called "ecology."

Frank and I met for the first time in December 1935 at the "First North Central States Fish and Game Conference," as it was called then—a conference that had a major impact on both our lives. The host and convener was T. H. Frison, Chief of the Illinois Natural History Survey, who would become our boss two years later. I was a University of Wisconsin graduate student of Aldo Leopold at the time. As students, we were somewhat awed by those in attendance at the conference; they represented a veritable Who's Who of the day in the new field of game management. A boat trip on the Illinois River following the conference provided an opportunity for students to rub elbows with many of those dignitaries. Frank recalls discussing prairie chickens with the venerated Leopold. We both remember "Ding" Darling's fiery keynote address at the conference and were inspired by it. Frank decided then and there that wildlife management was the field he would follow as a career. Darling had bemoaned the lack of information for proper management of the troubled continental duck population, and we both took the tip.

Frank and I joined the Illinois Natural History Survey in 1938, in the new two-man section of Wildlife Experiment Areas. Our first station was at Brussels, near the confluence of the Illinois and Mississippi rivers, but we soon decided that Havana was a better base for the waterfowl studies we intended to conduct. During a preliminary reconnaissance of the Havana area, Frank had initiated a study of wood ducks nesting in natural cavities. At nearby Chautauqua National Wildlife Refuge, manager Gil Gigstad and maintenance man Milford Smith had used a public works project to construct boxes for wood ducks out of heavy oak slabs and place them in trees. A check of these crude boxes confirmed that wood ducks would use them. Frank and I decided to try the box approach on a larger scale. Frank applied the information gained from natural cavities and the slab boxes to design a box made of boards—a design still in use today, with only slight modifications.

Frank's studies of wood duck use of nesting cavities, including artificial houses or boxes, were not without some peril. By the late 1930s, Frank

had been nipped often enough by fox squirrels when he reached into cavities to feel about to count woodie eggs that he was cautious when approaching known or potential nesting cavities. Yet on one occasion when he attempted to investigate a wood duck nest in a slab house, Frank let his guard down. As he approached the house, a hen woodie flushed from the opening. This signaled limited need for caution. But as Frank was groping for eggs—his arm inside the opening nearly to the elbow—a bull snake slithered out on his arm. Startled, Frank jerked his arm out and fell back. That might have been fine, except that the slab box, the snake, and Frank were a good 10 feet off the ground. And when Frank fell, so did the snake. Frank vividly recalls looking up as he began his backward free fall and seeing the apparently aggressive and equally nonplussed serpent also plummeting, and such that it likely would land on him. Frank was so focused on the snake that when he landed flat on his back in a dirt road, he was unhurt. The bull snake hit the ground next to Frank, and at least one of the two was greatly relieved to have the episode concluded. Tragedy averted, the humor of the event was not lost on Frank. Typically, however, in the telling, Frank highlights science rather than mishap. He and his assistant found that, in fact, there had been two bull snakes in the nest house. He had flushed the hen when it had been in the house apparently defending its eggs against the two predators. The hen's tenacity and snakes' persistence were equaled only by Frank's resilience.

Our duck studies, starting out as a two-man operation, soon involved many others, both within the Natural History Survey and along the Illinois and Mississippi rivers. Our chief, Dr. Frison, an aquatic insect specialist by training but also an excellent administrator, soon saw that our studies were filling a gap and gave us his support. At first, since we were bachelors and on the move much of the time, Frank and I rented rooms at the Windsor Hotel in Havana at $1 per night (there were no motels at that time). It was inconvenient moving all our equipment each day from hotel room to our car, so Dr. Frison arranged for us to live on the Survey's floating lab, the *Anax*, which was moored at the coal-loading dock in Havana. I still recall the clanging and banging of the bunks that hung by chains from the ceiling every time a tow of barges passed by. But still it was inconvenient carrying our equipment between boat and car. And as our need for storage space grew, it became evident that we needed a better home base. This problem was solved in 1939, when the Survey arranged a long-term lease for land on the Chautauqua National

Wildlife Refuge and built a well-equipped and spacious laboratory, with living accommodations for field personnel. This lab, now much modified and named the Stephen A. Forbes Biological Station, celebrated its fiftieth anniversary on May 5, 1989.

Frank had then, as now, a special gift for making friends easily. He soon had cooperators glad to help in any way they could along both the Illinois and Mississippi rivers. This cooperative network included commercial fishermen, hunting guides, duck club owners and caretakers, refuge personnel, game wardens, and even poachers, all of whom spent much time along the rivers and were good observers. One fisherman/poacher friend explained to Frank that young wood ducks in the "flapper" stage were fine eating. He and others liked to bag a fine woodie while tending their nets. The birds would be hidden in a sack of grapes in case a game warden happened by.

One encounter with poachers, however, was less than friendly. Frank and I were observing the opening of the 1939 duck season from the high Santa Fe bridge over the Illinois River at Chillicothe. We had an excellent view of the bottomlands below. Wood ducks were protected, as they had been for many years, so when we saw a hunter drop a woodie, we became concerned. After several more wood ducks were shot, Frank's mortification was upgraded to rage. Without benefit of boots, we waded out and confronted the hunters, with Frank in the lead. We made a citizen's arrest, since we lacked enforcement authority. The hunters claimed that they were novices, unaware that the birds they were shooting were protected, but their equipment and the skillful way in which the birds had been staked out as decoys belied their claim of innocence. Information obtained from the hunting licenses of the violators was turned over to a federal agent, who subsequently obtained convictions. We were informed that the violators were well-known gangsters from Cicero, Illinois. Hearing of the incident, Dr. Frison informed us in clear terms that we were researchers—out there to determine and record what was happening, good or bad—not enforcement officers. Thereafter, we were more discreet in the way we handled illegal situations, which were not at all uncommon at that time.

Aldo Leopold was very supportive of our studies. He insisted that we visit his family home at Burlington, Iowa, and meet his brother Frederic. With Frederic's help, we established a unit of nesting boxes at Crystal Lake Club across the Mississippi River from Burlington, where Aldo used to hunt and Frederic was a member. While we were talking to Fred in his yard high above the river one morning, a pair of wood ducks landed in a tree above us. Fred decided to put three boxes in his yard—the beginning of his half century of involvement in wood duck studies, lasting until his death in 1989. During that period, his boxes turned out more than 5,000 woodie ducklings from 500 successful nestings, most of which were carefully monitored by Frederic. It was fitting that the second North American Wood Duck Symposium held in 1988 was "dedicated to three individuals who symbolize efforts to conserve and manage the wood duck." They were Frank Bellrose, Frederic Leopold, and David Grice of Massachusetts.

A century ago, writers reported that the status of wood ducks was extremely precarious; some even claimed that these birds were on the verge of extinction. Overshooting was regarded as the main reason, and the first federal laws gave the woodie complete protection. Fifty years ago the ban was lifted, but only to the extent of permitting a single bird in the bag. And the remarkable comeback continued. In recent years, only the mallard surpasses the wood duck in numbers taken by hunters of the two eastern flyways. Perhaps even more spectacular has been the growing popularity of woodies among people who study them or who simply enjoy having them around. This trend is evidenced by the huge number of boxes being erected to benefit these colorful birds, and by such gatherings as the aforementioned symposium, involving 300 people from 31 states and Canada, at which 77 authors presented papers on the wood duck and its management.

Frank's experience with wood ducks spans most of this period of remarkable change. Nearly 60 years have passed since his chance encounter with wood ducks on Starved Rock Pool. One might wonder why anyone with Frank's proven talents in so many areas would devote so much of his energy to a single species. One practical reason is that anyone wishing to study ducks, including nesting, in Illinois, has no other choice, because only the wood duck nests there in significant numbers. A second reason might be that, among ducks, none is more interesting than the woodie, from both scientific and aesthetic viewpoints, and many of Frank's observations were previously unrecorded. Third, any intensive study of a single species and its habitat sheds light on management in general. This book makes that clear.

For stimulating the interest of both hunters and nonhunters and gaining their support on a wide range of wildlife conservation issues, the wood duck has few rivals. Frank understood these facts, and this book will be lasting testimony to that foresight.

Glen C. Sanderson

I first met Frank Bellrose in June 1947 at the Delta Waterfowl Research Station in Delta, Manitoba. Frank's formidable scientific reputation was well established by then and well known to me, a candidate for a Master's degree at the University of Missouri. After four years in the Army and one term back at the University to complete a Bachelor's degree in wildlife, I accepted an offer of transportation and lodging (but no salary) to spend the summer of '47 at Delta, as Dr. William H. Elder's assistant. There I met Frank (and Art Hawkins), even though he spent only a few days at the Delta station before going about his fieldwork for the summer.

I kept track of Frank for the next eight years through his publications and by seeing him at Midwest Wildlife Conferences. Our paths merged in 1955 when I joined the staff of the Section of Game Management at the Illinois Natural History Survey and became Frank's coworker. Soon I was working on raccoons and able to provide funds for a graduate student (Ken Johnson) at Western Illinois University to work on raccoon/wood duck relationships in the Havana area under Frank's direction. At that time, my primary research interest, the raccoon, was the number-one nemesis of Frank's primary research interest, the wood duck.

Despite our divergent biases, and the fact that Havana, where Frank was (and is) located, is 100 miles from my headquarters in Champaign, we remained friends and continued to work together. Our paths became even more closely entwined early in 1964, when I became Head of the Section of Wildlife Research at the Survey. Thus, I was Frank's supervisor—at least by title.

Shortly thereafter, I became deeply involved in studying the plight of the greater prairie chicken, which was about to disappear from Illinois and several other midwestern states. Frank always has had an abiding concern for conservation matters beyond those of his research scope. He suggested that we visit some of the individuals in duck clubs along the Illinois River and his other duck hunting friends to drum up support for saving the prairie chicken. As a result of these contacts, the Prairie Grouse Committee of the Illinois Chapter of the Nature Conservancy was formed. This group raised money and acquired land for prairie chicken nest sanctuaries and was primarily responsible for the greater prairie chicken's continued survival in Illinois. In commenting to Frank on the time and effort we spent on this project, I suggested that our efforts to save land for conservation purposes (in this instance, for the greater prairie chicken) in

Illinois probably have been of more lasting significance than our research contributions. Time will provide the ultimate answer to that opinion.

In 1968, Frank suggested to C. R. "Pink" Gutermuth of the Wildlife Management Institute that WMI's 1942 book, *Ducks, Geese and Swans of North America* by Francis Kortright, ought to be revised. Pink agreed and asked Frank to undertake the task. Frank accepted, but not to a relatively minor revision and updating as Pink proposed, but to a complete rewrite of the book. After struggling with the project for a few months on his own time, Frank approached me for permission to work on the book as part of his official duties. I agreed, and our lives became even more closely linked.

For many months, Helen Schultz, editorial assistant in the Section of Wildlife Research, and I agonized with Frank and WMI over the manuscript. Art Hawkins also was involved, urging Frank to make the text "warmer" and more readable. Although I agreed that Art's suggestion was a good one, it was virtually impossible to accomplish with the book as planned. Frank was concerned about criticism of the writing. I assured him that no one other than Helen Schultz and I would read the text from cover to cover—and we each had already done that several times! The material in the text, I believed, would stimulate the reader. As it turned out, I was wrong that no one would read the book from cover to cover. A number of readers reported that they had done exactly that.

Instead of relaxing when the new edition of *Ducks, Geese and Swans* was in print, Frank told me that he had two projects he wished to complete before he retired: a book on the waterfowl of Illinois and a book on his 50 years of study on the wood duck. He tentatively planned to work on the waterfowl of Illinois manuscript first. After our long struggle with *Ducks, Geese and Swans*, I wondered if Frank would have enough energy and time to complete both projects. I suggested that persons other than Frank could do a better job on the waterfowl of Illinois than they could on a wood duck monograph, which would include much of Frank's own research results. Frank readily agreed and the wood duck book became his top priority.

It has been a long effort, with some of the same types of problems attendant to the redo of *Ducks, Geese and Swans* plus a variety of new complications and intrigues. One great advantage was that, in the interim between the two books, word processing came into its own. The countless hours spent proofreading and correcting draft manuscripts for *Ducks, Geese and Swans* were greatly reduced for this wood duck volume. At the same time, however, the computer software used to prepare the manuscript at Havana was different from that used by me in Champaign. And both were different from that used by WMI. This resulted in a series of minor but time-consuming problems.

Frank was fortunate to find Dan Holm, a graduate student at Western Illinois University, who did a Master's degree on the wood duck. Dan was hired to tabulate data and enter the manuscript in a word processor. Frank's fortunes doubled when he learned that Dan, in addition to possessing great enthusiasm and familiarity with the subject matter and with the vagaries of word processing, also was a skillful writer. Dan worked with Frank on all chapters and wrote the initial drafts of a number of them. He also produced most of the final figures for this work. Sometimes there was money to pay Dan (certainly much less than he was worth) and sometimes he worked on the book without salary—a sterling measure of his devotion to science, to wood ducks, to the assignment, and to Frank.

Frank has remained concerned that the text of this book is not "warm" enough, and I continue to insist that the content will be sufficient to keep the reader's interest and that few people, if any, will read the book from cover to cover. However, based on our previous experience, I may be wrong . . . again . . . on the latter point.

Frank semiretired from the Illinois Natural History Survey at the end of August 1982 but continued to work full-time on partial salary until February 1991, when he retired after 53 years of employment with the Survey. Even after his second retirement, Frank continued to devote all his time and energy to the wood duck book. When I retired at the end of September 1990, Frank expressed great relief at my promise that, as friend, nagger, and counselor, I would continue to work with him and Dan to see the book to completion. I even persuaded my wife to do some illustrations for the book to speed the process.

This volume is a fitting capstone to Frank Bellrose's 53-year distinguished career in waterfowl research and conservation with the Illinois Natural History Survey. It is a well-earned cornerstone for Dan Holm's very promising career. As their friend and associate, I am pleased to have had a role in this important contribution to wildlife literature in general and to the science and management of wood ducks in particular.

Laurence R. Jahn

For some people, no horizon, whatever its twilight hues, is wholly breathtaking if it does not include waterfowl on the wing, or at least a high likelihood of seeing them. Kaleidoscopic panoramas provide considerable beauty, but without actual or potential flights of waterfowl, those vistas are not Nature's finest.

Anyone fascinated by wild things and places is certain to be mesmerized and somehow invigorated by the mere view of ducks playing tag with a skyline, of geese careening against a sharp headwind, or of swans in pinkish white synchrony overhead. Surely impoverished are those individuals not drawn to pause at such sights.

Observing waterfowl on a local horizon is much different than visualizing the international horizons of waterfowl. The latter—an expansive network of migration corridors and seasonal habitats—now is the realm of a few, a very few individuals. And perhaps foremost among them is Frank Bellrose.

Waterfowl management originated in the early 1900s, and the science of waterfowl ecology followed in the 1930s. The period since (1930s–1990s) of about 60 years is paralleled by Frank's professional career. His research, writings, and enthusiasm have helped waterfowl ecology and management in North America achieve much higher planes than would otherwise have been the case.

Nevertheless, by the 1980s and early 1990s, populations of many duck species (particularly some dabbling ducks) had declined. Prolonged drought and intensive agricultural uses of North America's prairie and parkland breeding grounds prevented duck populations from recovering. But without the insights, foresight, and voices of such rare men as John C. Phillips, Frederick Lincoln, Alexander Wetmore, Aldo Leopold, Clarence Cottam, Hoyes Lloyd, "Ding" Darling, Ira Gabrielson, J. Clark Salyer, Francis Uhler, H. Albert Hochbaum, Frank Bellrose, and a very few others, the ecological collision of civilization and waterfowl would have been much more severe. And the likelihood *and* opportunity for waterfowl population recoveries would have been less.

By the time I first met Frank Bellrose, in the late 1940s, he already had carved an important niche in waterfowl science, yet his contributions and legend were just beginning.

On a field trip Frank and I shared with others in the early 1950s to midcontinent and southern waterfowl habitats, I found in my gentle and genial companion a person who looked in detail yet perceived in broad horizons. Each important site and each duck we saw elicited from Frank careful scrutiny and a measure of poorly veiled excitement. And so it has been ever since. Waterfowl—ducks especially and wood ducks in particular—are Frank's intrigue and his passion. To this day, he cannot watch these birds at a marsh or discuss them in skyless meeting rooms without revealing his curiosity and infectious enthusiasm as vividly as when those traits became obvious to me 40-some years ago.

In subsequent decades, results from Frank's work have helped provide dimension, scope, and standards for assessing waterfowl populations, managing their seasonal habitats and harvests, and perpetuating their seasonal flights. Virtually every species of waterfowl in North America has benefited in one way or another from Frank's dedication to wildlife science. But the continent's most colorful species, *Aix sponsa*, the wood duck, has received his special attention, inquiry, and wisdom. And it now thrives, recovered from turn-of-the-century forecast levels of extermination, to be the foremost breeding waterfowl species in the United States east of the Mississippi River.

Whether scarce or present in rebounded abundance, the woodie is a prize to all who witness its spectacular beauty and unique behavior. That many people can share in this prize far into the future is a tribute to a rare individual, Frank C.

Bellrose. As biologist and visionary, his career has been spent in wetlands and laboratories, fashioning finer horizons for waterfowl and those who thrill to them.

Through his informative publications, Frank has demonstrated that an individual can improve his or her understanding of broad geographic areas and ecological relationships. This is the potential next step in expanding benefits from pursuing waterfowl, whether for hunting or observation. People must come to understand that many waterfowl seen at one place in one season depend on habitats elsewhere at other seasons. For example, some wood ducks observed wintering in South Carolina or Louisiana will occupy breeding habitats in northern states next spring.

Having people respect and enjoy waterfowl is essential. Having them extend that respect and stewardship to all seasonal habitats required to perpetuate waterfowl populations is the challenge for the balance of the 1990s and the next century. In this book, Frank Bellrose and Dan Holm have provided the insights to permit more of us the opportunity to participate more effectively.

Preface

The wood duck has made an astounding comeback from precarious population levels that prevailed during the early 1900s to become the third-ranking species (behind the mallard and green-winged teal) in the harvest of United States hunters. In the Atlantic and Mississippi flyways it is second to the mallard, and in several states it is the number-one duck in the bag.

Because of the wood duck's beauty, unique habits, and local breeding importance in the United States east of the Great Plains, many people from all walks of life have become interested in the species. Countless hours of pleasure have rewarded people who have been fortunate to have a pair or more nesting in their yards. Anecdotes from many of these chair-side observers have contributed to heightened awareness of the wood duck's infinite individual variations of behavior. In response to danger, environmental stimuli, or food choices, woodie behaviors are anything but stereotyped.

When Arthur Hawkins and I began studying nesting wood ducks in the spring of 1938, we found a large population in the Illinois River Valley—evidence that the closed season initiated in 1918 had already paid dividends. At that time, meaningful information on management of wood ducks was scant, even though the trail of knowledge about it had started in 1731 with Mark Catesby's *Natural History of Carolina, Florida, and the Bahama Islands*. Further knowledge about wood ducks resulted from early observations published in Alexander Wilson's *American Ornithology* (1828).

Pioneering ornithologists and aviculturists added bits and pieces about the biology and status of the wood duck in the late 19th and early 20th centuries. This information was ably summarized in 1923 by Arthur Cleveland Bent in his *Life Histories of North American Wild Fowl*. But not until 1924 did a meaningful life history study appear, *Nesting of the Wood Duck in California*, by Joseph Dixon. Edward Howe Forbush added his own observations and those of other ornithologists in discussing the wood duck in his 1924 opus *Birds of Massachusetts and Other New England States*. As waterfowler, ornithologist, and aviculturist, John C. Phillips gained much knowledge on the wood duck—his "Carolina duck"—which he included in his epic tome *A Natural History of the Ducks* (1925).

The wildlife profession developed in the mid-1930s, and research on waterfowl and other game species began to take on a new perspective. After World War II, scores of wildlife biologists began studying various aspects of wood duck biology and management, greatly expanding the scope of our initial studies. Because of several hundred technical bulletins, journal papers, and reports that have been published on wood ducks in the ensuing years, we now have an abundance of information on the species.

To appreciate how rapidly knowledge on the wood duck has progressed, one has only to examine the contents of the two symposia held on wood duck biology and management—December 8-9, 1965, and February 20-21, 1988. The first symposium proceedings consisted of 23 papers embracing 197 pages; the second featured 51 papers containing 385 pages.

Data seldom are interesting, but they are a necessary part of documented knowledge. For facts to be accepted, they must be supported by adequate findings and, as so often is the case in wildlife, data are neither black nor white but fall in gray areas where only an abundance of numerical findings evaluated statistically are meaningful. For this reason, we have tried to support our discussion of wood duck activities with substantive data fully cognizant of the resulting dullness.

On the other hand we—Dan Holm, Glen Sanderson, Audrey Hodgins, Dick McCabe, and I—have struggled to make this book as lucid as our individual skills permit. We have attempted to use nontechnical language as much as possible and provide a glossary for the limited "professional" words used—terms so specialized in meaning that a number of customary words would be required to define their substance. The objective of this book is to inform the wildlife manager, researcher, administrator, educator, and the dedicated hunter, bird watcher, and other conservationists—students all—about the welfare of the wood duck.

Approximately a decade of effort went into the preparation of this book. Without Dan Holm's collaboration, it would have taken me *at least* four additional years. Many others, dating back to 1977, helped collate and analyze data by calculator. Only banding data were analyzed by computer: David L. Swofford for migration and Richard Kasul for population survival. To them and to the scores who contributed and are recognized in the Acknowledgments, I am most grateful for their help in furthering understanding of the wood duck.

Frank C. Bellrose

Acknowledgments

This book materialized only because scores of people contributed to it. The assistance came in many different forms: financial support, editing, illustrating, data tabulation, statistical evaluation, behavioral observations, nest histories and house use, banding, analysis of band data, reference search, photo documentation, word processing, and many other logistical and informational services difficult to categorize but essential to the final product.

As Director of the Center for Wildlife Ecology of the Illinois Natural History Survey during the preparation of this book, Glen C. Sanderson contributed greatly to its development from beginning to end. He assisted in securing funds, provided information on raccoon and beaver numbers, edited the first drafts of every chapter, induced his wife Beverley to contribute several line drawings, transferred the text and tables from WordStar to WordPerfect to conform with the Wildlife Management Institute's word-processing equipment, and pressed us to complete the project in less than a lifetime.

Other editorial improvements in the text accrued because Audrey Hodgins of the Survey and Richard E. McCabe of WMI spent hundreds of hours of the most intense concentration to uncover errors and improve syntax.

Working closely with Glen, Audrey, and Dick, we have gained the utmost respect for their talents and their dedication toward making this a better book.

Experts on various aspects of avian biology reviewed early drafts of certain chapters: chapters 1 and 5—Henry M. Reeves, U.S. Fish and Wildlife Service (retired); Chapter 6—Scott K. Robinson, Illinois Natural History Survey; Chapter 10—Douglas H. Johnson, U.S. Fish and Wildlife Service, and Jeffrey D. Brawn, Illinois Natural History Survey; Chapter 13—Kenneth C. Parkes, Carnegie Museum, Milton W. Weller, Texas A & M University, Richard M. Kaminski, Mississippi State University, and Scott K. Robinson; chapters 18 and 20—Arthur S. Hawkins, U.S. Fish and Wildlife Service (retired), and R. Gary Hepp, Auburn University. The text benefited greatly from their suggestions and criticisms. However, we did not always adhere to their advice, so we accept full responsibility for any shortcomings of these and other chapters.

While a graduate student at Louisiana State University, Richard Kasul, currently of the U.S. Army Corps of Engineers, Waterways Experiment Station, Vicksburg, Mississippi, commenced analysis of band recovery rates pertaining to wood duck survival. When employed by the Corps, he continued the analysis at home. Richard is co-author of Chapter 18.

David L. Swofford, Illinois Natural History Survey, analyzed computer tapes provided by the Bird Banding Laboratory of the U.S. Fish and Wildlife Service for migration data as disclosed by band recoveries of wood ducks. We thank the Bird Banding Laboratory for making the banding tapes available to us for analyses of survival, recovery rates, migration chronology, and distribution. We are most grateful to the many biologists who banded 445,000 wood ducks at national wildlife refuges and state wildlife areas.

Carla Heister and Monica Lusk, librarians for the Survey, always graciously located difficult references and arranged for interlibrary loans of these and other materials; their help was invaluable. Jeffrey D. Brawn prepared the definitions of statistical symbols.

Among the scores of observers who provided unpublished information on the wood duck, we want to single out a few of the people outside the wildlife profession who made important contributions. Notable were Robert Ingstad, Valley City, North Dakota; Ray Cunningham, St. Paul, Minnesota; Don Helmeke, Maple Grove, Minnesota; and Frederic Leopold (deceased), Burlington, Iowa. In addition, Delbert Koke of Oquawka, Illinois, had recorded the calls of incubating wood ducks and pipping eggs before we met him. He placed radio receivers in six nest houses to determine when the broods would depart. Delbert also monitored the weights of ducks during laying and incubation and recorded the temporal activities at nest sites. We also must recognize Glen Welp. As a maintenance employee at Union Slough National Wildlife Refuge, Algona, Iowa, Glen built and erected innovative nest houses that resulted in the establishment of a thriving breeding population, which he closely monitored each year, 1966-91. Secretary Barbara Meyer helped keep meticulous records of Glen's house inspections. Also, Glen Kruse collated data at Forbes Station. Kevin Anderson, Harold Henderson, and Katherine Archer were especially helpful in initiating analyses of nest data, 1977–78. They made an unusually significant contribution in a brief time.

Wildlife biologists who made important contributions include:

Hugh Bateman, Louisiana Wildlife and Fisheries Commission
Karl Bednarik (retired), Ohio Department of Natural Resources
James Bartonek, U.S. Fish and Wildlife Service
Sam Carney (retired), U.S. Fish and Wildlife Service
Robert Eng, Montana State University
Kenneth Gamble, U.S. Fish and Wildlife Service
Arthur S. Hawkins (retired), U.S. Fish and Wildlife Service
James L. Hansen (formerly), Iowa Conservation Commission
William G. Minser, University of Tennessee
Robert Montgomery, Max McGraw Wildlife Foundation
Tim Moser (formerly), Indiana Department of Natural Resources
Fred Roetker, U.S. Fish and Wildlife Service
Paul Springer (retired), U.S. Fish and Wildlife Service
Dennis Thornburg, Illinois Department of Conservation
Harriet Wedger, Missouri Department of Conservation
Vernon Wright, Louisiana State University

The staff of the Chautauqua National Wildlife Refuge, especially William Watts, contributed data on wood duck nest house use and nest success. The long-term data and location adjacent to our Quiver Creek study area made their findings especially important. Fred Roetker helped check nest houses and band wood ducks at Nauvoo Slough, 1984.

In 1982 and subsequently, waterfowl biologists in each state and Canadian province, as well as certain biologists with the U.S. Fish and Wildlife Service, Canadian Wildlife Service, and Ducks Unlimited (Canada), were contacted for maps and descriptions of the relative wood duck breeding densities in their respective areas. We are grateful to the following cooperators for this detailed information:

Atlantic Flyway
Jerome R. Serie, U.S. Fish and Wildlife Service
Ian Goldie, Canadian Wildlife Service (Newfoundland)
Randy L. Dibblee, Prince Edward Island Department of the Environment
John C. Baird, New Brunswick Department of Natural Resources
Fred J. Payne, Nova Scotia Department of Lands and Forests
Austin Reed, Canadian Wildlife Service (Quebec)
Harry Lumsden, Ontario Ministry of Natural Resources
William R. Darby, Ontario Ministry of Natural Resources
Howard E. Spencer, Jr., Maine Department of Inland Fisheries and Wildlife
Harold C. Lacillade, New Hampshire Fish and Game Department
Thomas Myers, Vermont Department of Fish and Wildlife
H W Heusmann, Massachusetts Department of Fisheries, Wildlife and Environmental Law Enforcement
Tom Hoehn, Connecticut Department of Environmental Protection
James E. Meyers, Rhode Island Department of Environmental Management
Stephen Brown, New York Department of Environmental Conservation
Fred E. Hartman, Pennsylvania Game Commission
Fred Ferrigno, New Jersey Division of Fish, Game, and Wildlife
James M. Ruckel, West Virginia Division of Natural Resources
Larry J. Hindman, Maryland Department of Natural Resources
Charles P. Gilchrist, Jr., Virginia Department of Game and Inland Fisheries
Jack A. Donnelly, North Carolina Wildlife Resources Commission
Thomas Strange, South Carolina Wildlife and Marine Resources Department
Oscar Dewberry, Georgia Department of Natural Resources
Fred Johnson, Florida Game and Fresh Water Fish Commission
Frank Montalbano III, Florida Game and Fresh Water Fish Commission

Mississippi Flyway
Kenneth E. Gamble, U.S. Fish and Wildlife Service
Robert L. Jessen, Minnesota Department of Natural Resources
R. A. Hunt, Wisconsin Department of Natural Resources
Jerry Martz, Michigan Department of Natural Resources

Mark Hart, Michigan Department of Natural Resources

James L. Hansen, Iowa Conservation Commission

Dennis Thornburg, Illinois Department of Conservation

Tom Sporre, Indiana Department of Natural Resources

Karl Bednarik, Ohio Department of Natural Resources

David Graber, Missouri Department of Conservation

Dale D. Humburg, Missouri Department of Conservation

Vernon Anderson, Kentucky Department of Fish and Wildlife Resources

William G. Minser, University of Tennessee

Stephen Cottrell, Tennessee Valley Authority

James S. Walter, Arkansas Game and Fish Commission

Hugh Bateman, Louisiana Wildlife and Fisheries Commission

Richard K. Wells, Mississippi Department of Wildlife, Fisheries, and Parks

Keith D. Guyse, Alabama Department of Conservation and Natural Resources

Bruce C. Johnson, Alabama Department of Conservation and Natural Resources

Central Flyway

Wilbur N. Ladd, Jr., U.S. Fish and Wildlife Service

S. R. Barber, Saskatchewan Natural Resources

D. F. Hooey, Ducks Unlimited (Canada)

Elmer Mowbray, Jr., Ducks Unlimited (Canada)

Robert E. Jones, Manitoba Department of Natural Resources

Robert L. Eng, Montana State University

Don Childress, Montana Department of Fish, Wildlife, and Parks

Leonard Serdiuk, Wyoming Game and Fish Department

Terry McEneaney, U.S. National Park Service

Mike Johnson, North Dakota Game and Fish Department

Tom Kuck, South Dakota Department of Game, Fish and Parks

Lester D. Flake, South Dakota State University

Kenneth L. Johnson, Nebraska Game and Parks Commission

Joe Hylance, Nebraska Game and Parks Commission

Howard W. Funk, Colorado Division of Wildlife

Marvin J. Kraft, Kansas Department of Wildlife and Parks

Roger W. Tacha, U.S. Soil Conservation Service

Lem Due, Oklahoma Department of Wildlife Conservation

Charles Stutzenbaker, Texas Parks and Wildlife Department

Pacific Flyway

James G. Bartonek, U.S. Fish and Wildlife Service

W. T. Munro, British Columbia Ministry of Environment

Robert Jeffrey, Washington Department of Wildlife

Dick Norell, Idaho Fish and Game Department

Ralph Denney, Oregon Department of Fish and Wildlife

Watt Weber, Oregon Department of Fish and Wildlife

Dennis Woolington, Oregon Department of Fish and Wildlife

Fred Paveglio, U.S. Fish and Wildlife Service

Daniel Connelley, California Department of Fish and Game

Jack Helvie, U.S. Fish and Wildlife Service

Jessop Low (retired), Cooperative Wildlife Research Unit, Utah State University

Timothy Provan, Utah Division of Wildlife Resources

Tim Mitchesson, Cooperative Wildlife Research Unit, University of Arizona

John Taylor, U.S. Fish and Wildlife Service

We are indebted to the many investigators who contributed to the evaluation of wood duck nest houses and nest success on state and private areas scattered over much of the breeding range of the wood duck in the United States and Canada. These contributors are listed with their respective states in Appendix K.

We appreciate the National Wildlife Refuge System personnel who responded to our questionnaire on use and nest success of various types of nest houses and placement. These respondents are listed by refuge in appendices H and J.

Still others participated in evaluating wood duck nest houses, and we acknowledge their contributions: George Arthur, Ace Baxter, Lyle Bradley, Norman L. Brunswick, Richard Cullerton, William Keim, and Harvey Nelson.

We are grateful to Aleta Holt, Illinois Natural History Survey, for preparing maps showing the distribution of wood duck habitat, and to Beverley Sanderson for drawings of wood duck plumage topography and class development of ducklings. Bette Gutierrez of the Wildlife Management Institute provided valuable assistance in finalizing the book manuscript for press.

Several landowners along Quiver Creek permitted us to erect wood duck nest houses and have access to their property: Camille Cullinane Turk, the McHarry family, and Eldon Yetter.

Lee and Carmen Ourth permitted us to use their property as a base of operation for studying wood ducks at Nauvoo Slough.

Without financial assistance in the closing years of the wood duck study, this work would have been difficult to complete. Outside funding, for example, was used to employ the following part-time workers to collate data: Marie Ely, David Fisher, Glen Kruse, Greg Soulliere, Tamela Qualls, and Nanette Trudeau.

Donations were received from T. Stanton Armour, William T. Bacon, Jr., William Barnes III, Craig A. Buckingham, Clarissa H. and Henry T. Chandler, Charles F. Clarke, Jr., Sue and Wesley M. Dixon, Jr., Dorothy and Gaylord Donnelley, Ducks Unlimited, Inc., Jean C. Farwell, John K. Greene, Charles C. Haffner III, John H. Hobart, N. Landon Hoyt III, Max McGraw Wildlife Foundation, Kenneth Nebenzahl, Jay G. Neubauer, William L. Searle, Lawton L. Shurtleff, Henry M. Staley, Edmund Thornton, Waterfowl Research Foundation, and the Wildlife Management Institute. Also, the Illinois Department of Conservation contributed funds through P-R W-97-R-2, 1987–89, and provided the 80 nest house units erected on pipes at Nauvoo Slough, 1984.

Thousands of photo images were screened by Dick McCabe and the authors for supplemental use in this work. Among the many who generously lent slides or prints, we especially thank Jack Dermid, F. Eugene Hester, Scott Nielsen, David McEwen, and Stephen Kirkpatrick.

David A. Badger drew many of the migration graphs and the wood duck nest house.

For assistance in the production of this book, thanks to J. Richard King, Judith Schnell, David Uhler, and Mary McGinnis.

Finally, the authors and editors of this work wish to extend very special thanks to six individuals for particularly unselfish and valuable investments in the substance and quality of the book.

Eric Hopps of Bath, Illinois, recorded the calls of wood ducks and, with the help of Ronald Larkin, made audiospectrographs (sonograms) of the various calls. Eric contributed information on courtship behaviors, nocturnal roosts, and plumages, and he also counted, measured, and weighed the feathers on 10 wood ducks.

Stephen B. Simmons, California Waterfowl Association, provided exceptionally pertinent data on nesting and homing of wood ducks over a 19-year period.

At the waterfowl aviary in Hanna City, Illinois, **Bernard** and **Peter Van Norman** facilitated our studies of wood duck molting and plumage development. They also offered many pertinent observations on the behavior of captive birds.

As Dick McCabe's assistant at the Wildlife Management Institute, **Kelly Wadsworth** coordinated the frequent and complex refinements of the full manuscript's final drafts. She also assisted Dick with the layout and production proofs.

The artwork for this book was accomplished by internationally renowned wildlife artist **Francis E. Sweet** of Bowie, Maryland. To produce the illustrations for this work, Fran spent many hours studying the physiology, mannerisms, and habitat of the species. When particular behaviors, postures, or conditions could not otherwise be scrutinized clearly, Fran used as models images of woodies captured on film by Scott Nielsen. For this additional contribution, Scott is again acknowledged.

Even though, as we have found, many people are not devoted to the science and scientific management of wood ducks for the sake of personal recognition, we apologize to any contributor not mentioned and assure that such omission was inadvertent.

Contents

Foreword   vii
Preface   xiii
Acknowledgments   xv
List of Figures and Maps   xxi
List of Tables   xxvii

Chapter 1. Introducing the Wood Duck   1
Chapter 2. Distribution   15
Chapter 3. Habitat   37
Chapter 4. Migration   79
Chapter 5. Population Status   107
Chapter 6. Courtship and Mating System   123
Chapter 7. Natural Cavities   167
Chapter 8. Prebreeding and Breeding Behavior   185
Chapter 9. Physiology of Breeding and Wintering   201
Chapter 10. Nesting Biology   217
Chapter 11. Competitors and Nest Predators   275
Maps
Chapter 12. Brood Behavior and Survival   301
Chapter 13. Growth, Plumage, and Molt   323
Chapter 14. Postbreeding Activities   355
Chapter 15. Nocturnal Roosts   371
Chapter 16. Feeding Behavior and Food Habits   387
Chapter 17. Parasites and Diseases   419
Chapter 18. Population Dynamics *(coauthored with Richard Kasul)*   437
Chapter 19. Nest Houses   461
Chapter 20. Habitat and Population Management   495

Epilogue   519

Appendix A. Common and Scientific Names of Animals and Plants Cited in the Text   521
Appendix B. Glossary   525
Appendix C. Statistical Symbols and Definitions   527
Appendix D. Data used to determine wood duck populations for states and provinces
within the Atlantic Flyway, 1961–70.   528
Appendix E. Data used to determine wood duck populations for states and provinces
within the Mississippi Flyway, 1961–70.   528
Appendix F. Data used to determine wood duck populations for states and provinces
within the Atlantic Flyway, 1981–85.   530

Appendix G.   Data used to determine wood duck populations for states and provinces
within the Mississippi Flyway, 1981–85.   530
Appendix H.   Wood duck nest house information from national wildlife refuges
assigned to refuge wetland habitat types.   532
Appendix I.   Wood duck nest house information from publications.   538
Appendix J.   Wood duck nest house information from survey responses of national
wildlife refuge personnel; arranged by regions of flyways.   546
Appendix K.   Wood duck nest house information from unpublished reports.   552

References   555
Index   583

List of Figures and Maps

Figure 1. Relative size of adult male wood ducks and adult males of certain other duck species. 2

Figure 2. Relationship between eye diameter and body weight of adult wood ducks and selected species of other adult waterfowl. 4

Figure 3. Number of adult female wood ducks counted per stream kilometer in nine states of the Mississippi Flyway, 1973–78. 46

Figure 4. Relationship of islands to the number of wood duck broods per kilometer on nine stream areas surveyed in eastern Tennessee, 1990. 51

Figure 5. Palustrine wetlands available to wood ducks in the conterminous United States, 1974. 59

Figure 6. Net volume of hardwood growing stock on commercial timberland in the eastern United States, 1952, 1962, 1970, and 1977. 63

Figure 7. Net volume of hardwood sawtimber on commercial timberland in the eastern United States, 1952, 1962, 1970, and 1977. 64

Figure 8. Changes in the amount of bottomland hardwoods and agricultural lands present in the Lower Mississippi Alluvial Plain, 1937–77. 64

Figure 9. Average annual beaver harvest by 10-year intervals in the conterminous United States, 1931–79. 69

Figure 10. Chronology of autumn migration as disclosed by changing patterns of wood duck abundance on selected national wildlife refuges in regions of the Atlantic, Mississippi, and Pacific flyways. 84

Figure 11. Direct recoveries of wood ducks banded in the Atlantic Flyway north of 40 degrees, 1950–82, in relation to seasonal advancement and geographic region. 86

Figure 12. Direct recoveries of wood ducks banded in the Mississippi Flyway north of 43 degrees, 1950–82, in relation to seasonal advancement and geographic region. 87

Figure 13. Direct recoveries of wood ducks banded in the Mississippi Flyway between 37 and 43 degrees north, 1950–82, in relation to seasonal advancement and geographic region. 87

Figure 14. Direct recoveries of wood ducks banded at 44 degrees north and between 69 and 75 degrees west, in relation to latitude and number of days following banding. 88

Figure 15. Direct recoveries of wood ducks banded at 44 degrees north and between 78 and 85 degrees west, in relation to latitude and number of days following banding. 88

Figure 16. Direct recoveries of wood ducks banded at 40 degrees north and between 89 and 90 degrees west, in relation to latitude and number of days following banding. 89

Figure 17. Direct recoveries of wood ducks by sex and age class from banding sites located between 43 and 44 degrees north and 69 and 77 degrees west, in relation to latitude and number of days following banding. 89

Figure 18.   Direct recoveries of wood ducks by sex and age class from banding sites located between 43 and 44 degrees north and 78 and 85 degrees west, in relation to latitude and number of days following banding.   90

Figure 19.   Direct recoveries of wood ducks by sex and age class from banding sites located between 43 and 44 degrees north and 88 and 93 degrees west, in relation to latitude and number of days following banding.   90

Figure 20.   Direct recoveries of wood ducks by sex and age class from a banding site in Mason County, Illinois, in relation to latitude and number of days following banding.   90

Figure 21.   Chronology of spring migration as disclosed by changing patterns of wood duck abundance on selected national wildlife refuges in regions of the Atlantic, Mississippi, and Pacific flyways.   91

Figure 22.   Mean weekly wood duck numbers censused on Ermling and Cullinane units of Quiver Creek, Mason County, Illinois, 1947–76.   92

Figure 23.   Relationship of 10-percent arrival of the spring population of wood ducks at Quiver Creek, Mason County, Illinois, with March heating-degree days, 1952–67.   93

Figure 24.   Distance in meters that 326 wood duck hens nested in subsequent year from original nest sites, 1955–67, Quiver Creek, Illinois.   96

Figure 25.   Mean percentage and 95-percent confidence limits of adult and yearling wood duck occupancy of compartments in duplex houses, 1985–90, Nauvoo Slough, Illinois.   103

Figure 26.   Effect of return of web-tagged wood duck ducklings on the difference in return rate between web-tagged females and hens nesting for the first time at Mingo National Wildlife Refuge, Missouri.   104

Figure 27.   Linear regression of wood duck harvest in each of the four flyways, 1959–90.   113

Figure 28.   Linear and power curve regressions of calculated autumn populations of wood ducks in the north and central regions of the Mississippi Flyway, 1960–86.   115

Figure 29.   Linear and power curve regression of calculated autumn populations of wood ducks in the southern region of the Mississippi Flyway, 1962–85.   115

Figure 30.   Linear and power curve regression of calculated autumn populations of wood ducks in the northern region of the Atlantic Flyway, 1962–85.   115

Figure 31.   Linear and power curve regression of calculated autumn populations of wood ducks in the southern region of the Atlantic Flyway, 1959–85.   115

Figure 32.   Ten of the more frequently observed courtship displays in wood ducks.   130
Figure 33.   Sonogram of a female wood duck's inciting call.   141
Figure 34.   Sonogram of a female wood duck's nest searching call.   142
Figure 35.   Sonogram of a female wood duck's maternal call.   142
Figure 36.   Sonogram of a male wood duck's burp call.   143
Figure 37.   Sonogram of a male wood duck's turning-the-back-of-the-head call.   144
Figure 38.   Sonogram of a male wood duck's nest searching call.   145
Figure 39.   Sonogram of a male wood duck's basic call note.   145
Figure 40.   Sonogram of a male wood duck's incitement call.   146
Figure 41.   Sonogram of a male wood duck's winnowing call.   146
Figure 42.   Sonogram of a male wood duck's preen-behind-the-wing call.   146
Figure 43.   Sonogram of a male wood duck's chatter call.   147
Figure 44.   Sonogram of a female wood duck's coquette call.   148
Figure 45.   Sonogram of a female wood duck's high-intensity hauk call given while taking flight.   148

Figure 46.   Sonogram of a female wood duck's high-intensity hauk call given prior to landing.   149

Figure 47.   Sonogram of a female wood duck's low-intensity hauk call.   149
Figure 48.   Sonogram of a female wood duck's low-intensity hauk call.   150
Figure 49.   Sonogram of a female wood duck's low-intensity hauk warning call that was given to young ducklings.   151

Figure 50.   Sonogram of a female wood duck's winnowing call.   151

Figure 51.   Sonogram of a female wood duck's vocalization given after a second female entered her nest box.   151

Figure 52.   Sonogram of an alarm-distress call emitted by a wood duck duckling.   152

Figure 53.   Sonogram of a hiss call given by a wood duck duckling.   153

Figure 54.   Sonogram of a shriek call given by a wood duck duckling.   154

Figure 55.   Percentages of trees in diameter classes for available trees, trees with suitable cavities, and trees with wood duck nests at Muscatatuck National Wildlife Refuge, Indiana, 1984–85.   173

Figure 56.   Relationship between entrance sizes of available natural cavities and the proportion of each size used by wood ducks in central Illinois, 1958–61.   174

Figure 57.   Relationship between height of available natural cavities and the proportion of each height group used by wood ducks in central Illinois, 1958–61.   175

Figure 58.   Relationship between depth of available natural cavities and the proportion of each depth group used by wood ducks in central Illinois, 1959–61.   176

Figure 59.   Relationship between area of the bases of available natural cavities and the proportion of each area group used by wood ducks in central Illinois, 1959–61.   177

Figure 60.   Relationship between volume of available natural cavities and the proportion of each volume group used by wood ducks in central Illinois, 1959–61.   177

Figure 61.   Chronology of wood duck nest initiation in relation to weekly mean temperature, Quiver Creek, Illinois, 1957–67.   202

Figure 62.   Effect of the temporal initiation of wood duck nesting after March 1 on the span of nest initiation at Quiver Creek, Illinois, 1957–69.   203

Figure 63.   Temporal pattern of wood duck nest initiation by degrees of latitude for the Atlantic and Mississippi flyways.   203

Figure 64.   Chronology of nest initiation by 703 one- to four-year-old wood ducks at Quiver Creek, Illinois, 1957–67.   205

Figure 65.   Regression of the percentage that yearlings contributed to the total number of nesting wood ducks at Quiver Creek, Illinois, 1957–67, 1974; and Merced, California, 1975–92.   206

Figure 66.   Percentage of wood duck nests containing down, and the amount of down per nest in relation to the number of eggs laid, 1948–74.   218

Figure 67.   Interval between the day on which incubation was terminated by predation or desertion and the start of a new wood duck clutch, Mason County, Illinois.   220

Figure 68.   Clutch size of wood ducks nesting in natural cavities, Mason County, Illinois, 1938–59.   225

Figure 69.   Clutch size of wood ducks nesting in nest houses, Nauvoo Slough, Illinois, 1983–87.   225

Figure 70.   Clutch size of wood ducks nesting in board nest houses, Mason County, Illinois, 1939–55.   226

Figure 71.   Clutch size of wood ducks nesting in metal nest houses, Quiver Creek units, Illinois, 1956–74.   226

Figure 72.   Decline in mean clutch size of 602 normal wood duck nests with progression of the nesting season, 1956–74, Quiver Creek, Illinois.   227

Figure 73.   Length of incubation for 218 wood duck nests, Quiver Creek, Illinois, 1971–74.   228

Figure 74.   Mean percentage of successful dump nests in relation to total successful nests by year, compared with numbers of breeding females, Quiver Creek, Illinois, 1957–74.   244

Figure 75.   Weekly availability of nest sites for wood ducks and weekly proportion of total nests that were dump nests, Nauvoo Slough, Illinois, 1985–87.   246

Figure 76.   Relationship of initiation of wood ducks' normal and dump nests to chronology of distribution by adults and yearlings, Nauvoo Slough, Illinois, 1984–87.   249

Figure 77.   Hatchability of eggs in successful wood duck nests in relation to clutch size for Quiver Creek and Nauvoo Slough, Illinois.   250

Figure 78.   Percentage of dump nests among successful and unsuccessful wood duck nests in relation to percentage of eggs that hatched in successful nests.   251

Figure 79. Effect of nest density on wood duck nests deserted, based on 822 nesting attempts in Wake and Johnston counties, North Carolina, 1954–68. 256

Figure 80. Effect of the number of nesting pairs of wood ducks on the number of injured and dead nesting hens at Nauvoo Slough, Illinois, 1984–90. 257

Figure 81. Temporal distribution of 354 starling nests in wood duck houses, 1959–67, Quiver Creek, Illinois. 284

Figure 82. Flushing rate of incubating wood ducks for all nests in relation to the yearly percentage of nests destroyed by raccoons, 1939–65, based on 1,935 observations. 290

Figure 83. Regression of the number of raccoons harvested in several states and the United States for various years. 291

Figure 84. Predator destruction of wood duck nests in unprotected board houses at various stages from egg laying to hatching, 1939–43. 291

Figure 85. Chronology of wood duck nest destruction in wooden houses, Mason County, Illinois, by three predators, in relation to the proportion of active nests, 1939–47. 292

Figure 86. Development of young wood ducks. 302

Figure 87. Seasonal differences in wood duck brood survival on Nauvoo Slough, Illinois, 1984–87. 320

Figure 88. Logistic growth curve of known-aged wild wood ducks captured on Montezuma National Wildlife Refuge, New York, and wood ducks raised at the Van Norman Aviary, Illinois. 325

Figure 89. Cumulative percentage of mature (asymptotic) weight gained by young wood ducks during the first 14 weeks of life. 325

Figure 90. Culmen and tarsus growth of wood ducks raised at the Van Norman Aviary, Illinois, 1981. 328

Figure 91. Folded wing growth of wood ducks raised at the Van Norman Aviary, Illinois, 1981. 328

Figure 92. Topography of a wood duck, used here to delineate the specific tracts of feathers followed during changes in plumage. 330

Figure 93. Overview of the molt cycle in captive, wild-hatched, juvenile male wood ducks studied July 4 through November 28, 1990. 333

Figure 94. Development of wing feathers of juvenile wood ducks raised at the Van Norman Aviary, Illinois, 1981. 342

Figure 95. Percentage protrusion of feather vanes above their sheaths for three flight feathers as they grow in length on juvenile wood ducks. 342

Figure 96. Number of tail feathers in sheaths after September 1, 1981 through 1983 on wild wood ducks from central and southern Illinois. 345

Figure 97. Color intensity of covert feathers in adult and juvenile male wood ducks. 345

Figure 98. Color intensity of covert feathers in adult and juvenile female wood ducks. 345

Figure 99. Time frame of the prebasic molt to the definitive basic plumage of two adult male wood ducks—leading into the definitive alternate plumage. 347

Figure 100. Growth rate of primary and secondary feathers in adult wood ducks during the prealternate molt. 350

Figure 101. Social components of a wood duck population during breeding and postbreeding periods at Nauvoo Slough, Illinois, 1983. 356

Figure 102. Social components of a wood duck population during breeding and postbreeding periods at Nauvoo Slough, Illinois, 1984. 356

Figure 103. Social components of a wood duck population during breeding and postbreeding periods at Nauvoo Slough, Illinois, 1985. 357

Figure 104. Social components of a wood duck population during breeding and postbreeding periods at Nauvoo Slough, Illinois, 1986. 357

Figure 105. Ratio of male to female wood ducks during the postbreeding period in the area of Nauvoo Slough, Illinois, 1983. 359

Figure 106. Proportion of adult male wood ducks observed in the Nauvoo Slough area of Illinois showing evidence of basic plumage, in comparison with those with alternate plumage, 1983–86. 359

Figure 107.   Proportion of male wood ducks trapped or shot in central Illinois that had obtained full alternate plumage, compared with those that exhibited some basic plumage.   360

Figure 108.   Percentage of flightless and flighted adult male and female wood ducks per trapping episode at Green Island, Iowa, 1980.   361

Figure 109.   Seasonal changes in wood duck use of Hopps Pond roost, central Illinois, 1986.   376

Figure 110.   Pattern of roost usage by wood ducks at two backwater lakes in the central Illinois River Valley.   378

Figure 111.   Percentage of wood ducks in various-sized flocks entering and leaving a roost in the northeastern part of Anderson Lake, Illinois, September 4 through October 9, 1984.   378

Figure 112.   Percentage of wood ducks in various-sized flocks during spring roost flights at Nauvoo Slough, Illinois, 1985–86.   381

Figure 113.   Proportion of wood ducks arriving in various-sized flocks at three roosts in central Illinois, 1984–86.   383

Figure 114.   Changes in invertebrate consumption levels by breeding wood duck hens in relation to physiological condition.   403

Figure 115.   Effect of nest success in nest houses in a given year on the percentage of change in female wood ducks incubating the following year in nest houses at Merced, California, 1974–88, and at Quiver Creek, Illinois, 1957–68.   439

Figure 116.   Effect of wood duck nest success in nest houses in a given year on the percentage of change in use of nest houses the following year during two time periods at Mason County, Illinois.   439

Figure 117.   Effect of wood duck nest success in nest houses in a given year on the percentage of change in use of nest houses the following year at Union Slough National Wildlife Refuge, Iowa, 1966–89.   439

Figure 118.   Number of immature females per adult female wood duck, 1966–85, in regions of the Mississippi Flyway.   443

Figure 119.   Disappearance rate of 1,389 adult female wood ducks nesting at Quiver Creek, Illinois, and as ascertained from 1,211 band recoveries in the central region of the Mississippi Flyway.   455

Figure 120.   Disappearance of 100 immature male and female wood ducks, with time based on survival data summarized for all regions of the Atlantic and Mississippi flyways.   456

Figure 121.   Proportion of natural mortality and hunter kill of adult wood ducks in eastern North America.   457

Figure 122.   Proportion of natural mortality and hunter kill of immature wood ducks in eastern North America.   457

Figure 123.   Relationship of natural and hunting mortality to all mortality of wood ducks, based on variations between five regions of the Atlantic and Mississippi flyways and four sex and age classes.   458

Figure 124.   Construction plan for a standard wooden nest house with a "raccoon-proof" entrance.   464

Figure 125.   Average autumn weight of raccoons by sex and age in relation to degrees of latitude.   465

Figure 126.   Construction plan for a metal ("rocket") house.   468

Figure 127.   Effect of nest house diameter on wood ducks' mean clutch size at Chautauqua National Wildlife Refuge and Quiver Creek, Illinois.   470

Figure 128.   Subjective rating of the relative value of various types of aquatic habitats for the use of nest houses by wood ducks east of the Great Plains.   481

Figure 129.   Diameter of various tree species in relation to the age at which their minimum and mean sizes have potential for providing cavities for nesting wood ducks.   506

Figure 130.   Percentage of wood duck band recoveries within state of banding compared with recoveries from out of state, arranged by degrees of latitude.   512

Figure 131.   Development of the air cell in the wood duck egg under normal incubation.   514

Map 1.   Current breeding range of the wood duck.

Map 2.   Average density of wood duck harvest per square mile for each county in the United States, 1966–85.

Map 3.   Relative density (number counted per 100 party hours) and distribution of wood ducks counted during Audubon Christmas Bird Censuses, 1979–80.

Map 4.   Land use and physiographic features of the eastern United States.

Map 5.   Current and pristine distribution and abundance of bottomland hardwood wetlands in the Lower Mississippi Alluvial Plain (from U.S. Fish and Wildlife Service 1988).

Map 6.   Distribution and abundance of agricultural lands in drainage enterprises in the eastern United States, 1959 (U.S. Bureau of the Census 1959, U.S. Geological Survey 1970), and distribution and abundance of farm ponds, 1964 (U.S. Bureau of the Census 1964, U.S. Geological Survey 1970).

Map 7.   Migration corridors of wood ducks banded in northcentral New York and southwestern Wisconsin.

Map 8.   Migratory routes of wood ducks banded in northern regions of the Mississippi and Atlantic flyways.

List of Tables

Table 1. Comparative morphometrical data on wood ducks and hooded mergansers.   3

Table 2. Wood duck breeding population and density estimated for states and provinces within the Atlantic Flyway.   16

Table 3. Wood duck breeding population and density estimated for states and provinces within the Mississippi Flyway.   17

Table 4. Wood duck breeding population and density estimated for states and provinces of the Great Plains.   17

Table 5. Wood duck breeding and population density estimated for British Columbia and states within the Pacific Flyway.   18

Table 6. Estimated proportion of northern wood ducks harvested in the primary winter range of the Atlantic and Mississippi flyways.   32

Table 7. Localities in California south of 36 degrees latitude in which Audubon Christmas Bird Counts revealed wood ducks.   35

Table 8. Available habitat on Quiver Creek, Illinois and adjacent ponds, number of wood ducks observed, and number observed per year per unit of area, March 22 through April 26, 1948–62.   41

Table 9. Area of states in relation to length of streams and area of drainage.   42

Table 10. Number of potential breeding female wood ducks per kilometer of stream in various regions of states within the Mississippi Flyway, 1973–78.   44

Table 11. Number of wood ducks censused on summer stream surveys.   45

Table 12. Rivers with the largest numbers of potential breeding female wood ducks in certain states of the Mississippi Flyway, 1973–78.   46

Table 13. Wood duck brood observations on several reaches with varying gradients of the French Broad River, North Carolina, 1978.   49

Table 14. Relationship of stream width to number of female wood ducks observed in the northern half of Illinois.   50

Table 15. Relationship of stream width to number of female wood ducks observed in the southern half of Illinois.   51

Table 16. Area of wetland types considered of value to wood ducks in the Mississippi Flyway and Texas.   54

Table 17. Area of wetland types considered of value to wood ducks in the Atlantic Flyway.   55

Table 18. Area of wetland types considered of value to wood ducks in the Pacific Flyway.   56

Table 19. Distribution and extent of bottomland wetlands in the Mississippi Flyway and Texas around 1970.   57

Table 20. Distribution and extent of bottomland wetlands in the Atlantic Flyway around 1970.   57

Table 21. Wetlands considered of value to wood ducks in mid-Atlantic states, 1974.   58

Table 22. Distribution and area of farm pond habitat available to wood ducks in the Mississippi Flyway, 1964.   58

Table 23.   Distribution and area of farm pond habitat available to wood ducks in the Atlantic Flyway, 1964.   59

Table 24.   Land transferred to states under the authorization of the Swamp Land Acts of 1849, 1850, and 1860.   61

Table 25.   Land in drainage projects and estimated proportion of drained area that adversely affected potential wood duck habitat in the Mississippi Flyway and Texas, 1960.   62

Table 26.   Land in drainage projects and estimated proportion of drained area that adversely affected potential wood duck habitat in the Atlantic and Pacific flyways, 1960.   62

Table 27.   Distribution of land by state in the Lower Mississippi Alluvial Plain.   65

Table 28.   Distribution of potential wood duck habitat by state and river basin in the Lower Mississippi Alluvial Plain, 1978.   66

Table 29.   Average annual harvest of beaver in Mississippi Flyway states, 1977–81.   70

Table 30.   Average annual harvest and distribution of beaver in Atlantic Flyway states, 1977–81.   70

Table 31.   Some parameters of wood duck flocks observed migrating over farm fields in Mason County, Illinois.   80

Table 32.   Size of spring flocks of six or more wood ducks migrating into the Illinois River Valley.   81

Table 33.   Mean distance from locations of preseason bandings to sites of winter recoveries for wood ducks banded in eastern North America, 1970–86.   82

Table 34.   Homing of wood duck hens in a subsequent year to nest in the same areas where they had been initially banded as incubating birds.   95

Table 35.   Return in subsequent years to the same nest houses by banded wood duck hens experiencing previous successful and unsuccessful nesting at Quiver Creek (1954–67) and Nauvoo Slough (1985–87), Illinois.   96

Table 36.   Number of female wood duck ducklings that departed nest houses at Mingo National Wildlife Refuge, Missouri, compared with actual, adjusted, and potential recoveries in subsequent years.   98

Table 37.   Number of female wood duck ducklings that departed nest houses in the area of Merced, California (1976–78) and Nauvoo Slough, Illinois (1985).   98

Table 38.   Homing rate of certain dabbling ducks banded on their breeding grounds in North America.   100

Table 39.   Projected return of cohort representing adjusted return of web-tagged female wood duck ducklings, compared with the number of nonlocal hatched birds nesting for the first time.   100

Table 40.   Comments by ornithologists prior to 1900 on the status of wood ducks.   108

Table 41.   Comments by ornithologists, 1900–20, on the status of wood ducks.   109

Table 42.   Comments by ornithologists, 1920–45, on the status of wood ducks.   111

Table 43.   Changing status of wood duck populations, based on responses to inquiries of ornithologists and wildlife managers.   111

Table 44.   Seasonal harvest of wood ducks per duck hunter and day hunted during blocks of five years, 1961–90.   114

Table 45.   Yearly trend in calculated wood duck band recovery rates for regions of the Atlantic and Mississippi flyways, 1959–85.   114

Table 46.   Linear regression coefficients and calculated wood duck harvest in states of the Mississippi Flyway and Texas, 1959–87.   116

Table 47.   Linear regression coefficients and calculated wood duck harvest in states of the Atlantic Flyway, 1959–87.   116

Table 48.   Yearly percentage of change in wood duck harvest by regions in four states in the Mississippi Flyway during four time frames.   117

Table 49.   Yearly percentage of change in wood duck harvest by regions in four states in the Atlantic Flyway during four time frames.   118

Table 50.   Yearly percentage of change in wood duck harvest in four states in the Central Flyway during four time frames.   119

Table 51.   Comparative size of wood duck courting groups on Nauvoo Slough, Illinois during April and May, 1984–86.   125

Table 52. Number of wood duck displays per hour of observation during autumn and spring courtships in central Illinois. 126

Table 53. Ritualized wood duck displays and courting behaviors reported in the literature. 128

Table 54. Mean duration of some wood duck courtship displays. 128

Table 55. Synopsis of wood duck vocalizations. 137

Table 56. Sex composition of wood ducks flying in two-bird flocks to autumn roosts, central Illinois, 1984–87. 154

Table 57. Number of wood ducks arriving at autumn roosts as singles and in two-bird flocks, central Illinois, 1984–86. 155

Table 58. Pairing chronology of wood ducks in southeastern Missouri, August 29, 1977 through May 15, 1978. 155

Table 59. Comparison of pursuit flight frequencies in 10 species of ducks from the region of Minnedosa, Manitoba, May 16–28, 1983. 159

Table 60. Frequency of aerial pursuit flights by wood ducks at Nauvoo Slough, Illinois, 1985–86. 161

Table 61. Comparison of frequencies of aerial pursuit flights by mallards and wood ducks on Nauvoo Slough, Illinois, April 16–May 28, 1985. 161

Table 62. Temporal pattern of trio formation of wood ducks along Quiver Creek, Illinois, 1947–79. 163

Table 63. Number and proportion of live trees that contained cavities suitable for wood duck nesting, and the number and proportion used by wood ducks. 168

Table 64. Density and wood duck use of suitable natural nesting cavities and important cavity tree species. 170

Table 65. Diameter of trees containing cavities suitable for wood duck nests and of trees used by wood ducks. 172

Table 66. Use of natural cavities by wood ducks in years following successful and unsuccessful nesting attempts in central Illinois, 1959–61. 173

Table 67. Measurements of cavity trees and cavities excavated by pileated woodpeckers. 174

Table 68. Frequency of cavity suitability (for wood ducks) and of possible cavity entrances overlooked for tree species on Muscatatuck National Wildlife Refuge, Indiana, 1984–85. 178

Table 69. Major causes of cavity unsuitability for wood duck nesting in tree species on Muscatatuck National Wildlife Refuge, Indiana, 1984–85. 178

Table 70. Density of suitable natural cavities for nesting wood ducks in upland and bottomland hardwood forests of the same study areas. 180

Table 71. Tree species composition and abundance of cavities suitable for wood duck nesting in upland and lowland timber in northwestern Minnesota. 180

Table 72. Tree species with suitable nest cavities and number of wood duck nests found in Mason County, Illinois, 1958 and 1959. 182

Table 73. Percentage of time spent in various activities by paired, prelaying wood ducks at Nauvoo Slough, Illinois, 1986. 186

Table 74. Average percentage of time during stated periods that wood ducks spent searching for nest cavities on clear and overcast days at Nauvoo Slough, Illinois, March 27 through April 30, 1986. 189

Table 75. Estimated length of cavity-prospecting period of color-marked adult hen wood ducks at Nauvoo Slough, Illinois, 1986. 190

Table 76. Characteristics of wood duck pair associations along Quiver Creek, Illinois, 1947–79. 192

Table 77. Linear regression analyses of the relationship between day of laying and amount of time spent in nest cavity by four wood duck hens near Oquawka, Illinois. 193

Table 78. Percentage of time spent by paired wood ducks in various activities during prelaying, laying, and incubation periods at Nauvoo Slough, Illinois, 1986. 193

Table 79. Percentage of time spent by paired wood duck drakes in various activities throughout three daily time periods at Nauvoo Slough, Illinois, 1986. 193

Table 80. Percentage of time spent by paired wood duck hens in various activities throughout three daily time periods at Nauvoo Slough, Illinois, 1986. 194

Table 81. Comparison of average daily cavity entrance times by four egg-laying wood ducks near Oquawka, Illinois. 195

Table 82. Percentage of time spent by paired wood ducks in various activities during two incubation recesses at Nauvoo Slough, Illinois, 1985. 196

Table 83. Effect of latitude on the initiation and span of wood duck breeding within the Mississippi Flyway. 204

Table 84. Effect of latitude on the initiation and span of wood duck breeding within the Atlantic Flyway. 204

Table 85. Effect of latitude on the initiation and span of wood duck breeding within the Pacific Flyway. 204

Table 86. Relationship of the percentage of yearlings to the total number of nesting wood ducks at Nauvoo Slough, Illinois, 1985–91. 206

Table 87. Relationship of the percentage of yearlings to the total number of nesting wood ducks along Quiver Creek, Illinois, 1956–67 and 1974. 206

Table 88. Relationship of the percentage of yearlings to the total number of nesting wood ducks and their use of nest houses in the vicinity of Merced, California. 207

Table 89. Relationship of clutch size to the weight of female wood ducks, Quiver Creek, Illinois, 1964–68. 208

Table 90. Body mass of adult wood ducks by seasonal periods and sex in Mason County, Illinois, 1950–68. 210

Table 91. Body weights of wood ducks during early winter in Mississippi and Louisiana, 1979–83. 210

Table 92. Linear regression analysis for daily weight changes of seven laying wood ducks near Oquawka, Illinois, 1985. 211

Table 93. Linear regression analysis of total body weight changes of incubating wood ducks in Illinois. 212

Table 94. Invertebrate consumption rates needed to meet maximum daily protein requirements of wood ducks. 212

Table 95. Rate of egg laying by wood ducks at Burlington, Iowa and Mason County, Illinois. 218

Table 96. Change in the deposition of down in wood duck nests as the season advanced at Burlington, Iowa, 1948–56 and 1960–74. 219

Table 97. Occurrence of second broods in wood ducks. 221

Table 98. Wood duck egg dimensions and calculated volume for adult and yearling clutches in central Illinois. 222

Table 99. Dimensions and volumes of wood duck eggs. 223

Table 100. Dimensions, volumes, and weights of eggs of 17 species of ducks in comparison with body weight. 224

Table 101. Proportion of dump nests to total wood duck nests, breeding females, and nest sites at Nauvoo Slough, Illinois, 1983–90. 227

Table 102. Number of nights that wood duck females were on nests prior to completion of clutches. 228

Table 103. Criteria for determining the age of an excised wood duck embryo. 230

Table 104. Daily recess frequency for 14 female wood ducks. 231

Table 105. Components of the incubation rhythm of six hen wood ducks at Oquawka, Illinois. 233

Table 106. Percentage of wood duck males that returned with their mates, based on day of incubation in comparison with the progression of the nesting season after April 1. 233

Table 107. Clutch size for normal and dump nests and percentage of eggs hatched in successful nests in wood duck nest houses. 244

Table 108. Known age of wood ducks in relation to the proportion of dump nests and small clutch sizes under incubation, Quiver Creek, Illinois, 1956–67. 246

Table 109. Number of eggs laid per female wood duck at Nauvoo Slough, Illinois, 1983–90. 247

Table 110. Minimum rate of laying in nest houses receiving more than one egg from more than one wood duck hen per day for periods approximating a week, Nauvoo Slough, Illinois, 1984–87. 248

Table 111. Mean nest initiation dates and standard deviation for known-aged wood ducks incubating normal and dump clutches, Quiver Creek, Illinois, 1956–67. 248

Table 112. Percentage of wood duck dump nests and comparison of success between normal and dump nests, Nauvoo Slough, Illinois, 1983–90. 250

Table 113. Fate of unhatched wood duck eggs in normal and dump nests, and proportion of stranded ducklings. 253

Table 114. Effect of intraspecific strife on wood ducks as a result of population pressure, Nauvoo Slough, Illinois, 1984–90. 253

Table 115. Wood duck nest history activities with weekly progress of the breeding season, Nauvoo Slough, Illinois, 1984–90. 254

Table 116. Change in frequency of wood duck normal and dump nests as a result of the dumping of eggs in nests after incubation started, Nauvoo Slough, Illinois, 1984–87. 254

Table 117. Correlation matrix for several wood duck activities/dump nest histories at Nauvoo Slough, Illinois, 1984–90. 258

Table 118. Wood duck nest success in natural cavities, and agents of nest destruction. 264

Table 119. Wood duck nest histories in board and metal nest houses, Mason County, Illinois, 1939–74. 266

Table 120. Correlation matrix between agents of destruction among wood duck nests in board houses, Mason County, Illinois, 1939–52. 266

Table 121. Wood duck nest histories in sheet metal nest houses, Quiver Creek, Illinois, 1956–74. 268

Table 122. Correlation matrix between agents of destruction among wood duck nests in metal houses, Quiver Creek, Illinois, 1956–74. 268

Table 123. Wood duck nest histories in nest houses on posts (duplex compartments in 1984 and subsequent years), Nauvoo Slough, Illinois, 1983–87. 268

Table 124. Correlation matrix between agents of destruction among wood duck nests in houses, Nauvoo Slough, Illinois, 1983–87. 269

Table 125. Wood duck nest house use and nest success, Lake Chautauqua National Wildlife Refuge, Illinois, 1939–87. 270

Table 126. Wood duck nest house use and nest success in flyway regions, based on information from publications. 270

Table 127. Wood duck nest house use and nest success on national wildlife refuges. 271

Table 128. Wood duck nest house use in flyway regions, based on information from unpublished reports. 271

Table 129. Percentage use of potential wood duck natural cavities during spring and early summer by various animals. 276

Table 130. Percentage use of wood duck nest houses by various animals during spring and early summer. 278

Table 131. Use of wood duck houses by various animals on national wildlife refuges. 280

Table 132. Use of metal wood duck houses by starlings on 13 units, Quiver Creek area, Illinois, 1959–77. 283

Table 133. Temporal nesting of starlings by latitude for first and second nestings in North America. 283

Table 134. Effect of house diameter on starling nest occupancy of metal cylindrical wood duck houses, central Illinois, 1962–77. 284

Table 135. Percentage use of conventional wood duck houses with two types of entrances at Dulles International Airport, northern Virginia. 285

Table 136. Destruction of wood duck nests in houses by various predators. 286

Table 137. Principal losses of nests in wood duck houses on some national wildlife refuges. 288

Table 138. Growth criteria of wood duck ducklings in relation to development. 302

Table 139. Percentage of parentless wood duck broods on Nauvoo Slough, Illinois, 1983–87. 309

Table 140. Changes in the number of wood duck young comprising one cohesive brood on Nauvoo Slough, Illinois, 1985. 311

Table 141. Predators known to have consumed or pursued young wood ducks. 314

Table 142. Wood duck brood survivalship from selected areas throughout their breeding range. 316

Table 143. Comparative losses in broods among several species of ducks between hatching and Class II-developed ducklings. 318

Table 144. Survival of wood duck broods hatched at Great Meadows National Wildlife Refuge, Massachusetts, in relation to time of hatching, 1952–54. 319

Table 145. Seasonal changes in wood duck brood sizes at Nauvoo Slough, Illinois, 1984–87. 320

Table 146. Average body mass of day-old wood duck ducklings captured in nest boxes on Quiver Creek, Illinois. 324

Table 147. Average body mass of day-old wood duck ducklings from various locations throughout the species' breeding range. 324

Table 148. Relationship between levels of dietary protein to survival and primary development of growing wood ducks. 324

Table 149. Mean weights and standard error of wood duck weights from captive-reared wood ducks in central Illinois. 327

Table 150. Tarsus, culmen, and folded wing lengths in mature age and sex classes of wood ducks. 328

Table 151. Multiple correlation of weight and age of ducklings in relation to the development of various plumage tracts in captive and wild wood ducks. 329

Table 152. Number, size, weight, and calculated dietary protein necessary to synthesize feathers in various nuptial plumage tracts of an adult male wood duck. 330

Table 153. Number, size, weight, and calculated dietary protein necessary to synthesize feathers in various plumage tracts of the wing of an adult male wood duck. 331

Table 154. Comparison of mean number of sheathed feathers counted on five juvenile male wood ducks during their first prealternate molt, and the number of feathers counted on an adult male wood duck that had acquired definitive alternate plumage. 332

Table 155. Appearance of new feather sheaths among juvenile male and female wood ducks at the Van Norman Aviary. 334

Table 156. Percentage of incubating wood duck hens at Nauvoo Slough, Illinois that displayed some evidence of basic plumage on the belly, April 8 through June 19, 1990 and 1991. 334

Table 157. Number and percentage of captive wood ducks studied at Mississippi State University that showed evidence of winter molt in various plumage regions, December 21, 1990 to March 21, 1991, and seven plumage regions, December 21, 1991 to March 21, 1992. 335

Table 158. Age of seven wood duck ducklings when juvenile plumage replaced the downy plumage in various feather tracts of the head and body, July through August 1990. 336

Table 159. Age of wood duck ducklings during head plumage development, 1990. 337

Table 160. Age of five male wood duck ducklings when nuptial plumage replaced juvenile plumage in various feather tracts of the body, 1990. 339

Table 161. Mean number of feathers in sheaths enumerated in plumage tracts of 10 juvenile wood ducks during their 74- to 145-day periods of growth, 1990. 340

Table 162. Percentage of wood ducks with various numbers of secondaries. 341

Table 163. Length of the ninth primary, center secondary, and three tertials in wing feather tracts of wild wood ducks. 346

Table 164. Difference in measurements of most proximal greater secondary coverts of known-aged female wood ducks during the breeding season in South Carolina. 346

Table 165. Number of new rump, upper tail coverts, and tail feathers appearing on adult wood ducks raised at the Van Norman Aviary, Illinois, 1983. 348

Table 166. Number of new scapular and back feathers appearing on adult wood ducks raised at the Van Norman Aviary, Illinois, 1983. 349

Table 167. Development of primary and secondary wing feathers in relation to the beginning of definitive prebasic molt and completion of definitive prealternate molt in adult wood ducks, Van Norman Aviary, Illinois, 1983. 350

Table 168. Percentage distribution of postbreeding and autumn wood ducks observed flying in the Nauvoo Slough area, Illinois, 1983. 358

Table 169.   Size and composition of wood duck groups flushed by airboat from American lotus beds near Nauvoo Slough, Illinois.   358

Table 170.   Percentage of basic plumage among adult male wood ducks observed at Nauvoo Slough, Illinois, 1984–87.   360

Table 171.   Proportion of males among adult wood ducks banded during 10-day periods in late July and August in the upper Midwest and Ontario.   363

Table 172.   Proportion of direct wood duck recoveries in latitudes north of banding sites in comparison with direct recoveries for all latitudes by age and sex classes.   364

Table 173.   Percentage of direct recoveries from wood ducks killed north of their banding sites in the Atlantic Flyway.   365

Table 174.   Percentage of direct recoveries from wood ducks killed north of their banding sites in the Mississippi Flyway.   366

Table 175.   Weighted percentage of postbreeding season recoveries by age and sex classes of wood ducks banded in Alabama and shot their first autumn in other regions of the Atlantic, Mississippi, and Central flyways.   367

Table 176.   Proportion of direct band recoveries from wood ducks that occurred within one degree of latitude and of longitude of banding sites.   367

Table 177.   Spring evening roost flight characteristics of wood ducks arriving at Matthews Bay, central Illinois, 1989.   381

Table 178.   Proportion of wood ducks in evening roosting flights at Nauvoo Slough, Illinois, 1985–86.   381

Table 179.   Percentage of wood ducks in central Illinois flying to agricultural fields in flocks of various sizes, 1987.   394

Table 180.   Percentage of wood ducks departing on evening feeding flights from Chautauqua National Wildlife Refuge, Illinois, 1987.   395

Table 181.   Staple autumn plants in the diet of wood ducks as reported from selected food habit studies.   397

Table 182.   Nutrient composition of some major plant and animal foods ingested by breeding wood ducks.   398

Table 183.   Occurrence of corn in the gullets of incubating wood duck females captured on the nest, Nauvoo Slough (1985–87) and Quiver Creek (1961–85), Illinois.   404

Table 184.   Estimated percentage of animal matter consumed by young wood ducks on the Upper Mississippi River Wildlife and Fish Refuge, Minnesota and Wisconsin.   416

Table 185.   Seasonal occurrence of sick male and female wood ducks observed along Quiver Creek, Illinois, 1977–89.   422

Table 186.   Variation in the frequency of occurrence of hematozoal parasites in wood ducks from different geographical regions.   424

Table 187.   External parasites that have been found on wood ducks.   428

Table 188.   Nematodes that have been found parasitizing wood ducks.   430

Table 189.   Trematodes that have been found parasitizing wood ducks.   431

Table 190.   Cestodes that have been found parasitizing wood ducks.   432

Table 191.   Relationship between wood duck nest success in nest houses and nest house use the following year during three periods at the Chautauqua National Wildlife Refuge in Mason County, Illinois.   438

Table 192.   Factors affecting recruitment in mallards and wood ducks.   441

Table 193.   Relative vulnerability of immature and mature wood ducks in regions of the Atlantic and Mississippi flyways.   442

Table 194.   Immature wood duck females per adult female in nature.   443

Table 195.   Hunter selection of male to female wood ducks in regions of the Atlantic and Mississippi flyways.   445

Table 196.   Sex ratio of autumn wood duck populations in several regions of the Atlantic and Mississippi flyways, 1966–85.   445

Table 197.   Sex ratio of immature wood ducks trapped for banding during late summer, 1959–78, in several regions of the Atlantic and Mississippi flyways.   445

Table 198.   Summary of mean annual recovery and survival rates for adult and immature male and female wood ducks in regions of the Atlantic and Mississippi flyways for the years of available banding and recovery data.   446

Table 199.   Summary of results of hypothesis tests regarding differences between adult and immature wood ducks in regions of the Atlantic and Mississippi flyways.   446

Table 200.   Summary of results of hypothesis tests regarding differences between survival and recovery rates in male and female wood ducks in regions of the Atlantic and Mississippi flyways.   448

Table 201.   Summary of mean annual survival and recovery rates of male and female wood ducks by decade, 1950–85.   448

Table 202.   Differences in survival and recovery rates between sex and age classes of wood ducks for specified groups of years, 1950–85, in regions of the Atlantic and Mississippi flyways.   450

Table 203.   Pearson correlation coefficients between estimated recovery and survival rates of wood ducks in regions of the Atlantic and Mississippi flyways.   452

Table 204.   Summary tests of null hypothesis that wood duck recovery and survival rates are uncorrelated.   452

Table 205.   Results of z tests regarding geographic variation in mean annual survival and recovery rates of wood ducks.   454

Table 206.   Comparative annual survival rates and mean life span in years for sex and age classes of six duck species.   456

Table 207.   Comparison of percentage of recruitment with percentage of mortality among wood duck females in regions of the Atlantic and Mississippi flyways, 1966–85.   459

Table 208.   Partial regression coefficients of the relative importance of annual survival versus annual recruitment in affecting the calculated annual autumn populations of female wood ducks in regions of the Atlantic and Mississippi flyways, 1966–85.   459

Table 209.   Percentage of wood duck use of metal houses with different interiors and diameters at two study areas on the Illinois River, 1968–74.   470

Table 210.   Interior temperatures of wood duck nest houses composed of different materials, thicknesses, and colors in relation to ambient temperature.   476

Table 211.   First-year use of Ducks Unlimited, Inc. nest houses, 1988.   477

Table 212.   Average percentage of nest house use by wood ducks from studies with multiple designs available concurrently.   478

Table 213.   Percentage of wood duck use of wood nest houses in various wetland types in South Carolina, 1989.   482

Table 214.   Percentage of wood duck use of nest houses in various wetland habitats at national wildlife refuges.   483

Table 215.   Wood duck use of nest houses in four categories of vegetational obstruction on the alluvial flats of Benton County, Oregon, 1968.   483

Table 216.   Wood duck use of nest houses at various distances from water in the Illinois River Valley, 1939–56.   484

Table 217.   Use, nest success, and ducklings departed from wood duck nest houses monitored in 1992 in California.   487

Table 218.   Average wood duck use of nest houses determined from three information sources.   488

Table 219.   Percentage of wood duck use of nest houses in flyway regions.   489

Table 220.   Wood duck nest house programs in suburban areas of Minneapolis-St. Paul, Minnesota.   491

Table 221.   Amount and location of federal and state areas of bottomland forest in waterfowl and national forest reserves in the Mississippi Alluvial Plain, as of June, 1991.   500

Table 222.   Estimated percentage increase in duck kill with increase in bag limit, 1960–63.   510

Table 223.   Mean yearly harvest of wood ducks for a comparable number of years prior to and during special early hunting seasons that were part of the regular seasons.   511

Table 224.   Mean increase in harvest of wood ducks in three states accruing from a special five-day early extension to the regular season, 1981–88.   511

Table 225.   Harvest of wood ducks in provinces/states of the Mississippi Flyway from in-state and out-of-state breeding sources, 1981–85.   512

Table 226.   Harvest of wood ducks in provinces/states of the Atlantic Flyway from in-state and out-of-state breeding sources, 1981–85.   513

Chapter 1

Introducing the Wood Duck

The wood duck is one of 43 species of waterfowl that nest in North America. It is the most abundant breeding waterfowl between 30 and 43 degrees north latitude. The range of no other duck encompasses so much of the contiguous United States without spilling more extensively into Canada. Scattered records of wood ducks occur for Mexico, largely during winter (Williams 1987), but woodies are not known to breed there. Outside of the continent, a small number of wood ducks are permanent residents in Cuba (Barbour 1943). The hooded merganser approximates the wood duck's range in the contiguous United States but nests farther north and fails to nest as far south or as far west on the Great Plains (Bellrose 1976). Only the wood duck has a life-style that enables it to exploit nest sites, food, and cover from wetlands with water levels that fluctuate appreciably. It is uniquely adapted to breed in the deciduous forest biome, even to the point of nesting in cities and towns.

UNIQUE ATTRIBUTES AND BEHAVIORS

Over much of its range, the wood duck primarily nests in heavily populated regions of the United States, and that close association has endeared it to countless people. The wood duck's habit of nesting in natural cavities or in nest houses is shared by only a few other species (the black-bellied whistling duck, bufflehead, common and Barrow's golden-eyes, and hooded and common mergansers), but the wood duck has been the most successful in exploiting these sites.

No species of waterfowl occupies a greater variety of wetland breeding habitats than does the wood duck. It is at home in creeks, rivers, beaver ponds, bogs, swamps, marshes, lakes, and even in artificially constructed ditches and farm ponds. Its adaptability to such a variety of wetlands has enabled it to live with man yet become one of the most important ducks in the bag of hunters east of the Great Plains.

Wood ducks represent the only waterfowl species in North America known to regularly raise two broods per year. This nesting behavior is limited to wood ducks that nest at southern latitudes where the nesting season is relatively long and migration distances absent or short.

The wood duck forms nocturnal roosting sites with a greater degree of sophistication than does any other duck species. Throughout most of the year, nonbreeding woodies have a propensity to assemble in roosting sites provided with shallow water and low overhead cover. Other waterfowl species may feed in one area and roost elsewhere in open water, but none uses such specific locations and habitats as consistently as do woodies. Moreover, woodies use certain roost sites for many years.

Among all North American ducks, the male wood duck is the first to enter the molt, which leads to the basic (eclipse) plumage. It also is the first to acquire the alternate (nuptial) plumage in autumn.

Perhaps accordingly, it begins to form pairs earlier in autumn than do other duck species.

Probably more than any other species of waterfowl, the wood duck dabbles on the water surface for food. It "tips up" when choice food items are in shallow water and occasionally dives when they are beyond reach. The wood duck appears to be a more proficient diver than other dabbling ducks and does not hesitate to dive for acorns or corn in several feet of water. We observed a hand-reared adult wood duck swim underwater in a plastic wading pool about 2 meters (6.6 ft) in diameter. Partially opening and closing its wings, the duck propelled itself at a remarkable speed as it repeatedly circled the pool. Edwards (1931–1932) noted that flightless young also use their wings to propel themselves underwater when they dive to escape danger.

We timed an adult male wood duck swimming under no duress or apparent incentive at 3.4 kilometers (2.1 mi) per hour for 229 meters (250 yd) on Nauvoo Slough. This speed compares favorably with that of the canvasback; Hochbaum (1944) reported flightless adult canvasbacks swimming at 3.2 to 4.8 kilometers (2 to 3 mi) per hour.

Wood ducks probably are the fastest runners of all ducks. We have observed both mallards and wood ducks running in corn stubble fields, with the latter clearly faster. Stewart (1958) timed partially grown young wood ducks running at 8.9 to 11.4 kilometers (5.5 to 7.1 mi) per hour, almost as fast as ring-necked pheasants, which can run at 16 kilometers (10 mi) per hour. John James Audubon wrote: "On the ground the Duck runs nimbly and with more grace than other birds of its tribe" (Ford 1957: 80).

Wood ducks, among birds examined by Bang (1971), have well-developed odor-sensing organs. Of 124 species of birds rated by olfactory bulb ratio (diameter of olfactory bulb to diameter of hemisphere), wood ducks ranked seventeenth with a ratio of 25.6. Steller's eider had an olfactory ratio of 23.7, green-winged teal 20.0, mallard 19.0, and merganser 15.0. The highest ratio, 37.0, was found in the snowy petrel; the lowest, 3.0, occurred in the chickadee. Wood ducks, therefore, can detect odors better than most birds and better than any duck species that has been examined.

Physical Aspects

The wood duck is about half the size of the mallard; scaled with the dabbling ducks of the genus *Anas*, it falls between six larger species, three smaller species, and one similarly sized species—the northern shoveler (Figure 1). Although quite divergent morphologically, the wood duck is almost identical in size to the hooded merganser (Table 1).

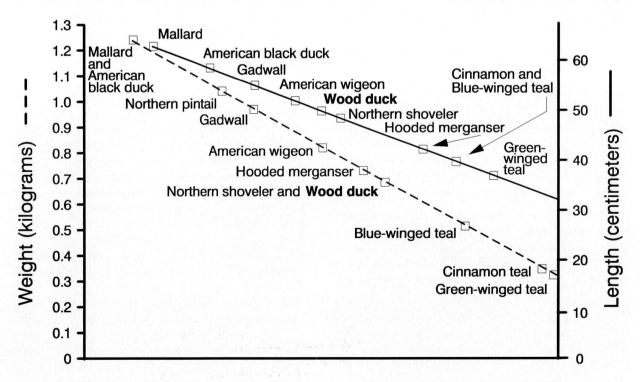

Figure 1. Relative size of adult male wood ducks and adult males of certain other duck species (from Bellrose 1976).

Table 1. Comparative morphometrical data on wood ducks and hooded mergansers.

Parameter[a]	Wood duck Male	Wood duck Female	Hooded merganser Male	Hooded merganser Female	Reference
Total length			43.2–48.8	40.6–45.7	Bellrose (1976)
	45.0–48.3	45.0			Heinroth (1910)
	43.2–52.1				Forbush (1925)
	47.8–53.9	47.0–51.1			Bellrose (1976)
	40.9–47.4	40.0–45.2			Thul (1979)
Folded wing			18.8–19.6	18.3–18.8	Bellrose (1976)
	23.0–23.5	23.0			Heinroth (1910)
	21.2–24.0				Forbush (1925)
	21.8-24.0	21.1–23.1	19.1–20.7	18.0–19.1	Palmer (1976)
	21.8–22.6	21.3–21.8			Bellrose (1976)
	20.8–23.9	18.8–23.0			Thul (1979)
Tail	12.5	10.3			Heinroth (1910)
	11.4				Forbush (1925)
	10.0–11.2	9.1–10.6	8.6–9.6	8.1–9.3	Palmer (1976)
	8.2–12.0	8.1–11.3			Thul (1979)
Culmen	3.5				Heinroth (1910)
	2.8–3.6				Forbush (1925)
	3.2–3.6	3.1–3.5	3.7–4.1	3.5–4.0	Palmer (1976)
	3.2–3.8	3.1–3.8			Thul (1979)
Tarsus	3.2–3.7				Forbush (1925)
	3.4–3.9	3.3–3.6	3.0–3.4	3.0–3.2	Palmer (1976)
	3.8–4.7	3.8–4.4			Thul (1979)
Weight	680[b]	640[b]	680	540	Palmer (1976)
	680[b]–670[c]	670[b]–610[c]			Bellrose (1976)
	670[b]–530[c]	590[b]–530[c]			Thul (1979)
			725[b]–635[c]	680[b]–680[c]	Bellrose (1976)

[a] Length measurements are in centimeters; weight means are in grams.
[b] Mean weight of adult birds.
[c] Mean weight of immature birds.

The wood duck and the hooded merganser compete for nest sites, and both species may have evolved their particular size and form to take advantage of cavities created by pileated woodpeckers. The ranges of these two species and the pileated woodpecker are highly similar.

Bellrose et al. (unpublished, 1990) have provided data on the wing parameters of adult male wood ducks: wing area—0.026 square meters (0.28 ft²); wing length, extended—0.288 meters (0.94 ft); wing width—0.118 meters (0.39 ft); and wing span—0.723 meters (2.37 ft). In proportion to its length, the wood duck has the broadest wing of any species of game duck, possibly an adaptation for flight among the branches of trees. The pectoral muscle, used for depressing the wing in flight, forms 18.18 percent of the body mass; the supracoracoides muscle, used for raising the wing, forms 2.53 percent.

The eye of the wood duck (12.3 ± 0.79 millimeters [0.48 in], n = 21) is the largest of any waterfowl (Figure 2). Although a large eye is advantageous under crepuscular or nocturnal light, there may be more involved in the evaluation of such a large eye than low light intensity. We have seen a number of other species of waterfowl—Canada geese, mallards, and teal—flying at the same low light intensity as wood ducks. Having observed woodies flying adroitly through a maze of branches, we suspect that their eyes perceive details that would not register with smaller eyes. The degree of visual acuity is determined by the *area centralis*, with its depressed fovea near the center of the retina and its density of visual cells (Van Tyne and Berger 1959, Terres 1980), but this aspect of the eye has not been studied in waterfowl.

The wood duck has a longer tail than that of other dabbling ducks except the northern pintail. We believe this long tail may have evolved, like the wings and eyes, to enable the wood duck to accommodate, with a minimum of injury, precarious flight through the tree mazes that dot its habitat.

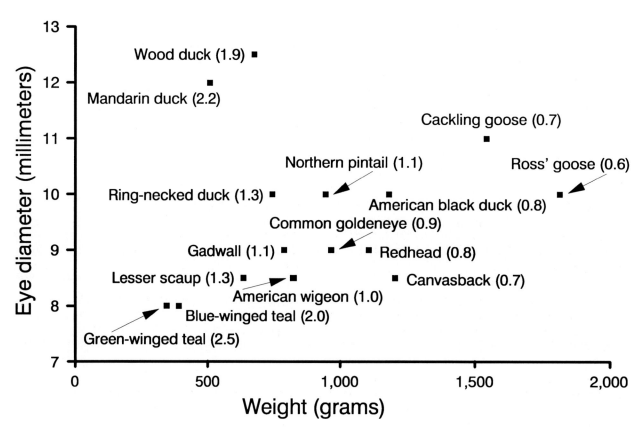

Figure 2. Relationship between eye diameter and body weight of adult wood ducks and selected species of other adult waterfowl. Percentages in parentheses compare eye diameter with body mass.

Large eyes dominate the head of the wood duck. Red eyelids and irises and red-margined bills with a black center stripe add to the luster of the male's multicolored head. A large white tear-shaped mark surrounding each eye distinguishes the female. Bills average about 3.18 centimeters (1.25 in) in length and are relatively narrow compared with those of other dabbling ducks. *Photo by George Arthur; courtesy of the Illinois Department of Conservation.*

CLASSIFICATION

In North America, only four duck species are sole representatives of their genus—wood duck, Steller's eider, harlequin duck, and oldsquaw. Worldwide, woodies share their genus, *Aix*, with the mandarin duck (*A. galericulata*), an Asiatic species.

First classified by Linnaeus (1758) as *Anas sponsa*, based mainly on "The Summer Duck" described by Catesby (1731–1743), the wood duck subsequently was placed in seven other genera by various taxonomists: *Aix, Dendronessa, Lampronessa, Aia, Cosmonessa, Dendrocygnus,* and *Aex* (Phillips 1925). One taxonomist classified it as *Aix promissa*, but all others held to the specific name *sponsa*, meaning "bridal." The genus *Aix* was first proposed by Boie (1828). Baird (1858), in a catalog of birds at the Smithsonian Institution, listed this species as *Aix sponsa*, with its common name as "summer duck." In his nomenclature of North American birds at the U.S. National Museum, Ridgway (1881) employed both common names—wood duck and summer duck—and the scientific name *Aix sponsa*. The genus *Aix* and species *sponsa* with the common name wood duck appended was adopted by the American Ornithologists' Union (AOU) in its *First Check-List of North American Birds* (1886). In the subsequent editions of 1895, 1910, 1931, 1957, and 1983, the AOU held to the same scientific and common names for this species.

Taxonomists have placed the genus *Aix* in the tribe Cairinini, which includes the Muscovy duck of Mexico. This tribe is a loose amalgamation of nine genera that, worldwide, include 13 species that exhibit perching and cavity-nesting traits; the plumages of many of these species exhibit extensive iridescent colors (Johnsgard 1978). Cairinini, along with seven other tribes, is placed in the subfamily Anatinae, which embraces most of the waterfowl that are considered typical ducks. The waterfowl family Anatidae includes whistling ducks, swans, and geese along with the typical ducks.

In a definitive study of the postcranial osteology of waterfowl, Woolfenden (1961) concluded that the genus *Aix* was closer to the genera *Cairina* (Muscovy duck) and *Chenonetta* (Australian wood duck) than to *Anas* (mallard). This relationship was evident from differences between humeri, carpometacarpi, the carcoid, and the sternum.

The wood duck has no less than 23 other common names: summer duck, Carolina duck, Carolina teal, acorn duck, black, branchier, bride duck, beau canard hupe, canard hupe, canard du bois, canard d'ete, black-billed whistling duck, whistler, squealer, plumer, scovy duck, widgeon, wood wigeon, crested wood duck, tree duck, king duck, regal duck, and rainbow duck (McAtee 1923, Phillips 1925). The names other than wood duck (or woodie) that were in the most widespread use were summer duck and Carolina duck.

A drake wood duck, resplendent in nuptial plumage, is a beautiful sight to behold. Even with its brilliant varicolored feathers, the male often is obscure in its world of light and shadow, primarily because of the broken pattern of the plumage that segments its conformation into bits and pieces that blend into the cover it seeks. *Photo by Jack Putnam; courtesy of the Denver Museum of Natural History.*

Similarities between the Wood Duck and Mandarin Duck

Both wood ducks and mandarins have behavioral and plumage characteristics that indicate a close relationship (Johnsgard 1978). The females of both species rely heavily on inciting to select a mate of their choice and on initiating copulation by assuming a prone position on the water. Females of both species are very similar in appearance, with differences largely in the amount of white around their eyes. Yet, despite their similar plumages, few hybrids ever form from their association in aviaries (Johnsgard 1978).

The woodie's failure to hybridize with the mandarin duck is particularly unusual because of the large number of species with which the wood duck is known to have hybridized in confinement (Gray 1958). The almost complete failure of these two closely related species to hybridize may relate to the apparent aberrant karyotype of the mandarin (Yamashina 1952). The chromosomal differences of the mandarin from other species of ducks may be responsible for limiting its ability to hybridize.

The only other bird in the same genus (*Aix*) as the wood duck is the mandarin duck of Asia. The two species not only share taxonomic and physiological similarities, they are also widely considered the most brilliantly colored ducks in their respective hemispheres. Although the females of the two species are similar, the mandarin hen has a thin white line behind the eyes, while the woodie hen has a white wedge-shaped marking. *Left photos of mandarins by Irene Vandermolen; top right photo of wood duck drake by Irene Vandermolen; bottom right photo of wood duck hen by Ed Bry; courtesy of the North Dakota Game and Fish Department.*

HISTORY

The unique and striking appearance of the wood duck has long been reflected in human artistic and cultural endeavors, encompassing the burials of prehistoric Indians, mythology and folklore of historic Indians, the history of the early colonies, exploration by pioneering adventurists and naturalists, and contemporary painting, sculpture, and photography. Through all the fabric of time that people have occupied eastern North America, they have been fascinated by the unique appearance and behavior of this species.

Indian Culture

Reeves (1990) concluded that prehistoric Indians not only were quite familiar with wood ducks but also revered them, especially in the Mississippi Valley. Hathcock (1976) devoted an entire chapter to bird effigies in his book about Indian pottery. Eight of 58 bowls illustrated there feature wood ducks; two more display ducks with crested heads (either wood ducks or hooded mergansers), and three have abstract effigies that may represent wood ducks. The bowls are from Arkansas, Missouri, and Illinois—in the heart of the wood duck's range. Only owls appear more often than wood ducks as effigies on these bowls.

Dockstader (1961) described a bowl uncovered in Walton County, Florida, that displays a wood duck's crested head; he noted that this design was a favorite of prehistoric potters.

The rim effigy heads on four bowls in the Dickson Mounds Museum, Lewiston, Illinois, are con-

sidered to represent wood ducks. Three bowls are from local excavations; one is unusually small. The fourth, an exceptionally large bowl, is from Madison County, Illinois.

Wood ducks often were carved by Indians as figures on ceremonial pipe or calumet bowls. Thruston (1890) showed three specimens, two of which were detailed body designs and one a probable wood duck effigy. Reeves (1990) considered a pipe representative of the Copena culture, Middle Woodland Period (A.D. 100–600), the finest wood duck steatite pipe he has seen. From Scott County, Virginia, this pipe is in the collection of the Smithsonian Institution. The use of wood duck ornamentation by Indians in historic times was observed by Wilson (1828: 315): "Among other gaudy feathers which the Indians ornament the calumet or pipe of peace, the skin of the head and neck of the Summer Duck is frequently seen covering the stem."

In discussing the Natchez Indians of the southeastern United States, Swanton (1946: 260) wrote: "He [Du Pratz (1763)] says there was a feast or ceremony on the new moon of each month showing how the economic and ceremonial cycles were intertwined. The second moon which corresponds to our month of April is that of the Strawberries. . . . The warriors then make their presents of wood ducks, which they have provided by a hunt made expressly for the purpose."

Abbott (1895: 249) found the attitude of Indians toward the woodie a natural outgrowth of their aesthetic values: "It is not strange that the wood duck should have strongly attracted the attention of the Indians. Its wondrous beauty naturally appealed to a savage people fond of personal decoration and

Four pottery vessels in the Dickson Mounds Museum, Lewiston, Illinois, have apparent rim effigies of wood ducks. The two shown are the best examples; both are from the Mississippian Culture, A.D. 1200–1300, one (left) from the Dickson Mound Site in Fulton County, the other (right) from the Vandeventer Site of Brown County, Illinois. *Photos by Kelvin W. Sampson; courtesy of Dickson Mounds Branch, Illinois State Museum.*

bright colors. They carved the head of this duck in steatite as an ornamental smoking-pipe, and we find it also moulded in clay in the elaborate pottery of the mound-builders." We concur that prehistoric and historic Indians were cognizant of the unusual beauty and the spectacular head form of the wood duck, and their application of its likeness to pottery and pipes is testament to their esteem for the species' unique appearance.

In addition to Indian appreciation of the wood duck's beauty, they found it a source of food. Parmalee (1957) examined vertebrate remains from the famous Cahokia site, occupied from 1200–1500 A.D., near East St. Louis, Illinois. He found 45 bones from wood ducks, compared with 480 from mallards, 199 from green-winged teal, 78 from blue-winged teal, and 426 from other ducks; swans and geese provided 453 skeletal remains.

Vanguards

Early explorers and settlers apparently considered the wood duck a singular bird, for at an early period in the history of the colonies, live wood ducks were sent to England and Europe, doubtless because they were beautiful and unique. According to Phillips (1925), wood ducks were known in Europe as early as the 17th century. The Condes at

Chantilly, France, obtained six specimens for a zoological collection in 1663, and others were kept by Louis XIV, King of France. The French Count G. L. L. Buffon (1707–1788) wrote of the wood duck (termed "branch duck") in his 36-volume opus, *Histoire Naturelle* (1783), incorporating findings of earlier French explorers in New France (eastern Canada). He quoted Friar C. Le Clercq (1691: 485): "There is a kind of duck we call branch ducks, which roosts in trees, and whose plumage is very beautiful on account of the agreeable diversity of colours which form it."

The wood duck attracted the attention of early naturalists exploring the wilderness of eastern United States (Reeves 1990). In *A New Voyage to Carolina*, published first in 1709, English naturalist John Lawson (1967: 152) noted: "We have another duck that stays with us all the summer. She has a great Topping, is pied, and very beautiful. She builds her nest in a Woodpecker's hole, very often sixty or seventy Foot high."

Mark Catesby explored the Carolinas and Florida and meticulously described the region's plant and animal life (see Feduccia 1985). Understandably, he named the wood duck the "summer" duck because it was almost the only one found in the Southeast during that season. Catesby (1731–1743) provided a detailed description of the wood duck's appearance and an excellent watercolor of an adult

Prehistoric and historic Native Americans appreciated the unique appearance of the wood duck sufficiently to represent its likeness on carved stone and baked clay pipes. The carved steatite pipe shown here with a wood duck head at one end and an owl head at the other is from the Copena Culture, Middle Woodland period, A.D. 100–600, Scott County, Virginia. *Photo courtesy of the Smithsonian Institution.*

The "Summer Duck," as Mark Catesby called the wood duck in the period 1731–1743, was the first painting of this species, a century before Audubon. The original art shows that Catesby had a remarkable ability to depict the complex plumage pattern of the drake. *Photo courtesy of the Smithsonian Institution.*

For his four volumes on the natural history of uncommon birds, English ornithologist George Edwards, 1743–1751, followed Catesby in illustrating the drake wood duck. Early naturalists neglected to portray the drab hen until 1821, when John James Audubon featured two females—one on a nest—with two males. *Photo courtesy of the Smithsonian Institution.*

male. He reported that wood ducks bred in Virginia and Carolina and nested in woodpecker holes in tall trees, particularly cypress growing in water.

Feduccia (1985: 52) quoted Catesby that, "While young and unable to fly, the old ones carry them on their backs from their nests into the water; and at the approach of danger, they fix with their bills on the backs of the old ones which fly away with them." This account and similar ones of the departure of ducklings from cavity nest sites in trees have been recounted by early ornithologists up to and including Forbush (1925).

In England, the eminent ornithologist George Edwards (1743–1751), as reported by Phillips (1925), described a wood duck shot before 1747 and mentioned seeing several live birds that had been sent from the Carolinas to London. Loisel (1912) reported that the wood duck was kept so commonly in Holland during the 17th and 18th centuries as to be used as a table bird by the nobility.

The naturalist Bartrams, father John and son William, commented sparingly on the wood duck during their travels in the eastern United States during the mid and late 1700s. William Bartram (1791) noted that it was a migrant in Pennsylvania, arriving in the spring season, nesting, rearing young, and returning south in autumn.

Charles C. Abbott (1895), pioneer naturalist of Georgia, noted that a few wood ducks remained all year but that their numbers were much greater in winter (Rogers-Price 1983: 63). Abbott observed that young placed in a pail would "readily climb out by the help of their bill and nails."

Philadelphia physician Benjamin Smith Barton wrote (1799: 17): "This beautiful species is the *Gi-gi-tschi-mu-is* of the Delaware Indians. It builds its nest in the holes of trees. Attempts have been made to domesticate it: but hitherto, they have not, I believe, been successful." However, Alexander Wilson, according to Phillips (1925), saw many captive woodies and mentioned a Mr. Nichols whose yard was "swarming" with summer ducks near Havre de Grace, Maryland.

John James Audubon (1840–1844) described the wood duck's morphology, distribution, nesting, behavior, rearing of young, movements, food, and feeding in a text of eight pages. His painting (1827–1838) of a perched pair, flying male, and incubating hen captured for the first time the bird's superb beauty. It was titled "Summer or Wood Duck"; the taxonomic name given was *Anas sponsa*.

Audubon's observation (1840–1844: 237) that, from nests placed over water, recently hatched young would scramble to the entrance hole, launch "into the air with their little feet and wings spread, and drop into their favorite element," was the first accurate account of their nest departure. Nevertheless, he continued to support the misconception that, at nests located some distance from the water, "the mother carries them to it [water] one by one in her bill, holding them so as not to injure their yet tender frame."

Explorers of the West, although they were not primarily naturalists, often took time to record the presence of the wood duck in their journals. Captain Meriwether Lewis and William Clark, in their account (Coues 1893) of their epic voyage to the Pacific, entered observations of the wood duck on at least five occasions (Reeves 1990). They were the first to report a western wood duck population, from an observation on March 13, 1806, along the Columbia River near present-day Washougal, Washington. They had not seen the bird since entering the Rocky Mountains at present-day Great Falls, Montana, where it was observed on June 19, 1805.

Prince Alexander Philip Maximilian of Prussia embarked from St. Louis on the steamboat *Yellowstone* on April 10, 1833. The Maximilian expedition was bound up the Missouri River as far as Fort Union to observe and paint the American West, particularly its Indians. On April 25, 1833, just above the mouth of the "Nadaway" [Nodaway] River in northwestern Missouri, Maximilian observed woodies from the deck of the *Yellowstone*: "We saw everywhere pairs of the beautiful *Anas sponsa*, which came out of holes in the bank, where they doubtlessly had their nests" (Thwaites 1906: 189).

As reported in his book *On a Tour of the Prairies*, Washington Irving departed Fort Gibson, Oklahoma Territory, on October 10, 1832. Two days later, along the Arkansas River, Irving (1835: 48) wrote: "In our course through a forest we passed by a lonely pool, covered with the most magnificent water-lilies that I had ever beheld, among which swam several wood ducks, one of the most beautiful of waterfowl, remarkable for their gracefulness and brilliancy of its plumage."

Naturalist and preeminent wildlife artist John James Audubon was particularly enamored of the woodie. He wrote: "I have always experienced a particular pleasure while studying the habits of that most beautiful bird, the Wood Duck" (Ford 1957: 76). His stylized treatment of the wood duck (left) and other birds set artistic standards in wildlife art that his contemporaries did not match, nor have many since. One of those contemporaries—also a friend and associate—was English engraver Robert Havell, Jr. In fact, Havell's principal fame was for engraving all but the first 10 plates in Audubon's *Birds of America*, which Havell accomplished between 1827 and 1838, prior to immigrating to the United States (where he lived for a time with Audubon). In his own painting of wood ducks (right), Havell virtually copied Audubon's birds but incorporated a background that features a distinctive European/Hudson River landscapist influence. Havell added the ducklings with the brooding hen. He also incorrectly repositioned Audubon's incubating female on a ground nest. *Left photo courtesy of the Library of Congress. Right photo courtesy of the Thomas Gilcrease Museum.*

Even Arctic explorers reported finding wood ducks. The Sir John Franklin expeditions collected two near Cumberland House, Saskatchewan (54 degrees north)—one in May 1820 and another in June 1827 (Houston 1984). A nest with two eggs was taken by MacFarlane (1908) at Fort Providence along Great Slave Lake on May 15, 1885.

Contemporary Appreciation

The beauty of the wood duck continues to inspire artists and fascinate the public at large. Its frequent portrayal on calendars, selection for federal and state duck stamps, and use by the U.S. Postal Service as the first (October 4, 1968) in an annual series of first-class postage stamps ($0.06) focusing on wildlife conservation demonstrate the public's admiration for this species. The U.S. Postal Service issued a second wood duck postage stamp ($0.29) on April 12, 1991. Because of that second stamp's popularity, it still was being issued in 1994 and represented sales in the tens of millions, according to a postal spokesman.

Fly fishermen appreciate the wood duck for its feathers, which they use in creating both wet and dry flies. McClane (1965) prescribed wood duck feathers for eight wet flies, six dry flies, three stream flies, a salmon fly, and a steelhead fly. For trout, Bergman (1970) recommended wood duck feathers for tying four kinds of wet flies and six dry flies. Indeed, the woodies' barred side feathers are known in the trade as "fly tiers' gold."

From a precipitously low population level in the early 1900s, the wood duck rebounded to an amazingly high level in the 1980s. While populations of such other important game ducks as the mallard, American black duck, and northern pintail have declined, wood duck numbers have steadily increased. During the first half of the 1980s, the wood duck ranked second to the mallard in the bag of hunters in the Atlantic and Mississippi flyways; by the mid-1980s, it ranked first in West Virginia, North and South Carolina, Georgia, and Kentucky.

After people became aware of the wood duck's low population levels in the early 1900s, conservation and research programs were initiated to increase its abundance. In addition to implementation of laws that restricted the kill, the comeback of the wood duck occurred primarily because of its high breeding potential and remarkable adaptability (Bellrose 1990). Wood ducks are able to use many different types of habitat because they can exploit a broad food base to meet their nutritional needs. Lack (1954) reported that the food base, more than any other factor, is responsible for affecting productivity and survival of birds.

The recovery of the wood duck has enabled it to resume a role as a game species. In addition, many people now have the opportunity to appreciate its unique beauty, unusual nesting habits, and association with towns and suburbia during the nesting season. Wood ducks have generated so much interest that thousands of nest houses have been privately erected by individuals in all walks of life. Many people have witnessed one of the greatest dramas in nature—woodie ducklings jumping from a nest house at the call of their mother.

Wood duck scenes have twice graced federal duck stamps: in 1943–1944 (left) with art by Walter E. Bohl, and in 1974–1975 (right) with art by David Maass. Federal duck stamps—required annually of all waterfowl hunters more than 16 years old in the United States—were first issued in 1934. Proceeds from the sale of these stamps are earmarked for waterfowl habitat purchase or lease. Since passage of the Migratory Bird Hunting Stamp Act on March 16, 1934, federal duck stamp dollars have contributed to the protection of about 1.62 million hectares (4 million ac) in the National Wildlife Refuge System. *Photos courtesy of the U.S. Fish and Wildlife Service.*

Stanley W. Galli's depiction of a wood duck pair in flight (top) was used on a 6¢ United States postage stamp (first class) issued on October 24, 1968. The stamp was the first in an annual series that emphasized the need to conserve wildlife. On April 12, 1992, the woodie's familiar visage appeared on a second U.S. first-class stamp (bottom), featuring the art of Robert Giusti. As of this book's press date, the second stamp still is being widely and extensively issued. *Top photo courtesy of Laurence R. Jahn. Bottom photo courtesy of the United States Postal Service.*

The widespread popularity of the wood duck is evidenced by its frequent appearance on state duck stamps. Over the past two decades the woodie has graced as many as 10 states' *first* duck stamps, including Ohio's in 1982 (top left, artwork by John A. Ruthven), Vermont's in 1986 (bottom left, artwork by Jim Killen), and Georgia's in 1985 (center left, artwork by Daniel Smith). Much like the federal duck stamp, state duck stamps are required for nearly all licensed waterfowl hunters within the state, and most of the revenue generated is used to acquire and protect wetland habitat. *Top left photo courtesy of the Ohio Department of Natural Resources. Bottom left photo courtesy of the Vermont Fish and Wildlife Department. Center left photo courtesy of the Georgia Department of Natural Resources.*

Currier & Ives lithographic prints were popular parlor and business establishment decorations in the 1800s. A fair number of the more than 7,000 different lithographs produced by that company featured contemporary "sporting life," including "American Dead Game" (above), produced in 1866 by artist Francis ("Fanny") Palmer. Currier & Ives sporting prints were calculated to appeal chauvinistically to males at a time when hunting and fishing were becoming more recreational choices than subsistence quests. Hunting and fishing scenes invariably portrayed a rich or dramatic pageant, interpreted with all the sentimentality, morality, and prejudices of the time. Scenes featuring dead game were common, evoking reflective illusions of success, skill, plenty, prosperity, diversity, prowess, and beauty. *Photo courtesy of the Library of Congress.*

Chapter 2

Distribution

The wood duck truly is a North American bird. Woodies occur naturally on no other continent. The need for suitable tree cavities in which to nest probably has delineated its breeding range more distinctly than any other factor. However, the presence of suitable natural cavities in the forested wetlands north of the wood duck's breeding range suggests that other factors—breeding physiology being the most notable—have limited the northward expansion of its range.

The life of the wood duck is intricately related to the range it occupies. Of all North American waterfowl, it is the most adept at living in forested wetland habitats. Woodies seldom venture far from woodlands and associated water areas, and their distribution is essentially confined to riparian corridors and other areas of lowland forest that are interspersed with freshwater ponds, lakes, marshes, and swamps.

HISTORICAL AND CONTEMPORARY RANGES

The wood duck's primary breeding range comprises two general areas: one includes southern British Columbia, northwestern Montana, the Pacific Northwest, and California; the other extends from the Great Plains eastward to the Atlantic Coast and from the southern Canadian provinces east of Alberta south to the Gulf Coast states (Map 1). Wood ducks also are known to nest in scattered locations in the Great Plains states adjacent to the primary breeding range, including New Mexico. An apparently self-sustaining population of wood ducks occurs in Cuba; unfortunately, little is known about the status of these birds or their habits.

Wood ducks have nested throughout the Pacific Northwest, California, and the Mississippi and Atlantic flyway states since presettlement times, but their range is dynamic in nature and has undergone changes in response to biological and environmental factors. Variations in distribution have resulted primarily from interactions between population production and survival, and from habitat enhancement, degradation, and destruction.

Little is known about the level and distribution of the wood duck population before and during the 19th century; however, the large amount of mature and overmature timber along the undisturbed watercourses that interlaced the deciduous forests of North America must have provided ideal breeding, brood-rearing, and wintering habitat. The literature suggests that wood ducks occurred in tremendous numbers during the 1700s and 1800s, probably in larger numbers than in later times. The breeding range of the wood duck likely encompassed all areas where wooded streams and other wooded wetlands occurred.

The historical distribution and contemporary status of the wood duck populations are discussed in Chapter 5, where the elimination and reoccupation of wood ducks in various portions of their range also are described.

Marked variations in local densities and distributions have occurred as the continental population rebounded from the low levels of the early 1900s. As a result of population increases, changes in vegetative communities, and the erection of nesting boxes and subsequent release of wood ducks in areas devoid of natural cavities, some present-day local populations are in larger numbers than occurred in the 19th century and in areas different from those occupied during the 1800s.

Descriptive accounts of the wood duck's range during the 20th century abound in scientific and popular literature. Comparisons between the historical range map prepared by Robbins and Aldrich (1966) and recent range maps make clear that wood ducks have appreciably expanded their primary range westward into the Great Plains and northward into much of southern Canada during the past five decades (Ladd 1990). Much of the westward expansion during the 1970s and 1980s is related to the development and maturation of floodplain forests (currently dominated by cottonwood and willow) along watersheds that transect the Great Plains. In certain areas of eastern North Dakota and southern Manitoba and British Columbia, wood ducks recently have become relatively common breeding birds because of nest box and release programs. Improved habitat conditions in Ontario were brought about by expanding beaver populations during the 1950s and 1960s and are thought to be partially responsible for increased numbers of wood ducks in eastern Canada (Cringan 1971).

Wood ducks undoubtedly have occurred in areas other than those on range maps, but their numbers were sparse or their presence undetected. Some apparent range expansions may merely reflect more precise information concerning the distribution of wood ducks or differences in the subjective delineation of range boundaries made by various authors.

BREEDING POPULATIONS

The wood duck's ability to hide in herbaceous and woody cover precludes the use of traditional survey techniques to estimate its status, and methods of estimating state and flyway breeding populations have ranged from educated guesses to the incorporation of banding data and hunter-kill information in involved calculations (tables 2 and 3). Although such indirect methods are not precise, they provide a reasonable basis from which comparisons between regional populations can be made.

Table 2. Wood duck breeding population and density estimated for states and provinces within the Atlantic Flyway.

State or province	This study[a] (1961–70)	Sutherland (1971)[b] (1965)	Bowers (1977)[c] (1962–68)	This study (1981–85) Number[d]	Number per square kilometer (mi²)	
Maine	15,063	17,000	35,099	31,016	0.36	(0.93)
Vermont	8,087	15,000	16,751	10,270	0.41	(1.07)
New Hampshire	16,469	25,000	16,514	23,925	1.00	(2.58)
Massachusetts	16,715	25,000	20,641	16,654	0.78	(2.01)
Connecticut	9,671	8,000	2,356	18,981	1.46	(3.78)
Rhode Island		2,000	1,818			
New York	86,501	40,000	57,612	86,993	0.68	(1.77)
Pennsylvania	34,904	23,000	57,594	45,094	0.38	(1.00)
West Virginia	11,750	5,000	22,067	27,410	0.44	(1.13)
New Jersey	32,622	18,000	20,876	76,940	3.81	(9.88)
Delaware	5,133	5,000	6,921	20,357	3.85	(9.96)
Maryland	29,283	11,000	4,002	103,623	3.82	(9.91)
Virginia	18,437	10,000	5,014	90,712	0.86	(2.23)
North Carolina	21,239	40,000	80,818	84,188	0.62	(1.60)
South Carolina	30,002	40,000	13,341	72,013	0.89	(2.31)
Georgia	18,098	30,000	181,679	55,083	0.36	(0.94)
Florida	36,652	60,000	92,701	32,778	0.22	(0.56)
Quebec	36,880	25,000	20,316	46,761	0.44	(1.14)
Ontario	113,839[e]	101,000[f]	53,612[f]	230,997	10.51	(2.34)
Total	541,345	500,000	709,732	1,073,795[g]		

[a] Average population estimates for the period 1961–70; calculations presented in Appendix D.
[b] Population estimates for 1965 based on educated but subjective estimates.
[c] Average population estimates for the period 1962–68 derived with simultaneous equations.
[d] Average population estimates for the period 1981–85; calculations presented in Appendix F.
[e] Based on kill data for the period 1974–78.
[f] Calculated adult population of Sutherland (1971) and Bowers (1977) prorated: 75 percent for Ontario's contribution to the Atlantic Flyway and 25 percent for its contribution to the Mississippi Flyway.
[g] Calculated on the basis of harvest, age ratios, and band recovery data for the entire flyway: 1,013,800 breeding numbers, close to the sum derived from calculating individual state and province populations.

Table 3. Wood duck breeding population and density estimated for states and provinces within the Mississippi Flyway.

State or province	This study[a] (1961–70)	Sutherland (1971)[b] (1965)	Bowers (1977)[c] (1962–68)	This study (1981–85)		
				Number[d]	Number per square kilometer (mi²)	
Minnesota	195,542	89,000	124,394	342,474	1.57	(4.06)
Wisconsin	164,232	70,000	138,449	236,982	1.63	(4.22)
Michigan	108,003	40,000	58,477	139,360	0.92	(2.39)
Iowa	44,155	30,000	26,994	80,625	0.55	(1.43)
Illinois	78,657	60,000	21,534	93,455	0.64	(1.66)
Indiana	56,954	40,000	40,058	66,273	0.71	(1.84)
Ohio	111,316	40,000	27,884	103,198	0.96	(2.50)
Missouri	43,153	29,000	71,614	86,840	0.49	(1.26)
Kentucky	2,025	12,000	13,561	7,044	0.07	(0.18)
Arkansas	74,876	34,000	40,653	117,503	0.85	(2.22)
Tennessee	42,310	13,000	0	45,577	0.41	(1.08)
Louisiana	60,915	31,000	34,225	134,346	1.09	(2.82)
Mississippi	38,685	44,000	137,590	81,983	0.66	(1.72)
Alabama	30,538	28,000	55,569	41,911	0.31	(0.80)
Ontario	37,951[e]	34,000[f]	17,871[f]	76,999		
Total	1,089,312	594,000	808,873	1,654,570[g]		

[a] Average population estimates for the period 1961–70; calculations presented in Appendix E.
[b] Population estimates for 1965 based on educated but subjective estimates.
[c] Average population estimates for the period 1962–68 derived with simultaneous equations.
[d] Average population estimates for the period 1981–85; calculations presented in Appendix G.
[e] Based on kill data for the period 1974–78.
[f] Calculated adult population of Sutherland (1971) and Bowers (1977) prorated: 75 percent for Ontario's contribution to the Atlantic Flyway and 25 percent for its contribution to the Mississippi Flyway.
[g] Calculated on the basis of harvest, age ratios, and band recovery data for the entire flyway: 1,627,300 breeding numbers, close to the sum derived from calculating individual state and province populations.

Our calculations (based on kill and band recovery data) indicate that, during 1981–1985, an average of more than 1 million (500,000 pairs) breeding wood ducks occurred in the Atlantic Flyway states and 1.6 million (800,000 pairs) in the Mississippi Flyway (tables 2 and 3). Recent estimates of the Central Flyway population range from 75,000 to 167,000 (Table 4). Recent estimates for the Pacific Flyway indicate approximately 60,000 (Table 5). Thus, there are a possible 1.4 million pairs of breeding wood ducks in North America, primarily in the United States.

Table 4. Wood duck breeding population and density estimated for states and provinces of the Great Plains.[a]

State or province	Population estimate	Number per square kilometer (mi²)		Source
Manitoba	2,800	tr	(tr)	This study
Saskatchewan	400	tr	(tr)	Dennis (1990)
North Dakota	13,100	0.164	(0.425)	Bellrose (1976)
Montana	7,500	0.029	(0.075)	Robert L. Eng
South Dakota	>8,600	0.090	(0.233)	Brewster et al. (1976)
Wyoming		tr	(tr)	
Nebraska	>4,000	0.037	(0.096)	Bellrose (1976)
Kansas	>5,000	0.031	(0.080)	Bellrose (1976)
Oklahoma	10,100	0.061	(0.158)	Prokop (1981)
Texas	24,000	0.067	(0.174)	May (1986)
Total	75,500[b]			

[a] Density based on area of state or province east of 100 degrees west, except for Montana which includes the region east of the Rocky Mountains.
[b] The average annual harvest of wood ducks in this flyway, 1971–80, was 76,100, of which 26,700 were adults. This harvest figure and the band recovery rates applicable to eastern North America (corrected for unreported bands) suggest an annual adult harvest rate of 0.1598 percent. This information indicates that the Central Flyway has a breeding population of about 167,000 (26,700/0.1598)—much higher than estimated by other methods.

Table 5. Wood duck breeding population and density estimated for British Columbia and states within the Pacific Flyway.[a]

State or province	Population estimate	Number per square kilometer (mi²)	
British Columbia	3,000		
Washington	7,900	0.045	(0.117)
Oregon	17,000	0.068	(0.175)
Idaho	3,730	0.017	(0.044)
Montana[b]	800–1,200	0.007–0.01	(0.018–0.026)
Wyoming	<50		
Nevada	>1,000		
Utah	<200		
California	26,000	0.063	(0.163)
Arizona	>24		
Total	59,904[c]		

[a] From Bartonek et al. (1990).
[b] West of the divide.
[c] This harvest figure and the band recovery rate of 0.0681 corrected for unreported bands at the rate of 3.32 suggests an annual harvest rate of 0.2261 percent. This information indicates that the Pacific Flyway has a breeding population of about 58,800, close to the sum of the state and province estimates in this table.

Many of the direct methods used to survey waterfowl populations are not practicable for assessing wood duck numbers because of the species' tendency to avoid open areas by seeking overhead cover. Band recovery data and other hunter-harvest information subject to statistical tests provide reasonable population estimates. Computation and analysis of such indirect measures indicated, for 1981–1985, a woodie population of approximately 2.8 million in North America. Since 1985, the population has shown slight or negligible annual increases. *Photo by Scott Nielsen.*

The Atlantic Flyway

Wood ducks may nest as far northeast as Newfoundland and perhaps Labrador. Peters and Burleigh (1951) recorded their casual occurrence in Newfoundland, and Todd (1963) stated that the wood duck was a straggler to the Labrador Peninsula. Ian Goldie reported their probable nesting at Serpentine Lake in 1957 and on Cape Spear, Avalon Peninsula, Newfoundland in June 1978. He also noted that wood ducks were seen during spring and autumn at Otter Creek, near Lake Melville, Labrador.

Only one wood duck, a male, has been reported from St. Pierre and Miquelon islands, which lie a short distance south of Newfoundland (Cameron 1967). On Prince Edward Island, off the coast of Nova Scotia, Dennis (1990) recorded 20–60 wood ducks breeding. Randy L. Dibblee noted that observations of adults and broods have been largely in the eastern and eastcentral regions, where better wetlands occur. Dibblee observed that a small influx of males occurred in late June and remained to early October. Breeding wood ducks in New Brunswick number about 3,000 (Dennis 1990) and, according to John C. Baird, are almost entirely south of a line from Woodstock to Fredericton to Moncton. The largest numbers occur along the St. John River, including its lakes and lower tributary courses, between Fredericton and Saint John. From there to the Maine border, moderate population levels occur.

An estimated 200 wood ducks occur in Nova Scotia (Dennis 1990). Fred J. Payne found them scattered throughout the province with pockets of larger numbers in the Medway, Shubenacadie, and

Musquodoboit valleys and in Cumberland County, where Tufts (1961) claimed more bred per square kilometer in the Amherst Bog than elsewhere in the province. Payne estimated one brood per 259 square kilometers (100 mi²) for the interior of the province. In the 1970s, he found a nest house with ducklings on nearby Cape Breton Island.

The number of wood ducks breeding in Quebec has been calculated at 2,000 (Austin Reed), 4,000 (Dennis 1990), 20,000 (Bowers and Martin 1975), and 47,000 (Table 2). Banding data, however, indicate that 90 percent of the annual harvest of 23,454, 1981–1985, were native birds. Apparently, many more birds nest in Quebec than previous estimates had indicated. (See appendices D–G for calculations of breeding population levels for provinces and states based on harvest, age ratios, and band recovery data.)

Austin Reed summarized the distribution of wood ducks in Quebec as follows. The bird probably breeds along the south shore of the St. Lawrence from Riviere-du-Loup to Quebec City to the Maine border. It nests sparsely from the border of the United States to 48 kilometers (30 mi) north of the Ottawa River as far as 47 degrees north. Along the St. Lawrence River, the distance north of the river—from Montreal to the St. Maurice River—increases to 80 kilometers (50 mi), declining east of there to a few kilometers at Quebec City. The area of highest nesting density extends from several kilometers north of the Ottawa and St. Lawrence rivers, Ottawa to Louisville, to the New York-Vermont border. Isolated northern records have been reported for broods at La Tuque and Naudville. Nest records exist for the north shore of the St. Lawrence extending to Cap-Tourmente. Apparently, the wood duck range in Quebec extends slightly beyond the St. Lawrence Lowlands onto the Precambrian Shield; however, significant numbers are found only in the Lowlands.

It has been calculated that 307,996 wood ducks bred in southern Ontario and 34,111 in northern Ontario, 1981–1985. Cringan (1971) estimated Ontario's adult wood duck population at 214,000–356,000, 1967–1969. Based on visual surveys of the Canadian Wildlife Service, Dennis (1990) reported about 155,000 breeding birds.

Eighty percent of the wood ducks harvested in Ontario, 1981–1985, were taken in the southern part (zones 1 and 2); only 20 percent were harvested in northern Ontario (Zone 3). Zone 2 extends from Montreal to Sault Sainte Marie at about 45.5 degrees north. The banding data used to determine the proportion of Ontario's wood ducks associated with the Atlantic and Mississippi flyways were from only the two southern zones. Of the 131 direct

recoveries that were tabulated from these bandings, 75.6 percent were in the Atlantic Flyway. Therefore, 75 percent of the calculated 307,996 woodies breeding in southern Ontario were allocated to the Atlantic Flyway and 25 percent to the Mississippi Flyway (tables 2 and 3). Wood ducks breeding in northern Ontario were assigned to the Mississippi Flyway.

According to Harry Lumsden, most of the wood ducks breeding in Ontario occur in the wedge of land that extends south of a line from Orillia to Brockville and is hemmed in by lakes Huron, Erie, and Ontario. Numbers are low north of this line to about 47 degrees north and absent to sparse north of there to about the 49th parallel. Lumsden remarked that densities are low on the Precambrian Shield and noted the difficulties of ascertaining where sparse densities fade to zero. Near the city of Kirkland Lake (48 degrees north) one or two wood ducks have been nesting in houses since 1977, and a nearby natural cavity was used several times. Although no evidence of breeding was found, the species has been seen as far north as James Bay (Godfrey 1966). Harry Lumsden saw a pair in May at Kinoje [now Kinosheo] Lake, 90 kilometers (56 mi) northwest of Moosonee, Ontario.

According to William R. Darby, a second breeding area occurs in southwestern Ontario, extending from Thunder Bay northwest to Sioux Lookout and then west to the Winnipeg River (50.2 degrees north). He bases these boundaries on more than 50 sightings of pairs during spring and summer and on several nesting records. Personnel from the Ontario Ministry of Natural Resources have reported several pairs north of Darby's delineated range, but sightings were few. Darby further notes that wood ducks are commonly seen in autumn and shot over a more extensive area of northwestern Ontario than the area in which they breed.

Despite its many lakes, woods, and streams, Maine has a relatively low breeding population of wood ducks (Table 2). The northern and western regions of the state are covered by dense fir and spruce forests, which contain few natural cavities. Howard E. Spencer, Jr., advised that these forests, along with the infertility of the soils, provide poor food resources. Moderate numbers breed 150 kilometers (93 mi) inland on the upper coast and increase appreciably for 100 kilometers (62 mi) inland along the lower coast as hardwoods replace conifers.

New Hampshire has twice the density of breeding wood ducks as Vermont (Table 2). The only apparent difference in these two very similar regions is the greater abundance of lakes and ponds in southern New Hampshire. Harold C. Lacaillade reported that the only poor habitats for woodies in

New Hampshire are the White Mountains area and the northern tip of the state. Five areas with high population densities are dispersed throughout the interior of the state where wetlands and woodlands are in the greatest juxtaposition. The remainder of the state has a moderate abundance of wood ducks.

We calculated 10,270 wood ducks breeding in Vermont, 1981–1985 (Table 2). Breeding numbers in Vermont in 1965 were estimated at 15,000 (Laughlin and Kibbe 1985). Lowest densities are in the Green Mountains region that extends the length of the state through its center. The greatest density occurs along the Lake Champlain lowlands in the northwest region, the Connecticut River marshes and set-backs on the eastern border, and the Lake Memphremagog marshes in the northcentral region, according to Thomas R. Myers.

Wood ducks are almost totally absent as breeders along the coastal marshes of the New England states. Were it not for their low density in the western half of Massachusetts and in Cape Cod, wood duck populations would be denser in that state than in New Hampshire or Connecticut (Table 2). H W Heusmann reported that wood duck nest houses were used at similar rates throughout eastern Massachusetts as far west as the Quabbin Reservoir.

Suitable wood duck habitat occurs scattered inland in scores of freshwater ponds, lakes, marshes, and swamps in Connecticut, according to Tom Hoehn, and in Rhode Island as per James E. Myers. Because of the bountiful interspersion of wetlands and woods, Connecticut has a high abundance of breeding wood ducks (Table 2).

New York has a moderately high breeding density of wood ducks, largely because of the Lake Plain and Central Lakes—a region of 25,167 square kilometers (9,717 mi²), or 19.6 percent of the state. Stephen Brown rated Long Island, the Champlain-Mohawk-Hudson valleys, and the southern tier of counties—71,010 square kilometers (27,417 mi²), or 55.3 percent of the state—as supporting moderate numbers of wood ducks. The Catskill and Adirondack mountains—embracing 32,230 square kilometers (12,444 mi²), or 25.1 percent of the state—had low numbers of breeding wood ducks.

Wood ducks in Pennsylvania are most abundant as breeders in the northwest in the Lake Plain province and in the southeast, partly due to the Great Valley that extends through Virginia and the southeast corner of Pennsylvania. Fred E. Hartman reported them to be low to sparse in the Appalachian Mountains as well as the Appalachian Plateau and moderate in abundance elsewhere, including the Pocono Mountains region.

As in other coastal states, wood ducks in New Jersey eschew the salt marshes, mouths of large rivers, and industrialized areas, according to Fred Ferrigno. Elsewhere in New Jersey, wood ducks are widely distributed but most abundant in the large drainage systems of the Pine Barrens and in upland swamps at the headwaters of streams. Most of the stream and interior wetland habitat was classified as good-to-excellent habitat by Ferrigno, the several extensive state forests as fair, and only the lower reaches of the larger rivers—including the Delaware below Willingboro—as poor. Because of the abundance of sluggish streams and wetlands in the extensive coastal plain, New Jersey has one of the highest populations of breeding woodies in the Atlantic Flyway (Table 2).

West Virginia has one of the lowest densities of breeding wood ducks in the Atlantic Flyway (Table 2). In view of that state's mountainous terrain, even this calculated number is surprising. According to James M. Ruckel, wood ducks breed along the larger, slower-moving rivers and in beaver ponds at their headwaters. He identified the following rivers as supporting moderate numbers: Ohio; Elk above Charleston; Buckhannon; Cheat above Morgantown; West Fork above Roanoke; Potomac; South Branch of the Potomac below Petersburg; Monongahela from Fairmont to Weston; New; and Gauley. Streams of more limited use are the Coal River, Bluestone River, Little Kanawha above Creston, Tug Fork from Matewan to its confluence with the Big Sandy, and Big Sandy to the Ohio River.

Except for coastal marshes, salt marshes of the lower Chesapeake Bay, and the Allegheny Mountains region, wood ducks breed commonly throughout Maryland. Data in Table 2 suggest that density there is among the highest in the Atlantic Flyway. Streams on the Eastern Shore with the highest densities, as rated by Larry J. Hindman, are Pocomoke, Marshyhope, Choptank, Tuckahoe, and Susquehanna. On the west side of Chesapeake Bay, the Patuxent River from Bristol through the Patuxent National Wildlife Refuge, Zekiah Swamp, Potomac River from Keyser, West Virginia, to Great Falls, and the Monocacy River all were ranked by Hindman as among the best production areas in Maryland. Other streams and wetlands support a more moderate level of breeders.

According to Charles P. Gilchrist, Jr., the wood duck—rare as a breeder along the coast of Virginia—is sparsely distributed for about 26 kilometers (16 mi) inland from the Potomac estuary south to the North Carolina line. This distribution appears related to the extensive broad river mouths created by land subsidence. Gilchrist identified the region supporting the largest breeding numbers in Virginia as the zone from the coastal estuaries west across the Coastal Plain to the Piedmont. The Piedmont and the Great Valley (a trough between ridges embracing the Shenandoah Valley) are rated of moderate value. Streams of the mountain ridges were ranked low.

Wood ducks are absent or rare as breeders from the off-shore islands and marshes that rim the coast of North Carolina, according to Jack A. Donnelley. Highest populations occur in the lower Coastal Plain, with the exception of Carteret County and a narrow coastal area south of Wilmington. The upper Coastal Plain to the Piedmont supports a moderate breeding population. With three large regional exceptions, Donnelley rated the Piedmont and mountain provinces as supporting low populations. He reported moderate populations in the northwest counties of Surry, Stokes, Yadkin, Davie, Forsyth, eastern Wilkes, and northern Iredell, in the westcentral counties of Burke, Cleveland, McDowell, Rutherford, Polk, Madison, Buncombe, and Henderson, and in the extreme southwest counties of Cherokee, Clay, and Macon.

Because of extensive regions that support low populations of breeding wood ducks, the statewide density of 0.62 bird per square kilometer (1.60/mi²) in North Carolina is lower than densities in New Jersey and Maryland (Table 2) where a larger proportion of the land is in the Coastal Plain.

Wood ducks are sparse breeders in the coastal region of South Carolina, especially south of Charleston where coastal marshes are extensive. Tommy Strange noted that they are most abundant in the Coastal Plain in the northeastern sector and along large river watersheds of the central and southern borders. The Great and Little Pee Dee and the Lynches rivers, with their tributaries in the northeast, support high populations of woodies, as do the Wateree, Congaree, Edisto, and Four Hole Swamp rivers in the central region. The Savannah River, bordering Georgia, has high breeding numbers from Augusta to its mouth, moderate numbers as far as Anderson, and low numbers above a large impoundment that alters the riverine habitat. Streams on the Coastal Plain ranked as possessing moderate populations are the Black, Pocotaligo, lower Santee, lower Cooper, Ashepoo, Combahee, Salkehatchie, and Coosawhatchie. In the Piedmont region, Strange ranked the upper Wateree, north and south forks of the upper Edisto, Broad, Tyger, and Enoree as rivers supporting moderate breeding populations. In the mountainous region, low populations occur on the Catawba, Fishing, upper Broad, Pacolet, Saluda, and Rocky rivers. Wood ducks are rare or absent on streams of the high mountain ridges.

Oscar Dewberry indicated that wood ducks breeding in Georgia are either sparsely distributed or absent from coastal islands and estuaries and from the mountainous region north of Atlanta. They are most abundant along the large rivers that drain the Coastal Plain and Piedmont. These include the Savannah, Ogeechee, Altamaha and its major tributaries, Oconee, Ocmulgee, Ochlockonee, and a network of rivers in the southwest that embraces the Flint River and its tributaries and the Chattahoochee River along the western border of the state.

Much of the southern part of the state as far north as Crisp and Jeff Davis counties supports low populations of wood ducks. Surprisingly, this region includes the 161,876-hectare (400,000 ac) Okefenokee National Wildlife Refuge — an area that looks ideal for wood ducks. The interspersion of marsh, swamp hardwoods, pines, cypress, and open water creates a diverse habitat that should support a larger breeding population than is apparent. The acidic waters, which may limit a suitable food base, and the abundance of alligators, a predator on adult and duckling wood ducks, may be responsible for the paucity of woodies.

Immediately south of the Appalachian Mountains in Georgia lies the Dahlonega Plateau which, according to Dewberry, supports a low wood duck breeding population. The remainder of the state has a moderate population amid a network of small streams and beaver ponds.

Few states possess the extensive wetlands that Florida does. Unfortunately for wood ducks, vast regions are in sawgrass, meadows, and pines — habitats that do not afford nest sites. These habitats are especially prevalent south of a line from St. Petersburg to Orlando and Daytona Beach. Swamps in the southern half of the state support either moderate or low wood duck populations, according to Frank Montalbano III. He reported that the Big Cypress Swamp and the pine flatwoods of south Florida have low numbers and that sparse numbers or none occur in the Everglades agricultural and conservation areas, the Gold Coast, and the uplands of sand pine/scrub oak and pine/oak.

The farthest south that wood duck broods have been recorded in Florida is the Loxahatchie National Wildlife Refuge, southeast of Lake Okeechobee, where three broods were observed in 1980. Jean Takekawa, formerly of the refuge staff, saw wood ducks numerous times, June through August, in cypress stands near the headquarters site. No evidence exists that wood ducks breed in Everglades National Park, but the banding of 316 woodies by personnel of the Florida Game and Fresh Water Fish Commission from June 12 to August 23, 1984, in the Everglades, 8–43 kilometers (5–27 mi) north of the park, suggests that they may do so. Fred Johnson reported that all age and sex classes were represented in the trapped sample, and one bird captured on June 12 was a young flightless female. There are three credible reports of nonbreeding wood ducks near Flamingo, Cape Sable, but all current authorities on south Florida birds report an absence of wood ducks on the Florida Keys.

For the northern half of Florida, where most of the breeding wood ducks occur, Frank Montalbano III reported that densities declined from highest to lowest according to habitat type: (1) swamps and river bottomland hardwoods; (2) flatwoods and hammocks; (3) pine/oak uplands; (4) sand pine/scrub oak; and (5) coastal regions except along large streams where riparian hardwoods and cypress extend to their mouths.

Most of the prime breeding habitat for wood ducks lies along the rivers that dissect the Florida panhandle and the Big Bend of the northwestern coast. These include the Perdido, Escambia, Coldwater, Blackwater, Yellow, Choctawhatchee, Econfina, Apalachicola, Ochlockonee, Aucilla, Suwannee, and Waccasassa rivers. In north interior Florida, the Santa Fe River, the St. Marys River, its tributaries the South and North Prong rivers, and

the St. Johns River also were ranked high by Montalbano. He considered the lake and wetlands between Ocala and Lakeland as supporting moderate populations of breeders. Elsewhere through the center of the state, wetlands have low numbers.

Cuba and the Western Indies. According to several authorities, the wood duck is a resident in Cuba. Barbour (1943) stated that no difference could be detected between continental and island specimens and that the Cuban wood duck was equally abundant during summer and winter. Bond (1961) reported that it occurred along shady streams and lagoons in western Cuba, particularly Laguna La Deseado in Pinar del Rio. In a letter of June 13, 1953, V. W. Lehmann wrote that "during a trip to Oriente Province in Eastern Cuba in March . . . I found wood ducks are very common along water ways."

Bond (1961) noted that the wood duck has been reported from New Providence in the northwestern Bahamas and in Jamaica (no recent records). Titman and Seaman (1978) recorded the recovery of a banded juvenile male wood duck that apparently was blown to Saba Island, Netherlands Antilles, during a storm. Wood ducks reported in Puerto Rico and the Azores are considered accidental occurrences (American Ornithologists' Union 1983).

The vast wetlands of southern Florida are suitable nesting habitat for only a sparse population of wood ducks, but bottomland swamps and certain riparian habitats in the northern part of the state support substantial numbers of breeding woodies. *Photo by J. Johnson; courtesy of the Florida Game and Fresh Water Fish Commission.*

The Mississippi Flyway

As noted in the previous section, about 25 percent of the wood duck population that breeds in southern Ontario (zones 1 and 2) migrates into the Mississippi Flyway. All of the small number (34,111) that breeds in northern Ontario (Zone 3) were assumed to migrate into the Mississippi Flyway because most of Zone 3 is north and northwest of Lake Superior. The combined breeding population of the three zones in Ontario that might contribute to migration numbers in the Mississippi Flyway is calculated at 110,900 — about 6.7 percent of the flyway population.

The Lake States of Minnesota, Wisconsin, and Michigan support more breeding wood ducks than any region of comparable size in the United States (Table 3). Minnesota, with its extensive surface water resources and abundance of deciduous forests, has more wood ducks than any other state. It has the most inland water of any state — 2.59 square kilometers (1 mi²) for every 52 square kilometers (20 mi²) of land. Robert L. Jessen found the highest breeding populations in the central and northcentral regions of the state, where fertile wetlands and deciduous woodlands are in close juxtaposition. Few wood ducks breed in the Precambrian Shield north of Lake Superior or in the unglaciated regions in the southeastern and extreme southwestern parts of the state. A low density occurs along the western border, except for the Red River Valley where moderate numbers breed.

Minnesota and Wisconsin have a high density of wood ducks breeding along their common border with the Mississippi River, probably the species' best extensive breeding habitat. Other high-density populations in Wisconsin occur in the northwestern lake district as well as in the eastcentral region south of Green Bay and north of Milwaukee, according to R. A. Hunt. Low populations occur in the northeastern lake district where conifers predominate and in the intensively farmed country of southeastern Wisconsin. Elsewhere through the midsection and including the unglaciated district in the southwestern part of the state, Hunt delineated population levels of moderate density.

In 1982, a visual estimate of breeding wood ducks in Michigan amounted to 77,250. Our calculated population (Table 3) is 139,360. As reported by Jerry Martz and Mark Hart, 10,100 (13.1 percent of the visual estimate) were in the Upper Peninsula, 15,075 (19.5 percent) were in the upper half of the Lower Peninsula, and 52,075 (67.4 percent) occurred in the lower half of the Lower Peninsula. The large proportion of wood ducks in the lower half of the Lower Peninsula coincides with better soils (dark clay loams); farther north, light sand loams prevail. In the Upper Peninsula, soils are thin, coniferous forests abundant, and lakes generally acidic.

Within these three geographic regions of Michigan, wood ducks are rather uniformly distributed as a result of the wide dispersal of more than 11,000 lakes and ponds. In the Upper Peninsula, Schoolcraft County, with the Seney National Wildlife Refuge, has an unusually high density of breeding wood ducks. Moderate densities are found in Houghton, Ontonagon, and Gogebic counties, all in the extreme west. In the upper half of the Lower Peninsula, only the counties of Muskegon and Mecosta have exceptional populations. Counties in the southwestern quarter of the lower half of the Lower Peninsula sustain the densest population of breeding birds; in the counties south and west of Saginaw Bay, moderate densities occur, as reported by Jerry Martz and Mark Hart.

The deciduous woodlands and abundant wetlands of Wisconsin, Minnesota, and Michigan support more breeding woodies than any other area of comparable size in the United States. Michigan alone accommodates approximately 5 percent of the continent's nesting woodies, and both Minnesota and Wisconsin support even greater numbers. *Photo by Miles Pirne; courtesy of Michigan State University.*

According to James L. Hansen, the Mississippi River and its tributaries in the eastern third of Iowa support the largest breeding populations of woodies in that state. The lake district in Emmet, Dickinson, and Palo Alto counties maintains high populations, as does the Union Slough National Wildlife Refuge. Hansen ranked as low the population in western Iowa, despite numerous streams there draining into the Missouri River. Elsewhere through the central and eastern regions of the state, moderate populations prevail.

The Mississippi River above Alton and the Illinois River—Bureau to Meredosia—support among the highest breeding populations of woodies in Illinois, as reported by Dennis Thornburg. Streams and swamps in the southern fifth of the state also maintain high populations. Moderate populations prevail in southcentral and westcentral Illinois, with major breeding populations on the Little Wabash River, Kaskaskia River north of Fayetteville, lower Embarras, Sangamon, and La Moine rivers. Moderate populations prevail in the northern reaches of the Little Wabash and Embarras rivers, in the Vermilion River in eastcentral Illinois, and along the Kankakee, Upper Illinois, and Fox rivers in northeastern Illinois. In other areas, especially the heavily farmed Big Prairie in eastcentral Illinois, wood duck populations are low to sparse.

The highest wood duck populations in Indiana, according to Tom Sporre, occur across the northern fifth of the state, embracing the former Great Kankakee marsh and the lake district in the northeast. The White River, from the Ohio border to its confluence with the Wabash River on the Illinois border, supports a high breeding population, as does the East Fork of the White and its tributary, the Muscatatuck. The Wabash and Ohio rivers, along with their principal tributaries, sustain a moderate breeding population. The following streams maintain low populations according to Sporre: Tippecanoe, Mississinewa (above Marion), Sugar, Raccoon, Big Walnut, Brandywine, Big Blue, Sand, Flatrock, Graham, Laughery and Little.

Data provided by Karl Bendarik show that wood ducks are broadly distributed throughout Ohio. Wood ducks reach their greatest breeding densities in northeastern counties where lakes and reservoirs are most numerous. The use of nest houses is high in Wayne County, as is the harvest of wood ducks. The Little Muskingum River in Washington County consistently yielded the highest number of breeding wood ducks among 23 streams surveyed, 1976–1980, in a sampling of diverse riverine habitats.

The densest wood duck populations in Missouri are along the Mississippi River above the mouth of the Missouri River to the Iowa line and below the mouth of the Ohio River to Arkansas, according to David Graber and Dale D. Humburg. Low to moderate numbers occur in the Mississippi River Valley between the entrance of these two major tributaries because of the dearth of wooded bottomlands. The remnants of the once vast swamps in southeastern Missouri provide a habitat that supports moderate breeding densities, as does the lake impoundment region north and west of the Ozark Plateau. Sparse populations occur in the Ozark Plateau and in western Missouri, except for the Missouri River, from Jefferson City northwest to Iowa. Other areas of the Missouri River Valley and the remainder of the state support low numbers.

The highest densities of wood ducks in Kentucky occur in the four counties flanking the Mississippi River and, as noted by Vernon Anderson, in the six counties south of the Wabash River's mouth that are associated with the Ohio River and its tributaries. The northeastern bluegrass region sustains a low population. Eastward, the Cumberland Plateau maintains only sparse breeding numbers. Elsewhere over the southern and central regions of Kentucky, populations are moderate. The paucity of swamps and other wetlands confines wood ducks largely to streams, and only 0.07 bird per square kilometer (0.18/mi²) is found statewide (Table 3).

Tennessee has a slightly higher density of breeding wood ducks than does Kentucky (Table 3). This higher density probably stems from Reelfoot Lake and adjacent swamps combined with several large rivers with extensive overflow bottomland hardwoods, including the Obion, Hatchie, and Forked Deer, all in west Tennessee. From Kentucky south to Baton Rouge, Louisiana, the Mississippi River—with its multitude of oxbow lakes—also plays an important role, increasing in magnitude downstream, in enhancing the abundance of breeding wood ducks.

The Tennessee River and its larger tributaries in the west—the Duck, Buffalo, and Indian rivers—support high numbers of breeding birds, as do the Cumberland and its tributaries—the Red, Yellow, and Harpeth rivers. In the eastern part of the state, the Tennessee River and many of its tributaries pass through broad valleys between the Cumberland and Appalachian mountains, thereby supporting moderate to dense populations of woodies in contrast to the sparse populations found in the Cumberland Plateau of eastern Kentucky. The upper Holston River, north of Knoxville, supports one of the highest populations of any stream in the nation. Only in the high Appalachian Mountains are wood ducks sparse or absent.

The highest density of wood ducks in Arkansas

occurs largely in the remnant of overflow bottomland forests along the waterways of the Mississippi Alluvial Plain north of the Arkansas River. Streams that support abundant wood duck populations include the Little, St. Francis, Bayou de View, Cache, Black, White, La Grue Bayou, and Bayou Meto in the northeast, the Bayou Bartholomew, Ouachita, and Saline rivers in the southeast, and the Saline, Little, and Red rivers in the southwest. Breeding populations are lowest in the Ouachita Mountains in the west and the Boston Mountains in the north and northwestern parts of the state. Elsewhere in Arkansas, moderate levels of wood ducks prevail.

Louisiana has the greatest density of breeding wood ducks of any state in the Mississippi Flyway south of Minnesota and Wisconsin. They occur in sizable numbers throughout the state except in the 1.2 million-hectare (3 million ac) coastal marsh, where they are absent or sparse breeders according to Hugh Bateman, and in the pine uplands and extensive agricultural developments where they occur in low numbers. The multitude of sluggish waterways that interlace the state, however, provides extensive bottomland forests for breeding habitat. Highest populations occur along the Mississippi River to New Orleans, particularly in the adjacent Atchafalaya Basin; in the Bayou Macon, Bayou Boeuf, and Ouachita rivers in the northeastern part of the state; in the Red River in the northwest and center; in the Pearl River on the eastern border; and in the Saline River on the western border. Most of the smaller bayous that drain the piney woods and agricultural uplands support moderate populations, according to Bateman.

In Mississippi, as in Arkansas and Louisiana, highest woodie populations occur where remnants of the once vast overflow bottomland forest remain, largely in the Yazoo Basin, Richard K. Wells reported. Other areas of high density are the Big Black River from its mouth to Mathiston, the Pearl River from upper Ross Barnett Reservoir to Philadelphia (moderate numbers as far as Louisville), and the lower Buffalo and Homochitto rivers. Moderate breeding densities occur on the Coldwater River above Arkabutla Lake, the Tallahatchie above Sardis Lake, the Tombigbee from Marietta to the Alabama border, Bogue Chitto from Brookhaven to the Louisiana border, the Pascagoula and its tributaries (the Leaf River as far as Raleigh and the Chickasawhay River as far as Buckatunna), the Escatawpa River, and Noxubee National Wildlife Refuge. Pearl River, south of Jackson to the Louisiana border, is the only large river, according to Wells, that supports low numbers of wood ducks. Few waterways are considered to have sparse populations, perhaps because all are in the Coastal Plain Province where streams have low gradients.

The Appalachian Mountains and Plateaus occupy about one-third of Alabama in the north and northeast and are responsible for low or sparse populations of wood ducks in that area. These low numbers partially account for the low breeding population in the state (Table 3); however, several large rivers—the Tennessee, Coosa, and Tallapoosa—cleave the mountains and sustain some of the higher populations in Alabama, according to Bruce C. Johnson. Before the Tombigbee was canalized, it and its major upper tributaries—the Black Warrior and Sipsey rivers—maintained high breeding populations. The Chattahoochee River, which forms a portion of the boundary between Georgia and Alabama, also ranks high. The southeastern quarter of the state sustains high to low populations from east to west.

High densities of breeding wood ducks persist in the remnant bottomland hardwood forests of the Lower Mississippi River Valley, but the woodie numbers there—like overflow habitats—are but a small fraction of their former abundance. *Photo by Stephen Kirkpatrick.*

The Great Plains

In the United States, the Great Plains sweep westward from 96 to 97 degrees west to the Rocky Mountains. The region west of 100–104 degrees is considered the High Plains and is higher and drier than the Eastern Plains. Because of the differences between the two Plains divisions in water resources, vegetation, and elevation, wood duck distribution of the Great Plains is covered by division.

The Eastern Plains. Manitoba, eastern Saskatchewan, the Dakotas, Nebraska, Kansas, Oklahoma, and Texas are included in the Eastern Plains. Even in this easternmost region of the Great Plains, wood duck abundance declines from east to west, particularly north of Nebraska, as deciduous woodlands are rapidly replaced by land that was once in grass and now is cropland.

Surprisingly, wood ducks nest as far north as the Saskatchewan Delta (54 degrees north) in eastern Saskatchewan and western Manitoba. D. F. Hooey listed a wood duck nest at Cumberland House, Saskatchewan in June 1980. It is here that Robert Hood of the ill-fated Franklin Expedition collected and illustrated wood ducks in 1819–1822 (Houston 1974). Robert E. Jones reported that Phil Older observed a brood on the Carrot River, near The Pas, Manitoba, on June 15, 1977. A 19th-century record still standing is a wood duck specimen taken at Fort Providence, Great Slave Lake, Northwest

Territories (51.33 degrees north) (Phillips 1925).

Elsewhere in eastern Saskatchewan, S. R. Barber and D. F. Hooey reported either wood duck nesting or broods in three areas: eastern Qu'Appelle River, Moose Mountain Provincial Park, and the Souris and Antler rivers east of Estevan.

Robert E. Jones reported that the wood duck range in southern Manitoba is more extensive than in Saskatchewan and embraces a region from the Winnipeg River in the southeast to north of Riding Mountain National Park in the west. Jones noted broods on the Assiniboine River near Portage la Prairie, June 15 and 28, 1982. He included Riding Mountain National Park, Turtle Mountain Provincial Park, and the Whitemud, Pipestone, Pembina, Souris, and Rat rivers as supporting breeding wood ducks.

With numerous streams and thousands of sloughs and potholes, North Dakota provides optimal dabbling duck breeding habitat as far west as the Missouri River. Where tree cavities or nest houses are available, wood ducks occur in small numbers compared with those of their prairie-nesting brethren. The Red River in the east and the Sheyenne and James rivers—in part due to nest house programs—have substantial breeding numbers, according to Mike Johnson. Where reservoirs on the Missouri River have not eliminated bottomland hardwoods, wood ducks breed in limited numbers as far west as the Montana line. In the

Wood ducks likely never nested extensively in the prairie states, despite the many streams and wetlands, because of a dearth of suitable cavity trees. Nevertheless, where bottomland hardwoods exist, and because of ambitious nest house programs, breeding woodies are not uncommon in scattered locations of this "grassland" region. *Photo by Ed Bry; courtesy of the North Dakota Department of Game and Fish.*

northern region, wood ducks nest across the state as far as Kenmare, particularly in the Pembina Hills, the Turtle Mountains, and along the Souris and Des Lacs rivers. Faanes and Andrew (1983) estimated that 13 pairs nested in the Pembina Hills; they found 0.32 pair per kilometer (0.51/mi) on the Pembina River. Mike Johnson opined that wood ducks have extended their breeding range westward in North Dakota from that outlined by Schroeder (1960).

The estimate of breeding wood ducks in South Dakota (Table 4) probably is low if the increase in kill since the calculations were made is considered. According to Tom Kuck and Lester D. Flake, the highest breeding densities in South Dakota occur east of the Missouri River, particularly in the southeastern corner of the state. Flake reported that wood ducks nest along the Big Sioux and James rivers and the lower half of the Vermillion River. Wood ducks are largely restricted on the Missouri River to that reach adjacent to Nebraska where they utilize ponds on islands to rear broods. An isolated nesting colony was reported by Kuck on a wooded island below the Oahe Dam, near Pierre.

West of the Missouri River isolated breeding areas were reported by Flake at Burke Lake, Gregory County; the lower 32 kilometers (20 mi) of the White River; Little Moreau state recreation area in Dewey County; and along the Redwater and Belle Fourche rivers north of Deadwood. Ladd (1990) reported that wood ducks nested near Rapid City, South Dakota.

Except for the Platte, Niobrara, and Republican rivers, most wood ducks in Nebraska breed east of the 98-degree meridian, as reported by Kenneth L. Johnson. Along the Niobrara, they extend westward to near Valentine, and on the Republican almost to McCook. But the Platte provides the greatest artery westward; wood ducks nest all the way to the confluence of the North and South Platte rivers. They use the North Platte into Wyoming and the South Platte as far as Colorado's Red Lion State Management Area west of Julesburg, according to Howard D. Funk.

Marvin J. Kraft observed that the highest density of breeding wood ducks in Kansas occurs along the Kansas, Big Blue, Republican, Marais des Cygnes, upper Neosho, Verdigris, Elk, Fall, and Cottonwood rivers, all east of 98 degrees west in the north and 96.5 degrees west in the south.

Rivers of moderate value for wood ducks are the Delaware, lower Neosho, Medicine Lodge, and Missouri. West of the 98-degree meridian, the Arkansas, Solomon, Smoky Hill, and Saline rivers provide limited habitat for small numbers of wood ducks. An isolated nesting colony supported by

nest houses occurs near Jennings (100.5 degrees west) in extreme northwestern Kansas, per information from Roger W. Tacha.

Eastern Oklahoma (east of the 97-degree meridian), except for several highland areas, has an abundance of streams that furnish habitat for breeding wood ducks (Table 4). There also are numerous stream impoundments, and the larger ones appear to have a negative influence on breeding populations. Nevertheless, Lem Due reported that the greatest density of breeding birds occurred in a triangular area of northeastern and northcentral Oklahoma, with the apex near Shawnee and the eastern base formed by the Arkansas line. Where the Boston Mountains in the northeast and the Ouachita Mountains in the southeast affect the terrain, wood duck abundance was low to moderate. Breeding density also was less in the Osage Hills region in the northeastern and northcentral parts of the state.

The Coastal Plain Province of southern Oklahoma as far west as Ardmore supports medium densities of breeding woodies. Low numbers populated streams surrounding the triangular region of high abundance to a line sloping southwest from Blackwell to Lawton. Lem Due observed that to the west, except for moderate numbers along the North Canadian River, Canton to Chester, wood ducks were sparsely distributed during the breeding season.

Charles Stutzenbaker reported that the highest densities of wood ducks in Texas occurred along scores of streams east of the 97-degree meridian. Abundance in this region decreased from northeast to southwest, with few to no wood ducks along the coast. Small numbers regularly nest in favorable stream habitats as far west as 99 degrees, but two nests in Live Oak County (98 degrees west) reported by Bolen and Cottam (1967) and Bolen and Cain (1968) are the farthest southwest that wood ducks are known to have nested. On March 31, 1989, Glen C. Sanderson observed 160–200 wood ducks—an unusually large number—on Lake McQueeney near San Antonio (98 degrees west). Several pairs were in, on, and around nest houses. Bellrose observed a nesting pair at Brownwood (99 degrees west) on March 1, 1982. Farther west, the wood duck breeds sparingly. Hawkins (1945) observed a brood at Palo Duro Lake near Canyon (102 degrees west), and reported that they regularly nested in Hemphill County in the northeastern Texas Panhandle.

The High Plains. Whether any wood ducks regularly breed in Alberta is unknown. Beacham (1957) reported a pair and, later, a brood 8 kilometers (5 mi) south of Calgary. Sadler and Myers (1976) considered any breeding woodies in the Calgary area to be escaped birds from the city zoo, but they noted that wood ducks regularly migrated through Banff on the edge of the Rocky Mountains.

The High Plains of Montana are unique in forming the only bridge between eastern breeding woodies and the western population indigenous to the Rocky Mountains and the Pacific Coast. According to Robert L. Eng and Don Childress, evidence of breeding has been found at various places along the Missouri and Yellowstone rivers (and their tributaries) from the North Dakota line to the Rocky Mountains. Childress reported 0.06–0.12 pair per kilometer (0.10–0.19/mi) along the Yellowstone River, Sidney to Big Timber, but solely on the reach from Sidney to Bighorn 1.8 nests per kilometer (2.9/mi). One stretch of the Clark Fork tributary near Edgar had 0.7 nest per kilometer (1.1/mi). Broods or pairs also were observed on the Tongue, Bighorn, and Boulder tributaries.

Broods and breeding pairs have been observed on the Musselshell River between Shawmut and Roundup. Near Lavina, an unusually high number of 3 pairs per kilometer (4.8/mi) have been recorded, according to Don Childress. On the upper Missouri River in the Charles M. Russell National Wildlife Refuge as many as 1.2–1.8 pairs per kilometer (1.9–2.9/mi) have been seen. Farther up the Missouri River, pairs and broods have been noted between Fort Benton and Craig, and from Townsend to Lombard.

A few kilometers above historic Three Forks (where the Missouri is formed by the confluence of the Jefferson, Madison, and Gallatin rivers), Robert L. Eng has established a viable group of wood ducks utilizing nest houses. From 15 to 24 houses have been maintained and checked annually, and from 25 to 57 percent of these were occupied, 1971–1983. On the most productive side channel, 2.4 houses per kilometer (3.9/mi) were occupied.

The Milk River, a major tributary from northern Montana, enters the Missouri River below Glasgow. On several float trips there from April to early June, Eng observed 0.6 pair per kilometer (1/mi).

Leonard Serduik identified stretches of the following streams in Wyoming's High Plains where sparse numbers of wood ducks have been known to breed: North Platte River, Colorado border to Seminoe Reservoir, Casper to Orin, and Guernsey to Nebraska border; Belle Fourche River, Keyhole Reservoir to South Dakota border; Powder River, Sussex to Montana border; Tongue River, Sheridan to Montana border; Bighorn River, Boysen Dam to Bighorn Lake; Wind River, Dubois to Shoshoni; and Shoshone River, Cody to Bighorn Lake.

According to Howard D. Funk, wood duck breeding numbers greatly increased in Colorado during the 1980s. Range expansion also resulted in the formation of isolated nesting colonies dispersed over about one-tenth of the state. Wood ducks are currently abundant along the eastern flank of the Front Range from Fort Collins to Denver in pond-type wetlands as well as along the Cache la Poudre and St. Vrain rivers. In northeastern Colorado wood ducks breed discontinuously along the South Platte River and adjacent reservoirs, particularly near Julesburg. Isolated breeding has been found on Bonny Reservoir in the extreme east, north of Burlington. Broods have been observed along a 64-kilometer (40 mi) stretch of the Arkansas River, including the John Martin Reservoir, from Fort Lyon to east of Lamar.

On the west slope of the Rocky Mountains in Colorado, wood ducks are known to breed in only a few places. The area of greatest nesting density is considered to be the Colorado River between Grand Junction and Fruita. Funk believes that there are breeding wood ducks along the Gunnison and Uncompahgre rivers between Montrose and Grand Junction, and there is evidence of sparse numbers nesting along the Yampa River from Steamboat Springs west to the Utah border.

Wood ducks are scarce on the Northern Plains, but there are pockets of breeding birds. The Northern Plains area provides the only bridge—via the Missouri, Bitterroot, and other rivers—between breeding woodies to the east and west of the Rocky Mountains region. *Photo courtesy of the Wyoming Game and Fish Department.*

New Mexico was the last state in the lower forty-eight to report breeding wood ducks, even though Hubbard (1978) stated that wood ducks were resident in the Farmington area since 1972–1973, probably the result of introductions. He reported several summer occurrences elsewhere at Patterson Pond and Burford and Elephant Butte lakes; the Santa Fe area; and Bosque del Apache National Wildlife Refuge.

However, the first solid evidence of nesting occurred in 1987 when Tim Mitchusson observed two different broods with hens on the backwaters of Elephant Butte Reservoir, San Marcial. He also saw a brood and its natural cavity nest site in a flooded borrow area near San Marcial on May 22, 1988. A pair searching for a nest site was seen at Luis Lopez. The first brood in the Bosque del Apache National Wildlife Refuge was reported by John P. Taylor on July 29, 1988. Both 1987 and 1988 were years of exceptionally high water, which perhaps played a part in the success of wood duck nesting attempts.

Except in Montana and to a lesser extent in Wyoming, wood ducks generally find suitable habitat at a minimum on the High Plains. This scarcity stems from a paltry food base and a lack of nesting cavities in the meager riparian timber of willow, cottonwood, and ash. It is apparent, however, that nest houses are enabling wood ducks to proliferate in many areas of the Great Plains.

The number of breeding wood ducks anticipated in provinces and states totals 75,000 for the Central Flyway (Table 4). However, harvest data and band recovery rates of adults imply a flyway breeding population closer to 170,000 (Table 4).

The Pacific Coast and Rocky Mountains

Kessel and Gibson (1976) listed the wood duck as a casual spring migrant and summer visitor to southeastern Alaska, but breeding pairs have not been observed.

According to Campbell et al. (1990), wood ducks in British Columbia breed along the coast from Victoria to Cortes Island (50 degrees north) and sparsely throughout the southern interior up to elevations of 1,200 meters (4,000 ft) north to the towns of Williams Lake and Anahim Lake.

W. T. Munro considered wood duck breeding numbers to be low in interior British Columbia as far north as Kamloops and sparse north from there to Williams Lake and Alexis Creek (52 degrees north). He reported sparse numbers breeding along the east coast of Vancouver Island to Campbell River (50 degrees north). Although Munro and other ornithologists observed woodies on Graham

Island (53–54 degrees north), Campbell et al. (1990) could find no hard evidence and regarded their occurrences as casual.

Most of the 3,000 wood ducks breeding in British Columbia (Table 5) are located in the lower Fraser and Creston valleys. Campbell et al. (1990) reported local populations reaching 1 pair per hectare (0.40/ac) in Maple Ridge, Pitt Meadows, White Rock, Burnaby Lake, and Westham Island. Numbers dramatically increased there during the 1970s with the placement of several thousand nest houses. On the South Alouette River wood ducks increased from one pair in 1968 to more than 50 pairs in 1979.

From the 14,500 breeding wood ducks in Washington during the early 1970s (Bellrose 1976), populations apparently declined to 7,900 during 1977–1986 (Bartonek et al. 1990). These numbers refer to birds that occur within their principal range—the west slope of the Cascade Mountains below 610 meters (2,000 ft) to the Pacific Ocean, excluding the Olympic Mountains. East of the Cascades across Washington north of the Columbia River, wood ducks are sparsely distributed with larger local populations in the Okanogan Valley and the Cusick Flats of the Pend Oreille Valley, according to Robert Jeffrey. They have been known to nest sporadically in the Turnbull National Wildlife Refuge near Cheney. Bartonek et al. (1990) reported nesting wood ducks along the Columbia River from Umatilla, Oregon, upstream to the Yakima River and the Toppenish Creek below Yakima, Washington.

Approximately 3,000 of the 3,730 wood ducks in Idaho breed near Coeur d' Alene in the northern panhandle (Bartonek et al. 1990). Dick Norell listed the highest populations on the Coeur d' Alene River, Pinehurst to Harrison, and the Kootenai River at Elmira and again near Bonners Ferry. Moderate breeding numbers occur on the St. Joe River below St. Maries and the Pack River near Kootenai. Low numbers occur on the Moyie River near Bonners Ferry, the Priest River from Priest Lake to Sandpoint, and the St. Joe River from Calder to St. Maries.

Some 362 kilometers (225 mi) to the south, about 600 wood ducks breed along the Snake River, Marsing to Weiser, and along its tributaries, the Boise and Payette rivers, according to Dick Norell and G. C. Will. Norell reported that sparse numbers breed in scattered localities along the middle Snake River—Blackfoot to Sterling, Burley, and below Twin Falls. Norell also reported breeding pairs on the lower Henry's Fork below St. Anthony, on Mud and Camas lakes west of Hamer, on the Portneuf River from Lava Hot Springs to its confluence with the Snake, on the Bruneau River from Bruneau Hot

Springs to the Snake, and in Deer Flat National Wildlife Refuge near Nampa.

From eastern Washington and the Idaho panhandle, the wood duck breeding range extends eastward into the Rocky Mountains of Montana, where Bartonek et al. (1990) reported 800–1,200 breeding birds (Table 5). Don Childress recorded wood duck distribution in this region as follows: Kootenai River from Libby to Libby Dam—10 observed during the breeding season; Blackfoot River from Lincoln to Missoula—1 pair per 3–5 kilometers (2–3 mi); Clark Fork from Huson to St. Regis—1 pair per 1.6 kilometers (1 mi); Clark Fork from Clinton to Huson—3 pairs per 1.6 kilometers (1 mi); and Bitterroot River from Darby to Missoula—2 pairs per 1.6 kilometers (1 mi). At the Lee Metcalf National Wildlife Refuge on the Bitterroot River near Stevensville, 15 percent of 50–55 nest houses were occupied annually by wood ducks.

Although there is a historical record of a wood duck nesting in Yellowstone National Park, Terry McEneaney believes that it was mistakenly identified. From its location at Yellowstone Lake, McEneaney considers it more likely a nest of a Barrow's goldeneye. McEneaney (1988) lists the wood duck as rare at Yellowstone, most likely to occur in May and September.

At Fortine, in extreme northwestern Montana, Weydemeyer (1975) recorded woodies only as a rare spring migrant. Terry McEneaney reported that wood ducks have nested at Lake McDonald on the west side of Glacier National Park, but the wood duck appears to be an irregular and rare breeder in the park. Homer Bradley reported a nest in a box east of the Ninepipe National Wildlife Refuge near Ronan.

Most of the 16,000 wood ducks breeding in western Oregon (Bartonek et al. 1990) occur in the Willamette River Valley, Eugene to Portland, and in the lower Columbia River Valley, particularly Sauvie Island from Bonneville Dam to Astoria. Relying on data assembled by Bartonek et al. (1990), it appears that about 1,000 breed elsewhere in Oregon: 24 in the Umatilla National Wildlife Refuge complex; 26–82 in the Malheur-Harney Lakes Basin; 100 in the upper Klamath Basin; 100 in Hood River, Wasco, and Sherman counties in north-central Oregon; and 20 in the Wallowa district of northeastern Oregon. The 1,000 estimated for the Snake River between Homedale, Idaho, and Farwell Bend State Park probably include some of the 600 estimated for the Idaho side of the river.

Ralph Denny singled out the Umpqua and Rogue rivers of the Coast Range as important breed-

In the Rocky Mountains region, habitat conditions are not highly suitable to wood ducks. But where the species' breeding requirements are met, local concentrations are impressive. In Idaho, for example, about 80 percent of the state's breeding population is located near Coeur d'Alene. *Photo by Charles and Elizabeth Schwartz.*

ing areas. Dennis Woolington added the Siuslaw River, Florence to Mapleton, and the Siltcoos Lake area near Dunes City. Walt Weber observed that wood ducks bred commonly in Clatsop County in the northwest corner of the state and had used 75 percent of several hundred nest houses placed there.

A wood duck nest and brood found by Kebbe (1956) 3.2 kilometers (2 mi) south of Adel in the Warner Valley is the farthest east that breeding has been recorded in arid southern Oregon.

The bulk of the 26,000 wood ducks breeding in California (Table 5) are found primarily in the Central Valley and secondarily in the Coast Range north of San Francisco Bay. Most of the streams of the Coast Range drain into the Pacific Ocean. Here, Daniel P. Connelley identified the Smith, Klamath, Mad, and Eel rivers as supporting low populations of breeding woodies and the Russian River as having a higher population. East of Healdsburg, on a small branch of the Russian River, Lawton L. Shurtleff developed a breeding population of 500 wood ducks. This population evolved after nest houses were placed on five small impoundments. These houses, incidentally, are shared with a feral population of 500 mandarin ducks.

Naylor (1960) identified the southern limit of the breeding range in California as the Tehachapi Mountains, but the principal range does not appear to extend south of the Kings River in the Sierra Nevada Mountains or south of Monterey County in the Coast Range. However, a quantum leap southward in the wood duck's breeding range in California came to light in 1992. Brian Davis and Stephen Simmons of the California Waterfowl Association discovered that Fred Pedley of Riverside had 68 wood duck nests in 200 nest houses. These were located on ponds and along the Santa Ana River near Riverside. This nesting "colony" was composed of native wild wood ducks augmented by an earlier release of 200 game farm birds. Pedley reported that with the first nest house in 1989, one-third of the nesting birds were wild, the others from previously released game farm wood ducks. Only 3 of 68 incubating wood ducks in 1992 were from the original game farm release, but unknown is the number that were the progeny of those birds.

According to Daniel P. Connelley, the Sacramento and San Joaquin rivers support only small numbers of breeding wood ducks. However, many of their tributaries are better, and he rated Deer Creek and the Feather, Cosumnes, Calaveras, Tuolumne, and Kings rivers as maintaining moderate populations. At the confluence of the Mokelumne and Cosumnes rivers near Thornton, 200 wood duck nests were reported in 230 houses with

135 hatched clutches in 1989 (Krammerer 1990). At Sutter Fort State Park in the center of Sacramento, all of the 10 houses were occupied by wood ducks in 1990. The Stanislaus and Merced rivers—tributaries of the San Joaquin River—were classed as having high populations of woodies. Near Merced, Stephen Simmons used nest houses to develop a population of 250 breeding wood ducks.

All accounts, however, place the most dense population of breeding wood ducks in the Butte Sink, an area of 4,450 hectares (11,000 ac) of marsh and riparian habitat between Colusa and Gridley.

Wood ducks breed on the small permanent streams, reservoirs, and beaver ponds in the eastern foothills of the Central Valley up to 1,524 meters (5,000 ft), according to Jack Helvie. Grinnell et al. (1918) listed a nest at Lake Tahoe, elevation 1,899 meters (6,230 ft).

Ryser (1985) estimated 700–800 wood ducks breeding along the Truckee, Carson, and Walker rivers east or south of Reno, Nevada. Part of this highly localized breeding population resulted from the use of nest houses.

Historical records exist of wood ducks nesting along the Bear River near its mouth in Box Elder County, Utah, but none has been known to nest there in recent years, according to Timothy Provan. Two pairs have been known to nest along the Ogden River in Weber County, and four pairs nested along Lost Creek and the Weber River in Morgan County. The Logan River in the city of Logan, Utah is the site of a small colony of 5–10 pairs, maintained 1985–1989 by the use of nest houses, as reported by Jessop B. Low.

Because the Rocky Mountains region of Wyoming and New Mexico has been placed in the Pacific Flyway for ecological and management purposes, we record here the fewer than 50 wood ducks nesting on the Snake River near Jackson, Wyoming, and on the upper Green River and New Fork River, near Pinedale (Bartonek et al. 1990).

Brown (1985) reported the first wood duck nesting in Arizona at Peck's Lake on the Verde River. An assumed breeding pair was observed on upper Eagle Creek on May 7, 1975. For two years, six pairs nested in the Havasu National Wildlife Refuge, but none has nested there since 1979. Bartonek et al. (1990) reported 12 nesting pairs in Yavapai and Coconino counties—a region of Arizona that contains atypical habitat for wood ducks.

The estimated breeding population of 59,900 wood ducks (Table 5) for the Pacific Flyway appears reasonably valid. Average annual flyway-wide harvest rates of adults related to comparable band recovery rates also indicate a breeding population of about 59,000 for the entire flyway (Table 5). Thus, the division of breeding wood duck populations among the states/province of the Pacific Flyway appears to be correct or approximately so.

AUTUMN DISTRIBUTION

From late summer through early autumn, wood ducks expand their summer breeding range. As discussed under migration (see Chapter 4) and post-breeding season movements (see Chapter 14), most woodies move only short distances, but some migrate hundreds of kilometers. Wood ducks expand their ranges to seek new and better sources of food when they are no longer restricted to breeding areas by the need for nest sites and habitat for brood rearing.

Map 2 shows the average density of the wood duck harvest per square mile for each county in the United States, 1966–1985. Areas of heavy harvest obviously mirror major breeding habitats. Nevertheless, the harvest is greater through the Great Plains and the intermountain valleys of the Rocky Mountains than is warranted by known breeding sites. At the same time that resident wood ducks disperse throughout this vast area, other woodies immigrate to the Central Flyway. Yet it is somewhat of a two-way street, because 41 percent of the wood ducks banded in the Central Flyway are shot in the Mississippi Flyway (Ladd 1990).

WINTER DISTRIBUTION

The winter range of the wood duck consists of three zones: (1) a northern zone where birds are absent in winter or are present sporadically when open water and favorable food conditions occur; (2) a central marginal zone where wood ducks commonly winter but where ice occasionally forces them to shift temporarily to nearby open water or move farther south; and (3) the terminal southern zone where frozen waters are not a factor and where the habitat stability needed by the majority of wintering birds is available. These three zones are most appropriately applied to the wood duck range east of the Great Plains. Wood ducks in the Pacific Flyway migrate, but appreciable numbers winter as far north as southern British Columbia.

Wood ducks counted during the annual Audubon Christmas Bird Counts (Map 3) provide a useful perspective on the species distribution in early winter, mid-December to early January. However, many of the wood ducks counted in the north and central zones may move farther south before the depth of winter is reached in mid-January.

The Atlantic Flyway

The northern zone extends as far south as 37 degrees north on the Atlantic Coast and 36 degrees north in the interior. A few individual and paired wood ducks and, more rarely, small flocks appear on Audubon Christmas Bird Counts in the New England states. Wood ducks are rare in winter in southern Ontario but have occurred as far north as Kingston (James et al. 1976). From Massachusetts south, a scattering of birds increases, but the wood duck has not been reported (1983–1987) in significant numbers north of 37 degrees north.

Bull (1964) recorded several instances of wood ducks wintering in the vicinity of New York City. In the lowlands of the Chesapeake Bay area, Stewart and Robbins (1958) considered them uncommon during the winter, and farther inland in Maryland they were rated rare. Small numbers of wood ducks consistently appear on Audubon Christmas Bird Counts in eastern Maryland, but numbers increase appreciably south through coastal Virginia.

The marginal wintering zone extends from 37 to 35 degrees north on the coast to 36 to 34 degrees north in the interior. Hester and Dermid (1973) found that wood ducks gathered at the Pungo River, coastal North Carolina (35.5 degrees north), when nearby swamps froze. Hester and Dermid (1973) knew of a few locations farther inland near Raleigh that consistently held wood ducks during winter, one of which was the Little River. Recoveries from wood ducks banded in the northern zone suggest that 27 percent winter in the intermediate zone and 73 percent in the southern zone (Table 6).

Table 6. Estimated proportion of northern wood ducks harvested in the primary winter range of the Atlantic and Mississippi flyways. Based on the relative number of band recoveries received from states north of the listed states, 1959–78.

State	Number of direct band recoveries	Relative percentage of recoveries
Atlantic Flyway		
Virginia	27	6.22
North Carolina	89	20.51
South Carolina	127	29.26
Georgia	104	23.96
Florida	87	20.05
Mississippi Flyway		
Tennessee	37	3.29
Arkansas	189	16.83
Mississippi	240	21.37
Alabama	133	11.84
Louisiana	524	46.67

The southern zone encompasses South Carolina, Georgia, and Florida. Band recoveries from northern states indicate that most of the migrants winter in South Carolina, followed by Georgia and Florida (Table 6). Burleigh (1958) noted that they were abundant winter residents in Georgia south of the fall line.

Few wood ducks in Florida winter south of a line from Sarasota to Fort Pierce, as determined from Audubon Christmas Bird Counts, band recoveries, and hunter-harvest distribution (maps 2 and 3). Apparently the abundant wetlands of South Florida fail to provide the type of habitat capable of supporting large numbers.

The Mississippi Flyway

The northern zone for wintering wood ducks in the Mississippi Flyway extends south into northern Arkansas on the west and to Knoxville, Tennessee, on the east (36 degrees north). Audubon Christmas Counts reveal only small, inconsistent numbers at dispersed locations north of this latitude; however, a few wood ducks have been recorded even in the northern states of Minnesota, Wisconsin, and Michigan (Map 3). In eastern Iowa, Kent and Kent (1975) occasionally recorded wood ducks in winter. Campbell (1968) reported several in 7 of 38 winters in the Toledo, Ohio, area. Keller et al. (1979) considered wood ducks to be rare during winter in Indiana.

In Audubon Christmas Bird Counts in Illinois, 1983–1987, wood duck numbers varied from 37 in 1983 to 762 in 1986—a mean of 206 ± 311. They have been found at numerous locations from Waukegan in the northeast and increasing in numbers southward to Union County and Horseshoe Lake State Wildlife areas in the south, where 724 were recorded in 1986.

In Missouri, small numbers of wood ducks were sporadically recorded in Audubon Christmas Bird Counts, 1983–1987, except at the Mingo National Wildlife Refuge (37 degrees north) where they were present in four of five years, with a mean of 16 ± 23.

Mengel (1965) reported the wood duck to winter occasionally in Kentucky. Several appeared on Audubon Christmas Bird Counts, 1983–1987, particularly at Louisville.

In west Tennessee, Ganier (1933) reported the wood duck to be a fairly common winter resident but largely absent from the middle and eastern regions. Audubon Christmas Bird Counts, 1983–1987, showed that small numbers consistently occurred on the Tennessee River and its tributaries at Kings-

Wood ducks are recorded annually in the Lake States during the Audubon Christmas Bird Counts. Their detection at that time probably indicates birds that have ready access to open water and such foods as acorns, corn, and aquatics that provide carbohydrates and protein. The sightings likely are of woodies not stressed by hunting pressure during the preceding months or by harsh winter weather, which usually peaks a month or so later. In very mild winters that allow for adequate open water and limited or infrequent snow cover, woodies may overwinter where there is a favorable food supply. When ice closes open water and foods disappear, they leave regardless of the lateness of the season. *Photo by Scott Nielsen.*

port, Knoxville, and Chattanooga. Moreover, substantial numbers of woodies appeared on counts at Reelfoot National Wildlife Refuge and in the vicinity of Memphis.

According to James and Neal (1986), wood ducks are rare to uncommon during winter in northern Arkansas but abundant in the southern lowlands.

Imhof (1976) reported that wood ducks were a common permanent resident in Alabama but were uncommon in the mountain region during winter.

Recoveries from wood ducks banded north of the states listed in Table 6 suggest that almost 40 percent of those birds winter in Louisiana, with 14–18 percent each in Arkansas, Mississippi, and east Texas. Audubon Christmas Counts indicate that large numbers of wood ducks winter through east Texas as far west as San Antonio and as far south as Corpus Christi. Substantial numbers were counted, probably on freshwater areas, along the Gulf Coast.

The Central Flyway

As unusual as it seems, several wood ducks were found in South Dakota in Audubon Christmas Bird Counts during 1983–1987. Twice, a single bird was recorded at Sioux Falls, and from one to three birds were observed in four of five years at Rapid City. Although Rapp et al. (1958) did not report wood ducks wintering in Nebraska, one was recorded twice at Omaha, one or two were observed in three of five years at Grand Island, and four were recorded once at Lincoln, 1983–1987 (Audubon Christmas Bird Counts).

Small numbers, inconsistent by years 1983–1987, were counted at six locations in Kansas in Audubon Christmas Bird Counts. Johnston (1965) did not consider the wood duck to be a wintering bird in Kansas.

Sutton (1967) reported wood ducks wintering in eight counties in Oklahoma. Audubon Christmas Bird Counts, 1983–1987, revealed seven locations, largely in the southern part of the state, where small numbers were seen; Stephens County held birds most consistently.

Wood ducks wintering east of 99 degrees west in Texas are considered to be local birds in addition to northern migrants from the Mississippi and Central flyways. West of the 99-degree meridian, we assign wood duck distribution solely to the Central Flyway.

An occasional wood duck has been found on Christmas Bird Counts at Big Bend National Park and nearby Presidio, Texas. However, the most consistent yearly records and the largest numbers, 1983–1987, occurred at such widely separated places as San Angelo, Del Rio, and El Paso.

The plains of Colorado and New Mexico are considered to be part of the Central Flyway, whereas the mountainous region is part of the Pacific Flyway. Of the seven locations in Colorado reporting wood ducks in Audubon Christmas Bird Counts, 1983–1987, six sites—from Fort Collins to Pueblo—were at the base of the Rocky Mountains; the seventh was at Grand Junction on the west side of the Rockies. Bird counters from Denver and Pueblo reported wood ducks all five years, with respective means of 27 ± 18 and 18 ± 21.

At Roswell, New Mexico, Christmas counts revealed small numbers of wood ducks in two of four years. Three other locations in New Mexico were within the Rocky Mountains Province.

In addition to the wood ducks in the states of the Central Flyway, small numbers migrate into eastern Mexico. Williams (1987) compiled winter records of wood ducks at three sites in the state of Tamaulipas, two in San Luis Potosi, two in Coahuila, one in southern Veracruz, and one in Distrito Federal. The most consistent yearly records have occurred at Rio Corona, Tamaulipas, where wood ducks were found in 8 of 10 Audubon Christmas Bird Counts, 1978–1987. At El Naranjo, San Luis Potosi, wood ducks were reported on five occasions, 1975–1987 (Williams 1987). Wood ducks in west Mexico are noted under the Pacific Flyway.

The Pacific Flyway

The wintering grounds for wood ducks in the Pacific Flyway extend far north of those in the other flyways. As a result of mild winter weather produced by maritime air and Asiatic current, wood ducks winter from southern British Columbia into Mexico.

Audubon Christmas Bird Count participants in British Columbia found an average of 271 wood ducks during 1983–1987, 87 percent of which were in the Fraser River Valley from Chilliwack to the mouth of the river at Vancouver. Small numbers were found on Vancouver Island at Nanaimo, Duncan, and Victoria.

Data compiled by Bartonek et al. (1990) indicated that about 1,000 wood ducks wintered in Washington. Audubon Christmas Bird Counts, 1983–1987, revealed consistently small numbers at such diverse localities as Seattle, Spokane, and Kennewick.

Bartonek et al. (1990) estimated that 8,300 wood ducks wintered in Oregon, of which 1,000–2,000 were on the Snake River border with Idaho. Audubon Christmas Bird Counts, 1983–1987, indicate that woodies are most abundant in the vicinity of Portland, including Sauvie Island, and the Willamette River Valley from Portland to Eugene. Appreciable numbers have been reported in the vicinity of Medford (mean = 78 ± 34) and Grants Pass (mean = 115 ± 129). Small and variable numbers have occurred east of the Cascade Range at Klamath Falls, Bend, John Day, and Malheur National Wildlife Refuge and in Wallowa County. A few have been reported at several places along the coast.

Audubon Christmas Bird Counts at Boise, Idaho, and nearby cities have regularly yielded moderate numbers (10–50) of wood ducks. An occasional record has been noted at Sun Valley, Rexburg, Pocatello, American Falls, and Hagerman.

In Utah, wood ducks have consistently appeared on Christmas Birds Counts at Logan (mean = 28 ± 13) and Salt Lake City (mean = 20 ± 11). Although Wauer (1969) cited two records in December near St. George, Utah, a perusal of Audubon Christmas Counts from 1979 through 1988 for the vicinity of St. George and Cedar City revealed no wood ducks. In three of five years, however, they were reported at Zion National Park, which is located about midway between these cities. Several wood ducks were reported during winter, 1967–1968, at Lorenzi Park, Las Vegas, Nevada, by Austin (1970). According to Audubon Christmas Bird Counts, wood ducks occur marginally in winter in two other areas of Nevada: the Carson and Truckee rivers near Fallon and on the Desert National Game Range north of Las Vegas. They were not found every year, 1983–1987, and then only between one and seven in number.

Wood ducks are broadly distributed in California during winter in small numbers all along the coast, at lower elevations in the Coastal Range, and on the west slope of the Sierra Nevada, and in substantial numbers in the Central Valley.

Naylor (1960) estimated that 55,400 wood ducks wintered in California—90 percent of the flyway population, 1958–1959. Helvie (1983) estimated that 80,000 wood ducks—75 percent of the flyway population—wintered in the Central Valley. Naylor (1960) identified areas of concentration as: Feather River in Butte, Sutter, and Yuba counties; Butte Sink, west of Gridley; streams of the Sierra Nevada Mountains as far south as the Kings River; and streams and reservoirs of the Coast and Diablo ranges south to Monterey County. He stated that the resident wood duck population moved for the winter from the higher elevations into the Central Valley and adjacent foothills but were rarely found on salt marshes. Bartonek et al. (1990) expressed the belief that during the past two decades more wood ducks have

wintered in the eastern foothill region than previously, perhaps as a result of the destruction of riparian wetlands in the Central Valley.

Harvest data and band recoveries indicate that the Butte Sink area has one of the greatest autumn/winter concentrations of wood ducks in California. In 1983, Jack Helvie estimated the winter population in Butte Sink at 3,000–5,000.

Because of the uncertain status of the wood duck in southern California during the winter, we compiled Audubon Christmas Bird Counts for all localities south of latitude 36 degrees that reported wood ducks during a five-year period, 1983–1987 (Table 7). These surveys indicate that wood ducks occur in small numbers at numerous locations, mainly near the coast, as far south as San Diego.

Wood ducks were recorded at several locations in Arizona by Vorhies (1947). Brown (1985) reported 140 wood ducks bagged by hunters, 1971–1980, of which 37.9 and 24.3 percent were in Maricopa and Yuma counties, respectively. During 1983–1987, Audubon Christmas Counts registered 286 wood ducks—95 percent of which came from Prescott, Camp Verde, and Jerome, all in the center of the state.

Borell (1948) cited several records of wood ducks in western New Mexico. Audubon Christmas Bird Counts disclosed a sporadic number at Espanola, Farmington, Albuquerque, and Santa Fe.

Wood ducks appear to be a recent addition to the avifauna of Mexico (Williams 1987). In addition to records reported for eastern Mexico under the Central Flyway, there are 10 winter observations in the west extending from Agua Prieta, Sonora, to San Blas, Nayarit. Most of the seven records in Sonora were in the Yaqui River Valley. There also are four spring or summer records—one in Sonora, two in Durango, and one in Jalisco.

Table 7. Localities in California south of 36 degrees latitude in which Audubon Christmas Bird Counts revealed wood ducks. Averaged for five years, 1983–87.[a]

Locality	Degrees latitude	Mean number	S.D.
Morro Bay	35.40	0.8	
Bakersfield	35.40	4.6	4.8
Lancaster	34.63	0.7	
Santa Barbara	34.45	2.2	1.9
Ventura	34.27	1.6	2.1
Claremont	34.15	2.0	3.1
Pasadena	34.01	2.6	3.3
Santa Ana	33.75	3.4	4.0
San Jacinto	33.86	2.2	1.9
Coastal Orange County	33.67	1.0	
Oceanside	33.22	0.6	
San Bernardino	34.05	2.2	1.9
Rancho Santa Fe	33.00	2.4	2.1

[a] Census period from approximately December 15–January 5. Year pertains to start of census period which extends into following year.

Chapter 3

Habitat

As a result of their morphological, physiological, and behavioral characteristics, wood ducks are able to utilize a wide variety of habitat types. Woodies use nearly every type of freshwater wetland—river, stream, lake, farm pond, beaver pond, marsh, swamp, ditch, or other water area that occurs near hardwood timber stands or provides inundated or overhanging shoreline vegetation. As a general rule, they shun salt and brackish marshes and large expanses of open water and turbulent streams; however, they often make foraging excursions into open water where beds of aquatic plants provide seeds, foliage, or invertebrates.

Woodies appear to be just as efficient at obtaining food from overflow bottomland forests where changing water levels alter the availability and abundance of food as they are at securing food from wetlands that have relatively stable water levels. They are proficient at perching in trees and maneuvering through flight lanes formed by intricate networks of tree limbs. They also are adept at walking on land and often seek food in dry woodlands, agricultural fields, and mast-producing orchards that are located up to 4.8 kilometers (3 mi) from the nearest water.

Extensive areas of overflow bottomland timber, cypress/tupelo swamps, and secluded ponds and streams often are considered the domain of wood ducks. Nevertheless, woodies do not require remote areas in which to live. In fact, they commonly breed in and around residential areas when habitats are available that meet their basic requirements for reproduction and survival.

Although wood ducks are able to find food and shelter in a wide variety of aquatic environments, they have definite habitat preferences. The largest concentration of wood ducks occurs over the eastern third of the United States where, for nesting and brood rearing, they rely on a diverse community of wetlands associated with the channel borders, backwaters, and floodplains of streams and rivers (Map 4). Basically, the deciduous forest biome is their home.

HABITAT TYPES

The habitat components required by wood ducks include suitable nest sites, shallow or slow-moving fresh water, abundant sources of food, and cover that affords concealment from predators, alternative escape sites from disturbances, some protection from adverse weather, and ample loafing sites. The types of habitat that provide these basic requisites vary throughout the wood duck's range because of regional differences in geography, soil, vegetation, climate, hydrology, water fertility, and other more subtle factors.

Two general types of wet environments are recognized by the U.S. Fish and Wildlife Service: wetlands and deepwater habitats (Cowardin et al. 1979). As these names suggest, wetlands are at least periodically inundated by shallow water, whereas deepwater habitats are permanently flooded lands where water depths are too deep to support emergent plant growth (see Cowardin et al. 1979 for more precise definitions). Marshes, swamps, bogs, and floodplain forests are common examples of wetlands. In addition, the littoral zones of rivers, lakes, and ponds and shallow areas of open water less than 2 meters (6.6 ft) deep are included in the wetland category.

Wetlands can be further divided into coastal and palustrine (inland) wetlands. Coastal wetlands are inundated by salt or brackish water, whereas most inland wetlands are saturated by fresh water. Characteristically, wood ducks restrict their use of aquatic habitats to freshwater inland wetlands,

Concerning the wood duck, John James Audubon wrote in the 1840s: "This beautiful species confines itself entirely to the fresh water of secluded retreats that occur in our woods. Well acquainted with man, it carefully avoids him, except during the breeding season when, if it finds a convenient place to deposit eggs and raise its young, it will now and then even locate itself near a miller's dam" (Ford 1957: 77). *Top left photo courtesy of the Illinois Natural History Survey. Top right photo by Glen R. Miller. Bottom photo by Charles and Elizabeth Schwartz.*

rarely inhabiting brackish or saline areas.

The types of aquatic habitats that wood ducks almost exclusively utilize are classified as freshwater emergent, scrub/shrub, and forested wetlands. These wetlands commonly occur on river floodplains, along the margins of many rivers, streams, lakes, and ponds, and in upland depressions. Each type is characterized by a dominant form of vegetation. Emergent wetlands are dominated by herbaceous (nonwoody) plants, scrub/shrub wetlands by woody vegetation (shrubs and trees) less than 6 meters (20 ft) tall, and forested wetlands by trees taller than 6 meters (20 ft). Included in the forested wetland category are permanently flooded swamps and seasonally flooded forested basins or flats (areas that support trees more than 6 meters [20 ft] tall and that become inundated at some time during the course of the year but remain largely dry during the growing season).

Overflow flats normally become inundated in late winter and early spring when stream channels cannot hold the increased water volumes brought about by melting snow and spring rains. Nonetheless, the flooding regime of live forests varies considerably, and the duration of floodwaters on overflow wetlands depends on precipitation, runoff, drainage velocity, and transpiration-evaporation. Most seasonal flooding ceases by early summer.

Regional differences are marked among the vegetative communities of the wetland types. Emergent wetland vegetation that serves as important cover for woodies in the South includes cattail, arrowhead, bulrush, arrowarum, waterprimrose, smartweed, pickerelweed, spatterdock, and lizardtail. In central regions, smartweed, American lotus, pickerelweed, bluejoint reedgrass, arrowhead, soft rush, spatterdock, arrowarum, clump sedge, and

Spring floods invariably inundate floodplains of thousands of streams in the eastern United States, greatly expanding early breeding habitats for wood ducks. A variety of aquatic invertebrates—isopods, amphipods, snails, and dipteran larvae—inhabits the flooded leaf litter and provides wood ducks an important source of preferred foods. In addition, the samaras produced by maple, elm, and ash trees are valuable for prebreeding and breeding woodies because of the concentrated energy and low fiber content. Wood ducks require a variety of wetland types during the course of the year because their behavioral and nutritional needs change constantly. *Photo courtesy of the Illinois Natural History Survey.*

certain grasses are important herbaceous emergents to wood ducks. Valuable emergents in the Great Lake states and the Northeast include cattail, bulrush, arrowhead, American lotus, giant burreed, reed canarygrass, wild rice, smartweed, pickerelweed, and sedge (McGilvrey 1968).

Because of their water chemistry and hydrology, northern and southern peat bogs are of little value as wood duck habitat. Most bogs lack seasonal flooding, and the stagnant, oxygen-depleted water of bogs becomes acidic. Among the characteristic northern bog plants are leatherleaf, sweet gale, bogrosemary, labrador-tea, cranberry, bog laurel, black spruce, larch, pond and loblolly pines, and balsam fir. Southern bogs are dominated by pond pine, sweet bay, inkberry, fetterbush, and titi (Tiner 1984). The scrub/shrub wetlands of most value to wood ducks are composed of such plant species as buttonbush, swamp privet, willow, dogwood, and young trees.

Hydrologic characteristics and climate exert a major influence on the vegetation that grows in a particular wetland. Forested wetlands in the northern portion of the wood duck's range that are flooded for an extended period during the growing season are characterized by red maple, ashes, northern white cedar, black spruce, and larch. By contrast, baldcypress, water tupelo, red maple, black gum, overcup oak, and black willow are characteristic southern wet swamp tree species. Trees such as sycamore, beech, silver maple, and pin oak are found on slightly higher sites in the central region, where floodwaters usually remain only briefly during the growing season. The drier forested wetlands of the South are characterized by sweetgum, loblolly pine, slash pine, tulip poplar, beech, black walnut, sycamore, water hickory, water oak, laurel oak, and willow oak (Tiner 1984). Cottonwood, silver maple, green ash, boxelder maple, willow, and various elms provide important habitat for wood ducks on the floodplain of many river systems throughout the United States.

Wooded wetland complexes provide essential habitat needs—food, cover, and nest sites—for wood ducks. Within this broad category are included creeks, rivers, ditches, beaver ponds, farm ponds, oxbow ponds and sloughs, wooded shorelines of lakes and reservoirs, overflow bottomland hardwoods, swamps, bogs, and marshes. The buttressed bases of baldcypress and tupelo are typical of their growth form in southern swamps. *Photo by Jack Dermid.*

Although many cavity-producing trees occur in forested wetlands, wood ducks also commonly use cavities in upland hardwood trees located within 1.6 kilometers (1 mi) of water for nesting. The value of a nest tree increases as its distance from water decreases. Silver, red, and sugar maple, American and slippery elm, quaking and bigtooth aspen, red ash, American basswood, red oak, bitternut hickory, black walnut, and black willow have been identified as important cavity-producing species in the northern portion of the wood duck's range (McGilvrey 1968, Prince 1968, Nagel 1969, Boyer 1974, Haramis 1975, Gilmer et al. 1978, Soulliere 1988). Sycamore, American beech, black oak, silver maple, red maple, and sugar maple provide most of the cavities in the central region (Bellrose et al. 1964, Grice and Rogers 1965, McGilvrey 1968, Robb 1986). The principal cavity trees in the South are tupelo gum, black gum, baldcypress, sycamore, cherrybark oak, water oak, willow oak, swamp white oak, American beech, and black willow (Almand 1965, McGilvrey 1968, Strange 1970, Teels 1975, Lowney 1987).

HABITAT PREFERENCES

Physiological demands, temporal activity, local weather conditions, and relative availability and quality of specific habitats are factors that influence the types of wetlands used by wood ducks in a given area. In general, wood ducks use the wetlands associated with streams and rivers more than any other habitat type. Along with overhanging stream shoreline vegetation, channel border, backwater, and floodplain wetlands constitute the backbone of the wood duck's habitat base throughout its extensive range.

Streams

Streams are the mainstay of wood duck breeding populations. Although streams rarely provide the best habitat for breeding birds, they provide the most extensive wetlands that woodies have been able to exploit. Wood ducks have evolved strategies that enable them to use a wide variety of stream habitats, from the smallest permanent streams to the largest rivers, from sluggish ditches to fast-moving streams, from streams of heavily forested regions to the skimpily clad riparian timber of the prairies. However, the density of breeding wood ducks varies appreciably among streams that have been surveyed, depending on the attributes of a given stream for reproduction and survival.

Streams that have oxbows, ponds, or other segments cut off by channel meanderings have supportive wetlands of added value to wood ducks, particularly during the breeding season. Islands double the shoreline and increase cover and food resources. The greater the stream's inherent meandering, the more likely the occurrence of oxbows and side-channel sloughs. Channelization by humans, however, may drain these side-channel wetlands as well as reduce eddies and quiet water pools that help make a stream productive.

Less commonly, channelized streams may retain viable oxbows and sloughs adjacent to the ditched bed. Such a condition occurred in the upper part of our Quiver Creek study area. Weekly counts of wood ducks on the Ermling and Cullinane units from March 22 through April 26, 1948–1962 (Table 8), revealed no significant difference between the use of the creek and that of adjacent ponds. The ponds, of course, added desirable water habitat to the limited aquatic resources of the creek.

Table 8. Available habitat on Quiver Creek, Illinois and adjacent ponds, number of wood ducks observed, and number observed per year per unit of area, March 22 through April 26, 1948–62.

Unit	Available habitat, in hectares (ac)		Average number of wood ducks observed per census		Average number of wood ducks observed per hectare (ac)		t-statistic
	Creek	Pond	Creek	Pond	Creek	Pond	
Ermling	1.96 (4.84)	4.87 (12.03)	6.57	20.21	3.35 (8.28)	4.15 (10.25)	
Cullinane	1.33 (3.29)	9.82 (24.27)	8.09	16.27	6.08 (15.02)	1.66 (4.10)	p>0.10
Total	3.29 (8.13)	14.69 (36.30)	14.66	36.48	4.46 (11.02)	2.48 (6.13)	

In the states east of the Great Plains, we have extrapolated 1,317,515 kilometers (818,688 mi) of stream courses from the 1,018,265 kilometers (632,738 mi) reported in 21 of 31 states (Table 9). Measured stream lengths, as derived from various state and federal sources, were not always based on the same parameters or measured in the same way. Some states may have included reaches with intermittent flow; some, such as Arkansas, limited stream measurements to fishable waters. One state—Minnesota—included drainage ditches. Nevertheless, these data provide a framework for evaluating the breeding distribution of wood ducks in political and physiographic areas.

Most of our knowledge of the use of streams by breeding wood ducks is derived from surveys of broods and adult birds enumerated on float trips by scores of biologists from state conservation agencies of the Mississippi Flyway, 1973–1978. The primary objective of these stream surveys was to measure yearly differences in wood duck numbers.

It should be borne in mind, however, that counts of wood duck broods (each representative of a breeding female) and lone females that are potential breeders seldom if ever provide more than an index of breeding numbers. Woodie broods and adult females often avoid detection by hiding under shoreline cover, scrambling up banks, and taking flight before being seen; during nonfeeding periods, some may consistently rest in upland areas away from the shoreline.

Studies made on the Holston River in eastern Tennessee clearly demonstrated that many more breeding wood ducks inhabit a stream than are seen on diurnal float censuses. Minser and Dabney (1973) and Cottrell and Prince (1990) made back-to-back nocturnal and diurnal floats for the purpose of evaluating differences in the occurrence of broods.

Table 9. Area of states in relation to length of streams and area of drainage.

State	Total area, in square kilometers (mi²)		Total length of streams, in kilometers (mi)		Land area per kilometer (mi) of stream	
Alabama	133,916	(51,705)	65,339	(40,600)	2.04	(1.27)
Arkansas	137,754	(53,187)	15,675	(9,740)	8.79	(5.46)
Connecticut	12,997	(5,018)	13,518	(8,400)	0.97	(0.60)
Delaware	5,294	(2,044)				
Florida	151,940	(58,664)				
Georgia	152,577	(58,910)	44,637	(27,736)	3.41	(2.12)
Illinois	145,934	(56,345)	21,250	(13,204)	6.87	(4.27)
Indiana	93,719	(36,185)				
Iowa	145,752	(56,275)	29,470	(18,312)	4.94	(3.07)
Kentucky	104,659	(40,409)	86,905	(54,000)	1.21	(0.75)
Louisiana	123,678	(47,752)				
Maine	86,156	(33,265)	51,499	(32,000)	1.67	(1.04)
Maryland	27,091	(10,460)				
Massachusetts	21,456	(8,284)	9,012	(5,600)	2.38	(1.48)
Michigan	151,585	(58,527)	58,500	(36,350)	2.59	(1.61)
Minnesota	218,599	(84,401)	144,841	(90,000)	1.51	(0.94)
Mississippi	123,515	(47,689)				
Missouri	180,513	(69,696)	84,635	(52,590)	2.14	(1.33)
New Hampshire	24,033	(9,279)				
New Jersey	20,168	(7,787)				
New York	127,190	(49,108)				
North Carolina	136,413	(52,669)	60,123	(37,359)	2.27	(1.41)
Ohio	107,045	(41,330)	70,678	(43,917)	1.51	(0.94)
Pennsylvania	117,348	(45,308)	72,420	(45,000)	1.63	(1.01)
Rhode Island	3,139	(1,212)				
South Carolina	80,583	(31,113)	17,864	(11,100)	4.51	(2.80)
Tennessee	109,153	(42,144)	30,957	(19,236)	3.52	(2.19)
Vermont	24,900	(9,614)	7,826	(4,863)	3.19	(1.98)
Virginia	105,587	(40,767)	43,839	(27,240)	2.41	(1.50)
West Virginia	62,758	(24,231)	36,196	(22,491)	1.74	(1.08)
Wisconsin	145,436	(56,153)	53,108	(33,000)	2.74	(1.70)
States with kilometer stream data	2,381,119	(919,351)	1,018,265	(632,738)	2.34	(1.45)
Total extrapolated	3,080,888	(1,189,531)	1,317,515	(818,688)	2.34	(1.45)

Minser and Dabney (1973) found four times more broods at night than during the morning on a 10.8-kilometer (6.7 mi) reach of the Holston River below Surgoinsville, Tennessee. Counts made during the morning on consecutive days varied by factors of 2 to 16, thereby revealing marked differences in diurnal behavior by maternal females. Cottrell and

Prince (1990) covered 35 kilometers (21.8 mi), including the same segment covered earlier by Minser and Dabney (1973). They found 13 times more marked females with broods on night floats than on morning ones, 1976–1979. During that same period, they observed 1,320 ducklings in morning float trips and 3,298 (2.5 times more) at night.

Overhanging riparian woody vegetation (top left) along Quiver Creek in Mason County, Illinois, provides ideal cover for breeding wood ducks and their broods. Because of the favorable foods and cover provided by the sluggish waters and by adjacent floodplain ponds, the lower 10 kilometers (6.2 mi) of the creek were selected for intensive study of wood ducks. The portion of Quiver Creek where nest houses were placed has an admixture of creek (9.6 hectares: 23.8 ac), open pond (29.8 hectares: 73.6 ac) (top right), shoreline shrub (37.2 hectares: 92 ac) (bottom left), marsh vegetation (42.6 hectares: 105 ac), and shrub/marsh (14.2 hectares: 35.2 ac) (bottom right). *Photos by Frank Bellrose; courtesy of the Illinois Natural History Survey.*

From May 20 to June 16, 1990, personnel of the Tennessee Wildlife Resource Agency conducted diurnal and nocturnal surveys of wood duck broods on six rivers in Tennessee (Minser 1993). They found twice as many broods on the nocturnal float trips, further confirming that a large proportion of broods are missed during diurnal surveys.

Observers obviously miss many broods during diurnal floats because of the females' awareness of the observers, out-of-sight brooding, and resting on banks after early morning feeding. Apparently, darkness reduces or eliminates some of the behavior that results in the oversight of broods.

Even if all broods were counted, no single float survey could encompass all breeders present during the brood season. Some broods become flighted prior to the hatching of others. Because this variation in hatching dates functions on an increasing gradient from north to south, counts on southern streams require larger adjustments. Also, the value of southern streams for breeding woodies is greater than that of more northern locations (see Chapter 9 for effect of latitude on duration of nest initiation).

We endeavored to evaluate differences in abundance of breeding woodies on streams within a state by comparing geographic or physiographic regions (Table 10) and, where possible, by identifying some of the characteristics of better streams.

David Fisher prepared an analysis for us that evaluated yearly counts of all wood ducks observed on streams, grouped by drainage systems, in the Mississippi Flyway. Two-way nested analysis of variance (ANOVA) was used to evaluate yearly and stream differences. His analysis showed no significant difference between years for streams within a given watershed (Table 11). However, statistically

Table 10. Number of potential breeding female wood ducks per kilometer of stream in various regions of states within the Mississippi Flyway, 1973–78.

State	Region	Females per kilometer (mi)	
Iowa	West (1)	0.313 ± 0.207	(0.194 ± 0.129)
	East (2)	0.151 ± 0.181	(0.094 ± 0.112)
Illinois	North (3)	0.348 ± 0.268	(0.216 ± 0.167)
	South (4)	0.463 ± 0.502	(0.289 ± 0.312)
Indiana	Central Lowlands (5)	0.469 ± 0.310	(0.291 ± 0.193)
	Lake Plain (6)	0.346 ± 0.114	(0.215 ± 0.071)
	Low Plateau (7)	0.643 ± 0.321	(0.400 ± 0.199)
Ohio	Central Plain (8)	0.306 ± 0.250	(0.190 ± 0.155)
	Appalachian Plateau (9)	0.303 ± 0.221	(0.188 ± 0.137)
Missouri	Core of Ozark Mts. (10)	0.118 ± 0.124	(0.073 ± 0.077)
	Peripheral Ozark (11)	0.204 ± 0.157	(0.127 ± 0.098)
	Northeast Quarter (12)	0.170 ± 0.133	(0.106 ± 0.083)
	West (13)	0.218 ± 0.177	(0.135 ± 0.110)
Kentucky	Mississippi Alluvial (14)	0.404 ± 0.345	(0.251 ± 0.214)
	Low Plateau (15)	0.584 ± 0.331	(0.363 ± 0.206)
	Cumberland Plateau (16)	0.354 ± 0.228	(0.220 ± 0.142)
Tennessee	Valley and Ridges (17)	0.782 ± 0.587	(0.486 ± 0.365)
	Cumberland Plateau (18)	0.344 ± 0.293	(0.214 ± 0.182)
	Low Plateau (19)	0.488 ± 0.208	(0.303 ± 0.129)
	Coastal Plain (20)	0.366 ± 0.218	(0.227 ± 0.135)
Arkansas	Mississippi Alluvial (21)	0.462 ± 0.298	(0.287 ± 0.185)
	Ouachita Mountains (22)	0.249 ± 0.210	(0.155 ± 0.130)
	Boston Mountains (23)	0.143 ± 0.132	(0.089 ± 0.082)
	Coastal Plain (24)	0.155 ± 0.071	(0.096 ± 0.044)
Alabama	Coastal Plain (25)	0.327 ± 0.300	(0.203 ± 0.186)
	Piedmont Plateau (26)	0.291 ± 0.306	(0.181 ± 0.190)

[a] Statistical comparisons (analysis of variance) were made among representative physiographic regions.

Table 11. Number of wood ducks (young and adults combined) censused on summer stream surveys. Streams were grouped by watershed for each year, 1973–77, and evaluated for significant differences by two-way nested analysis of variance.

Drainage system	Number of streams surveyed	Kilometers (mi) surveyed[a]		Mean number of birds per kilometer (mi)[a]		Between years		Between streams in basin	
						F	P	F	P
Lake Erie	4	488	(303)	1.34	(0.83)	1.08	>0.05	1.65	>0.05
Ohio River	8	1,035	(643)	2.25	(1.40)	1.01	>0.05	8.69	<0.01
Illinois River	4	369	(229)	1.00	(0.62)	0.68	>0.05	2.76	<0.05
Wabash River	7	851	(529)	2.40	(1.49)	0.63	>0.05	6.97	<0.01
Cumberland River	5	476	(296)	1.90	(1.18)	0.99	>0.05	3.82	<0.05
Tennessee River	8	1,180	(733)	2.25	(1.40)	0.56	>0.05	10.00	<0.01
Mississippi River	8	1,003	(623)	1.08	(0.67)	0.90	>0.05	3.89	<0.05
Missouri River	5	661	(411)	1.21	(0.75)	1.21	>0.05	6.86	<0.01

[a] Mileage figures (in parentheses) were rounded off during the conversion from kilometers.

significant differences in wood duck numbers were found between streams embracing seven of the

Table 10. (continued)

Statistically evaluated physiographic regions[a]	F statistic	P
1 and 2	17.04	<0.01
3 and 4	7.85	<0.01
5 and 6	3.11	>0.05
6 and 7	5.94	<0.01
5, 6 and 7	11.95	<0.01
8 and 9	0.006	>0.05
10 and 11	6.19	<0.05
12 and 13	1.13	>0.05
14, 15 and 16	0.98	>0.05
17, 18, 19 and 20	8.12	<0.01
17 and 18	16.81	<0.01
18 and 20	0.05	>0.05
19 and 20	1.68	>0.05
21 and 22	5.67	<0.05
21, 22 and 23	9.45	<0.01
21, 22, 23 and 24	7.30	<0.01
23 and 24	0.82	>0.05
25 and 26	0.21	>0.05

eight watersheds surveyed (Table 11). Streams flowing into Lake Erie in Ohio had similar wood duck populations, but individual streams in other drainage basins showed significant differences in abundance.

A further ANOVA by David Fisher of wood duck counts on nine streams in Indiana over a 12-year period, 1955–1967, did show a significant difference (P<0.05) in certain years: numbers were below average in 1955 and above average in 1963. However, differences between streams were significantly stronger (P<0.01).

Our analysis of adult females (alone or with broods) enumerated on float surveys, 1973–1978, in nine states of the Mississippi Flyway showed significant differences between states (Figure 3). The lowest number of females per kilometer occurred on streams surveyed in Iowa and Missouri; mid-level abundance occurred on streams in Ohio, Arkansas, and Alabama. Streams in Illinois, Indiana, Kentucky, and Tennessee had the largest number of potential female breeders. Tennessee and Kentucky streams appear to have had the greatest density of breeding females per kilometer among streams surveyed in the Mississippi Flyway (Figure 3).

Surprisingly, streams in western Iowa west of Interstate 35 supported significantly more wood ducks than those to the east (Table 10). In the western part of the state, woods are more confined to stream borders, more streams are less meandering or have channelized courses, and the landscape that surrounds streams is more undulating and in arable fields. Such an incongruous relationship of wood duck habitat between streams of the two regions defies ready explanation. Oxbows and sloughs are more prevalent along streams in eastern Iowa. Several years of high water occurred during the sample period, according to James L. Hansen, and more females and broods may have been con-

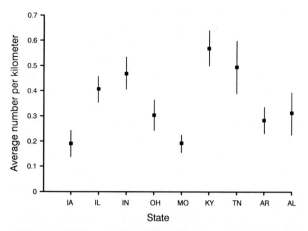

Figure 3. Number of adult female wood ducks counted per stream kilometer in nine states of the Mississippi Flyway, 1973–78. Bars represent 95-percent confidence limits to the mean. The data were obtained from reports submitted by the Wood Duck Subcommittee of the Mississippi Flyway Technical Committee.

centrated on these waters and fewer on the streams. Adjacent water areas may have dispersed broods, as Prokop (1981) observed lowest densities of wood ducks on those reaches of Oklahoma streams that contained marshes within 0.8 kilometer (0.5 mi). The most productive river surveyed in Iowa was the upper reaches of the Des Moines, north of Fort Dodge; the lower Iowa River in eastern Iowa supported the second largest number (Table 12).

More streams in southern Illinois provided superior habitat for breeding wood ducks than did those in northern Illinois (Table 10). Streams in southern Illinois have lower banks and broader, flatter floodplains per stream volume and are subject to frequent overflow, more meanders, more riparian timber, and larger forested watersheds. The three best streams for woodies in Illinois are located in the southern portion of the state (Table 12). The surveyed areas of Bay Creek and the Big Muddy have extensive riparian forests and low channel

Table 12. Rivers with the largest numbers of potential breeding female wood ducks in certain states of the Mississippi Flyway, 1973–78.

State	River	Counties	Number of observations	Kilometers (mi) sampled	
Iowa	Des Moines	Humboldt, Kossuth	8	129	(80.2)
	Iowa	Iowa, Louisa, Winneshiek	10	161	(100.0)
Illinois	Bay Creek	Pope	5	80	(49.7)
	Big Muddy	Jackson	21	338	(210.0)
	Little Wabash	Clay, Edwards, White	30	483	(300.1)
Indiana	St. Joseph	St. Joseph	4	71	(44.1)
	Muscatatuck	Jackson	6	159	(98.8)
	Patoka	Pike	4	76	(47.2)
	White	Bartholomew, Daviess, Madison, Morgan	16	396	(246.1)
Ohio	Muskingum	Washington	7	121	(75.2)
	Scioto	Marion	7	129	(80.2)
Missouri	Upper Sac	Dade	5	80	(49.7)
	Osage	Vernon	5	100	(62.1)
Kentucky	Green	Casey	4	64	(39.8)
	Salt	Mercer	4	68	(42.3)
	Dix	Lincoln	6	97	(60.3)
	Nolin	Hardin	5	80	(49.7)
Tennessee	Holston	Hawkins, Jefferson, Knox	9	217	(134.8)
	Red	Montgomery	4	84	(52.2)
	Nolichucky	Greene	5	182	(113.1)
	Little	Blount	4	64	(39.8)
Arkansas	Glaise	White	2	32	(19.9)
	Little Red	White	3	48	(29.8)
	L'Anguille	Lee	3	43	(26.7)
Alabama	Millers	Wilcox	2	48	(29.8)
	Flint	Morgan	3	80	(49.7)

velocity. The Little Wabash has an exceptional number of meanders and broad areas of riparian timber flanking its watercourse.

Indiana streams draining the Central Lowlands and Lake Plain physiographic provinces showed no statistical difference in density of breeding season wood ducks (Table 10). However, streams of the Low Plateau province in southcentral Indiana had significantly greater numbers of wood ducks per stream kilometer than did streams of the other provinces. Streams of the Low Plateau typically have broad, flat valleys and moderately timbered banks, as exemplified by the Muscatatuck River, which had the second highest density of wood ducks among streams in Indiana (Table 12). The Patoka and White rivers, which either originate or border the Low Plateau area, also rank among the best rivers for breeding woodies. The St. Joseph River on the Lake Plain is an exception (Table 12). Its high density of breeding birds may stem from enriched effluent downstream from the sewage treat-

Table 12. (continued)

Females observed per kilometer (mi)		State average	
0.49±0.19	(0.30±0.12)	0.19±0.17	(0.12±0.11)
0.32±0.20	(0.20±0.12)		
1.22±1.11	(0.76±0.69)	0.41±0.39	(0.25±0.24)
0.96±0.85	(0.59±0.52)		
0.55±0.50	(0.34±0.31)		
0.89±0.26	(0.55±0.16)	0.47±0.32	(0.29±0.20)
0.84±0.27	(0.52±0.17)		
0.76±0.46	(0.47±0.29)		
0.71±0.38	(0.44±0.24)		
0.75±0.25	(0.47±0.16)	0.32±0.29	(0.20±0.18)
0.60±0.24	(0.37±0.15)		
0.55±0.17	(0.34±0.11)	0.19±0.09	(0.12±0.06)
0.39±0.14	(0.24±0.09)		
1.08±0.27	(0.67±0.17)	0.57±0.36	(0.35±0.22)
1.06±0.39	(0.66±0.24)		
1.01±0.13	(0.63±0.08)		
0.99±0.12	(0.62±0.07)		
1.32±0.63	(0.82±0.39)	0.48±0.43	(0.30±0.27)
0.95±0.58	(0.59±0.36)		
0.88±0.29	(0.55±0.18)		
0.64±0.26	(0.40±0.16)		
0.87±0.70	(0.54±0.43)	0.29±0.26	(0.18±0.16)
0.60±0.28	(0.37±0.17)		
0.52±0.25	(0.32±0.16)		
0.95±0.77	(0.59±0.48)	0.32±0.30	(0.20±0.19)
0.86±0.50	(0.53±0.31)		

ment plant at South Bend, a city of 110,000. The fertile water, along with cavities in the large trees of city parks and suburban areas, apparently combine to produce the most productive section of stream in Indiana, according to Tom Sporre. The presence of a high-level food base is further evidenced by the large number of mallard broods produced.

There was no statistical difference in the use of streams by wood ducks in the Central Plain and Appalachian Plateau provinces of Ohio (Table 10). The best streams for woodies—the Muskingum and Scioto—are both in southern Ohio, in each physiographic province (Table 12).

Missouri has a wide variety of stream habitats created by diversified topography, particularly the Ozark Plateau (mountains). Streams of the central part of the Ozarks are clear and fast, occupy gravelly beds, and are relatively unproductive of aquatic plants. Although flowing through heavily forested watersheds, they supported the fewest breeding wood ducks of any of the stream groups analyzed (Table 10). Streams peripheral to the central Ozarks harbored more breeding wood ducks; they are not as swift and meander more. Streams elsewhere in Missouri do not sustain numbers that are statistically different among the several regions. The Osage and upper Sac rivers supported the greatest density of breeding wood ducks in Missouri (Table 12); both are in the southwestern part of the state, peripheral to the Ozarks.

The streams of Kentucky were populated by more breeding wood ducks per kilometer than the streams surveyed in other states (Figure 3), but no statistical difference in population densities was found among the collective streams in the three physiographic regions of the state (Table 10). Streams surveyed in the Cumberland Plateau region were those with moderate gradients. There was no statistical difference between the four streams supporting the largest density of wood ducks (Table 12). All are in the Low Plateau province in the central part of the state. The high breeding density for these streams and others in Kentucky may relate to the large number of meanders, moderately clear water, enhanced fertility stemming from their limestone beds, and extensive riparian forests.

Tennessee streams were surveyed for breeding wood ducks in four physiographic provinces: Coastal Plain, Low Plateau, Cumberland Plateau, and Valley and Ridge. The highest density was found among streams in the Valley and Ridge province, which flanks the Appalachian Mountains to the east and abuts the Cumberland Plateau to the west. Although streams of the Low Plateau contained the second highest density of wood ducks, there was no such statistical difference between that region, the Coastal Plain, and the Cumberland Plateau. Density in the latter was very similar to the density of woodies in the Cumberland Plateau of Kentucky.

The upper Holston River in Tennessee's Valley and Ridge province had the highest density of breeding wood ducks in Tennessee and, indeed, among all the streams recorded in the Mississippi Flyway (Table 12). Because of its high breeding density, the Holston River merits special attention. Fortunately, it has been studied extensively by Minser and Dabney (1973), Cottrell (1979a), Cottrell and Prince (1990), and Cottrell et al. (1990).

The Holston River arises amid the forested mountain ridges of southwestern Virginia and flows southwestward to form, with the French Broad River, the Tennessee River at Knoxville, Tennessee. It flows over a largely consolidated bed of limestone and sediments in Tennessee, with clear water, except in floods. At Kingsport, Tennessee—a city of 32,000 a few miles below the Virginia line—it receives effluent rich in nitrogen, phosphorus, and potash from the city's sewage disposal plant. The Holston drops an average of 0.69 meter per kilometer (3.6 ft/mi) during the first 24 kilometers (15 mi) below Kingsport. In the next 40 kilometers (25 mi), the river falls an average of 0.48 meter per kilometer (2.5 ft/mi) and contains long stretches of sluggish pools separated by short, rocky shoals. Luxuriant beds of submerged aquatic plants grow in numerous areas scattered over the river prior to its entering the John Sevier impoundment, which embraces the lower 8.9 kilometers (5.5 mi) of this river section (Cottrell 1979a). The average channel width of 128 meters (420 ft) is established in a floodplain 0.3–1.6 kilometers (0.2–1.0 mi) wide. The riparian vegetation is largely timber but often only 12 meters (39 ft) or less in width where pasture and arable land occupy the floodplain. Where the banks are at the base of steep ridges, extensive wooded lands stretch back from the channel. There are no oxbows, sloughs, or swamps adjacent to the channel, but there are nine large islands with the resulting side channels (Cottrell 1979a).

In response to our query about the unusual abundance of wood ducks on the Holston River, William G. Minser concluded that the high food base on the river, the source of which was aquatic plant beds, combined with an abundance of nesting cavities to create optimum nesting conditions for wood ducks. He further reported that the Clinch, Powell, and North and South forks of the Holston (above Kingsport) and the lower Holston below Cherokee Lake did not support the quantities of aquatic plants present in the upper Holston. As a result, fewer wood ducks were found breeding on these river areas than in the upper Holston. Thus, the discharge of rich organic-based effluents by the Kingsport sewage treatment appears to have created enriched aquatic habitats.

The importance of aquatic plants to wood duck production was further demonstrated in a study of the lower Holston River (below Cherokee Lake to Knoxville) by Minser et al. (1990). They found only 0.58 brood per kilometer (0.93/mi), 1976–1978, on the lower Holston compared with 2.7 broods per kilometer (4.34/mi) on the upper Holston, 1973 (Minser and Dabney 1973). Both sets of data were based on similar nocturnal surveys. The lower Holston River has sparse beds of aquatic plants, compared with the lush beds of the upper Holston. William Minser theorized that the nutrients of the upper Holston are reduced as the flow passes through two impoundments—John Sevier and Cherokee Lake. The coldwater discharge from the bottom of the deep Cherokee Lake impoundment may further inhibit development of aquatic plants and invertebrates.

Cottrell (1979b) also surveyed wood duck populations of the French Broad River. A view of this stream, popular for whitewater canoeing and raft trips, makes it difficult to believe that it supports breeding wood ducks; but it does. The river rises east of the Great Smoky Mountains near Rosman, North Carolina, and encircles them to the east and north before reaching the Douglas Lake impoundment near Newport, Tennessee. On morning float surveys in June 1978, Cottrell (1979b) found 0.32 brood per kilometer (0.52/mi) on 111 kilometers (69 mi) of stream. Over the entire reach surveyed, the French Broad River drops about 0.73 meter per kilometer (5.7 ft/mi)—a drop nearly twice that of the upper Holston River. However, the largest number of broods was found in the reach where the stream gradient was the lowest, and no broods were found where the stream gradient was the highest (Table 13). A surprisingly large number of broods was observed on the upper stream course in Transylvania County, where the stream descended at rates of 0.42–0.80 meter per kilometer (2.2–4.2 ft/mi).

Although wood ducks avoided the most turbulent sections of the French Broad River, the presence of broods on reaches of fast water demonstrates their ability to exploit a wide spectrum of streams. Smaller, more turbulent streams in the adjacent Great Smoky Mountains National Park, however, are not used by breeding wood ducks (Stupka 1963), thereby providing parameters on an upper limit of acceptable stream velocity.

Four physiographic regions—Mississippi Alluvial Plain, Coastal Plain, Ouachita Mountains, and

Table 13. Wood duck brood observations on several reaches with varying gradients of the French Broad River, North Carolina, 1978[a].

Date	County	Kilometers (mi) surveyed		Meters per kilometer (ft/mi) gradient		Broods per kilometer (mi)	
May 31	Henderson	25.7	(16.0)	0.265	(1.4)	0.73	(1.18)
June 14	Transylvania	19.3	(12.0)	0.417	(2.2)	0.47	(0.75)
June 15	Transylvania	30.6	(19.0)	0.795	(4.2)	0.03	(0.05)
June 16	Buncombe	20.9	(13.0)	0.909	(4.8)	0.34	(0.54)
June 30	Madison	14.5	(9.0)	2.44	(12.9)	0.00	(0.00)

[a] From Cottrell (1979b).

Boston Mountains—result in much stream diversity in Arkansas. Streams of the Mississippi Alluvial Plain supported significantly greater densities of breeding wood ducks than did the other three regions (Table 10). Streams surveyed in the Ouachita Mountains region were peripheral to the mountains; they supported a population density similar to the streams peripheral to the core of the Ozark Plateau in Missouri. Streams of the Boston Mountains region apparently are more turbulent and contained a lower density of wood ducks.

Most breeding wood ducks in Arkansas were found on Glaise Creek and the Little Red and L'Anguille rivers in the Lower Mississippi Alluvial Plain (Table 12). This is the region of the overflow bottomland hardwoods that, at one time, created the best extensive wood duck habitat in the United States. A remnant of this swampland in southeast Missouri was studied by Heitmeyer and Fredrickson (1990). They reported approximately one pair of breeding woodies for each 6.2 hectares (1/15.3 ac) of floodable land, and concluded that streams within overflow bottomland hardwoods were used because of the adjacent overflow hardwood habitat and not because of stream qualities per se.

Streams draining the Coastal Plain and the Piedmont Plateau of Alabama showed no significant difference despite variations in velocity (Table 10). Millers River in the Coastal Plain and Flint River in the Piedmont had the highest density of wood

Streams are the mainstay of breeding populations of wood ducks. Among the many significant stream characteristics that determine the attractiveness of such watercourses to woodies are rate of water flow, depth, width, temperature (relative to invertebrate and plant food growth), shoreline canopy, proximity to other wetlands, and type and size of riparian tree stands. *Photo by Frank Bellrose; courtesy of the Illinois Natural History Survey.*

ducks of streams censused in Alabama (Table 12).

Prokop (1981) surveyed 17 streams for wood ducks in the six physiographic provinces of Oklahoma. He found the greatest density along rivers in the Ozark Plateau in the northeast and the Dissected Coastal Plain in the southeast. These are the provinces where the bottomland forest predominates over that in other physiographic regions. The three streams with the largest spring population were Big Cabin Creek with 2.73 wood ducks per kilometer (1.70/mi), Caney Creek at 2.07 wood ducks per kilometer (1.29/mi), and the Illinois River with 1.68 woodies per kilometer (1.04/mi)—all in the Ozark Plateau province. Lowest numbers in the spring were found in streams of the Western High Plains, where scarce timber, steep cutbanks, and the numerous sand and mud flats all combine to provide little cover. According to Prokop (1981), these sparse riverine habitat conditions were reflected in negligible productivity.

Earlier surveys of breeding woodies were made on streams in Minnesota and Michigan. On 159 kilometers (99 mi) of streams in Minnesota, 1957, breeding females averaged 0.51 per kilometer (0.82/mi). Michigan reported 0.40 potential breeder per kilometer (0.64/mi) for 217 kilometers (135 mi) surveyed in 1959—a figure close to their 10-year average. These data suggest that breeding densities along streams in these two northern states in the late 1950s were comparable to those in Indiana and Illinois in the 1970s (Figure 3).

Stream surveys were conducted in Kansas concurrently with those of the Mississippi Flyway. An average of 0.185 ± 0.205 potential breeding female per kilometer (0.3/mi) was observed on 1,802 kilometers (1,120 mi) of surveyed streams in Kansas, 1975–1977. These numbers were similar to those found on surveyed streams of Missouri and Iowa (Figure 3).

Importance of stream width. Among the many variables of a stream that might be considered an important influence on its value to wood duck production is its width. We analyzed data on female wood duck numbers by stream width for the northern and southern halves of Illinois (tables 14 and 15). In the southern part of the state, no statistical difference was found among stream widths sampled and density of woodie hens (Table 15); however, the smallest streams floated had the largest number. Streams in northern Illinois showed a slight statistical significance for larger numbers on smaller streams, but these data covered only four years (Table 14). Overall, there is little evidence to suggest any appreciable effect of the width of floatable Illinois streams on the number of breeding woodies.

Because of the potential importance of stream size to wood duck production and management, we asked Tim Moser, former Waterfowl Research Biologist, Indiana Department of Natural Resources, to evaluate stream float data for Indiana. Moser employed linear regression to compare data for 21 streams over a 10-year period, 1977–1986. Widths were measured on large-scale maps at 10 section line crossings for each stream floated. His data showed no statistically significant difference among streams ranging in width from 17.6 to 90.3 meters (57.7–296.3 ft) ($r = 0.33$, $P > 0.10$). Even if the in-

Table 14. Relationship of stream width to number of female wood ducks observed in the northern half of Illinois.

| Year | Number of hens per kilometer (mi) by stream width category[a] | | | |
	1.0–6.1 (3.3–20)	6.2–30.5 (21–100)	30.6–91.4 (101–300)	>91.4 (300+)
1973	1.01	0.36	0.24	0.43
1974	0.93	0.23	0.47	0.62
1975	0.23	0.19	0.30	0.24
1976		0.25	0.33	0.56
1977	0.19	0.31	0.27	0.28
1978		0.20	0.08	0.49
1979		0.37	0.51	0.58
1980		0.28	0.47	0.74
1981		0.30	0.19	0.57
1983		0.39	0.26	0.19
1984		0.43	0.51	0.19
1985		0.51	0.39	0.15
1986		0.34	0.25	
Mean	0.59 ± 0.44	0.32 ± 0.09	0.33 ± 0.13	0.42 ± 0.20
95% C.L.	-0.02–1.20	0.26–0.38	0.25–0.41	0.29–0.55

[a] In meters (ft).

crease had proved statistically significant, it would have amounted to only a 0.0056-brood-per-meter (0.0017/ft) increase in width.

There is little information on the occurrence of wood ducks on streams too small to float. On unfloatable Salt Creek and seven still smaller tributaries near Lincoln, Nebraska, Cink (1977) walked 10 8-kilometer (5 mi) sections and found seven pairs and four broods. Considering the paucity of timber and other marginal qualities of these streams, that number is surprising.

We recognize that there is a point where streams become so wide that an increasing number of broods is overlooked. On diurnal floats of the 128-meter (420 ft) wide Holston River, Minser and Dabney (1973) found 1.27 times more broods when observers were used in two boats as compared to one. Most streams floated for wood duck brood counts are not as wide as the Holston River, thereby minimizing this variable in brood oversight.

Riverine habitat qualities. The lack of a significant relationship between stream width and occupancy by breeding wood ducks points to the extent of bank vegetation as a key element in the production and survival of wood duck broods. Certainly, the linear habitat stream banks provide is more important than the expanse of water streams provide. All of the broods found by Cottrell (1979a) on the Holston River were within 15 meters (49 ft) of the shoreline, most within 10 meters (33 ft), in a stream averaging 128 meters (420 ft) wide.

Islands increase the shoreline of reaches of streams where they occur. Their influence on wood duck brood abundance is evident in a 17.4-kilometer

(10.8 mi) stretch of the Little River, east Tennessee; this river was surveyed nocturnally under the direction of William G. Minser and J. C. Cole in 1990. Eight islands occur along the surveyed section of the Little River in an almost continuous chain. They found 1.4 broods per kilometer (2.3/mi), the highest density of broods on nine streams surveyed that summer in Tennessee. A linear regression of the relationship of islands in all nine stream areas to wood duck broods showed a positive correlation (Figure 4). Minser attributed the abundance of broods to the increased stream bank habitat provided by the islands and to abundant aquatic plant beds.

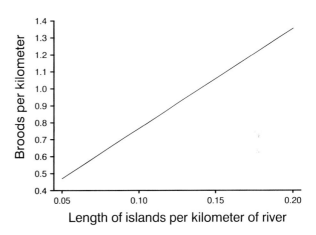

Figure 4. Relationship of islands to the number of wood duck broods per kilometer on nine stream areas surveyed in eastern Tennessee, 1990 (data provided by William G. Minser and J. C. Cole). The regression equation is: $y = 5.90x + 0.175$, $r = 0.775$, $P < 0.05$.

Table 15. Relationship of stream width to number of female wood ducks observed in the southern half of Illinois.

| Year | Number of hens per kilometer (mi) by stream width category[a] | | | |
	1.0–6.1 (3.3–20)	6.2–30.5 (21–100)	30.6–91.4 (101–300)	>91.4 (300+)
1973	0.71	0.36	0.70	
1974	0.43	0.28	0.47	
1975	0.85	0.35	0.71	
1976	0.25	0.24	0.37	
1977		0.32	0.30	
1978		0.30	0.53	
1979	0.21	0.29	0.86	
1980	0.55	0.34	0.85	
1981	0.29	0.31	0.61	0.51
1983	2.67	0.60	0.62	0.32
1984	1.95	0.63	0.72	0.20
1985	0.33	0.29	0.58	0.30
1986	0.25	0.32	0.34	
Mean	0.77 ± 0.80	0.36 ± 0.12	0.59 ± 0.18	0.33 ± 0.13
95% C.L.	0.24–1.30	−0.12–0.84	0.48–0.70	0.15–0.51

[a] In meters (ft).

Because impoundments of streams customarily expand water surface at the expense of wooded banks, they must be viewed in overall context as detrimental to riverine habitat for wood ducks. Hankla and Carter (1966) pointed out that flood-control reservoirs are particularly detrimental for the following reasons: (1) water levels fluctuate more above the impoundment structure and less below; (2) large acreages of bottomland hardwoods are destroyed in the impoundment area; (3) land-owners are prone to clear land below the impoundment because of reduced flooding; and (4) reduced flooding of bottomland hardwoods below the impoundment minimizes availability of food as a result of less bank overflow. Cottrell (1979a) raised the point, based on a report by Allen (1971), that wood duck production along streams impounded by the Tennessee Valley Authority probably was greater before flooding, channelization, and bank-side tree removal occurred.

In contrast, Prokop (1981) found about the same number of wood ducks above and below the Wister Dam on the Poteau River in Oklahoma. This impoundment of 1,619 hectares (4,000 ac) did not impact wooded habitat at the magnitude usually associated with the damming of rivers. Prokop (1981) found wood ducks in secluded coves of the impounded lake and speculated that during periods of low water the reservoir might provide a greater proportion of usable habitat than does the river. Although impoundments generally appear to be more destructive of wood duck habitat than beneficial to it, the size, shape, water fluctuation, and amount of shoreline timber left intact all are factors that need to be evaluated.

Cottrell et al. (1990) determined the relationship of female wood ducks and their broods to shoreline habitat of the upper Holston River in east Tennessee. They reported that the most used habitat was created by sloping wooded banks, fallen trees, and aquatic plant beds. A further enhancement was the exposure of tree roots and overhanging vegetation where currents were eroding banks at the shore-line/water interface. These conditions occur most often in a meandering stream, and they increase cover and attachment sites for aquatic insects.

Minser (1993) studied wood duck brood distribution by night lighting on 12 rivers in Tennessee. Brood density was correlated with aquatic vegetation, mud flats with overhanging woody vegetation, logs and limbs along the banks, and islands. Broods were absent from eroded and exposed stream banks and where rapids occurred. Frequently from two to four broods were found in a stream brush pile formed by downed trees and wooded flotsam that collected about the inundated branches. Islands doubled the edge of stream banks and, because of the lack of cultivation, provided more wooded cover and seclusion.

On the more barren rivers of Oklahoma, Prokop (1981) found that logjams and the proportion of overmature trees on stream banks were responsible for the highest density of wood ducks. Logjams not only provided cover but also enhanced the food supply because invertebrates used these structures as a substrate.

Many factors obviously enter into determining the value of a stream for breeding wood ducks. All of the variables fit broadly into three categories: food resources, cover, and nest sites. Of the three, food base is most important because it is necessary for survival and the least flexible of the variables. Adults and broods have mobility and the ability to adapt to a wide variety of cover types ranging from marsh, fallen trees, logs, stumps, overhanging woody cover of shrubs and young trees, and, where these are lacking, upland cover back from the shoreline. Although ranging to their maximum of 2.4 kilometers (1.5 mi) for a nest site usually is not productive, wood ducks have considerable flexibility in locating suitable sites near a watercourse.

The importance of the food base to wood ducks is exemplified by differences in the populations on the upper and lower Holston River, Tennessee, and on the streams of the Ozarks in Missouri. Because nutrients and aquatic plants are abundant on the upper Holston, wood duck use is high. Yet upstream on the North and South forks of the Holston above Kingsport, Tennessee, and downstream on the lower Holston (below Cherokee Reservoir), the aquatic plant food base is much reduced and wood duck production is 80 percent lower (Minser et al. 1990). Streams of the Ozarks are similar in appearance to the Holston River. Both river systems are associated with forested watersheds and are relatively clear, but the Ozark streams have comparatively little aquatic plant growth because of swift currents, gravelly beds, and low nutrients, and wood ducks occur at much lower densities.

Overflow Bottomland

Heitmeyer and Fredrickson (1990) evaluated habitat use by wood ducks on Mingo National Wildlife Refuge in southeastern Missouri. The flooding regime and nutrients characteristic of overflow bottomland hardwood forests in this northern reach of the Lower Mississippi Alluvial Plain—commonly referred to as the Mississippi Delta—allowed wood ducks to make extensive use of live forest habitat. Whenever more than 20 percent of the available live forests were flooded, at least 60 percent of all wood ducks observed were found in this habitat, regardless of season. Within the flooded live forests, wood ducks selected (P < 0.05) pin oak/high-elevation habitats over other representative tree stands (pin oak/low elevation, pin oak/hickory, and overcup oak).

During autumn, wood ducks on Mingo Swamp predominantly used live forests, green-tree reservoirs, and scrub/shrub wetlands. In fact, Heitmeyer and Fredrickson (1990) found that woodies utilized these habitats more than expected (P < 0.05) relative to availability. Nonetheless, nearly 50 percent of all wood ducks were observed on open marsh habitat during some sample periods in early autumn (1981 and 1982), and appreciable numbers used ditch/river habitats throughout October 1981.

As standing water habitats became ice-covered, wood ducks concentrated on rivers and ditches. When spring migrants returned to Mingo Swamp, riverine areas continued to receive more use than expected relative to availability (P < 0.05). Those woodies that remained to nest sought out the food resources and cover associated with live forests, green-tree reservoirs, and scrub/shrub swamps. Scrub/shrub swamps also received high use by females with broods.

Wood ducks made only sporadic use of dead tree habitats on Mingo National Wildlife Refuge. Use of dead tree wetlands was greatest in spring and increased as live forest areas dried. Stands of trees that had been dead for less than 10 years received higher use than did older stands of dead trees because of increased food associated with more recently dead stands (Heitmeyer and Fredrickson 1990).

Channelization, ostensibly to provide flood relief, and the conversion of bottomland swamps and riparian lands to cropland have greatly diminished the amount and quality of habitat for wood ducks and other wildlife in the South. Only in recent years have authorities begun to utilize guidelines and practices that retain and revitalize natural stream functions and provide normal flood relief for floodplains, as evidenced by sensitive restorative treatment of the East Fork of the Tombigbee River in Mississippi (above). Past drainage and channelization actions, while mostly well-intentioned, seriously jeopardized or actually eliminated a majority of bottomland acreage in the United States and the inherent values of those wetlands, including that of wood duck habitat. *Photo by Chester A. McConnell.*

WETLAND INVENTORIES

Hawkins and Addy (1966) addressed many of the problems associated with appraising wood duck habitat in the Mississippi and Atlantic flyways. They were unable to evaluate the amount of potential wood duck habitat accurately because past nationwide habitat surveys were either limited in scope or remiss by excluding many habitat types important to wood ducks. Although some additional information on habitat status has been brought to light since the mid-1960s, few steps have been taken to provide measures of habitat quality when documenting inventory data. Thus, only within very broad limits can the current national status of potential wood duck habitat be portrayed.

An estimate of the amount, type, and distribution of some wetland habitats available to wood ducks in the 1950s was determined by the U.S. Fish and Wildlife Service (tables 16, 17, and 18). Unfortunately, many wetlands under 16 hectares (40 ac) were omitted from the survey, as were thousands of stream kilometers. Nonetheless, the wetland surveys of the 1950s provided a valuable picture of the regional availability of select wetland habitats to wood ducks.

Table 16. Area of wetland types considered of value to wood ducks in the Mississippi Flyway and Texas.[a]

State	Scrub/shrub swamp	Wooded swamp	Overflow flats or basins	Emergent wetlands	Open water	Bogs	Total
	Wetland type, in hectares (ac)[b]						
Minnesota	464,179 (1,147,000)	424,925 (1,050,000)	0	306,755 (758,000)	170,374 (421,000)	68,393 (169,000)	1,434,626 (3,545,000)
Wisconsin	329,822 (815,000)	229,459 (567,000)	0	92,270 (228,000)	67,583 (167,000)	99,958 (247,000)	819,093 (2,024,000)
Michigan	376,362 (930,000)	511,528 (1,264,000)	0	31,971 (79,000)	39,660 (98,000)	20,639 (51,000)	980,159 (2,422,000)
Iowa	0	0	23,310 (57,600)	12,181 (30,100)	8,498 (21,000)		43,990 (108,700)
Illinois	2,185 (5,400)	364 (900)	39,417 (97,400)	13,517 (33,400)	101,577 (251,000)		157,060 (388,100)
Indiana	364 (900)	728 (1,800)	0	6,273 (15,500)	6,556 (16,200)		13,921 (34,400)
Ohio	364 (900)	283 (700)	0	14,852 (36,700)	3,683 (9,100)		19,182 (47,400)
Missouri	4,249 (10,500)	2,388 (5,900)	68,393 (169,000)	11,736 (29,000)	21,449 (53,000)		108,214 (267,400)
Kentucky	0	0	95,507 (236,000)	0	607 (1,500)		96,114 (237,500)
Tennessee	0	8,701 (21,500)	322,538 (797,000)	2,671 (6,600)	1,174 (2,900)		335,083 (828,000)
Arkansas	0	19,830 (49,000)	1,496,948 (3,699,000)	0	19,020 (47,000)		1,535,799 (3,795,000)
Mississippi	27,924 (69,000)	113,313 (280,000)	848,230 (2,096,000)	121 (300)	12,950 (32,000)		1,002,539 (2,477,300)
Alabama	445 (1,100)	1,700 (4,200)	595,299 (1,471,000)	0			597,444 (1,476,300)
Louisiana	1,862 (4,600)	290,163 (717,000)	1,230,258 (3,040,000)	0			1,522,282 (3,761,600)
Texas	0	15,783 (39,000)	909,743 (2,248,000)	13,759 (34,000)	6,070 (15,000)		945,356 (2,336,000)
Total	1,207,757 (2,984,400)	1,619,165 (4,001,000)	5,629,643 (13,911,000)	506,105 (1,250,600)	459,202 (1,134,700)	188,990 (467,000)	9,610,861 (23,748,700)

[a] Data from state wetland surveys conducted by the U.S. Fish and Wildlife Service, 1954–55.
[b] Omitted are freshwater meadows, bogs south of Michigan, and wetlands classed as having negligible value for ducks except overflow bottomland hardwood flats. Numbers were rounded off during the conversion from acres to hectares.

In the Mississippi Flyway, the largest acreage of wetland habitats considered of value to wood ducks occurred in the Great Lakes Region and in the lower Mississippi Valley (Table 16). There were marked regional differences in the acreage of major wetland types throughout the flyway. Ninety-seven percent of the scrub/shrub wetland habitat occurred in Minnesota, Wisconsin, and Michigan. These Great Lakes states also contained approximately 72 percent of the wooded swamp habitat and 85 percent of the emergent wetlands (Table 16).

By contrast, seasonally flooded bottomland hardwood basins were essentially restricted to the lower Mississippi River Valley (Table 16). Approximately 88 percent of the overflow bottomland flats or basins in the Mississippi Flyway, 1954, occurred

Table 17. Area of wetland types considered of value to wood ducks in the Atlantic Flyway.[a]

State	Scrub/shrub swamp	Wooded swamp	Overflow flats or basins	Emergent wetlands	Open water	Bogs	Total
	Wetland type, in hectares (ac)[b]						
Maine	688 (1,700)	3,723 (9,200)	0	931 (2,300)	567 (1,400)	2,995 (7,400)	8,903 (22,000)
New Hampshire	0	81 (200)	0	607 (1,500)	40 (100)	202 (500)	931 (2,300)
Vermont	4,371 (10,800)	11,008 (27,200)	0	6,273 (15,500)	364 (900)	3,804 (9,400)	25,819 (63,800)
Massachusetts	9,713 (24,000)	30,756 (76,000)	0	3,278 (8,100)	1,457 (3,600)	121 (300)	45,325 (112,000)
Rhode Island	405 (1,000)	1,295 (3,200)	0	850 (2,100)	809 (2,000)	324 (800)	3,683 (9,100)
Connecticut	243 (600)	324 (800)		283 (700)	0	0	850 (2,100)
New York	21,449 (53,000)	74,868 (185,000)	0	23,877 (59,000)	16,592 (41,000)	4,290 (10,600)	141,075 (348,600)
Pennsylvania	3,076 (7,600)	12,019 (29,700)	0	1,538 (3,800)	890 (2,200)	162 (400)	17,685 (43,700)
New Jersey	405 (1,000)	24,281 (60,000)	0	21,813 (53,900)	162 (400)	81 (200)	50,384 (124,500)
West Virginia	364 (900)	688 (1,700)	0	0	0	40 (100)	1,093 (2,700)
Virginia	0	16,997 (42,000)	30,756 (76,000)	0	202 (500)	0	47,956 (118,500)
Maryland	1,700 (4,200)	14,650 (36,000)	0	0	162 (400)	0	16,512 (40,800)
Delaware	0	769 (1,900)	0	0	0	0	769 (1,900)
North Carolina	0	86,604 (214,000)	628,484 (1,553,000)	0	23,877 (59,000)		738,964 (1,826,000)
South Carolina	0	330,227 (816,000)	183,729 (454,000)	2,145 (5,300)	4,654 (11,500)		520,755 (1,286,800)
Georgia	16,592 (41,000)	364,221 (900,000)	760,817 (1,880,000)	22,663 (56,000)	13,759 (34,000)		1,178,053 (2,911,000)
Florida	65,155 (161,000)	418,045 (1,033,000)		387,288 (957,000)			870,488 (2,151,000)
Total	124,159 (306,800)	1,394,198 (3,445,100)	1,603,786 (3,963,000)	471,545 (1,165,200)	63,536 (157,000)	12,019 (29,700)	3,669,243 (9,066,800)

[a] Data from state wetland surveys conducted by the U.S. Fish and Wildlife Service, 1953–55.
[b] Omitted are marine and coastal wetlands, freshwater meadows, bogs south of Virginia, and wetlands classed as having negligible value for ducks except overflow bottomland hardwood flats; additionally, shallow marshes, overflow flats, and open water were omitted in Florida. Numbers were rounded off during the conversion from acres to hectares.

Table 18. Area of wetland types considered of value to wood ducks in the Pacific Flyway.[a]

State	Wetland type, in hectares (ac)[b]						
	Scrub/shrub swamp	Wooded swamp	Overflow flats or basins	Emergent wetlands	Open water	Bogs	Total
Washington	2,023 (5,000)	4,856 (12,000)	0	5,382 (13,300)	6,677 (16,500)	567 (1,400)	19,506 (48,200)
Oregon	1,295 (3,200)	2,347 (5,800)	0	26,305 (65,000)	3,764 (9,300)		33,711 (83,300)
California	324 (800)	850 (2,100)	0	27,114 (67,000)	12,950 (32,000)	607 (1,500)	41,845 (103,400)
Total	3,642 (9,000)	8,053 (19,900)	0	58,801 (145,300)	23,391 (57,800)	1,174 (2,900)	95,062 (234,900)

[a] Data from state wetland surveys conducted by the U.S. Fish and Wildlife Service, 1954.
[b] Omitted are marine, coastal, and freshwater meadow wetlands. Numbers were rounded off during the conversion from acres to hectares.

in Arkansas, Mississippi, Alabama, and Louisiana. Mississippi and Louisiana also contained extensive areas of wooded swamps (Table 16).

Unlike the distribution of overflow swamplands in the Mississippi Flyway, scrub/shrub wetlands and wooded swamps were most abundant in southern Atlantic Flyway states. Eighty-six percent of the wooded swamp acreage in the Atlantic Flyway occurred within North Carolina, South Carolina, Georgia, and Florida (Table 17). Overflow flats in the Atlantic Flyway were almost entirely limited to the states where wood ducks spend the winter (Table 17). Overall, the Mississippi Flyway contained 2.6 times as many acres of wetlands considered of value to wood ducks as did the Atlantic Flyway, 1954 (tables 16 and 17).

The small amount of wetland acreage available to wood ducks in the Pacific Flyway (Table 18), in comparison to the amount available in the East (tables 16 and 17), accounts for the marked geographical differences in abundance of breeding populations (see Chapter 2). Within the Pacific Flyway, 1954, California supported the largest amount of total wetland areas considered of value to woodies (Table 18). However, the reported California acreage of scrub/shrub wetlands and wooded swamps was three to six times below the amount found in Oregon and Washington (Table 18).

Most of the wood ducks in the West occur west of the Cascade and Sierra Nevada mountains (Bartonek et al. 1990). Interspersed among the coniferous forest and turbulent streams of the northern California and Oregon coasts, woodies find acceptable habitat on lakes and associated drainages, river valley pasturelands, and coastal dune bogs, according to Dennis Woolington. Most of the wooded wetlands in Oregon are associated with the Willamette River; in Washington, most wooded wetlands are associated with the rivers flowing into Puget Sound. East of the Cascade Mountains, wood duck habitat is essentially limited to riparian corridors in arid regions.

Using U.S. Forest Survey information, Turner et al. (1981) calculated the distribution and combined area of forested wetlands and scrub/shrub swamps in 1970 for the Mississippi and Atlantic flyway states (tables 19 and 20). According to their calculations, around 11.7 million hectares (28.9 million ac) and 10.8 million hectares (26.7 million ac) of bottomland and swamp wetlands occurred in the Mississippi and Atlantic flyways, respectively, 1970. The most extensive areas of bottomland wetland acreage occurred in the southern portion of each flyway. More than 60 percent of the scrub/shrub and forested wetlands were concentrated in the southeastern portion of the Atlantic Coastal Plain, the Lower Mississippi Alluvial Plain, and southeastern Texas (tables 19 and 20).

An estimated 2.4 million hectares (6 million ac) of bottomland hardwood wetlands occurred in Louisiana, 1970 (Turner et al. 1981). Other states in the Mississippi Flyway that contained at least 0.8 million hectares (2 million ac) of bottomland wetlands included Mississippi, Arkansas, Alabama, and Minnesota (Table 19) (Map 4).

Florida contained the largest amount—2.3 million hectares (5.6 million ac)—of bottomland wetlands in the Atlantic Flyway. In addition, Georgia, South Carolina, North Carolina, Pennsylvania, and New York each contained in excess of 0.8 million hectares (2 million ac) of forested and scrub/shrub wetlands (Table 20).

Roughly half of the 1.6 million hectares (4 million ac) of bottomland wetland acreage in the Central Flyway, 1970, occurred in Texas (Turner et al. 1981). Oklahoma, Kansas, and Nebraska each con-

Table 19. Distribution and extent of bottomland (forested and scrub/shrub) wetlands in the Mississippi Flyway and Texas around 1970.[a]

State	Area of bottomland wetlands, in millions of hectares (ac)[b]		Percentage of state covered by bottomland wetlands
Minnesota	0.85	(2.1)	4.1
Wisconsin	0.53	(1.3)	3.8
Michigan	0.73	(1.8)	4.9
Iowa	0.24	(0.6)	1.6
Illinois	0.61	(1.5)	4.1
Indiana	0.24	(0.6)	2.5
Ohio	0.57	(1.4)	5.4
Missouri	0.40	(1.0)	2.3
Kentucky	0.36	(0.9)	3.6
Tennessee	0.28	(0.7)	2.7
Arkansas	1.21	(3.0)	9.1
Louisiana	2.43	(6.0)	20.7
Mississippi	1.46	(3.6)	12.0
Alabama	1.01	(2.5)	7.3
Texas	0.77	(1.9)	1.1
Total	11.70	(28.9)	

[a] From Turner et al. (1981).
[b] Numbers were rounded off and carried to two decimal places during the conversion from acres to hectares.

tained slightly more than 0.2 million hectares (0.5 million ac) of scrub/shrub and forested wetland habitat. The northern prairie states of North Dakota and South Dakota each supported roughly 0.08 million hectares (0.2 million ac) of bottomland hardwoods along their respective drainage systems. Less than 0.1 of 1 percent of the area of each state west of the Great Plains was scrub/shrub and for-

ested wetlands in 1970 (Turner et al. 1981).

Tiner (1987) presented U.S. Fish and Wildlife Service information on the quantity and distribution of wetland habitats, 1974, in the mid-Atlantic states of Delaware, Maryland, Pennsylvania, Virginia, and West Virginia (Table 21). Forested wetlands accounted for 68 percent of the wetland habitat considered of value to wood ducks in this

Table 20. Distribution and extent of bottomland (forested and scrub/shrub) wetlands in the Atlantic Flyway around 1970.[a]

State	Area of bottomland wetlands, in millions of hectares (ac)[b]		Percentage of state covered by bottomland wetlands
Maine	0.69	(1.7)	2.4
New Hampshire	0.28	(0.7)	11.3
Vermont	0.20	(0.5)	9.4
Massachusetts	0.28	(0.7)	15.0
Rhode Island	0.04	(0.1)	16.4
Connecticut	0.20	(0.5)	15.0
New York	1.38	(3.4)	11.1
Pennsylvania	0.93	(2.3)	7.9
New Jersey	0.16	(0.4)	8.2
Delaware	0.04	(0.1)	7.0
Maryland	0.20	(0.5)	7.4
West Virginia	0.32	(0.8)	5.1
Virginia	0.28	(0.7)	1.9
North Carolina	1.09	(2.7)	8.9
South Carolina	0.89	(2.2)	11.4
Georgia	1.54	(3.8)	10.1
Florida	2.27	(5.6)	16.0
Total	10.81	(26.7)	

[a] From Turner et al. (1981).
[b] Numbers were rounded off and carried to two decimal places during the conversion from acres to hectares.

Table 21. Wetlands considered of value to wood ducks in mid-Atlantic states, 1974.[a]

State	Wetland type, in hectares (ac)[b]				
	Emergent	Scrub/shrub	Forested	Ponds	Total
Delaware	2,388 (5,900)	2,347 (5,800)	53,945 (133,300)	1,093 (2,700)	59,773 (147,700)
Maryland	8,782 (21,700)	5,463 (13,500)	88,991 (219,900)	7,446 (18,400)	110,683 (273,500)
Pennsylvania	28,450 (70,300)	56,373 (139,300)	89,598 (221,400)	27,236 (67,300)	201,657 (498,300)
Virginia	25,495 (63,000)	25,860 (63,900)	253,255 (625,800)	22,379 (55,300)	326,990 (808,000)
West Virginia	8,134 (20,100)	9,632 (23,800)	16,795 (41,500)	6,637 (16,400)	41,197 (101,800)
Total	73,249 (181,000)	99,675 (246,300)	502,585 (1,241,900)	65,155 (160,100)	740,664 (1,830,200)

[a] From Tiner (1987).
[b] Numbers were rounded off during the conversion from acres to hectares.

region; half of the forested wetland habitat occurred in Virginia. Of the five mid-Atlantic states, Pennsylvania contained the largest acreage of emergent wetlands, scrub/shrub swamps, and freshwater ponds (Table 21).

The U.S. Bureau of the Census (1964) presented the distribution and total acreage of farm ponds (including artificial ponds, pits, reservoirs, and earthen tanks) in the United States, 1964 (Map 5). More than 860,000 hectares (2.13 million ac) of farm pond habitat were provided by nearly 2.2 million farm ponds. The number of ponds and the area of

farm pond habitat available to wood ducks in the Mississippi and Atlantic flyway states are presented in tables 22 and 23.

Eighty percent (975,755) of all farm ponds and 71 percent (255,938 hectares: 632,430 ac) of the farm pond acreage available to wood ducks in the eastern United States, 1964, occurred in the Mississippi Flyway (tables 22 and 23). Missouri contained more than 20 percent of the total farm ponds and pond acreage in the eastern United States. Although Kentucky and Tennessee each contained over 100,000 farm ponds, Georgia, Mississippi, and Arkansas

Table 22. Distribution and area of farm pond habitat[a] available to wood ducks in the Mississippi Flyway, 1964.[b]

State	Number of ponds	Total pond area, in hectares (ac)		Average pond size, in hectares (ac)	
Minnesota	15,079	4,083	(10,089)	0.28	(0.7)
Wisconsin	13,475	4,705	(11,625)	0.36	(0.9)
Michigan	8,185	2,636	(6,514)	0.32	(0.8)
Iowa	56,873	17,887	(44,200)	0.32	(0.8)
Illinois	65,968	20,242	(50,019)	0.32	(0.8)
Indiana	39,825	10,290	(25,426)	0.24	(0.6)
Ohio	31,189	8,265	(20,422)	0.28	(0.7)
Missouri	281,924	61,877	(152,899)	0.20	(0.5)
Kentucky	160,721	24,845	(61,392)	0.16	(0.4)
Tennessee	100,371	17,398	(42,990)	0.16	(0.4)
Arkansas	68,897	27,391	(67,684)	0.40	(1.0)
Mississippi	84,258	31,456	(77,729)	0.36	(0.9)
Alabama	29,179	15,538	(38,396)	0.53	(1.3)
Louisiana	19,811	9,326	(23,045)	0.49	(1.2)
Total/mean	975,755	255,938	(632,430)	0.24	(0.6)

[a] Includes artificial ponds, pits, reservoirs, and earthen tanks. Numbers were rounded off during the conversion from acres to hectares; in the case of average pond size, conversions were carried to two decimal places.
[b] From U.S. Bureau of the Census (1964).

Table 23. Distribution and area of farm pond habitat[a] available to wood ducks in the Atlantic Flyway, 1964.[b]

State	Number of ponds	Total pond area, in hectares (ac)		Average pond size, in hectares (ac)	
Maine	4,227	710	(1,755)	0.16	(0.4)
New Hampshire	1,739	305	(753)	0.16	(0.4)
Vermont	6,685	808	(1,997)	0.12	(0.3)
Massachusetts	3,202	1,127	(2,785)	0.36	(0.9)
Rhode Island	253	111	(274)	0.45	(1.1)
Connecticut	3,024	1,085	(2,681)	0.36	(0.9)
New York	35,445	8,898	(21,987)	0.24	(0.6)
Pennsylvania	24,281	6,802	(16,807)	0.28	(0.7)
New Jersey	2,752	1,087	(2,686)	0.40	(1.0)
West Virginia	15,856	2,198	(5,431)	0.12	(0.3)
Virginia	28,306	10,030	(24,784)	0.36	(0.9)
Maryland	4,493	1,351	(3,338)	0.28	(0.7)
Delaware	371	167	(412)	0.45	(1.1)
North Carolina	43,163	18,828	(46,525)	0.45	(1.1)
South Carolina	16,729	10,380	(25,650)	0.65	(1.6)
Georgia	37,515	36,371	(89,873)	0.97	(2.4)
Florida	8,414	5,548	(13,710)	0.65	(1.6)
Total	236,455	105,805	(261,448)	0.45	(1.1)

[a] Includes artificial ponds, pits, reservoirs, and earthen tanks. Numbers were rounded off during the conversion from acres to hectares; in the case of average pond size, conversions were carried to two decimal places.
[b] From U.S. Bureau of the Census (1964).

ranked second, third, and fourth, respectively, in total farm pond acreage (tables 22 and 23).

As with many other types of habitat, the value of farm ponds to wood ducks depends on the juxtaposition of the ponds to other wetlands and mature hardwood timber stands, the occurrence of concealing cover, and the presence of an adequate food base. Farm ponds appear to be of most value when they are part of a wetland complex, especially when located near a permanent stream that can serve as a travel route for females and their young.

A total of 37.9 million hectares (93.7 million ac) of inland wetlands were available to wood ducks in the conterminous United States during the mid-1970s (Figure 5). More than half (53 percent) of this wetland acreage was forested, whereas scrub/shrub and emergent wetlands made up approximately 11 percent and 30 percent of the total acreage, respectively (Frayer et al. 1983).

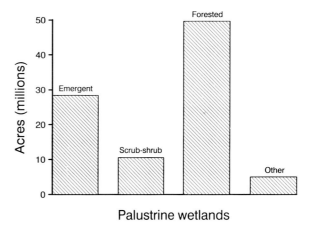

Figure 5. Palustrine wetlands available to wood ducks in the conterminous United States, 1974 (from Frayer et al. 1983).

HABITAT TRENDS

Because of their relatively small numbers and primitive implements, North American aborigines engaged in few activities that changed the virgin character of the land. Prior to European colonization, wood ducks found immense areas of habitat that provided their basic life prerequisites among the untouched wetlands and primeval forests east of the Great Plains. Undoubtedly, the mature forests contained a plethora of tree cavities suitable for wood duck nesting in close proximity to quality brood-rearing habitat. From the time that settlers began to move westward across the continent, tremendous changes to the original vegetation have occurred. Although some of these alterations have resulted in modest habitat gains for the wood duck, much more habitat has been destroyed than created.

Approximately 1.78 million hectares (4.4 million ac) of farm ponds in the United States provide wood ducks with much new habitat. Not all farm ponds provide the necessary food resources, cover, and nest sites in natural cavities, but a large proportion in or adjacent to deciduous woods is utilized by breeding wood ducks. A complex of ponds in the same area increases the value of each one for wood ducks. Ponds near permanent streams are more likely to be of value to breeding woodies than are those isolated from other wetland resources. *Photos by Dan Holm; courtesy of the Illinois Natural History Survey.*

Losses

In certain regions, the wetland habitat base essential to wood ducks suffered an early devastation similar to the recent destruction of nesting habitat that has occurred on prairie breeding grounds. Drainage, timber harvest and clearing for arable land development, channelization, leveeing of floodplains, and flood-control impoundments have been responsible for most of the wood duck's habitat losses. Early settlers viewed the extensive forests and wetlands as obstacles to human progress. Until recently, these improvident views were shared and supported by government agencies. Spectacular wetlands, such as the Black Swamp in northwestern Ohio that covered an area approximately 193 kilometers (120 mi) long and 64 kilometers (40 mi) wide (Trautman 1977) and the 161,876-hectare (400,000 ac) Kankakee Marsh of Indiana, as well as thousands of smaller water bodies, have been drained and developed into agricultural lands during the past two centuries.

Conversion of virtually all of the primeval forest into farmland, brush, and second-growth forest occurred by the 1930s, reducing available nesting habitat to a fraction of its former abundance. Many areas that once supported extensive forests were cropped to a condition of impoverishment and left to revert back to brush and second-growth forest. On cutover lands where forests were allowed to regrow, 50 to 100 years passed before trees became mature enough to provide cavities suitable for wood duck nesting.

Perhaps the most reliable estimate of presettlement wetland acreage for the conterminous United States is the 87-million hectare (215 million ac) figure determined by Roe and Ayres (1954) (Tiner 1984). By the mid-1950s, only 43.7 million hectares (108 million ac) of wetlands remained in the lower 48 states (Frayer et al. 1983). In the following 20 years, another 4.5 million hectares (11 million ac) were destroyed. At the same time, 0.81 million hectares (2 million ac) of wetlands were gained through the construction of ponds and reservoirs, resulting in a net loss of 3.6 million hectares (9 million ac). Inland wetlands were lost at an average rate of 177,659 hectares (439,000 ac) per year, 1954 through 1974 (Frayer et al. 1983). Most of the 46.9 million hectares (116 million ac) of wetlands that have been lost since settlement times were destroyed under the premise of improving areas for agricultural crop production, commercial and industrial development, flood and mosquito control, and commercial navigation.

In the West, livestock grazing is primarily responsible for the loss and degradation of riparian wetlands (Sather-Blair 1986). Hartmann (1988) noted that western lands supported 17 million cattle in 1983. Most of these animals utilize the vegetation and water associated with riparian wetlands. Cattle grazing and trampling often degrade watersheds by removing vegetation, impairing regeneration, creating conditions that favor the growth of invasive plants, and increasing erosion rates and thereby reducing water quality.

Other leading causes of wetland loss in the West include water projects (hydroelectric projects, multipurpose reservoirs, and irrigation), road construction, mining, and timber harvesting. Immense amounts of riparian habitat have been lost to multipurpose water projects. For example, more than 50 percent of the riparian wetlands along the Snake River in Idaho have been lost as a result of reservoir inundation (Sather-Blair 1986). Other western rivers such as the Humboldt, Columbia, Rio Grande, Payette, Boise, and Missouri (in Montana) have experienced similar rates of riparian wetland destruction (Hartmann 1988).

Throughout much of the West, the acreage of pristine wetland that has been lost is largely unknown. However, the U.S. Fish and Wildlife Service (1977) determined that approximately 91 percent of the original wetland area in California has been destroyed. Because of the limited amount of wood duck habitat in the West, any loss can severely curtail local wood duck production.

Frye (1986) estimated that only 37 percent of the original bottomland forest in Texas exists today. Likewise, Brabander et al. (1985) estimated that 75 percent of Oklahoma's original bottomland forest acreage has been lost. The severity of wetland destruction in the Great Lakes region has varied between states; Michigan, Minnesota, and Wisconsin are reported to have lost about 71 percent, 53 percent, and 32 percent, respectively, of their original wetland acreage (Michigan Department of Natural Resources 1982, University of Minnesota 1981, Wisconsin Department of Natural Resources 1976). Tiner (1984) noted that Ohio, Indiana, and Illinois probably have lost at least half of their wetlands. Only 50 percent of Louisiana's forested wetlands remain (Turner and Craig 1980), and about 80 percent of the original bottomland hardwood forest in the Lower Mississippi Alluvial Plain has been lost as a result of clearing and drainage activity (MacDonald et al. 1979).

Wetland drainage and channelization. Wetland drainage and degradation projects began in earnest when Congress passed the Swamplands Drainage Acts of 1849, 1850, and 1860. Under the provisions of these Acts, 15 states were allowed to sell swamplands and use the proceeds to finance flood-control and drainage projects. Nearly all of the 26 million hectares (65 million ac) of public domain wetlands that were transferred to the 15 states (Table 24) are now in private ownership (Shaw and Fredine 1956). A significant proportion of this land has been drained or otherwise altered, thereby reducing its value to wood ducks.

The drainage of vast areas of land by organized enterprises was well underway by 1900. Even without the assistance of modern drainage and land-clearing equipment, 26.5 million hectares (65.5 million ac) of land were incorporated into organized drainage enterprises by 1920 (U.S. Bureau of the Census 1950). In 1950, approximately 41.6 million hectares (102.7 million ac) of land were in organized drainage districts, and another 20.2 million hectares (50 million ac) of land outside of organized districts were modified through drainage (Shaw and Fredine 1956).

The relative abundance and distribution of agricultural lands in organized drainage enterprises in 1959 are depicted in Map 5. It should be noted that a significant proportion of these lands represented largely saturated soil areas that were of limited value to most waterfowl before drainage. Unfortunately, vast areas of overflow bottomlands were eliminated during the course of drainage operations in many areas. A breakdown of land area in drainage projects, 1960, in the Mississippi, Atlantic, and Pacific flyways, by states, is presented in tables 25 and 26. We estimate that drainage and clearing have

Table 24. Land transferred to states under the authorization of the Swamp Land Acts of 1849, 1850, and 1860.[a]

State	Transferred lands,[b] in hectares (ac)	
Minnesota	1,904,675	(4,706,503)
Wisconsin	1,360,076	(3,360,786)
Michigan	2,298,765	(5,680,310)
Iowa	484,168	(1,196,392)
Illinois	590,914	(1,460,164)
Indiana	509,598	(1,259,231)
Ohio	10,672	(26,372)
Missouri	1,389,091	(3,432,481)
Arkansas	3,110,680	(7,686,575)
Louisiana	3,841,907	(9,493,456)
Mississippi	1,354,845	(3,347,860)
Alabama	178,585	(441,289)
Florida	8,225,330	(20,325,013)
Oregon	115,785	(286,108)
California	887,435	(2,192,875)
Total	26,262,525	(64,895,415)

[a] From Shaw and Fredine (1956).
[b] Numbers were rounded off during the conversion from acres to hectares.

Table 25. Land in drainage projects (from U.S. Bureau of the Census 1959) and estimated proportion of drained area that adversely affected potential wood duck habitat in the Mississippi Flyway and Texas, 1960.[a]

State	Drained area, in hectares (ac)		Percentage of drained area that affected wood duck habitat
Minnesota	4,730,098	(11,688,201)	54
Wisconsin	237,878	(587,803)	100
Michigan	4,131,373	(10,208,735)	100
Iowa	2,786,051	(6,884,409)	34
Illinois	2,272,788	(5,616,121)	56
Indiana	4,500,532	(11,120,936)	100
Ohio	3,603,727	(8,904,907)	100
Missouri	1,264,015	(3,123,416)	100
Kentucky	382,640	(945,515)	100
Tennessee	295,770	(730,855)	100
Arkansas	1,970,883	(4,870,106)	100
Mississippi	1,263,939	(3,123,227)	100
Alabama	28,288	(69,901)	100
Louisiana	3,678,436	(9,089,516)	100
Texas	2,630,502	(6,500,043)	1
Total	33,776,921	(83,463,691)	

[a] Estimates of the amount of wood duck habitat affected by drainage projects were based on subjective interpretations of county drainage enterprises. Numbers were rounded off during the conversion from acres to hectares.

eliminated a minimum of 26.16 million hectares (66.64 million ac), 1.37 million hectares (3.38 million ac), and 0.77 million hectares (1.91 million ac) of wood duck habitat in the Mississippi, Atlantic, and Pacific flyways, respectively (tables 25 and 26).

During the course of drainage operations, ditches are constructed to lower the water table and provide an avenue for faster water removal from wetlands. Another landscape modification that often accompanies drainage operations is stream channelization. Streams usually are straightened and/or deepened through channelization so that large surface water volumes from floodplains move more quickly downstream.

Table 26. Land in drainage projects (from U.S. Bureau of the Census 1959) and estimated proportion of drained area that adversely affected potential wood duck habitat in the Atlantic and Pacific flyways, 1960.[a]

State	Drained area, in hectares (ac)		Percentage of drained area that affected wood duck habitat
Atlantic Flyway			
New York	20,079	(49,616)	100
New Jersey	4,758	(11,756)	100
Maryland	143,194	(353,837)	100
Delaware	144,354	(356,702)	?
Virginia	39,853	(98,478)	?
North Carolina	574,211	(1,418,892)	100
South Carolina	137,581	(339,966)	100
Georgia	38,335	(94,728)	100
Florida	3,732,260	(9,222,517)	12
Pacific Flyway			
Washington	102,986	(254,482)	100
Oregon	111,190	(274,754)	68
California	783,004	(1,934,825)	76
Total	5,831,807	(14,410,553)	

[a] Estimates of the amount of wood duck habitat affected by drainage projects were based on subjective interpretations of county drainage enterprises. Numbers were rounded off during the conversion from acres to hectares.

Landscape disturbances that accompany stream channelization projects have resulted in the degradation or destruction of an immense amount of wood duck habitat. As a result of channelization, the natural character of a meandering stream—with its diverse array of pool, riffle, and shoreline habitats—is transformed into a straight ditch essentially devoid of shoreline vegetation and stream obstructions. Channelization projects not only adversely affect the immediate area of disturbance but, through altering groundwater levels, stream velocity, and sedimentation rates, alter the plant and animal communities of backwater and floodplain wetlands, as well as the stream itself, for many miles downstream of the channelized area.

Farmers, municipalities, highway agencies, and private industry have been responsible for a large proportion of the channelization activity that has occurred. The U.S. Army Corps of Engineers and the Soil Conservation Service are the two principal federal agencies involved in channelization work. Nationwide, authorization has been granted to conduct channel modification involving 51.9 million hectares (128.2 million ac) of stream habitat (Fredrickson 1978). Between the early 1940s and the mid-1970s, the Corps and the Soil Conservation Service administrated at least 1,630 flood-control projects that called for the alteration of 54,716 kilometers (34,000 mi) of stream habitat (Conlin 1976).

Although ditches usually are employed to drain swamps and wooded bottomlands, they also may be of some value to wetland wildlife. Woodies occasionally seek low-gradient ditches, such as the one shown, that are blanketed with duckweed to use for feeding and as loafing sites during summer and early autumn. *Photo by Frank Bellrose; courtesy of the Illinois Natural History Survey.*

Bottomland hardwoods. Despite the marked increase in net volume of hardwood growing stock and hardwood sawtimber (more than 30 centimeters [11.8 in] diameter at breast height) that has occurred as the second-growth forest matures (figures 6 and 7), a tremendous loss of bottomland hardwoods has occurred throughout much of the wood duck's range, especially in the Lower Mississippi Alluvial Plain (Figure 8). The reduction of bottomland hardwoods is an especially severe loss to wood ducks because forested wetlands provide nest sites in close proximity to water, as well as concealing cover and food sources that are used in the South throughout the year.

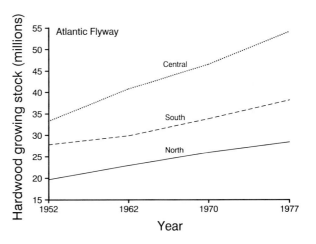

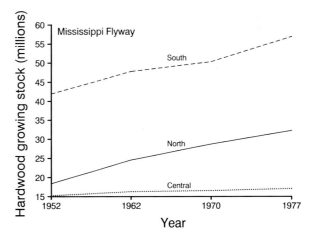

Figure 6. Net volume (million cubic feet) of hardwood growing stock on commercial timberland in the eastern United States, 1952, 1962, 1970, and 1977 (from U.S. Forest Service 1978). Top = Atlantic Flyway; North = CT, MA, ME, NH, NY, RI, and VT; Central = DE, MD, NJ, PA, VA, and WV; and South = FL, GA, NC, and SC. Bottom = Mississippi Flyway; North = MI, MN, and WI; Central = IL, IN, IO, MO, and OH; and South = AL, AR, KY, LA, MS, and TN.

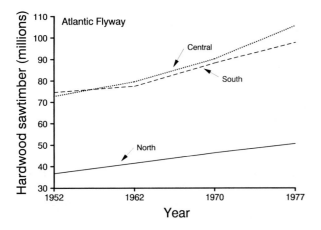

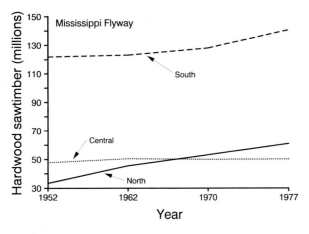

Figure 7. Net volume (million board feet, international 0.25-inch log rule) of hardwood sawtimber on commercial timberland in the eastern United States, 1952, 1962, 1970, and 1977 (from U.S. Forest Service 1978). Top = Atlantic Flyway; North = CT, MA, ME, NH, NY, RI, and VT; Central = DE, MD, NJ, PA, VA, and WV; and South = FL, GA, NC, and SC. Bottom = Mississippi Flyway; North = MI, MN, and WI; Central = IL, IN, IO, MO, and OH; and South = AL, AR, KY, LA, MS, and TN.

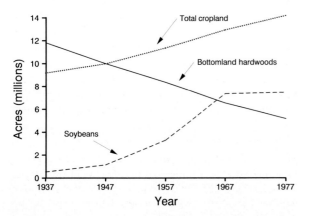

Figure 8. Changes in the amount of bottomland hardwoods and agricultural lands present in the Lower Mississippi Alluvial Plain, 1937–77 (from MacDonald et al. 1969).

Klopateck et al. (1979) estimated the original forested wetland acreage in the conterminous United States as 27.2 million hectares (67.2 million ac). Abernethy and Turner (1987) believed that Klopateck's estimate was conservative because it excluded many small tracts of land that, in aggregate, would comprise a significant area. Frayer et al. (1983) determined that forested wetlands covered 22.6 million hectares (55.8 million ac) in the mid-1950s. By 1974, forested wetland acreage was reduced to 20.1 million hectares (49.7 million ac). A total of 2.3 million hectares (5.8 million ac) of forested wetlands was lost to agricultural development between the mid-1950s and mid-1970s. Of this total area, 1.8 million hectares (4.5 million ac) were lost in the Mississippi Flyway, primarily in the states of Louisiana, Mississippi, and Arkansas (Tiner 1984).

The most dramatic and significant wetland loss in the entire United States has occurred in the Mississippi Delta region, where overflow wetlands serve as important habitats for fish and wildlife. The Lower Mississippi Alluvial Plain embraces roughly 10 million hectares (24 million ac) in Missouri, Kentucky, Tennessee, Arkansas, Mississippi, and Louisiana (Table 27) and serves as important breeding habitat as well as the primary wintering grounds for the Mississippi Flyway wood duck and mallard populations (Bellrose 1976). More than 80 percent of the original bottomland hardwood forest in this region has been lost (Tiner 1984), and 25 percent of the remaining bottomland hardwood vegetation likely will be destroyed by 1995 (MacDonald et al. 1979, National Research Council 1982).

Prior to 1928, the vast majority of land clearing and development projects that occurred in the lower Mississippi Delta region were undertaken by the private sector, under the authorization of the Swamplands Drainage Acts of 1849 and 1850. With the passage of the Flood Control Act of 1928, the federal government committed itself to providing flood protection to existing settlements in the lower Mississippi Valley. When Congress passed another Flood Control Act in 1944, the primary emphasis of federal water-development projects in the Delta shifted from providing catastrophic flood protection to existing developments to draining existing wetlands so that greater agricultural development could occur. Subsequent legislation—such as the Watershed Protection and Flood Prevention Act of 1954 and the Flood Control Act of 1965—gave federal agencies additional authority to promote agricultural development in the Lower Mississippi Alluvial Plain.

In the course of constructing an elaborate drainage and levee system, the Corps of Engineers and the Soil Conservation Service removed thousands

Table 27. Distribution of land by state in the Lower Mississippi Alluvial Plain.[a]

State	Land area, in hectares (ac)[b]		Percentage of total area
Arkansas	3,245,492	(8,019,700)	33.12
Louisiana	3,436,797	(8,492,420)	35.07
Mississippi	1,938,833	(4,790,910)	19.78
Missouri	924,170	(2,283,650)	9.43
Tennessee	214,688	(530,500)	2.19
Kentucky	39,732	(98,180)	0.41
Total	9,799,714	(24,215,360)	100.00

[a] From MacDonald et al. (1979).
[b] Numbers were rounded off during the conversion from acres to hectares.

of hectares of bottomland timber and adversely affected many hectares of remaining wetlands. Additionally, federal flood-control and drainage projects made conversion of forested wetlands to agricultural cropland economically attractive to many private landowners (U.S. Fish and Wildlife Service 1988). Protection of bottomland areas from frequent flooding presented landowners with the opportunity to convert wetlands to productive croplands without the risk of flood damage.

Approximately 56 percent (2.7 million hectares: 6.6 million ac) of the Mississippi Delta bottomland hardwood acreage existing in 1937 (4.8 million hectares: 11.8 million ac) was destroyed by 1978 (MacDonald et al. 1979), concomitant with the incentive of federal water-development programs. Concurrently, agricultural lands increased by approximately 2 million hectares (5 million ac). Unfortunately, many landowners removed extensive tracts of bottomland hardwoods from areas that received little protection from flood-control projects, and farming proved impracticable on those lands in most years. Forsythe (1985) noted that 19 percent of the cleared land (68,824 hectares: 170,066 ac) in the Upper Yazoo River Basin of Mississippi occurred within the one-year floodplain. Similarly, around 24 percent of the bottomland hardwood acreage that has been cleared in the Boeuf Basin of Louisiana (40,484 hectares: 100,038 ac) retains wetness levels that prohibit successful farming operations in most years. The peak period of land clearing in the Mississippi Delta region, 1937–1977, occurred between 1957 and 1967 when nearly 0.8 million hectares (2 million ac) of bottomland wetlands were destroyed (MacDonald et al. 1979).

The remaining 2.1 million hectares (5.2 million ac) of bottomland habitat in the Mississippi Delta, 1978, was distributed along eight principal river basins. MacDonald et al. (1979) determined the amount of seasonally flooded flats and wooded and scrub/shrub swamps remaining in the Lower Mississippi Alluvial Plain by river basin and state (Table 28). Louisiana, Arkansas, and Mississippi contained approximately 58 percent, 20 percent, and 18 percent, respectively, of the remaining bottomland wetland acreage in 1978. The largest area of overflow hardwood flats occurred in the Yazoo River Basin, Mississippi (254,930 hectares: 629,950 ac) and the Ouachita/Tensas River Basin, Louisiana (228,180 hectares: 563,840 ac). By contrast, the largest acreage of wooded and scrub/shrub swamp habitat was located in the Atchafalaya River Basin (375,700 hectares: 928,360 ac) and Lower Mississippi River Basin Complex, Louisiana (190,880 hectares: 471,660 ac). The largest acreage of bottomland wetlands in the Mississippi Delta region, 1978, occurred along the Atchafalaya River (0.56 million hectares: 1.4 million ac).

Since 1978, destruction of bottomland hardwoods in the Lower Mississippi Alluvial Plain by drainage and flood-control operations has continued virtually unabated; approximately 48,563 hectares (120,000 ac) of bottomland hardwoods are destroyed every year (Blue Ribbon Panel for Bottomland Hardwoods 1984, Tiner 1984). By 1988, less than 1.8 million hectares (4.5 million ac) of bottomland hardwoods remained in the Mississippi Delta; total land ownership by state and federal conservation agencies accounted for only around 18 percent (319,705 hectares: 790,000 ac) of the existing bottomland hardwoods (Forsythe 1985); the remaining 1.48 million hectares (3.66 million ac) are in private hands.

Primarily because of increased crop production costs and lower commodity prices, the incentive to clear forested wetlands in the Lower Mississippi Alluvial Plain has diminished somewhat during the last decade (U.S. Fish and Wildlife Service 1988). Nonetheless, approximately 80 percent of the existing Delta wetlands remains vulnerable to agricultural development whenever economic conditions make conversion feasible.

Table 28. Distribution of potential wood duck habitat in thousands of hectares (ac) by state and river basin in the Lower Mississippi Alluvial Plain, 1978.[a]

| State | River basin | Habitat type, in thousands of hectares (ac)[b] | | |
		Overflow hardwood flats	Wooded and scrub/shrub swamps	Total
Arkansas	Arkansas	47.52 (117.43)	9.72 (24.01)	57.24 (141.44)
	Ouachita/Tensas	84.44 (208.65)	18.80 (46.46)	103.24 (255.11)
	St. Francis	57.88 (143.03)	22.98 (56.78)	80.86 (199.81)
	White	153.16 (378.46)	16.32 (40.32)	169.48 (418.78)
Louisiana	Atchafalaya	184.09 (454.89)	375.70 (928.36)	559.79 (1,383.25)
	Lower Mississippi Complex	38.85 (96.00)	190.88 (471.66)	229.73 (567.66)
	Ouachita/Tensas	228.18 (563.84)	33.71 (83.30)	261.89 (647.14)
	Red	97.45 (240.79)	65.78 (162.55)	163.23 (403.34)
Mississippi	Mississippi Complex	46.56 (115.05)	13.59 (33.57)	60.15 (148.62)
	Yazoo	254.93 (629.95)	61.80 (152.72)	316.74 (782.67)
Missouri	St. Francis/White	21.85 (54.00)	5.89 (14.56)	27.75 (68.56)
Tennessee	Mississippi Complex	38.82 (95.93)	13.90 (34.35)	52.72 (130.28)
Kentucky	Mississippi Complex	10.11 (24.99)	3.82 (9.44)	13.93 (34.43)
Total		1,263.85 (3,123.01)	832.88 (2,058.08)	2,096.74 (5,181.09)

[a] From MacDonald et al. (1979).
[b] Numbers were rounded off during the conversion from acres to hectares.

Frayer et al. (1983) estimated that 87 percent of the wetland loss that occurred in the conterminous United States between 1954 and 1974 resulted from agricultural drainage operations. Urban development was responsible for 8 percent of recent losses, and other types of development resulted in the destruction of the remaining 5 percent. Flood-control and agricultural drainage projects continue to be the leading cause of wood duck habitat destruction. Fortunately, recent legislation—such as section 1221 of the Food Security Act of 1985 (the Swampbuster provision) and the Tax Reform Act of 1986—provides the farmer with less financial incentive to develop wetlands into agricultural croplands. Nevertheless, throughout the South, authorized Corps flood-control, drainage, and navigation projects continue to jeopardize large tracts of remaining bottomland timber along numerous river basins, such as the Atchafalaya, Yazoo, Hatchie, Obion, Forked Deer, Cache, and Bayou de View. The Water Resources Development Act of 1986 could eliminate construction of many inefficient Corps projects in the future

(U.S. Fish and Wildlife Service 1988). However, this legislation also authorizes the construction or study of 250 new water-development projects that could entail the destruction of valuable wetlands.

Alterations

Manmade lakes and reservoirs have impact on wood duck habitat—sometimes beneficial but more often detrimental. Existing wetlands often are destroyed during lake and reservoir construction. The incorporation of stream habitat, overflow hardwood bottomlands, and floodplain wetlands into open water bodies most often results in a net loss of habitat for wood ducks. On the bright side are gains in wood duck habitat resulting from the maturation of second-growth forests, expanding number of beaver ponds, increase in pileated woodpeckers, and erection of nest houses for wood ducks.

Second-growth forests. The increase in tree size of second-growth forests is steadily bringing a larger number of trees into size classes that produce cavities sufficiently large for wood ducks to use (figures 6 and 7). As a result of forest regrowth, protection, and perhaps adaptation to the use of smaller trees, pileated woodpeckers have steadily increased in numbers (Roberts 1932, Hoyt 1957, Cringan 1971). These large woodpeckers produce a new nest cavity each year, leaving older ones available as potential nest sites for wood ducks. Because the range of the pileated woodpecker almost encompasses that of the wood duck, its abundance plays an important role in the availability of nest sites for wood ducks.

The value of natural nest sites depends on the juxtaposition of hardwoods and wetlands. The dramatic reduction in total wetland acreage that has accompanied the maturation of second-growth timber stands reduces the value of some mature upland hardwood woodlands to nesting wood ducks.

The vegetative communities along many riparian corridors on the Great Plains have undergone a remarkable transformation in the last century. Often, the floodplain forests of entire watersheds were cut by early frontiersmen. In addition, trees were scarce along many prairie streams as a result of recurring prairie fires and early hydrologic characteristics. Control of prairie fires and regrowth of floodplain forests have resulted in increased bottomland forest acreage along some prairie streams during the 1900s (Farrar 1985, Knopf 1986). Today, the shorelines of many major streams are lined with mature stands of cottonwoods and willows. However, Ladd (1990) cautioned that wood duck habitat along river basins of the Great Plains actually may

decline dramatically in the next few decades because the cottonwood-dominated forest is not regenerating itself sufficiently. Russian-olive is expected to replace cottonwoods and other trees such as American elm and red ash along many streams in the future (Currier 1982, Knopf and Olson 1984), a phenomenon that would reduce the number of potential nesting sites available to wood ducks.

Impoundments, channels, and farm ponds. Frayer et al. (1983) reported that lacustrine (lakelike) wetlands increased by about 0.57 million hectares (1.4 million ac) between the mid-1950s and mid-1970s. Although wood ducks make little use of open water areas on manmade lakes, they may frequent wetlands that form along the shorelines of these open water bodies. Moreover, standing trees that are inundated as a result of impoundment provide temporary areas of new habitat for wood ducks. Unfortunately, permanently inundated trees soon die and, within a decade or so, lose much of their value as habitat for woodies (Heitmeyer and Fredrickson 1990). The value of wetlands that form along the edge of large lakes and reservoirs often is reduced because of excessive wave action.

According to Frye (1986) almost 242,814 hectares (600,000 ac) of bottomland hardwoods have been destroyed by the construction of more than 5,600 reservoirs in east Texas. Flood-control reservoirs also adversely affect downstream bottomland habitat by reducing over-bank flooding that invigorates the growth and food resources of bottomland hardwoods.

In addition, manmade navigation channels generally provide little new habitat for wood ducks, and important mast- and cavity-producing trees as well as brood-rearing habitat usually are destroyed during construction. Teels (1975) reported that more than 2,300 hectares (5,683 ac) of wood duck breeding habitat would be inundated as a result of impoundment construction on the 377-kilometer (234 mi) Tennessee-Tombigbee Waterway in Alabama and Mississippi. Since then, many trees have been destroyed because of permanent flooding, and others have been replaced by species tolerant of saturated soil conditions. Additional destruction and degradation of wetland habitats along navigation channels often occurs subsequent to their completion as industrial development and agricultural expansion occur.

The total area of farm ponds in the conterminous United States increased from 0.93 million hectares (2.3 million ac) to 1.78 million hectares (4.4 million ac) between 1954 and 1974 (Frayer et al. 1983). Tiner (1984) pointed out that although most of the new pond habitat represented new wetland acreage, 58,882 hectares (145,500 ac) of forested wetlands and 155,806 hectares (385,000 ac) of emergent wetlands were converted to open water.

Beaver ponds. Biologists have long recognized the importance of beaver ponds to wood ducks. In the past, some beaver release programs were intended to improve the habitat for wood ducks as well as to restore local beaver populations (Salyer 1946).

Through their feeding and dam-building activities, beavers can dramatically change the habitat along stream drainages. Most beaver dams occur on low-order streams (first through fourth; stream order advances from headwater streams to large rivers) where impounded waters change the nature of stream channels by reducing current velocity, expanding the inundated floodplain habitat, retaining larger quantities of sediments and organic matter, and modifying annual stream-discharge patterns (Naiman et al. 1988, Arner and Hepp 1989). These modifications to stream channels ultimately result in altered plant and animal communities.

Beaver ponds provide important habitat for wood ducks, especially during the breeding season. These shallow impoundments constructed in wooded flowages usually result in an ideal combination of food resources, cover, and natural cavity nest sites. To the right of the beaver lodge in the bottom photo, a wooden nest house protected by a metal guard has been placed on a sapling. The nest house in the top scene was fashioned from PVC pipe. *Top right photo by Dan Holm; courtesy of the Illinois Natural History Survey. Bottom photo courtesy of the U.S. Fish and Wildlife Service.*

Most ponds created by beavers develop chemical and physical characteristics that make them attractive to wood ducks. The composition of plant and animal communities that develop in a particular beaver impoundment depends on a large number of factors, including geographic location, acidity, pond age, stream gradient, and nutrient input.

Emergent and scrub/shrub wetlands usually develop in beaver impoundments, and these shallow water areas can support aquatic invertebrate populations that often are two to five times as dense and productive as comparative stream riffle habitats (Naiman et al. 1988). Although beaver ponds are transitory habitats, initially undergoing relatively rapid successional changes, some influence the wetland communities of watersheds for centuries (Naiman et al. 1988).

Normally, beavers create several ponds along a reach of stream; the number of impoundments varies with beaver density, topography, and food supply. Naiman et al. (1986) found an average of 10.6 dams per kilometer (17.1/mi) along the North Shore of the Gulf of St. Lawrence in Quebec. Similarly, in northern Minnesota where 0.4–0.8 beaver colony per square kilometer (1.0–2.1/mi²) often occurred in favorable areas, Naiman et al. (1988) reported that beavers constructed an average of 2.5 dams per kilometer (4/mi).

In the South, beaver ponds are used by wood ducks throughout the year. The diverse cover and food sources that develop in beaver pond complexes meet the wood duck's social and physiological needs throughout all phases of its annual cycle (Hepp and Hair 1977, Strader 1978, 1990, Luckett and Hair 1979, Arner and Hepp 1989). Likewise, beaver pond wetlands in northern states and Canada serve as important breeding, brood-rearing, and postbreeding habitats for woodies (Beard 1953, 1964, Cringan 1971, Kirby 1973, Gilmer et al. 1977).

An estimated 60–400 million beavers occurred in North America prior to the arrival of European explorers and settlers (Seton 1929, Hill 1987). Several centuries of commercial exploitation resulted in the extirpation or marked reduction of beavers throughout much of their range. By 1900, only 100,000 beavers were believed to exist in North America. Primarily through restoration efforts of conservation agencies, the continental beaver population has rebounded to 6–15 million (Hill 1987, Naiman et al. 1988).

The average annual harvest of beavers in the conterminous United States has increased throughout the 20th century (Figure 9), reflecting an increase in the number of harvestable animals (Novak 1987) and available beaver pond habitat. Beaver populations also have increased in Canada during

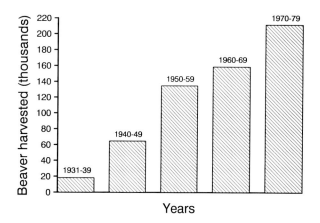

Figure 9. Average annual beaver harvest by 10-year intervals in the conterminous United States, 1931–79 (from Novak et al. 1988).

the 1900s. Cringan (1971) determined that beaver production within the principal breeding range of the wood duck in Ontario increased by an average of 2,700 per year between 1948 and 1968. He believed that the improved breeding and brood-rearing habitat conditions provided by beaver impoundments contributed to the dramatic expansion of Ontario's wood duck population.

Although beavers occur throughout the wood duck's range, densities vary markedly (Novak 1987). The largest number of beavers harvested per unit area in the Mississippi and Atlantic flyway states, 1977–1981, occurred in the northern tier of states from Minnesota eastward to Maine and in Alabama, Mississippi, and Virginia (tables 29 and 30). In some cases, however, harvest density information is too conservative an indicator of the area of habitat affected by beavers. In North Carolina, where an average of only five beavers was harvested per 1,000 square kilometers (386 mi²), 1977–1981, beaver impoundments covered at least 35,858 hectares (88,605 ac), 0.26 percent of the state (Woodward et al. 1985). By contrast, an average of 54 beavers was harvested per 1,000 square kilometers (386 mi²) in Arkansas, 1977–1981, where beaver impoundments covered approximately 66,199 hectares (163,580 ac), 0.48 percent of the state (Wigley and Garner 1987). The total area of land affected by beaver pond wetlands in Arkansas, Mississippi, Alabama, Georgia, North Carolina, and South Carolina is around 287,997 hectares (711,648 ac), 0.35 percent of the six-state area (Arner and Hepp 1989); the annual beaver harvest was 46,934 during 1977–1981 (tables 29 and 30).

Table 29. Average annual harvest of beaver in Mississippi Flyway states, 1977–81.[a]

State	Average annual harvest	S.D.	C.V.	Average harvest per 10 square kilometers (10 mi²)[b]	
Minnesota	54,200	17,964	33.14	2.49	(6.45)
Wisconsin	18,369	8,089	44.04	1.26	(3.27)
Michigan	12,613	8,305	65.84	0.84	(2.17)
Iowa	7,559	4,288	56.72	0.52	(1.34)
Illinois	4,928	2,286	46.39	0.34	(0.87)
Indiana	1,403	560	39.91	0.15	(0.39)
Ohio	3,403	1,696	49.84	0.32	(0.84)
Missouri	6,606	4,195	63.50	0.37	(0.95)
Kentucky	696	306	43.99	0.07	(0.17)
Tennessee	986	244	24.75	0.09	(0.23)
Arkansas	7,445	3,487	46.84	0.54	(1.40)
Louisiana	1,345	895	66.54	0.11	(0.28)
Mississippi	18,139	2,139	11.79	1.47	(3.80)
Alabama	13,794	5,731	41.55	1.03	(2.67)

[a] From Novak et al. (1988).
[b] Numbers were rounded off during the conversion from square miles to square kilometers.

Table 30. Average annual harvest and distribution of beaver in Atlantic Flyway states, 1977–81.[a]

State	Average annual harvest	S.D.	C.V.	Average harvest per 10 square kilometers (10 mi²)[b]	
Maine	10,979	4,970	45.27	1.28	(3.31)
New Hampshire	4,436	1,214	27.37	1.84	(4.77)
Vermont	2,499	1,281	51.26	1.00	(2.60)
Massachusetts	1,261	619	49.09	0.59	(1.53)
Connecticut	471	142	30.15	0.36	(0.94)
New York	11,948	4,636	38.80	0.93	(2.41)
New Jersey	161	72	44.72	0.08	(0.21)
Pennsylvania	4,036	2,529	62.66	0.34	(0.89)
Maryland	352	179	50.85	0.13	(0.33)
West Virginia	1,207	405	33.55	0.19	(0.50)
Virginia	8,785	3,593	40.90	0.83	(2.15)
North Carolina	721	310	42.00	0.05	(0.14)
South Carolina	388	109	28.09	0.05	(0.14)
Georgia	6,447	2,419	37.52	0.42	(1.10)
Florida	363	206	56.75	0.02	(0.06)

[a] From Novak et al. (1988).
[b] Numbers were rounded off during the conversion from square miles to square kilometers.

SEASONAL HABITAT NEEDS

During almost any time frame over the course of a year, the stage of physiological development of some members of local wood duck populations will vary quite dramatically from that of other members. For instance, courtship, egg laying, incubation, brood rearing, and molting are activities that different members of provincial populations may be engaged in at the same period in time. Seldom does any one wetland type meet all of the wood duck's nutritional, cover, and social requirements for long periods.

Breeding

In addition to suitable nest cavities (see Chapter 7), breeding wood ducks require wetland areas that provide a high-quality plant and invertebrate food base. Drobney and Fredrickson (1985) found that female woodies prepared for egg laying by assimilating large quantities of lipids; the most rapid accumulation of fat occurred two to three weeks preceding laying. At this time in their annual cycle, females must have access to appreciable quantities of high-quality plant and invertebrate foods. Plant foods that contain high concentrations of carbohydrates and fats are needed for lipid storage, whereas the proteins obtained from invertebrates are essential for follicle growth and oviduct synthesis.

Although a substantial proportion of the stored lipid reserves is used for egg production, female woodies must consume essentially all of the protein needed for egg formation on a daily basis during the laying period (Drobney 1977). When female wood ducks begin to lay eggs, their diet shifts from one of nearly equal proportions of plant and animal foods to one that emphasizes invertebrates. Therefore, abundant and available plant and invertebrate food bases in proximity to suitable nest sites are essential components of the wood duck's breeding habitat.

Paired wood ducks primarily use wetland areas that provide an interspersion of inundated shrubs, water-tolerant trees, and small areas of open water. They make frequent use of shorelines that support growths of overhanging woody vegetation. Persistent emergents—such as cattail, bulrush, and bur-reed—provide acceptable cover for adults in areas where desirable shrubs and trees are unavailable. In addition, canopies of fallen trees frequently are used as cover, as are the trunks as loafing sites, by breeding wood ducks. Stream banks and beaver and muskrat lodges also provide loafing sites.

Adult wood ducks seldom utilize areas with water depths greater than 1.8 meters (6 ft). Optimal breeding habitat is characterized by quiet or slow-moving water that is protected from forceful winds and has an average depth between 7.6 and 45.7 centimeters (3–18 in) (McGilvrey 1968). At an east Texas lake, Higgins (1979) observed that good habitats for adult wood ducks had a mean water depth of 26.4 centimeters (10.4 in); poor habitats had a mean of 48.3 centimeters (19 in).

Sousa and Farmer (1983) indicated that optimal cover for breeding wood ducks existed when inundated vegetation covered 50–75 percent of the water area. Ideal cover is provided by flooded trees, by shrubs that form a dense canopy approximately 0.6 meter (2 ft) above the water surface, or by a combination of both cover types (McGilvrey 1968). Higgins (1979) found that as the number of stems of buttonbush and planer tree increased, the density of wood ducks increased during autumn and winter.

In spring, duck potato tubers provide an important source of food for wood ducks at Nauvoo Slough in Illinois. Males there often wait for their incubating mates to join them in the emergent beds once or twice a day to feed or rest protected from view by the plants' canopy of leaves. *Photo by Dan Holm; courtesy of the Illinois Natural History Survey.*

The marshlike habitat of Nauvoo Slough, a 6-hectare (15 ac) backwater area along the Mississippi River at Nauvoo, Illinois, provides exceptional food resources and cover for breeding wood ducks. Forty duplex nest houses accommodate up to 75 breeding pairs of woodies annually (top). Early in spring, rice cutgrass and other wetland plants provide a detrital food base that supports an abundance of aquatic invertebrates. Luxuriant beds of emergent duck potato and submergent pondweeds develop later in spring. And still later, American lotus (bottom) occupies most of the remaining open water. Bottom soils are especially fertile, from an earlier time when sewage effluent from Nauvoo, a city of 1,100, was deposited in the slough area. *Photos by Dan Holm; courtesy of the Illinois Natural History Survey.*

Brood Rearing

Many of the same cover and food types that are important to breeding pairs are used extensively by young wood ducks. In addition, as submerged vegetation beds and stands of dense herbaceous vegetation become available, they are utilized by broods. Young ducklings feed extensively on aquatic and terrestrial invertebrates during their first few weeks of life before shifting to a diet of primarily plant foods. Females seem to prefer wetlands that contain herbaceous emergents along with flooded shrubs because they provide the types of cover, loafing sites, and nutritional substrates that are essential to quality rearing habitat (Ball 1973, Hepp 1977). McGilvrey (1968) reported that ideal wood duck brood habitat contained 30–50 percent shrubs, 40–70 percent herbaceous emergents, and 0–10 percent trees; open water should comprise approximately 25 percent of the habitat.

A notable difference between breeding and brood-rearing habitat is the availability of water. Although adults can easily move in response to low water levels, ducklings are exposed to an increased number of decimating factors when moving from isolated wetlands to alternate rearing sites. Moreover, broods become more concentrated as wetlands dry, and competition for food increases as do potential losses from predation and diseases.

Ball (1973) found a significant negative correlation (r = −0.44, P < 0.05) between the distance broods traveled overland before two weeks of age and the number of surviving ducklings. Broods that made the longest overland movements suffered the highest mortality rates. In northern Illinois, David (1986) determined that 1.55 ducklings were lost for each kilometer (0.62 mi) traveled from nest site to rearing area. Eighty-one percent of duckling mortality during the first two weeks of life was associated with movement to rearing areas. Ridlehuber (1980) reported that all young from nine wood duck broods in eastcentral Texas were lost within 10 days after hatching. He suspected that duckling mortality resulted from lengthy overland travel. Wood duck broods in the St. John River Valley, New Brunswick experienced 38-percent mortality traveling from nest site to water (Prince 1965). After reaching a rearing site, 80 percent of the remaining ducklings survived to flight stage.

Because of their experience and strength, older broods probably sustain lower mortality than younger broods when moving overland. Nevertheless, even older broods would seem to be more vulnerable to predation and accidents when traveling overland than when using a water route. McGilvrey (1968) emphasized that optimum brood-

rearing habitat must retain water and provide an adequate food base until ducklings are able to fly; stream channels provide valuable travel lanes for broods that must move from one wetland to another. He suggested that ideal brood-rearing habitat approximates the following distribution of water depths: 25 percent between 2.5 and 30.5 centimeters (1–12 in); 50 percent between 30.5 and 91.4 centimeters (12–36 in); and 25 percent between 91.4 and 182.9 centimeters (36–72 in). In many lake and marsh areas, the depth of water utilized depends on the depth that sunlight penetrates to produce submerged and floating aquatic plant beds. Such beds not only provide highly desirable invertebrate and plant foods but also reduce buffeting by waves.

Additionally, relatively stabilized water levels are a prerequisite to maintaining quality brood-rearing habitat because broods commonly use shoreline and adjacent upland areas for loafing sites, escape cover, and feeding areas. Boyer (1974) found that fluctuating water levels on the Shiawassee National Wildlife Refuge, Michigan, were partially responsible for low wood duck production because declining water levels diminished the value of shoreline habitat to broods.

Like adults, broods seldom use large expanses of open water or areas with depths greater than 1.8 meters (6 ft) except where submerged plant beds occur at greater depths. They also prefer quiet or slow-moving water that is protected from high winds. Nevertheless, we have seen young wood ducks, when required, skillfully contend with 30–46-centimeter (12–18 in) rolling waves while feeding on submerged vegetation beds in the Mississippi River at Nauvoo, Illinois. McGilvrey (1968) reported that brood-rearing habitat likely will receive higher use when at least 20 percent of the area remains calm during windy weather.

Many wood duck hens hatch their eggs before seasonal vegetational growth has advanced far enough to provide optimum brood cover. Early season cover generally is provided by inundated live forests (Hepp 1977, Fredrickson and Heitmeyer 1988), low overhanging shoreline vegetation, downed trees, scrub/shrub swamps, and persistent emergents. Webster and McGilvrey (1966) reported that the brood habitat preferred by wood ducks is a combination of inundated woody and herbaceous plants.

On many wetlands, young wood ducks frequent water areas that lack overhead cover to feed on plant and animal foods associated with submerged vegetation beds. In wetlands where only sparse stands of aquatic emergents grow, young woodies resort to the use of adjacent upland habitats for loafing and escape cover.

Plants used for brood cover vary with latitude and from one wetland to another. However, they typically have a dense, spreading low growth that allows easy access and swimming (Webster and McGilvrey 1966). Some of the most important brood cover plant species include buttonbush, swamp rose, swamp privet, swamp loosestrife, alder, willow, American lotus, smartweed, duck potato, spatterdock, soft rush, pickerelweed, blue-joint, bulrush, and cattail (Webster and McGilvrey 1966, McGilvrey 1968, Sousa and Farmer 1983).

Optimum wood duck brood habitat exists when inundated emergent vegetation covers at least 75 percent of the wetland (Webster and McGilvrey 1966). In northern Florida, Wenner and Marion (1981) found that seven of eight radio-tagged brood hens remained on wetlands where shrub cover occupied more than 76 percent of the area. Isolated wetlands that are less that 1.5 hectares (3.7 ac) generally receive little brood use regardless of their vegetative composition (McGilvrey 1968, Hepp 1977).

On eastcentral Texas wetlands, correlation analysis indicated a significant relationship (P < 0.05) between brood use and survival and wetland size, shoreline length, percentage of floating and emergent vegetation, and percentage of flooded shrubs (Ridlehuber 1980). As these habitat parameters increased in size or proportion, brood hens were more likely to use the wetland as a rearing site, and ducklings increased their survival chances. Brood use and survival decreased as maximum and average depth and percentage of open water increased.

A beaver pond of 4.8 hectares (11.9 ac) in south Louisiana that produced 35 wood ducks in 1977 failed to produce any fledged ducklings in 1976 because of low water levels (Strader 1990).

When adequate food and cover are available, the number of loafing sites in a wetland can directly influence the number of broods enticed to the area and the duration of their stay (Beard 1964). McGilvrey (1968) reported that loafing sites should be at least 46 by 46 centimeters (18 by 18 in) and extend 5–15 centimeters (2–6 in) above the water. He suggested that optimum brood habitat contains 10–20 loafing sites per 0.4 hectare (1 ac). Preferred loafing sites generally are located adjacent to escape cover.

Woody vegetation overhanging the margins of streams, ponds, and lakes provides concealment cover sought by wood ducks (particularly juveniles and molting birds). Ideally, foliage should extend 0.3–0.6 meter (1–2 ft) above water and several feet out from shore. *Photo by Robert A. McCabe.*

Postbreeding and Wintering

Because summer weather is least likely to present problems to wood ducks, adults and flighted juveniles are able to use a greater array of habitats during the postbreeding period than at other times of the year. Aiding in their welfare is the seasonal peak production of foods by many wetland plants. Postbreeding wood ducks may find suitable habitat close to their natal/breeding area, or they may fly hundreds of kilometers to unexploited habitats that reach optimum values at this season. Summer exodus may especially apply to wood ducks breeding along streams, because streams and overflow basins seasonally recede, thereby reducing cover and food resources.

The physiological and social demands of wood ducks change markedly during the postbreeding period. Accordingly, a variety of habitat types is required by postbreeding birds. As adult wood ducks enter into their prebasic molt and become flightless, they seek out secluded areas of wetlands that afford dense stands of inundated vegetation and abundant food. In most areas, adults utilize the protective cover and food resources associated with herbaceous wetlands (marshes) to a greater degree during wing molt than during any other period of the year.

Bands of buttonbush and swamp privet—plants capable of surviving prolonged inundation—often develop in the shallow margins of large bottomland lakes and enhance the value of such water areas for wood ducks during all seasons. In summer, beds of American lotus often cover extensive portions of these lakes, enhancing their value for developing wood duck broods and molting birds. *Photo by Frank Bellrose; courtesy of the Illinois Natural History Survey.*

A prominent activity of the postbreeding period is the formation of nocturnal roosts. They develop in midsummer at specific locations where cover and shallow water provide favorable habitat. In many cases, sites are traditional, existing for a decade or more; in other instances, they are impromptu, arising from a temporarily favorable mix of food, water levels, and cover. Numbers using roosts vary from a score to congregations of several thousand. Aspects of year-round roosting behavior and habitat needs are discussed in detail in Chapter 15.

Gilmer et al. (1977) noted that the principal habitat of wood ducks in northcentral Minnesota between the time of pair-bond dissolution and loss of flight feathers was emergent vegetation in shallow bays of lakes and in river and stream marshes. In addition to these cover types, flightless woodies made extensive use of scrub/shrub swamps. After regaining their flight feathers, wood ducks frequently utilized isolated small wetlands and beaver ponds. Thompson and Baldassarre (1988) found that postbreeding wood ducks in northern Alabama also utilized a wide variety of wetland habitats. Although forested wetlands were the preferred diurnal habitat from August through October, woodies used flooded hardwoods, wooded swamps, and marshes with herbaceous emergent vegetation.

At Union County Refuge in southern Illinois, Parr et al. (1979) reported that postbreeding wood ducks were located 75 percent of the time in scrub/shrub wetlands and 25 percent of the time in flooded timber. However, flooded timber composed only 15 percent (75 hectares: 185 ac) of the potential habitat whereas buttonbush swamp covered approximately 55 percent (275 hectares: 680 ac). These figures suggest a slightly greater preference for flooded timber. In southeastern Missouri, Heitmeyer and Fredrickson (1990) observed that postbreeding wood ducks preferred shallowly flooded live forests over all other habitat types.

Sousa and Farmer (1983) indicated that optimum wood duck winter habitat consisted of a complex of scrub/shrub, emergent, dead timber, and flooded forest wetlands. Flooded hardwood forests are used extensively by wintering wood ducks (Thompson and Baldassarre 1988, Fredrickson and Heitmeyer 1988), but large continuous stands of unaltered mature forested wetlands may receive little use by wintering woodies (Costanzo et al. 1983). None of the radio-marked wood ducks studied by Costanzo et al. (1983) in South Carolina was observed to move farther than 100 meters (328 ft) from open water into an extensive (500 hectare: 1,236 ac) cypress/tupelo swamp.

WETLANDS AND PRODUCTIVITY

This review of the parameters affecting the value of wetland habitats for breeding wood ducks and their productivity level emphasizes anew the importance of the juxtaposition of the food base and nest sites. One is of little value without the other.

The wetland food base runs the gamut from marshes to bogs, with marshes at the high end of productivity and bogs at the low end. The food base in marshes is high because of: clear and shallow water; extensive exposure to sunlight; submergent, floating, and emergent plant beds; plant matter that also provides structure and organic matter (via detrital pathways) for invertebrates; and a neutral pH. Bogs are low in productivity as a result of: generally acidic waters; tannins that reduce light penetration and are not easily utilized by microorganisms at the start of the food chain; and plants that, with few exceptions, produce little food.

Stream overflow is an important adjunct to food productivity for wood ducks. Small streams overflow frequently and briefly, sweeping organic matter and nutrients into the channel. Large streams do so less frequently, but their overflows cover the floodplain longer, often permitting woodies to take advantage of newly but temporarily created overflow habitat. Such habitat reaches maximum expansion on the Alluvial Plain of the Mississippi River. Organic matter and dead terrestrial invertebrates that are funneled into small stream channels by receding water often are trapped at logjams, protruding roots, and eddies where they are slowly processed by microorganisms and aquatic invertebrates.

During the leafless period, bottomland hardwoods permit a maximum of sunlight to reach channel and overflow waters, thereby providing the energy for phytoplankton and zooplankton development which, along with microorganism conversion of organic matter (chiefly fallen leaves), starts the aquatic food chain. Wood ducks exploit the small but visible organisms of this food chain plus terrestrial isopods and insects gleaned from shoreline vegetation.

The addition of nutrients to streams by agricultural fertilizers and the effluent of sewage disposal plants is an asset to food productivity up to the point where light penetration is reduced by algal blooms or oxygen levels are depleted by oxidation and microbial respiration. Sewage lagoons often provide a gold mine of invertebrates for wood duck broods.

The value of the vast areas overflowed by streams on the Mississippi Alluvial Plain—Cairo,

Illinois, to Baton Rouge, Louisiana—during late winter and early spring is manifest in its food base for wood ducks—the combined result of nutrient-rich soil, inundated organic matter, and maximum light penetration. When and where possible, wood ducks exploit this bonanza as they prepare for the energy demands of breeding (Heitmeyer and Fredrickson 1990).

Chapter 4

Migration

Of all North American waterfowl, the wood duck is the only species with large nonmigratory and migratory populations. Small populations of mottled ducks in Florida, Louisiana, and Texas are essentially nonmigratory, and the fulvous and black-bellied whistling ducks breeding along the Gulf Coast have limited migration (Bellrose 1976). The American black duck is the only other species with migration traits similar to those of the wood duck; small numbers in southern areas are non-migratory, but it breeds almost to 60 degrees north, resulting in migratory flights that may be up to 4,023 kilometers (2,500 mi).

Substantially all of the wood ducks breeding south of North Carolina, Tennessee, and Little Rock, Arkansas, are nonmigratory. For 161 kilometers (100 mi) north of there, wood duck populations are quasimigratory, partially remaining in mild winters but departing in severe ones. North of Arkansas, Tennessee, and North Carolina, almost all breeding wood ducks are migratory. Our calculations of the abundance of breeding wood ducks in each state suggest that about 40 percent of the wood ducks in the Atlantic Flyway, 30 percent in the Mississippi Flyway, and 75 percent of those breeding in the Pacific Flyway are nonmigratory. Because the migratory population breeds within 1,609–2,253 kilometers (1,000–1,400 mi) of the extremes in their winter grounds, the distance of migration is not as great as for other important game duck species.

Wood ducks, like other ducks, migrate primarily at night. On areas we have kept under daily surveillance over many years, wood ducks have appeared in the spring shortly after daybreak. Wildlife photographer Mike Male did not see any wood ducks from his blind on ice-covered Albert Lea Lake, Minnesota, at dusk on April 11, 1982. The following sunrise, he saw 30 wood ducks sitting in a hole in the ice.

On nine occasions, we have observed flocks of wood ducks migrating over the farmlands of Mason County, Illinois (Table 31). Most observations were within one hour of sunrise; three were within two hours, and one was within three hours. Flock size varied from 11 to 63, with a mean of 23. Flocks were flying at altitudes estimated at 46–244 meters (150–800 ft), a mean of 183 meters (600 ft) above the ground.

We saw flocks of 3, 12, 15, and 21 depart from Spring Lake, Tazewell County, Illinois, on October 24, 1983, 3:35–3:40 p.m. CST, 110 minutes prior to sunset. They ascended on a heading of 200 degrees, climbing rapidly into the sky until lost in the clouds. Eric Hopps observed an apparent migratory departure from a roost site near Snicarte, Illinois, on October 5, 1986, 5:50–5:58 p.m. CST. Three flocks of 30, 50, and 200 departed a roost of 1,500 wood ducks, 4–12 minutes prior to sunset under a largely overcast sky.

Bellrose (1951: 10–11) reported the following dramatic arrival of a large flight of wood ducks: "Out of the cold, gray November sky they came—group after group of ducks, plummeting down, down, down on slotted wings, checking their plunge to swirl about the willows, and then finally dropping into the water below. Following the line of descent we could see small sparrowlike birds suddenly materialize out of the leaden sky, to take the form of wood ducks as they drew nearer. Soon we heard their squeaking cries from every quarter as more and more birds found sanctuary in the flooded timber. . . . We were witnessing a tardy south-bound flight of wood ducks, which within the space of five minutes saw some 500 drop into the Chautauqua National Wildlife Refuge, near Havana, Illinois. Most of the woodies had left the Illinois Valley two weeks earlier, but these ducks had elected to remain farther north until a second cold wave had sent them scurrying south to central Illinois, and, by the next day, still farther south." The time was about 8:30 a.m. CST, two hours after sunrise; the exact date was lost but was close to November 10.

These observations suggest that woodies have a temporal pattern similar to other migrating ducks—they depart staging areas from shortly before sunset into the night. Bellrose (1964b) used radar to monitor waterfowl departures from the Chautauqua National Wildlife Refuge and found they extended from approximately sunset to about 11:00 p.m. CST.

Table 31. Some parameters of wood duck flocks observed migrating over farm fields in Mason County, Illinois.

Flight date	Time	Flight direction	Ground speed[a]		Flight speed[a]		Flock size	Estimated altitude[b]		Cloud cover
10/04/79	7:15 a.m.	175°	53	(33)	39	(24)	11	244	(800)	0/10
10/09/86	6:15 a.m.	360°	55	(34)	77	(48)	18	183	(600)	10/10
10/09/86	6:30 a.m.	180°	58	(36)	35	(22)	24	244	(800)	10/10
10/12/77	7:30 a.m.	190°	61	(38)	39	(24)	19	152	(500)	0/10
10/31/73	7:50 a.m.	175°	53	(33)	40	(25)	16	183	(600)	10/10
3/21/71	7:45 a.m.	355°	60	(37)	42	(26)	22	183	(600)	2/10
3/30/81	7:05 a.m.	360°					23	229	(750)	0/10
4/08/80	5:45 a.m.	30°					63	183	(600)	10/10
8/25/82	8:30 a.m.	90°	74	(46)	74	(46)	12	46	(150)	0/10
Mean			60	(37)	51	(32)	23.1	183	(600)	
S.D.			7.2	(4.5)	17.9	(11.1)	15.6	60.5	(198.4)	

[a] In kilometers per hour (mi/hr).
[b] In meters (ft).

Overall, about two-thirds of all wood ducks are migratory. Wood duck migration covers a shorter distance (less than 2,253 kilometers: 1,400 mi) from wintering to breeding grounds than is the case for other important game duck species. Woodies primarily migrate at night, in flocks of a few birds to several hundred, but usually about 20. When observed in early morning, migrating wood duck flocks have been estimated to fly at a mean altitude of 183 meters (600 ft) above ground level and at a mean speed of 51 kilometers per hour (32 mi/hr). The altitude of night-flying migrating woodies is unknown. *Photo by F. Eugene Hester.*

Once airborne, wood ducks probably continue to fly through the night to land in the predawn light, or later, in a predetermined wetland. The flocks observed migrating in early morning appear to be birds that failed to reach their destination by dawn.

The "chain" of flocks that Bellrose (1951) observed landing at the Chautauqua National Wildlife Refuge appears to represent a sequential departure of groups of birds migrating from a specific site (such as a roost) to a specific site. Perhaps their calls hold the chain together during darkness. From light aircraft, we have seen mallards migrating in "chains" of flocks in early morning on specific courses between the Mississippi and Illinois rivers.

The total of 500 in the Chautauqua-bound chain was composed of many small flocks. The flocks departing Spring Lake coalesced into two groups before reaching the clouds. Those that Eric Hopps observed leaving a roost site at dusk may have become more segmented once established in flight formation. Migrating flocks in autumn appear to be larger than those in spring.

The first birds to arrive in central Illinois in late February or early March are pairs and double pairs. Over a span of 50 years, we have observed many scattered pairs prior to March 14, but only a few flocks. From that date forward, migrating flocks appear among residential pairs up to as late as April 22. Some of the flocks that arrived in mid-March may have reached their destination locally, but most of those that arrived in April appeared to be transients bound for points farther north. Often they have been seen one day and gone the next.

Flocks were prone to be even rather than odd in numbers as a result of mated pairs, with odd-numbered flocks containing extra males (Table 32). Spring flocks were relatively small, with 32 the largest number recorded.

Table 32. Size of spring flocks of six or more wood ducks migrating into the Illinois River Valley.

Flock size	Number of flocks
6	26
7	13
8	10
9	6
10	13
11	5
12	10
13	1
14	10
15	0
16	4
17	3
18	1
19	0
20	2
≥ 21	8

A peculiar behavior on the part of migrating woodies is the penchant for flocks to perch in trees. From a number of such observations, we have selected two. On March 16, 1977, four flocks of 8–15 wood ducks flushed from the trees and waters of Quiver Creek and flew west; about half took flight from tree branches. All were gone the following morning. Thirteen wood ducks flushed from a sycamore tree to join 62 wood ducks in a roadside ditch on April 3, 1969. None was present the next day.

FLIGHT CHARACTERISTICS

Although the wood duck is one of the least migratory of North American ducks, its wing-to-body mass relationship differs little from that of species that make much longer migratory flights (Bellrose et al. unpublished, 1990). The wing loading of the wood duck is slightly higher than that of the American wigeon, slightly lower than that of the northern pintail, and much lower than that of the bay-diving ducks (Bellrose et al. unpublished, 1990). Because the wood duck's wings are proportionately broader than those of other game ducks, the aspect ratio is lower than that of other species. The broader wing has probably evolved to enable wood ducks to be more adroit in dodging branches as the birds thread a course among the trees—a task at which they excel.

We have determined ground speeds of migrating wood ducks by paralleling their flight by car for 0.4 kilometer (0.25 mi) or more (Table 31). Flight speed was the velocity of the birds alone, without assistance or impediment from the wind. Bellrose and Crompton (1970) reported that geese and mallards adjusted their flight speed within limits to compensate for changes in wind bearing and velocity. The data in Table 31 provide another example, with that of the mallard and geese, of birds adjusting their flight speed to conserve energy. The standard deviation for variations in wood duck flight speed was over twice that of ground speed (Table 31).

Our data indicate a slightly lower migration speed for wood ducks than that found by Lokemoen (1967), who recorded speeds of wood ducks flying to a roost from 63 to 89 kilometers per hour (39–55 mi/hr), with a mean of 76 kilometers per hour (47.1 mi/hr). The difference in ground speeds may occur because of differences between the speeds of local and migratory flights.

On the basis of wing parameters and body mass, Bellrose et al. (unpublished, 1990) used an equation formulated by Greenewalt (1975) to compute the most advantageous flight speed in relationship to a migrating wood duck's energy expenditure. This calculated flight speed of 53 kilometers per hour (33 mi/hr) for the greatest distance with the least energy cost is close to our finding of a mean flight speed of 51 kilometers per hour (32 mi/hr) (Table 31) during migration.

The width-to-length ratio of wood duck wings is greater than for other game ducks, but the wing loading is similar to several species of dabbling ducks, slightly lower than that of the northern pintail, and much lower than for bay-diving ducks. The broader wing and tail have probably evolved to provide better flight control for maneuvering among trees. *Photo by Scott Nielsen.*

Bellrose et al. (unpublished, 1990) calculated that wood ducks making a night-long flight of 800 kilometers (497 mi) would use 33.7 grams (1.19 oz) of fat—approximately 4.95 percent of an adult male's body weight.

The mean distances that wood ducks traveled from summer banding locations to winter recovery sites were examined by Nichols and Johnson (1990) for six regions of eastern North America (Table 33).

The most distant regions had means of 1,104–1,363 kilometers (686–847 mi); the shortest distances embraced 357–402 kilometers (222–250 mi). At these migratory distances, a wood duck would not significantly deplete its stored lipid resources; therefore, mortality during migration (see Chapter 18) would appear to be accidental or due to an increase in the number of days exposed to hunting activities, not an effect of depleted energy reserves.

Table 33. Mean distance from locations of preseason (July–September) bandings to sites of winter (December–January) recoveries for wood ducks banded in eastern North America, 1970–86.[a]

Reference area	Sample size	Mean distance, in kilometers (mi)		S.E. Kilometers	(mi)
Northeastern	967	1,363	(847)	17.7	(11.0)
Eastern Canada/New York	826	1,392	(865)	15.0	(9.3)
Lake States	1,150	1,061	(659)	9.5	(5.9)
Northcentral	2,662	1,104	(686)	8.4	(5.2)
Southeastern	1,138	357	(222)	12.9	(8.0)
Southern	2,308	402	(250)	6.8	(4.2)

[a] Adapted from Nichols and Johnson (1990).

In flooded bottomland woods, wood ducks take flight at an acute angle, adroitly avoiding trunks and branches that would pose a hazard to the flights of other species. To avoid flying through a maze of branches, mallards, in contrast, usually rise vertically in a towering takeoff to clear treetops before flying horizontally. *Photo by Stephen Kirkpatrick.*

CHRONOLOGY OF MIGRATION

Juvenile wood ducks undertake their first migration in autumn at the age of three to six months. Their motivation to migrate is brought about by a developing endocrine system, the deposition of fat for flight energy, the diminishing photoperiod, temperature decline, and the behavior of adults with whom they are associated. Owen (1968) observed that calling among blue-winged teal steadily increased prior to departure. Singles and doubles constantly joined loose flocks, apparently attracted by the calls. Preflight swimming maneuvers appeared to build up flock organization. Owen (1968) considered a few alert birds to be possible leaders of the flock.

Eric Hopps observed similar activity among wood ducks prior to evening flight departures for roosts or migration. The primary signals were pronounced increases in tail wagging, head shaking, body pivoting that eventually faced the ducks in the direction of flight, and erect posture; the female uttered a "winnowing" call note (see Chapter 6) that increased in intensity as the time for departure neared. Other signals that led up to the primary preflight activities included bathing, wing raising and flapping, body shaking, and males preening their backs. Immediately prior to departure signals, pairs and small flocks often came together and formed loose aggregations that departed at various intervals until darkness.

The restlessness that develops prior to autumn departures in adult wood ducks may be communicated to juveniles that are in a similar physiological state. For migration to occur, however, both intrinsic and extrinsic stimuli must mesh. The intrinsic state of readiness is brought about by the release of hormones—prolactin by the pituitary and corticosterone by the adrenal glands at different times of the day (Meier 1973, Meier and Davis 1967). Prolactin and corticosterone release, which is regulated by the photoperiod, stimulates the deposition of fat that will fuel migration flight and brings about a restlessness that is transmitted into an urge to migrate. In spring, an increase in activity of the pituitary results in the release of gonadotrophic hormones that affect both the migratory and breeding cycles (Berthold 1975).

Such extrinsic factors as wind direction and velocity, temperature, barometric pressure, hunting pressure, and food supply also affect the timing of migration. Our observations in autumn indicate that a northerly wind, with falling temperatures and overcast skies produced by approaching low pressure, resulted in periodic departures of ducks, including wood ducks, from the Illinois Valley.

An analysis of weather and blue-winged teal departures from Delta Marsh, Manitoba, by Owen (1968) disclosed that the most important stimulus was a wind shift to the north, usually from the passage of a cold front. In addition, Owen considered that falling temperature and a rising barometer, with skies clearing and a decline in humidity—all a result of approaching high pressure following a low—created the most favorable conditions for migration.

Hunting pressure on opening day of the duck season has resulted in a noticeable departure of wood ducks from the Illinois Valley. Even though roost sites were not hunted, wood duck numbers at some roosts declined precipitously immediately after the season opened. Lingle (1978) reported that, in Isabella County, Michigan, the number of woodies present declined by more than 90 percent with the opening of the hunting season. Heusmann and Bellville (1982) observed that local resident wood ducks remained until hunting pressure or a severe freeze caused them to migrate several hundred kilometers to the south.

Availability of food also may be a factor in determining autumn departures. Usually, most woodies have departed central Illinois by the end of October. However, as discussed in Chapter 15, more than 500 remained at the Chautauqua National Wildlife Refuge through December 15, 1987, when northwest winds of 32–40 kilometers per hour (19.9–24.9 mi/hr) and temperatures that dropped below freezing induced most of them to leave. They had apparently remained exceedingly late because of a bountiful supply of waste corn left in harvested fields within 3.2 kilometers (2 mi) of their diurnal resting area.

AUTUMN MIGRATION

Weekly waterfowl censuses taken at national wildlife refuges in 1952, 1962, and 1967 were used by Bellrose (1976) to analyze the chronology of waterfowl migration for various regions of the United States. From these data we have adapted Figure 10, which depicts the temporal wood duck population abundance in the delineated regions of the Atlantic, Mississippi, and Pacific flyways.

Atlantic Flyway

National wildlife refuge censuses show that wood duck populations in New England remained at peak abundance through September, followed by a gradual decline during October and a precipitous decline in November, with only a few remaining after November 20 (Figure 10). In Nova Scotia, Tufts (1961) reported latest departures in mid-November. Palmer (1949) considered that autumn departure in Maine occurred between September 15 and October 20. For Massachusetts, Grice and Rogers (1965) re-corded peak departures between October 10 and 20, with late ones from November 10–20. Departures of woodies from Pennsylvania occurred in September and early October (Wood 1973). Todd (1940) noted an influx of wood ducks in western Pennsylvania during October and an exodus by late November.

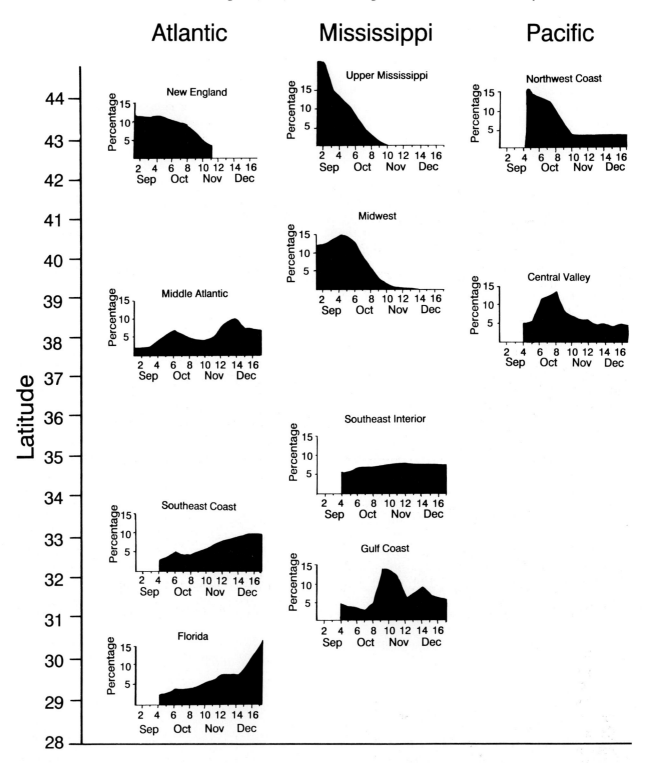

Figure 10. Chronology of autumn migration as disclosed by changing patterns of wood duck abundance on selected national wildlife refuges in regions of the Atlantic, Mississippi, and Pacific flyways.

The Middle Atlantic Region extends from New York south to northern North Carolina. Figure 10 shows an upward trend in wood duck numbers from mid-September to mid-October, followed by a temporary decline to late November, with the largest numbers through December. Peak autumn numbers occurred in Maryland from September 5 to November 7 (Stewart and Robbins 1958). Near Raleigh, North Carolina, Hester and Quay (1961) recorded that wood ducks at three roosts increased rapidly in October and decreased in November. They considered that roost numbers reflected the passage of migrants through the area. Winter populations consisted of no more than 10 percent of peak autumn numbers.

The Southeast Coast Region includes South Carolina and Georgia. Here, summer populations were steadily expanded by migrants from the end of September through December (Figure 10). Wood duck populations in Florida also increased from September through December as migrants arrived from the New England and Middle Atlantic states.

Temporal band recoveries. Band recoveries during the hunting season may not detect early southward migration of wood ducks from northern areas; however, most of the wood duck's migratory movements occur at the onset of and during the hunting season (figures 10 and 11). The temporal distributions of band recoveries in latitudinal zones of the Atlantic Flyway from bandings made north of 40 degrees indicate seasonal relationships in the three zones (Figure 11).

Banding, band recovery, and band analysis represent the primary steps in determining the migratory patterns of wood ducks and other waterfowl. On scores of federal and state wildlife areas, baited funnel traps have been used to capture wood ducks for the purpose of banding. Traps can be set on dry ground, in shallow water, or mounted on wooden platforms so that they float. The trap above is on a floating wood platform that can be adjusted as water levels change and is ideally positioned in shallow water where woodies typically feed on natural foods. Wheat and shelled or cracked corn are usual baits. Wood duck trapping operations are least successful during summer, when natural foods are most diverse, abundant, and widely accessible. Trapping during spring incubation periods must be done with caution or avoided, since lengthy entrapment of hens off their nests can cause the eggs to cool. Ideal trapping times are at daybreak and from late afternoon through dusk, when wood duck feeding activity is optimal. Raccoons, minks, and weasels have little difficulty getting at funnel trap captives and quickly habituate to areas of an easy food source; therefore, traps must be kept under close surveillance and should never be left closed overnight if checks at dusk (after sunset) are not made. *Photo by Dan Holm; courtesy of the Illinois Natural History Survey.*

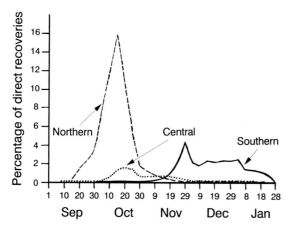

Figure 11. Direct recoveries of wood ducks banded in the Atlantic Flyway north of 40 degrees, 1950–82, in relation to seasonal advancement and geographic region.

Although hunting seasons opened on various dates over the years, the harvest (as reflected by the percentage of direct recoveries) of wood ducks in the northern zone consistently climbed sharply in early October (Figure 11). It fell just as quickly through the remainder of October as woodies departed southward. Small numbers of recoveries appeared in the central zone by October 10 and continued at a low level through November. By mid-November northern wood ducks began appearing in the bag of southern zone hunters; a peak was reached by the end of November, but recoveries remained high to mid-January.

Mississippi Flyway

The Great Lakes Region includes western New York, northern Ohio, Michigan, and eastern Wisconsin. Wood ducks in this region began departing in late September, with a continuous decline in abundance through November and small numbers persisting into December (Figure 10). For the Toledo, Ohio, area, Campbell (1968) gave an average departure date of October 13; some wood ducks departed as late as December 1.

The Upper Mississippi Region embraces Minnesota and western Wisconsin. Departure here commenced earlier—September 1—and ended earlier; only a few woodies persisted into November (Figure 10). Roberts (1932) gave October 3–18 as the major departure dates in northern Minnesota and October 12–31 for southern Minnesota.

The Midwest Region, which includes Iowa, Illinois, Indiana, most of Ohio, and Missouri, showed a slight increase in wood duck band recoveries through September as birds arrived from farther north to augment summer populations. From mid-October to mid-November, wood ducks steadily departed the region, with small numbers remaining into December (Figure 10). In eastern Iowa, Kent and Kent (1975) reported that most woodies departed between October 7 and November 7. From Ohio wood duck band recoveries, Stewart (1957) surmised that the largest southward migration occurred during the last days of October and early November. Widmann (1907) considered that major departures from Missouri occurred between October 20 and November 25.

The Southeast Interior Region embraces the heart of the wintering ground of the wood duck in the Mississippi Flyway—Arkansas, northern Louisiana, Mississippi, and Alabama. It also is the region of the second largest number of breeding woodies. Perhaps because of the local wood ducks and early migrants present in September, the number estimated on refuges showed only a slight but steady increase from October 1 through December (Figure 10).

Most wood ducks winter north of Gulf Coast refuges, but those that arrive there provide information on the chronology of arrivals from farther north (Figure 10). The big influx occurred in November, with numbers decreasing later as birds possibly moved out of refuges to flooded swamps.

Migratory flights arrived in Alabama in substantial numbers in mid-November with peak numbers by mid-December (Beshears 1974). In Louisiana, Bateman (1977) reported that the first wood duck migrants appeared during October and major flights occurred in November, with late arrivals to mid-December.

Temporal band recoveries. Seasonally distributed direct recoveries in three latitudinal zones of the Mississippi Flyway from bandings in the northern zone reveal southward migration by wood ducks (Figure 12). As in the Atlantic Flyway, recoveries in the northern zone soared in early October as hunting seasons opened variously among years and states. From October 10 to November 4, recoveries declined as ducks left the northern zone. The central zone began to record recoveries from the northern zone in early October. Recoveries increased in number up to November and gradually declined until late November. Recoveries from the northern zone began to appear in the southern zone in early November. They progressively rose in number to late December, after which a decline occurred through January.

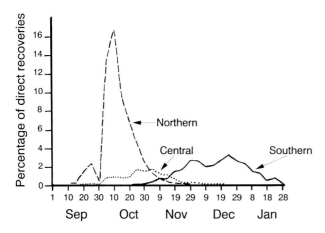

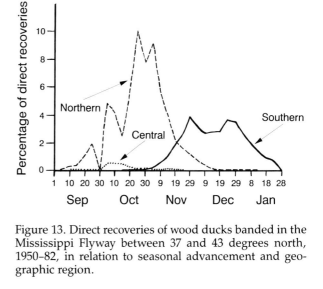

Figure 12. Direct recoveries of wood ducks banded in the Mississippi Flyway north of 43 degrees, 1950–82, in relation to seasonal advancement and geographic region.

Figure 13. Direct recoveries of wood ducks banded in the Mississippi Flyway between 37 and 43 degrees north, 1950–82, in relation to seasonal advancement and geographic region.

Bandings in the central region of the Mississippi Flyway are indicative of the wood duck's tenure there and the birds' passage into the southern zone (Figure 13). The upward surge of direct recoveries through October is the result of the staggered opening of the hunting season among the states of the Midwest. Wood ducks leave this region in a steady exodus from early November to early December, with small numbers remaining through December.

Pacific Flyway

The climate of the Pacific Flyway is much milder than that of the Atlantic and Mississippi flyways. As a consequence, wood duck migration is not prompted as much by weather as by food resources. Usually, a small number winter as far north as they breed. Nevertheless, there is a substantial decline in the populations of the Northwest Coast Region (western Washington, Oregon, and northwest California) from September to mid-November (Figure 10). After that, the remaining population appears to stabilize through the winter.

Most Pacific Flyway waterfowl winter in the Central Valley of California, which also is the most important wintering ground for wood ducks. At federal refuges, numbers increase through October; the decline in abundance in November and December probably represents local movements off refuge areas, because no appreciable numbers of wood ducks are known to leave the Central Valley. Naylor (1960) reported that wood ducks breeding at higher

elevations in the Coast Range of California migrate into the Central Valley for the winter.

Temporal/Spatial Relationship

A more visual but less measurable presentation of wood duck band recoveries in relation to time and space is provided by figures 14–16. These figures, which illustrate the temporal delay between recoveries from bandings on northern breeding grounds and southern wintering areas, help to evaluate the role played by staging areas between the two principal regions of seasonal activity.

It is apparent that the largest proportion of hunter harvest occurs locally, prior to departure from breeding areas. This kill extends over a period of 50–60 days. Recoveries from staging areas for latitudes up to 5 degrees south of northern banding sites—555 kilometers (345 mi)—have a temporal distribution similar to those at the latitude of banding (figures 14–16). South of the tagging areas on the wintering grounds (latitudes 35 to 28 degrees), recoveries are broadly distributed in time and show only casual responses to possible influxes from farther north. Obviously, no sizable numbers of northern wood ducks were on wintering ground areas at the opening of the hunting season (figures 14–16); most were still in northern areas.

Staging areas between breeding and wintering grounds are only lightly used by wood ducks. The low recovery rate at these latitudes (43 to 36 degrees) suggests that most wood ducks migrate directly from breeding areas to wintering areas.

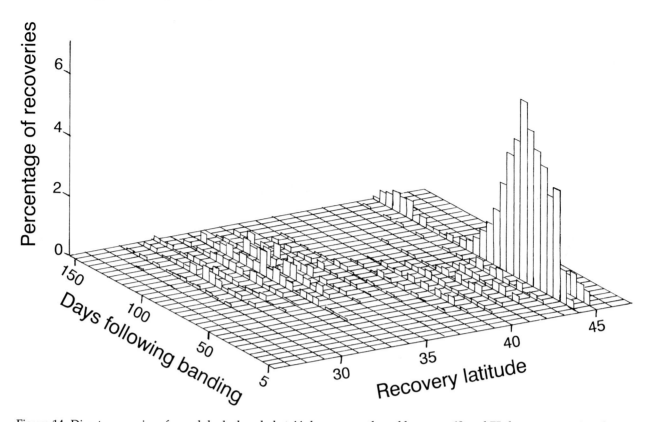

Figure 14. Direct recoveries of wood ducks banded at 44 degrees north and between 69 and 75 degrees west, in relation to latitude and number of days following banding.

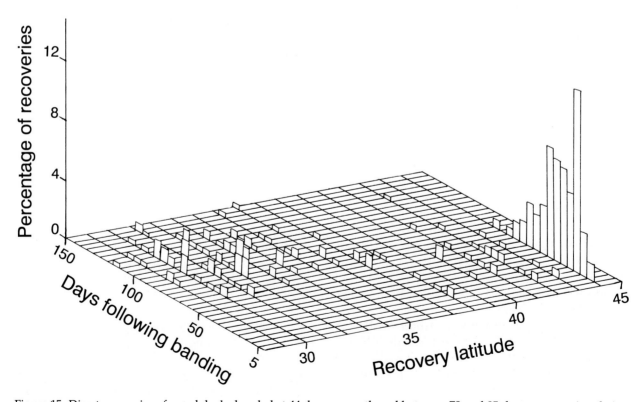

Figure 15. Direct recoveries of wood ducks banded at 44 degrees north and between 78 and 85 degrees west, in relation to latitude and number of days following banding.

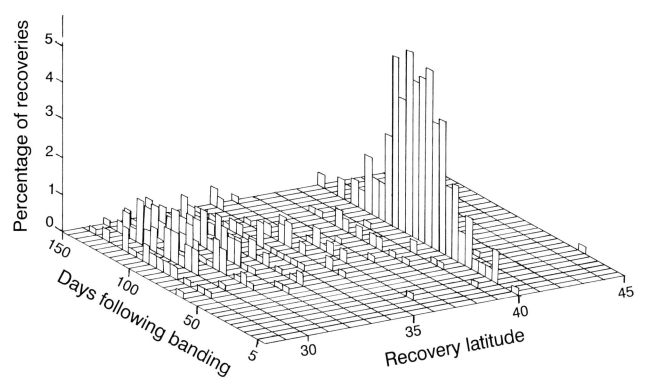

Figure 16. Direct recoveries of wood ducks banded at 40 degrees north and between 89 and 90 degrees west, in relation to latitude and number of days following banding.

Migration by Sex and Age Classes

A pertinent consideration of management is whether hunting regulations result in a disproportionate harvest of one sex or age class because of differential temporal migration. Our temporal and spatial analyses of direct recoveries from banding stations across the United States east of 93 degrees longitude – all between 43 and 44 degrees north latitude except one at 40.3 degrees north latitude (figures 17–20) – disclose slight differences between sex and age recoveries south of their banding sites.

In three of the four regions of banding (figures 18–20) one or both adult components departed, on the whole, about 10 days in advance of juveniles, both sexes of which migrated in almost identical temporal relationships. The trend lines represent the mean of population movements with all sex and age classes broadly overlapping. Therefore, ample numbers of adults remained to provide leadership when juveniles departed.

As measured by the temporal/spatial recoveries (figures 17–19), wood ducks from the northern zone (44 degrees north) progressed to the northern periphery (35 degrees north) of the wintering grounds in a mean of 47.4 ± 4.9 days (n = 12 for 3 regions × 4 sex and age classes). They would reach the southern periphery (30 degrees north) as a population in 73.8 ± 7.6 days.

Such a leisurely population movement fails to reflect on the rate of passage of its components. Individual elements respond differently to weather – some staying, some leaving. Consequently, some elements migrate early, some late (figures 14–16). The diversity of departures prolongs the entity of passage. Individual elements appear to migrate quickly from one destination to

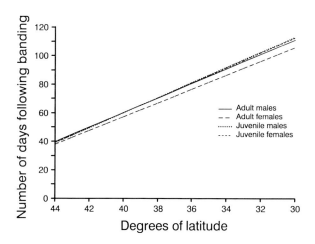

Figure 17. Direct recoveries of wood ducks by sex and age class from banding sites located between 43 and 44 degrees north and 69 and 77 degrees west, in relation to latitude and number of days following banding.

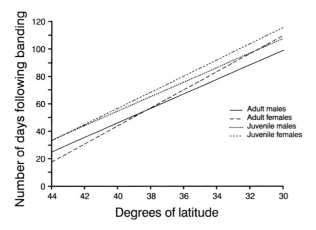

Figure 18. Direct recoveries of wood ducks by sex and age class from banding sites located between 43 and 44 degrees north and 78 and 85 degrees west, in relation to latitude and number of days following banding.

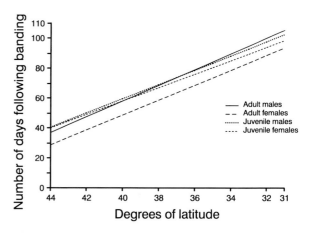

Figure 19. Direct recoveries of wood ducks by sex and age class from banding sites located between 43 and 44 degrees north and 88 and 93 degrees west, in relation to latitude and number of days following banding.

another and to spend considerable time there before departing for the next goal. Goals probably are widely separated for each component, so that a given flock might fly directly to the wintering ground as others stop once or twice en route. Heusmann and Bellville (1982) cited banded wood ducks that flew from New York to North Carolina in four days and another group that flew from New York to Florida in three days.

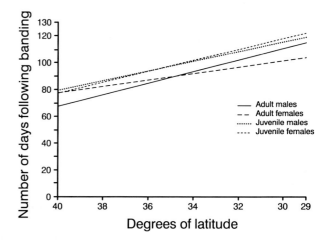

Figure 20. Direct recoveries of wood ducks by sex and age class from a banding site in Mason County, Illinois (40.3 degrees north, 90 degrees west), in relation to latitude and number of days following banding.

The banding of wood ducks captured in baited traps in late summer and in autumn prior to the hunting season provides knowledge about their autumn migration as gleaned from bands recovered and returned by hunters. Data provided by band recoveries help delineate migratory pathways and the chronology of southward passage. The high proportion of recoveries within a 56-kilometer (35 mi) radius of banding stations suggests that local hunters reap the reward of provincial enhancement of breeding productivity through nest house management programs. *Photo courtesy of the Illinois Natural History Survey.*

SPRING MIGRATION

Wood ducks begin leaving the more southern wintering areas in early February (Figure 21) and reach the more northern breeding areas in late March through April. Overall, migration is of shorter duration in spring than in autumn. In New England, the Upper Mississippi, and the Midwest, autumn migration (Figure 10) extended over a 10-week period, whereas it lasted 6 weeks in spring (Figure 21). However, departures from certain winter areas, such as Florida and the Southeast Coast, were protracted, extending over 12 weeks.

Atlantic Flyway

Because of maritime influence on weather, wood duck migration northward in the Atlantic Flyway differs from that in the Mississippi Flyway (Figure 21). A larger proportion of the Atlantic Flyway population winters farther north, and movements north lag compared with those of wood ducks in the Midwest.

Censuses of wood ducks in the Piedmont of Georgia during spring of 1963 and 1964 by Almand (1965) revealed a steady decline in abundance from

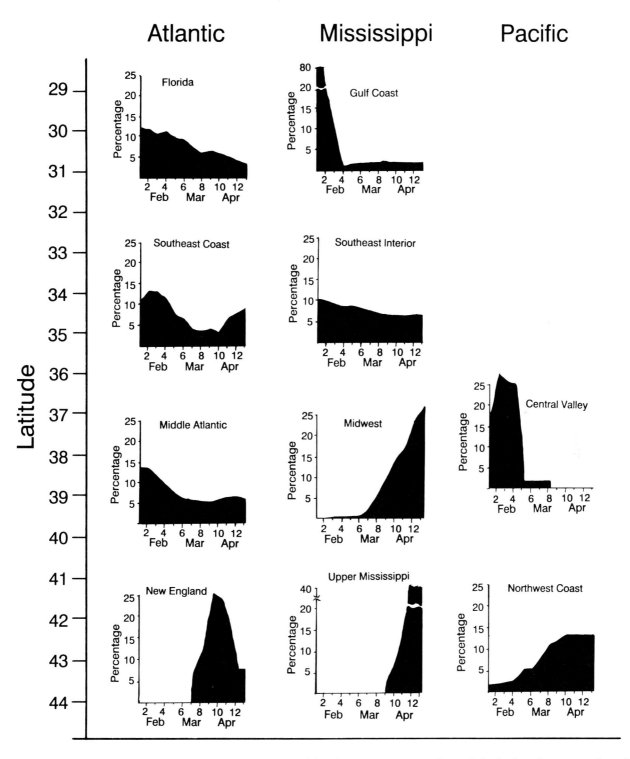

Figure 21. Chronology of spring migration as disclosed by changing patterns of wood duck abundance on selected national wildlife refuges in regions of the Atlantic, Mississippi, and Pacific flyways.

January through April. Although small numbers of wood ducks have wintered in the Chesapeake Bay region, Stewart and Robbins (1958) reported that peak numbers occurred during March. Spring migrants appeared in Pennsylvania during March and April (Wood 1973), and between March 27 and April 24 in western Pennsylvania (Todd 1940). Over a 40-year period, Saunders (1959) recorded the earliest woodie in Connecticut on February 28; the latest arrivals were on April 25. Wood ducks first appeared in Massachusetts March 10–17, with a peak on April 14 (Grice and Rogers 1965). Forbush (1925) reported that wood ducks were in Massachusetts from early March to late November.

According to Laughlin and Kibbe (1985), wood ducks arrived in Vermont late in March and populations peaked in April. Palmer (1949) reported that wood ducks arrived in Maine between April 2 and 23. The first appearance of wood ducks in Nova Scotia was April 16 (Tufts 1961). On the Rouge River in southwestern Quebec, Bouvier (1974) observed over a three-year period that wood ducks first appeared on April 10, 15, and 18, one or two days after the ice thawed.

Mississippi Flyway

By the end of February, most wood ducks in the marginal extremity of the Mississippi Flyway have moved north into the Southeast Interior Region (Figure 21). Because of the large permanent population in this region, migrants passing through produce only a slow, steady decrease in abundance of wood ducks through March. At Mingo National Wildlife Refuge in southeastern Missouri (37 degrees north), Heitmeyer and Fredrickson (1990) reported that wood ducks returned during February. Peak numbers of several thousand occurred February 18, 1983, March 6, 1981, and March 12, 1982.

A few woodies arrive in the Midwest in late February, but most do not begin to appear until mid-March; from that time through April, numbers increase steadily (Figure 21). In Kentucky, Mengel (1965) reported spring migrants from March 5 to 24. At Buckeye Lake in central Ohio, Handley (1955) reported the first migrating wood ducks on March 22, 1949, with numbers increasing through April. In the Toledo region of Ohio, Campbell (1968) gave March 1 as an early arrival date and April 10 as average.

For the state of Missouri, Widmann (1907) gave March 15 to April 20 as the period of spring migration. In eastern Iowa, Kent and Kent (1975) recorded the spring influx of wood ducks as March 7 to April 7.

Wood ducks arrived in the Upper Mississippi Region of western Wisconsin and most of Minnesota in early April, with numbers rapidly increasing through the month. Roberts (1932) gave spring migration as March 13–30 for southern Minnesota and March 31 to April 26 for northern Minnesota.

Arthur Hawkins reported that the first wood ducks appeared in the vicinity of White Bear Lake, Minnesota (45 degrees north) as soon as open water appears. From 1984 to 1988, the arrival dates varied from March 9 to 29, with a mean of March 21, ±7.9 days.

Wood ducks reach Winnipeg, Manitoba (49.9 degrees north) in early April. First arrivals have been observed as early as March 27 (1981) and as late as April 16 (1979). Other arrival dates include April 3 (1977), April 4 (1976), April 9 (1978), and April 14 (1982), according to N. E. Rodger.

There is good evidence to indicate that, as wood ducks migrate farther northward, they accelerate their passage to arrive in northern areas as the ice begins to melt.

Periodic censuses of spring wood duck numbers along Quiver Creek, 1947–1976, reveal the temporal pattern of arriving breeding birds and migrants passing through (Figure 22). Because of springs, Quiver Creek becomes ice-free ahead of nearby water areas and, therefore, wood ducks appear there in late February prior to their arrival in other central Illinois areas. Nauvoo Slough is 121 kilometers (75 mi) to the west and at about the same latitude, yet wood ducks do not appear there until it is ice-free, usually two weeks later than at Quiver Creek. Two female woodies banded at the same

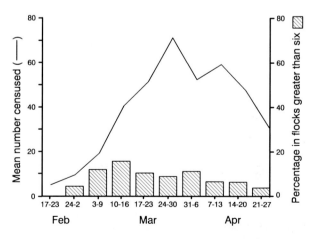

Figure 22. Mean weekly wood duck numbers censused on Ermling and Cullinane units of Quiver Creek, Mason County, Illinois, 1947–76. The bar graph shows the percentage of ducks in flocks larger than six, indicating arriving migrants or transients.

time on Quiver Creek on March 21, 1983, were found nesting at Nauvoo Slough on May 7 and June 6, 1984.

The effect of March temperatures on the arrival of 10 percent of the spring population of wood ducks on Quiver Creek is shown in Figure 23. The positive slope reflects increasing degrees of heat required to maintain a base of 18 degrees Celsius (65° F). The colder the March, the later wood ducks arrived over the 25-year period. Migration was delayed by cold weather in certain years by as many as four weeks, March 5–April 5. March of 1960 was particularly cold, requiring 709 Celsius (1308 F) degree days, compared with a low of 297 Celsius (566 F) degree days in 1973. For each increase heating degree day of Celsius that was required to maintain a base of 18 degrees Celsius (65° F), wood ducks delayed 0.06 days in arriving at Quiver Creek, 1952–1976.

Most of the migrants have passed through Quiver Creek by the last week in March, and the population in April is largely breeders (Figure 22). The seasonal decline of censused wood ducks stems from females beginning to incubate (Figure 22). Thus, the spring migration spanned a period of four to five weeks at Quiver Creek. As local breeders and transients arrived, the proportion of the population in flocks of six or more increased from none in mid-February to 16 percent the second week of March (Figure 22). Thereafter, as local breeding flocks dissolved and transients left, the proportion of birds in flocks declined to only a few by late April.

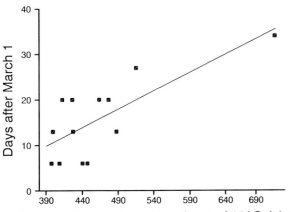

Figure 23. Relationship of 10-percent arrival of the spring population of wood ducks at Quiver Creek, Mason County, Illinois, with March heating-degree days (Celsius degrees above base of 18 degrees, 65°F), 1952–67 (three years of inadequate weekly population data omitted). The regression equation is: $y = -21.39 + 0.0802x$, $r = 0.75$, $P < 0.01$, $n = 13$.

Pacific Flyway

Because of the mild climate that prevails in the coastal region of the Pacific Flyway, wood ducks winter much farther north than elsewhere (Figure 21); however, most winter in the Sacramento River Valley of California. They begin departing there in late February with only small numbers remaining after mid-March. The Northwest Coastal Region begins to receive more wood ducks through March into early April.

MIGRATION CORRIDORS

Migration corridors embrace the direction of travel and geographic distribution of waterfowl between breeding and wintering areas (Bellrose 1976). Available population distribution data suggest that wood ducks maintain the same migration corridors between autumn and spring, but more data are needed to substantiate this premise. We have demarcated migration corridors for wood ducks on the basis of two-thirds the longitudinal recovery range of direct bands for each degree of latitude (Bellrose and Crompton 1970).

Mississippi and Atlantic Flyways

Direct recoveries from two banding stations—one in northcentral New York, the other in southwestern Wisconsin (Map 7)—illustrate migration corridors in the Atlantic and Mississippi flyways. The corridors achieve breadths of 209–595 kilometers (130–370 mi) in the Atlantic Flyway and 402–805 kilometers (250–500 mi) in the Mississippi Flyway. Hemmed between the Atlantic Ocean and the Appalachian Mountains, the New York corridor is narrower over most of its course than is the Wisconsin corridor, which is unrestricted by topography. The New York corridor is broadest near its south terminus where it expands south of the Appalachian Mountains to spread entirely across southern Alabama (Map 7).

The mean of wood duck band recoveries from Wisconsin approximates the course of the Mississippi River, with the western margin along the 95-degree meridian (western Missouri, Arkansas, and eastern Texas) and the eastern margin across central Tennessee and along the Mississippi/Alabama border.

Wood duck migration corridors in the Mississippi Flyway (Map 7) are much broader than those for the mallard (Bellrose and Crompton 1970). Outer standard deviations of mallard direct recoveries from banding in central Illinois cover breadths of 137–322 kilometers (85–200 mi) (Bellrose and Crompton 1970), less than half those of the wood duck.

The broader distribution of migrating wood ducks emanating from banding sites stems from the bird's penchant to exploit small, marginal habitats en route south and on wintering grounds. The habitats more specifically exploited by wood ducks than by other waterfowl are streams, ponds, and various small wetlands. Although these types of wetlands are not totally ignored by mallards, comparatively small numbers occupy them during the hunting season of autumn and early winter. Mallards are prone to concentrate by the tens of thousands in wetlands that afford undisturbed resting areas adjacent to natural or agricultural food resources. Food habits of the wood duck and mallard are similar. To reduce competition with a larger, more aggressive species, wood ducks apparently have evolved an autumn and winter distribution that optimizes the use of water areas more marginal for mallards. Thus, wood ducks disperse over a much broader area than do mallards during autumn migration.

The mean lines of band recoveries from banding sites across the northern United States, Maine to Minnesota, show the migratory flow between breeding and wintering areas (Map 8). Banding sites in eastern Maine and Massachusetts resulted in mean lines that closely followed the Atlantic seaboard; Vermont and central New York lines marked a north/south flight until reaching the Piedmont and Coastal Plain in Virginia, where they became part of the mass migrating through the eastern third of the Carolinas and the southeastern third of Georgia as far as the panhandle of Florida.

The axial recovery lines from western New York, southern Ontario, and northwestern Ohio stretch southward to the Appalachian Mountains of western Virginia, where they cross through North Carolina to central South Carolina then swing southwestward around the terminus of the Appalachian Mountains in Georgia.

For wood ducks banded in Michigan west through Minnesota, the mean lines of direct recoveries are largely on a north/south axis (Map 8). With the exception of axial lines emanating from banding sites in central Michigan and central Illinois, all lines tend to converge on the Mississippi River, especially south of Kentucky. The convergence of so many mean lines of band recoveries in eastern Arkansas and Louisiana and western Tennessee and Mississippi attests to the importance of this region of overflow bottomland hardwoods for wintering wood ducks.

Central Flyway

There is only one migration corridor of note in the Central Flyway. It extends down the east side of the Great Plains region, largely east of the 98-degree meridian. A smattering of wood duck migrants occurs as far west as 104 degrees; from there west to the Rocky Mountains, only a few woodie migrants occur.

These migrants of the Great Plains come from breeding grounds that extend across North Dakota and Montana and, farther south, from isolated pockets of supportive habitat along streams. The drainage pattern is at right angles to the southward line of flight. Consequently, there is no pattern of streams or other wetlands to provide a focal point for migrating woodies; they hurdle from one stream to another, dispersing broadly over mediocre stream and reservoir habitat. The majority of the migrants winters in Texas east of the 97-degree meridian (Dallas/Corpus Christi).

A review by Ladd (1990) of band data from the Central Flyway pointed out that 41 percent of the recoveries have come from the Mississippi Flyway, especially from bordering states.

Pacific Flyway

Most of the migrant wood ducks in the Pacific Flyway funnel into the Sacramento River Valley of California for the winter. They accrue largely from the Columbia River and its tributaries. The Willamette Valley of Oregon provides an important conduit south to the Sacramento Valley. Others entering this "funnel" come from breeding grounds on the Frazier River Delta of British Columbia and streams of the coastal ranges.

HOMING OF FEMALES

One of the most important keys to wood duck management is understanding homing (philopatry)—the ability to return to a specific site in subsequent years. The wood duck has a well-developed homing ability that plays a vital role in its productivity. Homing in wood ducks probably evolved to such a high degree through the necessity of returning to suitable but scarce and dispersed nest sites in following years. The importance of finding a suitable nest site that provides a successful hatch at least 40 percent of the time is instrumental to the species' survival. It is crucial, therefore, for a hen to be able to return to a site that has produced a successful nest.

Early ornithologists correctly surmised the homing capability of wood ducks. Wilson (1828) stated that a tree cavity had been occupied for four successive years probably by the same pair. Audubon (1840–44) remarked that wood ducks are attached to their "breeding places" and that, for three successive years, he found a nest in the same cavity originally created by an ivory-billed woodpecker.

We first became aware of the prominence that homing played in the use of nest houses from the large proportion of hens that returned to the same nest houses or to nearby nest structures (Bellrose 1953, Bellrose et al. 1964). Since then, numerous investigators have confirmed the large proportion of adult hens that return to nest in the same area (Table 34). Variation occurs in the return rate among studies for two basic reasons: (1) use of natural cavities or other nest sites has not been monitored; and (2) differential annual mortality among females occurs among sites and years.

Selecting Other Nest Sites

Returning hens that resort to new nest sites do so for a number of reasons: (1) low or high water makes the original wetland inhospitable; (2) the female returned to her original nest site but the nest was destroyed before her return; (3) the nest site is occupied by a conspecific or competing species; (4) the female was unsuccessful in her previous nesting effort; or (5) for unknown reasons the female pioneered to a new site.

Hester (1962) reported that, when four boxes became unavailable to returning wood duck hens, they nested within 3.2 kilometers (2 mi) of their original nest sites. From the site of a drained lake, two of these hens moved to a nearby lake. Grice and Rogers (1965) reported that, when a pond was drained in Massachusetts, a returned female nested nearby.

The event of wood duck nest desertion or destruction prior to incubation limited our opportunity to capture a nesting female. Occupancy of a former wood duck nest by starlings further reduced our chances of capturing a homing female at the same site where she nested the previous year. As early nest loss increased and use of houses by starlings rose, reoccupation of the same house by the same returning hen declined. The coefficient of determination (r^2) indicated that possibly 37 percent of the failure of returning wood duck hens to occupy the same houses was due to these two factors. Nest destruction and desertion were 2.5 times more likely than was starling occupancy to account for failure to recapture a homing hen at the same nest site. Nest desertion was largely caused by intraspecific strife among the competing females and harassment by starlings prior to wood duck incubation.

Destruction of incubated nests also results in less likelihood that a hen will return the following year to the same house (Table 35). A female that has suffered nest destruction seeks to nest in a different

Table 34. Homing of wood duck hens in a subsequent year to nest in the same areas where they had been initially banded as incubating birds.

State	Years	Number banded	Number recorded	Percentage recovered	Percentage captured in same nest house[a]	Source
Vermont	1949–51	52	17	32.7	35.2	Miller (1952)
Massachusetts	1950–56	536	232	43.3		Grice and Rogers (1965)
North Carolina	1961–62	30	14	46.7	50.0	Hester (1962)
	1965–66	72	44	61.1		Holloman (1967)
South Carolina	1979–86	277	124	44.8		Hepp et al. (1987)
Pennsylvania	1953–56	44	8	18.2	37.4	Decker (1959)
Wisconsin	1982–84	16	8	50.0	12.5	Soulliere (1985)
Illinois						
Mason County	1951–62	440	216	49.1		Bellrose et al. (1964)
Quiver Creek	1954–67	496	204	41.1	40.0	This study
Nauvoo Slough	1984–88	191	116	60.7		This study
Missouri	1967–70	177	103	58.2	56.4	Hansen (1971)
	1968–71	306	203	66.3		Hartman (1972)
	1973–74	169	122	72.2	20.6	Clawson (1975a)
Arkansas	1970–71	94	68	72.3		Brown (1972a)
Mississippi	1966–68	84	39	46.4		Cunningham (1968)
Alabama	1954–69	39	28	71.8		Beshears (1974)

[a] Based on the proportion of hens that returned to the nesting area.

Table 35. Return in subsequent years to the same nest houses by banded wood duck hens experiencing previous successful and unsuccessful nesting at Quiver Creek (1954–67) and Nauvoo Slough (1985–87), Illinois.

Area	Successful nests	Percentage return	Unsuccessful nests	Percentage return		P
Quiver Creek	866	40.76	49	36.7	0.568	(P>0.10)
Nauvoo Slough	135	65.93	56	48.2	2.266	(P<0.05)

but nearby location the same year. If the last nesting attempt results in failure, the female may return in a subsequent year to her original nest site or seek an entirely new location.

In a study of natural cavity use by woodies, Bellrose et al. (1964) found that natural cavities that produced successful nests were more likely to be occupied the subsequent year than those where nests had been destroyed.

At Quiver Creek, 40 percent of the adult hens that returned to the area occupied the same nest houses a second year (Figure 24). Although nest houses that extended along Quiver Creek for 10.1 kilometers (6.3 mi) were available, only 4.3 percent of the returning hens nested more than 1.6 kilometers (1 mi) from their original sites.

Hansen (1971) found that 56 percent of 88 successful hens returned the following year to nest in the same houses; 6 percent moved more than 0.8 kilometer (0.5 mi) to different houses, including one hen that moved 3.1 kilometers (1.9 mi). The mean distance moved in consecutive years by 10 unsuccessful females was 2.7 kilometers (1.7 mi), in contrast to a mean of only 0.24 kilometer (0.15 mi) for successful females. One unsuccessful female moved 7.9 kilometers (4.9 mi) the year following unsuccessful nesting, and four unsuccessful females moved more than 3.2 kilometers (2 mi).

A few years later, Clawson (1975a) studied wood duck nesting on the same area (Table 34) and found that only 20.6 percent of returning females used the identical house. This decline may have occurred because of increasing strife among hens as the breeding population increased (see Chapter 10).

At several areas in Massachusetts, Grice and Rogers (1965) found that 32 to 50 percent (mean = 43 percent) of 536 hens returned to the same nesting area (Table 34). On their larger study area – Great Meadows National Wildlife Refuge – they found that the majority failed to use the same nest house.

Female wood ducks are easily captured while incubating eggs in nest houses. When captured and handled in this manner, most hens will not abandon their nests as a consequence of the disturbance. The recapture of banded females in the same or nearby houses in subsequent years provides information on longevity and homing propensity. *Photo by Jack Dermid.*

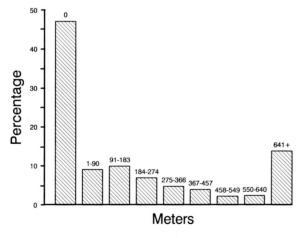

Figure 24. Distance in meters that 326 wood duck hens nested in subsequent year from original nest sites, 1955–67, Quiver Creek, Illinois.

However, of 163 banded females that returned to the Sundbury/Concord Valley, 83 percent were found nesting close to their original sites and an additional 16.6 percent nested within 3.2 kilometers (2 mi). One hen nested as far as 4.0 kilometers (2.5 mi) from its former nest site.

The homing rate of wood ducks reported for Quiver Creek (Table 34) is lower than that calculated from hens missed one year and found on nests after an absence of one or more years. Adjusting the homing rate for missed years of capture and factoring in a mortality rate of 50 percent for each missed year, we obtain data that more truly reflect the return of adult hens to Quiver Creek. The homing rate corrected for the missed ducks averaged 56 percent (n = 496), 1954–1967, which was higher than the mean survival rate of 49.2 percent calculated for adult female woodies in the central zone of the Mississippi Flyway, 1960–1984 (see Chapter 18). Thus, almost every wood duck hen still alive that had nested initially on the Quiver Creek study area returned to nest there. A few probably sought natural cavities the second year, especially those whose nests had been destroyed the previous year; we failed to capture on nests a few others that returned.

A comparison of survival rates with homing rates of adult females in Massachusetts led Grice and Rogers (1965) to conclude that about 90 percent of surviving females returned to the same area.

Hepp et al. (1989) calculated homing rates for 181 adult wood duck females captured in nest houses in southeastern South Carolina. They found that the homing rate of 55 percent compared closely with survival rates previously determined for the region by Johnson et al. (1986). Hence, Hepp et al. (1989) concluded that surviving females had a high probability of return and capture in nest houses.

Juveniles

Information on the homing of juveniles is derived from web-tagged ducklings in the nest and from flightless (local) juveniles bait-trapped on study areas containing nest houses.

Hansen (1971), at Mingo National Wildlife Refuge in Missouri, recorded a return rate by female ducklings of 8.6 percent (Table 36). Although return rates varied from 6.1 to 16.1 percent, 1966–1969, the number of hens breeding for the first time increased each year from 25 in 1966 to 44 in 1969.

Stephen Simmons recorded the returns from 1,351 web-tagged female ducklings, almost all of the 1,443 that departed nest houses, 1976–1978, near

Because wood ducks younger than four weeks of age are too small to leg-band, size #1 monel metal fish tags are used to mark day-old ducklings (left). The tags usually are attached by inserting them through two holes in the web and pressing the two ends together. Tags should never be pressed tightly against the web because necrosis will occur, causing the tag to fall out. When a tag is applied correctly, a tough ring of scar tissue forms around each hole, making it difficult for the tag to be torn loose. As with leg bands, each web tag is inscribed with a different number to allow identification of individual birds. Web-tagged wood ducks that are recaptured as adults provide information on the proportion that return to their natal area to nest, compared with those that pioneer to new breeding areas. Recapture of web-tagged ducklings later in the season (right) by bait traps can furnish facts on plumage development, survival, and local movements. *Photos by Jack Dermid.*

Table 36. Number of female wood duck ducklings (web-tagged and unmarked) that departed nest houses at Mingo National Wildlife Refuge, Missouri, compared with actual, adjusted, and potential recoveries in subsequent years.[a]

Year banded	Number[b] 1	Number[b] 2	Year 1 Actual	Year 2 Actual	Year 2 Adjusted[c]	Year 3 Actual	Year 3 Adjusted[c]
1966	83	76	4	1	2		
1967	160	157	6	3	5		
1968	247	242	9	2	3	1	3
1969	391	124	10	4	7	1	3
Total/mean	881	599	29	10	17	2	6

[a] Data from James L. Hansen (1971, personal communication).
[b] Number of female ducklings (based on 50-percent sex ratio) that departed (column 1) and were web-tagged (column 2).
[c] Adjusted number based on 58-percent yearly mortality for yearlings and 50 percent the second year to compensate for birds that returned but were not found.
[d] Adjusted for ducks that missed capture and for unmarked ducklings.
[e] Based on females surviving from hatching to flight of 46 percent, and on a yearly survival rate of 41.6 percent.

Merced, California (Table 37). His data show an actual return of 7.77 percent of web-tagged ducklings. However, a number of web-tagged birds were not found nesting until the second, third, and even fourth year and no doubt are representative of others that returned but were not found. Adjusting for mortality that occurred in this group (52 percent the first year and 41 percent in each subsequent year) suggests that about 10 percent of all birds actually homed back to the general area. Twenty-eight percent of those that departed nest houses would be anticipated to survive, based on standard duckling and juvenile survival rates (Table 37). Return rates of 11.3, 6.4, and 12.2 were followed for the first time by increases in nesting ducks in succeeding years from 42 to 44 to 65.

At Nauvoo Slough, Illinois, the adjusted web-tagged duckling return rate of 12.9 percent in 1986 was in part responsible for an increase in yearling breeding hens from 33 in 1985 to 41 (19.5 percent) in 1986 (Table 37).

In Massachusetts, Heusmann (1975) web-tagged 2,042 female wood duck ducklings, 1963–1972. Heusmann later recaptured 73 individuals on nests and 15 others from bait trapping and shot recoveries on or close to their natal marshes. Fifty-one (2.5 percent) of these wood ducks returned the first year to nest, 14 were not found until the second year, and 8 were seen for the first time in the third year, indicating that these birds and others of their cohort that had survived the first year returned to nest nearby.

Table 37. Number of female wood duck ducklings (web-tagged and unmarked) that departed nest houses in the area of Merced, California (1976–78)[a] and Nauvoo Slough, Illinois (1985).

Year banded	Number[b] 1	Number[b] 2	Year 1 Actual	Year 2 Actual	Year 2 Adjusted[c]	Year 3 Actual	Year 3 Adjusted[c]	Year 4 Actual	Year 4 Adjusted[c]
Merced									
1976	363	317	17	8	13	0		1	6
1977	471	454	21	2	3	2	5	0	
1978	609	580	34	15	24	5	12	0	
Total/mean	1,443	1,351	72	25	40	7	17	1	6
Nauvoo Slough									
1985	287	132	11	2	3	1	3		

[a] California data provided by Stephen Simmons.
[b] Number of female ducklings (based on 50-percent sex ratio) that departed (column 1) and were web-tagged (column 2).
[c] Adjusted number based on 58-percent yearly mortality for yearlings and 50 percent the second year to compensate for birds that returned but were not found.
[d] Adjusted for ducks that missed capture and for unmarked ducklings.
[e] Based on females surviving from hatching to flight of 46 percent, and on a yearly survival rate of 41.6 percent.

Table 36. (continued)

Number of adjusted returns[d] (marked and unmarked)	Percentage of adjusted returns (all ducklings)	Number of potential returns[e]
7	8.4	16
11	6.9	31
15	6.1	47
63	16.1	75
96	8.6	169

Heusmann (1975) used a mortality rate of 53 percent for yearling females and 34.6 percent for older birds to adjust homing rates for hens that lived but were not represented in second- and third-year samples. Thus, he estimated that 106 female ducklings (5.2 percent) returned as potential nesting birds. Records of 15 non-nesting returns in subsequent years indicated that at least an additional 0.73 percent homed back to the general area of their hatch.

Near Wendell, North Carolina, Holloman (1967) web-tagged 785 ducklings (392 assumed to be females) at four large ponds. The following year, 12 (3.1 percent) were found nesting in houses on their natal ponds and 3 (0.8 percent) nested at ponds where they were reared. No follow-up occurred the second year to determine the status of ducklings that might have returned but were not captured the first year.

At Big Lake National Wildlife Refuge in Arkansas, Brown (1972a) web-tagged 1,290 ducklings (645

Table 37. (continued)

Number of adjusted returns[d] (marked and unmarked)	Percentage of adjusted returns (all ducklings)	Number of potential returns[e]
41	11.3	60
30	6.4	90
74	12.2	117
145	9.4	276
37	12.9	55

assumed to be females) in 1970. He reported that 28 (4.3 percent) were captured on nests in 1971. No study was made in 1972 to determine if additional ducklings returned.

Of 2,945 web-tagged ducklings (1,459 females) that departed nest houses 1982–1987 on the Department of Energy's Savannah River Plant in west-central South Carolina, 5.2 ± 0.7 (SE) percent (adjusted for mortality after year one) returned to nest (Hepp et al. 1989). Of 67 recoveries for first nesting attempts, 58 occurred the first year, 8 the second year, 1 the third year, and none thereafter.

The return rate of juvenile hens among dabbling duck species (Table 38) was broadly lower than that of juvenile female wood ducks (tables 36 and 37). It should be noted that, with the exception of Doty and Lee's (1974) banding of day-old mallards, all other juvenile bandings were of birds six or more weeks of age. These older ducks would be at a higher level of survival than day-old ducklings, thereby promulgating a doubling of their return rates.

Although data are too fragmentary to be conclusive, available evidence points to both adult and yearling wood duck hens as homing to a greater degree than do female prairie-nesting dabbling ducks. This greater degree of homing may be a favorable evolutionary development, considering that the nest requirements of wood ducks are more site-specific than those of prairie-nesting ducks. Homing would be a greater asset to the productivity of wood ducks nesting in natural cavities—dispersed and difficult to locate—than to the productivity of duck species nesting in prairie landscapes where variations in precipitation constantly are changing the availability and conformation of wetland habitats.

DISPERSAL OF FEMALE DUCKLINGS

Unmarked incubating hens appeared in significantly greater numbers than could be accounted for by yearlings returning to their natal areas (Table 39). The result was especially apparent at Mingo National Wildlife Refuge, where Hansen (1971) web-tagged 92–98 percent of the ducklings departing nest houses, 1966–1969. Despite this high tagging rate, 27–84 percent of the new incubating females were not of the cohort represented by web-tagged birds (Table 39). Similarly, Stephen Simmons, at Merced, California, web-tagged 87.3–96.3 percent of the ducklings hatched, 1976–1978, but 45–55 percent of the ducks nesting for the first time in his nest houses were unmarked and presumably had not hatched on his study area (Table 39).

Table 38. Homing rate of certain dabbling ducks banded on their breeding grounds in North America.[a]

| | Females | | | | Males | |
| | Adult | | Juvenile | | Adult | |
Species	Number banded	Percentage returned	Number banded	Percentage returned	Number banded	Percentage returned
Mallard	15	13.3	20[c]	5.0		
	24	41.7	122[c]	5.7		
	113	46.0	140	5.0		
	150	33.3	52	22.8		
American black duck	89	24.7	289[c]	2.4		
Northern pintail	44	39.0	115[c]	13.0		
Gadwall	16	37.5	8[c]	12.5		
	52	28.8				
	33	63.6	47	6.4	242	9.1
	200	48.5	184	8.7		
Northern shoveler	19	42.1	12[c]	8.3		
	20	15.0	116	3.4	19	10.5
Blue-winged teal	58	13.8	30[c]	0.0		
	16	0.0	200[c]	0.0		
	136	4.4	42	2.4		
American wigeon	21	43.0				

[a] Adapted from McKinney (1986).
[b] References: 1 = Sowls (1955); 2 = Coulter and Miller (1968); 3 = Doty and Lee (1974); 4 = Gates (1962); 5 = Blohm (1978); 6 = Poston (1974); 7 = McHenry (1971); 8 = Wishart (1983); 9 = Lokemoen et al. (1990).
[c] Banded as captive-reared juveniles six to eight weeks old.

Table 39. Projected return of cohort representing adjusted return of web-tagged female wood duck ducklings, compared with the number of nonlocal hatched birds nesting for the first time.

| | | | Number of yearlings | Percentage of nesting yearlings | | Number of |
Place	Year of return	Calculated number of returns[a]	nesting (no leg bands)[b]	Hatched locally	Not hatched locally	nesting adults
Mingo National Wildlife Refuge, Missouri[c]	1967	4	25	16.0	84.0	14
	1968	6	29	20.7	79.3	21
	1969	9	39	23.1	76.9	35
	1970	32	44	72.7	27.3	34
Total/mean		51[d]	137[d]	37.2	62.8	104
Merced, California[e]	1977	19	42	45.2	54.8	42
	1978	22	44	50.0	50.0	52
	1979	36	65	55.4	44.6	37
Total/mean		77[f]	151[f]	51.0	49.0	131
Nauvoo Slough, Illinois	1986	24	41	58.5	41.5	32

[a] Combined total of number of web-tagged and unmarked females that departed nest houses and returned to nest the following year assuming survival of unmarked females was similar to large samples of web-tagged birds from tables 37 and 38.
[b] New, unbanded females—both web-tagged and unmarked—found incubating.
[c] Data from James L. Hansen (1971, personal communication).
[d] Difference: $t = 5.80$, $P \leq 0.05$.
[e] Data from Stephen Simmons (personal communication).
[f] Difference: $t = 11.28$, $P < 0.10$.

Table 38. (continued)

Males		
Juvenile		
Number banded	Percentage returned	Reference[b]
13[c]	0.0	1
		2
		3
		9
		2
132[c]	1.5	1
9[c]	0.0	1
		4
25	4.0	5
		9
12[c]	0.0	1
134	0.7	6
19[c]	0.0	1
		7
		9
		8

Of 107 bait-trapped flightless females (locals) that we banded on Quiver Creek, 1964–1969, only 17.8 percent (adjusted) were found nesting in subsequent years. An expected survival of 43 would result in a return of about 40 percent. Because of few natural cavities more than half probably nested elsewhere.

A substantial ingress of nonlocal hens nesting for the first time in nest houses was apparent at Mingo National Wildlife Refuge and Merced, California. Only 37–64 percent could be accounted for by the return of web-tagged birds (birds hatched on the area).

Many of the marked birds not found on nests until the second, third, or even fourth years probably represent individuals that nested in natural cavities near their natal sites. Heusmann's (1975) records of 15 non-nesting ducks shot or retrapped in years following marking suggest that new sites are utilized to a substantial degree. One duckling web-tagged at Nauvoo Slough was found for the first time three years later in a residential fireplace near its natal site, and one was found in a nest house three years later.

Yearling hens also appear to disperse farther from their natal breeding sites than do adult hens. Hansen (1971) found that 88 successful females moved 0.24 ± 0.47 kilometer (0.15 ± 0.29 mi); unsuccessful females returning in subsequent years moved 2.74 ± 2.46 kilometers (1.70 ± 1.53 mi); females renesting the same year moved 1.29 ± 0.80 kilometers (0.80 ± 0.5 mi); and web-tagged ducklings moved 2.08 ± 2.46 kilometers (1.29 ± 1.53 mi). A web-tagged duckling was found nesting 9.5 kilometers (5.9 mi) from its natal site, whereas the greatest distance for an unsuccessful adult was 7.9 kilometers (4.9 mi). Grice and Rogers (1965) reported that 23 percent of 113 flightless young were captured in later years outside of their natal areas; one was found 7.2 kilometers (4.5 mi) distant.

Stephen Simmons' study area near Merced, California, consists of eight grouped units of wood duck nest houses at intervals over an area 16 kilometers (10 mi) long and from 0.6 kilometer (0.4 mi) to 9.6 kilometers (6 mi) wide. The 101 web-tagged ducklings that Simmons found in subsequent years in nest houses on his study area moved an average of $1,575 \pm 2,121$ meters ($1,722 \pm 2,320$ yd). Although one-fourth (28.7 percent) nested within 91 meters (100 yd) of their natal nest sites, eight nested from 4.8 kilometers (3 mi) to 8 kilometers (5 mi) from their place of origin. Three others nested off the study area at 8 kilometers (5 mi) to 16 kilometers (10 mi) from where they hatched. Twenty of 45 adult hens (44.4 percent) returned to the same nest house; the others—all successful nesters—moved from 9.1 meters (10 yd) to 3.6 kilometers (2.25 mi), a mean of $785 \pm 1,373$ meters ($858 \pm 1,502$ yd). The yearlings dispersed to nest sites much farther from their natal homes than did their mothers, even those that pioneered new nest sites.

Hepp et al. (1989) noted that 60 percent of the wood duck yearlings returning to their Savannah River, South Carolina, study area dispersed to nesting sites with a mean distance of only 1.6 kilometers (1 mi) from their natal sites.

Rarely is one fortunate enough to obtain data from marked birds found outside study areas during the breeding season. H W Heusmann reported that a duckling web-tagged at Hopedale, Massachusetts, was found the following year near Boston, 37 kilometers (23 mi) to the north. Another duckling marked near Paxton, Massachusetts, was found nesting in a box at Sutton, 26 kilometers (16 mi) to the south. Ray Cunningham of St. Paul, Minnesota, released a banded wood duck hen he raised in 1966. The following March, she entered a residence, via a fireplace, in Eudora, Arkansas, 1,336 kilometers (830 mi) south of St. Paul. The date and site suggest that she was seeking a nesting place.

A flightless juvenile bait-trapped on Quiver Creek was found the following year nesting in a house 16 kilometers (10 mi) distant. A fledged juvenile female banded at the Chautauqua National Wildlife Refuge on July 31, 1980, entered the basement of a house in Havana, Illinois, via a furnace flue on May 5, 1981; she was about 11 kilometers (7 mi) from the banding site. A flightless juvenile (local) banded on the Chautauqua National Wildlife Refuge, August 6, 1963, was found nesting near Wapello, Iowa, on June 24, 1964, some 135 kilometers (84 mi) distant. A fledged female banded near Quincy, Illinois, on August 11, 1963, was found nesting near Keithsburg, Illinois, in 1964, 130 kilometers (81 mi) away.

Although these exceptional movements of yearlings are few, we do not have comparable information of adults moving such extensive distances. From the tentative evidence, we conclude that a moderate proportion of yearling females does extensive pioneering.

The enigma of why some yearling females pioneer and others show philopatry may lie in where they were located immediately prior to autumn migration, or at least that phase of the activity rhythm that results in autumn restlessness (Zugunruhe). Cursory evidence suggests that the location of a wood duck during the development of this particular phase of aging results in the imprinting of local environmental cues used for homing. Thus, immature females that remained in the natal area would return, while those that had dispersed to new and sometimes distant areas would seek to return to that particular location to breed rather than to their natal area.

Imprinting has been defined as a type of permanent knowledge acquired in the brief period that the brain is receptive to a particular stimulus. Welty (1979) reviewed some of the findings of imprinting pertaining to homing in birds.

At least some of the wood duck females that we raised for six to eight weeks at Havana, Illinois, and transported to Madison, Wisconsin, Medaryville, Indiana, and Wheaton, Illinois, where they were held prior to fall migration, returned to their respective release sites the following spring (McCabe 1947, Bellrose 1958). Thus, apparently the cues received during the later part of maturity motivated the return to displaced areas rather than to natal sites.

Among the immature female wood ducks banded during the summer in Alabama, we calculate that 43 percent of recoveries the first hunting season were in areas outside of Alabama (from data in Hayden and Pollock 1990). Thus, even in a state where there are no environmental reasons to migrate, a substantial number of females apparently

developed autumn restlessness (Zugunruhe) and moved distantly from their natal area. It is probably this segment of the immature females that becomes imprinted with environmental cues (sun, star constellations, landscape, Earth's magnetic field) at a distance from their natal area, resulting in the development of pioneering to new nesting areas.

Why some young become restless and leave their natal environs while others remain relatively sedentary may stem from genetic differences among ducklings in the same brood as well as between broods. Martinson and Hawkins (1968) found that mallard brood mates were killed at widely dispersed migration and winter areas, a suggestion that genetic differences might be responsible for differing behavior by brood mates as well as broods.

Effect of Mothers

We have no concrete evidence that mothers influence the nest site selection of their yearling daughters. The ability of birds to recognize kin has been demonstrated in the Japanese quail (Bateson 1982), the Florida scrub jay (Woolfenden and Fitzpatrick 1984), and other species of birds. The grouping of two or more wood duck pairs during the nest search period has caused us to speculate that mothers and daughters were involved.

In order to evaluate this hypothesis, we asked Stephen Simmons of Merced, California, to analyze his data on the distance that web-tagged yearlings nested from their natal sites in relation to the presence or absence of their mothers. His data showed that there was no significant difference in the pioneering distance of the two groups of yearlings: those whose mothers returned (n = 45) moved an average of 1,559 ± 2,003 meters (1,705 ± 2,190 yd); those whose mothers failed to return (n = 56) moved 1,450 ± 2,027 meters (1,586 ± 2,217 yd) from their natal sites.

At Nauvoo Slough, eight yearlings whose mothers returned nested 439 ± 317 meters (480 ± 347 yd) from their natal sites. All but one of the eight mothers nested in the same duplex used the previous year. Three yearlings whose mothers failed to return nested an average of 122 meters (133 yd) from natal sites. Again there appeared no association of nesting mothers and daughters. Thus, available data do not support our hypothesis of mother/daughter association during the breeding season.

There does, however, appear to be an association of yearlings with older females. At Nauvoo, we found that a large proportion of yearlings occupied a duplex compartment adjacent to one used by an adult (Figure 25).

Over the six years, the number of hens nesting in houses was almost equally divided between adults (245) and yearlings (232). Yet the occupancy of duplex houses was strongly skewed toward an adult in one compartment and a yearling in the other (Figure 25) rather than an adult/adult or yearling/yearling occupancy. Thus, there appeared to be a definite association between many unrelated yearlings and adult females at Nauvoo Slough.

The association of yearling females with breeding adult females has three possible roots. First, juveniles may affiliate with adult females on staging or wintering areas and return with these surrogate mothers to their nest locations and type of site selections. Second, juvenile females may home back to their natal areas independently of adults and then ally with adult females on the breeding area. Third, juvenile females may home to their previous fall dispersal site where imprinting of navigational cues occurred and there ally with indigenous adult females.

The return of yearling females to their premigration or natal areas independent of adults has been demonstrated through the release of hand-reared wood ducks in areas where there had been no previous breeding birds (McCabe 1947, Bellrose 1953, 1958, Doty and Kruse 1972).

McCabe (1947) and Bellrose (1958) reported on young wood ducks released after flight stage at Madison, Wisconsin, 322 kilometers (200 mi) from where they were hatched. Several returned to the Madison area the following year. Doty and Kruse (1972) released 132 young females, of which 100 survived to migrate from the Arrowwood National Wildlife Refuge in North Dakota, where no wood ducks had been known to breed in the previous 33 years. The translocated females were hatched at the Northern Prairie Research Center, 31 kilometers (19 mi) to the south. A minimum of 15 returned to nest at Arrowwood, where natural cavities were absent but 73 nest houses were available. On the basis of mean juvenile female survival in the northern region of the Mississippi Flyway, we would anticipate that 47 would have survived (see Chapter 18). Thus, substantial numbers of yearlings may have nested elsewhere.

In the spring of 1957, we artificially hatched wood duck eggs obtained from Louisiana. A small but unknown number escaped that May. Two females were found nesting in subsequent years at the Baldwin Beach unit, within 400 meters (437 yd) of the pen from which they escaped. One was found incubating on May 9, 1958; the other was not found until May 2, 1960. The latter bird returned an additional three years.

All the evidence from displaced releases of juvenile wood ducks further suggests that homing affinity is not transmitted directly but acquired by environmental cues imprinted some weeks after hatching. It appears that imprinting overwhelmed genetics in this instance.

Data in Table 39 show that 42–63 percent of the females nesting for the first time at Mingo National Wildlife Refuge in Missouri, Merced, California, and Nauvoo Slough, Illinois, did not originate in nest houses on these areas. Moreover, as local production declined at Mingo National Wildlife Refuge, recruitment of first breeders increased from outside the nest house units (Figure 26). This information suggests that some juvenile females on wintering grounds may "adopt" adult females prior to returning to their indigenous breeding areas. Other juveniles that are not attached to either their real or surrogate mother may return to their natal areas independent of adults, as apparently many unattached males do. Still others may return to their autumn location prior to migration.

Among 1,073 incubating hens captured on nests over 13 years, we found a yearly ratio of 1:1.06 banded adults to unbanded (ostensibly) yearlings, and a combined year ratio of 1:1.22 ± 0.52; standard deviation shows that two-thirds of the yearly range occurred between 1.74 and 0.70 yearlings per adult. Thus, the proportion of breeding adults and yearlings was remarkably balanced through the years. This points to the importance of yearling females affiliating with adults during nest selection and egg laying to enhance their breeding knowledge.

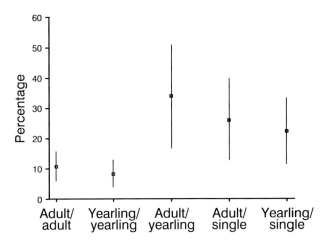

Figure 25. Mean percentage and 95-percent confidence limits of adult and yearling wood duck occupancy of compartments in duplex houses, 1985–90, Nauvoo Slough, Illinois, based on 167 adjacent-occupied compartments and 143 single-occupied compartments. F-statistic for percentage distribution: $F = 5.04$, $P < 0.01$.

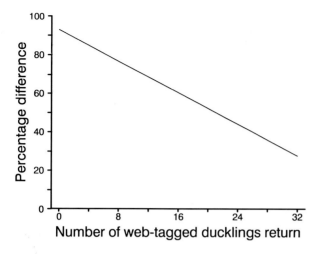

Figure 26. Effect of return of web-tagged wood duck ducklings on the difference in return rate between web-tagged females and hens nesting for the first time at Mingo National Wildlife Refuge, Missouri. The regression equation is: $y = -2.04x + 92.9$, $r = -0.99$, $P < 0.01$, $n = 4$.

HOMING OF MALES

Male wood ducks do not home to their natal or breeding areas to the degree exhibited by females. Grice and Rogers (1965) found that 9 percent of 210 trapped males returned in a subsequent year, compared with 48 percent of 217 trapped females. They also reported returns from outside the wintering ground migration corridor of males banded on their Massachusetts study area, but no similar flyway dispersion in females.

At Big Lake National Wildlife Refuge in Arkansas, Brown (1972a) found a return the following year of 15.2 percent of 46 web-tagged and leg-banded males, compared with 58.3 percent of 48 similarly web-tagged females. Leigh Fredrickson (in Palmer 1976) reported that, of 30 males captured in southeastern Missouri during spring, none had been previously banded, but of 30 trapped females, 57 percent had been previously marked there.

At late summer bait traps at Demopolis Lake in Alabama, Beshears (1969) recorded a subsequent-year recapture of 7.8 percent of 526 females, compared with 5.5 percent of 489 males. Robert Montgomery reported that wood ducks were captured in a decoy-type trap March through May 1984 at the Max McGraw Wildlife Foundation in Dundee, Illinois. Of 29 adult male wood ducks banded in 1984, 17.2 percent returned in 1985. Of 34 adult females banded in 1984, 35.3 percent returned in 1985.

From 253 hand-reared wood ducks of both sexes released during summer 1968 at Arrowwood National Wildlife Refuge in North Dakota, 9 (7.1 percent) females and 3 (2.4 percent) males were captured in bait traps during autumn 1969. During bait trapping in autumn 1970, 6 females and 4 males were still in evidence from the 1968 release.

Near St. Paul, Minnesota, Ray Cunningham released 75 banded wood duck drakes in 1966 and observed 1 that returned with a banded female in 1967. Of about 100 banded hens released, Cunningham observed that 30–35 returned in spring to glean grain at a feeding station.

Hunt and Smith (1966) observed two hand-reared, bill-marked wood duck drakes that returned to their propagation pen near La Crosse, Wisconsin, in 1961 and 1962—an observation that indicates that unmated males do return to their natal areas.

Exclusive of areas where no males or only one male returned in a subsequent year (Missouri and Minnesota), male-to-female return ratios varied from 1:1.2 to 1:5.3, with a mean of 1:2.7.

Available evidence points to male wood ducks returning to their former breeding or natal sites at higher rates than males of other species of dabbling ducks (Table 38). This relatively higher rate of homing for male woodies may reflect differences in the temporal pairing activity of the various species. Because wood ducks pair earlier in autumn than do other species of ducks, their hens may be expected to retain more indigenous drakes as mates upon their return in spring.

Lincoln (1934) was the first to point out that, among ducks, the female determines the place of nesting by returning to her natal area. Males that form pair bonds with hens on the wintering grounds are conditioned therefore to return to their mates' breeding areas. The more frequently that pair formation occurs on the wintering grounds, the less likely that drakes will return to their own natal areas.

Three behavior mechanisms apparently govern the relationship of male attachment to a natal or breeding site. First, males that pair with females in autumn on their mutual breeding areas return to the same breeding grounds the following spring when the pair bond remains intact. Second, males that did not mate on the wintering grounds return in all likelihood to their natal areas. Third, the majority of males appears to form fixed pair bonds on the wintering grounds and follow their mates back to their natal or previous breeding areas. Because these males follow their homing mates, only limited numbers of males return to their natal areas; most return to the natal site of the female.

Because wood ducks form pair bonds during late summer and early autumn to a greater degree than other game ducks, they are more likely to have a higher proportion of homing drakes than do species that form pairs later in the season. However, in view of the limited proportion of males that return, fall pair bonds must often be temporary and subject to termination by hunting.

Chapter 5

Population Status

In all probability, the wood duck was the most abundant duck in the United States east of the Mississippi River during the 19th century. Unfortunately, meaningful data on its relative abundance among ducks were not available until after the mid-20th century, by which time the wood duck population status had been drastically altered by human activities. Nevertheless, we do have numerous comments by early naturalists regarding its remarkable abundance in the East.

Phillips (1925) remarked that earlier ornithologists, notably Audubon, wrote about the great abundance of the wood duck throughout the eastern United States. Phillips (1925: 65) further stated: "Information as to the former abundance and present diminution of the Carolina [wood] Duck is so voluminous and writers are so generally in agreement as to its present and past status that only a few of the more important investigations need to be noted here. In general this species was exceedingly abundant all over the eastern United States until the early eighties."

Comments by ornithologists on the wood duck's status prior to 1900 in various regions of the United States are given in Table 40. They generally support Phillips' (1925) contention of great abundance until near the close of the 19th century. As late as the 1890s, Askins (1931) described a 32.2-kilometer (20 mi) horseback ride through the lowlands of Arkansas, with vivid portrayal of wood ducks constantly in sight, leading him to surmise that thousands were nesting in the swamp.

Even in the northern part of its breeding range, the wood duck was impressively abundant according to Hatch (1892: 51), who wrote about its arrival in Minnesota in March: "when they come, like the rains of the tropics, they pour in until every pool in the woodlands has been deluged with them." Writing on the bird life of Michigan, Barrows (1912: 88)

stated: "Twenty years ago it was one of the most abundant ducks in the state and nested commonly in the hollow trees bordering most of our streams and ponds." A market hunter at Faville Grove, Wisconsin, told Hawkins (1940) that, in the 1880s, wood ducks were the most abundant duck, with mallards a close second.

John Townsend, 1834–36, reported that wood ducks in the lower Columbia River region of Washington were "very plentiful here in the summer, but are never seen in the winter" (Jobanek and Marshall 1992).

Our premise that the wood duck was even more abundant than the mallard east of the Mississippi River also is based on the extensive quality of breeding habitat formerly available to this species. The deciduous forest was practically intact. Mature and overmature trees in the forests must have been commonplace, producing an abundance of natural cavities. These were augmented by cavities produced by ivory-billed and pileated woodpeckers. Almost every 19th-century naturalist mentions the use of woodpecker holes by wood ducks. Although the ivory-billed woodpecker was never numerous, the pileated woodpecker was apparently abundant throughout the eastern United States during the 19th century (Bent 1939) and undoubtedly provided an abundance of cavities that wood ducks could exploit for nest sites.

The high quality of stream water and wetlands during the 19th century would have supported a good invertebrate food base for egg production and brood survival. The myriad streams and other water areas formed a network of wetland areas through the deciduous forest that provided the wood duck with an extensive, quality breeding habitat. Early naturalists' reports indicated that the wood duck indeed must have exploited to its fullest the potential that this habitat provided.

Table 40. Comments by ornithologists prior to 1900 on the status of wood ducks.

Region	Status	Reference
Massachusetts	General decrease starting 1870	Phillips (1925)
Massachusetts	Abundant breeder near Ipswich, 1888	Phillips (1925)
Pennsylvania	Widely distributed	Warren (1890)
Hancock County, Ohio	Most numerous of waterfowl	Phillips (1925)
Buckeye Lake, Ohio	Most numerous of waterfowl; decline started 1890–1900	Trautman (1940)
Lake St. Marys, Ohio	Abundant prior to 1900	Clark (1955)
Michigan	Common breeder	Gibbs (1879)
Indiana	Resident; occurring in some numbers	Butler (1898)
Northeast Illinois	Rather common	Nelson (1876)
Faville Grove, Wisconsin	Most abundant duck, 1883	Hawkins (1940)
Madison, Wisconsin	Last known breeding, 1890	McCabe (1947)
Minnesota	Abundant breeder	Hatch (1892)
South Dakota	Common in southeast	Agersborg (1885)
Washington County, Oregon	Common resident	Anthony (1886)
Fort Klamath, Oregon	Common resident	Merrill (1888)
Salt Lake, Utah	Common resident in autumn	Allen (1872)
North Carolina	Nests abundantly	Coues (1871)
Kentucky	Common in summer	Pindar (1889)
Kansas	Common summer resident	Snow (1875)
Louisiana	Plentiful	McIlhenny (1897)
San Antonio, Texas	Fairly common	Dresser (1866)
San Antonio, Texas	Becoming rare	Attwater (1892)

Market hunting of waterfowl prevailed from the late 1800s to the enactment of the Migratory Bird Treaty Act in 1918. Wood ducks were sold in many eastern markets because they were delectable and readily shot. Day (1949) reported that one hunter along the Mississippi River shot 122 wood ducks before 9:00 a.m. The Christmas menu in 1879 of the Maxwell House in Nashville, Tennessee, epitomized the general availability of game. Note that wood duck, blue-winged teal, canvasback, and redhead were part of the game fare. *Photo courtesy of the Wildlife Management Institute.*

PERIOD OF DECLINE

The rosy status of the wood duck began to deteriorate in the late 1800s. Naturalists began to report a diminution of wood duck numbers that continued during the first two decades of the 20th century (Table 41). In some regions, particularly the Northeast, the decline was so rapid that fears were raised that the species would become extinct.

The most noteworthy comments were made by Grinnell, Forbush, and Cooke. An ardent hunter and conservationist, George Bird Grinnell was one of the first to raise the alarm. In his classic book on duck hunting, Grinnell (1901: 142) reported: "Being shot at all seasons of the year they are becoming very scarce and are likely to be exterminated before long." Forbush (1925: 228), an eminent New England ornithologist, wrote, "Spring shooting which went on merrily even after the ducks had laid their eggs brought the species nearly to extinction in the early part of the twentieth century." In his important report on distribution and migration of waterfowl, Cooke (1906: 8) stated, "So persistent has this duck [wood duck] been pursued that in some sections it has practically been exterminated. . . . As a result the wood duck is constantly diminishing in numbers, and soon is likely to be known only from books or by tradition."

Commenting on the status of the wood duck in California, Grinnell et al. (1918: 146) concluded, "From the foregoing evidence it can be seen that the wood duck although existing in California in considerable numbers in the early days, is now nearly extinct."

Table 41. Comments by ornithologists, 1900–20, on the status of wood ducks.

Region	Status	Reference
General	In danger of extermination	Fisher (1902)
General	Becoming scarce; likely to be exterminated	Grinnell (1901)
General	Practically exterminated in some areas	Cooke (1906)
Maine	Decline began about 1900	Brewster (1924)
Massachusetts	Rapidly growing rare early 1900s	Forbush (1912)
Massachusetts	104 of 117 observers reported a decrease, 1908	Phillips (1925)
Western New York	Holding its own, pre-1910	Eaton (1910)
New Jersey	Now rare	Stone (1909)
Pennsylvania and New Jersey	Almost exterminated; only few breed	Harlow (1918)
Western Maryland	Breeding but rare	Eifrig (1904)
Virginia	Not rare breeder	Bailey (1912)
North Carolina	May still nest	Pearson et al. (1919)
South Carolina	Locally nests in some numbers	Wayne (1910)
Big Cypress, Florida	Okaloacoochee Slough teemed with wood ducks	Kennard (1915)
Lake region of Ontario	Common summer resident	Macoun and Macoun (1909)
Michigan	Few breeding; becoming rare by 1904	Barrows (1912)
Ohio	Once common, now rare	Dawson (1903)
Wisconsin	Considerable numbers nest in north and central and few places in south, pre-1903	Kumlien and Hollister (1903)
Illinois	Common in parts of Illinois and Wisconsin; decreasing in numbers	Cory (1909)
Alabama	Once abundant, now uncommon	Howell (1924)
Missouri	Fairly common	Widmann (1907)
Southeast Missouri	Very common	Howell (1910)
Louisiana	Plentiful	Beyer et al. (1907)
Iowa	Almost ceased breeding, past 10 years	Anderson (1907)
Sanborn County, South Dakota	Only few breed	Visher (1913)
Fraser Delta, British Columbia	Regular breeder	Brooks (1918)
Puget Sound, Washington	Once common, now rare	Edson (1908)
Lower Columbia River, Washington	Common	Dawson and Bowles (1909)
Lower Columbia River, Washington	Rare by 1912	Gabrielson and Jewett (1970)
California	Once abundant/common; on verge of extinction by 1913	Dawson (1923)

Fortunately, the wood duck was not in such uniformly dire straits as these comments and others imply (Table 41). Other naturalists afield in the early 1900s reported more favorable populations. Beyer et al. (1907) stated that wood ducks were plentiful in Louisiana. Kennard (1915) found wood ducks "teeming" on Okaloacoochee Slough, Big Cypress, Florida. Howell (1910) reported that, in the lowlands of southeastern Missouri, wood ducks were very common. Widmann (1907) considered the wood duck to be fairly common throughout Missouri. Phillips (1925) was cognizant of the wood duck remaining common in areas of eastern Maine and fairly common in vast areas of the Carolinas, Georgia, Florida, and other Gulf states.

Regions where wood duck populations remained at viable levels during the depressed levels of the early decades of 1900 were: (1) areas difficult for human access—often swamps or river bottomlands subject to prolonged seasonal flooding; (2) regions of low human population where sport hunting and market hunting were at low levels; and (3) areas where populations of wood ducks were not fragmented by small or isolated habitats that made the ducks highly vulnerable to hunters. Thus, in certain regions of the Deep South, because of lower hunter pressure and more extensive wooded wetlands, woodies were able to maintain higher populations than elsewhere.

RESPONSES TO POPULATION DECLINE

By World War I, wood ducks were at such low levels over much of their range as to evoke national concern. The Weeks-McLean Bill, placing custody of migratory birds with the federal government and prohibiting hunting of wood ducks, became a law on March 4, 1913. No provision for its implementation was made until the Migratory Bird Treaty Act with Canada was ratified on July 3, 1918. This treaty resulted in a nationwide closed season on wood ducks that lasted until 1941, when 14 states in the Atlantic and Mississippi flyways were permitted one wood duck in the bag and possession.

Among all species of waterfowl, the wood duck was the only game duck singled out for complete protection by the Migratory Bird Treaty Act (see Lawyer 1919). More than any other species, it had suffered from market hunting and open seasons that extended in most states from September to April. Prior to 1918, no other species was exposed more to hunting than was the wood duck because its range—largely confined to areas populated by humans—made it vulnerable for longer periods

than species that bred in more sparsely inhabited areas of Canada.

Some states had appreciated the problem that wood ducks faced from overhunting. According to Reeves (1966), Louisiana closed the season on wood ducks for five years in 1904. Five states—Maine, New Hampshire, Vermont, Massachusetts, and South Carolina—prohibited the hunting of wood ducks in 1911. They were followed a year later by Connecticut, New York, and New Jersey, by Rhode Island, Pennsylvania, West Virginia, Ohio, Indiana, and Wisconsin in 1913, by Michigan, Iowa, Illinois, Kansas, Washington, Oregon, and California in 1914, and by Alabama in 1916.

Protection that the wood duck began to receive from states during the second decade of the 1900s, combined with federal protection that followed, resulted in a favorable population response. The recovery of the wood duck rivals that of beaver, white-tailed deer, pronghorn, and wild turkey.

The comeback of the wood duck was dutifully noted by ornithologists (Table 42). Griscom (1948), a most respected ornithologist, stated that populations in New England began to increase by 1919. In writing about birds in Massachusetts, Forbush (1925: 228) observed, "now at last its numbers are beginning to increase." The rate of the comeback differed in many areas, probably depending on illegal kill, the potential of the breeding habitat, and the nearest source of breeding birds.

We were able to obtain information on population status during the 1940s and early 1950s from inquiries we sent to ornithologists and wildlife biologists (Table 43). Respondents generally reported increases over decreases in most areas within the eastern flyways from pre-1942 through 1951. In 1952, respondents in the Mississippi Flyway reported that, for the first time, wood ducks had decreased in more areas than they had increased. Waterfowl biologists in six states of the Mississippi Flyway reported a decrease in 1952 and 1953; one state reported an increase in both years (Bellrose 1955).

Because of an apparent setback in the previous favorable population trend, the Mississippi Flyway Council recommended a closed season on wood ducks in 1954 and again in 1956. One wood duck in the bag was permitted in flyway regulations in 1957 and 1958, but eight states in 1957 and nine states in 1958 kept the season closed (Reeves 1966).

On the basis of stream surveys, general observations, banding, and nest house use, state waterfowl biologists in the Mississippi Flyway considered that the status of the wood duck had improved sufficiently by 1962 to permit a daily bag limit of two woodies.

Table 42. Comments by ornithologists, 1920–45, on the status of wood ducks.

Region	Status	Reference
General	Increased greatly, especially in Mississippi Valley	Phillips and Lincoln (1930)
New England	Protection showed results by 1919; reached peak numbers in 1938; hurricane resulted in decline	Griscom (1948)
Massachusetts	Now increasing	Forbush (1925)
Winous Point, Ohio	Most abundant duck, summer 1930	Cristy (1931)
Milwaukee, Wisconsin	Presently in dozens or hundreds; previously rare	Gromme (1930)
Minnesota	Apparently increased	Roberts (1932)
California	Marked increase past few years	California Fish and Game (1930)
North Carolina	Increased numbers past 20 years	Pearson et al. (1942)

According to Griscom (1948), the upward trend of wood ducks in Massachusetts and the Northeast ended with the 1938 hurricane, which destroyed countless natural cavities. He considered that numbers in 1948 were 60 percent below those of 1938. Apparently for this reason, Massachusetts closed the season on wood duck hunting from 1941 through 1950. Two other Atlantic Flyway states also had closed seasons on wood ducks—West Virginia in 1947–1953 and New Jersey in 1947 and 1948.

Although wood duck populations had partially recovered from their low of the early 1900s, they had not reached optimum levels by the 1950s. What had been achieved in population recovery was due solely to limiting the harvest to reasonable levels. The recovery of wood duck populations had been so rapid that gradually improving forest resources could not have accounted for it.

Table 43. Changing status of wood duck populations, based on responses to inquiries of ornithologists and wildlife managers.

Years	Area	Status[a] Increase		Decrease		Stable	
Pre-1943	Atlantic Flyway	79	(66)	8	(7)	33	(27)
	Mississippi Flyway	66	(62)	10	(9)	30	(29)
	Central Flyway	7	(87)	0	(0)	1	(13)
	Pacific Flyway	7	(59)	1	(8)	4	(33)
1942–46	Wisconsin	46	(42)	31	(28)	32	(30)
	Indiana	23	(48)	12	(25)	13	(27)
1946–49	Atlantic Flyway	9	(30)	3	(10)	18	(60)
	Mississippi Flyway	20	(41)	13	(26)	16	(33)
	Central Flyway	3	(43)	0	(0)	4	(57)
	Pacific Flyway	1	(7)	3	(20)	11	(73)
1949–50	Atlantic Flyway	13	(34)	4	(13)	20	(53)
	Mississippi Flyway	27	(47)	13	(22)	18	(31)
	Central Flyway	6	(67)	0	(0)	3	(33)
	Pacific Flyway	1	(6)	3	(18)	13	(76)
1950–51	Atlantic Flyway	12	(31)	6	(16)	20	(53)
	Mississippi Flyway	27	(42)	12	(18)	26	(40)
	Central Flyway	3	(27)	0	(0)	8	(73)
	Pacific Flyway	2	(10)	4	(20)	14	(70)
1951–52	Atlantic Flyway	14	(39)	3	(8)	19	(53)
	Mississippi Flyway	12	(18)	30	(44)	26	(38)
	Central Flyway	3	(30)	0	(0)	7	(70)
	Pacific Flyway	2	(10)	8	(38)	11	(52)

[a] Percentage in parentheses.

Market gunning, unregulated sport hunting, semiautomatic shotguns, and spring hunting were reasons given for the decline of wood ducks in the late 1800s and early 1900s. Ornithologists and sportsmen alike feared that the species was rapidly nearing extinction, but records now show that healthy populations remained in certain areas away from the "profitable" reach of gunners. Nevertheless, the woodie was particularly vulnerable to spring hunting, since it was the foremost nesting species in the continental United States. When protection came in the early 1900s, first by many individual states and then by ratification in 1918 of the Migratory Bird Treaty Act, the wood duck was the only game duck (eiders also were similarly protected, but were not considered "game" ducks) to be accorded complete protection from harvest—protection that continued until 1941. This East Coast hunter shown during the spring of 1890 has bagged a drake woodie and a drake blue-winged teal. While the waterfowler's attire has not changed much in the century since then, the oarlocks and the double-barrelled shotgun with external hammers evidence a sport hunt of early vintage. *Photo courtesy of the Library of Congress.*

As discussed in Chapter 3 on wood duck habitat, during the past four decades there has been a widespread increase in the abundance and size of deciduous trees, a dramatic increase in beaver ponds, and a proliferation of farm ponds. However, these improvements in habitat for wood ducks were offset by the draining and clearing of bottomland forests, particularly in the Mississippi Alluvial Plain. Although benefited by improving habitat conditions in many regions of the United States, wood ducks increased at rates greater than those warranted by a gradual change in the environment.

That the wood duck still had not achieved an optimum population in all breeding habitats by the 1950s is shown by events that followed in the next three decades.

HARVEST AND BAND
RECOVERY DATA

Annual computed harvest related to band re-covery rates provides the only solid data available to determine with some degree of reliability the yearly status of the wood duck within a state or a flyway. Annual direct (recovered the same fiscal year as banded) recovery rates provide an index to the pro-portion of the population harvested by hunters. Not all hunters report bands, but the proportion that does is believed to be relatively constant from year to year. Within the framework of band recovery rates, the computed kill furnishes information on the yearly status of the wood duck. The unfortunate aspect of this method is the year delay in accumu-lating the information.

Suitable annual harvest data for all waterfowl species have been made available on a nationwide basis by the U.S. Fish and Wildlife Service since 1959. The wood duck data analyzed on a regression basis show a yearly increase in kill in all flyways except the Pacific (Figure 27). The yearly increment in flyway harvest, 1960 through 1990, amounted to 11,721 in the Mississippi, 7,021 in the Atlantic, 1,391 in the Central, and minus 47 in the Pacific Flyway. The high correlation coefficient (r) for the three flyways east of the Rocky Mountains points to a fluctuation in yearly harvest that was close to the indicated trend line, especially through 1984 (Figure 27). After 1984, the harvest of wood ducks declined appreciably in the Atlantic and Mississippi flyways (Figure 27), partly the result of fewer hunters. For those afield, the number of days hunted remained

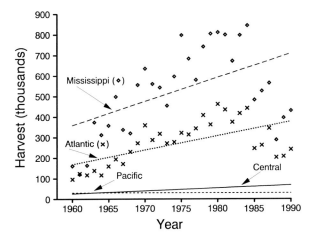

Figure 27. Linear regression of wood duck harvest in each of the four flyways, 1959–90. The regression equa-tions for the Mississippi, Atlantic, Central, and Pacific flyways, respectively, are: y = 140,700 + 28,900x, r² = 0.88; y = 70,900 + 15,000x, r² = 0.91; y = 8,611 + 2,635x, r² = 0.72; and y = 23,030 + 638x, r² = 0.29.

remarkably similar (Table 44). In the Pacific Flyway, the wood duck harvest oscillated through the years without a significant trend.

Harvest data alone only inform us that hunters took an increasingly large number of wood ducks as the years passed. The increased harvest might have resulted from an increase in the proportion of wood ducks harvested. However, regression of band re-covery rates for several regions of the Atlantic and Mississippi flyways, 1959–1985, shows only slight increases in recovery rates over time in four of the five regions, and these were not significant (Table 45). The only significant trend was found in the northern region of the Atlantic Flyway, where a decline in recovery rates occurred. Although har-vest rates have varied from year to year, hunters apparently have not taken an increasingly larger proportion of autumn wood duck populations.

By using yearly band recovery rates (x 3.12 for unreported bands) and harvest data, we have calcu-lated the wood duck's yearly autumn populations for regions of the two flyways. This justification for multiplying band recoveries by 3.12 to account for unreported bands is based on recent studies on mallards by the U.S. Fish and Wildlife Service, in which return rates by hunters who received mone-tary compensation were compared with standard band return rates. In comparison with reward re-turns, only 32 percent of the standard bands taken were reported (Nichols et al. 1991). Geis and At-wood (1961) found that the failure rates of hunters to report mallard and wood duck bands were similar.

We examined the rate of increase in autumn populations of wood ducks, 1959–1986, for the vari-ous regions of the Mississippi and Atlantic flyways (figures 28–31) and found a remarkably steady population growth in all regions. Because of the influx of wood ducks from the north, southern re-gions had considerably larger autumn populations than did more northern areas. Nevertheless, the yearly trends among regions are reasonably com-parable because of the large component of provin-cial birds in each region's population (see Chapter 2 for calculated state breeding population numbers).

Mississippi Flyway wood duck populations in-creased at the rate of 9.2 percent per year in the northern region 12.1 percent in the central region, and 15.7 percent in the southern region. Autumn populations in the Atlantic Flyway increased at an annual rate of 7.1 percent in the northern region and 8.7 percent in the southern region.

The power curve regressions compared with the linear regressions (figures 28–31) suggest that the rate of increase in all regions was the greatest in the 1960s, leveled off in the 1970s, and weakened in the 1980s.

Table 44. Seasonal harvest of wood ducks per duck hunter and day hunted during blocks of five years, 1961–90.*

Period	Atlantic Flyway		Mississippi Flyway	
	Harvest/Hunter[a]	Days hunted[b]	Harvest/hunter[c]	Days hunted[d]
1961–65				
Mean	0.6399	4.74	0.5575	6.38
S.D.	0.0663	0.236	0.1983	0.595
C.V.	10.36	4.98	35.57	9.33
1966–70				
Mean	0.7484	5.34	0.6570	7.17
S.D.	0.1168	0.339	0.1452	0.668
C.V.	15.61	6.35	22.10	9.32
1971–75				
Mean	0.7868	6.02	0.7139	8.07
S.D.	0.0967	0.268	0.2117	0.235
C.V.	12.29	4.45	29.65	2.91
1976–80				
Mean	1.0854	6.53	1.0216	8.69
S.D.	0.1968	0.142	0.1702	0.377
C.V.	18.13	2.17	16.66	4.34
1981–85				
Mean	1.2285	6.43	1.2011	8.78
S.D.	0.2209	0.308	0.2038	0.434
C.V.	17.98	4.79	16.97	4.94
1986–90				
Mean	0.9854	5.72	0.8951	7.83
S.D.	0.1770	0.295	0.1328	0.419
C.V.	17.96	5.16	14.84	5.35

* One-way analysis of variance ($v_1 = 5$, $v_2 = 24$).
[a] $F = 10.35$, $P < 0.01$.
[b] $F = 13.34$. $P < 0.01$.
[c] $F = 9.14$, $P < 0.01$.
[d] $F = 18.71$, $P < 0.01$.
Significant difference (3.90 at 1-percent level of chance) in five-year block variations. As regulations reduced harvest, numbers of hunters declined, but surprisingly, days hunted each season remained relatively flat.

The effect of a steady increase in the wood duck population, 1961–1985, is reflected in an increasingly successful season harvest for each active hunter in the Atlantic and Mississippi flyways. However, the season harvest per hunter declined in both flyways during 1986–1990.

As shown by the percentage of coefficient of variation, the block changes in hunter harvest were

Table 45. Yearly trend in calculated wood duck band recovery rates for regions of the Atlantic and Mississippi flyways, 1959–85.

Flyway	Region	n	r	P	Intercept	Yearly slope	Percentage	
							1959	1985
Atlantic	North	25	−0.51	<0.01	7.63	−0.066	7.56	5.92
	South	24	0.28	>0.10	3.53	0.040	3.57	4.57
Mississippi	North	25	0.15	>0.10	5.95	0.356	5.99	6.88
	Central	25	0.21	>0.10	5.10	0.031	5.14	5.92
	South	24	0.04	>0.10	3.51	0.006	3.52	3.67

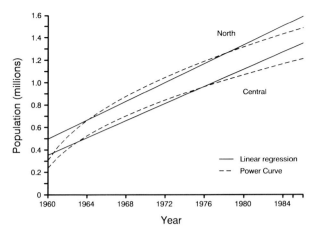

Figure 28. Linear and power curve regressions of calculated autumn populations of wood ducks in the north and central regions of the Mississippi Flyway, 1960–86. The linear and power curve regressions from the northern and central regions are: $y = 455,389 + 41,920x$, $r^2 = 0.79$; $y = 306,272$ $(x^{0.479})$, $r = 0.95$; $y = 316,401 + 38,205x$, $r^2 = 0.95$; and $y = 237,004$ $(x^{0.495})$, $r^2 = 0.85$, respectively.

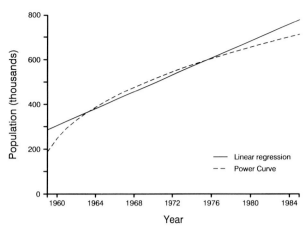

Figure 30. Linear and power curve regression of calculated autumn populations of wood ducks in the northern region of the Atlantic Flyway, 1962–85. The linear and power curve equations are: $y = 267,208 + 18,878x$, $r^2 = 0.64$; and $y = 187,400$ $(x^{0.405})$, $r^2 = 0.66$, respectively.

several times greater than the block changes in the days hunted per season. Thus, the seasonal harvest per hunter was not entirely the result of more days hunted. For example, on a daily bag basis, the harvest of wood ducks per hunter declined from 0.190 ± 0.0293 in 1981–1985 to 0.172 ± 0.0248 in 1986–1990 in the Atlantic Flyway, and from 0.137 ± 0.0216 to 0.114 ± 0.0123 in the Mississippi Flyway during the same periods.

Thus the reduced seasonal harvest per hunter, 1986–1990, suggests that the prolonged increase in wood duck populations has "bottomed out."

The trend in state harvest of wood ducks, 1959–1987, in the Mississippi and Atlantic flyways (tables 46 and 47) provides data on those flyway states where populations have prospered most. In those Mississippi Flyway states on the western margin of the flyway – Minnesota, Iowa, Missouri, Arkansas, and Louisiana – the increase in harvest has been higher than the flyway mean (Table 46). The more eastern states in the Mississippi Flyway – Michigan, Indiana, Ohio, and Alabama – have had the lowest annual rates of increase. Although Mississippi is in neither the western nor eastern sector

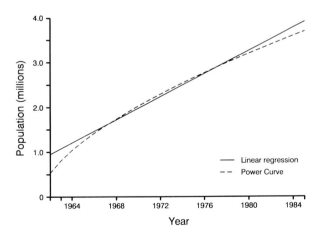

Figure 29. Linear and power curve regression of calculated autumn populations of wood ducks in the southern region of the Mississippi Flyway, 1962–85. The linear and power curve equations are: $y = 819,532 + 128,672x$, $r^2 = 0.69$; and $y = 529,339$ $(x^{0.611})$, $r^2 = 0.81$, respectively.

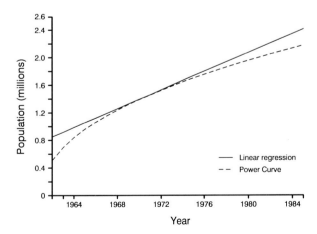

Figure 31. Linear and power curve regression of calculated autumn populations of wood ducks in the southern region of the Atlantic Flyway, 1959–85. The linear and power curve equations are: $y = 781,691 + 68,096x$, $r^2 = 0.66$; and $y = 506,800$ $(x^{0.459})$, $r^2 = 0.79$.

Table 46. Linear regression coefficients and calculated wood duck harvest in states of the Mississippi Flyway and Texas, 1959–87.

State	r^2	Intercept	Slope	Number harvested 1959	Number harvested 1987	Annual percentage of increase
Minnesota	0.602	36,230	4,033	40,270	153,375	9.69
Wisconsin	0.284	43,700	1,954	45,738	100,462	4.13
Michigan	0.256	18,340	799	19,143	41,526	4.03
Iowa	0.511	12,140	1,656	13,791	60,168	11.60
Illinois	0.472	16,330	1,364	17,695	55,877	7.44
Indiana	0.236	5,930	330	6,256	15,489	5.09
Ohio	0.051	21,250	139	21,385	25,277	0.63
Missouri	0.432	3,800	773	4,577	26,216	16.30
Kentucky	0.868[a]	130	184	151	26,183	
Tennessee	0.578	−220[b]	901	679	25,914	
Arkansas	0.359	13,080	1,445	14,524	54,972	9.60
Mississippi	0.501	9,110	1,652	10,768	57,012	14.81
Alabama	0.262	9,070	581	9,648	25,914	5.81
Louisiana	0.587	28,250	5,509	33,758	188,000	15.76
Entire Flyway	0.660	213,310	21,330	234,650	831,990	8.78
Texas	0.478	9,210	1,350	10,560	48,370	12.35

[a] Power curve regression was used for Kentucky.
[b] Negative intercept caused by low harvest in early years followed by greatly increased levels in later years.

of the flyway, it has had a remarkable yearly increment in its wood duck harvest (Table 46). An appreciable proportion of wood ducks originating in the Mississippi Flyway winter in Texas (see Chapter 4), where the percentage increase has been similar to that of the western sector of the Mississippi Flyway.

In the Atlantic Flyway, appreciable gains in the trends of the annual wood duck harvest have occurred in New Jersey, West Virginia, North Carolina, South Carolina, and Georgia (Table 47), with a nominal yearly increase experienced in Maine, Vermont, New Hampshire, Connecticut, and Pennsyl-

Table 47. Linear regression coefficients and calculated wood duck harvest in states of the Atlantic Flyway, 1959–87.[a]

State	r^2	Intercept	Slope	Number harvested 1959	Number harvested 1987	Annual percentage of increase
Maine	0.598	3,460	267	3,731	11,214	6.92
Vermont	0.265	3,480	131	3,609	7,281	3.51
New Hampshire	0.479	2,620	250	2,868	9,870	8.02
Massachusetts	0.073	5,070	94	5,160	7,798	1.76
Connecticut	0.346	1,530	137	1,671	5,494	7.89
New York	0.008	34,660	165	34,828	39,448	0.46
Pennsylvania	0.449	14,120	689	14,811	34,113	4.49
New Jersey	0.517	3,110	408	3,518	14,939	11.19
West Virginia	0.448	710	108	815	3,840	12.80
Delaware	0.286	−50[b]	94	45	2,673	
Maryland	0.480	−670[b]	311	−359	8,359	
Virginia	0.755	−4,110[b]	1,343	−2,768	34,838	
North Carolina	0.724	−2,930[b]	2,664	5,599	80,195	45.94
South Carolina	0.591	16,530	1,984	18,519	74,074	10.34
Georgia	0.624	5,930	1,825	7,754	58,861	22.73
Florida	0.048	21,200	270	21,469	29,041	1.22
Entire Flyway	0.684	107,890	11,110	119,000	430,000	9.01

[a] Rhode Island data are too small and inconsistent to be meaningful.
[b] Negative intercept caused by low harvest in early years followed by greatly increased levels in later years.

vania. Exceptionally low rates of increase in harvest were recorded in Massachusetts, New York, and Florida. Except for Florida, the greatest gains have been associated with the southeastern states and West Virginia.

Further information pertinent to an evaluation

of the wood duck's geographic expansion can be derived by comparing 10-year sets of harvest data for groups of counties (tables 48 and 49). Each of the four 10-year data sets has a 5-year overlap with the subsequent data set (Carney et al. 1975, 1978, 1983, S. M. Carney personal communication: 1988).

Table 48. Yearly percentage of change in wood duck harvest by regions in four states in the Mississippi Flyway during four (five-year overlap) time frames: 1961–70, 1966–75, 1971–80, 1976–85.

State and region	Base period	Percentage of yearly rate of change from base period		
		1966–75	1971–80	1976–85
Minnesota				
Northwestern	1961–70	18.9	16.8	37.2
	1966–75		7.5	4.8
	1971–80			1.5
Southwestern	1961–70	9.2	7.9	10.5
	1966–75		4.5	7.6
	1971–80			8.8
Northeastern	1961–70	14.8	10.8	5.8
	1966–75		3.9	0.8
	1971–80			−2.0
Central	1961–70	9.1	6.0	5.8
	1966–75		1.9	2.8
	1971–80			1.4
Southeastern	1961–70	5.1	3.5	2.9
	1966–75		1.5	1.5
	1971–80			1.4
Wisconsin				
Northern	1961–70	5.2	3.8	4.1
	1966–75		1.9	2.9
	1971–80			3.5
Western	1961–70	11.1	6.2	1.8
	1966–75		0.9	−3.6
	1971–80			−4.2
Eastern	1961–70	11.9	8.5	4.4
	1966–75		3.2	−0.8
	1971–80			−2.1
Michigan				
Northern	1961–70	5.2	9.1	12.3
	1966–75		10.2	12.5
	1971–80			9.8
Central	1961–70	8.2	9.6	6.3
	1966–75		7.8	3.8
	1971–80			−0.2
Southern	1961–70	12.9	6.8	3.2
	1966–75		0.4	−1.0
	1971–80			−2.4
Iowa				
Western	1961–70	16.8	18.8	13.8
	1966–75		11.4	6.7
	1971–80			1.2
Eastern	1961–70	12.8	12.0	7.8
	1966–75		6.7	3.3
	1971–80			−0.3

Table 49. Yearly percentage of change in wood duck harvest by regions in four states in the Atlantic Flyway during four (five-year overlap) time frames: 1961–70, 1966–75, 1971–80, 1976–85.

State and region	Base period	Percentage of yearly rate of change from base period		
		1966–75	1971–80	1976–85
Virginia				
Western	1961–70	−5.2	136.7	144.6
	1966–75		349.0	275.5
	1971–80			10.9
Central	1961–70	1.2	10.0	15.8
	1966–75		17.6	21.7
	1971–80			13.8
Eastern	1961–70	6.4	15.4	27.5
	1966–75		18.5	28.9
	1971–80			20.4
North Carolina				
Western	1961–70	5.5	19.2	20.0
	1966–75		25.9	21.4
	1971–80			7.3
Central and southeastern	1961–70	11.5	15.4	17.2
	1966–75		12.2	12.7
	1971–80			8.2
Northeastern	1961–70	10.2	12.3	11.5
	1966–75		9.5	8.0
	1971–80			4.4
South Carolina				
Western	1961–70	10.0	18.5	23.4
	1966–75		17.9	20.0
	1971–80			11.7
Northcentral and northeastern	1961–70	10.0	7.3	4.9
	1966–75		3.1	1.6
	1971–80			0.02
Southcentral and southeastern	1961–70	12.9	1.6	11.1
	1966–75		3.3	6.2
	1971–80			7.9
Georgia				
Northern	1961–70	47.9	43.7	38.1
	1966–75		11.6	9.8
	1971–80			5.0
Southwestern	1961–70	9.6	8.5	7.6
	1966–75		5.1	4.5
	1971–80			3.0
Southeastern	1961–70	16.9	22.2	17.3
	1966–75		14.9	9.5
	1971–80			2.3

Harvest data from Minnesota show that the greatest increases, 1966–1985, occurred in the northwestern and southwestern sectors (Table 48). In Wisconsin, the largest rate of increase was in the northern sector, followed by the eastern. The western, embracing the Mississippi River, had the lowest rate of increase. Michigan had the highest rate of increase in the northern sector, a much lower rate in the central, and the lowest in the southern. Of the two regions of Iowa, the western sector had a much larger rate of increase than did the eastern, which includes the Mississippi River. Thus, the Mississippi River region, which has by far the best wood duck habitat in the three-state area of Minnesota, Wisconsin, and Iowa, had the lowest rate of harvest increase.

EXPLOITING HABITATS
OF SECONDARY QUALITY

The greater increases in the harvest rates of the northern regions of the three Great Lakes states as well as the western regions of Minnesota and Iowa (Table 48) indicate that, during 1961–1985, the wood duck experienced its greatest population increase in habitats of marginal quality. These regions are marked by a lessening of the influence of the deciduous forest. In the northern regions, the coniferous forest assumes an increasing proportion of land coverage; in the western regions, the prairie does. These regions do not provide the abundance of natural cavities found in the more southerly and easterly areas of the deciduous forest biome, and the woods are more fragmented. In many peripheral regions, streams do not provide as favorable a brood habitat as they do in the other areas.

Wood duck harvest in the eastern states of the Great Plains showed an increasing rate during the first two periods (Table 50). In the third period, 1976–1985, the rate of harvest continued to be slightly higher in South Dakota, Nebraska, and Texas. In Kansas and Oklahoma, however, the harvest rate declined (Table 50).

The rate of increase in South Dakota and Nebraska was comparable to the exceptional increase recorded in southwestern Minnesota and western Iowa and provides further evidence that, during 1966–1985, wood duck populations were expanding into prairie stream habitats. Although prairie streams and wetlands do not provide the cavities found in the deciduous forest biome, the food base in marshes and sluggish streams may be exceptional. Most prairie streams south of Nebraska, however, have characteristics that make for poor brood survival, including high banks, turbid waters, and a paucity of riparian cover.

Even within the heart of the wood duck breeding range, there were areas devoid of or underpopulated by wood ducks that took time for pioneering birds to fill. An example was provided by Hugh Bateman, biologist and administrator with the Louisiana Wildlife and Fisheries Commission. Since the late 1960s, he has observed small streams in the pine woods of central Louisiana where no breeding wood ducks were found. Then a few were observed, followed by increasing numbers as the years passed.

Likewise, we know of areas in the Chicago region that once were devoid of woodies but now support modest numbers of breeding birds. Similarly, many ditches and small streams in central Illinois—where woodies were absent in the 1940s—had small breeding numbers in the 1970s.

Table 50. Yearly percentage of change in wood duck harvest in four states in the Central Flyway during four (five-year overlap) time frames: 1961–70, 1966–75, 1971–80, 1976–85.

| State | Base period | Percentage of yearly rate of change from base period | | |
		1966–75	1971–80	1976–85
South Dakota	1961–70	6.8	10.4	10.4
	1966–75		10.4	9.1
	1971–80			5.1
Nebraska	1961–70	12.1	14.8	17.8
	1966–75		10.8	12.8
	1971–80			9.6
Kansas	1961–70	11.9	10.4	4.6
	1966–75		5.5	0.6
	1971–80			−4.0
Oklahoma	1961–70	18.6	7.0	2.8
	1966–75		−2.8	−3.7
	1971–80			−4.0
Texas	1961–70	5.6	6.9	6.3
	1966–75		6.4	5.3
	1971–80			3.1

Data in Table 49 indicate that the mountain regions of Virginia, North and South Carolina, and Georgia experienced the greatest increase in rate of wood duck harvest in recent years. These increases imply that wood duck populations are expanding at a faster rate in the streams of and adjacent to the Appalachian Mountains than they are in the Piedmont and Coastal Plain. Because streams in the more rugged mountain terrain fall faster, they are lower in quality for wood ducks than those in the lower provinces, where there also are more swamps and marshes. Consequently, much of the increase of wood ducks in the southeastern states and in West Virginia has resulted from the exploitation of habitats of secondary quality. This pattern suggests that wood duck expansion in the optimum habitats of these states occurred earlier, and that the birds currently are approaching a limit to their carrying capacity.

Data from the western sectors of the Mississippi Flyway also suggest that the increased rate of wood duck harvest in prairie areas is due to the birds' ability to exploit new and underpopulated habitats. Optimum habitats, as exemplified by those along the Mississippi River, apparently have reached the point of full occupancy.

The poorer quality of breeding habitat in marginal areas of the wood duck's range results in a lower productivity potential than does the better-quality habitat. However, as the more optimum habitats approach a point of occupancy saturation, the wood duck's reproductive rate ceases to rise and the woodies occupying underpopulated secondary habitats have the greater potential for increase.

It has taken the wood duck 60 years to exploit its available habitats and reach the population levels evident in the mid-1980s. Our conception of the scenario that produced these dramatic results follows. During the early 1900s, wood ducks were largely extirpated from marginal habitats where breeding pairs were dispersed and productivity was nominal. In wetland habitats where nesting sites were minimal and where cover and food for broods were minimal, productivity was insufficient to support a population that was being overharvested by hunters. The more marginal the breeding conditions, the earlier a given wetland became bereft of breeding birds.

Water areas that might be considered marginal, yet were the most extensive, include the network of streams and rivers of the deciduous forest. Wood ducks inhabiting streams probably were the most vulnerable to hunting losses because they were often the only ducks in those habitats. These wood ducks were available to farm folk, small-town Nimrods, and urbanites who did not have to travel a

great deal or expend much effort to reach the birds. The wood ducks least likely to be decimated were those inhabiting extensive swamps and overflow hardwood bottomlands, particularly in the South.

Wetland areas on the western and northern periphery of the deciduous forest were marginal because of relatively limited food resources and adverse climatic conditions. Marginal habitats in juxtaposition to better habitats probably were the first to be reoccupied as the wood duck started its comeback. Because of strong homing by adult and yearling wood duck females, pioneering into vacant habitats may have been limited. Consequently, habitats that were either ecologically or geographically removed from centers of production tended to be reoccupied on a time scale related to the distance and degree of isolation. The time required to reach habitat saturation probably was dependent on the yearly increment of a given wood duck population. Regional woodie populations with the highest surplus numbers (where yearly productivity exceeded mortality) therefore provided the birds capable of filling underpopulated habitats and expanding into vacant ones.

The 60 years it has taken the wood duck to reach or nearly reach habitat saturation suggest that surpluses were low and pioneering slow. The recovery of the wood duck might have proceeded at a faster rate if the hunting season had remained closed beyond 1941. Although the harvest apparently did not affect survival on an extensive scale, it may have curtailed the exploitation of new breeding habitat by reducing the abundance of pioneering birds.

The time it has taken the wood duck to reoccupy and exploit its former range suggests that hunting regulations that would permit a still larger proportion of the population to be harvested should be carefully considered. Certainly, populations in marginal habitats and peripheral areas would not cope successfully with an increase in harvest rates.

The wood duck has come back more than Bellrose (1953: 43) anticipated when he wrote, "The woodie came back, part way at least, during the 1920s and 1930s because it was protected from shooting, and probably also because raccoon populations were low. Whether this duck will return to the ranks of the endangered species will, of course, depend upon the balance between productivity and mortality." As future events revealed, Bellrose (1953) was overly concerned and failed to recognize the remarkable productivity of the species and the degree to which habitats were underpopulated. Thirty-five years later, we believe that wood ducks in better habitats have reached or are approaching maximum population levels. Filling in or expanding into vacant or underpopulated habitat continues but at reduced rates. Population increases are lessening (figures 28–31), yet the wood duck evidently has recovered from the excessive kills of the past and reached population levels that are increasingly constrained by the availability and quality of habitat.

Chapter 6

Courtship and Mating System

We believe that wood ducks, like most other species of waterfowl, are basically monogamous. Pair bonds, however, seldom persist from one reproductive season to the next, and surviving pair members usually establish new bonds with different birds each year. Although we have seen paired wood ducks together through the entire summer on our central Illinois study areas, the low return rate of male wood ducks to their natal areas (see Chapter 4) suggests that those cases where bonds remained intact from one season to the next are exceptional and probably of little consequence to production.

Wood ducks instigate courtship activities at least six to seven months before the nesting season. In central Illinois, social courtship usually begins in mid-September. By October, female courtship vocalizations are frequently heard emanating from scrub/shrub and forested wetlands. Unpaired males are attracted to these vocalizations and form small displaying groups around females.

Through ritualized displays and vocalizations that indicate courtship intentions, wood ducks are able to evaluate potential mates. The formation of pair bonds appears to occur gradually. Most of the earliest bonds are temporary associations that may only last for a few minutes or several hours (Armbruster 1982). As autumn advances, the sexes continue to assess the quality of potential mates, and many bonds become firmly established before autumn migration. Once paired, courtship activity strengthens the bond and deters intruders.

McKinney (1986) discussed the early establishment of pair formation in migratory dabbling ducks. He noted that in most species there are more males than females and early pairing assures the male a mate; a male that fails to obtain a mate early is less likely to breed that year. Bellrose (1976) reported the presence of approximately one extra drake wood duck for every four hens during autumn. A paired female receives protection from the male while on wintering grounds and can feed with lessened harassment from unpaired males, thereby maintaining or building nutrient reserves for the breeding season.

REPRODUCTIVE MATURITY

A high percentage of wood ducks forms pair bonds and nests their first year. Factors that influence breeding attempts by yearlings include hatching date, latitude, breeding density, and age structure of populations. In many species, adults are dominant over juveniles because of their experience in performing displays that apparently highlight their plumage colors and patterns and because they are usually larger than juveniles (Weller 1965, Wishart 1983, Kodric-Brown and Brown 1984). Although young wood ducks attain their breeding plumage during their first autumn, slight differences in plumage exist between adults and yearlings of both sexes. Adult wood ducks are heavier than immatures (Bellrose 1976), and many adults acquire their breeding plumage at least one month earlier than most juveniles (see Chapter 13).

From their studies on captive wood ducks Korschgen and Fredrickson (1976) noted that when a female was able to choose between a yearling and adult male, she always chose the adult for her mate.

These authors detected age-related differences in the form, timing, and orientation of some male courtship displays.

The age composition of wood duck pairs is unknown. For gadwalls, Blohm (1982) found that adult male/adult female (51 percent) were the most common pair combinations, followed by adult male/yearling female (23 percent), yearling male/ yearling female (18 percent), and yearling male/ adult female (8 percent). Stotts and Davis (1960) concluded that juvenile American black duck females began pairing at the age of six to seven months—one or two months before juvenile males. The evidence they presented indicated that pair bonds from August to November were exclusively between adult black ducks. The first paired juvenile they collected was a female shot on November 22.

Grice and Rogers (1965) explained how high breeding densities may cause yearling female wood ducks to delay nesting. From 1951 through 1956, 2–24 percent of the nests on Great Meadows National Wildlife Refuge were established by two-year-old females nesting for the first time. Heusmann (1975) found that 58 percent of the wood duck hens on eastern Massachusetts study areas failed to nest as yearlings.

Hepp et al. (1991) studied wood ducks under confinement in South Carolina and found that early hatched young conducted courtship more frequently and formed pair bonds earlier than late-hatched birds. However, they found that behavioral differences were not related to differences in hormonal levels.

Earlier, Hepp et al. (1989) reported that date of hatch did not affect the time when females first nested in South Carolina. Grice and Rogers (1965) found that females from late-hatched broods in Massachusetts often failed to nest as yearlings.

Differences between the findings of Hepp et al. (1989) in South Carolina and studies that were conducted farther north may relate to differences in sexual development resulting from earlier nesting in the South, where substantial migration is absent and where photoperiods do not change as rapidly.

Maturity in breeding behavior of yearling drakes seems to depend partly on the physiological development of the nervous and endocrine systems. The date of hatch directly influences when a male attains reproductive maturity, and drakes that hatch in the northern part of the breeding range are less likely than those that hatch in southern areas to reach sexual maturity in autumn. For example, ducklings that hatch on the Yazoo National Wildlife Refuge, Mississippi, can reach two months of age before the first ducklings appear in central Minnesota (Cunningham 1968, Fiedler 1966).

In some instances, male wood ducks that retain noticeable amounts of their "basic" (eclipse) plumage engage in courtship activity. We observed two paired males in basic plumage over a period of several days in September at the same location in an isolated backwater lake. On three occasions in late September and early October 1988, Eric Hopps observed five male wood ducks in various stages of their prealternate molt perform courtship displays—"preen-behind-the-wing," "bill-jerk," "wing-and-tail-flash," and "bill-jab." The form and function of wood duck courtship displays are described later in this chapter. We suspect that the observations made by Hopps may reflect a common behavior in wood ducks and that courtship by males when in partial basic plumage functions to establish pair bonds between adult birds of proven breeding capability. Female wood ducks apparently solicit displays from male wood ducks by giving the "coquette call" (Heinroth 1910) as early as August in central Illinois. Most males that respond to courtship vocalizations in July and August undoubtedly retain noticeable amounts of their basic plumage. Some wood ducks, therefore, apparently establish pair bonds before they attain "definitive alternate" (nuptial) plumage and in advance of the period of social display.

As latitude increases, adult birds probably comprise a higher proportion of the individuals involved in autumn courtship. We documented age-related differences in courtship activity of captive female wood ducks at the Van Norman Aviary, Hanna City, Illinois, during the afternoon hours on October 9, 1986. Although at least twice as many immatures as adults were present, adults gave coquette calls six times more frequently than did yearlings (2.30 versus 0.37 calls per minute). Most immatures probably start pairing after they arrive on the wintering grounds or during the following spring (Armbruster 1982). Mate selection by adult and yearling wood ducks occurs prior to reproductive fertility.

BEHAVIOR OF COURTING PARTIES

Many of the wood duck's ritualized displays and vocalizations are performed during discrete time frames known as display bouts. Each display period consists of several sequences where a number of unpaired drakes gather around a female, frequently vocalizing and performing displays.

Armbruster (1982) reported that display sequences varied in length from 1 to 20 minutes and were separated by 1–90 minutes of preening and feeding. A display sequence usually started as one or several males began whistling or giving bill-jerks. Shortly thereafter, a female usually gave either the "hauk" or coquette call, stimulating the males to vocalize and display with an increased level of activity.

Intensity of pairing activity is reflected in the duration of display sequences. Armbruster (1982) found that display sequences tended to be longer (P < 0.05) in autumn than in spring (1.9 versus 1.0 minute). Although average display sequences in September, October, and November continued for 2.0, 1.3, and 2.5 minutes, respectively, sequences lasted for only 1.0 minute in January, February, and March.

Courting parties are dynamic in nature, with males repeatedly joining or leaving the group during the course of a day. Armbruster (1982) also found that the average size and sex ratios of courting parties varied from month to month. Group size on Duck Creek Wildlife Management Area, Missouri, fluctuated from 9.5 to 16.3 between September and November. Similarly, male to female sex ratios of courting groups increased from 1.94:1 in September to 3.42:1 in November. In February, when wood ducks were forced by ice to concentrate on small areas of open water, group size increased to 33 birds. By April, each courting group averaged only 4.5 birds and the average sex ratio was 2:1. Armbruster (1982) observed no courting parties in southeastern Missouri during May.

Although early arriving wood ducks return to Nauvoo Slough, Illinois, in mid-March, no courting groups have been observed until early April. We have observed courting groups on Nauvoo Slough throughout the month of May, 1984–1986. Although groups ranged from 3 to 20 birds, 75 percent were between 5 and 12. We found no significant (P > 0.05; Mann-Whitney Test) difference in courting group size between April and May, 1984 and 1985 (Table 51). In 1986, the average number of wood ducks per courting group declined (P < 0.05) from April to May (Table 51). Late spring courting parties on

Nauvoo Slough were nearly twice as large as those observed by Armbruster (1982) on Duck Creek Wildlife Management Area. This difference may reflect differences in latitude, habitat, population sex ratios, and population densities.

Because wood ducks formed larger courting groups, engaged in longer display sequences, and performed nearly four times as many display sequences in autumn as in spring, Armbruster (1982) concluded that courtship activity in southeastern Missouri was greatest during autumn. We utilized data provided by Eric Hopps to evaluate seasonal differences of courtship display rates in central Illinois (Table 52). His observations were restricted to courting groups of wood ducks. Males performed nearly twice as many displays per hour of observation in autumn (110.41) as in spring (56.43). They gave more (P < 0.01) "display shakes," "burps," bill-jabs, bill-jerks, preen-behind-the-wing displays, "rush" displays, and wing-and-tail-flashes during autumn (Table 52). "Turning-the-back-of-the-head," "inciting," and "pseudo mock-preen" displays were performed at similar rates (P > 0.05) during each season. Females performed rush and inciting displays at significantly higher (P < 0.01) rates during autumn, and they gave more (P < 0.01) bill-jabs during the spring. Nearly equal (P > 0.05) numbers of bill-jerks and preen-behind-the-wing displays were performed by females each season (Table 52). These observations are consistent with those of Armbruster (1982) and indicate that more courtship occurred in central Illinois in autumn than in spring. This seasonal difference in courtship activity indicates that a large proportion of the population forms pair bonds during autumn and winter.

Other aspects of the wood duck's courtship behavior also are dramatically different in autumn and spring. Most confrontations between males in autumn stop short of actual combat. In spring, however, males occasionally engage in 15- to 30-second fights in which they grab at each other and

Table 51. Comparative size of wood duck courting groups on Nauvoo Slough, Illinois during April and May, 1984–86.

Year	Month	Number of groups observed	Size[a]	S.D.	P
1984	April	16	7.00	2.97	>0.05
	May	33	9.64	4.15	
1985	April	10	11.70	6.20	>0.05
	May	7	7.29	5.35	
1986	April	27	8.26	2.93	<0.05
	May	16	6.38	2.60	

[a] Mean number of wood ducks in observed courting groups.

Table 52. Number of wood duck displays per hour of observation during autumn and spring courtships in central Illinois.[a]

Display	Male				Female			
	Autumn[b]	Spring[c]	Chi²	P	Autumn[b]	Spring[c]	Chi²	P
Turning-the-back-of-the-head	9.66	11.19	1.98	>0.05				
Preen-behind-the-wing	8.90	3.57	38.46	<0.01	0.14	0	2.55	>0.05
Burp	10.07	6.70	10.95	<0.01				
Display shake	4.34	1.95	14.77	<0.01				
Bill-jerk	34.69	10.27	229.58	<0.01	2.83	2.27	0.78	>0.05
Bill-jab	20.34	9.84	61.46	<0.01	0.21	1.30	12.15	<0.01
Rush	17.52	11.35	21.87	<0.01	22.76	3.35	258.61	<0.01
Inciting	0.34	0.32	0	>0.05	12.56	4.65	62.02	<0.01
Wing-and-tail-flash	3.79	0.76	36.86	<0.01				
Pseudo mock-preen	0.76	0.49	0.81	>0.05				

[a] Data collected by Eric Hopps. Observations were restricted to the first three hours following sunrise and preceding sunset. No groups of loafing birds were observed.
[b] During 14.5 hours of observation between September 21 and October 30, 1988, 1,601 male and 558 female displays were observed.
[c] During 18.5 hours of observation between March 7 and June 6, 1988, 1,044 male and 214 female displays were observed.

beat each other with their wings. These skirmishes often involve one male rapidly pursuing another as both swim in a tight circular pattern. The pursuing drake may grab the other's tail, rump, or wing feathers with his bill while simultaneously beating with his wings. Other than the loss of a few feathers, wood ducks apparently suffer little if any physical injury as a result of these confrontations.

Four male wood ducks court a female in a typical small wetland with excellent cover. The pair bond between the hen and nearest drake apparently was not sufficiently firm to discourage the other suitors. Wood ducks form courting parties as early as September, earlier than most species of ducks. *Photo courtesy of the Wildlife Management Institute.*

Aerial Courtship Flights

Little information has been published on aerial courtship flights by wood ducks. Nevertheless, such flights appear to be an important component of the pairing process. From 1984 to 1986, we made detailed observations of 30 courtship flights by wood ducks at Nauvoo Slough. Unlike the gyrating, twisting, display flights flown over prairie marshes by many species of dabbling ducks, wood duck courtship flights were characteristically flown in a straightforward manner with only slight undulations. Many courtship groups flew in patterns that required several sharp banking maneuvers and generally returned to within 100–150 meters (328–492 ft) of their takeoff points. Almost all flights were flown at altitudes between 12 and 21 meters (39–69 ft). They were of considerable duration, lasting an average of 2.05 ± 1.24 minutes. Flight characteristics differ in more wooded habitats where female woodies maneuver through standing timber. We once saw two drakes pursue a female on a twisting flight about 2 meters (6.6 ft) above the ground through a wild plum thicket; their passage was comparable in dexterity of flight to that of a woodcock.

Wood duck courtship flights serve as an additional means by which females can evaluate the skills and persistence of the individual drakes that court them. As in the social courtship that occurs on the water surface, drakes maneuver in flight to attract the female's attention and to obtain a position close to her. In several flights, one male was observed to remain close to the female while the others flew in a tight, maneuvering group slightly above and behind the hen. Occasionally, drakes joined and dropped out of flights as they proceeded. Courting groups normally began another display sequence after landing.

COURTSHIP DISPLAYS

Male and female wood ducks have been reported to perform at least 21 and 11 ritualized courtship displays and behaviors, respectively (Table 53). Of the displays performed by wood ducks that have evolved a specific duration, most occur very rapidly, lasting less than one second (Table 54). Although some displays generally are performed singly, others are given in combination with another display.

Fourteen drakes pursue a female wood duck in an aerial phase of courtship. In comparison with other species of dabbling ducks, aerial display by woodies is at a lower level of performance; they place a greater emphasis on water courtship. This emphasis may be an adaptation to the wooded habitat typically used by woodies, as opposed to the relatively open habitat of other duck species. *Photo by Scott Nielsen.*

Table 53. Ritualized wood duck displays and courting behaviors reported in the literature.[a]

Function	Male	Female
Preflight synchronization	Neck-craning Lateral head-shaking	Neck-craning Lateral head-shaking
Pair bond establishment and maintenance	Bill-jab Rush Bill-jerk Preen-behind-the-wing Inciting Turning-the-back-of-the-head Display shake Drinking Burp Chin-lifting Wing-and-tail-flash Introductory shake (rare) Pseudo mock-preen Mutual preening Courtship feeding Supplanting	Bill-jab Rush Bill-jerk Preen-behind-the-wing Inciting Mutual preening Courtship feeding
Precopulatory displays	Bill-jerk Bill-dipping Drinking Bathing	Bill-jerk Prone position
Postcopulatory displays	Facing Turning-the-back-of-the-head Wing-and-tail-flash (adults) Preen-behind-the-wing (rare) Bathing (rare)	Bathing

[a] References: Johnsgard (1965); Korschgen (1972); Korschgen and Fredrickson (1976); Scherpelz (1979); Armbruster (1982).

Researchers have assigned functions to various displays by observing the circumstances they believed were responsible for bringing about a given display and noting how other individuals reacted to that display. The messages conveyed by certain displays vary depending on the situations in which they occur (McKinney 1975). Courtship behaviors also vary with the stage of pair formation and time of year.

Original descriptions of wood duck courtship displays and vocalizations were presented by Heinroth (1910), Lorenz (1951–1953), Korschgen (1972), Korschgen and Fredrickson (1976), Scherpelz (1979), and Armbruster (1982). Johnsgard (1965) summarized the observations of Heinroth (1910) and Lorenz (1951–1953) and presented some data of his own. Ten frequently observed displays in wood ducks are shown in Figure 32.

Table 54. Mean duration of some wood duck courtship displays.[a]

Display	Number analyzed		Display duration, in seconds			
	Female	Male	Female	(S.D.)	Male	(S.D.)
Display shake	0	2			0.76	(0.007)
Preen-behind-the-wing	1	29	1.00		0.86	(0.009)
Wing-and-tail-flash	0	15			0.31	(0.008)
Bill-jerk	20	63	0.23	(0.006)	0.32	(0.020)
Burp	0	7			0.23	(0.030)
Pseudo mock-preen	0	7			1.57	(0.190)
Facing[b]	0	9				

[a] From Korschgen and Fredrickson (1976).
[b] See text for explanation of display duration.

Male

"Introductory shaking" is uncommon in woodies and does not function to introduce major displays as it does in ducks of the genus *Anas* (Johnsgard 1965). This display may be given by a drake in a state of low sexual motivation, when unexpectedly confronted by a female (Korschgen 1972).

According to Johnsgard (1965), ritualized "drinking" by male wood ducks occurs frequently during courtship. The movement is similar to regular drinking, but the uplifting of the head appears to be slightly exaggerated. Drinking always precedes preen-behind-the-wing displays. Moreover, it is frequently given in conjunction with an introductory shake (Lorenz 1951–1953) and following burp displays, according to Eric Hopps.

While performing preen-behind-the-wing displays, drakes usually position themselves beside or in front of the female and turn their heads, with partially erected crests, toward the hen before reaching around to their backs. A male always raises the wing that is closest to the hen (Korschgen and Fredrickson 1976). He moves his bill behind the wing as the primaries and secondaries are spread and displayed to the female.

Captive yearling males that had been isolated from adult drakes failed to assume the exaggerated postures taken by adults and oriented themselves differently when performing the preen-behind-the-wing display. Korschgen and Fredrickson (1976) reported that the display positions of adults were concentrated (P < 0.05) in front of and lateral to the female, whereas yearlings showed no uniformity in orientation when performing the display. Under their experimental conditions, Korschgen and Fredrickson (1976) did not observe preen-behind-the-wing during mate selection, suggesting that this display functions mainly to strengthen and maintain pair bonds. We have seen unpaired males in courting parties at Nauvoo Slough synchronize their performance of this display. Armbruster (1982) observed a paired male give the preen-behind-the-wing display as part of a postcopulatory sequence.

In a variation of the preen-behind-the-wing display, drakes may perform a pseudo mock-preen (Korschgen 1972). The stereotyped sequence of initial movements remains the same as that of preen-behind-the-wing, but instead of lifting a wing the drake preens his back.

Johnsgard (1965) reported that only wood ducks and mandarin ducks perform a wing-and-tail-flash. This display apparently is analogous to the "head-up-tail-up" display given by male dabbling ducks (Korschgen 1972). As in preen-behind-the-wing, drakes often orient themselves with the long axis of their body perpendicular to the female. During this display the crest is erected and the head, tail, and wings are raised in unison. A guttural call is given as the male raises his head (Korschgen and Fredrickson 1976). Following this display, the male usually swims a short distance and wags his tail (Korschgen and Fredrickson 1976). Because both paired and unpaired males perform the wing-and-tail-flash, it probably functions to establish and maintain pair bonds. The wing-and-tail-flash is a common postcopulatory display.

The bill-jerk consists of a rapid upward snap of the head, exposing the white chin to the female. Drakes often give a short whistle during this display (Lorenz 1951–1953). A bill-jerk is frequently given as a greeting when a pair reforms after having been separated for a short time. This display also functions to synchronize pairs for copulation (Korschgen and Fredrickson 1976) and is used by paired males as a threat display toward other drakes (Johnsgard 1965). Bill-jerks performed during social courtship in the fall often appear to cause rushing displays by females, according to Eric Hopps.

Prior to the initiation of a burp display, a drake stretches his head and neck vertically and partially erects the crest. The display begins with a quick lateral head shake in which the male points his bill at a female (Korschgen and Fredrickson 1976). Korschgen (1972) reported that this display functions primarily in pair maintenance. He indicated that it was normally performed by drakes that tried to attract the attention of their mates after they had become separated by other birds. Eric Hopps indicated that males also may give this display in conjunction with female low-intensity inciting movements, as a warning signal, or in response to potential danger.

"Chin-lifting" may be performed alone or in combination with turning-the-back-of-the-head. With chin-lifting, in contrast to bill-jerking, a drake continues to hold his head tilted slightly back, exposing the white chin to a female for several seconds (Johnsgard 1965). While performing turning-the-back-of-the-head, drakes swim just ahead of the hen and off to one side. The wings and tail are held high and the tail is tilted away from the female, emphasizing the elongated feathers along the side of the rump. According to Johnsgard (1965), the combination of inciting by the female and turning-the-back-of-the-head by the male is the most important display in pair bond maintenance. Moreover, turning-the-back-of-the-head is an important display during pair formation. Adult males were found to use a more exaggerated posture than did yearlings when performing turning-the-back-of-the-head displays (Korschgen and Fredrickson 1976).

Figure 32. Ten of the more frequently observed courtship displays in wood ducks: (above, clockwise from top left) bill-jab, hen inticing, display shake (1), bill-jerk, rush, and display shake (2); (opposite page, clockwise from top left) facing, burp, preen-behind-the-wing, wing-and-tail-flash, and turn-the-back-of-the-head. *Illustrations by Francis E. Sweet.*

Instead of or in addition to bill-dipping, drinking, and bathing displays, male wood ducks perform bill-jerks to signify readiness to copulate. Bill-jerking also is frequently performed when a pair reforms after being separated. *Photo by Stephen Kirkpatrick.*

Male wood ducks lower the head and neck off to one side or completely over the shoulder and make rapid direct pointing movements toward another bird when performing the inciting display (Lorenz 1951–1953, Korschgen and Fredrickson 1976). Paired males are probably the only drakes to perform this display. They normally incite against unpaired males when confronted during preening or resting (Korschgen and Fredrickson 1976) or in conjunction with inciting by the female (Lorenz 1951–1953).

The display shake has been regarded as the most elaborate courtship movement performed by male wood ducks (Johnsgard 1965). Korschgen and Fredrickson (1976) observed paired males and unpaired drakes involved in a trio perform this display. They believed that display shakes function in pair formation and maintenance.

After a male orients himself broadside to the female and within 0.6 meter (2 ft) of her, he prepares for a display shake by erecting the crest and lowering his head. The display begins as the male lowers and extends his head. He then briefly rears up on the water, exposing the white belly. Johnsgard (1965) reported that males emit a whistling note in conjunction with the display shake. Display shakes are occasionally followed by a tail wag (Korschgen and Fredrickson 1976).

The white chin is not exposed during bill-jabbing. Instead, rapid vertical head movements result in the head being jabbed straight downward. Armbruster (1982) noted that bill-jabbing is used frequently at the start of a courtship sequence and probably functions more in pair formation than in pair maintenance during autumn. Both paired and unpaired males perform this display. Paired males often give bill-jabs when other wood ducks approach their mates, and occasionally when no conspecifics are nearby, according to Eric Hopps. Moreover, they frequently perform bill-jabbing in conjunction with female rushing. In spring courtship, female bill-jabbing often is given in conjunction with male turning-the-back-of-the-head and appears to function in pair maintenance.

Rush displays are a common component of courting parties and symbolize a high level of courtship activity. This display begins when a drake lowers and extends his head, becoming prone on the water. With bill open, he dashes at another nearby drake, leaving a wake in his path. Both males usually "bathe" following a confrontation (Armbruster 1982). Paired males will also rush conspecifics of either sex whenever they approach too closely.

Pairs often engage in "mutual preening." Bernard Van Norman reported that, of the 20 species of ducks raised at his aviary, only paired wood ducks and mandarin ducks have been observed to engage in bouts of mutual preening. Eric Hopps observed 0.41 mutual preening bouts per hour of observation in autumn (14.5 hours of observation) and 0.81 in spring (18.5 hours of observation); the difference was not significant (P > 0.05; chi-square = 1.75). On several occasions, Korschgen (1972) observed the extra drake of a trio preen the hen. As noted by Johnsgard (1965), hens often nibble at the white feathers on a drake's chin and crest. Similarly, males restrict most of their preening to the female's head and neck. Woodies may engage in mutual preening bouts that last anywhere from several seconds to several minutes. Mutual preening apparently functions to strengthen the pair bond.

Heinroth (1910) reported that paired males occasionally offer large pieces of food to females that subsequently consume them. While observing captive birds, Korschgen (1972) observed drakes offering females a piece of wood, string, and even a feather in what appeared to be a form of "courtship feeding." The hens picked the material up and rolled it around in their bills before dropping it. We have seen similar behavior several times at Nauvoo Slough. On each occasion, a drake carried a duck potato tuber in his bill and dropped it in front of his mate. She then proceeded to ingest the tuber.

Female

As with males, inciting by females consists of rapid direct pecking movements. According to Korschgen and Fredrickson (1976), this display confirms the establishment of a pair bond.

No appreciable difference exists between male and female bill-jerk displays. The function of this display also appears to be the same for both sexes. It is used as a threat (Johnsgard 1965), greeting, and precopulatory display (Korschgen and Fredrickson 1976). Females in the "prone" position also may give this display to attending males.

Korschgen and Fredrickson (1976) have observed both adult and yearling females perform preen-behind-the-wing displays. In every case, the display was given while the hen stood on land and within 0.6 meter (2 ft) of her mate. Eric Hopps observed a female perform two preen-behind-the-wing displays while floating on the water. He stated that the female gave a coquette call following the display performance. Movement sequences during preen-behind-the-wing are similar for both sexes.

Both male and female wood ducks perform bill-jabbing in a similar manner. Bill-jabbing by a female apparently signals her mate to defend her.

Wood ducks are the most avid mutual preeners, or "allo-preeners," among 15 species of ducks observed at the Van Norman Aviary in Illinois. Most often the drake nibbles at his mate's head feathers, which are nearly impossible to self-preen; head scratching also may function to distribute preen oil on the head. The hen sometimes reciprocates, but at a lower level of intensity. Not only does allopreening aid in the vitality of the feathers by cleaning them, removing ectoparasites, and adding oil, but it also may serve to strengthen the pair bond. *Photo by David McEwen.*

In contrast to males, which normally remain prone for only a few seconds prior to rushing, some females remain in the prone position for about one minute before rushing. Armbruster (1982) suggested that this combination of displays may be a form of inciting. She noted that whenever a female rushes a male, all other males in the courting group usually rush the same male. Females also rush away from a group of attending males; the drakes generally follow quickly behind the female and often respond by performing a sequence of displays. Eric Hopps has heard females give the inciting call just before and during a rush. He believes that this combination of display and vocalization stimulates drakes to become aggressive and begin performing displays.

Both sexes perform rush displays at a nearly equal rate during the autumn. In spring, rushing remains a common male display but is used less frequently by females (Table 52, Armbruster 1982). Like paired males, paired females frequently rush intruders. Thus, depending on the circumstances, females may use this display to signal either sexual or aggressive intentions.

Rush and inciting displays by female wood ducks are used to aid in establishing and maintaining the pair bond. At times these displays are directed at an intruding male or, less frequently, an intruding female. *Photo by Scott Nielsen.*

BEHAVIORS ASSOCIATED WITH COPULATION

Ducks use a variety of ritualized movements that appear to signal their intention to copulate. Because wood ducks typically isolate themselves from conspecifics before copulating, it is not surprising that their major precopulatory displays are relatively inconspicuous and probably not accompanied by auditory signals. Male woodies exhibit four ritualized precopulatory displays: bill-jerking, "bill-dipping," drinking, and bathing (Table 53). The bill-jerking and prone posture of females are used along with male precopulatory movements to synchronize a pair for copulation.

Many precopulatory sequences fail to terminate in copulation because of interference by conspecifics. In other cases, one member of the pair often fails to respond to precopulatory displays and simply swims away. Females may attempt to arouse a disinterested male by rising from the prone position and giving a bill-jerk or by giving a bill-jerk from the prone position. A hen sometimes swims after her mate while in the prone position or swims toward another male, causing the mated drake to perform a turning-the-back-of-the-head display (Korschgen and Fredrickson 1976). Armbruster (1982) observed that, after females assumed the prone position, copulations occurred about 20 percent of the time. When hens fail to perform precopulatory displays, drakes try to interest them by performing repeated bill-jerks, inciting movements, and drinking displays (Korschgen and Fredrickson 1976).

The number of precopulatory displays performed before attempted copulation takes place varies greatly among and within pairs. Age and responsiveness of each bird to displays are key factors that determine the length of precopulatory sequences.

In a similar fashion to observations made by Johnsgard (1965), we have seen females assume the prone position without performing mutual bill-jerking. Korschgen and Fredrickson (1976) recorded 22 bill-jerks and 16 drinks by a drake and 8 bill-jerks by the hen during a two-minute precopulatory sequence.

It is of interest to note that wood ducks engage in precopulatory displays, copulations, and post-copulatory displays during autumn as well as during the spring. Hester and Dermid (1973) and Armbruster (1982) observed wood ducks copulate as early as October 13 in North Carolina and Missouri. Eric Hopps has seen copulation between wood ducks in central Illinois as early as September 25. Interestingly, he observed more copulations during the period of autumn courtship (n = 14; 0.97 copulation per hour of observation) than in the spring (n = 11; 0.59 copulation per hour of observation); however, the difference was not significant (P > 0.05; chi-square = 1.46). By contrast, Armbruster (1982) reported that only 9 percent (n = 2) of the copulations that she observed between wild-trapped wood ducks occurred during autumn; confinement may have influenced the behavior of these birds.

Drobney (1977) found that the testes of paired males during autumn courtship were in a regressed state, weighing significantly less (P < 0.01) (0.08 gram, 0.003 oz) than testes of paired males collected in spring (2.30 grams, 0.08 oz). Thus, it is unlikely that viable sperm could be produced and transferred to females during autumn courtship. Also, it seems improbable that females would store sperm at this time of year. Obviously, copulations occur during the fall for reasons other than fertilization. Copulations outside of periods when male spermatogenesis and female sperm storage are likely may serve as a form of mate-quality evaluation or function in the maintenance and strengthening of pair bonds, or both.

The frequency with which paired wood ducks copulate during the spring is unknown. Because stored sperm can remain viable in a female's oviduct for several weeks, in theory a single insemination during the female's fertile period probably is sufficient to fertilize most eggs of a clutch. Elder and Weller (1954) found that some sperm stored by domestic mallard females remained viable for 17 days. However, egg fertility decreased from 64 percent to

Bathing by the male is part of the precopulatory display and is rarely engaged in after copulation, but bathing by the female is a regular behavioral activity after mating. Note the pronated hen to the left of the bathing drake. *Photo courtesy of the Minnesota Department of Natural Resources.*

37 percent to 3 percent during the first, second, and third weeks, respectively, following insemination. Therefore, female wood ducks may require several inseminations to ensure fertilization of their entire clutch.

Copulation frequency during the breeding season appears to be related to sperm viability and sperm competition (Birkhead et al. 1987). Because of declining viability with age and the manner in which sperm is stored and released, an egg usually is fertilized by sperm from the most recent insemination (Cheng et al. 1983). In species that lay large clutches and engage in extra-pair copulations, frequent pair copulations are needed to assure mate paternity.

Research conducted on captive northern shovelers and mallards indicated that established pairs normally copulate once or twice daily throughout the prelaying and laying reproductive phases (McKinney 1967, Barrett 1973, Abraham 1974). We expect that copulations occur at a similar rate in the wood duck.

The copulation behaviors of three adult and two yearling drakes were analyzed by Korschgen and Fredrickson (1976). Although the adult drakes mounted by swimming up behind the female, year-

lings approached from the side or front. This behavior resulted in additional time spent in a reorientation process and could result in proportionally more unsuccessful copulations.

No differences were detected between the copulatory movements of adult and yearling drakes. An average of 5.09 ± 0.22 seconds elapsed between grabbing and releasing the nape of the hen (Korschgen and Fredrickson 1976).

In wood ducks, both sexes perform postcopulatory displays that apparently indicate a successful copulation. McKinney (1975) felt that these displays function in pair maintenance by reaffirming pair identity. The vocalizations that often accompany male postcopulatory displays direct the female's attention toward her mate. Male postcopulatory displays include "facing," turning-the-back-of-the-head, wing-and-tail-flash, bathing, and preen-behind-the-wing (Table 53). After dismounting, the drake moves rapidly away from the hen for about 0.5–1.0 meter (1.6–3.3 ft). He then usually turns toward the bathing hen and erects his crest (facing). Yearling drakes were found to face hens longer ($P < 0.05$) (2.39 ± 0.20 seconds) than were adult drakes (1.02 ± 0.27 seconds) (Korschgen and Fredrickson 1976).

Copulation by wood ducks is preceded and followed by stereotyped rituals distinctive for both sexes. Copulation itself is initiated by the hen pronating herself to indicate receptiveness to being mounted. The drake will mount the hen from behind, grasp her nape in his bill, and achieve penetration by forcing her nearly under the water. Repeated copulations by pairs, at a rate of once or twice a day, usually ensure insemination. *Photo by Scott Nielsen.*

VOCALIZATIONS

Wood ducks communicate among one another by uttering calls, performing displays, or both. Although wood ducks use calls to convey specific messages to conspecifics during all seasons of the year, they appear to be most vocal during the breeding season and autumn courtship. Vocal communication is a necessary form of information transfer between individual wood ducks because they live in habitats where dense vegetative growth often prohibits the effective use of visual displays. When wood ducks become visually separated, calls provide a ready means of transferring messages and allowing location contact.

Like most Anatinae, wood ducks exhibit considerable variation in tracheal structure between sexes. Male wood ducks have an asymmetrical osseous bulla—an enlarged chamber of the tracheal tube at the syrinx—whereas the female's syrinx is comparatively small and apparently unmodified (Johnsgard 1961). These morphological variations are at least partly responsible for the marked differences in voice exhibited by each sex. As air is forced out of the air sacs and past the osseous bulla of male woodies, a whistlelike call normally is produced. These soft calls are highly variable and often exhibit considerable frequency modulation. Although female wood ducks tend to have louder and harsher voices than do woodie males, they also produce several soft calls.

Woodies have voice traits that facilitate the transmission of sound through dense vegetation. Both sexes produce calls that are relatively low pitched; fundamental frequencies usually are below 1,500 hertz. Most wood duck calls have a narrow, highly developed harmonic spectrum. In the loud calls used by females to attract conspecifics, sound energy often is concentrated around the fundamental. Female hauk and coquette calls can be heard up to 0.8 kilometer (0.5 mi).

Like most species of birds that communicate through the use of calls, the wood duck meets its needs with a relatively modest vocabulary. The number of distinct calls given by different bird species ranges from about 4 to 30, partly depending on the criteria used to classify calls (Brown 1975). Heinz and Gysel (1970) reported that the ring-necked pheasant had a vocabulary of 16 known calls, whereas the wild turkey is believed to utter at least 28 distinct calls (Williams 1984). Abraham (1974) reported that mallards gave at least 14 different calls. Biologists have described at least 29 different wood duck vocalizations based on apparent meanings and variations in sound (Table 55). It is entirely possible that some wood duck calls that observers interpret as mere variations are in fact separate calls and vice versa. Moreover, wood ducks may give a number of calls that have yet to be described or understood.

Table 55. Synopsis of wood duck vocalizations.[a]

Type of call	Seasonal distribution	Place	Situation	Probable function
Female				
Nest search	Mar-Jun	Tree; on top of nest box	Nest searching	Reinforces pair bond; incites mate to guard female
Maternal	Apr-Jul	Nest	While incubating	Auditory imprinting of ducklings
	Apr-Jul	Water, land, tree	Calling ducklings from nest	Aids in inducing duckling departure
	Apr-Aug	Water, land	Female with brood; impending danger or after sudden disturbance; during visual separation	Enables female to lead or gather brood
Hauk low-intensity	Apr-Aug	Water, land	Female with brood; during visual separation with members of brood	Enables female to lead or gather brood
	Aug-May	Water	Courtship; during pair formation	Advertises presence; attracts males; coordinates social activity
	All year	Water, land	During visual separation with mate or conspecifics; response to conspecific low-intensity hauk vocalization	Attracts mate or conspecifics or determines their location
	Apr-Jun	Water	During incubation following arrival at male waiting area	Attracts or determines location of mate
Hauk low-intensity warning	All year	Water, land	Impending danger; prior to taking flight	Alerts mate or conspecifics
	Apr-Aug	Water, land, tree	Impending danger during and following brood exodus from nest	Enables female to "freeze" brood when danger is sensed
Hauk high-intensity	Apr-Jun	Air	Prior to landing or while flying over male waiting area during incubation recess	Attracts or determines location of mate
	Mar-Jun	Air	Following exodus from nest during egg laying; after leaving trees during nest searching	Signals departure and direction to mate
	All year; infrequent during Jun-Aug	Air	Following accidental separation of pair	Attracts or determines location of mate

Table 55. (continued)

Type of call	Seasonal distribution	Place	Situation	Probable function
Hauk high-intensity	All year; infrequent during Jun-Aug	Air	Single, pair, or flock in flight prior to landing	Aids in announcing and/or synchronizing landing
	All year; infrequent during Jun-Aug	Air	Pair or flock in flight	Establishes flock contact
Hauk high-intensity warning	All year	Air; while in or taking flight	Alarm; impending danger or after sudden disturbance	Alerts mate or conspecifics and signals direction of flight
Coquette	Aug-May	Water, logs, trees, top of nest box	Courtship; during pair formation and maintenance; frequent at roosts; frequent during social courtship; while nest searching	Coordinates social activity; attracts males for mate selection; establishes contact following separation; reinforces pair bond; draws attention to female
Incitement	Aug-May	Water, land	Courtship; during pair formation and maintenance; frequent during social courtship; occasionally precedes coquette call; also associated with rush and bill-jab displays	Attracts males for mate selection; incites males to perform displays and utter calls; incites mate to guard female; draws attention to female; aggression
Winnowing	All year	Water, land, tree	Impending danger or after sudden disturbance; prior to taking flight; under confinement; while flocking with conspecifics	Alerts mate or conspecifics; informs and synchronizes impending takeoff; expresses impatience; promotes flock cohesion
Hiss	All year	Nest, water, land	Confrontation with predator	Intimidates or threatens
Repulsion	Apr-Jul	Nest	Response of incubating female to intrusion by female conspecific	Repulsion of intruder; aggression
Copulation	Sep-May	Water	Upon union during copulation	Signals successful copulation

Table 55. (continued)

Type of call	Seasonal distribution	Place	Situation	Probable function
Male				
Call note	All year; infrequent during Jul-Aug	Water, land, tree	During visual separation with mate or conspecifics; response to conspecific call note vocalization	Attracts mate or conspecifics or determines their location
	Aug-May	Water, land	Courtship; response to female coquette and hauk vocalizations	Advertises presence; attracts female or determines her location
	All year; infrequent during Jun-Aug	Water	Following landing of lone male	Attracts conspecifics or determines their location
	All year; infrequent during Jun-Aug	Air	Single, pair, or flock in flight prior to landing	Aids in announcing and/or synchronizing landing
	All year; infrequent during Jun-Aug	Air	Pair or flock in flight	Establishes flock contact
	All year; infrequent during Jun-Aug	Air; while in or taking flight	Following sudden disturbance	Alerts mate or conspecifics; signals direction of flight
Call note warning	All year; infrequent during Jun-Aug	Water, land, tree	Alarm; impending danger or after sudden disturbance	Alerts mate or conspecifics
Winnowing	All year; infrequent during Jun-Aug	Water, land, tree	Impending danger or after sudden disturbance; prior to taking flight; under confinement	Alerts mate or conspecifics; expresses impatience; informs and synchronizes impending takeoff; promotes flock cohesion
Nest search	Mar-Jun	Tree; on top of nest box	Nest searching	Incites female to nest search; reinforces pair bond
Burp	Sep-May	Water, land, tree	Accompany burp display; during visual separation of pair; impending danger	Draws attention to male; establishes contact with female; warning; signals specific display
Preen-behind-the-wing	Sep-May	Water, land	Accompany preen-behind-the-wing display	Draws attention to male; signals specific display

Table 55. (continued)

Type of call	Seasonal distribution	Place	Situation	Probable function
Turning-the-back-of-the-head	Sep-May	Water, air, tree	Accompany turning-the-back-of-the-head display; aerial courtship flight; aggressive encounter with conspecifics	Draws attention to male; aggression; signals specific display
Wing-and-tail-flash	Sep-May	Water	Accompany wing-and-tail-flash display	Draws attention to male; signals specific display
Display shake	Sep-May	Water	Accompany display shake display	Same as above
Bill-jerk	Sep-May	Water, land	Accompany bill-jerk display	Same as above
Incitement	Sep-May	Water, land	Courtship; during pair formation and maintenance; frequent during social courtship; accompany bill-jab and inciting displays; response to female incitement vocalization	Incites female to display; signals specific display; aggression
Hiss	All year	Water, land	Confrontation with predator	Intimidates or threatens
Duckling Click	Apr-Jul	Nest	Two or three days before hatching	Synchronizes hatching
Alarm/ distress	Apr-Jul	Nest	Two or three days before hatching	Expresses physical or emotional condition; enables ducklings to recognize maternal call; stimulates female to utter maternal call
	Apr-Jul	Nest	After hatching and prior to nest exodus	Informs hen of physical or emotional condition
	Apr-Aug	Water, land	After nest exodus; lost; cold or alarmed	Establishes location contact with female and brood mates; informs hen of physical or emotional condition; alarm
Contact contentment	Apr-Jul	Nest	Two or three days before hatching	Expresses physical or emotional condition; enables ducklings to recognize maternal call; stimulates female to utter maternal call
	Apr-Jul	Nest	After hatching and prior to nest exodus	Informs hen of physical or emotional condition

Table 55. (continued)

Type of call	Seasonal distribution	Place	Situation	Probable function
Contact contentment	Apr-Aug	Water, land, log	After nest exodus; while flocking with conspecifics; while feeding and during brooding	Promotes flock cohesion; informs hen of physical or emotional condition
Shriek	Apr-Aug	Water, land	Alarm; sudden disturbance	Alerts female and brood mates
Hiss	Apr-Aug	Water, land	Confrontation with predator	Intimidates or threatens

[a] Table compiled by Eric Hopps; format after Abraham (1974). Months of nesting and courtship vocalizations are for central Illinois.

Some vocalizations sound to the ear like the same call, yet researchers have assigned different names to them because they are given in different situations. For example, the female's "nest searching," "inciting," and "maternal" vocalizations (given at the time of nest exodus) all sound similar, according to Eric Hopps. Sonograms of these calls reveal that nest searching and inciting probably are the same call (figures 33 and 34) and not two separate vocalizations as previously believed (they are presented as separate calls in Table 55). Each call may convey a unique message based on the context in which it is uttered (Table 55). The structure of the maternal call note appears identical to the call note given during nest searching and inciting except that it lacks harmonic development (figures 33–35). Thus, these three vocalizations are easily confused if the listener does not know the behavioral activity in which a call is used. We suspect that Miller and Gottlieb (1976) were misled by the similar sounds of the female's inciting and maternal vocalizations when they stated that nonmaternal females may use the maternal call to attract their mate to a source of food. Additional research is needed to ascertain whether each described wood duck call is in fact a separate vocalization.

Until recently, no serious attempt has been made to study the characteristics of many wood duck calls. Previous studies of wood duck vocalizations, outside of the work of Gottlieb (1963, 1965, 1974, 1977, 1980), Miller and Gottlieb (1976), and Miller (1977b), have been essentially restricted to creating onomatopoeic renditions of individual calls. Although these phrases provide some insight into what a call sounds like to the listener, they should be used with caution. There are a number of accepted call descriptions in which minor variations of the same phrase are used to describe two or more calls that exhibit dramatic structural differences. In addition, some researchers have coined phrases that are markedly different to describe calls that sound similar to the human ear.

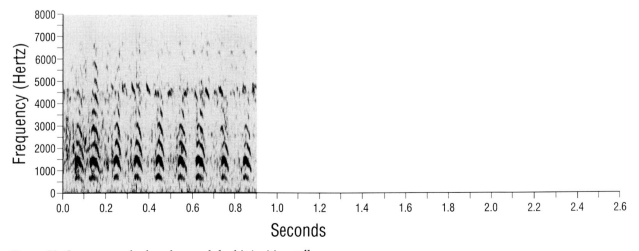

Figure 33. Sonogram of a female wood duck's inciting call.

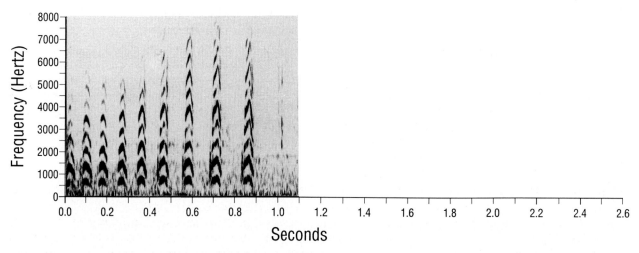

Figure 34. Sonogram of a female wood duck's nest searching call.

The conversion of sound to visual images (sonograms) by a sound spectrograph enables us to analyze wood duck calls visually. Sonograms characterize certain components of calls such as number of notes, pitch of the notes, number of notes delivered per unit of time, and amplitude or relative loudness of each note. With this information, each call can be described and compared with the others.

We were fortunate to have the assistance of two people—Eric Hopps and Delbert Koke—who spent many hours of their personal time collecting recordings of wood duck vocalizations. Through their considerable efforts, we are able to present sonograms that show the main characteristics of many wood duck calls.

Most recordings were made with a Uher 4000 Report-S tape recorder (speed 7.5 inches per second) and a Sennheiser ME80 shotgun microphone. Sound spectrograms were made using a 150- to 300-

hertz wide-band filter on a Kay Elemetrics Sonagraph, Model 7800.

Although we have attempted to select sonograms that clearly represent the major characteristics of certain calls, it should be noted that there is considerable individual variation in the voices of wood ducks, and even characteristics of calls given by the same individual may vary at different times (Miller 1977b). Nevertheless, each type of call has a definite sound energy pattern that separates it from all others. These major sound features are especially evident on sonograms.

Eric Hopps compiled a synopsis of wood duck vocalizations (Table 55). Male and female wood ducks each utter at least 12 distinct vocalizations, whereas ducklings have a known vocabulary of 5 calls. Descriptions of the context in which specific calls are given and the probable function of each vocalization also are presented in Table 55.

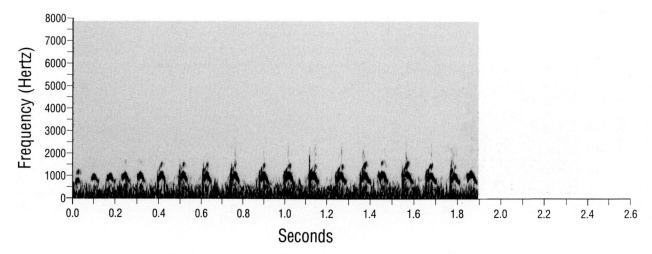

Figure 35. Sonogram of a female wood duck's maternal call.

Male

Male wood ducks give distinct calls when they perform the preen-behind-the-wing, wing-and-tail-flash, bill-jerk, burp, display shake, and turning-the-back-of-the-head displays (Lorenz 1941, Johnsgard 1965, Korschgen and Fredrickson 1976, Armbruster 1982). Eric Hopps believes that they give the same call during inciting and bill-jabbing (Table 55). Each call probably carries a unique message. Thus, females may be able to evaluate the physiological state and pair status of a male without ever seeing the displaying bird. Male courtship calls also may serve to attract the woodie female's attention (Table 55).

In addition, male wood ducks often utter a "winnowing" call, a "chatter" call, a basic "call note," a "warning call note," a "hiss" call, and a nest searching call. Eric Hopps collected recordings of the following male vocalizations: burp, turning-the-back-of-the-head, nest searching, basic call note, inciting, winnowing, preen-behind-the-wing, and chatter call.

Lorenz (1941) characterized the burp vocalization as a short "pfit" sound. Korschgen (1972) noted that burp displays were often linked together and double burps apparently were common. He observed an unpaired yearling drake give 23 burps in succession on one occasion.

A typical burp call begins with a whistle that consists of several harmonics and lasts for approximately 0.70 second (Figure 36). It starts with an apparent fundamental frequency at about 1,000 hertz that rises somewhat gradually in pitch to 4,000 hertz and then drops sharply. The maximum amplitude of the whistle note appears to occur between 4,000 and 7,000 hertz.

After a pause that may last as long as 0.10 second, the "fit" portion of the burp call is emitted. This note begins abruptly and is composed of a mixture of pitch frequencies that range from a level that is too low to interpret on a sonogram to approximately 14,000 hertz; the maximum amplitude occurs between 2,000 and 5,000 hertz (Figure 36). The "fit" note lasts about 0.10 to 0.15 second.

Many burp vocalizations are composed of three notes. After a pause of about 0.03–0.05 second, the second note ("fit") is often followed by a soft whistle that lasts for approximately 0.05–0.10 second (Figure 36). The maximum amplitude of this terminal note occurs around 3,000 hertz. Burp calls generally are about 1 second long, but the timing of the notes and of pauses between notes varies markedly.

A "jib . . . jib . . . jib" vocalization is given during the turning-the-back-of-the-head display (Lorenz 1941) in apparent attempt to focus the female's attention on the displaying drake. This call is composed of a series of simple ascending and descending notes, each note having several harmonics. The fundamental frequency appears to range from 1,000 to 2,000 hertz; major amplification occurs between 3,000 and 7,000 hertz. This multinote call series can last more than 2.5 seconds, and we have presented only a portion of the call in Figure 37.

Heinroth (1910) described the male nest searching vocalization as a "jibjibjibjibjib" sound. This call appears to function to encourage the female to search for nest cavities and to reinforce the pair bond (Table 55).

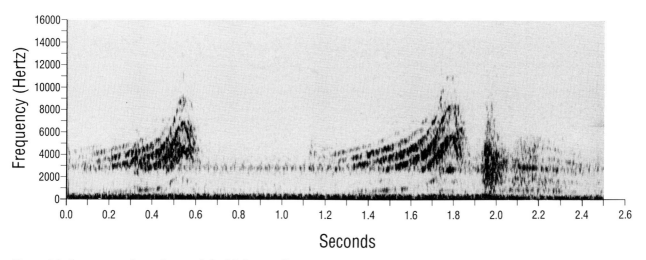

Figure 36. Sonogram of a male wood duck's burp call.

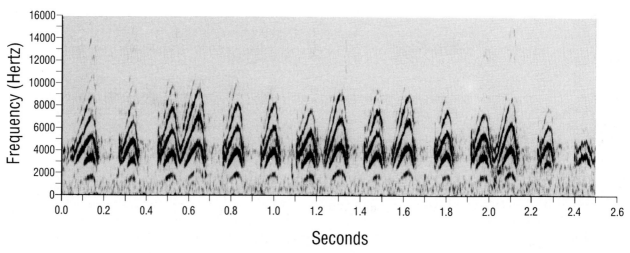

Figure 37. Sonogram of a male wood duck's turning-the-back-of-the-head call.

A sonogram of a male nest searching call is presented in Figure 38. This multisyllabic call consists of rising and falling harmonic notes that last for about 0.25 second and range in maximum amplitude from 4,000 to 8,000 hertz. A 0.20-second pause separates each note.

The basic call note of the male wood duck has been described as a "jiib" sound by Heinroth (1910)

All through pair formation and the pair bond period, the male wood duck maintains an unrelenting communication with his mate. His calls are low and soft, often inaudible only a few yards away, and phonetically described as "jibjibjib" or a goldfinchlike "chi-di di-di." These vocalizations can mean many things, depending on the display and events unfolding at that particular moment. *Photo by Stephen Kirkpatrick.*

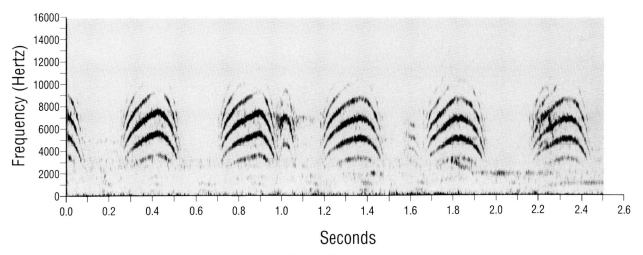

Figure 38. Sonogram of a male wood duck's nest searching call.

and a "ji-ihb" sound by Lorenz (1941). It is a prolonged whistle that functions primarily as a contact call for the male wood duck (Table 55). The whistle is an ascending call that ends abruptly as it drops in pitch (Figure 39). This call may last 1.5–1.7 seconds and have as many as seven harmonics. It has a fundamental frequency that starts at approximately 700 hertz and rises in pitch to 2,500 hertz.

Lorenz (1951–1953) reported that the male wood duck utters a soft "dih" during each lunge in inciting displays, and Armbruster (1982) indicated that male woodies give a variation of the "jibjibjib" nest search call during bill-jabbing. However, it appears that males actually vocalize with the same sound during inciting and bill-jabbing (Table 55). Although characteristics of inciting and nest searching calls resemble each other in general form, inciting notes are usually shorter and exhibit a more pronounced descending frequency modulation (figures 38 and 40).

One way that drakes alert conspecifics of potential danger is to utter a winnowing call (Table 55). This vocalization also is used as a preflight call. Heinroth (1910: 123) stated that male woodies give a soft "jii" just prior to taking flight; he described the note as "quite drawn out at the end and dying softly away." A sonogram of this vocalization reveals that the call begins with several sharp frequency fluctuations that last for approximately 0.50 second before rising and falling gradually in pitch over a 0.60-second interval (Figure 41). The fundamental frequency appears to occur between 1,000 and 2,500 hertz and the maximum amplitude ranges from 3,000 to 7,000 hertz.

Eric Hopps recorded a male vocalization given during preen-behind-the-wing displays that has not been described in the literature. It appears that drake woodies utter this call as they move the head behind the wing. This call is composed of two distinct sounds (Figure 42). The first part, represented

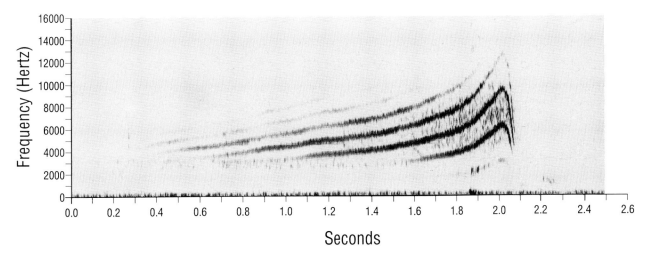

Figure 39. Sonogram of a male wood duck's basic call note.

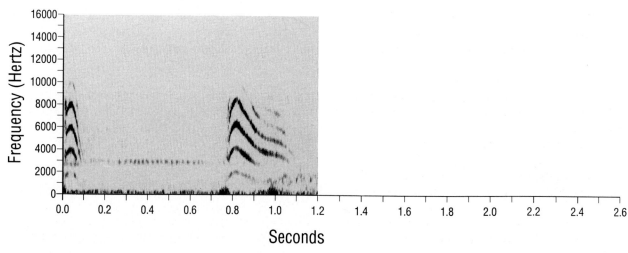

Figure 40. Sonogram of a male wood duck's incitement call.

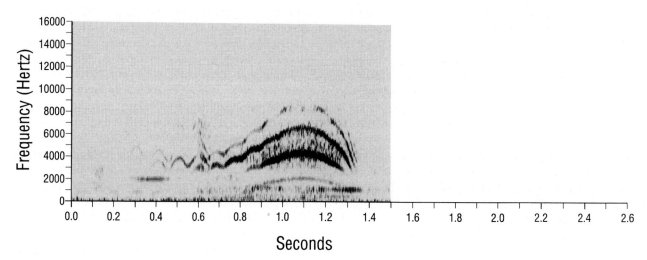

Figure 41. Sonogram of a male wood duck's winnowing call.

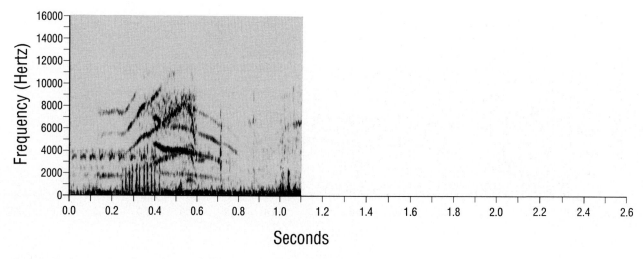

Figure 42. Sonogram of a male wood duck's preen-behind-the-wing call.

by vertical energy bands on the sonogram, is weak in amplitude and has a very wide frequency range, with no apparent harmonic structuring; the sound resembles a "putt." These notes are followed by a short, harmonically structured hum that appears to be made up solely of descending frequency modulation. The entire call may last for approximately 0.55 second (Figure 42).

Males also utter a variety of soft call notes when in close proximity to conspecifics. Messages conveyed by this vocalization—the chatter call—are unknown. Moreover, there are so many variations that several calls actually may be involved. Heinroth (1910) noted that this call is used under a variety of circumstances and may indicate an amicable or aggressive state. The sonogram that we chose as a representative example of the male chatter call was collected at a bait site where several birds had gathered (Figure 43).

Female

Females appear to utter the same multisyllable call notes when performing inciting, nest searching, rushing, and bill-jabbing displays (Johnsgard 1965, Armbruster 1982, Eric Hopps). Other sexually motivated calls include the hauk and coquette calls (Heinroth 1910). Based on the apparent function, context, and variation in sound of hauk vocalizations, Eric Hopps distinguishes four categories: hauk low- and high-intensity calls and hauk low- and high-intensity warning calls (Table 55).

A winnowing call is used for preflight synchronization and to signal impending takeoff. The call given by a female woodie when confronted by a potential predator in the nest resembles the hiss of a snake. We believe that this call also is used to harass squirrels in an endeavor to oust them from nest cavities. Female wood ducks use the maternal call to communicate with their young (Gottlieb 1963). They also give a specific call ("repulsion") when a second female enters an occupied nest (Table 55). Heinroth (1910) reported that female wood ducks give a soft call note upon union during copulation. We have never heard the call given during wood duck copulation and therefore cannot provide additional information about its sound.

Armbruster (1982) characterized the vocalization given by female wood ducks during bill-jabbing as a soft, rapid "dihdihdih" sound. She noted that this call resembled the nest searching call of female wood ducks that Heinroth (1910) described as a "tetetete" sound. Eric Hopps collected recordings of the female's inciting and nest searching calls. Both calls not only sound alike but appear similar on sonograms (figures 33 and 34). The calls are made up of a relatively large number of well-defined harmonically composed notes that begin and end abruptly as they rise and fall in pitch. Each call lasts for a variable length of time up to several seconds; the average duration of a call note is about 0.04 second. The pause between notes also varies considerably but generally does not exceed 0.15 second. The fundamental frequency appears to begin at about 500 hertz, rising to nearly 1,000 hertz in about 0.02 second before exhibiting a pronounced descending frequency modulation. The messages conveyed by these structurally similar vocalizations may depend on the activity appropriate to the behavior at the time the call is issued (Table 55).

The coquette call—a one-syllable note that has remarkable harmonic development and a great many variations (Figure 44)—has been described as sounding like "houi" by Lorenz (1941) and "kuri" or "kerri" by Heinroth (1910). To us, it sounds like a

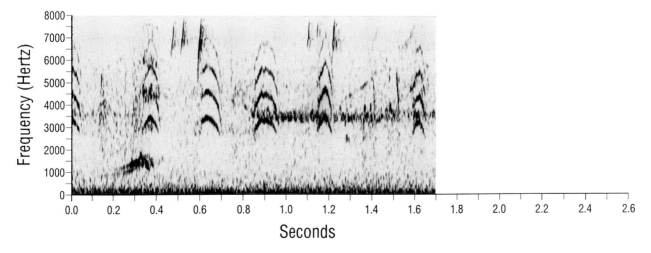

Figure 43. Sonogram of a male wood duck's chatter call.

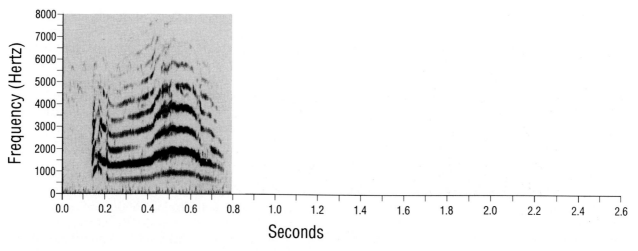

Figure 44. Sonogram of a female wood duck's coquette call.

piercing "ter-wee." The coquette call is given as the female rapidly lowers her head vertically. When the call is given on water, the tip of the bill is often submersed, which can cause a noticeable difference in sound quality. As can be seen on the sonogram (Figure 44), the call exhibits a great deal of frequency modulation. It begins abruptly with a sharp rise and fall in pitch, followed by a second gradual rise, then another sharp rise and a gradual drop, all taking place in about 0.60 second. Eric Hopps heard individual females give as many as seven coquette calls per minute. This call frequently is given during the pairing process to elicit courtship displays from males. Paired females also utter coquette calls during nest searching when they become visually separated from their mates; the paired drake responds by immediately flying to the female, according to Eric Hopps.

Perhaps more people are familiar with the female's high-intensity hauk warning call than with any other wood duck vocalization. This sound has been characterized by such descriptions as "huick" (Heinroth 1910), "oo-eek, oo-eek" (Palmer 1976), and "wee-e-e-ek, wee-e-e-ek" (Bellrose 1976). Females characteristically utter this vocalization as they take flight after being disturbed, as well as under a variety of other circumstances (Table 55). Figure 45 illustrates characteristics of a high-intensity hauk warning call that was given as a female took flight. The fundamental frequency occurs between 500 and 1,000 hertz, and maximum amplitude appears to occur around 1,000–1,500 hertz; call duration lasts slightly more than 0.30 second. This vocalization exhibits rapid and sharp frequency fluctuations, whereas other high-intensity hauk calls often show a more gradual change in pitch.

A representative high-intensity hauk call given by a female as she flew into an isolated backwater area is presented in Figure 46. This vocalization is an unusually prolonged, harmonically structured

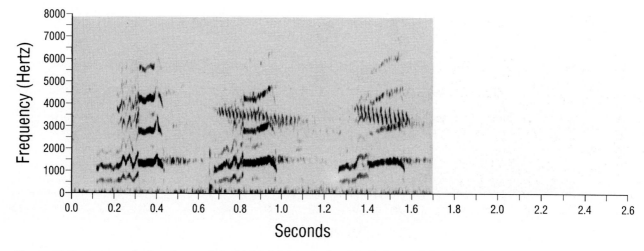

Figure 45. Sonogram of a female wood duck's high-intensity hauk call given while taking flight.

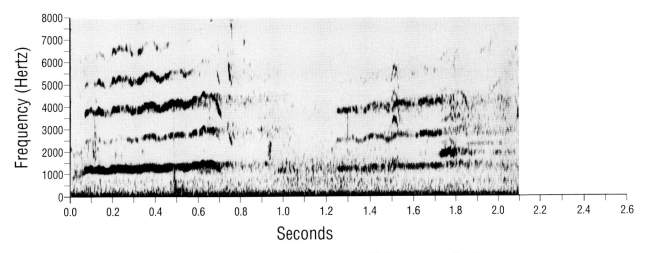

Figure 46. Sonogram of a female wood duck's high-intensity hauk call given prior to landing.

single call note that lasted approximately 0.70 second. The fundamental frequency appears to occur at about 1,000–1,500 hertz, and this frequency band has the greatest amplitude. The second, third, and fourth harmonics reveal that the call began abruptly and modulated throughout a frequency range of about 500 to 750 hertz, dropping sharply in pitch before dying out.

A sonogram of a low-intensity hauk vocalization that courting females apparently use to advertise their presence, attract males, and coordinate social activities is shown in Figure 47. Apart from its relatively constant frequency modulation, this call shares many acoustic characteristics with high-intensity hauk vocalizations (figures 45 and 46).

The low-intensity hauk vocalization presented in Figure 48 was given by a female floating on the water. The fundamental frequency began at about 500 hertz and rose gradually over a period of about 0.25 second to 1,000 hertz before undergoing a

Hen woodies tend to be more vocal and more audible than are woodie drakes. Most distinctive of the hen's vocalizations is the high-intensity hauk call—a warning or alarm call of such high frequency and volume that it sometimes can be heard by humans at a distance of 0.8 kilometer (0.5 mi). *Photo by Scott Nielsen.*

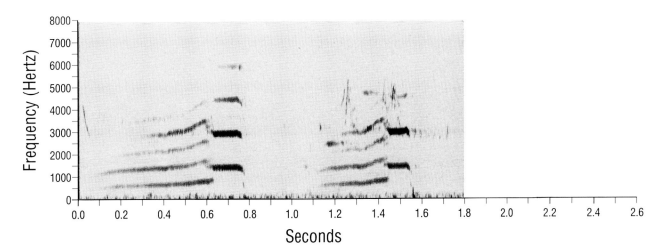

Figure 47. Sonogram of a female wood duck's low-intensity hauk call.

rapid (0.05 second) rise in frequency to 1,500 hertz, which was immediately followed by a sharp drop (Figure 48). This contact call functions as an important means of communication between females and their young and among adult birds (Table 55).

Female woodies often give a low-intensity hauk warning vocalization when they sense danger. The context in which the call is given influences how conspecifics react (Table 55). We elicited a low-intensity hauk warning call from a female at the Van Norman Aviary, Illinois, by suddenly appearing from a concealed location as she prepared to call her young from the nest (Figure 49). The ducklings reacted to the vocalization by becoming quiet and still. Within five minutes after we evoked the hauk warning call, the female uttered her maternal call and the young wood ducks exited the nest box. These markedly different responses to distinct female vocalizations illustrate that day-old ducklings are able to distinguish among calls.

Heinroth (1910: 121) reported that "When a Wood Duck intends to fly up . . . the duck as well as the drake usually utter a very definite sound." Eric Hopps noted that females characteristically utter a winnowing call prior to taking flight. A sonogram of a winnowing vocalization (Figure 50) reveals that this call consists of a series of short (0.05–0.07 second) notes, each exhibiting considerable descending frequency modulation followed by a single drawn-out note that gradually declines in pitch and lasts more than 0.50 second.

Miller and Gottlieb (1976) presented sonograms that showed individual variation in the structure of nest exodus (maternal) calls. One of these sonograms appeared very similar to the winnowing vocalization in Figure 50. However, the sound of maternal nest exodus vocalizations contrasts with the sound of winnowing calls and, according to Eric Hopps, each signals a different message (Table 55).

It is not uncommon for a female wood duck to enter a nest where another female is egg laying or incubating (see Chapter 10). Delbert Koke recorded the repulsion calls uttered by an incubating female after another female entered her nest (Figure 51). As seen on the sonogram, the incubating female gave a series of modified low-intensity hauk vocalizations interspersed with several short high-pitched sounds characterized by rapid ascending and descending frequency modulation. Presumably, the female in attendance of a nest is attempting to repel the conspecific intruder by uttering a mixture of call notes.

No other aspect of the wood duck's vocabulary has received as much study as the female's maternal call (Gottlieb 1963, 1965, 1974, 1977, 1980, Miller and Gottlieb 1976, Miller 1977b). Characteristics and functions of this vocalization are discussed in detail in Chapter 10 and summarized in Table 55.

Gottlieb (1974) reported that wood duck embryos began giving two types of calls two or three days prior to hatching. The female responded to these calls with her maternal vocalization—a low-pitched "kuk" sound. The communication that occurs between mother and young while in the nest allows ducklings to identify the female voice of their species (Gottlieb 1963, 1965).

Gottlieb (1974, 1980) conducted several experiments to determine what acoustic features of the maternal call made it attractive to young ducklings. He demonstrated that the critical acoustic feature of the maternal call was the descending frequency modulation. In addition, he discovered that young woodies were aided in recognition of the maternal call through hearing their own vocalizations, which also have a distinct descending frequency modulation.

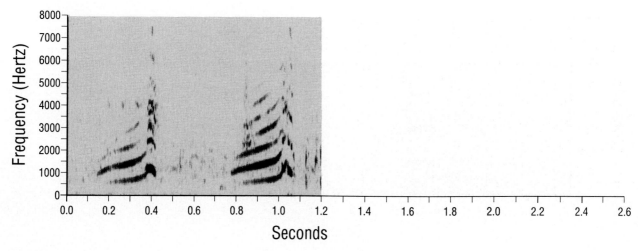

Figure 48. Sonogram of a female wood duck's low-intensity hauk call.

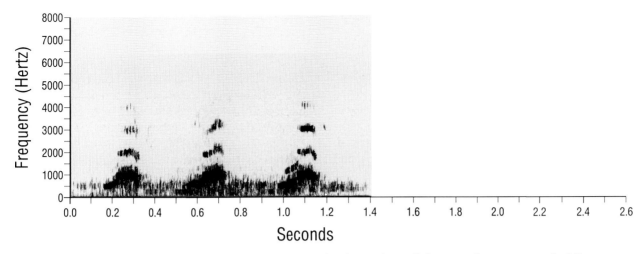

Figure 49. Sonogram of a female wood duck's low-intensity hauk warning call that was given to young ducklings.

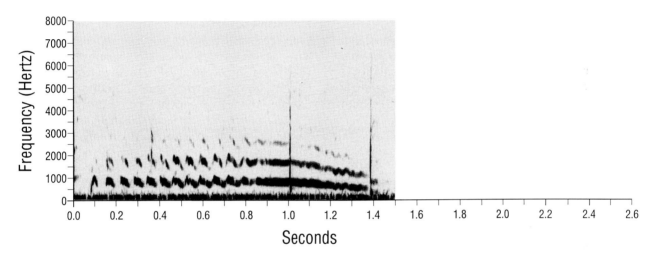

Figure 50. Sonogram of a female wood duck's winnowing call.

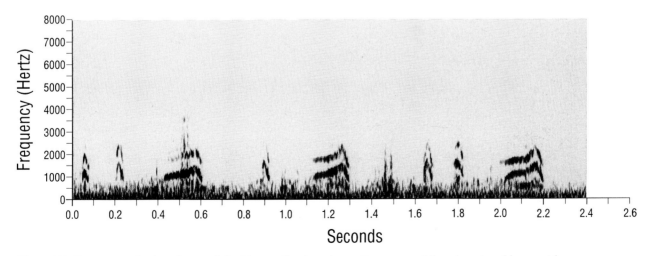

Figure 51. Sonogram of a female wood duck's vocalization given after a second female entered her nest box.

When wood duck eggs were hatched by a bantam hen on scores of occasions at the Van Norman Aviary, Illinois, the ducklings responded to the bantam hen's clucks for feeding and brooding. The ducklings were able to adapt in a meaningful way to the calls of another species.

Female wood ducks are capable of simultaneously producing two or more separate, nonharmonically related tones when uttering the maternal call (Miller 1977b). They are able to control separately the internal tympaniform membranes that are located in each bronchus. Thus, woodies can simultaneously produce two sounds that differ in frequency, amplitude, or both. The extent to which wood ducks use both acoustical sources when uttering calls other than the maternal vocalization is unknown.

Miller (1977b) found a great variation in the pitch composition of the maternal call from one hen to another. Some birds uttered a simple tone, whereas other females simultaneously emitted two, three, and four harmonically unrelated tones. The ability of female wood ducks to produce maternal calls that are often composed of two or more sounds at the same time may be one means that ducklings use to distinguish the voices of their mothers from those of other females (Miller 1977b).

Miller and Gottlieb (1976) reported that a typical maternal call had the following characteristics: (1) each note contained nonharmonically related tones that occurred between 900 and 1,500 hertz; (2) each note was composed primarily of descending frequency modulation and increasing amplitude modulation; (3) each note lasted an average of 0.040–0.045 second; (4) notes were repeated at an average of 9 per second during nest exodus; and (5) females uttered an average of 19 notes per burst when calling their young from the nest.

Delbert Koke recorded a maternal call that was uttered just prior to nest exodus (Figure 35). As seen on the sonogram, the female uttered about 9–10 notes per second. The repetition rate of the maternal call varies markedly between hatching and nest exodus. Gottlieb (1965) found that females uttered an average of less than one call per five seconds during the 36-hour period prior to nest exodus. The increased frequency of calling around the time of nest departure must signal the female's intention to lead her brood from the nest.

Duckling

As previously noted, wood duck embryos begin producing a variety of sounds two to three days before hatching when they start to breathe with their lungs. Known vocalizations include a "clicking" sound as well as "alarm/distress" and "contact-contentment" calls. Based on the occurrence, amplitude, and rhythm of the clicking sound, wood duck embryos may be able to synchronize their hatching (Vince 1969). All ducklings from a single clutch normally hatch within an hour or so of one another.

Sonograms of the alarm/distress and contact-contentment calls given by young wood ducks were presented by Gottlieb (1974). He noted that both duckling vocalizations showed a pronounced descending frequency modulation. The alarm/distress call, however, was much higher in pitch than the contact-contentment call.

We collected a recording of an apparent alarm/distress "peep" given by a young wood duck shortly after it was called from its nest at the Van Norman Aviary, Illinois (Figure 52). The single-note call rose abruptly (0.02 second) in pitch from about

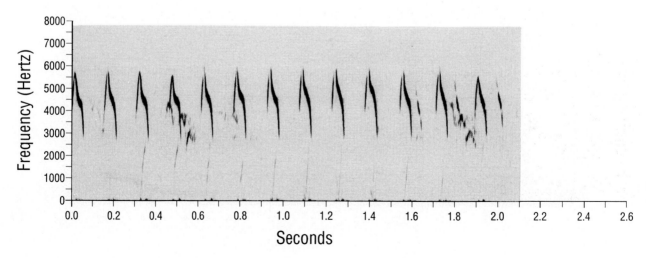

Figure 52. Sonogram of an alarm-distress call emitted by a wood duck duckling.

3,750–6,250 hertz. Descending frequency modulation occurred over a period of 0.04 second. The repetition rate of this particular alarm/distress vocalization was eight calls per second.

Eric Hopps studied the vocabulary of 13 wood ducks as they matured from day-old ducklings until they reached approximately 140 days of age. He found that after hatching, young wood ducks communicated with a minimum of four calls until fledging (Table 55). The "hiss" and "shriek" calls have not been previously described for young wood ducks, although a number of other waterfowl are known to give these vocalizations (Kear 1968). Hopps noted that ducklings began giving shriek and hiss calls at one and five days of age, respectively. Sonograms of woodie duckling hiss and shriek calls are presented in figures 53 and 54.

Heinroth (1910: 124) recognized little distinction in the sound quality of the voices of male and female wood ducks before they reached approximately two months of age. He stated that a hauk vocalization given by a female around the time of fledging sounded "so thin and sharp that it resembles very much the 'jiib' of the old drake."

Eric Hopps followed the chronological development of an adult vocabulary in young wood ducks that he raised. He noted that females gave low-intensity hauk warning notes at 50 days, winnowing calls at 62 days, and coquette calls at 124 days. In contrast, the first adult male vocalizations were heard at 80 days and consisted of winnowing calls and basic call notes; a warning burp (not preceded by a whistle) was heard at 99 days and inciting notes were given at 104 days. It appears that most young wood ducks utter some recognizable adult vocalizations by the time they reach three months old.

Some calls, such as the female maternal vocalization, would not be used until the birds are approximately one year old.

PAIRING CHRONOLOGY

By the time wood ducks arrive on the wintering grounds many pair bonds are firmly established. Armbruster (1982) concluded that most females have established pair bonds by late January. Bellrose (1976) noted that at least 90 percent of the females he observed had mates by late February.

The proportion of two-bird flocks in autumn and winter roost flights serves as an indicator of pairing activity (Hester and Quay 1961). As autumn advances, two-bird flocks become proportionally more abundant, an indication that pairing is increasing. The onset of the waterfowl hunting season in autumn often disrupts wood duck roosting flights and changes behavior patterns. Therefore, the pattern of pairing chronology relative to seasonal advancement may not be accurately reflected in roost flight counts conducted during the hunting season.

Not all wood ducks flying in two-bird groups are true pairs. Some consist of male/male or female/female associations, and some male/female two-bird flocks undoubtedly are incidental associations. Nonetheless, the ratio of male/female associations in Illinois steadily increased as autumn advanced (Table 56). We believe that this increase represents a reasonable portrayal of pairing chronology during autumn courtship.

At roost sites along the Illinois River, male/female associations occurred more frequently than

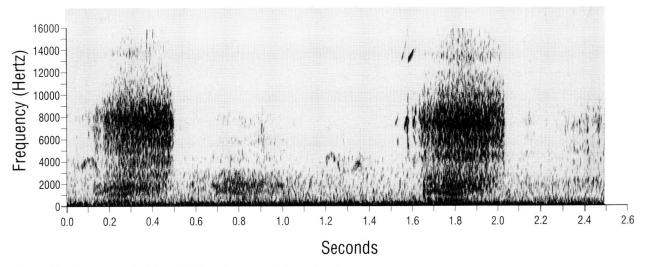

Figure 53. Sonogram of a hiss call given by a wood duck duckling.

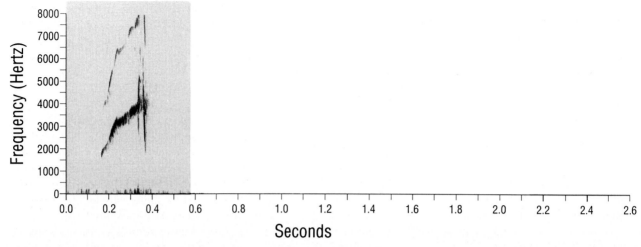

Figure 54. Sonogram of a shriek call given by a wood duck duckling.

expected (P < 0.05) during September and October (Table 56). During July and August a similar number (P > 0.05) of male/male, male/female, and female/female associations arrived at roost sites. Generally, about 75 and 90 percent of the two-bird flocks in central Illinois are male/female associations during September and October, respectively (Table 56).

Hester and Quay (1961) found that the proportion of two-bird groups in roosting flights in east-central North Carolina increased from 34 percent in October to 36 percent, 43 percent, and 47 percent in November, December, and January, respectively. Perry (1977) reported a similar trend in northeastern

North Carolina. He noted that 84 percent arrived in groups of two during March. The proportion of all wood ducks arriving at Louisiana roosts in two-bird flocks fluctuated between 25 and 35 percent during July–December (Tabberer et al. 1971) and increased to approximately 45 and 37 percent during January and February, respectively.

Changes in the percentage of single wood ducks arriving at roosts in relation to seasonal advancement also serve as an index to pairing chronology. Because flocks represent an unknown ratio of single and paired wood ducks, we analyzed the seasonal changes of unpaired wood ducks in relation to birds arriving in two-bird flocks (Table 57).

Table 56. Sex composition of wood ducks flying in two-bird flocks to autumn roosts, central Illinois, 1984–87.[a]

Roost	Year	Observation interval	Number of flocks	Percentage		
				Male/female	Male/male	Female/female
Rat Lake	1984	Oct 13–25	137	91	4	4
Rat Lake	1985	Aug 14–28	25	60	28	12
		Sep 3–29	23	78	4	17
		Oct 2–21	20	95	0	5
Hopps Pond	1986	Aug 15–30	14	57	14	29
		Sep 1–28	49	73	8	18
		Oct 3–22	31	81	6	13
Rat Lake	1987	Jul 17–28	5	40	20	40
		Aug 19–29	9	66	11	22
		Sep 6–30	10	80	10	10
		Oct 9–19	15	100	0	0
Hopps Pond	1987	Jul 3–20	4	50	50	0
		Aug 11–24	5	20	20	60
		Sep 3–27	70	71	14	14
		Oct 2–20	98	98	1	1

[a] Data provided by Eric Hopps.

Table 57. Number of wood ducks arriving at autumn roosts as singles and in two-bird flocks, central Illinois, 1984–86.

Roost	Year	Observation interval	Number arriving as		Percentage of singles
			Singles	Two-bird flocks	
Anderson Lake	1984	Sep 4–Sep 23	760	1,500	33.63
		Sep 24–Oct 13	598	2,412	19.87
		Oct 14–Nov 2	330	1,452	18.52
Anderson Lake	1985	Jul 11–Jul 30	138	360	27.71
		Jul 31–Aug 19	136	302	31.05
		Aug 20–Sep 8	348	696	33.33
		Sep 4–Sep 23	274	704	28.02
		Sep 24–Oct 13	361	1,312	21.58
		Oct 14–Nov 2	265	1,112	19.24
Rat Lake[a]	1984–86	Jul 11–Jul 30	49	104	32.03
		Jul 31–Aug 19	202	456	30.70
		Aug 20–Sep 8	129	192	40.19
		Sep 4–Sep 23	463	1,260	26.87
		Sep 24–Oct 13	673	3,012	18.26
		Oct 14–Nov 2	778	4,476	14.81
Hopps Pond[a]	1985–86	Sep 4–Sep 23	371	560	39.85
		Sep 24–Oct 13	450	1,186	27.51

[a] Data provided by Eric Hopps.

As the season advanced from August to November, roosting flights contained proportionally fewer single wood ducks, suggesting that these birds were either forming pairs or joining flocks. Although we were unable to document the proportion of birds that joined flocks as singles, the decline in single birds undoubtedly reflected increased pairing activity with seasonal advancement.

Armbruster (1982) was able to document pairing chronology by making daily behavioral observations of wood ducks on Duck Creek Wildlife Management Area in southeastern Missouri. Pair formation began in late September, and 18 percent of all females were found to be paired during this month (Table 58). During October, 67 percent of all females were paired. From December through February wood duck behavioral patterns were influenced by harsh weather conditions, making it difficult to distinguish paired birds (Armbruster 1982). Eighty-three, 91, and 95 percent of all females were paired in March, April, and May, respectively (Table 58).

Table 58. Pairing chronology of wood ducks in southeastern Missouri, August 29, 1977 through May 15, 1978.[a]

Month	Total observed		Percentage paired	
	All birds	Females	All birds	Females
August	59	0	0	0
September	1,436	256	5	18
October	487	60	14	67
November	232	52	27	60
January	448	22	4	46
February	379	56	13	45
March	1,027	413	66	83
April	680	281	76	91
May	113	40	67	95

[a] From Armbruster (1982).

Value of Autumn Roosts to Pair Formation

Wood ducks are known to initiate courtship and form pair bonds earlier than most other ducks (Bellrose 1976). The American black duck is the only other species that forms pairs as early. Moreover, unlike other waterfowl, woodies show remarkable fidelity to traditional roost sites. The beginning of social courtship and formation of roosting aggregations appear to occur simultaneously. Hein and Haugen (1966a) suggested that wood ducks are attracted to roosts because of some social need. We believe that, in addition to other functions (see Chapter 15), autumn roosting stimulates and synchronizes courtship activities. By observing adult displays, yearlings also may learn certain aspects of courtship behavior at these gatherings.

If coquette calls given during autumn function only to attract males and solicit displays, the degree of courtship at autumn roosts should be reflected in the occurrence and frequency of these vocalizations. Eric Hopps has heard hens at evening roosts in central Illinois give this call as early as July 25. The number of hens giving a coquette call and the frequency at which it is uttered increase as autumn advances. At mid-September roosts in central Illinois, females commonly give coquette calls continuously until nearly an hour after sunset.

At an early autumn roost (September 10) of approximately 170 birds, Eric Hopps recorded 120 coquette calls in the evening and 492 the following morning. He felt that the evening calling rate, after all birds had arrived, equaled the frequency of morning vocalizations. The incessant calling of courting females illustrates the importance of autumn roosts to pair bonding.

Eric Hopps also has heard female wood ducks continue to give courtship vocalizations (hauk, coquette, and inciting calls) until well after sunset, especially on calm, clear nights when light from a three-quarters to full moon was present. However, factors such as high winds, overcast skies, and no moonlight apparently curtail the frequency and intensity of nocturnal vocalization. During a 16-minute period (11:00 p.m.–11:15 p.m. CST) on September 19, 1988, under clear skies, light from a half moon, and 24–40-kilometer-per-hour (15–25 mi/hr) winds, Hopps recorded no calls at a roost of approximately 2,250 birds. Similarly, on two nights when the moon was absent or obscured by cloud cover, only 0.53 and 3.3 coquette calls per minute were recorded at a roost where more than 1,000 wood ducks had gathered.

During 10-minute periods on October 3 (8:06–8:15 p.m. CST) and October 6 (10:06–10:15 p.m. CST), 1987, when light from a three-quarter moon was present and a slight breeze was noticeable, Hopps recorded 3.4 and 2.0 coquette calls per minute, respectively, at a central Illinois roost of approximately 100 birds. Similarly, on September 26, 1988, 14 coquette calls per minute were recorded at a roost of approximately 800 birds (10:40–10:49 p.m. CST). The apparent courtship activity that occurs throughout the night at autumn roosts may accelerate the pairing process of adult birds.

In addition to hearing these vocalizations, we have seen wood ducks perform various courtship displays at roost sites. Autumn courtship activity appears to be most intense around sunrise and sunset (Armbruster 1982)—times when woodies are most frequently at a roost. Many associations between birds forming courting groups probably result from encounters and evaluations made at roost sites. Certainly, numerous temporary pair bonds first are established and then retested as birds come into contact at these aggregations.

REPRODUCTIVE STRATEGY

As with other types of birds, monogamy is not a rigidly fixed form of pair bond in many species of ducks. Some species exhibit mixed breeding strategies, occasionally shifting between monogamy and polygyny or promiscuity (McKinney et al. 1983). Gilmer (1971) found evidence that wood ducks may exhibit a mixture of monogamy and contemporaneous polygamy. He observed that on at least one occasion, three of seven radio-tagged drakes each associated with a female other than his mate. The four males that exhibited strong pair bonds were located with their mates 59 percent of the time and established an average home range of approximately 202 hectares (500 ac). In contrast, drakes that associated with females other than their mates were located with their mates only 36 percent of the time and established an average home range of about 546 hectares (1,350 ac).

Wood duck pair bonds may remain intact until the final week of incubation (see Chapter 10). Drake woodies apparently remain with their mates for this relatively long time in order to: (1) protect females against predators during the prelaying and laying periods, thereby enabling the females to concentrate on reaching nutritional levels that will meet the high lipid and protein requirements associated with egg laying; (2) prevent forced copulation attempts prior to and during egg laying; (3) guard against excessive male harassment during incubation recesses and thus reduce nest desertions; and (4) fertilize renesting hens and consequently increase their opportunities for paternity.

Although many species of ducks are gregarious during autumn and winter, they generally become intolerant of one another and disperse during the nesting season. Indeed, the aerial pursuits of many dabbling duck species may result in the dispersion of breeding pairs. Females apparently learn to avoid areas where pursuits by territorial males originate or where males may attempt forced copulation. Subsequently, hens are forced to seek alternate areas where territories are not established or where the chances of sexually motivated pursuits are less frequent. However, breeding wood ducks apparently make no attempt to avoid specific areas. Pairs frequently remain in close proximity to one another while feeding and resting and show no prolonged site attachment. Nest site availability plays an important role in controlling dispersion of local wood duck populations.

Even socially inclined wood ducks like to maintain a small space of separation from others. Their social intolerances build as pair bonds strengthen. In the top left photo, the female on the stump threatens another female as she approaches, apparently with a drake; in the top right scene, a male on a log threatens a female mallard; and in the bottom photo, a male threatens a male as it approaches too closely. *Photos by David McEwen.*

Firmly paired wood duck males maintain vigilance against other males approaching their mates. Because land/water territory is not involved, this defended water area around a female is aptly termed a "moving territory," for as the hen swims over an extensive home range, only a small area centering on her presence is guarded against the trespass of other males. *Photo courtesy of the Minnesota Department of Natural Resources.*

The wood duck's nonterritorial breeding strategy may have developed in response to nest site availability and water level fluctuations. Breeding wood ducks traditionally have used riverine habitat where varying water levels and wind often dramatically alter local cover and food sources. The rise and fall of spring floodwaters may force pairs to seek new resting and feeding places several times during the nesting season. Consequently, wood ducks have little to gain, in terms of reproductive fitness, by defending a particular area. Development of a fixed-location territorial system has been inhibited, at least in part, by the transitory nature of cover and food sources (Brown 1964).

Aerial Pursuits

We believe that dabbling ducks instigate aerial pursuits for one or a combination of the following reasons: courtship, territorial defense, or forced copulation. The motivation of males that engage in aerial pursuits varies greatly with and within species. Intentions of pursuing males are influenced by their pair status and the strength of their pair bonds. In territorial species, paired males actively pursue conspecifics that cross their territorial boundaries (McKinney 1973, Titman and Seymour 1981). These pursuits commonly are known as three-bird flights. Blue-winged teal, gadwalls, and northern shovelers engage in aerial pursuits involving male-to-male aggression (Seymour 1974, Titman and Seymour 1981). In the African black duck and northern shoveler, the motivation of pursuing males appears to be related only to territorial defense (McKinney et al. 1983). In contrast, the mallard, blue-winged teal, and American black duck may initiate three-bird flights for the purpose of territorial defense, forced copulation, or forming liaisons with renesting hens (Seymour and Titman 1978, Titman and Seymour 1981, McKinney et al. 1983). In such nonterritorial species as the northern pintail and green-winged teal, three-bird flights usually result in attempted forced copulations (Smith 1968, McKinney and Stolen 1982). The males of these species combine pair bonding with promiscuity.

From May 16 to 28, 1983, Arthur Hawkins and Robert Jones collected information on the frequency of three-bird flights exhibited by 10 species of ducks nesting in the Minnedosa pothole region of Manitoba (Table 59). Because the temporal pattern of peak nesting and territorial defense varies with species, the flight frequencies reported probably are less than maximum. Nevertheless, the wide range of pursuit flights per hour among different species indicates that some are more prone to initiate aerial chases than others. Hawkins pointed out that although the aerial pursuits of canvasbacks, mallards, and northern pintails reached a peak before the sample period, gadwalls and lesser scaups peaked later. Northern shovelers and blue-winged teal were sampled when most pairs were selecting nest sites and establishing territories. The mallard exceeded all other species in its intensity of pursuit flights (Table 59), even though it was past its maximum pursuit activity.

Most pursuit flights during the prelaying, laying, and renesting periods are directed against females that are looking for nesting sites or laying eggs. Males that engage in three- or multiple-bird flights for reasons other than territorial defense increase their chances of paternity by inseminating prelaying, laying, or renesting females. Both Seymour (1974) and Seymour and Titman (1978) observed the highest frequency of pursuit flights early in the morning, coinciding with the time of ovulation and the daily peak of nest site exploration.

The three-bird chase in the wood duck is somewhat different from the territorial defense in the mallard. Here, an intruding male follows a mated pair. The pair may have taken flight to escape the advances made by the unmated drake and will take evasive action either in the air, by diving into water, or by seeking dense cover. Some woodie pairs appear to tolerate an extra male; trios of two males and a female may be found together through the breeding season, the intruding male invariably at the greater distance from the female. After incubation commences, the tag-along drake usually leaves the mated pair, but nonincubating hens often are seen throughout the breeding season with an attendant extra male. *Photo by F. Eugene Hester.*

Table 59. Comparison of pursuit flight frequencies in 10 species of ducks from the region of Minnedosa, Manitoba, May 16–28, 1983.[a]

Species	Number of pairs counted on transects	Number of observed pursuit flights[b]	Flight frequency per hour	Flight frequency per pair
Mallard	548	38	0.38	0.069
Northern pintail	205	1	0.01	0.005
Gadwall	103	3	0.03	0.029
Green-winged teal	78	2	0.02	0.026
Blue-winged teal	546	11	0.11	0.020
Northern shoveler	294	9	0.09	0.031
Canvasback	291	1	0.01	0.003
Redhead	163	1	0.01	0.006
Lesser scaup	503	3	0.03	0.006
Ruddy duck	109	0	0.00	0.000

[a] Data collected by Arthur S. Hawkins and Robert Jones while surveying 12 breeding ground transects that extended for 322 linear kilometers (200 mi) and encompassed 131 square kilometers (50.6 mi²).
[b] From 100 hours of observations collected between 8:00 a.m. and 6:00 p.m.

Aerial pursuit behavior in the wood duck is much more limited than it is in many prairie dabbling ducks. Although wood ducks exhibit no territorial defense, they do engage in both aggressively and sexually motivated aerial pursuits. Only rarely has one of these chases been observed to end in attempted forced copulation.

We have not seen aerial pursuit of one male by another. Aggressively motivated pursuit flights invariably involved a paired male chasing an intruding pair. This type of pursuit normally originated near a nesting site while the female inspected a potential cavity or laid an egg in the nest. Usually the mated, pursuing male approached an intruding pair, instigated a short skirmish, and subsequently generated a three-bird flight. The pursuing male generally gave an intensive, short chase before terminating the flight. These chases probably serve to repel intruding females from the nest site, thereby reducing the opportunity of dump nesting, and to drive paired males away from the egg-laying female at a time when forced copulation would be the most effective.

Many of the wood duck pursuit flights we have observed appeared to be sexually motivated. These flights generally were prolonged and males commonly joined in or dropped out as the pursuit progressed. The most common type of pursuit flight involved a lone male pursuing a pair of wood ducks. More often than not, the lone male followed the pair when it took flight. In some instances, however, the pursuing drake intercepted a pair in flight.

Many pursuing males seemed content to trail behind and seldom attempted to overtake the passing pair. They often veered off and terminated the chase after a few seconds or a minute or two of flight. In other instances, all three birds landed near one another and the lone drake followed the pair at a fairly close distance. The response that the pursuing male elicited from the pair likely influenced how persistent the attachment became.

Males may undertake low-intensity, nonaggressive, aerial pursuits in order to evaluate the response of the female. The pair status of males that participate in these pursuits allows speculation as to their purpose. Although unpaired drakes probably undertake these pursuits in an effort to establish a pair bond, intruding paired males probably are more concerned with evaluating their chances of a successful forced copulation. Unpaired males that are permitted to accompany a pair may eventually establish a trio, thus improving the unpaired male's chance of mating. If the female's original mate dies or terminates the bond, the second male will be available to establish a new pair bond.

We have seen two multiple-bird flights—one involving four drakes and the other eight—terminate in attempted forced copulation. In each instance, the female swam away with one of the males, indicating that she was paired. We could not determine if her mate engaged in attempted forced pair copulation (copulation between pair members despite resistance by the female).

One or several drakes sometimes pursued a pair intensely, in what appeared to be flights that would terminate in attempted forced copulation. During some of these chases, the pursuing male tried to position himself between the paired drake and hen. In one instance, we observed a paired male undertake such a pursuit after his mate had entered a nest box to continue incubating her eggs. On several other occasions, we saw drakes pursue an egg-laying hen immediately after she left her nest in the morning. These drakes probably were either the third bird of a trio or paired males that intended to attempt forced copulation. The form of these pursuit flights and the behavior of the pursuing male lead us to believe that attempted forced copulation in wood ducks may occur more often than previously believed. Because wood ducks typically seek heavy cover and many flights terminate beyond the vision of observers, many forced copulations may go unobserved.

We observed that the paired female usually tried to terminate these chases by abruptly landing in emergent vegetation. In one instance, however, a pair was pursued for about 250 meters (820 ft) before the birds landed in open water. The pursuing male landed about 10 meters (33 ft) from the pair. Both members of the pair dove underwater upon landing. After surfacing, they swam about 150 meters (492 ft), followed by the pursuing drake, before taking flight. The lone male continued to pursue the pair for about 200 meters (656 ft) before he landed separately.

On Duck Creek Wildlife Management Area in southeastern Missouri, Clawson (1975a) observed only one aerial chase in 277 hours of wood duck observation. This pursuit involved a paired female chasing a lone female. The drake remained on the water, passive throughout the encounter.

In Table 60, we summarized how frequently wood ducks instigated aerial pursuits, excluding courting parties, on Nauvoo Slough, 1985–1986. Pursuit flights began in late March and continued to June, coinciding with the peak periods of nest site exploration and egg laying. No aerial pursuits were observed after June 2. Wood ducks engaged in aerial pursuits throughout the day and did not appear to favor any one time period. Only 18 percent of the drake woodies that engaged in pursuit flights

Table 60. Frequency of aerial pursuit flights by wood ducks at Nauvoo Slough, Illinois, 1985–86.

	Year	
	1985	1986
Observation period	Apr 17–Jun 1	Mar 27–Jun 2
Number of nesting pairs	63	74
Hours of observation	118.2	155.9
Total flights[a]	17	23
Flight frequency per hour[a]	0.14	0.15

[a] Three-bird flights and attempted forced copulation flights were considered together.

returned to the vicinity from which their flights originated.

In 1985, we compared the frequency of mallard and wood duck aerial pursuits during 35 observation periods (Table 61). Even though the number of territorial mallards on Nauvoo Slough was only a tenth the number of breeding woodies, mallards engaged in significantly ($P < 0.05$, $Z = 2.94$) more aerial pursuits (Table 61). The main purpose of mallard pursuit flights appeared related to territorial defense. By contrast, wood ducks appeared to engage in nearly equal numbers of sexually and aggressively motivated flights. Distinguishing between these two forms of pursuit often was difficult, however, because both paired and unpaired male woodies instigated chases in order to determine the female's reproductive condition.

Although the breeding population density at Nauvoo Slough increased by about 18 percent between 1985 and 1986 (Table 60), no significant ($P > 0.05$, chi-square = 0.0041) difference in the frequency of aerial pursuit was detected.

Table 61. Comparison of frequencies of aerial pursuit flights by mallards and wood ducks on Nauvoo Slough, Illinois, April 16–May 28, 1985.[a]

	Species	
	Mallard	Wood duck
Estimated number of nesting pairs	6[b]	63
Hours of observation	66.7	66.7
Total flights[c]	35	15
Number of flights per pair	5.8	0.24
Flight frequency per hour	0.52	0.22

[a] Only sample periods during which observers recorded aerial flight frequencies of both species were used in this analysis.
[b] Territorial pairs; approximately 15 total pairs.
[c] Three-bird flights and attempted forced copulation flights were considered together.

Our observations suggest that, as the pair bond between early-nesting wood ducks begins to wane and males are freed from mate guarding, some males, prior to their annual molt, attempt forced copulation with laying females of other pairs. The extent to which this behavior occurs and the importance of sexually motivated aerial chases to the wood duck's mating system are unknown. However, females that nest late may be more susceptible to forced copulation because many paired males have been freed from mate guarding and can chase without exposing their own mates to the risks of outside paternity.

Forced Copulation

Forced copulation chases, attempts, or both have been observed in 39 species of waterfowl (McKinney et al. 1983). Much variation occurs among species, however, and forced copulation attempts appear to be absent in some species and rare to common in others (McKinney et al. 1983).

Extra-pair. Armbruster (1982) concluded that wood ducks rarely engage in forced extra-pair copulation attempts, and little evidence of the occurrence of extra-pair copulation has been reported in the literature (Heinroth 1910, Miller 1977a). Heinroth (1910) indicated that female wood ducks usually resisted attempted forced copulation by diving and swimming rather than by flying. This behavioral characteristic may be one reason forced copulation attempts have seldom been observed under natural conditions.

During the second week in April 1986, we observed male wood ducks on Nauvoo Slough attempt forced copulation on three different occasions. In two instances the females initially tried to avoid the attacks by flapping at the surface and swimming rapidly away from the drakes. Both retreats eventually developed into aerial chases. We were unable to document the events associated with the beginning of the third attempt.

Pair. In reviewing the literature we found no reports of attempted or successful forced pair copulations by wood ducks. However, our observations at Nauvoo Slough indicate that forced pair copulation may occur. In two cases of attempted forced copulation, the paired drake accompanied the group of pursuing males in flight. After landing, events occurred so rapidly that we were unable to determine if the paired male copulated with his mate during the attack. Although he was observed with the males as they piled on top of the female, his intent may have been to dislodge the other drakes.

The third observation of attempted forced copulation did not result in an aerial chase. Two males were observed to copulate with a female in a manner that suggested forced pair copulation; however, their pair status was unknown.

Paired males of many dabbling duck species (northern pintail, American black duck, northern shoveler, blue-winged teal, American wigeon, green-winged teal, gadwall, and mallard) are known to attempt forced copulation (McKinney et al. 1983). Although most of the drake wood ducks that we observed attempting forced copulation were of unknown pair status, one was known to be paired with another female.

The high breeding density and open marsh habitat on Nauvoo Slough may have increased the frequency of forced copulation behavior because females may more easily escape males in more wooded habitats. Nonetheless, our observations at Nauvoo Slough indicate that forced copulation among wood ducks may not be as uncommon as previously believed. Further study is needed to determine whether forced copulations occur frequently enough to function as a secondary insemination strategy.

Unpaired males. Most unpaired male dabbling ducks initiate only those courtship activities associated with pair formation (Smith 1968, Dwyer 1974, Seymour 1974, Derrickson 1977, Seymour and Titman 1979, Afton 1985). Among all ducks, only unpaired male blue-winged teal and lesser scaups have been observed to attempt forced copulation (Bailey et al. 1978, Afton 1985). Because the unpaired male blue-winged teal were observed to perform displays before attempting forced copulation, Bailey et al. (1978) considered their behaviors to be associated with pair formation. Presumably, lesser scaups increase their chances of paternity by form-

Forced copulation is mating of a hen by a male with which the hen is not paired. It is a fairly uncommon event. Usually (but not always) the hen is unreceptive to the aggressive advances of one or more males (probably unmated males). It seems to take place most often in wood ducks with hens whose clutches have failed or been destroyed late in the incubation period and after their mates have departed or the pair bond has diminished. *Photo by Scott Nielsen.*

ing pair bonds through mate switches rather than engaging in forced copulation.

We believe that a similar situation exists among wood ducks. Paired males generally can protect their mates from conspecifics with threat displays and on-water chasing activities. Mate guarding, prior to and during egg laying, is highly developed in the wood duck. Moreover, because most unpaired males probably are yearlings with little copulation experience (Armbruster 1982), it seems likely that forced copulation is a less successful breeding strategy than pair formation through trios.

Trios

Trios made up of a hen wood duck with two drakes commonly are seen during the spring. There seems to be a social tendency for paired wood ducks to acquire an extra male near the beginning of nest initiation. An extra drake is permitted to follow the pair, but he seldom gets as close to the hen as her mate. Nevertheless, an extra male often accompanies the paired birds while they feed, rest, preen, and search for a nest site, without eliciting the ordinary challenges associated with such a close approach. A threat by either member of the pair usually only momentarily deters the extra drake from attachment; after a brief hesitation, he usually resumes pair association.

Korschgen's (1972) observations of captive wood ducks indicated that the unpaired male of a trio can replace the paired drake as the hen's mate. The extra male performed several displays and tried to lead the hen away from her original mate. After the paired drake was removed from the observation pen, the extra drake immediately established a pair bond. Copulation was observed between the hen and the extra drake three days after her original mate had been removed from the pen. When an extra drake is allowed to follow a pair, his compatibility as a mate probably can be assumed. Under natural conditions, this association may ensure that a female acquires a new mate if the paired male dies or prematurely terminates the pair bond.

From February 8 through June 20, 1947–1979, we surveyed the wood duck population on Quiver Creek by walking established transects and recording the social status of observed individuals. An extra male accompanied 17.4 percent (n = 385) of all pairs encountered. During May, nearly 66 percent of all pairs encountered were accompanied by an extra drake (Table 62). We found a significant correlation (r = 0.763, P < 0.01) between the number of nest starts per week and the number of trios observed during that week. Because the greatest number of trios was observed during peak egg-laying periods, it seems likely that unpaired males were able to increase their chances of mating by joining pairs around the time females began laying.

Table 62. Temporal pattern of trio formation of wood ducks along Quiver Creek, Illinois, 1947–79.

Date		Total number of pairs[a]	Number of trios	Percentage of pairs with an extra male
February	8–14	5	0	0
	15–21	16	4	25.00
	22–28	18	2	11.11
March	1–7	67	6	8.96
	8–14	135	13	9.63
	15–21	206	37	17.96
	22–28	311	36	11.58
	29–4	317	33	10.41
April	5–11	363	46	12.67
	12–18	352	69	19.60
	19–25	227	40	17.62
	26–2	66	22	33.33
May	3–9	29	20	68.97
	10–16	42	29	69.05
	17–23	27	10	37.04
	24–30	18	16	88.89
	31–6	8	0	0
June	7–13	9	2	22.22
	14–20	1	0	0

[a] Includes trios.

A female wood duck, with head down and bill agape, appears to be inciting her mate to threaten the intruding male on the ground below. They seem, however, to have accepted the affiliation of another drake. Why certain drakes are tolerated by a breeding pair while other drakes are not is unknown. *Photo by David McEwen*.

Renesting Courtship

The average incubation period of wood ducks is approximately 31 days (see Chapter 10). If an incubated nest is destroyed early in the nesting season, most adult females will lay another clutch. How long eggs have been incubated prior to nest destruction strongly affects the renesting interval. Because females lose about 2 grams per day (0.07 oz/

day) while incubating (see Chapter 9), they require proportionally more time to replenish depleted nutrient reserves when nest destruction occurs later into incubation. Just as importantly, drakes are more likely to abandon their mates at earlier stages of incubation later in summer, thereby increasing the likelihood that renesting females will need to establish new pair bonds as the breeding season progresses.

Courtship events that lead to the fertilization of renesting females are poorly understood. If the pair bond has been broken, the female must either pair again or be inseminated through forced copulation. Because of potential physical damage (including death), females are unlikely to signal males to engage in forced copulation (McKinney 1975). McKinney et al. (1983) summarized the available evidence among ducks and concluded that most renesting females are fertilized after they form another pair bond.

Female mallards, gadwalls, and northern pintails perform a type of aerial pursuit that has been characterized as "renesting courtship" by Sowls (1955). At some point during these flights the hen slows her climb and appears to hesitate momentarily in midair. Sowls (1955) believed that the calls given by the hen and the behavior she exhibits during these flights encourage drakes to pursue her. Johnsgard (1965) indicated that these flights are given when males pursue a female whose mate is absent. According to Palmer (1976), her mate may participate in these flights if the pair bond is nearly dissolved. We have seen female wood ducks at Nauvoo Slough engage in a similar type of pursuit flight. Although their head and neck movements were not as exaggerated as those of hen mallards, female woodies stalled their flight and hovered momentarily at times during the pursuits.

Survival favors males over females (see Chapter 18), leading to a sex ratio biased toward males. Because there is a surplus of males in wood duck populations, females have more than one choice in selecting a mate. The process of choosing a mate has led through the eons of time to development of calls and displays that provide a means of evaluation.

SUMMARY

The wood duck—along with other species in the subfamily Anatinae—has a predominance of males, brief pair bonds, and complex courtship rituals (Johnsgard 1965). On the other hand, whistling ducks, swans, and geese of the subfamily Anserinae have mostly even sex ratios, permanent pair

Within their home range, pairs of wood ducks use stumps, logs, muskrat houses, or shorelines as convenient sites to rest. When food is plentiful and pair bonds strong, they have ample time for resting before and during egg laying. A few drakes remain with their spouses through the incubation period, but about half leave by the time the midpoint is reached. As the breeding season progresses, males desert their mates increasingly early in incubation. *Photo by Charles and Elizabeth Schwartz.*

bonds, and more simple courtship displays. Thus, where waterfowl species have had to make frequent selection of mates, it appears that intricate displays have evolved to indicate the physiological state and physical condition of competing birds. This may be reflected in males by the vigor and persistence of their pursuit of a female whose calls and displays have indicated a readiness to find a mate. The end result may be that the female selects a mate that, at that time, is most likely to defend her from attacks by other males and provide the most vigor to the offspring.

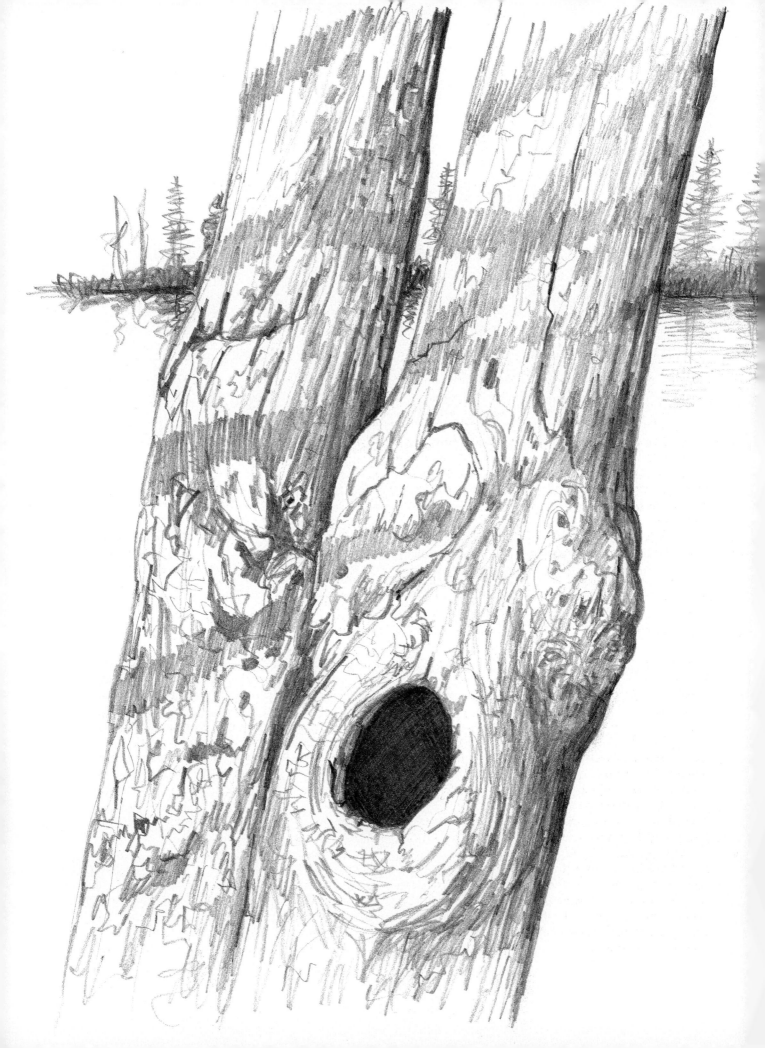

Chapter 7

Natural Cavities

Although wood ducks nest in houses made and erected specifically for them, all but a small proportion nest in natural cavities. The abundance of natural cavities in or adjacent to wetlands is an important factor that defines the status of a local breeding population. Because of the wood duck's relatively large body size, suitable nest cavities must have entrances large enough to admit them and platforms large enough to provide space for a dozen or more eggs plus the incubating bird. Other animals also covet natural cavities, including raccoons, opossums, squirrels, owls, and rat snakes, to name a few. Thus, in many woodlands, cavities available for nesting wood ducks are at a premium.

CAVITY FORMATION

A typical wood duck nest cavity is in the trunk of a tree and has a stable floor that will hold eggs, a covered top, and a side entrance hole. Hollows of this sort are the products of different processes, often in combination. Cavities of suitable size for wood ducks sometimes are excavated by other species. A number of researchers (Weier 1966, Prince 1968, Hansen 1971, Robb 1986) have found wood duck nests in the former nests of pileated woodpeckers or in cavities where the entrances had been made by this bird and the cavities hollowed further by another animal. Pileated woodpeckers normally excavate cavities in a snag (Bull and Meslow 1977) but sometimes in the dead limb of a live tree (Hoyt 1957). Although most wood duck nests have been found in live trees, site selection appears proportional to the availability of suitable cavities in dead and live trees (Table 63). Thus, in areas used for nesting by both species, pileated woodpeckers may be an important source of nest sites for wood ducks.

Cringan (1971) suggested that increased wood duck numbers in Ontario may be attributed partly to increased numbers of pileated woodpeckers; both species greatly increased in number in that province over a period of several decades. In addition, Nagel (1969) found that woodpecker activity appeared to be the main cause of cavity formation in aspen and birch. Although abandoned pileated woodpecker nest and roost cavities generally are of low to moderate importance—ranging from 4 percent (Weier 1966) to 7 percent (Prince 1968, Robb 1986) to 25 percent (Haramis 1990) of the suitable wood duck nest sites—woodpeckers are nevertheless important for their role in assisting, in conjunction with other factors, with cavity formation.

Tree cavity formation more commonly occurs through the slower process of natural decay. Physical injury to the tree stem instigated by wind, lightning, frost, snow damage, or breaking of a branch often is a beginning point (Gayle 1986). Other tree injuries include false nest starts by woodpeckers, basal fire scars, insect infestation, or a combination of these. Of 237 cavities inspected in central Illinois by Johnson (1959), 60 percent were formed through the breaking of dead limbs, 38 percent resulted from external forces (such as wind or lightning), 1 percent from woodpecker action, and 1 percent from deformity in the growth of the tree. Broken or dead limbs and subsequent heartwood decay accounted for 60 percent of 411 cavities found at Tamarac National Wildlife Refuge in Minnesota (Nagel 1969). At Mingo National Wildlife Refuge in Missouri, broken and dead limbs were the origin of 61 percent of 109 cavities (Weier 1966). About 18 percent were due to fire scar decay, 8 percent to lightning and logging damage, and 4 percent to woodpeckers; 9 percent were of undetermined origin. In Mississippi, Lowney (1987) found that 65 percent of cavities suitable for nesting were formed

167

Table 63. Number and proportion of live trees that contained cavities suitable for wood duck nesting, and the number and proportion used by wood ducks.

Location	Suitable cavities found		Suitable cavities used		Reference
	Total number	Number in live trees (percentage)	Total number	Number in live trees (percentage)	
Indiana	122	99 (81.1)	37	30 (81.1)	Robb (1986)
Michigan	90	88 (97.8)	4	4 (100.0)	Boyer (1974)
Illinois			58	47 (81.0)	Gigstead (1938)
New Brunswick	46	43 (93.5)	24		Prince (1965)
Mississippi	30	30 (100.0)	8	8 (100.0)	Teels (1975)
Mississippi	23	23 (100.0)			Lowney (1987)[a]
Minnesota			28	25 (89.3)	Gilmer et al. (1978)
Missouri	23	21 (91.3)	6	5 (83.3)	Weier (1966)
Wisconsin	13	11 (84.6)	1	1 (100.0)	Soulliere (1985)

[a] Data collected on Noxubee National Wildlife Refuge and Delta National Forest.

as a result of broken branches. Other causes of suitable cavity formation in his study included woodpeckers (13 percent) and lightning (4 percent); 17 percent of the causes were unknown.

During the normal course of events, a fungus enters through injuries and further weakens the wood so that birds or tree-using mammals can more readily excavate a cavity in the affected area (Gayle 1986). Decay occurs in the center of trees because, in most cases, dead heartwood is more easily rotted. Because fungi do not rot live bark or the outer rim of sapwood in the tree trunk, they must gain access to the heartwood through a break. Squirrels and woodpeckers excavate or expand cavities by removing the dead, punky wood that results as decay progresses (Allen 1943). Fox squirrels (Nixon et al. 1978) and gray squirrels, according to Stephen Havera, also gnaw the scar tissue surrounding entrances to their tree dens. This process often enlarges small holes to a size useful to wood ducks and prevents cavity entrances from closing; squirrels normally move from tree dens to leaf nests during the warm months, making their cavities available to wood ducks.

Hardwood forest stands generally contain the tree species that develop wood duck nest cavities. Some species tend to produce more cavities than others, although quality and durability may vary. In addition, environmental and genetic factors govern the production in species and individual trees. Finally, susceptibility of tree species to cavity formation can vary depending on soil fertility, exposure, and other extrinsic factors. Some of these factors include the ability of the sap to attract insects, birds, or mammals (Gayle 1986). An injury during the period when sap is flowing may draw a particular species of insect that in turn may draw a bird. An excavation by that bird may, in turn, introduce a rotting fungus. The same tree injured during a period of dormancy may attract neither birds nor insects. The form of the crown also may affect the tree's tendency to suffer mechanical damage.

As a result of their extensive distribution in bottomland and upland forests, about 90 percent of the breeding wood duck females use natural cavities for nest sites. However, few natural cavities exclude arboreal predators, resulting in heavy nest losses, particularly from raccoons. *Photo by William Clark; courtesy of the Illinois Natural History Survey.*

Weather conditions—primarily ice, snow, and wind—affect wide-crowned trees more than those with narrow crowns. Sprouting stumps provide another major avenue of infection by rotting fungi (Hansen 1966). Hardwood trees that originate from stump sprouts are more subject to heartrot decay than are conifers and hardwoods that originate from seeds. Consequently, trees originating from sprouts produce more cavities. Pine forests generally are not good cavity producers, although usable cavities can be found in old growth (Gayle 1986).

Sprouting vigor from stumps and the age to which sprouting continues vary considerably among hardwoods. Decay cannot occur until heartwood is formed and until fungi reach the heartwood (without penetrating bark or sapwood tissues). Information on decay from basal origin among various oak species indicates that cavity formation under natural conditions generally is a very slow process (Hansen 1966). Local situations may vary, however, as was the case with black oaks growing on sandy soils in Mason County, Illinois. Because the taproot of a black oak dies when the tree is about 20 years old, according to Leo Tehon, decay can enter through the taproot and proceed through the heartwood. A variety of sources of external damage to trees resulted in rapid cavity formation and relatively high cavity abundance in the black oak woodlots of Mason County.

CAVITY TYPES AND WOOD DUCK USE

Tree cavities used by wood ducks have been described in numerous ways. The three basic types include: the most common or typical, enclosed with a side entrance; the bucket or cavity with a top entrance; and a combination of side and top entrances (Gilmer et al. 1978, Robb 1986). Dreis (1951) and Prince (1968) described nest cavities as either closed or bucket. Cavities that have top entrances and tend to fill with water or debris usually are unsuitable sites. Lowney (1987) reported that 60 percent of the bucket-type cavities examined on the Noxubee National Wildlife Refuge in Mississippi contained water, even though no rain had fallen for a month. However, bucket cavities apparently are more valuable sites at northern latitudes than they are farther south (Prince 1968, Robb 1986).

More wood duck nests are found in typical cavities than in other types. Gilmer et al. (1978) found 58, 31, and 11 percent of 28 nests in cavities with side, top, and combination entrances, respectively. Prince (1968) examined 24 nests and found only slightly more in enclosed cavities (58 percent) than

Natural cavities suitable for wood duck nests vary widely in size and shape, but sites with small entrances (top) and shafts 38–63 centimeters (15–25 in) deep are preferred. Most of the trees selected have cavity base diameters varying from 20 to 25 centimeters (8–10 in) (center); smaller and larger ones are less used. Cavities with side openings are created by a limb breaking off (bottom), which either opens a passage to a core cavity created by heartrot or initiates the decay of heartwood by permitting the entrance of moisture, fungi, and bacteria. Bucket-type cavities are formed where wind breaks the top of tree trunks in which heartwood has decayed a core area. *Photos by Dan Holm; courtesy of the Illinois Natural History Survey.*

in bucket cavities (42 percent); however, the proportion of each cavity type available was unknown. Most (10 of 16) of the common goldeneye nests on the same area were in bucket cavities.

Robb (1986) compared the characteristics of all suitable cavities that he found with those actually used by wood ducks. He determined that a greater (P < 0.05, 1 df, chi-square = 4.53) number of typical cavities was used in proportion to their availability; 27 of 36 nests (75 percent) were in typical cavities, but only 51 percent of the suitable cavities were classified as typical. Cavities created by woodpeckers normally are classed as typical (enclosed

with a side entrance), and four of six wood duck nest entrances studied by Weier (1966) were made by pileated woodpeckers. Five of eight pileated woodpecker cavities found by Robb (1986) were used by wood ducks, and this use also was more than expected (P < 0.05, 1 df, chi-square = 3.91).

During surveys to determine the density of suitable cavities, researchers have found the use of such cavities to range from 0 to 52 percent (Table 64). In Mason County, Illinois, the same woodlots were surveyed in 1939–1940 (Bellrose et al. 1964), 1958–1961 (Johnson 1959, Meyers 1962), and 1964–1965 (Shake 1967). The percentage of wood duck use of

Table 64. Density and wood duck use of suitable natural nesting cavities and important cavity tree species from surveys of timber stands used by nesting wood ducks.

Location	Suitable cavities Per hectare (ac)[a]		Found	Used (percentage)		Tree species[b]
SC New Brunswick	5.50	(2.23)	46	24	(52.2)	Silver maple, American elm
NC Minnesota	4.20	(1.70)	28			Quaking aspen, American elm, sugar maple
WC New York	3.95	(1.60)	26	8	(30.8)	Red maple, red ash, American elm
SC Indiana	1.23	(0.50)	122	37	(30.3)	American beech, red maple, sycamore
SE Missouri	1.19	(0.48)	8	0	(0.0)	Bottomland hardwoods
C Georgia	0.67	(0.27)	22	9	(40.9)	Sycamore, boxelder
C Wisconsin	0.67	(0.27)	13	1	(7.7)	Silver and sugar maple, quaking aspen, American basswood
WC Mississippi	0.66	(0.27)	27	0	(0.0)	Black willow, baldcypress
NW Minnesota	0.63[c]	(0.25)	54	9	(16.7)	American basswood, quaking and bigtooth aspen, American and slippery elm
NE Mississippi	0.57	(0.23)	30	8	(26.7)	Tupelo gum, baldcypress
C Illinois[d]	0.51[e]	(0.21)	105	39	(37.1)	Black oak
SE Missouri	0.33[f]	(0.13)	23	0	(0.0)	Black gum, oak (4 species), elm (3 species), sycamore
C Mississippi	0.19–0.23	(0.08–0.09)	23	0	(0.0)	Bottomland hardwoods
SE Iowa	0.13	(0.05)	11	4	(36.4)	Bottomland hardwoods
SC Michigan	0.11	(0.04)	90	4	(4.4)	Red maple, red oak, bitternut hickory, black walnut, black willow
C Mississippi	0.075	(0.03)	1	0	(0.0)	Oak, sweetgum
C Illinois			211	48	(22.7)	Upland hardwoods
W Massachusetts			22	10	(45.5)	Apple, ash, maple, oak, pine (species not identified)
Total/mean[g]			834	201	(24.1)	

[a] Some density figures were not given in the publication but are calculated or estimated from available data.
[b] When species were not provided, they are listed in order of their importance in a given habitat type.
[c] From three habitat types combined: upland (40 hectares: 16.2 ac), lowland (9 hectares: 3.6 ac), and hardwoods and aspen (36 hectares: 14.6 ac) had 1.00, 0.64, and 0.22 suitable cavities per hectare (0.40, 0.26, and 0.09/ac), respectively.
[d] Numbers are averages found over six years on the same study areas.
[e] Density in upland (black oak) woodlots. A preliminary survey of 147 hectares (363 ac) of bottomland timber revealed a suitable cavity density of 0.15 per hectare (0.06/ac).
[f] Suitable cavity densities were 0.11 and 0.31 per hectare (0.04 and 0.125/ac) in two bottomland timber types and 0.72 per hectare (0.29/ac) in upland hardwoods.
[g] Gilmer et al. (1978) omitted.

suitable cavities dropped from 50.7 (1940) to 33.0 (1960) to 22.7 (1965). This drop appeared related to an increase in nest predation and a decline in survival of young (see Chapter 18).

The highest use rate reported for natural cavities was 65.5 percent (n = 142) in Minnesota (Strom 1969). However, many cavities in that study had been modified to suit the requirements of nesting woodies, causing increase in the opportunity of selection. Cavities were improved by creating or enlarging entrances in hollow trees and by forming platforms or plugging trunks that were hollow throughout their length. Of 52 modified cavities, 26 (50 percent) were used by woodies the first year.

Table 64. (continued)

Reference
Prince (1968)
Gilmer et al. (1978)
Haramis (1975)
Robb (1986)
Hartowicz (1963)
Almand (1965)
Soulliere (1988)
Strange (1970)
Nagel (1969)
Teels (1975)
Bellrose et al. (1964)
Weier (1966)
Lowney (1987)
Dreis and Hendrickson (1952)
Boyer (1974)
Woods (1964)
Shake (1967)
Grice and Rogers (1965)

CAVITY AVAILABILITY

A number of factors may affect the use of natural cavities by wood ducks: juxtaposition of cavities to wetlands, quality of brood-rearing areas, abundance and durability of large trees containing suitable nest cavities, competition for existing nest sites, and previous productivity of breeding woodies inhabiting a particular area.

Location

Hens will travel long distances inland to find nest sites, but cavities less than 0.8 kilometer (0.5 mi) from wetlands likely will be selected first. Grice and Rogers (1965) and Nagel (1969) found few nests farther than 180 meters (197 yd) from water. In Minnesota, Gilmer (1971) found that 68 percent of the natural cavities used by wood ducks were situated within 161 meters (176 yd) of a wetland. Similarly, Robb (1986) found 70 percent of wood duck nests in Indiana within 30 meters (33 yd) of a wetland. The average distance from water of three natural cavities used by wood ducks in Mississippi was 1 meter (1.1 yd) (Lowney 1987).

Grice and Rogers (1965) noted that very large trees and trees standing alone seldom were used, and that wood ducks preferred to nest in rows or clusters of large trees of similar size. This preference may relate to their greater exposure to predators when in large, isolated trees. Often the use of particular cavities may depend on open areas of approach for easy access and entrance visibility, as well as an earlier history of nest success. Sites close to water normally are discovered first and, because of homing and higher brood survival, have the potential to contribute more ducklings to local wetlands than do those sites more distant from water. Nevertheless, because of predation, nest success often is higher farther inland than closer to water. Robb (1986) found that the distance to nearest water was significantly (P < 0.05) greater for successful nests than for unsuccessful nests.

During 1938–1939, we found 14 (21 percent) of 68 wood duck nests in cavities between 0.8 and 1.6 kilometers (0.5–1.0 mi) from water in central Illinois; only one nest was more distant, and the rest (78 percent) were less than 0.8 kilometer (0.5 mi). In the same area, during 1958–1959, Johnson (1959) found that the distance from water of trees with active nests averaged 176 meters (192 yd) and ranged from 6 to 594 meters (7–650 yd). Robb (1986) found that the average distance from nest site to nearest wetland (water available in July) was 207 ± 190 meters (226 ± 208 yd); the average distance to nearest brood habitat was 446 ± 318 meters (488 ± 348 yd).

Gilmer et al. (1978) examined the habitat around 31 nest sites and found brood-rearing areas present within 0.5 kilometer (0.3 mi) of 21 nests (68 percent); for 8 nests (26 percent), this distance exceeded 1 kilometer (0.6 mi). Distances from nesting cavities to nearest water ranged from 0 to 350 meters (0–383 yd) and averaged 80 meters (87 yd). They also observed that when hens (n = 31) were away from cavities, most (70 percent) of their activity was within 1 kilometer (0.6 mi) of the nest sites. Thus, woodlots farther than 1.6 kilometers (1 mi) from water are of limited value to nesting wood ducks.

Tree Size

Generally, trees 30 centimeters (12 in) or larger in diameter at breast height are adequate to contain suitable nest sites (Table 65). Boyer (1974) found evidence in Michigan of wood duck nesting in a red maple with an 18-centimeter (7 in) diameter at breast height; however, the diameter of the tree was larger in the upper trunk at the site of the nest cavity; the inside diameter of the cavity was also 18 centimeters (7 in). In New York, a hen nested in a dead elm that was 22 centimeters (8.7 in) in diameter at breast height, but Haramis (1975) found the remaining (96 percent) acceptable sites in trees 33 centimeters (13 in) or larger. Two of 30 (6.7 percent) suitable nest sites found by Teels (1975) in a Mississippi tupelo/cypress area were in trees that ranged

from 25 to 36 centimeters (10–14 in) in diameter. Trees in the 64–86-centimeter (25–34 in) range contained the largest proportion of suitable cavities. Only 20 percent of the trees surveyed were in the larger size group, but they were responsible for 40 percent of the cavities. Robb (1986) reported that wood ducks in Indiana nested more frequently in trees 41–58 centimeters (16–23 in) in diameter than in trees of other size groups (P < 0.05) (Figure 55).

Forest age determines cavity density, but the time required for trees to reach adequate size to produce suitable cavities varies with species and local growing conditions. Northern hardwoods have the potential for producing high densities of cavities, but the time required to develop suitable sites for wood ducks in this type of timber may be on the order of 100 years, compared with about 50 for aspen (Gilmer et al. 1978). According to Weier (1966), black willow and ash trees in Missouri produced cavities before reaching a diameter at breast height of 38 centimeters (15 in); overcup oak, on the other hand, contained few cavities until it reached about 69 centimeters (27 in).

Johnson (1959) found that black oaks with cavities of minimum diameter were 60–70 years of age. The red maples with cavities studied by Boyer (1975b) were about 40 years old with a diameter at breast height of 25–28 centimeters (10–11 in). Mature and overmature trees, however, have the greatest potential to provide nest sites. The highest cavity densities yet reported (Table 64) were in virgin bottomland hardwoods that averaged 230 ± 93 years (Prince 1968).

Table 65. Diameter at breast height (dbh)[a] of trees containing cavities suitable for wood duck nests and of trees used by wood ducks.

Location	Trees with suitable cavities			Trees used by wood ducks			Reference
	Number	Dbh average	Dbh range	Number	Dbh average	Dbh range	
Minnesota	142			93	66	38–91	Strom (1969)
Illinois	139		31–104	62	48	31–104	Johnson (1959)
Indiana	100	70	27–186	34	59	33–91	Robb (1986)
Michigan	90			4	86	18–135	Boyer (1974)
Minnesota	54			9	46	36–56	Nagel (1969)
New Brunswick	46	62	33–127	24	66	33–127	Prince (1965)
Minnesota				22	47		Gilmer et al. (1978)
New York	26	42	22–64	8	42	22–64	Haramis (1975)
Missouri	23			6	53	33–69	Weier (1966)
Massachusetts	22	69	33–91	10			Grice and Rogers (1965)
Mississippi[b]	15	55		0			Lowney (1987)
Wisconsin	13	61	36–140	1	140		Soulliere (1985)
Mississippi[c]	8	67		0			Lowney (1987)
Mississippi[d]				3	70		Lowney (1987)

[a] Measurements in centimeters.
[b] Noxubee National Wildlife Refuge.
[c] Delta National Forest.
[d] Yazoo National Wildlife Refuge.

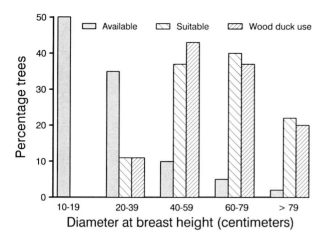

Figure 55. Percentages of trees in diameter (dbh) classes for available trees (estimated from 31 sample plots), trees with suitable cavities (n = 107), and trees with wood duck nests (n = 37) at Muscatatuck National Wildlife Refuge, Indiana, 1984–85 (from Robb 1986).

Longevity

Cavity life can be affected by intrinsic and extrinsic factors. The standing time of dead timber obviously is less than that of live timber of the same species. Cavity longevity in dead trees, because it is not impaired by tree growth, simply is as long as the tree remains standing and the walls of the cavity remain intact. Availability of cavities in live timber, however, is affected by tree growth, with cavity entrances often closing or becoming covered by bark. During a two-year study in Indiana, Robb (1986) estimated the annual duration of 122 suitable cavities to be 91.3 percent (range = 85.9–97.0 percent). Honey bees were responsible for the loss of three cavities, and two cavity trees fell. Cavity instability, primarily caused by cavity bottoms becoming unplugged and making the cavity too deep for wood

duck nesting, made four cavities unsuitable. However, Robb (1986) found that cavity formation and cavity renovation by fox squirrels probably were equal to or greater than the annual losses of suitable cavities.

Bellrose et al. (1964) obtained tree cavity data from the same areas in 1939–1940 and again in 1958–1961. The occurrence of natural cavities suitable for nesting wood ducks was relatively stable over this 22-year period; densities increased from 0.48 per hectare (0.19/ac) to 0.52 per hectare (0.21/ac) between survey periods. Although some cavities were destroyed by winds each year, new cavities were created by squirrels or by winds that broke off treetops and large branches.

SELECTION OF CAVITIES

Previous nest success is an important factor in the selection of natural cavities for wood duck nesting. Along the Illinois River, we found that a high proportion of cavities that had been used successfully was selected again the following year (Table 66). Cavities in which nests had been destroyed the previous year were less than half as likely to be used the following year. This behavior suggests that previous nest predation affects the selection of cavities by returning adult females.

A variety of cavity characteristics may affect nest success and the subsequent use of individual sites. In central Illinois, a unique situation existed— almost all nesting took place in black oak uplands. Thus, wood duck selection of nest sites could be evaluated in fairly similar settings, with fewer variables than would normally be possible. The following descriptions include important cavity characteristics in Illinois and comparisons with what others have found elsewhere.

Table 66. Use of natural cavities by wood ducks in years following successful and unsuccessful nesting attempts in central Illinois, 1959–61.[a]

Year	Following successful nesting		Following unsuccessful nesting		t	P
	Number of cavities	Percentage used	Number of cavities	Percentage used		
1959	16	75.0	12	50.0	1.37	>0.10
1960	18	88.9	31	32.3	4.23	<0.001
1961	14	71.4	18	38.3	1.90	<0.10
Total	48		61			
Weighted mean		79.2		37.7	4.52	<0.001

[a] From Bellrose et al. (1964).

Entrance

The entrance is the first cavity feature noticed by nest-searching females and is one of the most important features in site selection. Cavities with relatively small entrances are used at higher rates than are those with larger entrances (Figure 56). A high proportion of cavities with 9- by 10-centimeter (3.5 by 4 in) entrances—the smallest openings through which hens can readily pass—was used. Entrances ranging from 65–252 square centimeters (10–39 in²) received notably higher use than did cavities with larger openings. The largest entrance to an occupied cavity measured 30 by 61 centimeters (12 by 24 in). Average size for all entrances was 11 by 20 centimeters (4.3 by 7.9 in).

Wood ducks at Muscatatuck National Wildlife Refuge in Indiana also selected cavities with smaller entrances significantly more (P<0.001) than cavities with larger entrances (Robb 1986). The smallest wood duck entrance found by Prince (1968) in New Brunswick was 8 by 10 centimeters (3 by 4 in); the largest was 15 by 76 centimeters (6 by 30 in); and the average was 13 by 25 centimeters (5 by 10 in). Stuewer (1943b) observed a woodie using a cavity with an entrance 6 by 10 centimeters (2.4 by 3.9 in).

Wood ducks evidently find cavities made by pileated woodpeckers to be desirable nest sites, because they select them at a high rate (Robb 1986).

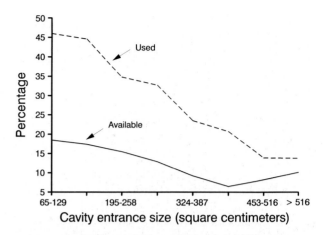

Figure 56. Relationship between entrance sizes of available natural cavities and the proportion of each size used by wood ducks in central Illinois, 1958–61 (graphed lines represent a three-way moving average) (adapted from Bellrose et al. 1964).

Entrances to these nest sites are uniformly small (Table 67) and are normally round or have a vertical ellipse rather than a horizontal ellipse for an opening. Haramis (1990) reported the average entrance size of 13 pileated woodpecker cavities as 8.6 by 10.9 centimeters (3.4 by 4.3 in).

Selection of small entrances no doubt is a mechanism of survival developed through evolution, because raccoons are less likely to penetrate these

Table 67. Measurements of cavity trees and cavities excavated by pileated woodpeckers.

Characteristic	Mean	S.D.	Range
Tree			
Diameter at breast height[a]	76[b]	29.7	58–99
	74[c]	26.9	53–91
Height[d]	21[b]	2.2	12–37
Cavity			
Height[d]	13[b]	1.2	7–19
	8[c]	2.1	6–11
Depth[a]	56[b]	16.6	43–61
	41[c]	5.8	36–46
Diameter[a]	23[b]	6.2	18–28
	19[c]	1.5	18–20
Cavity entrance			
Vertical[a]	13[b]	3.9	10–15
	12[c]	1.5	10–13
	12[e]	1.6	11–15
Horizontal[a]	10[b]	2.2	10–10
	10[c]	0.6	9–10
	12[e]	1.1	11–14

[a] In centimeters.
[b] From 13 active wood duck nests in ponderosa pine and western larch on the Starkey Experimental Forest and Range in northeastern Oregon (Bull and Meslow 1977).
[c] From four active roost or nest trees (shagbark hickory, white oak, sycamore, and dead stub) in central and southern Illinois (from Richard R. Graber).
[d] In meters.
[e] From 10 trees (primarily tupelo) in the Four Hole Swamp (Francis Beidler Forest), South Carolina (from Norman L. Brunswig).

The use of pileated woodpecker excavations in dead snags and partially decayed tree trunks as nest sites illustrates the small cavity size that wood ducks are capable of utilizing. Pileated nest shafts are 19.1–23.1 centimeters (7.5–9.1 in) in diameter and 40.6–55.9 centimeters (16–22 in) in depth, with entrance holes 11.9–13.0 centimeters (4.7–5.1 in) vertical and 9.9–11.9 centimeters (3.9–4.7 in) horizontal. To enter the vertical ellipse, wood duck hens have been observed to turn sideways. Note, too, the close proximity of the cavity in the right photo to a water area – a circumstance especially attractive to nesting wood ducks. *Left photo by Scott Nielsen. Right photo by Dan Holm; courtesy of the Illinois Natural History Survey.*

cavities. At Tamarac National Wildlife Refuge, predation of nests in cavities with entrances ranging from 52–97 square centimeters (8–15 in²) was 23 percent, compared with 50 and 39 percent in cavities with entrances ranging from 103–148 and 155–903 square centimeters (16–23 and 24–140 in²), respectively (Nagel 1969).

The direction an entrance faces has little bearing on its use (Grice and Rogers 1965). Robb (1986) found the aspect of a nest site unrelated to the nearest forest opening or nearest water (P > 0.10); cavity entrances also were not clustered in any particular compass direction (P > 0.10).

We have observed wood ducks turn on their sides to enter cavities with long, narrow, vertical openings.

Height

Height is another important factor in the selection of cavities for nest sites (Figure 57). Generally, the higher the cavities, the greater the use rate; those 9 meters (30 ft) or more above ground were more acceptable than lower ones. However, three occupied cavities were only 1.8 meters (6 ft) above

the ground. Average height of cavities containing wood duck nests was 7.6 meters (25 ft); maximum height was 16.8 meters (55 ft).

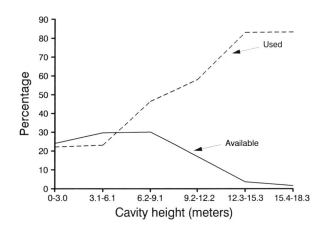

Figure 57. Relationship between height of available natural cavities and the proportion of each height group used by wood ducks in central Illinois, 1958–61 (graphed lines represent a three-way moving average) (adapted from Bellrose et al. 1964).

Hens searching for nest sites often enter woodlots from a fairly high aspect, where high cavities are more noticeable in less dense parts of the forest canopy. Cavity-seeking wood ducks usually land about one-third of the way below a tree's top canopy, where branches are at least 2.5 centimeters (1 in) in diameter. In addition, nests in high cavities are less subject to predators than are nests in low cavities, thereby increasing nest success and return of hens in following years to high cavities. Cavity entrances found by Gilmer et al. (1978) were more than 4 meters (13 ft) above the ground; 54 percent (n = 28) were at least 9 meters (30 ft) high. Prince (1968) found wood duck cavities located 2.4–15.2 meters (8–50 ft) above ground, with an average height of 7.9 ± 3.0 meters (26 ± 10 ft). Wood duck cavities studied by Grice and Rogers (1965) averaged 5.2 meters (17 ft) and ranged from 0.9 to 14.6 meters (3–48 ft) high. Lowney (1987) reported that the average height of three cavities used by wood ducks in Mississippi was 14.3 meters (46.9 ft).

According to Robb (1986), wood ducks selected higher sites significantly more (P < 0.02) than lower cavities; 34 wood duck nest cavities averaged 11.0 ± 3.6 meters (36 ± 12 ft) high, whereas 100 unused suitable sites averaged 8.6 ± 5.7 meters (28 ± 19 ft). Successful nests averaged 12.4 ± 3.0 meters (41 ± 10 ft) high and unsuccessful nests averaged 10.3 ± 3.8 meters (34 ± 12 ft), but there was no significant difference (P > 0.14).

Depth

Cavities less than 1.3 meters (50 in) deep were used most frequently for nest sites (Figure 58). Data

showing highest use of shallow cavities with depths from 10.2 to 22.9 centimeters (4–9 in) may be misleading because some of these hollows extended horizontally into trees for 51 centimeters (20 in) or more. Thus, nests were out of sight even though the cavities were shallow. Minimal depth of occupied cavities was 10.2 centimeters (4 in), average depth was 56 centimeters (22 in), and maximal depth was 4.5 meters (178 in).

Hens in an Indiana study (Robb 1986) also were commonly found nesting in very shallow cavities where the cavities extended back into the trees. Robb (1986) noted that, as long as the hen was concealed from the entrance, shallow cavities were selected at rates similar to those of deeper sites. Grice and Rogers (1965) found hens nesting in hollows from 12 to 122 centimeters (5–48 in) deep and averaging 46 centimeters (18 in). Gilmer et al. (1978) found the average depth of wood duck cavities to be 69 centimeters (27 in); the deepest cavity used was 157.4 centimeters (62 in). Lowney (1987) reported an average vertical depth of wood duck nest cavities (n = 3) as 24 centimeters (9.4 in).

Prince's (1968) measurements of wood duck cavity depth ranged from 2 to 183 centimeters (0.8–72 in) with a mean of 61 ± 61 centimeters (24 ± 24 in). He stated that cavity depth appeared to be the major factor related to raccoon predation of wood duck nests. Raccoons did not destroy wood duck nests in cavities more than 76 centimeters (30 in) deep (n = 6); 8 of 14 (43 percent) of the nests at shallower depths were destroyed by raccoons.

Surviving wood duck females of successful nests usually return to the same nest site; yearlings may follow adults and observe where and how natural cavities are selected. Therefore, wooded areas that produce successful nests have higher breeding densities than do those with histories of high nest failures. Cavities high in trees are selected most often by wood ducks, perhaps because these nests are more successful than lower ones. Predators, especially raccoons, are less likely to find high nest sites. *Photo by Glenn D. Chambers; courtesy of the Missouri Department of Conservation.*

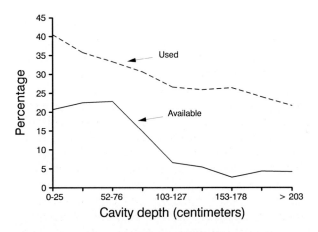

Figure 58. Relationship between depth of available natural cavities and the proportion of each depth group used by wood ducks in central Illinois, 1959–61 (graphed lines represent a three-way moving average) (adapted from Bellrose et al. 1964).

Basal Area

Size of the base area at the bottom of the nest cavity was, within broad limits, an unimportant factor in the selection of nest sites (Figure 59). Wood ducks tended to reject cavities with bases less than 258 square centimeters (40 in²) and larger than 703 square centimeters (109 in²). Cavities with bases ranging from 258 to 703 square centimeters (40–109 in²) appeared equally acceptable.

Prince (1968) also found basal area to be quite variable, with average inside diameters measuring 26 ± 18 centimeters (10.2±7 in). At a New York study area, Haramis (1975) discovered a hen nesting in an extremely small cavity, with a platform of 14 by 15 centimeters (5.5 by 5.9 in); average base dimensions for 26 suitable sites were 20 by 20 centimeters (7.9 by 7.9 in). The smallest active nest site found by Grice and Rogers (1965) contained 516 square centimeters (80 in²) of floor space. Nine nesting bases measured by Nagel (1969) varied from 213 to 406 square centimeters (33–63 in²) and averaged 284 square centimeters (44 in²).

Volume

Volume (basal area times total inside height) varied considerably in cavities selected by hens in Illinois, ranging from less than 16 liters (976 in³) to 82 liters (5,000 in³) (Figure 60). Data on volume provide some measure of use of cavities that are shallow vertically but long horizontally. Cavities of more than 82 liters (5,000 in³) were not as acceptable for nest sites as were smaller cavities. The smallest

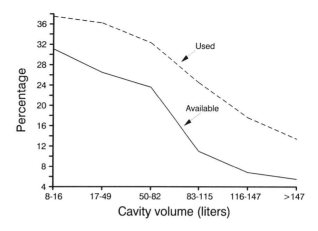

Figure 60. Relationship between volume of available natural cavities and the proportion of each volume group used by wood ducks in central Illinois, 1959–61 (graphed lines represent a three-way moving average) (adapted from Bellrose et al. 1964).

cavity used measured 13 by 18 centimeters (5 by 7 in). Average horizontal dimensions of occupied cavities were 23 by 25 centimeters (9 by 10 in). The diameter of the largest cavity used was 41 centimeters (16 in).

Robb (1986) found cavities used by wood ducks to be smaller (P<0.0001) than unused suitable cavities. Mean volume was 25.6 ± 20.8 liters (1,560±1,270 in³) for wood duck nest sites and 111.9 ± 162.3 liters (6,830±9,900 in³) for unused sites. Soulliere (1985) determined that the volume of 13 cavities suitable for nesting averaged 22 liters (1,360 in³) in Wisconsin, but only one site (20 liters, 1,230 in³) contained an active nest.

CAVITY DENSITY

Tree cavities generally are difficult to find. Determining the occurrence of suitable cavities in a wooded tract is labor intensive, not only because of the thorough ground search necessary but also because of the work involved in examining cavity characteristics. Detection of all cavities is nearly impossible. After climbing trees to inspect hollows observed from the ground, Robb (1986) found cavities that had been missed but were visible from a higher vantage point. He found a total of 789 possible nest sites (visible entrances), of which 13 percent were detected while perched in other trees. Upon close inspection, only 15 percent of the total possible nest sites were deemed suitable for wood duck nesting. Table 68 indicates species differences in apparent (from ground) versus actual cavity suitability and in ground-sighted versus total sighted cavities.

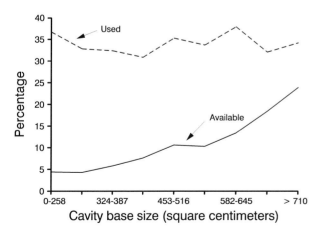

Figure 59. Relationship between area of the bases of available natural cavities and the proportion of each area group used by wood ducks in central Illinois, 1959–61 (graphed lines represent a three-way moving average) (adapted from Bellrose et al. 1964).

Table 68. Frequency of cavity suitability (for wood ducks) and of possible cavity entrances overlooked for tree species on Muscatatuck National Wildlife Refuge, Indiana, 1984–85.[a]

Tree species	Number of possible cavity trees	Number of possible cavity entrances	Frequency rate of cavity trees suitable[b]	Frequency rate of cavities suitable[c]	Frequency rate of overlooked cavity entrances[d]
American beech	147	336	0.28	0.15	0.16
Red maple	101	148	0.21	0.16	0.10
American sycamore	31	54	0.42	0.28	0.19
Sweetgum	23	27	0.26	0.22	0.07
Ash spp.	27	39	0.22	0.15	0.15
Pin oak	29	36	0.17	0.14	0.06
Silver maple	18	24	0.11	0.08	0.13
River birch	33	35	0.06	0.06	0.06
Miscellaneous spp.	48	61	0.21	0.18	0.10
Unidentified (dead)	19	29	0.05	0.07	0.07
Total	476	789			
Weighted mean			0.22	0.15	0.13

[a] From Robb (1986).
[b] Number of suitable cavity trees per number of possible cavity trees sighted; a possible cavity tree contained an opening that appeared suitable for nesting.
[c] Number of suitable cavities per number of possible suitable entrances sighted.
[d] Frequency of overlooked suitable cavity entrances after ground searching trees; plots with possible entrances were revisited and cavity trees and neighboring trees were searched more thoroughly while tree climbing.

Normally, only a portion of the tree cavities observed from the ground prove to be suitable nest sites. A total of 356 potential sites were inspected by Boyer (1974) in Michigan; 90 (25.3 percent) were considered to have characteristics suitable for use by wood ducks. Of 119 cavities inspected in a Missouri survey (Weier 1966), 17 (14.3 percent) were suitable for duck nesting. Another Missouri study revealed 8 (30.8 percent) suitable nest sites out of 26 cavities inspected (Hansen 1971). Teels (1975) found 30 (31.9 percent) of 94 cavities observed near a Mississippi lake to be suitable for use by waterfowl.

And in Iowa, 11 (21.2 percent) of 52 cavities inspected were suitable for wood ducks (Dreis and Hendrickson 1952). Lowney (1987) found 15 of 107 cavities (14 percent) in bottomland hardwood habitat on the Noxubee National Wildlife Refuge in Mississippi suitable for wood duck nesting. Potential wood duck cavities are most often unsuitable because of too small or too large interior dimensions. Robb (1986) found that 28.7 percent of possible entrances led to small cavities in very early stages of formation. Table 69 indicates the causes of cavity unsuitability by species at this Indiana study area.

Table 69. Major causes of cavity unsuitability for wood duck nesting in tree species on Muscatatuck National Wildlife Refuge, Indiana, 1984–85.[a]

Tree species	Percentage cause of unsuitability[b]								N[c]
	NC	DTS	ND	TD/HTG	HW	BN	ED	UC	
American beech	31.1	31.5	9.9	20.2	2.7	0.9	3.2	0.5	222
Red maple	26.2	34.6	13.1	7.5	6.5	2.8	1.9	7.5	107
River birch	29.4	58.8	5.9	2.9	2.9				34
Pin oak	26.7	23.3	6.7				3.3	40.0	30
American sycamore	38.5	15.4	11.5		7.7	3.8	7.7	15.4	26
Ash spp.	36.0	36.0	16.0	8.0		4.0			25
Miscellaneous spp.	26.5	43.4	14.5	4.8		1.2		9.6	83
Unidentified (dead)	11.1	22.2	7.4	3.7				55.6	27
All species	28.7	34.1	11.0	11.0	2.9	1.4	2.2	8.7	554

[a] From Robb (1986); cavities detected by one or more possible entrances.
[b] Variables were defined as NC = no cavity; DTS = interior or entrance dimensions too small; ND = no depth; TD/HTG = too deep or tree cavity hollow to ground; HW = holds water; BN = bee or hornet nest; ED = excessive debris; and UC = tree unclimbable but cavity suitability doubtful.
[c] Number of cavities unsuitable for wood duck nesting.

Highest suitable cavity densities have been found in virgin hardwoods (average = 233 years old) in New Brunswick (Prince 1968), mature aspens (average = 68 years old) and northern hardwoods (average = 107 years old) in Minnesota (Gilmer et al. 1978), and mature bottomland hardwoods in New York (Haramis 1975) (Table 64). Soulliere (1988) found only 0.67 suitable cavity per hectare (0.27/ac) in a typical second-growth forest in Wisconsin, but cavities were considered abundant overall because of the vast hardwood forests available. With the exception of Robb (1986), most researchers have reported higher cavity densities in uplands than in lowlands (Table 70).

In many regions of the deep South, low densities of natural cavities prevail (Table 64). Tree species that are prone to form cavities and occur commonly in the North generally are found in low numbers in the South. Lowney (1987) reported that the best cavity producers on Noxubee National Wildlife Refuge were sycamore and beech, which accounted for only 2.6 percent of the forest but contained 60 percent of the suitable cavities. In addition, hardwoods often are cut before they reach an age where suitable cavity formation is most likely, and it appears that injuries to trees in the South heal more quickly than injuries to northern trees, thereby reducing the chance of cavity formation (Lowney 1987). Because of the apparent low availability of suitable natural cavities in the South, Lowney (1987) recognized that wood duck box programs probably contribute substantially to southern wood duck populations. He recommended that box programs be promoted in the South until sufficient densities of natural cavities develop.

TREE SPECIES

Various species of trees have different potentials for cavity formation. Some species seldom produce cavities, no matter how much damage they may suffer or how seriously they are infected with disease (Gayle 1986). Others, such as aspen, may contain numerous cavities, yet be so structurally weak that the cavities decay rapidly and have little long-term value (Gayle 1986). Poplar trees were the major source of nest sites for buffleheads breeding in British Columbia, but few cavities in these trees lasted more than 10 years (Erskine 1961). White oaks, on the other hand, may not produce many cavities, but those produced will persist because of the strength of the wood. Because of differences in structure strength, susceptibility to rot, and the relationship of site conditions to individual tree health, there is no consistent rule as to which tree

species are most important to nesting wood ducks (Gayle 1986).

Generally, tree species important for natural cavity production vary regionally (Table 64) due simply to species abundance, which is determined by latitude (climate). Tree species of documented importance at northern latitudes include silver, red, and sugar maple, American elm, quaking and bigtooth aspen, and American basswood. Sycamore, American beech, black oak, and to a lesser degree various other species of oak, elm, and maple are the primary cavity producers in central regions. Baldcypress, tupelo, black gum, and, to a lesser extent, species of oak and elm are the main sources of tree cavities in the South. Wood ducks breeding in the San Joaquin and Sacramento valleys of California were found using willow, cottonwood, and valley oaks (Dixon 1924). Uncharacteristic species can be important in local areas. Apple trees, for example, contained a majority of the wood duck nest sites in a Massachusetts study (Grice and Rogers 1965), and suitable cavities also have been found in various ashes (Nagel 1969, Haramis 1975, Robb 1986) and pine species (Bent 1923, Almand 1965).

The most frequently reported cavity-producing maples (silver, red, and sugar) not only are common but also are often the dominant hardwood species in northern forests. Silver maple accounted for 54.1 percent of the large tree composition in a floodplain forest of New Brunswick (Prince 1968). Sugar, silver, and red maples accounted for 25.5, 17.5, and 7.6 percent, respectively, of the large trees in a Wisconsin forest (Soulliere 1985). Red and silver maple grow on wetter sites than does the upland sugar maple (Curtis 1959) and therefore are more available for nest sites. Red maple made up 48 percent of the trees in bottomlands studied in both New York (Haramis 1975) and Michigan (Boyer 1975b). Strom (1969) reported that red maple was the dominant tree form in the bottoms of the Upper Mississippi Wildlife and Fish Refuge in Minnesota; he also found a high rate of heartrot in these trees.

In New Brunswick, a relationship was found between the type of site and the tree species with the most cavities (Prince 1968). Silver maple dominated wet sites and elm dominated wet-mesic sites in the floodplain forest. Elm usually had more cavities when growing on wet sites, and silver maple had more cavities when growing on wet-mesic sites. Prince (1968) concluded that trees growing on marginal sites are more likely to contain cavities.

American elm once was one of the most abundant trees growing on wet-mesic soils along many river systems. It was nearly as important as silver maple in virgin forest stands of New Brunswick (Prince 1968) and historically rivaled red maple for

Table 70. Density of suitable natural cavities for nesting wood ducks in upland and bottomland hardwood forests of the same study areas.

	Upland				Bottomland		
	Area in hectares (ac)		Suitable cavities found	Suitable cavities per hectare (ac)		Area in hectares (ac)		Suitable cavities found
Illinois	206.8	(511.0)	105	0.51	(0.21)	146.6	(362.3)	23
Minnesota	40.1	(99.0)	40	1.00	(0.40)	9.3	(23.0)	6
Wisconsin	7.5	(18.5)	8	1.07	(0.43)	12.5	(30.9)	5
Missouri[a]	16.6	(41.0)	12	0.72	(0.29)	28.3	(70.0)	3
						6.4	(15.8)	2
Indiana	20.9	(51.6)	29	1.39	(0.56)[b]	37.6	(92.9)	70
	11.5	(28.4)	3	0.26	(0.11)[c]	11.5	(28.4)	4
Total/mean	303.4	(749.7)	197	0.65	(0.26)	272.2	(672.6)	113

[a] Lowland timber types included pin oak/overcup oak (28.3 hectares: 70 ac) and elm/ash/maple (6.4 hectares: 15.8 ac).
[b] Large trees.
[c] Small trees.

dominance in bottomlands at Montezuma National Wildlife Refuge in New York (Haramis 1975). In recent times, however, this tree has been severely infected by Dutch elm disease and virtually eliminated from many areas. Because it is less prone to heartrot, its dead trunks are much more persistent than those of maple or ash (Haramis 1975). Widespread death of the elm has had an important impact on the forest community, opening much of the canopy and allowing greater floral and faunal productivity on the forest floor. At the same time, the many dead trees have enhanced pileated woodpecker activity, which may be an especially important link to wood duck nest cavity formation in elm.

Aspen has not been considered an important species for producing wood duck nest sites, mainly because it is short-lived and does not grow to a large size except under favorable conditions (Hansen 1966). Nevertheless, those aspens containing suitable wood duck cavities at age 60 probably would remain viable for at least 10 years (Gilmer et al. 1978). Decay in aspen sets in at a later age in northern regions, allowing these trees to reach the large diameter necessary for adequate-sized nest hollows. Relatively fertile glacial soils and optimal moisture conditions enabled aspen stands in north-central Minnesota to attain the sizes required for excellent cavity development (Gilmer et al. 1978). The large-diameter trees (diameter at breast height greater than 51 centimeters: 20 in) studied there produced potential wood duck cavities at a rate of 0.49 cavity per tree—nearly five times the rate (0.10 per tree) observed in smaller trees (28–51 centimeters: 11–20 in) on the same study areas. Nagel

Table 71. Tree species composition and abundance of cavities suitable for wood duck nesting in upland (U) and lowland (L) timber in northwestern Minnesota.[a]

Tree species[b]	Number of trees		Percentage of trees		Number with cavities		Percentage with cavities		Trees per hectare (ac)	
	U	L	U	L	U	L	U	L	U	
American basswood	1,930	519	32.3	48.0	17	3	0.9	0.6	48.2	(19.5)
Sugar maple	1,832	38	30.7	3.5	9	0	0.5	0.0	45.7	(18.5)
American and slippery elm	1,436	333	24.1	30.8	6	1	0.4	0.3	35.8	(14.5)
White and red oak	287	0	4.8	0.0	2	0	0.7	0.0	7.2	(2.9)
Red and black ash	188	16	3.1	1.5	4	1	2.1	6.0	4.7	(1.9)
Quaking and bigtooth aspen	119	33	2.0	3.1	2	1	1.7	3.3	3.0	(1.2)
All others	178	142	3.0	13.1	0	0	0.7	0.0	4.4	(1.8)
Total	5,970	1,081	100.0	100.0	40	6	0.7	0.6	149.0	(60.3)

[a] From Nagel (1969); upland = 40.1 hectares (99 ac), lowland = 9.3 hectares (23 ac).
[b] Only live trees 24 centimeters (9.5 in) diameter at breast height or larger are included.

Table 70. (continued)

Bottomland

Suitable cavities Reference		Source
0.16	(0.06)	Bellrose et al. (1964)
0.64	(0.26)	Nagel (1969)
0.40	(0.16)	Soulliere (1988)
0.11	(0.04)	Weier (1966)
0.31	(0.13)	
1.86	(0.75)[b]	Robb (1986)
0.35	(0.14)[c]	
0.42	(0.17)	

(1969) found wood ducks nesting in 3 of 8 aspen cavities, compared with 3 of 46 cavities in upland and lowland hardwoods in northeastern Minnesota. Although cavity abundance was lower in aspen stands, Nagel felt that use by wood ducks was greater.

Despite the relatively short cavity-producing life of aspen, this species has tremendous potential as a source of nest sites for wood ducks and other cavity-dwelling wildlife in the northern regions of the Lake States (Gilmer et al. 1978). Wood duck production estimates in northcentral Minnesota indicated an upward trend in the mid-1950s. This apparent population increase occurred at a time when large areas of aspen that had sprouted after the logging era of the early 1900s were beginning to reach maturity (Shirley 1936). Potentially, these trees were capable of producing many cavities and may have contributed to the wood duck population increase (Gilmer 1971).

Table 71. (continued)

Trees per hectare (ac)		Cavities per hectare (ac)			
L		U		L	
55.8	(22.6)	0.42	(0.17)	0.32	(0.13)
4.2	(1.7)	0.23	(0.09)	0.00	(0.00)
35.8	(14.5)	0.15	(0.06)	0.11	(0.04)
0.0	(0.0)	0.05	(0.02)	0.00	(0.00)
1.7	(0.7)	0.10	(0.04)	0.11	(0.04)
3.5	(1.4)	0.05	(0.02)	0.11	(0.04)
15.3	(6.2)	0.00	(0.00)	0.00	(0.00)
116.3	(47.1)	1.00	(0.40)	0.65	(0.26)

Basswood and oak generally grow on dryer upland soils. In certain areas they are significant as cavity tree species. In Minnesota, Breckenridge (1956) observed numerous wood ducks nesting in hollow basswoods along the Mississippi River. At the Tamarac National Wildlife Refuge in Minnesota, basswood was the most abundant large tree and contained more usable cavities than did other species in both upland and lowland hardwoods (Table 71). The range of American basswood is largely confined to the northeastern quarter of the United States, whereas there is a variety of oak species scattered throughout the nation. Oak has only limited cavity-producing importance in northern reaches but was second only to black gum in producing suitable cavities in Missouri (Weier 1966) and second to sycamore in Indiana (Mumford 1952). Because of its abundance and proclivity for cavity formation, black oak was the tree species used almost exclusively by wood ducks in uplands of Mason County, Illinois (Bellrose et al. 1964). In addition, all oaks with suitable nest cavities in this area were in the red (black) oak family (Table 72).

Most hardwoods can produce sprouts from stumps (a trait important to the decay process), but sprouting vigor and the age to which trees can continue to produce sprouts vary considerably. Basswood is one of the most vigorous of all species in this respect, whereas sprouting vigor in oaks depends on species and age of the parent tree (Hansen 1966). The ability of white oak stumps to generate sprouts declines earlier than does that of red oak stumps (Kittredge and Chittenden 1929). Sprouts generated from old stumps are more subject to decay than are those from smaller and younger stumps—a phenomenon that partially explains the greater abundance of cavities reported in the red oak as opposed to the white oak family. Another factor affecting this comparison is the greater resistance of white oaks to decay. Scheffer et al. (1949) compared the decay resistance of seven oak species (four from the white oak group and three from the red [black] oak group) and found that all of the red oaks decayed faster than all of the white oaks. The chestnut oak was the most resistant to decay, followed by Oregon white oak, white oak, and swamp chestnut oak. The black and northern red oaks were comparable and lower in resistance, with the scarlet oak the least resistant to decay caused by four important species of fungi. This study suggested that, if other characteristics are similar, areas dominated by red rather than white oak groups will provide more cavities for wood ducks.

Sycamore has been the most important cavity-producing species reported in Georgia (Almand 1965), Missouri (Hansen 1971), Indiana (Mumford

Table 72. Tree species with suitable nest cavities and number of wood duck nests found in Mason County, Illinois, 1958 and 1959.[a]

Tree species	Number of cavities	Percentage of cavities	Number of nests[b]	Percentage of nests
Black oak	115	82.7	72	80.9
Northern red oak	9	6.5	4	4.5
Blackjack oak	3	2.1	2	2.3
Silver maple	3	2.1	1	1.1
Hackberry	2	1.5	6	6.7
American elm	2	1.5	3	3.4
Hickory	2	1.5		
American basswood	1	0.7	1	1.1
Green ash	1	0.7		
Sycamore	1	0.7		
Total	139	100.0	89	100.0

[a] From Johnson (1959).
[b] Some cavities were occupied during both years, contained two nests during a single nesting season, and/or contained two nests during both nesting seasons.

An investigator probes the depth of a natural cavity in a black oak to determine its suitability as a wood duck nest site. Because of the low fertility of sandy soils adjacent to the Illinois River Valley in Mason County, Illinois, a substantial proportion of black oaks developed heartrot, forming large, shaftlike cavities. It appears that as long as cavity entrance and shaft characteristics are suitable, the tree species is not a significant nest-site selection factor for wood ducks. *Photo courtesy of the National Archives.*

1952), and Tennessee (Minser 1968). In southeastern Missouri, Weier (1966) conducted a survey in which he found no suitable sycamore cavities; however, two of the six wood duck nests he found outside the study transects were in sycamores. The others were in willow, pin and white oaks, and a dead slippery elm. Of the cavity entrances observed by Robb (1986), those that upon closer examination most frequently led to a suitable cavity were found in sycamores (Table 68). Although not producing as many cavities as the associated beech at Muscatatuck National Wildlife Refuge, sycamore appeared to produce optimum-sized nest cavities that were frequently found in relatively young (>80 years old) trees (Robb 1986).

Cavities in American beech trees often consist of hollow branches connected to large, deep, hollow trunks. In southern Indiana, this characteristic was observed to cause many cavities to be unsuitable for wood duck nesting (Table 69); nevertheless, beech was the most important source of suitable nest sites (41 percent of 122). It was second only to sycamore as the species most frequently used by nesting wood ducks in eastern Tennessee (Minser 1968). Lowney (1987) found beech to be the most important cavity-producing tree on Noxubee National Wildlife Refuge in Mississippi. Beech contributes significant numbers of cavities in old growth (Gysel 1961) but often is culled in forest management as an undesirable species (Robb 1986).

Both tupelo gum and baldcypress are potentially important to wood ducks in the South because of their cavity-forming properties and preference for wetland habitats, usually in or close to standing water. In northern Mississippi, tupelo gum (also called water tupelo) contained 76.7 percent of 30 cavities that were deemed suitable for wood ducks (Teels 1975). Baldcypress contained the remaining (23.3 percent) suitable cavities on the area and was proportionately more important than tupelo gum; tupelo accounted for 92.7 percent of the forest stand, while baldcypress made up only 6.3 percent.

In a 10-transect (40.8 hectares: 100.7 ac) survey of natural cavities at the Yazoo National Wildlife Refuge in Mississippi, cypress accounted for 4 of 27 (14.8 percent) suitable cavities (Strange 1970). Most (70.4 percent) cavities were found in black willows, but waterelm, pecan, overcup oak, and sweetgum each contained one (3.7 percent) suitable cavity. Taken together, sweetgum and black gum (also called black tupelo) accounted for 6.5 percent of the 122 suitable cavities inspected by Robb (1986). In southern Missouri, Hansen (1971) determined that 2 of 12 suitable nest sites were in sweetgum; Strange (1970) also found cavities in sweetgum in Mississippi.

Even though increasing numbers of nest houses are being erected, most of the continental wood duck population will continue to nest in natural cavities. Thus, sizable blocks of mature and overmature trees along riparian corridors must be maintained. Because streams east of the Great Plains in the United States embrace an estimated 1,317,515 kilometers (818,688 mi), riverine habitats make a major contribution to wood duck production (see Table 9). Depending on the species, it takes from 50 to 100 years for a tree to reach a stage that produces natural cavities suitable for wood duck nesting.

Forestry programs in riverine woods need to consider the importance of large cavity-producing trees for wood ducks and other wildlife. Land management agencies need to promote the establishment of riparian forest belts among streams for a number of reasons; one of the most important reasons is to reduce stream bank erosion.

Chapter 8

Prebreeding and Breeding Behavior

Activities engaged in by wood ducks during the nesting season vary with changes in breeding physiology and pair status. Throughout most of the wood duck's range, the daily activities of unpaired males are centered around courting unpaired or renesting females until late May or early June, when most drakes begin their prebasic (eclipse) molt. However, some unpaired males appear to show little interest in spring courtship and simply spend the days feeding and resting.

Although most females nest as yearlings, varying proportions of local populations delay egg laying until they are two years old (see Chapter 9). Small groups of noncourting birds occur during the breeding season and probably are composed principally of sexually immature birds.

Daily activities of paired wood ducks change markedly as the birds advance from searching for a nest site to egg laying, incubation, and brood rearing. Predominant behavioral patterns also vary throughout the day and between sexes during each reproductive phase.

PRELAYING ACTIVITIES

The onset of nest site inspections may indicate the beginning of prelaying activities for wood ducks that remain in the South to nest. In the case of wood ducks that migrate north, the interval between spring return and egg laying represents the prelaying period. Gonadogenesis (development of reproductive organs) in many of the female woodies that nest in the South normally begins in February. The northward migration of wood ducks that nest at higher latitudes also normally begins in February.

By early April, some wood ducks usually are present on all portions of the breeding range. Their numbers continue to rise throughout April on the more northern areas, and essentially all birds have returned to the breeding grounds by early May (Bellrose 1976).

Most wood ducks that return to northern breeding grounds appear to travel in groups of fewer than a dozen birds (see Chapter 4). Although some pairs begin nest searching shortly after they arrive, a minimum of one or two weeks normally elapses before females become physiologically capable of egg laying (Drobney 1980). During this time, rapid follicle growth and oviduct maturation occur.

Drobney (1977) found that female wood ducks obtained nearly all of the nutrients needed for gonadogenesis on nesting areas. During the two weeks immediately preceding egg laying, female wood ducks spend a large proportion of their time acquiring nutrients. Paired birds can be seen actively feeding throughout the day. Prelaying female woodies use plant food primarily for lipid deposition, whereas animal food provides the protein needed for follicle growth and oviduct maturation (Drobney 1980).

The social behavior of prelaying wood ducks depends on a number of factors, including habitat characteristics and population densities. On a large-river marsh habitat in westcentral Illinois, we documented how paired prelaying wood ducks allocated their time (Table 73). By using a scan sampling technique (see Altmann 1974), the combined daily activities of about 20 pairs were recorded during six one-hour sample periods. Although habitat quality probably influences the proportion of time

Table 73. Percentage of time spent in various activities by paired, prelaying wood ducks at Nauvoo Slough, Illinois, 1986.

Activity	Female				Male			
	Morning[a]	Afternoon[b]	Evening[c]	Mean	Morning[a]	Afternoon[b]	Evening[c]	Mean
Feeding	43.55	29.47	27.70	33.57	32.64	18.43	18.71	23.26
Resting	11.74	39.63	4.03	18.47	9.34	35.30	4.03	16.22
Swimming and walking	14.58	12.22	35.87	20.89	16.01	17.42	37.63	23.69
Comfort	3.12	11.26	9.79	8.06	3.65	12.62	6.49	7.59
Aggression	0.19	1.00	0.00	0.40	1.31	2.46	0.08	1.28
Nesting	20.95	0.00	1.64	7.53	20.95	0.00	1.64	7.53
Courtship	0.18	0.46	0.49	0.38	0.18	0.46	1.04	0.56
Alert	1.84	4.88	13.17	6.63	12.05	12.22	23.07	15.78
Flying	3.87	1.10	7.33	4.10	3.87	1.10	7.33	4.10

[a] Morning = 5:00 a.m.–11:00 a.m.
[b] Afternoon = 11:00 a.m.–5:00 p.m.
[c] Evening = 5:00 p.m.–7:00 p.m.

wood ducks devote to specific activities, behavioral patterns should remain relatively constant throughout their breeding range.

At Nauvoo Slough, prelaying females spent considerably more time feeding (34 percent) than did their mates (23 percent) (Table 73). No data are available that allow comparison between the amount of food consumed by prelaying hens and the amount ingested by breeding drakes. However, Drobney (1977) felt that paired females fed more often and with greater intensity than did paired males. Conversely, males may spend more than twice as much time in alert posture and aggressive activities as females do (Table 73). As a result of paired male behavioral patterns, females apparently spend longer periods feeding and thus are able to meet the high nutritional demands associated with the prelaying reproductive phase.

On breeding areas north of the wintering grounds, wood ducks arrive in small flocks or in single pairs. Nearly all females are paired by the time they depart their southern wintering grounds. Hens tend to return to their natal or previous nesting area, and their mates follow. Because woodies form pair bonds over an extended period—September through March—when populations from different breeding areas mix, males may pair with and follow mates to areas far from where the males hatched. *Photo by F. Eugene Hester.*

During the breeding period and well into the incubation period, drake woodies are especially alert to threats, including advances toward their mates by unpaired males. Such alertness presumably allows paired hens to allot most of their time to foraging and storing nutrients prior to the rigors of egg laying and incubating. *Photos by Scott Nielsen.*

Overall, prelaying woodies allotted more time to feeding than to any other activity (Table 73). Feeding was most intense during the early morning hours, when hens and drakes spent 44 percent and 33 percent of their time, respectively, pecking at and consuming food. Although females allotted considerably more time to feeding than did drakes during all periods of the day, neither sex exhibited much variance in their respective feeding rates during afternoon and evening hours.

The most common afternoon behaviors of prelaying wood ducks, listed in descending order of occurrence, were resting, feeding, and swimming and walking. Prelaying wood ducks on Nauvoo Slough spent considerably more time preening and bathing (comfort movements) during midday hours than during either of the other daily time periods (Table 73). Both sexes allotted more than 75 percent of their time to feeding, swimming and walking, and alert behaviors during evening periods.

Preening by wood ducks is an important comfort activity that helps remove lice, clean and oil feathers, and realign feather vanes. Woodies have a "preen (uropygial) gland" at the base of their upper tail feathers. The oil produced by this gland is worked into the feathers to keep them flexible and waterproof. Preening is performed following bathing or without preliminary comfort behavior. *Photos by David McEwen.*

From their first day out of the nest, wood duck ducklings commence vigorous bathing. Adult woodies bathe frequently to keep their plumage neat and to release tension in courtship. *Photo by Scott Nielsen.*

Wood duck comfort activities at rest include leg and wing stretching (top left), drinking (top right), shaking, wing flapping (bottom left), and even yawning (bottom right). The gamut of all the comfort activities plays a role in the well-being of each individual. No doubt they also reflect the state of a duck's well-being: the more stored energy, the more time for resting, which leads to more comfort movements. *Top photos by David McEwen. Bottom photos by Scott Nielsen.*

Although we documented no nest searching activity during afternoon observations, prelaying wood ducks do engage in this activity during all daily periods. Most nest searching, however, occurs between daylight and 11:00 a.m. Behaviors that occurred at relatively low levels during a particular portion of the day were less likely to be observed because of our small sample size; nevertheless, we feel that these data reflect the general behavior of prelaying wood ducks.

Apparently, local weather conditions have an important influence on nest searching activities. Bellrose (1976) noted that woodies spend more time in timber stands searching for nest sites on cloudy days than on clear days. We documented a significant increase during midday hours in the amount of time woodies allocated to cavity searching on overcast days at Nauvoo Slough, 1986 (Table 74).

Even though a number of investigators have published accounts of pair behavior during nest searching (Leopold 1951, Bellrose 1953, Grice and Rogers 1965, Beshears 1974, Bateman 1977, Bellrose 1976), little quantitative information detailing this important phase of the reproductive cycle is available. It is generally accepted that cavity inspection and selection are performed exclusively by female wood ducks. Males accompany their mates during nest searching and occasionally peer into cavities, but only rarely do they enter potential nest sites (Leopold 1951, Bellrose 1953, Grice and Rogers 1965).

Cunningham (1968) cautioned against assuming that males have no active role in nest site selection. On occasion, the male may induce his mate to inspect a cavity that he has located (Dixon 1924, Cunningham 1968). This inducement probably occurs when the female is inexperienced at locating cavities or overly apprehensive about entering. This behavior by the male is relatively uncommon.

The time pairs spend searching for nest sites is influenced by their physiological condition along with density and availability of suitable cavities. At Nauvoo Slough, where artificial nest cavities are located on an open marsh, prelaying wood ducks spend about one hour a day inspecting cavities (included under nesting activity in Table 73). Pairs generally spend one to several hours a day searching for natural cavities (Bellrose 1953, Grice and Rogers 1965).

Mated pairs generally begin prospecting for nest sites shortly after daybreak. After alighting in a tree, a female typically cranes her neck, looking in all directions, as she attempts to locate a cavity. Pairs often move along branches as they survey nearby trees for cavities. Females may investigate several potential nest hollows, peering into some but occasionally entering one partially or completely before moving on to another. When nest boxes are located on posts over water, pairs often swim or fly from one box to another. Moreover, females commonly peer into cavities from atop artificial nest boxes.

Prospecting females are less likely to enter a cavity that contains an incubating female or eggs. After peering inside, females on Duck Creek Wildlife Management Area, Missouri, entered unoccupied cavities 82 percent of the time (Clawson 1975a). In contrast, they entered cavities where egg laying was underway or where a completed clutch was located 76 and 53 percent of the time, respectively. Hens that subsequently nested made an average of 9.1 (range = 0–38) visits to 5 (range = 0–16) nest boxes before choosing a nest site (Clawson 1975a). Upon entering nest houses at Nauvoo Slough, prelaying hens (n = 10) spent an average of 12.8 (range = 0.17–90) minutes inside.

By following morning activities of color-marked (plastic pigeon bandetts) adult hens (at least two years old) on Nauvoo Slough, we were able to document the approximate number of days they prospected for nest sites (Table 75). On an average, 11.9 ± 8.6 days elapsed before females initiated laying. Although 83 percent of the nest cavities were under close observation, 11 color-marked hens that incubated clutches were never seen investigating

Table 74. Average percentage of time during stated periods that wood ducks spent searching for nest cavities on clear and overcast[a] days at Nauvoo Slough, Illinois, March 27 through April 30, 1986.

Weather condition	Morning (5:00–11:00 a.m.)	Afternoon (11:00 a.m.–5:00 p.m.)	Evening (5:00–8:00 p.m.)	Daily average
Clear (8)[b]				
Percentage	36.46	0.72	9.98	15.72
S.D.	13.13	1.38	9.26	17.85
Overcast (7)[b]				
Percentage	45.92	12.82	14.50	24.42
S.D.	9.89	7.52	5.86	17.32

[a] Overcast = greater than 70-percent cloud cover.
[b] ( ) = number of observation days.

When a drake wood duck accompanies his mate to inspect a prospective nest site, he seldom enters (though he may peer inside) the house or cavity; instead he stands guard and invariably utters a continual, soft vocalization, which increases in intensity whenever his mate enters the cavity or danger threatens. *Photo by Scott Nielsen.*

nest sites—an observation that suggests that some hens spent little time searching for nest sites. They may have been hens that had successful nests the previous year and returned to their former nest sites without inspecting other sites.

Clawson (1975a) also noted that individual female wood ducks searched for nest sites over a wide range of days. On Duck Creek Wildlife Management Area in Missouri, 14 hens each spent an average of 25.1 (range = 3–64) days searching for a nest site. In westcentral Mississippi, cavity inspection generally begins about one week prior to egg laying (Cunningham 1968). Similarly, Strader (1978) observed that wood ducks in southern Louisiana

spent 8–13 days inspecting cavities before laying their first eggs.

Wood duck pairs may search for cavities by themselves or in small flocks. Prospecting activity by one pair of woodies usually attracts others to the same area. Small groups of two to five pairs frequently follow one another from tree to tree (Bellrose et al. 1964, Grice and Rogers 1965, Jones and Leopold 1967, Zipko 1979, Armbruster 1982). Females of prospecting groups often investigate, in turn, the same cavities. Moreover, two hens occasionally inspect a cavity at the same time. Don Helmeke has observed as many as five wood duck hens in a nest house at the same time.

Table 75. Estimated length of cavity-prospecting period of color-marked adult hen wood ducks at Nauvoo Slough, Illinois, 1986.

Bird number	Date first observed on study area	Date first observed inspecting cavities	Date egg laying initiated	Length of prospecting period (days)
865	March 25	March 25	April 19	25[a]
861	March 19	March 28	April 18	21[a]
869	April 5	April 5	April 11	6
544	April 5	April 5	April 18	13[a]
479	April 15	April 15	April 27	12[a]
478	April 28	April 28	May 13	15[a]
866	April 18	April 19	April 20	1
890	April 15	April 15	April 17	2

[a] Possible instances of a female laying in conspecific nests (i.e., dump nesting) before initiating her own nest.

In early spring, many wood duck pairs fly into the upper canopies of large trees (top left). From that vantage, the female cranes her neck and bobs her head in search of potential nest cavities (top right). Espying one, she will fly to it, perch at the entrance in the manner of a woodpecker, and look in (center left). Occasionally, two or more pairs will simultaneously examine the same nest house or cavity (center right). If the cavity looks suitable and there is no predator inside or nearby, the hen will enter. Her mate will wait impatiently close by while she makes the inspections (bottom left). (Note, too, one of two mated drakes in the upper left corner of the center right photo.) The pair then may return to a wetland or fly elsewhere to continue exploring for other cavities (bottom right). *Top right photo by Stephen Kirkpatrick. Center right photo by George Kammerer; courtesy of the California Waterfowl Association. Other photos by Scott Nielsen.*

Paired woodies appear to have a strong social tendency to associate with other pairs during nest searching. This relationship between breeding pairs is reflected in the yearly breeding wood duck surveys that we conducted along Quiver Creek, 1947–1979 (Table 76). In March, 47 percent of all pairs encountered were in the company of at least one other pair. This percentage declined to 35, 28, and 27 percent in April, May, and June, respectively (Table 76). We believe that a majority of these multiple-pair associations include only one pair with an adult female, whereas the females of the additional pairs are yearlings.

Aggression among members of prospecting groups is rather common. Agonistic behaviors are especially evident near groups of nest boxes because prospecting pairs often congregate around these conspicuous nesting structures. Usually one pair or one pair member from a prospecting group will alight on top of a nest house. If another hen attempts to investigate the cavity, she frequently provokes aggression from any male or female atop the box. Aggressive postures include head and neck extension, with bill open, combined with short rushes or repeated jabbing movements at the intruder. In addition, occasionally we have observed a female peck at and grab the back feathers of a hen that is peering into a cavity. These aggressive interactions, for the most part, do not appear to diminish prospecting activities. In fact, females frequently enter cavities despite these aggressions.

EGG-LAYING ACTIVITIES

A drake usually accompanies his mate to the nest site and waits nearby while she deposits an egg. Females may spend as little as five minutes or longer than one hour inside a cavity while laying. Delbert Koke found that the laying patterns in three of four wood ducks near Oquawka, Illinois, showed a significant (P < 0.01) correlation between day of laying and amount of time spent at the nest site (Table 77). The total time spent inside the nest cavity increased significantly as laying progressed. For each additional egg, the four hens spent an average of 18 minutes longer in egg-laying activities. This increase may be accounted for by the hen's time spent depositing down (see Chapter 10).

On Duck Creek Wildlife Management Area, Missouri, a female wood duck tended to spend less than one hour (range = 17–120 minutes) inside a cavity when depositing each of the first several eggs of a clutch (Clawson 1975a). As laying neared completion, a hen consistently spent more than 90 minutes in the nest. Overall, a female spent an average of 117 minutes inside the cavity while laying an egg. In Minnesota, Breckenridge (1956) found that one female spent an average of 108 minutes (range = 8–191 minutes) in the nest cavity while depositing an egg.

After laying an egg, the female normally buries it in the debris at the bottom of the cavity. Consequently, eggs remain concealed beneath a low mound of material while the female is away from the nest during the laying period. In addition to being hidden from potential predators, the eggs are insulated against temperature fluctuations.

Unlike species of waterfowl that rely on endogenous (originating internally) sources of lipids and protein to meet the energetic costs of laying and incubation (Ryder 1970, Ankney 1974, MacInnes et al. 1974, Korschgen 1976), wood ducks rely on dietary sources of protein for egg production. Thus, females must allot a significant portion of their time to foraging for invertebrates during egg laying.

We documented the daily activities of breeding wood ducks at Nauvoo Slough in 1986. One hour was spent observing wood ducks at randomly selected times within morning (5:00–11:00 a.m.), afternoon (11:00 a.m.–5:00 p.m.), and evening (5:00–7:00 p.m.) periods on 27 days between March 25 and June 5. Unfortunately, after egg laying had been initiated, no distinction could be made between prelaying and laying pairs. Thus, the results presented in tables 78–80 represent composite activities of birds from these two reproductive categories. Attention was paid to behavioral characteristics and nesting chronology so that observations of incubating birds were minimized.

Table 76. Characteristics of wood duck pair associations along Quiver Creek, Illinois, 1947–79.

Month	Number of surveys	Percentage of single pairs	Percentage of double pairs	Percentage of triple pairs	Percentage of more than triple pairs
March	109	52.7	24.1	11.2	12.1
April	114	65.3	22.3	7.0	5.4
May	80	72.3	20.0	4.4	3.8
June	15	72.7	23.1		4.2

Table 77. Linear regression analysis of the relationship between day of laying and amount of time (minutes) spent in nest cavity by four wood duck hens near Oquawka, Illinois.[a]

Number of eggs laid	Number of observations	Intercept	Slope	r	P
8	5	12.17	22.01	0.98	<0.01
11	11	35.49	32.51	0.74	<0.01
10	7	12.83	13.21	0.67	>0.05
6	5	178.20	60.20	0.97	<0.01

[a] Data provided by Delbert Koke.

Table 78. Percentage of time spent by paired wood ducks in various activities during prelaying, laying, and incubation periods at Nauvoo Slough, Illinois, 1986.[a]

Activity	Male	Female	P
Feeding	14.16	22.93	<0.01
Resting	13.26	15.23	>0.05
Swimming and walking	21.96	18.02	<0.01
Comfort	10.75	12.14	>0.05
Aggression	1.30	1.09	>0.05
Nesting	19.21	19.21	>0.05
Courtship	0.53	0.52	>0.05
Alert	13.71	5.75	<0.01
Flying	5.12	5.12	>0.05

[a] Statistical differences determined by paired t-tests.

Females spent significantly (P<0.01) more time feeding (pecking at and ingesting food) than did their mates (Table 78). In fact, feeding was the dominant activity of females, whereas it ranked third in the daily time budget of males. Paired drakes and hens spent an average of 2.0 and 3.2 hours a day feeding, respectively. Although drakes exhibited a constant diurnal feeding rate (Table 79), hens allotted significantly (P<0.05) more time to feeding during evening hours (Table 80).

Drobney and Fredrickson (1979) recorded selected behaviors of breeding wood ducks during

two one-hour periods of continuous observation on Duck Creek Wildlife Management Area in southeastern Missouri. They partitioned wood duck behaviors into three categories: feeding, maintenance and reproductive activities, and alert postures. Because several important and time-consuming activities (such as swimming, resting, and flying) were not included, these data only reflect time allotments for the specific periods of observation and cannot be extrapolated to represent daily activity patterns.

Paired males and females in southeastern Missouri allotted 34 percent and 73 percent of their time, respectively, to feeding activities (Drobney and Fredrickson 1979). Woodies nesting on Nauvoo Slough spent less than half as much time on their average daily feeding activities as did the Duck Creek birds. Because we recorded feeding only when birds pecked at or consumed food, individuals searching for food while swimming or walking were not included in our feeding category.

Both males and females showed substantial increases in resting behavior during the afternoon hours (tables 79 and 80). However, neither sex appreciably altered the amount of time it spent resting between morning and evening periods. Time allotted to comfort movements by paired woodies was lowest during morning hours but increased to a relatively constant level during afternoon and evening periods (tables 79 and 80).

Table 79. Percentage of time spent by paired wood duck drakes in various activities throughout three daily time periods at Nauvoo Slough, Illinois, 1986.

Activity	Morning (5:00–11:00 a.m.)	Afternoon (11:00 a.m.–5:00 p.m.)	Evening (5:00–8:00 p.m.)
Feeding	14.03	13.36	14.90
Resting[a]	*4.50*	29.97	*5.28*
Swimming and walking[a]	*19.52*	*19.32*	27.69
Comfort[a]	8.13	13.59	11.66
Aggression	1.26	1.09	1.44
Nesting[a]	37.05	5.90	12.58
Courtship	0.44	0.32	0.80
Alert[a]	9.48	14.44	17.95
Flying[a]	5.59	2.01	7.69

[a] Denotes statistical significance, P<0.05, except that italicized means for the same activities are not significantly different. Data were tested with Kruskal-Wallis and nonparametric Tukey multiple-comparison tests.

Table 80. Percentage of time spent by paired wood duck hens in various activities throughout three daily time periods at Nauvoo Slough, Illinois, 1986.

Activity	Morning (5:00–11:00 a.m.)	Afternoon (11:00 a.m.–5:00 p.m.)	Evening (5:00–8:00 p.m.)
Feeding[a]	*20.33*	*21.74*	26.15
Resting[a]	*5.87*	33.67	*5.92*
Swimming and walking[a]	*16.18*	*16.33*	22.43
Comfort[a]	8.50	13.34	*15.59*
Aggression	1.25	0.71	1.20
Nesting[a]	37.05	5.90	12.58
Courtship	0.44	0.32	0.76
Alert	4.79	5.97	7.69
Flying[a]	5.59	2.01	7.69

[a] Denotes statistical significance, $P < 0.05$, except that italicized means for the same activities are not significantly different. Data were tested with Kruskal-Wallis and nonparametric Tukey multiple-comparison tests.

Male and female wood ducks use logs for resting (loafing) wherever possible. As the day progresses, they spend more and more time at rest, culminating with long periods of repose in afternoon hours. Where logs are not available as resting sites, woodies use mud banks, gravel bars, muskrat houses, mats of vegetation, and other sites selected presumably based on security and weather conditions. *Left photo by David McEwen. Right photo by F. Eugene Hester.*

Paired males on Nauvoo Slough devoted considerably more time ($P < 0.01$) than females to alert behaviors (14 percent versus 6 percent) and locomotor (swimming and walking) activities (22 percent versus 18 percent) (Table 78). Moreover, males altered the amount of time they spent in alert postures ($P < 0.05$), whereas females exhibited a constant diurnal pattern of alert behavior (tables 79 and 80).

Drobney and Fredrickson (1979) also found a dramatic difference between the amount of time male and female wood ducks engaged in alert postures. Drakes in southeastern Missouri were observed in alert postures 44 percent of the time. Conversely, hens were never observed in an alert posture during data collection.

At Nauvoo Slough, both sexes spent considerably more time in locomotor (swimming and walking) activities during evening hours than during either morning or afternoon periods (tables 79 and 80). Apparently, drake wood ducks directly alter the amount of time they spend in alert postures and locomotor activities in response to female feeding activity. Similar sexual differences in feeding and alert behavioral patterns have been reported for several other waterfowl species (Dwyer 1975, Seymour and Titman 1978, Afton 1979, Dwyer et al. 1979).

Afton (1979) reported that harassment by male northern shovelers prevented one female shoveler from spending sufficient time feeding during her incubation recesses, resulting in nest abandonment. We could attribute no wood duck nest desertions at Nauvoo Slough, 1984–1987, to harassment of incubating hens by males. Despite exceptionally crowded breeding conditions on Nauvoo Slough in 1986 (74 nesting pairs), paired males apparently were able to maintain isolation for their mates throughout all phases of the reproductive period and successfully protect their reproductive investment. By contrast, intraspecific interactions between females at the nest site resulted in high levels of nest desertion (see Chapter 10).

The predominant morning (5:00–11:00 a.m.) behavior of breeding pairs along the Mississippi River in westcentral Illinois was associated with nesting (nest box inspection or egg laying) (tables 79 and 80). Apparently the egg-laying interval of wood ducks corresponds with the 24-hour solar day. It is generally accepted that, for the most part, egg laying occurs early in the morning (before 9:00 a.m.) and at a rate of one egg per day until the clutch is completed (Leopold 1951, Bellrose 1953, Breckenridge 1956, Grice and Rogers 1965). Leopold (1951) observed that hens usually laid eggs within one or two hours after daybreak.

Delbert Koke recorded the egg-laying patterns of four wood ducks near Oquawka, Illinois. Average cavity entrance times ranged from 5:35 to 9:12 a.m. (Table 81). Individual hens exhibited considerable daily variation in the times they entered their nests to lay. Close placement of five to seven nest boxes may have exacerbated this variation. Semel and Sherman (1986) described how female woodies avoided approaching and entering their nests when other pairs were nearby. Thus, wood ducks that nest in natural cavities may exhibit more uniform cavity entrance times because of the increased likelihood of entering concealed and well-dispersed nest sites without notice from other pairs.

While their mates feed or rest, wood duck drakes usually remain alert (left). At Nauvoo Slough in Illinois, mated males were observed to spend more than twice as much time in an alert posture as did paired females. Drakes altered the amount of time spent alert and swimming depending on their mates' feeding activity. *Photo by Scott Nielsen.*

Breckenridge (1956) found that one female laid regularly between 5:00 and 8:00 a.m. Clawson (1975a) observed that wood ducks arrived on his study area in southeastern Missouri at approximately the same time each day. The females frequently spent time loafing and preening prior to laying.

Table 81. Comparison of average daily cavity entrance times by four egg-laying wood ducks near Oquawka, Illinois.[a]

Number of eggs laid	Number of observations	Average entrance time[b]	S.D. (minutes)	Range[b]
8	5	9:12 a.m.	123.9	6:55–11:10 a.m.
11	11	6:28 a.m.	43.3	5:25–8:05 a.m.
10	7	5:57 a.m.	24.8	5:22–6:40 a.m.
6	5	5:35 a.m.	16.1	5:15–5:57 a.m.
Mean		6:40 a.m.	93.4	5:15–11:10 a.m.

[a] Data provided by Delbert Koke.
[b] Central standard time.

Stewart (1957) found that, when a female was disturbed and departed the nest before laying, she did not return and lay an egg in the nest on that day. The hen probably abandoned the egg after laying it in another cavity or dropping it at some random location. In most cases, laying resumed in the original nest the following day.

INCUBATION ACTIVITIES

During egg laying, paired wood ducks normally become separated only when the hen enters a cavity to deposit an egg. After the onset of incubation, most pairs spend less than three hours per day together. Female woodies incubate the eggs without assistance from their mates. In order to assure the normal rate of embryonic development, most hens remain on their nests for at least 20 hours a day (see Chapter 10).

The behavior of the hen on the nest has received relatively little study. She probably spends most of her time resting, turning eggs, and occasionally preening. Leopold (1951) noted that the position of eggs in a clutch changed constantly; in one half day, marked eggs on the perimeter were replaced by other eggs. Stewart (1971a) outlined the process of egg turning by one hen in Ohio. He found no consistent pattern of egg movement during a four-day observation period. Although the female wood duck moved some eggs from the outside of the clutch towards the center and across the nest, others were only moved short distances and remained on the same side of the clutch.

Delbert Koke determined how frequently one incubating female turned her eggs during the course of a day (6:45 a.m. to 8:47 p.m.). Portions of the clutch were rearranged on 30 occasions within a 12-hour period. An average of 26 ± 11.6 minutes elapsed between egg turnings. Overall, the female spent more than 49 minutes (average of 98 ± 57.3 seconds per turning) turning the eggs during the 14-hour observation period.

Up until the time that pair bonds dissolve, hens attempt to locate their mates when they leave their nests for short periods to feed and perform maintenance behaviors. We observed male woodies ranging over 0.40–4.05 hectares (1–10 ac) of wetlands while the female was incubating. At such times, they often associated with one or more males. Unlike many other species of ducks, wood ducks do not have specific waiting sites where the females can find their mates during incubation recesses. Instead, the female usually flies to a wetland area that is part of the pair's home range and calls to attract her mate. If her calls do not bring a response,

she ceases calling and either commences to feed or flies to another area to search for food. In response to calls given by their mates after leaving their nests, some drakes will take wing to join them in the air. It is apparent that a drake wood duck can recognize his mate by her call. On numerous occasions, we have seen a drake leave a group of conspecifics and swim or fly to his calling mate even though she was not then in view.

We made continuous observations of paired wood ducks during two incubation recesses at Nauvoo Slough (Table 82). Whereas the most common recess activities of incubating hens were feeding (64 percent) and swimming (20 percent), drakes allotted most of their time to alert postures (40 percent) and swimming (36 percent). As expected, females spent considerably more time (14 percent) than did males (5 percent) in comfort activities—preening, bathing, and stretching.

Early in incubation, the male usually accompanies his mate back to the nest site. Leopold (1951) observed that the hen led the drake and that neither member called when approaching the nest tree. Flight characteristics probably are dependent on the stage of incubation and amount of previous nesting experience (Jones 1964, Clawson 1975a). During the early stages of incubation, a pair often alights near the nest, and the female may wait for a short period before entering the cavity (Dixon 1924, Jones 1964). During early incubation, males may remain perched near the nests for an hour or more before returning to their loafing areas. Another flight behavior, seen at all stages of incubation, is typified by the female flying directly to the cavity entrance as the drake veers off and returns to a nearby wetland.

Pair bonds of most wood ducks dissolve before the female completes incubation (see Chapter 10). Apparently, drakes begin their prebasic (eclipse) molt shortly after the termination of pair bonds. On rare occasions, a male may follow a female and her young, but these attachments are tenuous; females receive no assistance from males in rearing their young.

Table 82. Percentage of time spent by paired wood ducks in various activities during two incubation recesses at Nauvoo Slough, Illinois, 1985.

Activity	Male	Female
Feeding	19.65	63.75
Alert	40.04	1.65
Swimming and walking	35.50	20.40
Comfort	4.50	13.90
Aggression	0.30	0.30

While his mate incubates, the drake wood duck swims about an extensive and variable home range. She usually joins him (especially early during the incubation period) once or twice a day. Her calls attract him to swim or fly to where she has landed. In some cases, a drake will fly in early morning to the nest site occupied by his mate. He will wait for her to depart, then follow her to their feeding area. Generally, after half an hour to one hour of feeding, resting, and preening, the female returns to the nest. The male often follows her back to the nest site, veering off at the last moment to return to a nearby wetland. *Photo by Ed Bry; courtesy of the North Dakota Game and Fish Department.*

BREEDING HOME RANGE

Wood ducks more or less restrict their daily activities to an area known as the "home range." They have adapted to living in habitats where floodwaters readily change the availability of cover and food. As water levels rise and fall, woodies seek alternate areas for loafing and feeding.

Wood ducks do not establish a true territory (a portion of the home range defended against conspecifics) within their home range. Nonetheless, paired drakes are intolerant of conspecifics during the breeding season. As he swims about, a paired drake establishes a moving "territory" of sorts, and conspecifics that approach within several feet of the hen are repelled (Bellrose 1976).

Pairs generally find food and cover in wetlands in close proximity to the nest sites. In northcentral Minnesota, 7 of 10 radio-marked preincubating hens confined their daily (home range) movements to within 1 kilometer (0.62 mi) of the cavities they eventually chose for nesting (Gilmer et al. 1978). Robb (1986) reported similar patterns at Muscata-

tuck National Wildlife Refuge in southern Indiana. He found that hens nested an average of about 0.8 kilometer (0.5 mi) from the sites of their capture and radio-tagging. The extent of daily movements by breeding woodies varies with the quality of the habitat. Larger home ranges would be expected in areas where essential habitat components are dispersed over extended areas or where constantly fluctuating water levels alter cover, loafing sites, and food availability.

Most female wood ducks return to the vicinity where they nested the previous year or, in the case of yearlings, near their natal sites (see Chapter 4). Pairs usually establish home ranges that include the nest sites well before egg laying is initiated (Gilmer et al. 1978). Often, the same wetlands are used for feeding and resting throughout the prelaying, laying, and incubation phases of reproduction.

Following the movement patterns of 31 nesting hens on the Chippewa National Forest in northcentral Minnesota, Gilmer et al. (1978) found that most pairs restricted their movements to a land area of about 3.1 square kilometers (1.2 mi²). Some hens

Decoy traps often are employed in spring to capture male wood ducks (top). Pen-raised hens are used as live decoys to attract wild drakes, which can be difficult to lure to bait traps in springtime, when food is abundant. Leg bands and nasal tags (bottom left) secured on woodies captured before and during the breeding season provide means of assessing individual and population home range parameters, activity patterns, pair bond associations, and numerous other behavioral characteristics. Nasal tags are especially helpful in assisting with researchers' visual identification of woodies; each tag carries a unique number that can be read with a spotting scope. Nasal tag observation is an economical way to collect information on individual birds without having to recapture them. Because wood ducks in their usual spring and summer haunts often are hidden from view or simply difficult to detect, radio-telemetry can be used to pinpoint their location. Signals from a small transmitter usually are receivable at ground level at distances as far as 1.6 kilometers (1 mi). Mounted on a small horseshoe-shaped nylon collar (bottom right), these transmitters do not significantly affect the subject woodies' daily movements or overall survival: in one study, approximately 70 percent of radio-collared hens returned the next year to the nesting area where they had been captured and tagged. *Top and bottom left photos by Robert A. Montgomery; courtesy of the Max McGraw Wildlife Foundation. Bottom right photo by Dan Holm; courtesy of the Illinois Natural History Survey.*

selected nest sites in locations where wetlands comprised less than 0.3 percent of the surrounding landscape. Suitable natural cavities located in close proximity to water areas probably occurred at suboptimal levels on this study area.

Robb (1986) found that wetlands covered 18–82 percent of the home ranges of six nesting hens on Indiana's Muscatatuck National Wildlife Refuge. The home ranges of these birds averaged 30.3 hectares (74.9 ac).

The home ranges of 28 to 74 breeding pairs of wood ducks at Nauvoo Slough, 1983–1987, were largely confined to the slough and the adjacent margin of the Mississippi River. The combined area encompassed a water surface of about 25 hectares (62 ac). Many pairs ranged over the entire area, but some confined their activities to a portion of the area. A few pairs departed from the slough; one nesting pair used a narrow pond 1.4 kilometers (0.9 mi) across the Mississippi River. A small proportion temporarily used night roosts 2.4 and 6.4 kilometers (1.5 and 4.0 mi) distant. Several other pairs used Nauvoo Slough for feeding and resting but nested off the area.

Thus, Nauvoo Slough provided home ranges that were smaller than customary for wood ducks. This reduction in size of home range occurred because of overwater nest houses, a rich food base, and stable water levels that minimized the area required to support prelaying and laying needs. Late in incubation, a small number of female wood ducks were observed feeding on waste corn in fields 0.8–1.6 kilometers (0.5–1.0 mi) from Nauvoo Slough, briefly enlarging their home ranges to meet nutritional requirements.

In keeping with their riverine habitats, often the scene of fluctuating water levels, wood duck home ranges may be large and flexible, unlike those of prairie-nesting ducks. Moreover, unlike many prairie-nesting ducks, wood ducks have no established waiting site during nest site selection, egg laying, and early incubation. When wood duck pairs become separated, the female relies on calls to locate her mate, often in flooded timber where home ranges are large and dense vegetation restricts visibility.

Chapter 9

Physiology of Breeding and Wintering

Age, genetics, photoperiod, temperature, and nutrition are all factors that interrelate to determine the breeding season in wood ducks. About one-third of the wood ducks that spend the winter in the South remain there to breed; the others migrate northward, returning to former breeding grounds or, in the case of yearling females, to their natal areas.

Genetics sets the stage for the internal (endogenous) rhythm of annual behavior, which in turn is modified by external (exogenous) stimuli (Gwinner 1986). Thus, the internal cycles of resident and migratory wood ducks are subject to the same external stimuli prior to the start of spring migration. Yet some resident wood ducks in the deep South begin breeding before most northern birds begin migrating. Berthold (1990) experimented with subpopulations of the European blackcap warbler that were migratory or resident and found from cross-breeding that migratory activity was transmitted genetically to the hybrids. We therefore can speculate that differences between the genetics of resident and migratory wood ducks may explain differences in response to photoperiod by birds wintering in the same area. A reasonable hypothesis is that the exogenous cycle in the wood duck developed as it matured from a duckling.

Ornithologists generally agree that photoperiod is the primary exogenous stimulus in adjusting the annual internal rhythm of activities—migration, breeding, and molting—to local conditions. Gwinner (1986) and colleagues made a strong case with altricial (born with few or no feathers and unable to leave the nest for days or weeks) species, particularly blackcap warblers, for genetically programmed "circannual" cycles fine-tuned by photoperiod. We suggest that the wood duck, a precocial (born covered with down and able to leave the nest shortly after hatching) species, may further refine its genetically based endogenous rhythm by relying on photoperiod. Wood ducks that were hatched from local eggs, raised to near flight stage at Quiver Creek, and released at two distant areas shortly before flight returned to their released home the following year (McCabe 1947, Bellrose 1958).

In another experiment, we obtained wood duck eggs from Ferriday, Louisiana, about 885 kilometers (550 mi) south of Quiver Creek. We banded the woodies that hatched from these eggs, and several birds escaped captivity in 1957. One of the banded females was found nesting on May 9, 1958, and a second banded female was found on April 22, 1960; both birds were within 1 kilometer (0.62 mi) of their escape site. Because no wood ducks wintered in the Quiver Creek area during those years, these birds must have migrated to Quiver Creek. Therefore these woodies, which were presumably genetically programmed to be residents, became migratory. Although the evidence is meager, it implies that exogenous factors—most likely the photoperiod—imprinted over the genetic resident traits. In mature wood ducks, the exogenous factors influencing the circannual cycle appear to be primarily the photoperiod modified by temperature and body fat. Increases in the photoperiod and temperature as days lengthen in spring set the stage for migration and/or breeding in the wood duck.

Sexual maturity is an endogenous factor that contributes to temporal parameters of breeding and perhaps migration. Although juveniles assume breeding plumage in early autumn, their small penises or closed oviduct openings through autumn indicate that many do not reach sexual maturity before late winter, if then. As late as January 15, 1988, at the Van Norman Aviary near Hanna City, Illinois, all eight juvenile males checked had immature penises. Drake wood ducks raised in captivity at Delta, Manitoba, developed adult penises between eight and nine months of age (Hochbaum 1942).

Stephen Simmons of Merced, California, had 74 web-tagged woodie ducklings return to nest the year following marking. A comparison of their dates of hatch with their dates of nest initiation disclosed that there was no correlation between the two (r = −0.0281). The mean Julian day for nests initiated as yearlings was 140±21.06. Twenty-eight ducklings were not found until the second year; their mean date was 149.4±22.76. Thus there was no statistical difference between the seasonal dates when the two groups started nesting as one-year-old or two-year-old birds.

Wood ducks nesting in eastern Massachusetts and westcentral South Carolina exhibited no difference in age at nesting. Heusmann (1975) and Hepp et al. (1989) found no correlation between chronology of hatch and ducklings nesting as yearlings (n = 87 in Massachusetts; n = 58 in South Carolina). However, Grice and Rogers (1965) believed that females from late-hatched broods in Massachusetts were more likely than early-hatched females to delay nesting until their second breeding season.

In South Carolina, 82 percent of the females nested when they were yearlings (Hepp et al. 1989). Grice and Rogers (1965) and Heusmann (1975) found 75 percent and 58 percent of returning females nesting as yearlings in Massachusetts. As latitude increases, a higher proportion of ducklings from late-hatched broods appears likely to delay nesting as yearlings. Hepp et al. (1991) suggested that the additional time and energy expended during spring migration by females that nest in the North may preclude some yearlings from nesting.

CHRONOLOGY OF NESTING

Among wood ducks of all ages at Quiver Creek, 1957–1967, a few hens were found that were starting to lay the first week in March (Figure 61); appreciable numbers did not begin to nest until the third week. By the end of March, large numbers of hens were beginning to lay. More nests were initiated through April than at any other time (Figure 61). Nest starts declined steadily through May and tapered off through June. Only a few nests were started in July and early August, and most of these clutches were infertile.

From 1957 through 1967, 10–90 percent of all nests at Quiver Creek were initiated over a 62.3± 11.6-day period, April 1 to June 3. The mean span for all nest initiations was 98±17 days, March 23 to June 4. Over the 11 years, the yearly span of nest initiation was largely dependent on the date that the early nests were started (Figure 62). Each day of delay in initiation among all nests resulted in a reduction of 1.43 days in the yearly span. Birds that started nests within a 10–90-percent time frame of the population experienced a 1.31-day shorter nesting span for each day of delay. Later initiation also resulted in wood ducks not initiating as many late nests—a seemingly paradoxical situation that apparently resulted from a reduction of renesting effort because of a shortened breeding period in years when nesting started late.

Ornithologists have long recognized that birds nesting at high latitudes have shorter breeding seasons than their counterparts at lower latitudes (Baker 1939, Ricklefs 1966, Wyndham 1986). Duration of the breeding season is partially controlled by the influence of temperature and day length on food supply. Birds nesting at high latitudes in temperate zones generally have a compressed breeding

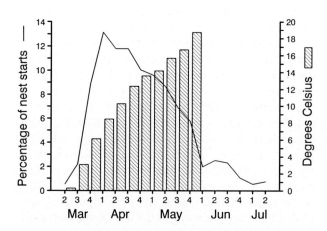

Figure 61. Chronology of wood duck nest initiation (n = 794) in relation to weekly mean temperature (degrees Celsius), Quiver Creek, Illinois, 1957–67.

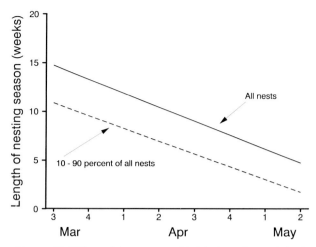

Figure 62. Effect of the temporal initiation of wood duck nesting after March 1 on the span of nest initiation at Quiver Creek, Illinois, 1957-69. The regression equation for first to last nest starts is $y = 21.86 - 1.43x$, $r = -0.71$, $P < 0.05$. The regression equation for 10-90 percent of nest starts is $y = 17.40 - 1.31x$, $r = -0.67$, $P < 0.05$.

season because of the relatively short time in which environmental conditions remain favorable for brood rearing. Because female wood ducks need access to invertebrate foods during follicle growth and egg laying, birds nesting at high latitudes must delay nest initiation until after ice breakup. As latitude decreases, milder temperatures allow for extended breeding seasons.

We selected several areas within the Mississippi, Atlantic, and Pacific flyways to illustrate the effect of latitude on wood duck nesting chronology (tables 83-85, Figure 63). Nest initiation in the deep South usually begins in late January or early February and may continue through late June to early July, often spanning 140-150 days. In the northern portion of their breeding range, woodies usually begin nesting during the first half of April; however, harsh weather in some years may cause delays. At latitudes above 41 degrees north, woodie nests generally are initiated over a period of 60-70 days. Woodies nesting near Riding Mountain National Park, Manitoba (latitude 50 degrees 45 minutes) began nesting on May 4, 1975, April 3, 1976, and April 25, 1977, according to N. E. Rodger.

Initiation of wood duck nests along the northern Pacific Coast often occurs over a longer time span than those at similar latitudes within the Mississippi and Atlantic flyways. For example, Morse and Wight (1969) found that nest initiations spanned an average of 102 days at latitude 44.5 degrees north in Benton County, Oregon, 1965-1967. Wood ducks nesting at approximately the same latitude in the Mississippi and Atlantic flyways normally lay eggs over a 60- to 65-day period (tables 83 and 84). This difference in nesting

chronologies reflects the moderating influence of the California Current on the Pacific Coast of the United States. The Gulf Stream may influence wood duck nesting duration along the southern Atlantic Coast in a similar manner.

As expected, periods of peak nesting also vary with latitude (Bellrose 1976) (Figure 63). Local wood duck populations that occur below 31 degrees north latitude usually exhibit peak nest initiations during February (Strader 1978). At latitudes between 31 and 37 degrees north, peak egg-laying periods often occur during March (Baker 1971, Hansen 1971, Bellrose 1976). Wood ducks that nest above 37 degrees north latitude usually reach their height of egg laying during April and early May (Morse and Wight 1969, Bellrose 1976).

Environmental conditions, predation rates, population age structure, and nesting densities are important factors influencing peak nesting (and hatching) periods of wood ducks. Primarily as a result of these factors, and throughout much of their breeding range, local populations normally exhibit two or three periods of peak nesting during the course of a breeding season. Whenever nest initiations are restricted to a 60- to 70-day period, wood ducks normally have one period of peak egg laying that often lasts for about 15 to 20 days. Generally, the first group of incubating birds are adults; most yearlings begin incubating nests two to four weeks later. Renesting and double-brooded females account for the majority of birds involved in the third peak of egg laying.

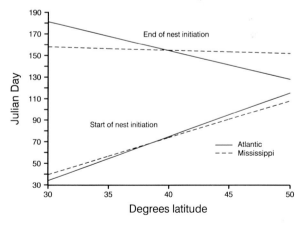

Figure 63. Temporal pattern of wood duck nest initiation by degrees of latitude for the Atlantic and Mississippi flyways. The regression equations for the start and termination of nest initiations in the Mississippi Flyway are: $y = -62.7 + 3.41x$, $r = 0.92$, $P < 0.001$; and $y = 167.1 - 0.305x$, $r = -0.24$, $P > 0.05$, respectively. The regression equations for the start and termination of nest initiations in the Atlantic Flyway are: $y = -87.7 + 4.06x$, $r = 0.91$, $P < 0.001$; and $y = 261.0 - 2.66x$, $r = -0.85$, $P < 0.01$, respectively.

Table 83. Effect of latitude on the initiation and span of wood duck breeding within the Mississippi Flyway.

Location	Degrees latitude	Study period	Average date of first nest start	Average date of last nest start	Peak nesting period
Louisiana	30.5	1976–77	Feb 12	Jun 2	Feb 12–28
Louisiana	31.5	1976–77	Feb 26	May 28	
Mississippi	33.1	1967–68	Feb 3	Jun 28	Mid-Mar to mid-Apr
Mississippi	33.3	1969	Feb 7	Jun 3	Mid-Mar
Tennessee	36.3	1977	Mar 3	May 28	
Missouri	37.0	1962–74	Mar 4	Jun 13	Mar 8–28[a]
Illinois	40.2	1954–67	Apr 1	Jun 3	Mid-Apr to early May
Wisconsin	44.0	1982	Apr 5	Jun 1	
Minnesota	45.0	1985–86	Mar 31	May 26	
Minnesota	46.0	1964–75	Apr 13	Jun 3	Apr 11–21
Minnesota[b]	48.8	1985	Apr 7	Jun 6	
Manitoba	49.8	1982	Apr 13	May 25	

[a] Data from Hansen (1971).
[b] Polk County.

Table 84. Effect of latitude on the initiation and span of wood duck breeding within the Atlantic Flyway.

Location	Degrees latitude	Study period	Average date of first nest start	Average date of last nest start	Peak nesting period
Florida	30.5	1978	Feb 28	Jul 5	
Alabama and Georgia	32.0	1985–86	Feb 4	Jun 25	
Georgia	33.1	1969	Feb 7	Jun 12	Mar
South Carolina	33.1	1982–86	Feb 14	Jun 20	
North Carolina	35.5	1961–62	Feb 19	Jun 28	
Maryland	39.1	1966	Mar 6	May 30	
New Jersey	41.2	1976	Mar 12	May 16	
Massachusetts	42.3	1950–56	Apr 1	Jun 6	Mid-Apr to mid-May
New York	43.0	1973–74	Mar 29	Jun 2	Mid-Apr to mid-May
New Brunswick	45.5	1963–64	Apr 15	May 21	

Table 85. Effect of latitude on the initiation and span of wood duck breeding within the Pacific Flyway.

Location	Degrees latitude	Study period	Average date of first nest start	Average date of last nest start	Peak nesting period
California	37.2	1975–79	Mar 5	Jun 8	Apr
California	39.1	1957–65	Mar 25	Jun 15	Late Mar to late Apr
Oregon	44.5	1965–67	Mar 1	Jun 17	Early Apr
Washington	47.5	1983	Mar 25	Jun 3	

Effect of Age

On Quiver Creek, one-year-old hens were found incubating nests started later than those of two-year-old birds (Figure 64); two-year-old birds were found on nests extending later than those of three- and four-year-old females. This finding suggests that both one- and two-year-old hens were involved in dump nesting early in the season and afterwards initiated nests that they incubated. As discussed under dump nesting (see Chapter 10), differences in the times that birds belonging to different age classes initiate nesting are clouded by the probability that young birds dump an inordinate number of eggs early in the nests of older-aged hens. Over an 11-year period, 1957–1967, yearling hens were found incubating nests later than expected relative to adults (P<0.0005, chi-square=

Table 83. (continued)

Approximate number of nests examined	Source
57	Strader (1978)
19	DiGiulio (1978)
453	Cunningham (1968)
74	Baker (1971)
14	Goetz and Sharp (1981)
924	Fredrickson and Hansen (1983)
919	This study
27	Kim Mello
61	Arthur S. Hawkins
278	Fiedler (1967)
26	Michael Zicus
5	N. E. Rodger

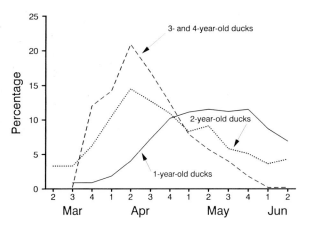

Figure 64. Chronology of nest initiation by 703 one- to four-year-old wood ducks at Quiver Creek, Illinois, 1957–67. Data subject to a moving average of 3.

Table 84. (continued)

Approximate number of nests examined	Source
26	Wenner and Marion (1981)
240	Moorman (1987)
67	Odom (1970)
429	Kennamer and Hepp (1987)
55	Hester (1962)
22	Uhler and McGilvrey (1967)
180	Zipko (1979)
468	Grice and Rogers (1965)
65	Haramis (1975)
9	Prince (1965)

Table 85. (continued)

Approximate number of nests examined	Source
578	Stephen Simmons
86	Jones and Leopold (1967)
202	Morse and Wight (1969)
19	Jack Beall

282.6). Approximately one month separated the peak nest initiation dates of adults (April 5–11) and yearlings (May 3–9).

Similarly, at Mingo National Wildlife Refuge, Missouri, Hansen (1971) found that adults nested significantly (P < 0.001) earlier than yearlings. Over a three-year period, the mean nest initiation dates for adults and yearlings were March 28 and April 27, respectively.

Grice and Rogers (1965) believed that yearlings may sometimes dump eggs in established nests before starting nests of their own. They also indicated that temporal differences in age-related peak nesting dates could result from differential migration patterns, nest site competition, latent sexual maturity, or combinations of these factors.

Although yearlings are known to return to nesting areas at the same time as adults (Bellrose et al. 1964, Grice and Rogers 1965, Clawson 1975a), age ratios of arriving birds are largely unknown. Nest initiations on Nauvoo Slough, 1986, began during the last week of March. We captured nine incubating females on April 16 during our weekly nest box inspections. One of these birds was a yearling that we had web-tagged as a day-old duckling the previous year, indicating that some yearlings begin egg laying at the same time as adults.

Over most of their breeding range, yearlings appear unlikely to delay nesting because cavities are so scarce that adults occupy all available nesting space before yearlings return (Baker 1971, Heusmann 1975, Gilmer et al. 1978, Soulliere 1986). However, in areas where natural cavities are extremely rare or when nest box programs build up exceptionally high breeding densities, yearlings may dump eggs, pioneer new areas, fail to nest, or delay nesting because they are unable to compete with adult hens for available nest sites.

At Nauvoo Slough and Quiver Creek, Illinois, and Merced, California, yearlings comprised 49.1, 55.2, and 53.8 percent, respectively, of the nesting wood ducks over periods of 7, 13, and 18 years (tables 86–88). At Nauvoo Slough, where house use averaged over 100 percent (Table 86), there was no significant correlation between the yearly variation

Table 86. Relationship of the percentage of yearlings to the total number of nesting wood ducks at Nauvoo Slough, Illinois, 1985–91.

Year	Total number of females	Number of yearlings	Percentage of yearlings	Percentage nest house use by all females
1985	60	32	53.3	91.3
1986	73	41	56.2	126.3
1987	71	25	35.2	105.0
1988	51	25	49.0	100.0
1989	64	29	45.3	108.9
1990	75	39	52.0	106.3
1991	74	39	52.7	
Total/mean	468	230	49.1 ± 7.04	106.3 ± 11.60

in numbers of yearlings and adults ($r = -0.105$, $P > 0.10$). At Merced, California, where nest house use also was over 100 percent (Table 88), the number of yearlings declined 0.45 for each increase in an adult ($r = -0.58$, $P < 0.05$). For each increase of an adult hen at Quiver Creek, yearling hens declined by 0.64 ($r = -0.93$, $P < 0.001$); nest house use averaged 71.2 percent (Table 87). Although not reflected in year-to-year changes in the proportion of yearlings at Nauvoo Slough, the comparatively low 49.1 percent in the yearling cohort (Table 86) suggests that in all years substantial numbers of yearlings pioneered new sites.

We surmise that the decline in the yearling component as the numbers of house-nesting wood ducks increased (Figure 65) resulted in more yearlings nesting in natural cavities or nesting farther afield. Some of these yearlings may have dumped eggs in nest houses on these areas before nesting elsewhere later in the season.

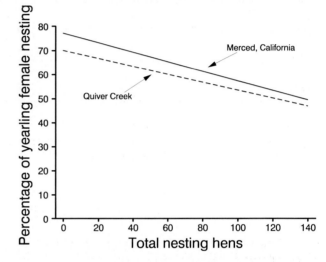

Figure 65. Regression of the percentage that yearlings contributed to the total number of nesting wood ducks at Quiver Creek, Illinois, 1957-67, 1974 ($y = 70.0 - 0.1647x$, $r = -0.87$, $P < 0.001$, $n = 13$); and Merced, California, 1975-92 ($y = 77.2 - 0.198x$, $r = -0.57$, $P < 0.05$, $n = 18$).

Table 87. Relationship of the percentage of yearlings to the total number of nesting wood ducks along Quiver Creek, Illinois, 1956–67 and 1974.

Year	Total number of females	Number of yearlings	Percentage of yearlings	Percentage nest house use by all females
1956	22	14	63.6	27.8
1957	21	14	66.7	34.3
1958	34	24	70.6	40.0
1959	45	28	62.2	41.1
1960	61	32	52.5	60.8
1961	84	47	56.0	90.4
1962	99	45	45.5	90.6
1963	93	47	50.5	97.8
1964	91	57	62.6	106.5
1965	98	50	51.0	70.6
1966	142	67	47.2	102.8
1967	129	61	47.3	86.7
1974	154	54	35.1	76.1
Total/mean	1,073	540	54.7 ± 10.05	71.2 ± 27.68

Table 88. Relationship of the percentage of yearlings to the total number of nesting wood ducks and their use of nest houses in the vicinity of Merced, California.[a]

Year	Total number of females	Number of yearlings	Percentage of yearlings	Percentage of nest house use by all females
1975	38	35	92.1	52.0
1976	84	59	70.2	98.0
1977	90	42	46.7	90.0
1978	99	44	44.4	107.1
1979	108	65	60.2	95.0
1980	161	100	62.1	145.1
1981	146	80	54.8	141.2
1982	182	85	46.7	154.1
1983	171	83	48.5	176.6
1984	141	53	37.6	127.4
1985	146	75	51.4	134.6
1986	118	56	47.5	124.1
1987	104	54	51.9	92.6
1988	97	42	43.3	84.9
1989	109	59	54.1	88.8
1990	106	57	53.8	97.3
1991	98	57	58.2	117.7
1992	129	68	52.7	130.8
Total/mean	2,127	1,114	54.2 ± 12.1	114.3 ± 30.2

[a] Total number of females compared to percentage of nest house use: $r = 0.93$, $P < 0.001$, intercept = 19.8, slope = 0.80. Yearly number of adult females compared to number of yearlings: $n = 18$, $r = 0.58$, $P < 0.05$, $a = 35.85$, $b = 0.450$, $5x = 38.1y$; $90x = 76.3$. Data provided by Stephen Simmons.

Grice and Rogers (1965) also found proportionally fewer yearlings establishing nests as the breeding population increased on Great Meadows National Wildlife Refuge in Massachusetts. Prior to 1954, more than 60 percent of the females captured in nest boxes were yearlings. Thereafter, only about 40 percent of all nesting attempts were undertaken by one-year-old birds. Grice and Rogers (1965) believed that nesting boxes were too few in relation to the number of breeding wood ducks and that yearlings simply were unable to compete successfully with adults for the limited number of nest boxes, but other more subtle factors appear to be involved.

Some adults may nest earlier than yearlings because they are more efficient foragers. Most fat deposition during spring (60 percent) occurs during the six- to seven-day period of rapid follicular growth (Drobney 1980). Protein requirements also steadily increase during this period and reach a maximum on the day before laying (Drobney 1977). Consequently, some yearlings may delay nesting because they are unable to acquire enough nutrients to initiate laying during the early part of the nesting season when food is less abundant (Drobney and Fredrickson 1985).

We captured and weighed 114 yearling and 95 adult female wood ducks on Quiver Creek (1964–1968) during their first week of incubation. One-year-old hens weighed an average of 15.56 grams

(0.55 oz) less than adult females (634.80 ± 4.68 [SE] grams [22.39 ± 1.50 oz] compared to 650.36 ± 4.49 [SE] grams [22.94 ± 0.16 oz]).

At the start of incubation, female wood duck weights varied only slightly for various clutch sizes of normal nests (Table 89). The lowest weights were recorded among hens incubating the fewest eggs. This anomaly apparently occurred because these were largely yearlings whose lower weights reflected previous laying of eggs in dump nests.

Hepp et al. (1987) found no correlation ($r = 0.32$, $P > 0.05$) between female body mass and number of eggs laid. Nevertheless, age-related differences in incubation dates, foraging experience, and lipid reserves may preclude many yearlings from undertaking renesting attempts, or they may disproportionately parasitize nests of conspecifics. Adults accounted for 69.2 percent ($n = 36$) of the renesting wood ducks that we captured in central Illinois. If both age groups renested at equal rates, we would have anticipated a 50-percent renesting rate by adults.

Yearling hens of many duck species are known to lay smaller clutches than adult hens do (Mendall 1958, Dane 1965, Coulter and Miller 1968, Morse et al. 1969, Krapu and Doty 1979). Because the final clutch size of any wood duck nest may be the product of two or more hens, the number of eggs laid by individual females is difficult to determine.

Table 89. Relationship of clutch size to the weight of female wood ducks calculated to the first day of incubation, Quiver Creek, Ilinois, 1964–68.

Number of clutches	Clutch size	Mean weight, in grams (oz)		S.E.
10	4–6	599.9	(21.16)	7.08
20	7–8	629.4	(22.20)	11.98
31	9–10	641.6	(22.63)	8.10
33	11–12	647.2	(22.83)	8.04
32	13–14	649.0	(22.89)	9.79
21	15–16	641.3	(22.62)	9.77

The smallest clutch sizes among wood ducks nesting along Quiver Creek, 1956–1967, were incubated by one-year-old females, but evidence suggests that the larger clutch sizes of older birds probably resulted from younger hens adding eggs to the older birds' nests. Thus, even though one-year-old wood ducks normally incubate smaller clutches than older birds, individuals from both age classes may well lay a similar number of eggs. Hepp et al. (1987) found no differences in wood duck clutch sizes among age groups in South Carolina.

Effect of Temperature

The earliest nesting wood ducks begin laying along Quiver Creek in March when daily ambient temperatures reach a mean of 0 degrees Celsius (32°F) (Figure 62). By the time this temperature is reached, many water areas have become ice-free. The number of hens initiating nests rapidly increases as daily mean temperatures rise at an average rate of 0.24 degree Celsius (0.43°F) until early April, when the first peak in nest initiations is reached and mean ambient temperature is 8 degrees Celsius (46°F). As the mean temperature continues to rise at the rate of 0.22 degree Celsius (0.40°F) per day (mid-April), the number of females initiating egg laying reaches a plateau and begins a steady decline during the remainder of the breeding period, during which time mean temperatures rise from 11 degrees Celsius (52°F) to 19 degrees Celsius (66°F).

An evaluation of heating-degree days from February through April 1960–1969 in relation to nest initiation revealed strong negative correlations between the number of heating-degree days in March (above a base of 8 degrees Celsius: 46°F), the date when the first nests were begun, and the date by which 10 percent of all nests had been started (r = −0.58, P<0.05; r = −0.69, P<0.05). The higher the number of March heating-degree days (the lower the ambient temperature), the later the

date in March when nests were initiated. No correlation was found between heating-degree days in February or April and nest initiation.

The early nest initiation and low temperature at which the majority of wood ducks initiate active breeding in central Illinois imply that this temporal response is an advantage to survival of the species. An improvement in species survival may stem from the opportunity to renest more frequently or to raise more than one brood (especially in the South), and possibly from the greater survival of broods hatched early.

At latitudes above 39 degrees north, eggs of early-nesting wood ducks are exposed at times to subfreezing temperatures. Although most clutches are protected and insulated against cold temperatures because they are laid in tree cavities and covered with decayed wood and other debris, a few eggs occasionally are cracked by freezing. We have examined several thousand wood duck nests in central Illinois (40 degrees north) during the last 50 years and have encountered frozen eggs on only a few occasions. Glen Welp found several frozen wood duck eggs at Union Slough National Wildlife Refuge in Iowa (43 degrees north). However, it appears that the few unincubated or slightly incubated eggs lost from freezing have no appreciable effect on overall production.

Early nesting would not seem to favor survival of the individual nesting hen. The earlier the hen commences to lay, the greater the lipid drain to maintain homoiothermy at a time when lipids are needed for egg-laying energy. Moreover, the protein required for the egg mass usually becomes increasingly available as the season advances.

Hansen (1971) found wood ducks nesting two to four weeks after arrival in spring at Mingo National Wildlife Refuge in southeastern Missouri. He indicated that temperature probably was the most important factor influencing nest initiation. Egg laying began sooner during years when mean daily temperatures stayed above freezing for at least a 20-day period following return in spring.

Haramis (1975) also found evidence that cold temperatures caused female woodies to delay nesting. During the last 16 days of March 1974, the average mean daily temperatures on Montezuma National Wildlife Refuge in New York were about 10 degrees Fahrenheit lower than temperatures during the same period in 1973. By determining when 23 percent of each year's total nests had been initiated, Haramis (1975) discovered that hens had delayed nesting for 6.8 days in 1974.

Individual Response

We found that, after year one, an individual wood duck hen has a predisposition to initiate egg laying at similar times each year. A two-way analysis of variance test was used to compare the nest initiation dates of 117 hens for two to five years; there was significantly less ($F = 2.27$, $P < 0.05$) temporal variability by individuals than among individuals. Further testing of age groups showed a significant relationship ($F = 2.01$, $P < 0.01$) in the adherence to a temporal pattern by 99 individuals between years one and two; by 46 hens ($F = 2.10$, $P < 0.01$) across years one, two, and three; and by 9 birds ($F = 3.09$, $P < 0.05$) over a four-year span. Thus, there appears to be a genetically programmed clock influencing the chronology of nesting along with exogenous factors. An extension of the genetic program would explain why many individual wood ducks breed where they winter rather than migrate (see Chapter 4).

Krapu and Doty (1979) reported on the nesting chronology of 21 wild mallard females during a seven-year study in eastern North Dakota. Although they determined that mean nest initiation dates were significantly different ($P < 0.05$) among years, individual hens showed no appreciable differences ($P > 0.01$) in their respective nesting dates. Most of the variation was attributed to annual differences in snow cover and temperatures during April. Mallards began nesting about two weeks earlier in years when there was no snow cover during April and daily temperatures rose above 10 degrees Celsius (50°F).

Under controlled tests with captive mallards of wild ancestry, Batt and Prince (1979) found that, over a three-year period, a given hen was significantly more restricted in yearly date of nest initiation than the yearly variation in dates by individuals. Because diets and other environmental factors were similar for the 30 pairs of mallards in the experiment, they concluded that differences in the temporal pattern of breeding individuals resulted from differences in their heredity traits.

Thus, an individual wood duck's proclivity to nest at a particular time may have roots in its genetic constitution or the time that it hatched. The genetic control or initial breeding age of early-nesting individuals is subject to modification by ambient temperature.

BODY MASS CHANGE

Body mass reflects three aspects of a wood duck's life: (1) physical size; (2) changes in internal organs; and (3) changes in lipid and protein content. Delnicki and Reinecke (1986) used a comparison of wing length and weight of wood duck specimens to obtain a condition index that minimizes body mass variations. We found a good correlation between their wood duck weight and condition index data ($r = 0.96$, $P < 0.01$), suggesting that weight data alone are useful in evaluating condition, especially when samples are sufficiently large to minimize size differences.

Each stage of the wood duck's annual cycle of behavior is accompanied by physiological changes. Body weights may fluctuate during the course of a year as much as 141 grams (5 oz) in females and 108 grams (3.8 oz) in males from changes in visceral mass and lipid reserves (Table 90). There appear to be only small variations in the protein content of a wood duck's carcass throughout the year (Drobney 1982). Because of the seasonal change in viscera and lipid mass, a weight that reflects a bird's health status at one phase of annual activity may not reflect the same condition in another phase.

Seasonal Weight Changes

Wood duck weight data that we obtained in Mason County, Illinois, from March into December showed pronounced seasonal changes (Table 90). Weights were highest at the onset of the breeding season and in autumn; they were lowest during July. Female body mass was much more reduced than that of males during the period July 11–September 4. Most of the year, females averaged 6–7 percent below the weight of males, but during summer, female weight was 9–16 percent less than that of males. Apparently, nesting and brood rearing unduly depleted female energy resources despite favorable temperatures and food resources during summer.

Prelaying and laying weights. Dennis Thornburg found that wood ducks arrived in southern Illinois, February 22 to March 14, 1983, at weights averaging 652.1 ± 8.7 (SE) grams (22.9 ± 0.3 oz) for

Table 90. Body mass of adult wood ducks by seasonal periods and sex in Mason County, Illinois, 1950–68. Birds were live-trapped until October 11; hunter-shot birds were used thereafter.[a]

Period	Males			Females			Percentage difference of females to males
	Number	Weight, in grams (oz)	S.E.	Number	Weight, in grams (oz)	S.E.	
Mar 7–20	33	656 (23.1)	10.7	36	598 (21.1)	9.9	−8.8
Mar 21–Apr 3	82	722 (25.5)	6.5	57	675 (23.8)	9.4	−6.5
Apr 4–17	24	709 (25.0)	8.5	37	667 (23.5)	6.7	−5.9
Apr 18–May 1	32	685 (24.2)	10.6	19	663 (23.4)	8.2	−3.2
Total/mean	171	693 (24.4)	9.1	149	651 (23.0)	8.6	−6.1
Jul 11–24	16	655 (23.1)	15.0	21	562 (19.8)	15.8	−15.7
Jul 25–Aug 7	31	640 (22.6)	10.3	35	579 (20.4)	11.4	−9.5
Aug 8–21	59	670 (23.6)	8.5	72	604 (21.3)	7.1	−9.9
Aug 22–Sep 4	76	684 (24.1)	6.8	76	622 (21.9)	5.5	−9.1
Total/mean	182	662 (23.4)	9.5	204	589 (20.9)	10.0	−11.0
Flightless[b]	35	655 (23.1)	2.4	73	617 (21.8)	1.3	−5.8
Sep 5–18	165	700 (24.7)	4.2	85	645 (22.8)	5.2	−7.9
Sep 19–Oct 2	117	696 (24.6)	6.7	42	630 (22.2)	7.1	−9.5
Oct 3–16	93	694 (24.5)	4.4	108	652 (23.0)	5.1	−6.1
Oct 17–30	61	709 (25.0)	5.0	28	664 (23.4)	8.5	−6.3
Total/mean	436	700 (24.7)	4.6	263	648 (22.9)	6.0	−7.4
Oct 31–Nov 13	9	711 (25.1)	4.1	8	684 (24.1)	7.4	−3.8
Nov 14–27	10	734 (25.9)	13.6	4	669 (23.6)	47.0	−8.9
Nov 28–Dec 11	27	743 (26.2)	6.4	12	683 (24.1)	4.3	−8.1
Dec 12–25	20	748 (26.4)	4.9	19	703 (24.8)	4.3	−6.0
Total/mean	66	734 (25.9)	7.3	43	685 (24.2)	15.8	−6.7

[a] One-way ANOVA excluding flightless group. Sex difference: $F = 20.09$, $P < 0.01$; period difference: $F = 7.15$, $P < 0.01$.
[b] Period of flightless capture was July 17 through August 31.

34 males and 621.9 ± 9.1 (SE) grams (21.9 ± 0.3 oz) for 24 females. These weights were an insignificant 3.3 percent lower for males and were similar to female weights obtained the previous winter in

Louisiana (Table 91). When wood ducks reached Quiver Creek in central Illinois the same year, March 21–30, 21 males averaged 676.4 ± 7.5 (SE) grams (23.9 ± 0.3 oz) and 11 females averaged

Table 91. Body weights of wood ducks during early winter in Mississippi and Louisiana, obtained from hunters' bags, 1979–83.[a]

State	Year	Males			Females			Percentage difference of females to males
		Number	Weight, in grams (oz)	S.E.	Number	Weight, in grams (oz)	S.E.	
Mississippi[b]	1979–80	55	703 (24.8)	8	28	645 (22.8)	10	−8.3
	1980–81	59	673 (23.7)	7	41	639 (22.6)	7	−5.1
	1981–82	85	685 (24.2)	7	47	637 (22.5)	8	−7.0
Subtotal/mean		199	687 (24.2)	7	116	640 (22.6)	8	−6.8
Louisiana[c]	1980–81	142	637 (22.5)	5	81	585 (20.6)	5	−8.1
	1981–82	33	652 (23.0)	8	27	620 (21.9)	11	−4.9
	1982–83	26	674 (23.8)	11	22	621 (21.9)	14	−7.9
Subtotal/mean		201	654 (23.1)	6	130	609 (21.5)	8	−6.9
Total/mean		400	671 (23.7)		246	625 (22.0)		−6.9

[a] One-way ANOVA sex difference: $F = 12.47$, $P < 0.01$; one-way ANOVA state difference: $F = 3.69$, $P > 0.05$.
[b] Mississippi weight data from Delnicki and Reinecke (1986).
[c] Louisiana weight data from Hugh Bateman.

638.6±8.2 (SE) grams (22.5±0.3 oz); both sexes weighed slightly but not significantly (P>0.05) more than weights recorded in Louisiana and southern Illinois. This evidence suggests that wood ducks added slightly to their body mass as they migrated northward. Later in spring, prior to nesting, males on Quiver Creek reached 715.1±6.5 (SE) grams (25.2±0.2 oz) and females reached 667.2±8.4 (SE) grams (23.5±0.3 oz). It is apparent that either late-migrating woodies increased their weight as they migrated north or resident woodies rapidly accumulated weight after their arrival on Quiver Creek.

In southeastern Missouri, Drobney (1982) found that, when wood duck females returned in late winter, they weighed 612 grams (21.6 oz), a weight that was not significantly different from their mean weight during autumn courtship (618 grams: 21.8 oz). Drobney (1977) recorded a 10.8-percent body weight increase of 66 grams (2.3 oz) during the prelaying period when follicle development advanced rapidly, largely as a result of lipid deposition. We found that weights of 209 females calculated for the onset of incubation in Mason County, Illinois, averaged 639.6±3.32 (SE) grams (22.6±0.12 oz). These weights were 23 grams (0.81 oz) lower than those recorded from prelaying bait-trapped birds (Table 90) and 38 grams (1.2 oz) lower than Drobney (1982) recorded at this stage of breeding activity.

It appears that laying wood ducks lose an amount of weight that may relate to the number of eggs they lay; at some threshold, females may cease laying because of depleted energy reserves. However, Delbert Koke documented daily weight changes of wood ducks during laying and found that five of seven females showed no significant change in body weight from the first through the last day of laying (Table 92). Two hens actually gained weight as laying progressed, but the increase was only significant in one instance. Overall, the seven females lost an average of 1.25 percent

(range = 8.62–13.54 percent) of their body mass during the laying of an average clutch of 9.86±2.54 eggs.

At Nauvoo Slough, 1987, we captured a female on the day before she initiated egg laying. The following week she was recaptured and weighed again. Although she had deposited six eggs that together weighed approximately 256 grams (9.03 oz), her total body weight had declined by only 14 grams (0.49 oz) or 2.2 percent. Drobney (1982) reported that the female wood ducks he studied gained weight up to the deposition of the sixth egg; however, body weight declined almost 90 grams (3.2 oz) by the time laying terminated. He noted that laying females expended nearly all visceral and abdominal fat and 76 grams (2.7 oz) or 71 percent of carcass fat in egg laying; most of the visceral and abdominal lipids were depleted by the time the fifth egg was laid.

Drobney (1977) observed that, although most lipids were depleted during egg laying, weights of the reproductive organs, liver, and lower digestive tract increased; changes in body weight were caused primarily by changes in weight of reproductive organs. Thus, changes in body mass at this time would not necessarily mirror changes in lipid reserves.

A clutch of 12 eggs requires about 73 grams (2.6 oz) of lipids and 69 grams (2.4 oz) of protein (see Chapter 10). Wood duck hens that engage in dump nesting lay more eggs than this average clutch. Lower weights of female wood ducks at the onset of incubation at Nauvoo Slough, Illinois (where food sources were optimum), compared with higher weights of females nesting on Quiver Creek, Illinois (where food sources were mediocre), probably reflected a high proportion of dump eggs laid at Nauvoo Slough, which further depleted fat reserves (Table 93). The lack of significant body mass depletion among laying wood ducks reported by Delbert Koke may have occurred as a result of the limited clutch sizes.

Table 92. Linear regression analysis for daily weight changes of seven laying wood ducks near Oquawka, Illinois, 1985.[a]

Number of eggs laid	Number of weights taken	Intercept Grams (oz)		Slope	r	S.E.	P
8	7	633.01	(22.33)	−0.23	−0.05	1.00	>0.05
11	11	723.48	(25.52)	−5.67	−0.69	0.72	<0.05
10	10	685.00	(24.16)	−4.55	−0.50	0.87	>0.05
8	6	655.59	(23.12)	−2.54	−0.68	0.73	>0.05
9	6	672.76	(23.73)	0.36	0.05	1.00	>0.05
15	13	573.88	(20.24)	5.18	0.78	0.63	<0.01
8	8	623.15	(21.98)	−1.53	−0.13	0.99	>0.05

[a] Dependent variable = total body weight; independent variable = day of laying. Data provided by Delbert Koke.

Table 93. Linear regression analysis of total body weight changes of incubating wood ducks in Illinois.

Location	Year	Number of weights taken	Intercept Grams (oz)		Slope	r	S.E.	P
Quiver Creek	1964	73	610	(21.5)	−2.01	−0.48	0.88	<0.01
	1965	201	610	(21.5)	−2.06	−0.38	0.93	<0.01
	1967	65	605	(21.3)	−2.84	−0.60	0.80	<0.01
	1968	141	633	(22.3)	−3.60	−0.51	0.86	<0.01
Nauvoo Slough	1985	113[a]	599	(21.1)	−1.29	−0.32	0.95	<0.01
	1985	78[b]	581	(20.5)	−1.37	−0.34	0.94	<0.01
	1986	109[a]	629	(22.2)	−0.81	−0.21	0.98	<0.05
	1986	77[b]	607	(21.4)	−0.74	−0.19	0.98	>0.05

[a] Adult females.
[b] Yearling females.

Although the lipid content in eggs can be obtained from the female's fat reserves, protein for egg production must be acquired on a contemporary basis. Drobney (1980) found that female wood ducks acquired nearly all their protein needs for oviduct maturation and egg formation from dietary sources. He detected no significant change in carcass protein levels during laying. The need for dietary protein during the three weeks preceding incubation underscores the importance of invertebrate food resources being abundantly available at that time.

Drobney (1977) calculated the approximate number of invertebrates that a wood duck consumes in order to meet daily protein requirements for egg formation (Table 94). Assuming a protein-conversion efficiency of 100 percent, nearly 4,000 invertebrates must be ingested to produce one egg. Because wood ducks are unlikely to be 100-percent efficient, the actual number of invertebrates needed

Table 94. Invertebrate consumption rates needed to meet maximum daily protein requirements of wood ducks, at conversion efficiencies of 100 and 55 percent.[a]

Invertebrate food	Number of individuals needed at ingestion rates of	
	100-percent PCE[b]	55-percent PCE
Chironomidae	14,342	26,076
Gammaridae	5,711	10,384
Asellidae	4,724	8,589
Gerridae	2,610	4,745
Dytiscidae	2,056	3,738
Coenagrionidae	1,823	3,345
Limacidae	1,765	3,209
Aranae	442	804
Hydrophilidae	382	695
Mean rate	3,762	6,843

[a] From Drobney (1977).
[b] PCE = Protein conversion efficiency.

to produce an egg probably is greater than 5,000 (Drobney and Fredrickson 1985).

Incubation weights. Because availability and quality of local food bases vary throughout a year and from one year to another, incubating wood ducks often experience different degrees of weight loss on a local, seasonal, or yearly basis. We documented the weight changes of incubating wood ducks at two locations in Illinois (Table 93). Along Quiver Creek and Nauvoo Slough, weight loss was negatively correlated (P < 0.01) to day of incubation. At Quiver Creek, females lost an average of 12.8 percent of their weight during incubation.

Wood ducks nesting at Nauvoo Slough, 1985 and 1986, lost an average of 5.26 percent of their body mass during incubation (Table 93). This variance in weight loss between study areas may reflect the presence of a higher quality food base at Nauvoo Slough. The lower weights of wood ducks at the initiation of incubation at Nauvoo Slough probably stem from the inordinately large number of eggs laid in dump nests prior to incubation (see Chapter 10).

Harvey et al. (1989b) found that wood ducks in South Carolina lost an average of 1.8 ± 0.2 (SE) grams (0.06 ± 0.01 [SE] oz) and 1.2 ± 0.2 (SE) grams (0.04 ± 0.01 [SE] oz) per day, or about 9 and 6 percent of their body mass during incubation in 1986 and 1987, respectively. They also found considerable variation in the weight lost by individual hens; some females gained weight throughout incubation, whereas others lost as much as 4 grams (0.14 oz) per day. Although Harvey et al. (1989b) found that heavier females lost proportionally more (P < 0.0001) body mass than did lighter hens, they found no significant differences (P = 0.092) in weight loss between yearlings and adults.

Harvey et al. (1989b) also detected no relationship (P = 0.13) between the weight lost by incubating wood ducks in South Carolina and the time of nest initiation. This seasonal consistency in weight loss during incubation indicates that woodies are adaptable foragers throughout the reproductive season and are able to change food items with changing availability to maintain their body mass.

Incubating wood ducks at Quiver Creek, Illinois, lost about 2.63 grams (0.09 oz) of weight per day (Table 93); at Nauvoo Slough 1.05 grams (0.04 oz) were lost per day. The more abundant food resources at Nauvoo Slough apparently made the difference. Over a 30-day incubation period, female weights declined about 78 grams (2.8 oz) at Quiver Creek and 32 grams (1.13 oz) at Nauvoo. Hepp et al. (1990) found in a three-year study that incubating wood duck hens lost about 25 grams (0.9 oz) from early to late in the incubation period: 40.5 grams (1.4 oz) in 1986; 31.0 grams (1.1 oz) in 1987; and 8.4 grams (0.3 oz) in 1988.

Lipid reduction accounted for much but not all of the weight loss that occurred during incubation. Hens that Drobney (1977) examined started incubation with an average of 31 grams (1.1 oz) of fat and by termination were down to 14 grams (0.5 oz)—a loss of 17 grams (0.6 oz).

Some of the weight loss we recorded in wood duck hens during incubation apparently was due to a reduction in size of the ovary and oviduct, which Drobney (1977) found amounted to 32.4 grams (1.14 oz). Thus, by usually feeding twice a day, wood duck hens are able to maintain most of their lipid reserves during incubation. Incubating hens compensate for limited feeding time by shifting from the protein-rich animal diet consumed during laying

to a diet of high-energy carbohydrate plant foods (Drobney and Fredrickson 1979). We have seen that female wood ducks make extensive use of residual corn in harvested fields during incubation recesses; they often fly 1.6 kilometers (1 mi) or more to obtain this carbohydrate-rich food. The frequent capture of female wood ducks at banding sites baited with corn is another example of their exploitation of foods high in carbohydrates at this physiological stage.

Posthatching period. Body weights that we obtained from female wood ducks during the posthatching period—July to September—represented birds that were either rearing young or engaged in the prebasic (postnuptial) molt (Table 90). Biweekly weights during this period ranged from 562 to 622 grams (19.8–21.9 oz), increasingly higher than the mean weight of 538 grams (19 oz) recorded when females departed nest sites with their broods on Quiver Creek and, late in summer, the 572 grams (20.2 oz) of departing hens at Nauvoo Slough. Thus it appears that, for an extended period in midsummer, female wood ducks slowly but steadily increase their body mass.

During the posthatching period, the spread in body mass between male and female wood ducks was the greatest, averaging 11 percent (Table 90). Differences that were statistically significant between the sexes in other seasons ranged from 6.4 to 7.6 percent. Although we have little data on male weights during the period of nesting, their body mass apparently does not decline as much as that of females; average male body weights in mid-July

Wood ducks were weighed throughout the year to document their physiological stage and evaluate how different behavioral activities influenced their condition. During incubation wood duck hens were weighed at weekly intervals to determine the effect of 30 days of incubation on their well-being. At Quiver Creek, Illinois, average weight loss of incubating hens was 12.8 percent; at Nauvoo Slough, Illinois, the loss averaged 5.6 percent. *Left photo by Dan Holm. Right photo of Frank Bellrose at Nauvoo Slough by Mike Beno.*

were only 54 grams (1.9 oz) lower than those in mid-April (Table 90).

Wood ducks begin a flightless period that lasts three to four weeks about one month after they begin the prebasic molt (see Chapter 13). Because of considerable individual variation in timing of the wing molt, flightless males and females were recorded from early July to late September. While the birds are flightless, large flight feathers and their coverts develop at a rapid rate. These feathers are replaced at a calculated cost of about 18 grams of protein (0.6 oz) (see Chapter 13). Thus, the energy expended to produce wing feathers is only one factor responsible for low body weights of flightless woodies. At this time of physiological change, the difference in body weights between males and females was the lowest recorded at any time during the year (Table 90).

Pre-autumn migration. As more and more males and females regained their nuptial (alternate) body plumage from late August through September, their body mass increased (Table 90). In Illinois, this is the time of autumn courtship and lipid storage in preparation for migration. During the last two weeks of October, a sizable proportion of the wood ducks weighed probably were migrants from farther north (see Chapter 4). For the most part, those weighed in November were local birds that were more prone to remain later than northern transients. At Quiver Creek, body mass of each sex at this time was similar to that recorded on the birds' return in early spring, and the seasonal disparity in weights between the sexes was similar (Table 90).

Migration and winter. We calculated that a wood duck making a night-long flight of 800 kilometers (497 mi) would use 33.7 grams (1.2 oz) of fat (see Chapter 4). Thus, males departing Quiver Creek, Illinois, at 734 grams (26 oz) might arrive on northern wintering grounds weighing about 700 grams (25 oz) and on southern wintering areas at 667 grams (23.5 oz). Females weighing 685 grams (24 oz) would weigh around 652 grams (23 oz) and 619 grams (22 oz), respectively, when they arrived on the same wintering grounds.

The calculated body mass of male and female wood ducks on their arrival on wintering areas was between the high weights actually recorded in early winter in Mississippi and the lower weights taken in Louisiana (Table 91).

Wood duck weights on wintering areas were affected by water levels and resulting availability of mast—primarily acorns. According to Hugh Bateman, water levels were particularly low in the Mississippi Alluvial Plain (Mississippi Delta) during the 1980–1981 winter. The low body mass of wood ducks in Mississippi and Louisiana reflected these conditions (Table 91). Bateman reported that the paucity of mast food resulted in wood ducks turning to feeding in soybean fields and visiting coastal marshes in greater numbers than previously observed. Landers et al. (1977) noted a decline in wood duck weights in South Carolina when they were forced to shift from their stable diet of acorns to a secondary diet of weed seeds.

Low temperature is suspected of being another factor influencing body mass. Early January weights of male wood ducks wintering in central Illinois averaged more than 65 grams (2.29 oz) heavier than those of male wood ducks wintering in Mississippi and Louisiana. The wood ducks in central Illinois may have responded to lower ambient temperatures by consuming larger quantities and different types of food. Concomitantly, body mass probably increased as a result of lipid storage and increased size of digestive organs.

Baldwin and Kendeigh (1938) illustrated the inverse relationship between temperature and body weight of birds. They found that as temperature decreased, passerine birds ingested more food and subsequently attained a greater body mass. William H. Long found a similar temperature-related feeding pattern in bobwhite quail and ring-necked pheasants (Baldwin and Kendeigh 1938). Food consumption rates of these upland birds in winter were three to four times higher than their summer feeding rates. Because of the influence of temperature on feeding activity, wood ducks that winter farther north than Mississippi and Louisiana might be expected to feed more actively and, therefore, temporarily weigh more than their southern counterparts.

Our weight data at Quiver Creek (Table 90) disclosed body masses for males and females on their return in spring that were higher than during winter (Table 91) but lower than immediately prior to their autumn departure. Drobney (1982) observed slight declines in the body mass of both sexes between autumn and spring. The fat content of autumn and spring males was almost identical, but the lipid content of females increased in spring by 26.5 grams (0.9 oz) as the endocrine system prepared them for the demands of egg laying.

THE PHYSIOLOGY OF REPRODUCTION

Drobney (1977) made an intensive study of physiological changes and energy costs of reproductive activity in wood ducks. The amount of productive energy required for gonadogenesis (development of reproductive organs) by female woodies is about 31 times that needed for testicular growth.

Male wood ducks require only about 7.48 kilocalories for production of the testes. This level of energy represents approximately 14 percent of their daily basal metabolic rate. Conversely, females need approximately 232.69 kilocalories to synthesize a mature ovary and oviduct.

A fully functional, nonovulating wood duck ovary normally contains seven developing follicles (Drobney 1977). Thus, the period of ovarian development usually lasts about a week, during which large amounts of subcutaneous, abdominal, and mesenteric lipids are stored. Prelaying females collected during the period of follicle development in southeastern Missouri contained an average of 107 grams (3.77 oz) of carcass fat and 25.5 grams (0.90 oz) of visceral and abdominal fat. Nearly 20 percent of the body weight of prelaying females was fat reserves. In contrast, the fat content of autumn females represented only about 7 percent (40.4 grams: 1.42 oz) of total body mass.

Drobney (1977) determined that the basal metabolic rate of female wood ducks was about 54.4 kilocalories per day. Although their daily energy requirements for reproduction vary with stage of follicular growth and egg laying, energy demands reached a maximum (114.9 kilocalories) on the last day before egg laying began and continued at this level during the first five days of laying. Prelaying hens must expend at least 191.35 kilocalories and 41.34 kilocalories in order to produce a fully developed ovary and oviduct, respectively.

Because the diet of laying females consists primarily of invertebrates (Drobney and Fredrickson 1979), stored lipid reserves that were accumulated during the seven-day follicle growth period are used to supplement dietary sources of energy during egg laying. About 77 percent (101.5 grams: 3.58 oz) of the prelaying fat deposits were expended during egg laying (Drobney 1977). Abdominal and mesenteric fat reserves were essentially depleted by the time the fifth egg had been laid (Drobney 1977). Moreover, only approximately 29 percent (31 grams: 1.09 oz) of the carcass fat remained after females had laid 12 eggs.

Drobney (1980) reported that nearly 75 percent of the female's total estimated costs for reproduction were associated with the energy requirements for biosynthesis (342.37 kilocalories) and the nonprotein fraction of the oviduct and clutch (709.47 kilocalories). He reported that about 88 percent of these costs (927.32 kilocalories) were met by expending stored lipid reserves during laying.

The ovaries of the prelaying females that Drobney (1977) collected contained from two to seven developing follicles. Hence, some lipid reserves were expended prior to his analysis. Consequently, Drobney (1980) concluded that wood ducks can meet all nonprotein and biosynthetic energy requirements for a 12-egg clutch and oviduct by expending endogenous lipid reserves.

On Duck Creek Wildlife Management Area, Missouri, the carcasses of laying females contained significantly ($P < 0.04$) more (21 percent) ash than did prebreeding hens. Drobney (1982) felt that this difference resulted from changes in medullary bone. Calcium can be stored in medullary bone and used to supplement dietary calcium during egg production (Sturkie 1965). The ash content of females reached a maximum during the terminal laying period. Because no significant ($P > 0.05$) change in ash was observed between early and terminal laying females, Drobney (1982) suggested that wood ducks can obtain sufficient amounts of dietary calcium to meet most of the requirements for eggshell formation.

Breeding females required about 67 grams (2.36 oz) of protein for oviduct maturation and full development of a 12-egg clutch (Drobney 1980). Although follicle cells secrete yolk material into ova throughout the period of development and laying, albumen is deposited only during the period of egg formation (Drobney 1977). Thus, the reproductive stage of an individual hen influences her protein requirements, which range from 0.9 to 5.1 grams (0.03–0.18 oz) per day (Drobney 1977). The amount of protein required increases in proportion to the number of developing follicles.

There is almost a complete absence of information on the effect of physiological changes and lipid reserves on survival. Hepp et al. (1990) found one year during a three-year study in which females that were the heaviest at the end of incubation survived better to the following breeding season than did lighter hens; during the other two years, there was no significant difference. We analyzed the degree of weight loss among 153 incubating hens in relation to survival to the following nesting season. There was no significant difference in survival ($P > 0.05$) among individuals that lost an average of 3–11 grams (0.1–0.4 oz) per day. Mortality that occurs at other seasons of the year may mask that caused by body mass loss during the laying and incubation periods of activity.

Genetics, modified by environmental variables, has evolved an annual physiological cycle that adjusts for the changing energetic costs of courtship, reproduction, molt, and migration. Seasonal body mass and organ weight variables point to the physiological anticipation of these events and the endeavor to prepare the body through endocrine secretions for the energy demands of these major activities.

Chapter 10

Nesting Biology

The wood duck hen demonstrates her interest in a cavity or nest house as a nest site by rounding the base material into a saucer-shaped scrape or depression an average of 5.31±1.91 centimeters (2.09±0.75 in) deep and 20.47±2.69 centimeters (8.06±1.06 in) in diameter. This depression may remain for several days or up to two weeks before she lays the first egg; some scrapes are never used. As each egg is laid the hen covers it with material from the bottom of the cavity, and a slight mound soon accrues.

LAYING ACTIVITY

After egg laying has begun, hens usually lay one egg each day, but data in Table 95 show that hens skipped 69 days while laying 775 eggs (8.9 percent). Significantly more days were missed by hens that laid small clutches than by hens that laid large clutches. Small clutches are most likely during the last quarter of the breeding season and may indicate that the level of energy available for egg production has been reduced. Hens with reduced energy levels may interrupt their daily egg-laying regimens to rebuild their nutrient reserves. If this "time off" indicates dwindling energy levels, smaller clutches are a manifestation.

Each ovum normally is retained by the ovary and not released into the oviduct until the wood duck has laid the previously formed egg. Intervals between eggs, therefore, depend on the time required by the oviduct to secrete the various egg layers around the yolk—usually one day (Welty 1979). The normal sequence of laying can be delayed, however, by the onset of cold weather or by the unavailability or inadequacy of food. Changes

in the temporal pattern of laying also may occur. Typically, wood ducks lay their eggs in early morning, but on several occasions we have witnessed a hen laying an egg during midday hours and, more rarely, in the evening. Although these hens may have been prevented from laying their eggs earlier in the day, they also may have deviated from the morning pattern because of a delay in ovum development.

Because females use only small amounts of endogenous protein during laying, the cessation of laying is thought to be caused by the depletion of fat reserves (Drobney and Fredrickson 1985). In a study on the Duck Creek Wildlife Management Area in Missouri, for example, Drobney (1977) found that hens with depleted fat reserves terminated laying prematurely (after three to four eggs). Nevertheless, protein can be considered the ultimate determinant of clutch size.

Protein, unlike fat, cannot be stored in large quantities, and woodies must therefore forage during egg laying for aquatic and terrestrial invertebrates to supply the protein needed for follicular growth (Drobney and Fredrickson 1979). When invertebrates are scarce or the bird is an inexperienced forager, fat reserves may be depleted in the search for invertebrates and, consequently, are unavailable for egg production. As a result, individual, regional, seasonal, and annual differences in clutch size can be attributed to local differences in invertebrate densities and to the foraging skill of each bird (Drobney and Fredrickson 1985). Moreover, because females must forage for invertebrates to replace essential protein, they are unlikely to fill lipid requirements from dietary sources. Thus, the search for protein ultimately governs clutch size because it governs the rate at which fat reserves are depleted.

Table 95. Rate of egg laying by wood ducks at Burlington, Iowa and Mason County, Illinois.[a]

Clutch size	Number of eggs laid[b]	Number of days skipped	Percentage of days skipped
9	48	6	12.5
10	114	17	14.9
11	86	10	11.6
12	190	13	6.8
13	150	13	8.7
14	79	9	11.4
15	75	0	0.0
16	33	1	3.0
Total/weighted mean	775	69	8.9

[a] Data from nest records of Frederic Leopold and the present study.
[b] All clutches were complete, but some had more than one egg when first examined.

We used an analysis of variance test to evaluate variation in clutch size among 177 marked wood ducks over two to five years. When dump nests were excluded, the variation in clutch size for normal nests (<17 eggs) was not significantly related to individual birds (P = 0.31). Neither did an analysis of the same birds by five age groups find significant differences between clutch size and age of bird. Analysis that combined both normal and dump nests, however, revealed that certain of the 177 hens consistently incubated clutches that were larger or smaller than average. Thus, certain individual ducks were responsible for incubating dump nests; in this case, these were the older ducks.

Batt and Prince (1979) studied mallards under controlled conditions for three years and found that some birds laid more eggs than others did. Because variations in diet could not have been a factor, Batt and Prince attributed these significant variations in clutch sizes to genetic differences among individuals. Because our study was conducted with wild birds, endogenous differences among individuals may have been masked by such exogenous influences as nutrition.

Addition of Down to Nests

The female usually makes use of the indigenous base material to cover the first few eggs of her clutch. In natural cavities, this material customarily is decayed wood from the sloughing interior of the cavity, but it may be leaves brought in by squirrels or grass carried in by starlings or other birds. Occasionally, eggs are left uncovered because of insufficient base material. Under certain conditions of dump nesting by more than one female, eggs may be left uncovered and in disarray and rarely incubated.

The addition of breast down to the covering material begins with a trace amount appearing with the first three eggs (Figure 66). After the fourth egg, an increasing number of birds begin to add down, which then accumulates until the last egg is laid, at which time more than 1,639 cubic centimeters (100 in³) of down may have been added. As much as 3,278 cubic centimeters (200 in³) were recorded in a dump nest of 23 eggs. We have noted that the largest amount of down in a nest is usually deposited between the eighth and thirteenth eggs.

Data provided by Frederic Leopold indicated that, as the season progressed beyond late April at Burlington, Iowa, the amount of down covering declined from 2,016 cubic centimeters (123 in³) to 754 cubic centimeters (46 in³) (Table 96). A linear regression, excluding the last period of two observations, disclosed a significant decline of 151 cubic centimeters (9 in³) of down deposition with each

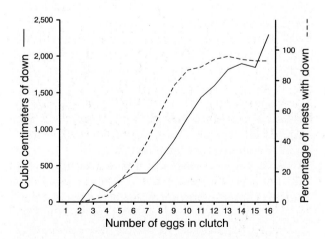

Figure 66. Percentage of wood duck nests containing down, and the amount of down per nest in relation to the number of eggs laid, 1948–74 (compiled from data provided by Frederic Leopold).

Table 96. Change in the deposition of down in wood duck nests as the season advanced at Burlington, Iowa, 1948–56 and 1960–74.[a]

Period	Sample size	Mean amount of down, in cubic centimeters (in³)	
Mar 15–21	6	2,589	(158)
Mar 22–28	20	2,196	(134)
Mar 29–Apr 2	13	1,999	(122)
Apr 3–9	20	2,524	(154)
Apr 10–16	15	2,196	(134)
Apr 17–23	9	2,016	(123)
Apr 24–30	14	2,016	(123)
May 1–6	20	1,917	(117)
May 7–13	11	1,196	(73)
May 14–20	9	1,295	(79)
May 21–27	8	754	(46)
May 28 +	2	1,475	(90)

[a] Data from records of Frederic Leopold. Linear regression, Mar 15–May 27: $r = -0.88$, $P < 0.001$, intercept = 2.79, slope = -150.7 cubic centimeters per week.

week reduction in the nest initiation period. Renesting female wood ducks have smaller amounts of down or none at all for covering clutches, but if sites previously used by successful birds are chosen by renesters, the old down serves as insulating material.

Renesting

If the first clutch is destroyed, female woodies often will renest until they successfully hatch a brood. In areas where many nests are lost during egg laying, most renesting occurs as a continuation of laying (Grice and Rogers 1965). Because of recurrent nest losses, some females may lay up to three clutches in a reproductive season before they hatch one brood (Bellrose 1953, Grice and Rogers 1965, Holloman 1967, Baker 1971, Odom 1970).

The stage of incubation at which a nest is destroyed affects the time the female requires to replenish depleted endogenous reserves (Sowls 1955, Grice and Rogers 1965). In Massachusetts, the relaying interval became proportionally longer as clutch destruction occurred later into incubation. For each additional day of incubation beyond the first, females waited an average of 0.33 day before renesting (Grice and Rogers 1965).

In central Illinois we found that, for each day in which incubation had occurred prior to termination of the nest, the new clutch was delayed 0.72 day (Figure 67). The mean delay (n = 16) was 14.4 ± 10.1 days. Eight additional records for which the initial incubation period was unknown averaged 12.9 ± 3.5 days.

Twelve eggs constitute the average wood duck clutch size, but there can be considerable variation. During laying and incubation, woodie hens cover their clutches (left) before periodic departures principally to feed and rest in the company of their mates. Until the fourth, fifth, or sixth egg is laid, the clutch is covered with base material. Thereafter, down from the female's breast and abdominal areas (often resulting in a brood patch) is added and used to insulate the eggs when the hen is gone. While on the nest, a laying hen may turn on her side (much as when preening on water) and push her bill through her side feathers to roll out a small ball of down which then is tucked around the eggs. The down accumulation may amount to 1,639 cubic centimeters (100 in³) for single clutches and 3,278 cubic centimeters (200 in³) for dump nests. When a hen returns to her nest and clutch, material or down is removed from the eggs in a pattern to conform to the hen's incubating shape (right). *Left photo by Chuck Scott; courtesy of the Illinois Natural History Survey. Right photo by Frederic Leopold; courtesy of the Starr's Cave Nature Center (Burlington, Iowa).*

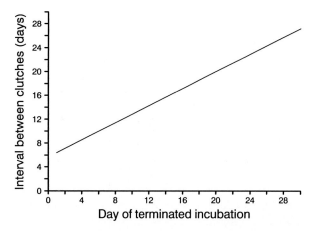

Figure 67. Interval between the day on which incubation was terminated by predation or desertion and the start of a new wood duck clutch, Mason County, Illinois. The regression line is: $y = 5.69 + 0.72x$, $r = 0.63$, $P < 0.05$.

At the Piedmont National Wildlife Refuge in Georgia, four hens with unsuccessful first nests delayed an average of 34 days before renesting (Odom 1970). Although one female in Massachusetts delayed only 5 days before initiating her second nesting attempt, all others waited at least 11 days (Grice and Rogers 1965). On Mingo National Wildlife Refuge in southeastern Missouri, hens delayed renesting for at least 9 days following the destruction of their first clutches (Hansen 1971).

When a nest is destroyed, the hen invariably selects a different cavity for renesting. We found that wood ducks ($n = 26$) whose nests were destroyed or deserted moved an average of 312 ± 411 meters (341 ± 450 yd) to renest. If we omit four hens whose new nesting locations exceeded 1,000 meters (1,094 yd), we found a mean displacement of 175 ± 191 meters (191 ± 209 yd). One female moved 12.1 kilometers (7.5 mi) to renest, although there were available sites in the same nest house unit and two other nest house units were located between the two nest sites.

Renesting intervals also are influenced by variations in quality of local food sources and their availability to renesting hens (Drobney 1982). Apparently, renesting wood ducks seldom build up their endogenous energy reserves to the levels attained when their initial nesting attempts were undertaken. At Nauvoo Slough, we found that weights of nine females (621 grams: 21.9 oz) during their first week of incubation differed ($P < 0.05$, Mann-Whitney Test) from weights during renesting attempts (580 grams: 20.5 oz). One female, however, weighed 50 grams (1.8 oz) more at the start of incubation of her second clutch.

Double-brooded Females

Adding support to the claim that wood ducks are persistent renesters is the fact that some females renest after successfully hatching a first clutch (Table 97). Key factors affecting the occurrence of second broods are food supply and, most importantly, length of the breeding season (Fredrickson and Hansen 1983). Females are most likely to produce two broods in the southern portion of the breeding range where nesting often begins in early February and may last for 130 days (Rogers and Hansen 1967). With his own data plus information summarized by Fredrickson and Hansen (1983), Moorman (1987) determined that the occurrence of second broods decreased 1.2 percent with each degree increase in latitude.

Nesting chronology and duration often vary from year to year. At the Savannah River Plant in South Carolina, Kennamer and Hepp (1987) reported that the average length of the nesting season (days from initiation of the first clutch to hatching of the last nest), 1982–1986, was 157 ± 83 (SE) days. The incidence of second brood production increased as the nesting season lengthened. In 1985, no double broods were produced when the nesting season spanned only 134 days. In contrast, 18 percent ($n = 11$) of the females produced two broods in 1986 when the nesting season lasted for 179 days (Kennamer and Hepp 1987).

From 1962 through 1974, the nesting season on Mingo National Wildlife Refuge averaged 132 ± 5.7 days. During this time, approximately 4 percent of the females nesting on Mingo Swamp produced two broods per season (Fredrickson and Hansen 1983). However, up to 10 percent of the nesting hens produced two broods in years when the nesting season lasted for at least 139 days.

In California, 1974–1986, Thompson and Simmons (1990) found that the wood duck's nesting season (days from first nest initiation to last successful nest initiation) averaged 94 ± 2 (SE) days (range = 81–103). The proportion of woodie females that laid second clutches varied from 0 to 11 percent (average = 3.6 percent) during their study. No second clutches were laid in 1984, when the nesting season spanned 81 days. Conversely, 11 percent of all wood duck females laid a second clutch in 1977, when the nesting season continued for approximately 102 days.

In order to produce two broods in one season, most females abandoned the first brood at about four to five weeks of age (Table 97). Because the hen/brood bond of wood ducks is usually broken at about five weeks (Beard 1964, McGilvrey 1969, Ball et al. 1975), many females that raise two broods

Table 97. Occurrence of second broods in wood ducks.

State	Number of second brood attempts	Average interval between clutches[a]		Reference
		Days	Range	
North Carolina	4	62	29–90	Hester (1962)
Massachusetts	1	27		Grice and Rogers (1965)
Maryland	2	27	18–35	McGilvrey (1966c)
North Carolina	17			Holloman (1967)
Missouri	5	37	29–44	Rogers and Hansen (1967)
Georgia	8	41	28–69	Odom (1970)
Mississippi	4			Baker (1971)
Arkansas	29			Brown (1972a)
Texas	1			Labuda (1977)
South Carolina	2	43	34–51[b]	Luckett (1977)
Louisiana	2	46	45–47	Strader (1978)
Louisiana	2	53	47–58	Rothbart (1979)
Missouri	30	33	11–62	Fredrickson and Hansen (1983)
Alabama and Georgia	23	37	15–71	Moorman (1987)
South Carolina	21	47	19–92	Kennamer and Hepp (1987)
California	56	26	6–47	Thompson and Simmons (1990)

[a] Interval between hatching of first brood to initiation of laying for the second nest.
[b] Based on a 30-day incubation period.

may remain with their young for normal rearing periods. Some females, however, obviously deserted their first broods, or the broods were decimated or lost before the fourth week of rearing (Table 97).

Rogers and Hansen (1967) discussed why hen/brood bonds dissolve prematurely. A female could, of course, lose her brood through predation or accidental separation. As latitude increases, moreover, females probably spend proportionally less time with first broods because of the time required to raise two (Fredrickson and Hansen 1983). Haramis (1990) pointed out that the minimal time and energy expended in migration by wood ducks that nest in the South enhance their ability to produce two broods per season.

Fredrickson and Hansen (1983), Moorman (1987), Kennamer and Hepp (1987), and Thompson and Simmons (1990) reported minimum mean ages for females that produced two broods as 3.0, 2.6, 2.3, and 2.2 years, respectively. Only three yearlings have been known to lay second clutches after successfully hatching one brood (Kennamer and Hepp 1987, Thompson and Simmons 1990). Because adults usually initiate laying earlier than yearlings do and probably are more proficient at obtaining essential nutrients, they account for most of the females that raise two broods per season (Fredrickson and Hansen 1983).

Occasionally, hens utilize the same cavity for first and second clutches. Seventeen, 13, and 34 percent of all females that produced double broods in southeastern Missouri, on Eufaula National Wildlife Refuge in southern Alabama and Georgia, and in California, respectively, used the same nest boxes for both nests (Fredrickson and Hansen 1983, Moorman 1987, Thompson and Simmons 1990). This double residency did not occur when nests were destroyed by a predator. Double-brooded females in southern Missouri and California moved an average of 877 meters (959 yd) and 892 meters (976 yd), respectively, between first and second nests. In comparison, most double-brooded hens on Eufaula National Wildlife Refuge initiated second clutches in nest boxes that were within 500 meters (547 yd) of the first nest sites. The distance females move between two nesting attempts depends largely on the availability of cavities (Fredrickson and Hansen 1983).

Kennamer and Hepp (1987) found significant ($P < 0.01$) differences in mean egg weights (43.9 grams [1.55 oz] versus 41.7 grams [1.47 oz]) and clutch sizes (13 versus 10) between the first and second nests of double-brooded hens. Similarly, Fredrickson and Hansen (1983) found that the mean clutch size of first (16 ± 0.8 [SE]) and second (12 ± 0.8 [SE]) clutches were different ($P < 0.05$). Thompson and Simmons (1990) found mean clutch sizes of 16.1 ± 0.8 (SE) for the first and 14.3 ± 0.7 (SE) for the second nests in California, but the differences were not significant because of small sample sizes. Because dump nests probably result in inflated average first-clutch sizes, comparisons of the number of eggs in first and second clutches of double-brooded females must be viewed with caution.

THE EGG

Our data indicate that wood duck eggs vary in size within each clutch and between clutches (Table 98). A slight significant difference was found in length but not in width or volume between the egg size of adult and yearling birds. Calculated mean weights of wood duck eggs ranged for several studies from 36.3 grams (1.28 oz) to 47.6 grams (1.68 oz) (Table 99). All studies combined have a mean egg weight of 43.1 grams (1.52 oz).

Hepp et al. (1987) found that most of the variation in the size of wood duck eggs was related to the weight of the female—the heavier the bird, the larger the egg. As eggs increased in weight, so did their components, particularly the shell and albumen, and to a lesser degree the yolk.

A larger egg reflects the better condition of the laying female (Hepp et al. 1987). A larger egg also produces a duckling of larger mass, with the potential for increased survival (Batt and Prince 1979), as Howe (1976) also found for the common grackle. The larger eggs produced by some females are a factor in the ability to hatch and raise a larger number of ducklings to flying stage. In an analysis of duckling weights compared with returns in subsequent years at Savannah River, South Carolina, Hepp et al. (1989) found statistical significance in the slightly positive relationship between duckling mass and survival the first year.

As with many cavity nesters, wood ducks lay eggs that are dull white but often become stained brown from the leaching of tannins from decayed wood and leaves. Hooded mergansers occasionally

Table 98. Wood duck egg dimensions and calculated volume for adult (n = 15) and yearling (n = 12) clutches in central Illinois.[a]

Age	Number in clutch	Length Mean	Length S.D.	Breadth Mean	Breadth S.D.	Volume (cc)	S.D.[b]
Adult	11	4.92	0.052	3.78	0.090	36.70	
	14	5.03	0.238	3.87	0.092	39.34	
	12	5.25	0.131	3.93	0.078	42.33	
	12	5.18	0.186	3.96	0.131	42.40	
	10	4.87	0.101	3.92	0.047	39.06	
	10	5.06	0.081	3.97	0.034	41.63	
	9	5.09	0.143	4.01	0.088	42.72	
	12	5.08	0.072	3.90	0.081	40.33	
	12	5.06	0.128	4.04	0.090	43.11	
	14	5.23	0.202	3.95	0.060	42.60	
	8	4.86	0.113	3.78	0.070	36.25	
	10	4.71	0.147	3.88	0.092	37.01	
	12	4.98	0.094	3.74	0.060	36.36	
	11	5.01	0.107	3.80	0.063	37.76	
	12	5.05	0.178	3.80	0.071	38.07	
Total/mean	169	5.03	0.132 0.144[b]	3.89	0.076 0.092[b]	39.71	2.59
Yearling	13	5.04	0.223	3.94	0.069	40.84	
	12	5.02	0.175	3.90	0.086	39.86	
	6	4.87	0.093	3.96	0.038	39.86	
	9	5.13	0.146	3.86	0.055	39.90	
	9	5.06	0.161	3.93	0.087	40.79	
	13	5.19	0.133	3.87	0.078	40.58	
	12	4.82	0.137	3.75	0.052	35.38	
	10	4.88	0.158	3.79	0.070	36.59	
	12	4.97	0.127	3.77	0.066	36.87	
	11	4.86	0.143	3.78	0.065	36.25	
	11	4.95	0.144	3.78	0.060	36.92	
	12	4.93	0.108	3.76	0.060	36.38	
Total/mean	130	4.98	0.146 0.114[b]	3.84	0.066 0.078[b]	38.35	2.10

[a] Length—adult versus immature: t = 2.22, $P \leq 0.05$.
 Width—adult versus immature: t = 1.82, $P > 0.05$.
 Volume—adult versus immature: t = 0.46, $P > 0.10$.
[b] Standard deviation among clutches.

Table 99. Dimensions and volumes of wood duck eggs.

Location	n	Length[a] Mean	Length[a] S.D.	Breadth[a] Mean	Breadth[a] S.D.	Volume[b]	Weight[b]	Source
New York	174					40.20	42.89	Haramis (1975)
South Carolina	105	5.13	0.35	3.94	0.11		44.18	Hepp et al. (1987)
Ohio	13	5.55		3.93		44.74	47.57	Stewart (1957)
Illinois[c]	164	5.15	0.22	3.87	0.11	40.26	42.81	This study
Iowa	108	5.24		3.96		42.86	45.61	Dreis (1951)
	85	5.09		3.85		39.35	41.87	
Tennessee	203	4.99	0.24	3.85	0.14	38.00		Spero et al. (1983)
California	26	5.23		3.90		41.49	44.15	Dixon (1924)
	51	4.68		3.74		34.14	36.33	Robinson (1958)
Various areas	99	5.11		3.88		40.16	42.70	Bent (1923)

[a] In centimeters.
[b] Calculated for all except Haramis (1975), Spero et al. (1983), and Hepp et al. (1987). Calculated volume (cubic centimeters) = Kv/LB^2. Calculated weight (grams) = Kw/LB^2.
   L = average length of wood duck egg in centimeters (5.15).
   B = average width of wood duck egg in centimeters (3.87).
   V = mean volume of wood duck egg in cubic centimeters (40.26).
   W = mean weight of wood duck egg in grams (42.81).
   Kv (constant for volume) = 0.522.
   Kw (constant for weight) = 0.555.
[c] These are random eggs measured in addition to those in Table 98.

nest with wood ducks; both use similar cavities and nest houses. Eggs of hooded mergansers are slightly larger, as shown by comparative length and breadth (Table 100), and are more ovate than the elliptical-ovate eggs of the wood duck.

Other cavity-nesting ducks have eggs slightly smaller (bufflehead) in diameter or considerably larger (common goldeneye and common merganser) than those of the wood duck (Table 100).

The average thickness of the wood duck eggshell is 0.255 millimeter (0.010 in), while that of the hooded merganser egg is 0.541 millimeter (0.021 in) (Soulliere 1987). These data are particularly useful in determining the source of shell fragments in hatched nests.

Each egg weighs about 6.4 percent of the wood duck hen's body mass (Table 100)—a percentage comparable to that of other duck species of similar sizes. The eggs of small ducks (such as the green-winged teal, bufflehead, and ruddy duck) weigh more than 9 percent of the hen's body weight. The eggs of larger ducks (such as the mallard and canvasback) form smaller proportions.

A comparison of the clutch weights of eggs—based on average clutch size (Bellrose 1976)—with the body weights of adult females for 17 species of ducks (Table 100) revealed the comparative energy expended in egg laying. Except for the small teals and ruddy duck, cavity-nesting ducks—wood duck, common goldeneye, bufflehead, and hooded merganser—have a larger egg mass to body mass ratio than that of other species. The ratio for the wood duck is lowest of the four cavity species. The early nesting mallard and northern pintail have the lowest ratio of egg to body mass; late-nesting dabbling ducks—blue-winged teal, gadwall, and American wigeon—have higher ratios. Canvasbacks nest early; redheads, ring-necked ducks, and lesser scaups nest considerably later. This difference in nesting chronology parallels their comparative ratios of egg weight to body weight. Thus, differences in the ratio of egg mass to body mass among similar phylogenetic species suggest that early nesting ducks do not have the amount of stored lipids (essential to laying) that is found in species that nest later. On the other hand, early nesters gain time for additional renesting.

Composition

An analysis of the contents of eight wood duck eggs by Drobney (1977) revealed these percentages: water 69.5, lipid 14.1, protein 13.5, ash 1.7, and carbohydrates 1.2. Eggs that averaged 42.6 grams (1.5 oz) were composed of 53.5 percent albumen, 35.8 percent yolk, and 10.7 percent shell. Data derived from the composition of 105 wood duck eggs by Hepp et al. (1987) provided similar percentages: albumen 53.5, yolk 36.8, and shell 9.7; water made up 62.7 percent of the contents (46.2 in the albumen and 16.5 in the yolk). Ricklefs (1977) reported mallard eggs composed of 51 percent albumen, 35.9 percent yolk, and 10.9 percent shell, proportionately almost identical with wood duck eggs. An average wood duck egg is composed of 23.1 grams (0.81 oz) albumen, 15.9 grams (0.56 oz) yolk, and 4.2 grams (0.15 oz) shell.

Table 100. Dimensions, volumes, and weights of eggs of 17 species of ducks in comparison with body weight.

Species	Length[a] Mean	S.D.	Breadth[a] Mean	S.D.	Volume[b]	Weight[b]	Adult female[c] (grams)	Percentage egg per body weight	Percentage clutch per body weight
Wood duck	5.15	0.220	3.87	0.114	40.26	42.81	671	6.38	77.84
Green-winged teal	4.59	0.143	3.38	0.110	27.37	29.10	308	9.45	81.25
Mallard	5.81	0.192	4.17	0.103	52.74	56.07	1,107	5.07	45.59
Northern pintail	5.37	0.123	3.79	0.117	40.26	42.81	866	4.94	38.59
Blue-winged teal	4.66	0.142	3.35	0.085	27.30	29.02	376	7.72	75.64
Northern shoveler	5.30	0.180	3.72	0.118	38.29	40.70	635	6.41	60.25
Gadwall	5.47	0.190	3.88	0.073	42.99	45.70	835	5.47	54.73
American wigeon	5.50	0.248	3.84	0.138	42.33	45.01	767	5.87	49.88
Canvasback	6.28	0.204	4.38	0.200	62.89	66.87	1,157	5.78	54.91
Redhead	5.98	0.378	4.30	0.263	57.72	61.37	971	6.32	73.58
Ring-necked duck	5.54	0.270	3.92	0.157	44.44	47.25	671	7.04	64.78
Lesser scaup	5.74	0.166	3.99	0.126	47.70	50.27	748	6.72	61.03
Ruddy duck	6.23	0.170	4.61	0.113	69.11	73.48	540	13.61	110.22
Common goldeneye	6.05	0.156	4.37	0.128	60.31	64.12	789	8.13	74.77
Bufflehead	5.16	0.164	3.66	0.072	36.08	38.36	367	10.45	91.98
Hooded merganser	5.43	0.256	4.37	0.098	54.13	57.55	680	8.46	89.71
Common merganser	6.60	0.240	4.65	0.097	74.49	79.20	1,238	6.40	67.17

[a] In centimeters; data from Palmer (1976).
[b] Calculated volume = Kv/LB². Calculated weight = Kw/LB².
   L = average length of wood duck egg in centimeters (5.15).
   B = average width of wood duck egg in centimeters (3.87).
   V = mean volume of wood duck egg in cubic centimeters (40.26).
   W = mean weight of wood duck egg in grams (42.81).
   Kv (constant for volume) = 0.522.
   Kw (constant for weight) = 0.555.
[c] Adult female weights and clutch sizes from Bellrose (1976).

Drobney's (1977) analysis showed that yolk provided 69.7 kilocalories and albumen 18.8 kilocalories dry weight—a combined 88.5 kilocalories of energy (2.08 per gram). Hepp et al. (1987) calculated total egg energy at 88.6 kilocalories—16.9 from albumen and 71.7 from yolk.

Because the yolk contains the bulk of energy found in a bird's egg, its relative proportion to overall contents provides an index to the amount required for embryonic development and hatchling survival. Altricial birds have the lowest yolk content, and precocial birds have the highest (Carey et al. 1980). Yolk increased from 24 percent in altricial eggs to 65 percent in the most precocial ones. The yolk content in wood duck eggs ranks slightly above the median given by Carey et al. (1980) for a number of waterfowl species.

Loss in Weight

From 115 wood duck eggs that we weighed from unmatched clutches in various stages of incubation, a regression analysis revealed a consistent rate of weight loss (r = −0.85, P<0.001) as incubation progressed. Between laying and hatching, eggs declined from 39.9 grams (1.41 oz) to 29.4 grams (1.04 oz)—a loss of 25.6 percent. The diffusion of water through the shell and its replacement by air account for the change in weight, according to Romanoff and Romanoff (1949).

Rahn and Ar (1974) stated that bird eggs generally lose about 18 percent of their weight during incubation, subject to limited species variation. They reported that the length of incubation is proportional to the water vapor conductance of the eggshell—a factor of shell thickness and a function of pore area.

CLUTCH SIZE

Determining normal clutch sizes in wood ducks is difficult because of the proclivity of females to lay eggs in more than one nest (dump nesting). Dump nesting became especially prevalent with the establishment of nest houses. Few other phases of wood duck biology have attracted so much interest. Despite much study, however, many aspects of dump nesting remain enigmatic.

Unlike the redhead and ruddy duck, which not only dump eggs among conspecifics but also in the nests of numerous other species, the wood duck—because of its cavity nesting—is largely limited to nests of its own species. Nevertheless, small numbers of wood ducks and hooded mergansers have been found laying together, with incubation usually by the wood duck (Morse et al. 1969, Hartman 1972, Doty et al. 1984).

Clutch size in natural cavities or nest houses that have been checked daily provide information on the range and means of clutches. Early records based on clutches in museums were taken exclusively from natural cavities. Bent (1923) reported the typical clutch to be 10–15, with some clutches as few as 6 or 8 eggs, some larger sets of 18–29 eggs, and even one joint clutch of 31 wood duck eggs and 5 eggs of the hooded merganser. Forbush (1925) listed 8–15 eggs as customary; the largest clutch he reported was 19 eggs. Phillips (1925) stated that the average number in a clutch was more than 11, ranging usually from 9 to 14, but most often 10–13. He cited clutches of 19 and 21 eggs and surmised that they resulted from the laying of two females. In California, Dixon (1924) found eight clutches—three with 10 eggs each, one of 12 eggs, one of 13 eggs, and three with 14 eggs each (mean = 12.13 ± 1.89). In New Brunswick, Prince (1965) found nine clutches in natural cavities—two with 10 eggs each, and one clutch each with 8, 11, 12, 13, 19, 21, and 22 eggs (mean = 14 ± 5.2).

In a 1985–1986 study of the use of natural cavities by wood ducks at the Muscatatuck National Wildlife Refuge, Joe Robb recorded four clutches of 8 eggs each, three of 10 eggs each, and one clutch each of 9, 11, 12, 13, and 17 eggs (an average of 10.3 ± 2.67). In Missouri, Clawson et al. (1979) found that the mean number of eggs laid by female wood ducks that did not engage in dump nesting was 11.8 (range = 7–14). During a three-year study of wood duck nesting in Oregon, Morse and Wight (1969) documented average clutch sizes of normal nests as 9.8, 9.9, and 11.2. Although female wood ducks laid normal clutches as large as 15 eggs, all nests that contained 16 or more eggs were considered dump nests.

An evaluation of clutch size in Illinois is based on four styles of nesting: (1) nests in natural cavities; (2) nests in board houses subjected to mammalian predation; (3) nests in metal houses subjected to little predation; and (4) duplex houses at Nauvoo Slough subjected to an unusually dense breeding population and intraspecific strife.

Clutches in natural cavities had the most limited range and the highest mode (Figure 68); those in duplex units at Nauvoo had no modes (except

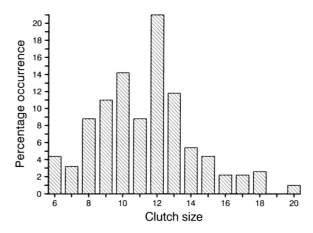

Figure 68. Clutch size of wood ducks nesting in natural cavities, Mason County, Illinois, 1938–59. The average size of 91 clutches was 11.34 ± 2.94 eggs (95-percent confidence limit = 10.74–11.94). Nests (n = 85) that contained 6–16 eggs had a mean of 10.87 ± 2.40 eggs per clutch (95-percent confidence limit = 10.36–11.38). Nests containing more than 16 eggs (n = 6) averaged 18.0 ± 1.10 eggs per clutch (95-percent confidence limit = 17.12 – 18.88).

where class sizes were lumped) and the most extensive range (Figure 69). Differences in the distribution of clutch sizes between board houses and metal ones (figures 70 and 71) are believed to be due to the greater nest destruction in board houses and consequent renesting. The more frequent renests show up in the large proportion of clutches with fewer than 12 eggs.

Two completely different patterns of clutch distribution are shown by hens nesting in natural cavities compared with those in duplex houses (figures 68 and 69). This extreme disparity is caused by

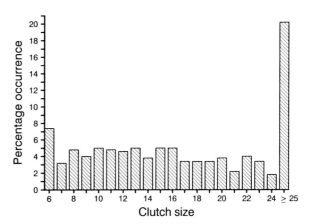

Figure 69. Clutch size of wood ducks nesting in nest houses, Nauvoo Slough, Illinois, 1983–87. The average size of 370 clutches was 17.33 ± 8.67 eggs. Nests (n = 198) that contained 6–16 eggs had a mean of 10.74 ± 3.53 eggs per clutch. Nests containing more than 16 eggs (n = 172) averaged 24.92 ± 6.30 eggs per clutch.

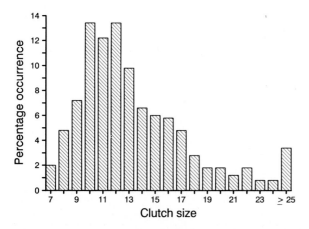

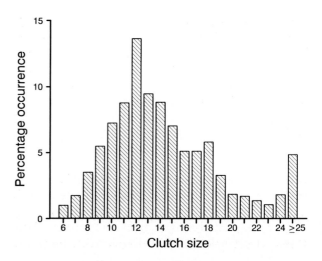

Figure 70. Clutch size of wood ducks nesting in board nest houses, Mason County, Illinois, 1939–55. The average size of 481 clutches was 13.48 ± 4.48 eggs (95-percent confidence limit = 13.08–13.88). Nests (n = 383) that contained 6–16 eggs had a mean of 11.64 ± 2.33 eggs per clutch (95-percent confidence limit = 11.40–11.87). Nests containing more than 16 eggs (n = 98) averaged 20.67 ± 3.47 eggs per clutch (95-percent confidence limit = 19.98–21.36).

Figure 71. Clutch size of wood ducks nesting in metal nest houses, Quiver Creek units, Illinois, 1956–74. The average size of 1,893 clutches was 14.17 eggs. Nests (n = 1,385) that contained 4–16 eggs had a mean of 11.89 eggs. Nests containing more than 16 eggs (n = 508) averaged 20.33 eggs per clutch.

differences in the magnitude of dump nesting. Our natural cavity data show the presence of only a few dump nests. Indeed, all studies concerning nests in natural cavities record a low level of dump nesting. (We have made the assumption that any nest con-

taining fewer than 17 eggs was laid by one female, but we recognize that a proportion of these "normal-sized" clutches may actually have been dump nests.) In contrast, at least 47.2 percent of the 614 nests in duplex houses were dump nests (Table 101).

A duplex wood duck nest house at Nauvoo Slough, Illinois, shows an unusually small clutch of seven eggs and an exceptionally large compound clutch of 35 eggs in the adjacent compartments. The small clutch—started on May 26—represented that of a renesting female (note the absence of down), and the compound clutch probably represented eggs from at least three hens. Clutches of 16 eggs or more indicate laying by more than one female and have been termed "dump nests." *Photo by Dan Holm; courtesy of the Illinois Natural History Survey.*

Table 101. Proportion of dump nests (more than 16 eggs) to total wood duck nests, breeding females, and nest sites at Nauvoo Slough, Illinois, 1983–90.

Year	Number of breeding females	Number of nest sites	Total number of nests[a]	Number of dump nests	Percentage of dump nests	Nests per female
1983	28	28	42	13	31.0	1.50
1984	46	81	71	24	33.8	1.54
1985	60	80	73	37	50.7	1.22
1986	73	80	101	55	54.5	1.38
1987	76	80	85	43	50.6	1.12
1988	51	80	70	39	55.7	1.37
1989	67	80	87	37	42.5	1.30
1990	75	80	85	42	49.4	1.13
Total/weighted mean (years)	476	589	614	290	47.2	1.29

[a] Excludes number of dropped clutches (less than four eggs); includes both successful and unsuccessful nests.

Of 80 nests that each contained 25 or more eggs, 5 held 40 or more eggs and 1 held 49. The largest clutch that we know of contained 69 unincubated eggs; it was found by John Staab, Ohio Department of Natural Resources, on May 30, 1979, on the Killbuck Wildlife Area.

Sizes of wood duck clutches in nest houses range tremendously, depending primarily on the degree of dump nesting that occurred and secondarily on the degree of renesting. A comparison of the records of 25 renesting females not involved in dump nests revealed that the initial mean clutch was 12.44 ± 1.8 eggs, whereas their second clutches averaged 10.84 ± 2.67 eggs. Four females laid identical-sized clutches in renests; in six instances, the renests were one or two eggs larger than the initial clutches. Clutch size was not influenced by the weight of the laying female, according to Hepp et al. (1987).

The size of normal clutches declines slightly as the nesting season progresses until June 1, when the occurrence of smaller clutches becomes increasingly frequent (Figure 72). Variation among clutch sizes was lowest for nests initiated in March and early April and highest in June when ducks were renesting. The earliest nesters were older hens that apparently returned with more stored lipids than did later-nesting birds. Because protein becomes increasingly available as water temperature rises and aquatic and marsh vegetation develop, reduced clutch sizes and greater variability during June suggest that stored lipids are lower and more variable among renesting hens. The low weight of incubating females at this time further points to reduction in lipid reserves. Clutch sizes of woodies nesting in southeastern Missouri showed a marked seasonal decline in dump nests, but a decline in normal nests was barely perceptible (Clawson et al. 1979).

The larger the clutch size of wood duck eggs, including dump nests, the lower the proportion that hatches. In most instances, however, dump nesting is an asset for production, resulting in more ducklings leaving a nest site. A woodie hen that dumps her eggs usually later incubates her own separate clutch. *Photo by Jack Dermid.*

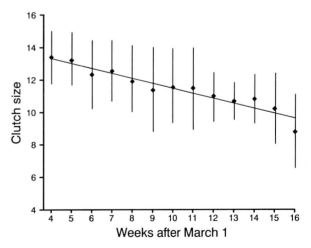

Figure 72. Decline in mean clutch size of 602 normal wood duck nests with progression of the nesting season, 1956–74, Quiver Creek, Illinois (vertical lines represent standard deviation). The regression equation is: $y = 14.57 - 0.307x$, $r = -0.95$, $P < 0.001$.

INCUBATION

The precise beginning of incubation is difficult to determine. The problem is compounded because some females lay eggs during the night or prior to early morning departures, and intruding females may add one or more eggs to an otherwise normal and nearly complete clutch. Frederic Leopold recorded the ducks he found on nests at night in relation to clutch deposition and completion (Table 102). Presence of a hen on a nest at night was most often observed on the night prior to completion of the clutch. However, females were found on nests overnight for up to five days prior to completion of the clutch. In each instance, an egg was added to the clutch during the nocturnal visit. Breckenridge (1956) also observed a female that spent the last three nights prior to incubation on the nest and deposited an egg each night. Delbert Koke reported that several females under his close observation spent nights on nests during which they laid eggs.

Whether sufficient heat is applied by contact to eggs previously deposited to initiate embryo development is a moot question. Kennamer et al. (1990) reported that embryo development early in incubation in a single clutch varied from 0 to 5 days (mean = 2.2 ± 1.0 day). Thus, it is possible that nocturnal occupancy of a nest site prior to circadian incubation may initiate early embryo development.

Our data on the lengths of incubation of 218 nests are presented in Figure 73. The mode was 31 days, the minimum 28 days, the maximum 37 days, and the mean 30.8 ± 1.69 days. Frederic Leopold's data for 61 incubation periods provided a mean of 31.7 ± 1.53 days. His earlier published findings (Leopold 1951) for 35 nests ranged from 27 to 33 days, with a mean of 29.9 ± 1.38 days. Haramis and Thompson (1985) reported on 16 incubation periods that ranged from 27 to 30 days and averaged 28.8 ± 1.2 days. Heinroth (1910) considered the wood duck incubation period at the Berlin Zoological Garden to be 31 days.

At the Van Norman Aviary, Hanna City, Illinois, the minimum incubation period has been 28 days

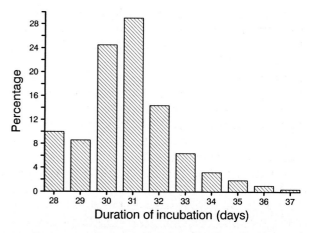

Figure 73. Length of incubation for 218 wood duck nests, Quiver Creek, Illinois, 1971–74.

for clutches under laying wood ducks and for clutches placed under bantam hens. However, there are some records of incubation periods that are inexplicably brief: Breckenridge (1956) reported that a wood duck nest in Minnesota hatched at 25 days, and Wilkins et al. (1990) reported that some wood duck nests in the South hatch at 25–26 days.

The spread in incubation periods is in part due to variations in the daily amount of heat applied to the eggs; reducing incubation temperature slows embryonic development. Individual hens vary in attentiveness to incubation, and low ambient temperatures have the potential to reduce heat applied to the eggs (Breckenridge 1956). An incubating bird also has more difficulty applying equal amounts of heat to eggs in a large clutch. We frequently have noticed hens attempting to cover large clutches with partially spread wings, a tactic that obviously reduces heat exchange to individual eggs. A regression of 120 clutch sizes, containing 10–20 eggs each, in relation to incubation periods indicated a slight correlation ($r = 0.15$, $P \leq 0.10$), with incubation periods increasing 2.13 hours for each egg above 10. Hepp et al. (1990) also reported that length of incubation increased as the clutch size from parasitic laying increased. Zipko (1979) found that the temperature of eggs in normal nests averaged 35.4 degrees Celsius (95.8°F) whereas eggs in dump nests averaged 33.4 degrees Celsius (92.1°F); the difference was statistically significant.

Breckenridge (1956) reported on several incubating birds that spent many hours off their nests yet whose eggs hatched in 29–31 days. These examples of embryos surviving substantial periods (9.6 hours and 13.6 hours) without the application of heat are important in evaluating hatchability.

We observed one female that incubated addled eggs for at least 43 days before we removed them.

Table 102. Number of nights that wood duck females were on nests prior to completion of clutches.[a]

Number of nights	Number of females	Percentage
1	13	34.2
2	10	26.3
3	8	21.1
4	6	15.8
5	1	2.6

[a] Data from the records of Frederic Leopold, Burlington, Iowa.

After we removed another clutch of rotten eggs, the hen returned to incubate the empty nest. Grice and Rogers (1965) found hens incubating 45, 54, and 60 days. Leopold (1951) observed a female that incubated for 62 days. Heusmann and Pekkala (1976) also reported one wood duck hen that attempted in two consecutive years to incubate a nest with no eggs. The maternal desire to incubate is strong in many individual woodies, and not so strong in others that readily desert clutches.

In thousands of wood duck nests studied by us and others, only the female has been found incubating. Rollin (1957), however, reported a captive male in eclipse plumage incubating a nest deserted by the female. Karl C. Wenner found both a drake and a hen brooding still wet ducklings in a nest box in northern Florida. The female was captured as she flushed, leaving the male in the box to be banded later. Upon release, the male flew nearby; the female returned to the nest with the brood, remained overnight, and departed with the brood the following morning. Although the female and the brood were monitored visually through radiotelemetry, the male was not observed again.

Hanson (1954) photographed and outlined the changing appearance of a candled wood duck egg as incubation progressed. Burke et al. (1978) excised the developing embryo from day 1 through day 30 of incubation. They recorded selected measurements and the most pertinent developmental changes to provide criteria necessary to determine the stage of incubation (Table 103).

Wood duck incubation periods range from 28 to 37 days and average 30 days. The greater the interruptions in heat application—and the lower the ambient temperature—the longer the eggs take to hatch. Incubation by woodie drakes is rare if it occurs at all. *Photo by Wilmer Zehr; courtesy of the Illinois Natural History Survey.*

Table 103. Criteria for determining the age of an excised wood duck embryo.[a]

Day of incubation	Length[b]				Remarks
	Head and torso	Wing bud (wing)	Leg bud[c] (tarsus)	Bill bud (culmen)	
0					Blastodisc about 5 millimeters in diameter; infertile eggs lack blastodisc.
2	1.8				Blastodisc 9.2 millimeters in diameter.
4	4.2				Heartbeat present.
6	8.6				Eyes present; embryo forming shape of letter C.
8	10.7	2.5	2.5		Head and tail folds developing; midbrain forms bulge.
10	19.2	5.7	6.2		Midbrain bilobed; neck elongating.
12	22.5	7.9	9.4	1.8	Spinal, femoral, and crural tracts have colorless feather germs; egg tooth present (0.2 millimeters in diameter).
14	50.0	9.1	7.0	4.8	Dark feather papillae on spinal, femoral, crural, and crudal tracts.
16	55.0	10.0	8.2	5.6	Nostrils appear as white depressions; ear openings and claws visible.
18	67.0	11.3	11.5	6.1	Black feather papillae cover all tracts except ventral side of humerus.
20	74.6	12.8	12.6	6.8	All tracts feathered; ear openings covered with feathers; eye one-third closed.
22	79.0	15.7	14.6	7.5	Back of neck against blunt end of egg; beak turning upward.
24	81.4	17.3	16.8	8.0	Embryo on left side with beak angled toward air cell; lids cover eyes.
26	85.5	17.9	18.3	8.5	Eye and bill partly covered by right wing and left leg; nostrils open.
28	92.0	18.6	20.0	9.1	Bill touches chorion; pipping starts in some eggs.
30	104.6	19.2	22.0	10.4	Egg tooth penetrates shell membrane and shell.

[a] Adapted from Burke et al. (1978).
[b] In millimeters.
[c] Leg bud measurements include the foot until fourteenth day of incubation; thereafter only the tarsus was measured.

Recess Patterns

We relied on published and unpublished information along with our own data to determine the most common daily recess patterns (Table 104). Incubating females most often (46 percent) left nests once in the morning and once in the afternoon. Days with one recess in the afternoon were the second most common pattern. Breckenridge (1956) emphasized that hens show wide variation in daily temporal (or regimen) distribution of recesses, and Stewart (1962) concurred.

Not only are there differences among hens, but individuals also occasionally show wide variance in the temporal pattern of rest flights. Leopold (1951) noted that some females changed recess patterns during incubation. Breckenridge (1956) and Stewart (1962) documented this behavior more closely. Each observed one hen with no consistent pattern of daily recess.

Jobes et al. (1976) found that four hens in the St. Paul, Minnesota, area were fairly consistent in the timing of morning departures. Eighty-five percent of all morning recesses occurred between 4:00 and 5:00 a.m. In southeastern Iowa, Leopold (1951) observed that morning recess flights commonly started as early as one hour before sunrise. Similarly, Breckenridge (1956), Jones (1964), and Stewart (1962) each observed that morning recesses generally were initiated before 6:00 a.m.

Wood ducks show greater variation in afternoon departures. They generally leave the nest between 3:00 and 6:30 p.m. Jobes et al. (1976) observed that 65 percent of all afternoon recesses occurred between 3:20 and 5:00 p.m. Results from several studies indicate that hens rarely depart the

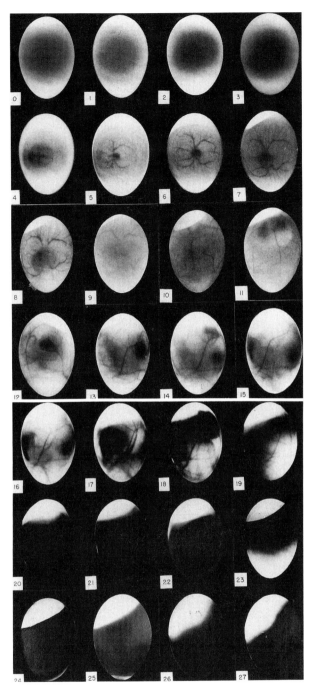

Candling of wood duck eggs often is used to obtain information on the stage of incubation, the fate of unhatched eggs, and whether dump nesting occurred after incubation started. By placing an egg in one end of a flexible tube, such as a radiator hose, and holding it up to the sun so that all light must pass through, developmental stages can be observed. The above photographs reveal the daily development of wood duck embryos over a 27-day period in a normal 30-day incubation. In addition to the darkening occasioned by the developing embryo, notice the increase in white area at the blunt end of the egg as a result of a slow but steady increase in the air chamber. At laying, the air chamber is minuscule; it encompasses about 5 percent of the contents by the seventh day, 10 percent at 10 days, and 33 percent at 30 days. *Photos from Hanson (1954); courtesy of Harold C. Hanson.*

Table 104. Daily recess frequency for 14 female wood ducks (not necessarily consecutively during incubation period).[a]

Recess pattern	Number of days	Percentage of all days
No recesses	17	5.6
1 in a.m.	39	12.9
1 in p.m.	86	28.5
2 in a.m.	2	0.7
2 in p.m.	6	2.0
1 in a.m.; 1 in p.m.	139	46.0
1 in a.m.; 2 in p.m.	8	2.6
2 in a.m.; 1 in p.m.	5	1.7
Total	302	100.0

Mean = 1.52 ± 0.67 recesses per day

[a] Information from Breckenridge (1956) (three females), Stewart (1962) (one female), and Jobes et al. (1976) (four females) was combined with our data on six females.

nest during midday (Leopold 1951, Breckenridge 1956). We examined 411 nests between 8:00 a.m. and 3:00 p.m. and found 92.5 percent of all females in attendance. In central Ohio, however, one female left her nest nearly 25 percent of the time between 9:00 a.m. and 3:00 p.m. (Stewart 1962).

At Oquawka, Illinois, Delbert Koke observed the incubation patterns of six female wood ducks through an entire nesting season (Table 105). Morning and afternoon recesses were of comparable duration, but not every hen took a recess twice a day. The total time that hens were absent from their nests averaged 71.6 minutes per day. A mean of 749 minutes occurred between departures from the nest. The standard deviation and range expressed considerable individual variation, much of which was attributed to prevailing inclement weather—

cold, rain, fog, and wind.

In Minnesota, Jobes et al. (1976) found a significant negative correlation ($r = -0.49$, $P < 0.05$) between time of departure and length of morning recess. Hens took proportionally shorter recesses when they left nests earlier in the day. The researchers indicated that length of a preceding session was the most important factor influencing morning departure time. Length of afternoon recess was positively correlated ($r = 0.73$, $P < 0.05$) with the sum of the previous day's recesses. Timing of afternoon departure was negatively correlated with temperature ($r = -0.12$, $P < 0.05$) and time spent off the nest the day before ($r = -0.55$, $P < 0.05$). Breckenridge (1956) and Grice and Rogers (1965) also found that wood ducks tended to incubate longer on cooler days.

Upon returning to her nest site early in incubation, a wood duck hen usually is followed by her mate, who "peels off" close to the nest as the hen quickly enters (left). At times, a female appears to fly directly through the entrance without perching first. One experienced observer witnessed a female return to a nest house at an unusually fast rate and on direct course, closely trailed by a male. As the hen virtually shot through the entrance, the male collided with the nest house. The very groggy drake took half an hour to recover sufficiently to fly off. The drake may not have been the hen's mate and was perhaps intent on forced copulation. Late in the incubation period, wood duck hens usually return to the nest unaccompanied by their mates. When a nest house is over water, the female may land in the water nearby before springing upward to the nest site (right). Such a "false" return may be an antipredator strategy, giving the hen an opportunity to identify threats in the vicinity before she exposes the cavity location by her own flight. *Photos by Jack Dermid.*

Table 105. Components of the incubation rhythm (in minutes) of six hen wood ducks at Oquawka, Illinois.[a]

Component	Mean	S.D.	C.V.	n	Range
Total time spent off nest per day[b]	71.61	45.83	64.0	77	0–205
Duration of morning recesses	54.78	36.04	65.8	36	10–188
Duration of afternoon recesses	62.55	34.70	55.5	58	15–205
Session duration[c]	749.12	261.56	34.9	66	295–1,464
Incubation constancy[d]	91.27				

[a] Data provided by Delbert Koke.
[b] Includes days when females took no recesses.
[c] The time that a female remained on a nest between recess departures.
[d] Percentage of day spent incubating. Calculated as (100 times session duration) divided by (session duration plus recess length).

Pair-bond Duration

Leopold (1951) described how nesting season chronology influenced the duration of pair bonds in southeastern Iowa. In early spring (April and May), 7 of 10 drakes remained with their mates until the fourth week (22–28 days) of incubation. In contrast, during midsummer (June and July) he found that males deserted their mates immediately after clutches were completed. Delbert Koke observed a drake in late June that stopped accompanying his spouse during egg laying.

We used data provided by Frederic Leopold to illustrate more precisely how pair-bond duration changed with progression of the breeding season (Table 106). Estimates from the regression indicate that after three days of incubation in early spring, 64 percent of the incubating hens were accompanied by their mates during recess periods. This behavior contrasts with the behavior of pairs that started nests later in the year. By the first week of June, only 3 percent of incubating hens were estimated to be accompanied by their mates after three days of incubation. Fifty-seven percent of all pair bonds appeared intact after 28 days of incubation on April 6; however, only 17 percent of incubating females were accompanied by drakes following 28 days of incubation in mid-May (Table 106).

Table 106. Percentage of wood duck males that returned with their mates, based on day of incubation in comparison with the progression of the nesting season after April 1.[a]

	Days after April 1		
Day of incubation	5	45	65
3	64	25	3
8	63	23	1
13	61	22	0.1
18	60	19	
23	59	18	
28	57	17	

[a] Multiple regression equation in standard format = $(Z = 0.023980 + (-0.000350X_1) + (-0.000092X_2))$; $r^2 = 0.25$; $N = 183$.

On the Chippewa National Forest in north-central Minnesota, Gilmer et al. (1977) observed wide variation in the length of time male wood ducks remained with their mates. On average, drakes were found to abandon their hens after 6.5 days of incubation. Although one pair bond dissolved 4 days before the female terminated laying, another drake remained with his mate for 25 days after the start of incubation. The short time that males accompanied females to nest sites in northern Minnesota, compared with the longer time in Iowa, may stem from the shorter breeding season in Minnesota.

During laying and into the incubation period, wood duck drakes accompany their mates to the nest site. During the laying period, drakes attempt to be as inconspicuous as possible while waiting for their mates to complete laying. Most males are patient and wait 15–60 minutes for their spouses to reappear. However, some give up and fly back to loafing areas, and a few fly to the nest cavity and look inside. Incubating hens usually depart the nest twice a day—early morning and mid to late afternoon—for a respite and food. *Photo by Gary Kammerer; courtesy of the California Waterfowl Association.*

At Great Meadows National Wildlife Refuge in Massachusetts, most drake woodies deserted their mates about midway through incubation (Grice and Rogers 1965). Clawson (1975a) observed that most pair bonds in southeastern Missouri were broken during the third week of incubation. Similarly, pair bonds of nesting wood ducks in the Sacramento Valley of California were broken about three-quarters of the way through incubation (Jones 1964).

Some drakes that accompany late-nesting females have entered into the prebasic molt. Because late-season nests have proportionally more infertile eggs than do early nests, Grice and Rogers (1965) speculated that drakes in Massachusetts may not be physiologically capable of fertilizing a complete clutch after mid-June.

PIPPING AND HATCHING

Up to 48 hours prior to hatching, small starlike cracks begin to appear between one-fourth and one-third from the top of the blunt end of the egg, where a large air cell developed as incubation progressed. In 10 records, we found great variability from a mean of 32 hours ± 11.3. Faint intermittent peepings and the scraping sound of the egg tooth as it presses against the shell foretell the end of the embryonic term. Over several hours, the egg tooth (a horny tubercle at the tip of the upper mandible) cuts a hole in the shell. The duckling turns within the shell, cutting an opening around the blunt end through which it extricates itself by kicking from the shell in 0.5–2.0 hours. The time required for the entire hatching process varies considerably within a clutch and between clutches of eggs; it apparently depends on the vigor of the embryos and the toughness of the egg membrane. For the first few hours, ducklings are wet, limp, and almost lifeless. When dry, they become animated balls of down that increasingly keep their mother preoccupied with their activity and clamorous peeping.

The eggshell is now in two parts, the blunt cap forming about 30 percent and the lower base about 70 percent. The shells soon become fragmented by the movements of young and mother. Evidence of a hatched nest is demonstrated by the shell membranes—white envelopes 35–40 millimeters (1.2–1.4 in) long. These membranes are a good index of eggs recently hatched, but starlings remove them and, according to Wilkins et al. (1990), wood duck hens may consume them, so their presence must be judiciously interpreted.

By placing a microphone in a wood duck nesting box and studying the recorded calls by sonogram, Gottlieb (1963, 1965, 1974, 1977, 1980) made a number of significant findings on auditory perception between ducklings and their mother. With the pipping of eggs, the mother wood duck begins a dialogue with the hatching embryos that lasts at least until the young leave the nest and sometimes even to flight stage.

A pecking at the shell, faint peeps, and a slight protuberance one-third below the top of the egg are indications that hatching has started. From an initial "window," woodie ducklings use an egg tooth—a temporary horny growth on the upper mandible—to cut the upper third of the shell in a circle. At left, the initial opening has been slightly enlarged to reveal the egg tooth. The more vigorous ducklings are able to kick themselves from the shell in about six hours after pipping (right). Within an hour or two after hatching, the down dries and the hatchlings become animated. During the hatching process, the peeps of the most advanced embryos appear to stimulate the less advanced ones to commence pipping activities, enabling the hatch to be fairly synchronous. *Photos by Jack Dermid.*

A hen wood duck broods her ducklings, which are only a few hours old (left). Two eggs remain and probably will not hatch; they may be infertile, contain dead embryos, or be out of synchronization with the clutch as a whole. Grass stems forming the nest base indicate a previous nest by a starling. Hatched wood duck eggs are trampled by a hen and her ducklings (right), breaking the shells into small pieces and exposing egg membranes. Large shell fragments usually indicate that the egg contents were eaten by a predator. Occasionally a hatched eggshell is sufficiently intact to show the "trap door" cut by an emerged duckling. *Photos by Wilmer Zehr; courtesy of the Illinois Natural History Survey.*

NEST EXODUS

Gottlieb (1965) reported that the female wood duck began calling to young 36 hours before nest exodus at an average rate of less than one note per five seconds. At two hours prior to exodus, the calling rate increased to four notes per second, and at the time of exodus from the nest site the rate of calling increased to seven to nine notes per second (Miller and Gottlieb 1976).

In later experiments, Gottlieb (1977, 1980) discovered that the ducklings exposed solely to their own vocalizations during hatching would, after hatching, respond to the maternal call of the species. He attributed this ability to the similarity in the descending frequency modulation of their notes, even though the ducklings' calls were in a higher frequency range than those of the adults. Gottlieb (1974) found that the ducklings had two distinctive notes: low-pitched contact contentment cheeps and loud, high-pitched distress peeps.

Several years ago, Delbert Koke of Oquawka, Illinois, placed microphones in five wood duck nest houses within a few yards of his home. He wanted to know when to watch for the departure of broods from nest sites, an event that theretofore had es-

caped him. Koke was surprised to hear the females "talking to the embryos" more than two to three days prior to departure. Because of our interest, he taped numerous "dialogues" between mothers and young.

As the time within the nest lengthened after hatching, Koke recorded that the calls of both young and mother increased in intensity. After prolonged brooding, the young became restless, moving about with increasing frequency. On occasion, the mother left the brood for brief intervals one or more times prior to departure. When she did, Koke's taped recordings revealed that the ducklings were dramatically quiet.

While assisting wildlife photographer Mike Male obtain motion pictures of wood ducks leaving nest houses at the Van Norman Aviary, we noticed that the mother used two calls: the one that enticed the ducklings from the house was rapid (a maternal call); the other, which silenced and immobilized them, was longer and slower (a hauk warning call). The rapid "kuck, kuck, kuck" of the maternal call is in contrast to the slower hauk warning call that froze the young in the nest cavity (see Chapter 6). Until released by the maternal call, the ducklings remained quiet in the nest.

Wood duck hens brood their ducklings for about 24 hours prior to the young's departure. During this time, the ducklings become increasingly noisy and animated, crawling over their mother's back and about the nest site (top). The brooding hen leaves her ducklings the day of their departure in order to feed and apparently scout out the route she will take them to water. In Havana, Illinois, author Frank Bellrose has observed hens flying an entirely different course over the town the morning of brood departure—a direction they later took their young. Note the egg membranes and shell fragments (bottom). *Top photo by Ray Cunningham. Bottom photo by Jack Dermid.*

Prior to calling her ducklings from the nest—usually about midmorning—the wood duck hen makes several appearances at the nest entrance that typically last 3–10 minutes each, possibly looking for potential predators (top). When satisfied that there is no danger present, the hen flies to a short distance away in preparation for calling her ducklings (center). Hens call to their ducklings from the water (bottom), the ground, or a tree limb near the nest site. *Photos by Jack Dermid.*

Upon hearing the maternal call, the ducklings immediately began springing upward toward the entrance. The initial leap carried some to within a few inches of the entrance, others only partway. Some make the distance in two; a few take three or more continuous upward hitches. Because the ducklings are jumping like corn popping, they frequently collide and have to start over again. In less than five minutes, most broods have departed the nest cavity. Sometimes two at a time appear at the entrance in their hurry to leave. Once at the entrance the duckling pauses momentarily, peeping loudly, before jumping outward, with tiny wings fluttering and tail outspread, to the terrain below.

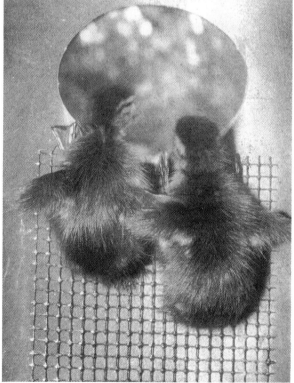

The wood duck hen's maternal call stimulates her brood in the nest cavity to commence jumping upward and toward the lighted entrance, clinging to the side of the nest site as they hitch upward a few inches at a time (left). Where nest house sides are smooth, a hardware cloth "ladder" is absolutely essential for the young woodies to climb to the entrance (top right). Even with sharp claws, ducklings are unable to cling to smooth surfaces, and we have found entire broods "marooned" in plywood houses without ladders. The mother's call incites a virtual pandemonium in the nest, and her offspring compete with one another to gain purchase to follow her urgings (bottom right). *Left photo by William E. Clark; courtesy of the Illinois Natural History Survey. Right photos by Mike Male.*

Siegfried (1974) described changes in body position and patterns of movement of woodie ducklings ascending an artificial chimney of cement blocks. With the aid of needle-sharp decurved toe claws that averaged 3.3 millimeters (0.12 in) in length, they could cling to the rough surface for the next leap upward. The stiff caudal (tail) down feathers served as a brace to assist the ducklings in maintaining a vertical position while extending their feet upward for the next ascension. At the peak of the body lift, the feet were released and the wings swung outward, upward, and then inward. Ducklings that successfully reached the top averaged 7.9 jumps per minute. Unsuccessful ducklings averaged only 0.7 jump per minute, suggesting that the successful ones had the greater energy.

Ducklings that leap from nest sites over water have comfortable landings; those that exit over land may have uncomfortable landings but usually complete them without serious injury. We have seen ducklings drop 15 meters (50 ft) without injury. On one occasion, a duckling jumped 8 meters (26 ft) to a cement walk, bounced a foot in the air and, without the slightest indication of impairment, scurried to join mother and brood.

However, 4 of the 11 ducklings that jumped from a natural cavity 11 meters (36 ft) above the ground in the Bellrose yard at Havana were stunned when they landed on their backs. Apparently they struck twigs or branches on their downward plunge, upsetting their balance. It took them a few seconds longer to recover than those landing right side up and, like them, scurry to their mother 10 meters (9.5 yards) away.

The mother calls to the young from either a branch on a tree within a few feet of the nest site or from the ground (or water) near the base of the nest tree. She nervously walks or swims while collecting her brood as the loudly peeping ducklings land and make a beeline for the ever-expanding group. She may delay escorting the brood from the nest area for minutes to an hour when a duckling remains in the nest. In time, however, she leaves even if one or more ducklings still call from the nest cavity. Broods usually leave between 9:00 and 12:00 a.m. (mean = 10:00 a.m.) standard time, but some leave shortly after daybreak and some as late as dusk.

On one occasion in May 1988, Delbert Koke saw a partial wood duck brood depart before the mother returned from a brief absence. Unexpectedly, one of the ducklings had jumped out, peeping loudly, and six more followed before the female returned. Two ducklings were still in the entrance. As the female entered the nest, one duckling was knocked to the ground and the other back into the nest. Taped calls revealed unusual and high-pitched calling by the woodie female before she flew to the ground to call the remaining members of the brood from the nest house.

On July 4, 1987, at 6:50 a.m. CST, Bellrose witnessed a female wood duck on his neighbor's front yard looking up into a tree, apparently calling. As pedestrians passed 6.1 meters (20 ft) away, she took refuge under shrubs. At 8:00 a.m., she appeared with only one duckling trailing her as she moved back and forth between clumps of shrubs. At 8:45 a.m., she appeared with 10 ducklings. Apparently this mother, perhaps because of the location near a busy street, attempted to entice her young to depart their nest cavity before they were sufficiently conditioned or strong enough to leave.

Don Helmeke reported a similar incident at Maple Grove, Minnesota. On June 10, 1982, a female wood duck remained near the base of the nest tree for several hours. She scrambled about, calling, and was followed by a lone duckling. Later investigation revealed one duckling in the nest, apparently too weak to climb out, and 12 unhatched eggs.

By contrast, at Delbert Koke's residence we have heard taped calls of ducklings that were so active in the nest that it appeared their mothers were having difficulty restraining their departure. There appears to be a particular time in development when it is most propitious for the ducklings to leave the nest. Departing too early or too late, the young apparently lack sufficient energy to engender their departure.

Siegfried's (1974) observations of hatchery wood duck ducklings climbing out of an artificial chimney suggest that ducklings one or two days of age are not yet at optimum strength. Success in exiting the structure increased from 71 percent for one-day-olds to 75 percent for two-day-olds and 100 percent for three-day-old chicks.

We witnessed ducklings climbing up the interior of an opened nest house on several occasions. On one occasion the mother, off the nest at our arrival, gave the maternal call from nearby when we removed the top of the nest house. Immediately all of the young sprang upward, clinging to the rough-surface wall 15.2–30.5 centimeters (6–12 in) from the bottom, then made another leap up to the entrance and out. Sharp claws and light weight (about 28 grams: 1 oz) enable ducklings to climb rough surfaces that are many feet high. We found them successfully climbing out of chimneys and cavities as deep as 4 meters (13 ft). On the other hand, we found entire broods trapped in nest houses made of plywood or of dressed rather than rough-cut lumber that were only 46 centimeters (18 in) deep. Obviously the ducklings could not cling to the slick surface to reach the entrance.

It may take only a moment for the first departing woodie duckling to appear at the entrance, peeping loudly in response to the mother's soft staccato "kuh, kuh, kuh," which she will use later to entice her young to food, loafing sites, and brooding. After a brief pause, the duckling jumps into space with tiny wings beating and feet extended. The height of the fall rarely poses a problem, even when the ducklings must land on concrete walks and patios. *Photos by Mark Wilson.*

We have witnessed the departure of a score of broods, and our colleagues collectively have viewed several scores more. Yet in all observations by serious students of wood duck behavior, the calling by the female, followed by the jumping of young from the nest site, has followed this pattern we have described. Fishermen and other river folk have told us of seeing a wood duck carrying her young to water by her bill or on her back. According to Phillips (1925), such noted early ornithologists as Alexander Wilson and John J. Audubon wrote that wood ducks use their bills to carry ducklings from the nest. After describing young jumping from the nest

site, Forbush (1925: 229) wrote: "There is incontestable evidence, however, that the young often are conveyed to the water by the parent not only when the nest is at a considerable distance from the water but sometimes when the nest almost overhangs it." Three of his correspondents told of a mother, carrying ducklings on her back, scaling downward from the nest cavity to water, the young falling from her back as she alighted. After reviewing Forbush's extensive correspondence on the subject, Phillips (1925) remained unconvinced that wood ducks employ these unconventional methods. We, too, are not convinced of this; if they do it is most unusual.

The hen starts to collect her brood as they begin their exodus from a nest site. This may take 5–10 minutes, depending on how fast the ducklings reach the entrance. Weak young, unable to climb to the entrance, may be left behind. Some ducklings found dead in nests may result from eggs that hatched late, possibly from eggs dumped by intruding hens during incubation. Hens display considerable variation in the time they wait below the nest site for the appearance of tardy young. *Photo by Jack Dermid.*

TREK TO WATER

Comparatively few wood ducks find nest sites in natural cavities or in nest houses over or adjacent to water, and the vast majority of broods are led by their mothers overland to water that may be a few meters to 1.6 kilometers (1 mi) or more distant. We have had small numbers of wood ducks use nest houses situated 2 kilometers (1.25 mi) across sand-loam fields from the nearest wetland. We have seen more than one recently hatched brood with their mother crossing a road more than 3.2 kilometers (2 mi) from a ditch, creek, or body of water larger than a swimming pool.

It is essential for woodie ducklings to reach water and obtain food before their stored energy is depleted. In a study of mallard ducklings, Kear (1965) found that recently hatched birds obtained energy from yolk residue and liver, which initially developed from the energy provided by yolk. By the onset of bill tapping on the shell, about 10 grams (0.35 oz) (half of the original amount) of yolk was utilized. About 5.9 grams (0.21 oz) of yolk were used during the two-day hatching period; the remaining 3–4 grams (0.11–0.14 oz) were drawn into the abdomen. Residual yolk is passed into the liver for future energy demands. Kear (1965) believed that an unfed mallard duckling would survive at least 48 hours after hatching.

Burke et al. (1978) reported that wood duck ducklings lost 33 percent of their yolk between day 22 of incubation and the onset of pipping. The remaining 6.3 milliliters (0.38 in³) were drawn into the abdomen for future energy needs, probably a sufficient amount to last 48–60 hours, 24 hours of which are normally spent in a nest cavity. Hence, it is necessary for woodie ducklings to obtain food before the stored energy expires. Ducklings that become separated from their mothers rarely eat when confined, and we have observed that they seldom survive more than 24 hours.

Several long-distance records for wood ducks nesting in cities have been reported. In Manhattan, Kansas – where a pair nested on the campus of Kansas State University – John L. Zimmerman noted that the nest site was 2.1 kilometers (1.3 mi) from a perennial creek and 2.6 kilometers (1.6 mi) from the Kansas River. In Lincoln, Illinois, a recently hatched brood was observed by Michelle Georgi (Illinois Natural History Survey staff) near the center of the residential area, 3.2 kilometers (2 mi) to the nearest water at Lincoln Lakes or 4.8 kilometers (3 mi) to Salt Creek. In Williamsville, Illinois, a recently hatched brood was observed by Neil Gunkel near the center of town, 2 kilometers (1.25 mi) from the nearest water at Wolf Creek.

Each year for a number of years, Rick Kaminski has received several records of wood duck broods on or near the campus of Mississippi State University, adjacent to Starkville. Indeed, a nest searching female descended his fireplace flue on February 17, 1991. The only available water areas, according to Kaminski, are small ponds in an urban setting. The ponds are partially or completely surrounded by well-groomed lawns, yet wood ducks persist there as a viable breeding population.

Because wood ducks often nest away from water, hens must lead their broods from a few meters to 1.6 kilometers (1 mi) or more. After collecting her brood near the base of the nest tree, a woodie hen heading for water darts from one copse to another in an attempt to cover open areas quickly when no danger is evident. Many ducklings can be lost along the way, but these may represent the weaker ones that ultimately may not have survived. *Photo by Frederic Leopold; courtesy of the Starr's Cave Nature Center (Burlington, Iowa).*

Wood ducks nest in cities and towns throughout the eastern United States, especially those adjacent to rivers and wetlands. Each year we know of 10–20 pairs of wood ducks that nest in Havana, Illinois, a town of 2,700 (1991). One cavity 27.4 meters (30 yd) from a window wall in the Bellrose home has been used for at least eight years. This house is near the center of town, 0.4 kilometer (0.25 mi) from the Illinois River. Some broods pass through the yard from more distant points. Following broods partway through town, we have noticed that mothers take zigzag courses seeking the shadows of shrubs, flower beds, and other cover. Biding her time until pedestrian or car traffic slackens, a mother may scoot across a street, lawn, or other open area to the next shaded shelter. When crossing open areas, she maintains a low profile with head down and neck extended. The ducklings are immediately behind in a compact ball or strung out in a line moving at incredible speed for such tiny creatures.

The trek through town takes a mother wood duck and her brood several hours, usually most of the day until evening. We have known some broods to spend four hours traveling one block. On occasion, a brood may spend many hours near the nest site waiting for human activity to decline. Bellrose saw one such instance on May 30, 1987, when a female feigning injury tumbled across his yard at 9:35 a.m. CST, leaving her brood under a clump of shrubs. She returned to her brood in 10 minutes and was content to remain within a few yards of her initial waiting site until at least 3:25 p.m., when Bellrose lost contact with them.

Entire broods are lost to pursuit by cats, dogs, children, and the occasional overly concerned or inquisitive adult. Other broods lose weak or adventuresome members that fall behind or fall into structures that trap them. When the brood is threatened, the mother endeavors to lead the predator or human away from the young by flapping and tumbling as if she has a broken wing. Later she usually returns to a tree near the brood and, when the coast is clear, rejoins them. By uttering calls, a female attempts to rally her brood, but she is seldom completely successful. She may accept the appearance of one, two, or, if fortunate, more ducklings and continue her trek without searching for those left behind.

Leopold (1951) observed broods of woodies leaving nest houses in his yard atop a 40-meter (130 ft) bluff overlooking the Mississippi River at Burlington, Iowa; a railroad track runs between the bluff and the river. In leading their young through dense vegetation down the bluff and across the railroad tracks, hens have lost 61 of 189 ducklings (32 percent). No doubt the longer and more hazardous the trek overland to water, the more broods and ducklings are lost along the way. Some of this loss represents weak ducklings that would have succumbed during their first week of life—a time when brood losses are heavy.

While taking her brood to water, a hen may temporarily desert her ducklings because of human presence or other imminent danger. She usually will try to lure a human or predator away from her brood by feigning a broken wing. Depending on perceived circumstances, she may return in a few minutes or one to several hours later. Especially in cities, the abandonment is likely to be protracted. During that interval of abandonment, the brood typically remains together and seeks shelter nearby. *Photo by Larry Stone; courtesy of the Starr's Cave Nature Center (Burlington, Iowa).*

Frederic Leopold examines a day-old woodie duckling left behind on a brood's travel through his yard in Burlington, Iowa. Many ducklings become separated from their brood because they do not keep up with other members. By and large, these ducklings are relatively weak. *Photo by Larry Stone.*

DUMP NESTING

"Dump nesting," also commonly called compound nesting or brood parasitism, occurs when two or more females contribute eggs to a single clutch and is a common behavior in wood ducks. Woodies engage in this behavior regardless of the nesting situation, although it is more pronounced in areas where nest boxes are grouped together and conspicuously placed. Semel et al. (1988) reviewed potential costs and benefits that parasitizing and host females may derive from dump nesting. Ultimately, production is enhanced as a result of this behavior; exceptions usually occur when people manipulate the wood duck's nesting biology by supplying nest cavities in unusual densities.

Researchers have used three criteria to identify a dump nest: (1) the laying of more than one egg a day; (2) a hatched nest that contains eggs with living embryos retarded in development; and (3) a clutch that contains more than 15–17 eggs. Grice and Rogers (1965) considered that clutches of more than 15 eggs were laid by more than one female. Morse and Wight (1969) classified all nests with more than 16 eggs as dump nests. Haramis (1975) found clutches of 12 and 13 eggs that contained one dumped egg each and observed that all clutches of

15 or more eggs contained dumped eggs. Zipko (1979) reported that, at Great Swamp National Wildlife Refuge in New Jersey, most dump nests contained 18 or more eggs. At Duck Creek, Missouri, Clawson et al. (1979) rated a dump nest as one with 18 or more eggs.

From our own and other studies, we recognized that any clutch above one may have a dumped egg, and that as the clutch size increases the likelihood is greater that one or more eggs have been added to the host clutch. Dumped eggs become especially evident in clutches above 14; on the other hand, evidence suggests that a single female may lay as many as 16 eggs during an initial term. In order to facilitate the analysis of factors influencing dump nesting, we made the following arbitrary division in clutch sizes: normal nests were defined as those containing 4–16 eggs; dump nests were those with more than 16 eggs. These divisions were made with the understanding that many normal-sized clutches actually are dump nests. On their study area in Oregon, Morse and Wight (1969) found that 52 percent (n = 62) of the clutches containing fewer than 16 eggs were parasitized nests. Hence, inferences drawn about the costs and benefits of dump nesting, and which are based solely on clutch sizes, must be viewed with caution.

In most analyses of clutch size, we do not consider unincubated clutches of one to three eggs, because these clutches appear to be a corollary of dump nesting—females depositing eggs on an exigency basis with little attempt to complete a clutch or to incubate. Eggs may even be deposited on the ground.

In most dump nests, the eggs are arranged neatly and covered during laying; however, some nests of 20–40 eggs are untidy. The eggs are scattered and uncovered, making clear that none of the laying females intended to incubate them. In these dump nests, little if any down is found, in contrast to the heavy down blanket in most incubated dump nests. We believe that most of these aggregate layings are entirely by yearlings, perhaps caused by a lack of nesting experience.

Numerous researchers have classified 8,461 successful wood duck nests into those with apparently normal-sized clutches and those with obviously compound clutches (Table 107). Normal-sized clutches accounted for 60.7 percent of these successful nests; dump clutches accounted for 39.3 percent. Individual study means of normal clutches ranged between 10.1 and 13.3 eggs, with an overall mean of 11.6 ± 0.77. Clutches formed with the known addition of dumped eggs ranged from individual study means of 15.8 to 28.7, with an overall average of 21.7 ± 3.53.

Table 107. Clutch size for normal and dump nests and percentage of eggs hatched in successful nests in wood duck nest houses.[a]

Location	Normal nests				Dump nests		
	n	Mean clutch size	Percentage of hatch		n	Mean clutch size	Percentage of hatch
New York	95	10.3	77.4		105	22.7	70.3
Massachusetts	70	10.9	86.8		98	21.5	81.0
Massachusetts	135	11.2	88.4		99	20.5	76.8
New Jersey	919	13.3	65.3		541	27.8	58.2
South Carolina	25	11.5	91.4		10	16.3	88.3
Illinois[b]	383	11.5	88.7		98	20.4	78.4
Illinois[c]	1,527	11.9	95.4		507	20.8	90.8
Illinois[d]	123	12.0	72.4		161	24.0	62.0
Iowa[e]	1,048	11.6	80.3		472	21.6	73.7
Missouri	115	11.8	83.5		108	19.5	73.2
Missouri	239	11.4	77.9		330	20.2	62.9
Mississippi	76	11.1	87.5		22	18.2	72.1
Mississippi	239	11.9	74.8		326	25.4	50.0
Louisiana	19	12.6	78.7		19	20.9	83.9
Louisiana	58	11.7	71.9		84	24.0	66.5
Louisiana	111	12.2	75.2		260	28.7	51.1
Oregon	63	10.1	92.4		86	15.8	75.7
Total	5,245				3,326		
Mean by item		11.6±0.77				21.7±3.53	
Mean by item			81.6±8.43				71.5±11.85

[a] Only successful nests were used to determine average clutch size because many unsuccessful nests contained incomplete clutches.
[b] Board nest houses, Mason County, 1939–42.
[c] Metal nest houses, Quiver Creek, 1956–74.
[d] Duplex nest houses, Nauvoo Slough, 1983–90.
[e] Data from Glen Welp, Union Slough National Wildlife Refuge, Iowa.
[f] Data from files at Yazoo National Wildlife Refuge, Mississippi, 1983–86.

In our studies of wood duck nesting in three areas in Illinois (Table 107), we found that dump nesting was most prevalent at Nauvoo Slough, where 56.7 percent of all nests were dump nests, compared with 24.9 percent at Quiver Creek and 20.4 percent in Mason County. The mean clutch size of dump nests at Nauvoo Slough was also higher (24.0) than elsewhere in Illinois (20.8 at Quiver Creek and 20.4 in Mason County).

Factors Affecting Dump Nesting

Investigators of dump nesting behavior in wood ducks have looked for various factors that might account for this phenomenon, including: (1) density of breeders; (2) scarcity of nest sites; (3) nest destruction; (4) yearlings or other individuals nesting for the first time; and (5) chronology of nest starts.

Density of breeders. At Quiver Creek, the density of breeding birds played an important role (Figure 74), 1957–1966, in the yearly level of dump

nesting. For each additional breeding hen an increase of 0.48 in the number of dump nests occurred ($r = 0.89$, $P < 0.001$).

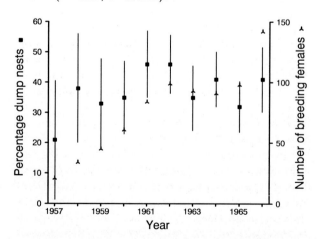

Figure 74. Mean percentage of successful dump nests in relation to total successful nests by year, compared with numbers of breeding wood duck females, Quiver Creek, Illinois, 1957–66. The lines extending from percentage dump nests values reflect 95-percent confidence limits of the mean.

Table 107. (continued)

Dump nests	
Percentage of dump nests	Source
52.5	Haramis and Thompson (1985)
58.3	Grice and Rogers (1965)
42.3	Heusmann (1972)
37.1	Zipko (1979)
28.6	Luckett (1977)
20.4	This study
24.9	This study
56.7	This study
31.1	Glen Welp
48.4	Hansen (1971)
58.0	Clawson et al. (1979)
22.4	Baker (1971)
57.7	f
50.0	Strader (1978)
59.2	Davis (1978)
70.1	Moore (1981)
57.7	Morse and Wight (1969)

45.6 ± 15.36

Nauvoo Slough—a 1.4-kilometer (0.9 mi) long, 6.1-hectare (15 ac) body of water—probably has had the densest population of wood ducks ever recorded. The combination of a rich food base and 80 artificial nest structures produced an amazingly high breeding population, 1984–1990. It also produced an increasing proportion of dump nests, 1983–1990 (Table 101). For each additional breeding female, dump nest activity increased by 0.67 nest ($r = 0.89$, $P < 0.05$, $y = -3.47 + 0.673x$).

Zipko (1979) noticed at Great Swamp National Wildlife Refuge that, in three of four years, dump nesting declined from 46.1 to 35.5 percent of all nests as nest house use increased from near saturation to over the 100-percent level. The following year nest house use declined to 80.3 percent, and dump nesting declined to 29.8 percent of all nests.

At Montezuma National Wildlife Refuge in New York, Haramis and Thompson (1985) reported that dump nesting increased from 14 percent of all nests in 1973 to 73 percent in 1976, concomitant with an increase in breeding numbers. With the decline of water levels in later years, breeders scattered, and dump nesting declined to 20 percent by 1979.

As the number of wood duck nests increased from 20 in 1967 to 244 in 1987 at Union Slough National Wildlife Refuge, Iowa, the number of clutches that contained dumped eggs increased

0.49 for each 1.0 increase in the total number of yearly nests. The equation $r = 0.95$, $P < 0.001$, $y = -15.29 + 0.49x$ was based on 1,811 nests.

In the Sacramento Valley of California, Jones and Leopold (1967) found that, as breeding numbers increased, so did the proportion of dump nests. However, both that study and the New York study of Haramis and Thompson (1985) may have been influenced by a shortage of nest sites to accommodate the maximum number of breeding ducks. As a result, both the dense population and the inadequate nest sites may have partly accounted for the high proportion of dump nests reported.

Scarcity of nest sites. Obviously, when the number of breeding females exceeds the number of nest sites, as occurred during certain years at Quiver Creek in Illinois and in the Sacramento Valley in California (Jones and Leopold 1967), an increase in the number of dump nests is to be anticipated. A scarcity of nest sites was considered to have exacerbated dump nesting at Montezuma Marsh, New York (Haramis and Thompson 1985).

At Quiver Creek, the proportion of dump nests increased only moderately as the percentage of nest houses occupied rose during 1957–1966. For each 1-percent increase in nest house occupancy, dump nests increased at the rate of 0.17 percent ($r = 0.65$, $P < 0.05$). Even when 103–108 percent of the houses were occupied in each of two years, dump nesting amounted to only 40.9 percent of all nests. The mean percentage of dump nests for all years was 37.0 ± 7.6.

The increased proportion of dump nests, 1984–1987, at Nauvoo Slough failed to parallel the increase in total nests. A comparison of the weekly availability of nest sites with the weekly proportion of dump nests at Nauvoo, moreover, disclosed the unexpected: as nest sites were more available, the proportion of dump nests actually increased (Figure 75). This anomaly occurred because of the seasonal distribution of dump nests and available nest sites. Maximum levels of both occurred early in the breeding season and were obviously independently related. At Nauvoo Slough, limited availability of nest sites played a minor role at best in severe dump nesting activity.

Semel and Sherman (1986) noticed at Duck Creek, Missouri, that 95 percent of the woodie nests they studied were parasitized by conspecifics even though 46 percent of the nest houses were unoccupied. Likewise, Morse and Wight (1969) found that the availability of nest boxes had no influence on the degree of dump nesting that occurred in Benton County, Oregon. Nest box availability exceeded 40 percent throughout the breeding season, yet 59.4 percent of the nests were dump nests. In Massachu-

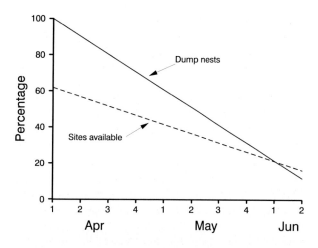

Figure 75. Weekly availability of nest sites for wood ducks and weekly proportion of total nests that were dump nests, Nauvoo Slough, Illinois, 1985–87. The regression equations for the dump nests and nest sites available lines are: $y = 109.78 - 9.78x$, $r = -0.84$, $P < 0.001$; and $y = 66.56 - 5.06x$, $r = -0.64$, $P < 0.001$, respectively.

setts, Heusmann et al. (1980) reported conflicting evidence. When they added houses to the two already on a pond, the dump nesting of four hens in one box stopped. Yet on another pond that had 11 nest houses, dump nesting occurred in four of the first five nests initiated early in spring.

When the number of nesting birds exceeds the number of nest sites, dump nesting may well expand because of the paucity of nest sites. Our overall data may hide individual instances of this happening, but they show little evidence that the number of available nest sites is related to the degree of dump nesting. Dump nesting increased as the local breeding density increased more than it did as a result of limited numbers of nest sites. It appears evident that the greater the concentration of breeders, the more likely certain females will follow another female to a nest site for the purpose of depositing an egg.

Nest destruction. We have no evidence that destruction of nests increases dump nesting. A comparison of the rates of nest destruction and dump nesting on Quiver Creek nesting units revealed no significant correlation. Haramis et al. (1983), however, tracked eggs marked by a tetracycline-injected female that deserted during laying. She laid an additional six eggs in three occupied nest houses; two nests were being incubated, the third was unincubated. As in this case, where nest loss resulted in parasitic laying at a low incidence of egg dispersion, we might not be aware of dumped eggs by females whose nests were destroyed.

Dump nesting by yearlings and older birds. Clawson et al. (1979) and Heusmann et al. (1980) presented evidence that wood ducks of all ages lay parasitically. Unanswered is the question of the degree of dump nesting by different age groups.

Our data from Quiver Creek imply that the bulk of dump nesting there is done by yearlings and appreciably less dumping is done by older birds. Table 108 lists the percentage of dump nests being incubated by yearling females and older birds. The percentage was lowest for first-year nesting birds and increasingly higher for each subsequent year until the fifth. We assume that a larger proportion of older birds incubated dump nests because younger ducks had added eggs to the normal clutches of older birds. The size of normal clutches is lowest for one-year-olds (10.6 ± 0.153 [SE]) and higher (12.0 ± 0.33 [SE]) for older ducks; the mean of all clutches — normal and dump — increases from 13.53 ± 0.264 (SE) for yearlings to 16.99 ± 0.59 (SE) for older birds.

Hepp et al. (1987) found that the age of laying hens had no effect on clutch size; therefore, differences in clutch sizes between yearlings and older ducks is best explained by differences in levels of dump nesting. Females incubating the fewest eggs were the most likely to have laid the most eggs parasitically.

Further credence to the role yearlings exercise in dump nesting is evident from a positive correlation ($r = 0.79$, $P < 0.05$) between the proportion of their return and that of dump nests. For every 10-percent increase in the return of local yearlings, the rate of dump nesting increased 1.38 percent. Because the proportion of yearlings declined among nesting wood ducks on Quiver Creek as the population increased, density of breeding birds did not compound the increase in dump nesting resulting from yearling hens.

Table 108. Known age of wood ducks in relation to the proportion of dump nests and small clutch sizes under incubation, Quiver Creek, Illinois, 1956–67.

	Age of female (years)		
	1	2–5	Significance
Total nests	506	344	
Percentage of dump nests	25.9	48.8	$t = 6.87$ $P < 0.001$
Percentage of clutches ≤ 8	16.8	5.8	$t = 12.72$ $P < 0.001$

Older birds were involved in dump nesting to a greater extent at Nauvoo Slough than were such birds at Quiver Creek. The large number of eggs laid during the course of each breeding season at Nauvoo Slough, 1983–1990, prorated for each breeding hen, averaged two full clutches and appears near the maximum possible number of eggs. If we attributed the dumped eggs only to the yearling class, which made up 53 percent of the 1985–1990 breeding population, the number laid per female would be prohibitively high (Table 109). Counts and visual identification of marked birds indicated that all females on the area eventually attempted to nest.

Robert Montgomery reported that, at Max McGraw Wildlife Foundation in Dundee, Illinois, where wood ducks are raised in captivity, each of 892 breeders averaged 22.8 eggs per season, 1977–1987. The largest yearly average was 33.3 eggs. These birds are fed a high-protein ration for maximum egg production. Therefore, the large egg production per female at Nauvoo Slough suggests that birds of all age classes were involved in either dumping eggs or renesting.

The dense breeding population and the closeness of highly visible nest houses at Nauvoo Slough seem to have stimulated some older ducks to dump eggs. At Quiver Creek, the lower density of breeding birds and the less visible and more dispersed houses appear for the most part to have restricted large-scale dumping of eggs by yearlings.

At Nauvoo Slough, 1984–1987, we found that the number of nest houses in which more than one female laid eggs each day for a period of six to eight days (usually seven) reached a high of 82 nest houses in 1986 (Table 110). The highest number of

eggs laid per day at a single nest site averaged 2.5 for the week period, but the more typical range was 1.5–2.0 eggs. Because egg laying did not occur evenly throughout the period at any one nest site, some nests had more eggs than the average deposited in a single day. The greatest activity in egg dumping occurred in April; the lowest occurred in June, paralleling breeding activity. We have seen as many as five hens enter a nest site at various times in a single morning, but we do not know the number of eggs laid. Semel and Sherman (1986) observed five hens enter one nest at various times during a 21-minute period; four eggs were deposited. They observed a mean of four hens contributing eggs to 21 nests, on the basis of maximum daily egg accumulation in each nest.

Chronology of nesting. Yearlings are presumed to nest later than adults (Bellrose et al. 1964, Grice and Rogers 1965, Hartman 1972, Clawson 1975a). Because dump nests appear early during the breeding season, often prior to initiation of yearling nesting, Hartman (1972) concluded that early dump nests were produced by older birds. However, yearlings may be more involved with early dump nesting than the data provided by nest capture indicate. Because of parasitic laying at the beginning of the breeding season and laying a normal clutch later, early laying activity by yearlings may go undetected.

At Quiver Creek, yearlings were captured on dump nests earlier than yearlings on nests with normal-sized clutches, but not as early as older birds (Table 111). Individuals that dump an entire clutch of eggs before laying a normal-sized clutch to incubate appear to be late nesters. We believe that the late initiation of normal clutches by one-year-

Table 109. Number of eggs laid per female wood duck at Nauvoo Slough, Illinois, 1983–90.

Year	Number of incubating females	Number of eggs laid[a]	Number of eggs per female	Calculated eggs above normal clutches[b]	Additional eggs per female
1983	28[c]	692	24.7	362	12.93
1984	46[d]	979	21.3	487	10.59
1985	60[d]	1,252	20.9	553	9.22
1986	73[d]	1,890	25.9	1,009	13.64
1987	76[d]	1,635	21.5	973	14.10
1988	51[d]	1,261	24.7	673	12.70
1989	67[d]	1,388	20.7	678	10.12
1990	75[d]	1,479	19.7	586	7.81
Total/mean	476	10,576	22.4 ± 2.31	665 ± 225	11.31 ± 2.18

[a] Excludes number of dropped clutches with less than four eggs.
[b] Normal clutch size was calculated as the mean size of clutches that contained 4–16 eggs.
[c] Based on weekly counts and active nests.
[d] Based on the number of banded females captured on nests and the number of unbanded dead females found on nests.

Table 110. Minimum rate of laying in nest houses receiving more than one egg from more than one wood duck hen per day for periods approximating a week, Nauvoo Slough, Illinois, 1984–87.

	1984			1985			1986			1987		
Week	n[a]	Mean[b]	S.D.	n[a]	Mean[b]	S.D.	n[a]	Mean[b]	S.D.	n[a]	Mean[b]	S.D.
April												
1st				9	2.5	1.19	8	2.2	0.98			
2nd				11	2.0	0.92	9	2.3	0.70	5	1.6	0.26
3rd				10	1.9	0.79	10	1.9	0.59	9	2.4	0.79
4th	6	1.8	0.45	11	1.6	0.41	13	1.9	0.77	14	1.9	0.84
May												
1st	3	1.7	0.47	7	1.6	0.72	13	1.8	0.63	7	1.6	0.42
2nd	5	1.5	0.41	8	1.6	0.31	9	1.8	0.60	15	1.7	0.55
3rd	3	1.4	0.12	3	1.3	0.22	7	1.8	0.67	12	1.8	0.60
4th	5	1.5	0.45	3	1.8	0.63	6	1.9	0.68	8	2.4	0.86
June												
1st	4	1.4	0.14	1	1.4		4	1.8	0.58	7	1.9	0.63
2nd	2	1.9	0.70	1	1.1		3	1.7	0.76	2	1.5	0.00
3rd												
4th												
Total[c]	28			64			82			79		

[a] Number of nest houses in which egg deposition exceeded an average of one egg per day for a period of about one week.
[b] Mean number of eggs for all samples.
[c] Sum numbers may be larger than the total number of nests because a single nest frequently is involved in more than one period.

old females (Table 111) resulted, in a large measure, from earlier dump nesting. The seasonal distribution of nesting activity also implicates two-year-old birds more than older birds in dump nesting episodes.

Seasonal nest initiation at Nauvoo Slough (Figure 76) shows similar trends for yearling and older ducks. As the number of normal nests for both age groups increased with seasonal advance, the proportion of dump nests declined, especially for older birds that had nested in previous years. Although more adults were involved in egg dumping at Nauvoo Slough than at Quiver Creek, it is apparent that yearlings still were the more important parasitizers.

Effect of Dumping on Production of Young

Germane to the problem of dump nesting is its effect on the production of young. Because the production of young involves a sliding scale of increased nest desertion and reduced hatching success as clutch sizes increase, and because an unknown proportion of small clutches are dump nests, definitive parameters are difficult to establish.

One of the most important questions is the degree to which dumping eggs terminates the egg laying of the parasitizing female. Clawson et al. (1979) found that 6 of 14 marked hens observed dumping eggs in nest houses later were found incu-

Table 111. Mean nest initiation dates and standard deviation for known-aged wood ducks incubating normal and dump clutches, Quiver Creek, Illinois, 1956–67. Julian days in parentheses.

Female age in years	Normal nest				Dump nest			
	n	Mean[a]		S.D.	n	Mean[a]		S.D.
1	375	May 3	(123)	18.9	137	Apr 16	(106)	15.6
2	107	Apr 15	(115)	23.3	94	Apr 5	(95)	12.5
3	44	Apr 10	(100)	16.9	41	Apr 4	(94)	13.6
4 and 5	25	Apr 11	(101)	18.7	33	Apr 3	(93)	13.0
Total/mean	551	Apr 29	(119)	18.9	305	Apr 9	(99)	14.1

[a] t: normal versus mean dump nest dates = 3.75, $P < 0.05$

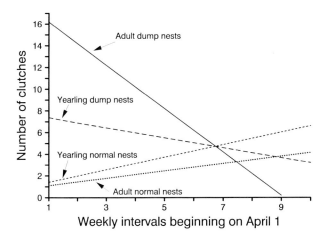

Figure 76. Relationship of initiation of wood ducks' normal and dump nests to chronology of distribution by adults and yearlings, Nauvoo Slough, Illinois, 1984–87. The regression equations for adult dump and normal nests are: $y = 18.2 - 2.00x$, $r = -0.86$, $P < 0.01$; and $y = 0.76 + 0.34x$, $r = 0.51$, $P > 0.10$, respectively. The regression equations for yearling dump and normal nests are: $y = 0.78 - 0.46x$, $r = -0.43$, $P > 0.10$; and $y = 0.82 + 0.58x$, $r = 0.59$, $P > 0.05$, respectively.

bating nests of their own. Heusmann et al. (1980) reported that 12 of 16 ducks that dumped one or more eggs later established their own nests. In both studies, the investigators noted that some or all of the females not observed later in nest houses may have nested in natural cavities.

Our evidence points toward the conclusion that almost every egg-dumping hen eventually lays a clutch that she incubates. At both Quiver Creek and Nauvoo Slough, our spring counts of breeders were consistently below the minimum number of breeding hens, which had been determined from the banding of almost every incubating bird. The counts were below actual breeding numbers because of differences in temporal activities; not all of the breeding ducks were present on the study areas at any one time. Any increase accorded nonincubating hens (parasitic individuals that did not nest) would exacerbate the difference between counts and the number banded as nesting birds.

The number of eggs deposited during each breeding season at Nauvoo Slough, prorated among the number of breeding hens, is of such a magnitude (Table 109) as to suggest that all or almost all hens that parasitically laid eggs, or whose nests were destroyed, established new nests.

Another item of evidence that dump nesters form an additional nest is found in the correlation between dump nesting activity and clutches with fewer than eight eggs on the Quiver Creek area, 1956–1974. For every additional dump nest, nests with small clutches increased by an average of 0.15

nest ($r = 0.40$, $P < 0.10$). In addition, for every nest deserted or destroyed, nests with fewer than eight eggs increased by 0.14 nest ($r = 0.79$, $P < 0.001$). Thus, the significance of correlation coefficients suggests that most small clutches represented renesting hens primarily and dump nesting birds secondarily. Small clutches appeared largely during the last month of the breeding season. Early second clutches – laid by birds that had initially been parasitizers and by renesting females – apparently have more eggs than second clutches laid later and were not detected among the mélange of normal clutches.

The second issue is whether sufficient eggs hatch in dump nests to contribute to production. In determining the production of ducklings from normal as well as dump nests, we must consider the hatch of ducklings in successful nests and the relative proportion of entire clutches lost through desertion or predation. Of 1,943 normal-sized clutches on the Quiver Creek area, 1956–1974, 78.5 percent hatched eggs. Of the 593 dump-sized clutches during that period, 85.5 percent hatched eggs ($P < 0.05$). Of the dump-sized clutches that failed to hatch, 51.7 percent were deserted; the others were destroyed by predators. At Nauvoo Slough, dump nests hatched more frequently (53 percent) than normal nests (43.7 percent) (Table 112). Although nest success at Yazoo National Wildlife Refuge in Mississippi, 1983–1986, was relatively low, dump nests hatched at a higher rate (44.9 percent) than did normal-sized clutches (33.2 percent). Clawson (1975a) also found that a larger proportion of dump nests were successful at the Duck Creek Wildlife Area, Missouri, 1966–1974. He reported that only 52 percent of the normal nests were successful compared with 87 percent of those classed as dump nests. Little difference was found at Union Slough National Wildlife Refuge, where 83 percent of the 1,263 normal-sized clutches hatched eggs and 83.1 percent of the 568 dump nests were successful. At Great Swamp National Wildlife Refuge in New Jersey, Zipko (1979) had almost identical nest success rates between 1,719 normal nests and 1,010 dump nests. However, Morse and Wight (1969) in Benton County, Oregon, reported a slightly greater hatch of normal nests (76.8 percent) than dump nests (71.7 percent).

Available evidence points to dump nests in houses as hatching successfully at a generally higher rate than nests with normal-sized clutches. On their study area in Oregon, Morse and Wight (1969) found that dump nesting contributed 32 percent more young to the population than would have been produced from an equal number of normal nests. Similarly, Clawson et al. (1979) reported that

Table 112. Percentage of wood duck dump nests and comparison of success between normal and dump nests, Nauvoo Slough, Illinois, 1983–90.

	Normal nests[a]				Dump nests				
Year	n	Percentage success	Total eggs	Percentage hatch	n	Percentage success	Total eggs	Percentage hatch	Percentage dump nests
1983	29	51.7	343	42.9	13	30.8	349	23.8	31.0
1984	47	61.7[b]	502	47.8	24	54.2	477	34.6	33.8
1985	36	52.8[c]	400	45.3	37	64.9	852	46.7	50.7
1986	46	30.4[d]	525	17.5	55	58.2[e]	1,365	31.1	54.5
1987	42	28.6	434	24.2	43	55.8	1,201	23.1	50.6
1988	31	41.9	345	28.1	39	41.0	916	25.0	55.7
1989	50	34.0	530	24.7	37	56.8	858	32.5	42.5
1990	43	48.8	512	29.3	42	61.9	967	31.1	49.4
Total/mean[f]	324	43.7	3,591	31.8	290	53.0	6,985	30.9	46.0

[a] Although all nests with fewer than 17 eggs were classified as normal, some of the clutches that were deserted may have been incomplete dump nests.
[b] Although 30 normal nests hatched successfully, ducklings failed to leave one nest.
[c] Although 20 normal nests hatched successfully, ducklings failed to leave one nest.
[d] Although 15 normal nests hatched successfully, ducklings failed to leave one nest.
[e] Although 33 dump nests hatched successfully, ducklings failed to leave one nest.
[f] Percentage nest success for normal versus dump nests: $t = 1.498$, $P > 0.10$. Percentage egg hatch for normal versus dump clutches: $t = 0.398$, $P > 0.10$.

dump nesting contributed 30 percent more ducklings than would have hatched from an equal number of nonparasitized nests.

The mean clutch size of successful dump nests reported from 17 studies conducted throughout the wood duck's range was 21.7 (Table 107). An average of 71.5 percent of the eggs in the dump nests hatched. Thus, 15.5 ducklings were produced per successful dump nest. By contrast, the average clutch size of a successful normal nest was 11.6 (Table 107). A hatching rate of 81.6 percent resulted in an average of 9.5 ducklings per normal clutch. When Grice and Rogers (1965) examined the hatching rate of successful normal and dump nests at Great Meadows National Wildlife Refuge in Massachusetts, they found that dump nests contributed 72 percent more young to the population than would have come from an equal number of normal-sized nests.

The hatch of eggs in successful nests in houses at our three study areas (Figure 77) generally declined as clutch sizes increased. The relative percentage of eggs that hatched in normal clutches at Quiver Creek was slightly larger than the percentage that hatched in smaller clutches as a result of small, late clutches that failed to hatch the customary percentage of eggs. The decrease in hatching success was more pronounced among dump nests than among normal-sized nests. This difference stems from three factors: (1) inability of the female to provide each egg in a large clutch with as much heat transfer as in a normal clutch; (2) deposition of

parasitic eggs after incubation has begun; and (3) disturbance to the incubation regimen of the proprietor female resulting from harassment by intruding parasitic females.

The deposition of eggs after incubation has begun results in either unhatched embryos or duck-

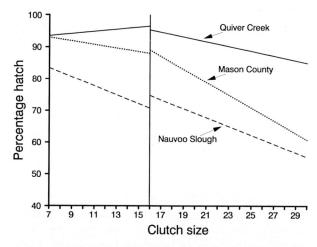

Figure 77. Hatchability of eggs in successful wood duck nests in relation to clutch size for Quiver Creek and Nauvoo Slough, Illinois. The regression equations, which show hatchability of normal clutches for Quiver Creek and Nauvoo Slough, are: $y = 96.92 - 0.56x$, $r = -0.71$, $P < 0.01$; and $y = 93.27 - 1.41x$, $r = -0.71$, $P < 0.01$, respectively. The regression equations, which show hatchability of dump clutches for Quiver Creek and Nauvoo Slough, are: $y = 121.32 - 2.02x$, $r = -0.58$, $P < 0.05$; and $y = 96.94 - 1.39x$, $r = -0.36$, $P > 0.10$, respectively.

lings left behind because their energy levels are insufficient to respond to their mother's departure call. Reduced hatches of both normal and dump clutches at Nauvoo Slough compared with Mason County and Quiver Creek areas (Figure 77) are indicative of the disturbance factor caused by intruding females upsetting the regimen of incubating hens.

For each egg in successful normal-sized clutches at Union Slough National Wildlife Refuge in Iowa, hatchability decreased 0.90 percent ($r = -0.80$, $P < 0.01$). In dump nests (those with more than 16 eggs), hatchability declined 1.23 percent for each additional egg ($r = -0.70$, $P < 0.01$). The large range in variability of hatch in normal and dump nests shown by the wide standard deviation is explainable.

We compared the proportion of dump nests for 17 studies (Table 107) with the hatch in normal and dump nests by linear regression. The results showed that, as dump nesting increased, hatchability of both normal and dump clutches decreased (Figure 78). This effect of parasitic intruding hens on established nests probably explains the wide variability in hatch rate among studies. It also may serve as an index to population density intolerance among nesting females. Our observations suggest that parasitic exploring hens enter both normal and dump nests. Even if no egg is laid, the regimen of the incubating hen may be upset, and a reduced hatch rate may result from temporarily tentative incubation.

The supernumerary eggs in a wood duck dump

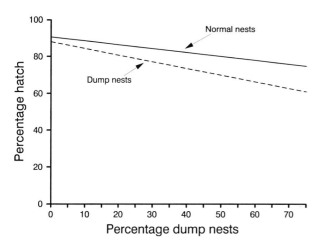

Figure 78. Percentage of dump nests among successful and unsuccessful wood duck nests in relation to percentage of eggs that hatched in successful nests. Data from 17 areas are listed in Table 107. The regression equations for normal and dump clutches are: $y = -0.26 + 93.63$, $r = -0.48$, $P < 0.05$; and $y = 0.73 + 92.90$, $r = -0.68$, $P < 0.01$, respectively.

nest reduce hatchability, as demonstrated in an experiment Barry (1992) conducted at the Yazoo National Wildlife Refuge, Mississippi, 1987–1991. From a combined 207 parasitized nests, Barry removed 550 damaged, infertile, or asynchronous eggs from approximately half the nests in a variety of comparable nest house sites. The egg hatching rate in nests where aberrant eggs were removed was 73.4 percent; those where dumped clutches remained intact hatched at the rate of 10.9 percent. Although increased heat application by those hens incubating the reduced clutches may have helped increase their rate of hatching, we think that the removal of nonviable eggs reduced desertions, thereby accounting for such a remarkable improvement in hatch success.

There is little evidence to suggest that dump nesting is anything but beneficial to production when wood ducks nest in natural cavities. The small amount of information on clutch size from natural cavities indicates that most nests contain fewer than 16 eggs. Apparently, females that dump eggs have more difficulty locating active nests in natural cavities than in nest boxes that are placed in conspicuous locations. The addition of a few eggs to a nest in a natural cavity normally results in the production of additional young without reducing the hatch or survival rates of ducklings.

The detrimental effects of dump nesting often become evident in areas where nest box programs build up large breeding populations. Large numbers of eggs are laid, but proportionally fewer young are produced. In the worst case scenario from density of houses, a rapid population growth is followed by a dramatic decline in hatch rate, resulting in a reduction in the subsequent breeding population (Semel et al. 1988); but overall, dump nesting usually aids productivity (Table 107).

Infertility, Nonterm Embryos, and Stranded Ducklings

The fate of unhatched wood duck eggs, as ascertained from various studies (Table 113), shows wide variations in relative infertility and nonterm embryos. Our infertility data from Quiver Creek include addled eggs that may have contained embryos that died at such early stages of development as to leave no trace. The high percentage (14.3 percent) of nonterm embryos reported by Hansen (1971) occurred because 73 percent of these embryos were in dump nests; in normal nests, embryonic losses were 8 percent. Zipko (1979) found 489 dead ducklings in nest houses—3.3 percent of the hatched eggs and 0.95 percent of all eggs laid.

No significant weekly correlation (r = −0.39, P > 0.10) was found at Quiver Creek between temporal distribution (March 14 to May 31, 1957–1974) of normal successful nests and percentage of eggs that failed to hatch, including both infertile eggs and dead embryos. During this period, only 6.37 percent of 28,714 eggs (mean = 0.90 per nest) failed to hatch in all successful normal and dump nests.

In June-initiated nests of normal clutches, 8.14 percent of the eggs failed to hatch, whereas all normal clutches encompassing the entire breeding season had a mere 4.86-percent failure. The difference was significant: t = 2.53, 13 d.f., P < 0.05. Thus, only during the last month of the breeding season when nest activity was rapidly declining did the rate of hatching success change significantly.

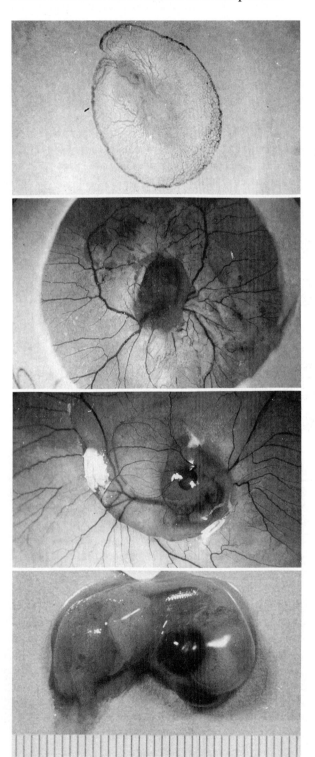

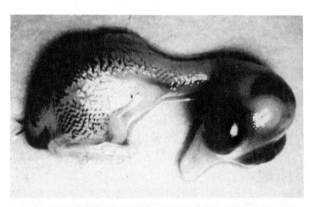

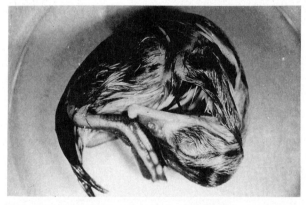

By examining the contents of unhatched wood duck eggs, the proportion infertile or with dead embryos can be determined. Also, the stage of embryonic development can be obtained by such distinctive features as degree of embryo elongation, circulation of blood, and development of eye, head, limb bud, and egg tooth. Wood duck embryo stages are shown for (left column, top to bottom) day 4, day 6, day 8, day 13, and (right column, top to bottom) days 14–18, day 20, days 24–29. *Photos by Robert Montgomery; courtesy of the Max McGraw Wildlife Foundation.*

Table 113. Fate of unhatched wood duck eggs in normal and dump nests, and proportion of stranded ducklings from various studies.

Location	Total eggs	Percentage			Source
		Infertile	Nonterm embryos[a]	Stranded ducklings[b]	
Quiver Creek	26,774	4.3	2.3	1.8	This study
Nauvoo Slough[c]	5,756			3.1	This study
Iowa	868	4.0			Leopold (1951)
Iowa	132	2.3			Schreiner and Hendrickson (1951)
Massachusetts	12,180	8.0	7.0		McLaughlin and Grice (1952)
Massachusetts	1,377	4.4			Heusmann and Bellville (1982)
Vermont	693	6.9			Miller (1951)
New Hampshire	640	2.5	3.6		Lee (1956)
Ohio	449	9.1	5.8		Stewart (1957)
New York	644	5.7	2.8	1.2	Haramis (1975)
Missouri	2,301	3.9	14.3		Hansen (1971)
New Jersey	51,269			1.0	Zipko (1979)

[a] Nonterm embryos include dead embryos and those in retarded development that would fail to hatch during term incubation.
[b] Stranded ducklings are those left behind at a nest site after the female has exited with her brood. They either are too weak or hatched too late to participate in the brood departure.
[c] 1984–87.

Doty (1972) found that 73 percent of 662 wood duck eggs obtained from captive birds were fertile. With the hens on a high-protein diet and with incubation started by ducks (as opposed to an incubator), hatchability was 70 percent.

We examined 349 eggs containing dead embryos from 134 successful nests in wooden nest houses in Mason County, Illinois, 1939–1955. The daily distribution of embryos by age at death was as follows: 2–8 days, 0.94 percent; 9–16 days, 1.61 percent; 17–24 days, 3.93 percent; and 25–30 days, 8.03 percent. The differences were significant ($P < 0.05$), indicating that, as incubation progressed, greater numbers of embryos died. There was no significant relationship between clutch size and the proportion of dead embryos, suggesting that dump laying did not play a discernible role in this particular cohort of nests.

Parasitic Laying During Incubation

At Nauvoo Slough, 1984–1990, intruding females laid 877 eggs while host hens were incubating (Table 114). If we assume that all eggs above the normal clutch size (11) were dumped, then 3,388 were parasitically deposited (computed from Table 112), 1984–1990. Of those parasitically deposited

Table 114. Effect of intraspecific strife on wood ducks as a result of population pressure, Nauvoo Slough, Illinois, 1984–90.

Year	Number of females laying[a]	Number of dump nests[b]	Number of eggs			Number of females	
			Dumped late[c]	Crushed[d]	Disappeared[e]	Injured[f]	Killed[g]
1984	149	24	46	2	54	0	0
1985	206	37	105	45	59	0	3
1986	291	55	191	246	83	10	4
1987	241	43	278	379	229	9	11
1988	181	39	77	106	92	4	2
1989	200	37	98	27	57	6	2
1990	211	42	82	29	75	8	6
Total	1,479	277	877	834	649	37	28

[a] Cumulative weekly number for breeding season.
[b] Number of nests that contained more than 16 eggs.
[c] Eggs dumped by intruding female in nest being incubated by host female.
[d] Eggs crushed by other wood duck females (includes cracked eggs that resulted from intraspecific fighting).
[e] Eggs that disappeared from completed clutches; ostensibly removed by either the intruder or the host female.
[f] Females injured about head in altercations with other wood duck females.
[g] Females killed on nest by other wood duck females.

eggs, 25.9 percent were laid while nests were being incubated; 74.1 percent were deposited during the laying period. According to Clawson et al. (1979), 22 percent of 1,361 dumped eggs in southeastern Missouri were laid after incubation had begun; 80 percent of those laid postincubation occurred during the first two weeks of the 30-day incubation period. A similar finding was made by Zipko (1979), who reported that at Great Swamp National Wildlife Refuge, 20 percent of 3,179 eggs were deposited after commencement of incubation; 91.5 percent of these eggs were laid during the first two weeks of the incubation period.

The temporal distribution of eggs added parasitically to nests under incubation at Nauvoo Slough (Table 115) showed that eggs were deposited throughout the breeding season but largely from mid-April through May—the period of highest nesting activity among all breeders.

As a result of dumped eggs, 23.4 percent of the clutches under incubation at Nauvoo Slough, 1984–1987, expanded from normal-sized (≤16 eggs) clutches to dump clutches (≥17 eggs) (Table 116). Dumping eggs into small clutches, however, can occur without altering clutch size sufficiently for the clutch to be identified as a dump nest.

Table 115. Wood duck nest history activities with weekly progress of the breeding season, Nauvoo Slough, Illinois, 1984–90.

Week	Number of females laying[a]	Number of dump nests[b]	Number of eggs Dumped late[c]	Lost[d]	Number of females injured or killed[e]
April 1	78	10	6	9	0
2	126	36	48	23	3
3	171	39	140	60	2
4	179	42	113	116	6
May 1	191	40	173	160	7
2	188	36	144	106	10
3	170	24	108	198	8
4	149	21	90	153	9
June 1	126	18	28	85	10
2	60	8	18	260	7
3	30	3	8	169	1
4	10	0	1	76	2
July 1	1	0	0	68	0
Total	1,479	277	877	1,483	65

[a] Minimum number of females laying eggs throughout week.
[b] Number of nests that contained more than 16 eggs.
[c] Number of eggs deposited parasitically after host female began incubation.
[d] Number of eggs crushed, cracked, or carried out of nest by female wood ducks.
[e] Females killed or injured on nest by other female wood ducks.

Table 116. Change in frequency of wood duck normal and dump nests as a result of the dumping of eggs in nests after incubation started, Nauvoo Slough, Illinois, 1984–87.

Year	Number of predumping size clutches ≤16 eggs	≥17 eggs	Percentage of dump nests	Number of postdumping size clutches ≤16 eggs	≥17 eggs
1984	8	4	33.3	5	7
1985	20	12	37.5	15	17
1986	18	33	64.7	8	43
1987	24	27	52.9	7	44
Total/weighted mean	70	76	52.1	35	111
Mean (years)			47.1±14.5		

Intraspecific Strife

Intraspecific strife affects wood duck productivity in a number of ways. Away from the nest site, aggression between pairs may upset the laying or incubation rhythm, and energy can be expended in short charges on the water, bill-thrusts, and other stress behaviors.

At Nauvoo Slough, the population buildup from a minimum of 28 breeding pairs in 1983 to 46 in 1984, 60 in 1985, 73 in 1986, 76 in 1987, 51 in 1988, 67 in 1989, and 75 in 1990 resulted in bizarre strife between females within the nest site (Table 114). The first manifestation of this behavior occurred in 1984, when we detected two crushed eggs in a nest. At that time we were uncertain about the cause, but as the number of crushed eggs increased each year to 379 in 1987, we became convinced that intruding wood duck females were crushing the eggs of proprietor females. Crushing apparently was accomplished by the intruding hen grasping the egg between her mandibles until the shell caved in through the midportion or at one end, or by the intruding hen repeatedly hitting the egg with her bill. In many instances, the proprietor female deserted the nest because of crushed eggs. In an almost equal number of cases, however, she prevailed despite this disturbance and seemed to recognize that egg destruction was not life threatening, as it would be from a raccoon invasion.

When eggs are punctured or crushed, either the intruding female or the incubating female, or both, carries the eggs out of the nest. The eggs may be dropped (in water at Nauvoo) or consumed. In nest houses from which eggs were removed, yolk was invariably smeared on the interior sides and at the entrance of the house. When the crushed egg(s) were carried out, the contents leaked, further fouling the nest.

On several occasions we have seen a wood duck carrying an egg out of a house, carrying an egg while swimming, and once carrying an egg while in flight. Moreover, Semel and Sherman (1986) report that, in five instances, they observed females removing damaged eggs in their bills from nest houses to the water, where they broke the eggs open further and ingested the contents. Cunningham (1968) observed a female wood duck fly out of a nest box with an egg grasped in her bill. Six eggs disappeared from this nest before nine hatched; a woodpecker was suspected of causing damage to the eggs. Strader et al. (1978a) also witnessed an egg being carried out of a nest house by a female; several eggs in the nest had been punctured by a woodpecker. At Oquawka, Illinois, Delbert Koke observed five eggs being carried out of two nest houses—three eggs from one house during laying and two from another during incubation.

Graham (1980) observed a wood duck carry an egg from a nest house and fly away with it. From the same nest on two occasions, a hooded merganser was seen to carry out an egg and drop it into the adjacent river. The wood duck apparently deserted and selected a nearby nest site.

The known number of eggs that disappeared from wood duck nests at Nauvoo increased from 54 in 1984 to 229 in 1987 (Table 114). In 1984 and 1985, most missing eggs were removed by persistent hens because those eggs had been punctured by flickers. Flicker predation, however, was almost negligible in 1986, 1987, 1988, 1989, and 1990 when 83, 229, 92, 57, and 75 eggs, respectively, disappeared. Most of the missing eggs in 1986–1990 were crushed or cracked eggs that probably were removed by the proprietor females. The broken and missing eggs amounted to 329 in 1986, 608 in 1987, 198 in 1988, 84 in 1989, and 104 in 1990. Obviously, intruding females had a pronounced adverse impact on productivity during those years.

The extent of egg losses from intraspecific strife among wood ducks is difficult to determine. At Yazoo National Wildlife Refuge in Mississippi, Cunningham (1968) reported 53 occasions in 1968 when 216 eggs disappeared without a trace. Despite close surveillance, including a nest in his yard, he could detect no agent (other than a single observation of a female wood duck removing an egg) that might have been responsible.

Semel and Sherman (1986) found six cracked wood duck eggs and attributed the damage to intraspecific strife. They reported that 18 of 20 eggs that disappeared were known to have been damaged. Several investigators reported instances of an intruding female entering an occupied nest house with resulting clashes (Clawson et al. 1979, Semel and Sherman 1986). On several occasions, Delbert Koke taped the vociferous squawks that occurred as

Table 116. (continued)

Percentage of dump nests	Percentage increase to dump nest status
58.3	25.0
53.1	15.6
84.3	19.6
86.3	33.3
76.0	24.0
70.5 ± 17.2	23.4 ± 7.6

a result of confrontations between intruders and hosts in nest houses adjacent to his home near Oquawka, Illinois. On May 26, 1977, Ray Cunningham observed an intruding hen enter a nest box in which another female was incubating. Twice the hens made considerable noise with calls and by wings striking the interior "as they fought for minutes at a time."

Walter J. Breckenridge described a fracas between two females that eventually led to nest desertion. On April 21, 1981, a duck entered the nest house of an incubating female. Breckenridge heard calls and wing strikes that shook the box intermittently for almost 30 minutes. The following day a similar event occurred; for 30 minutes the proprietor and intruder battled before both left at 10:00 a.m. CST. The nest contained 19 eggs on April 19 and 24 eggs on April 22. Because of a lack of activity at the nest site, Breckenridge checked it on April 30 and found the 24 eggs had been deserted, apparently a consequence of the clashes between the two hens.

McLaughlin and Grice (1952) pointed out that as density of nesting increased, rate of abandonment increased. Data that we calculated from Stephenson (1970) also demonstrated (Figure 79) that as nest density increased, the number of nests deserted increased as a result of increasing intraspecific strife.

Conspecific Injuries and Fatalities

The first indication to us that altercations between dump nesting and incubating females might be serious became evident in early April 1985, when blood specks were noticed high on the interior sides of a nest compartment at Nauvoo Slough. The "predator-proof" situation eliminated all but a few bird predators—woodpeckers, starlings, and screech-owls. Particles of blood were observed on the interior walls of several more houses. Then a dead female was found on a nest with another female incubating beside the carcass. The dead female had lacerations about the top of the head and behind the eye. A similar incident occurred and another dead female was found a few weeks later.

The nest houses at Nauvoo Slough parallel and are within 46 meters (50 yd) of state highway 96, "The Great River Road." No evidence of a culprit was uncovered, even though these houses were under intensive surveillance during daylight hours. Ultimately, by elimination of other explanations, we concluded that altercations between female conspecifics were the cause of the injuries and fatalities we found.

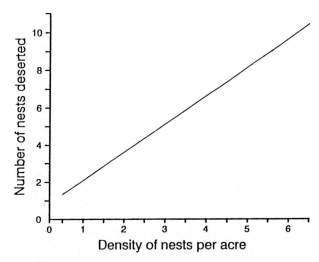

Figure 79. Effect of nest density on wood duck nests deserted, based on 822 nesting attempts in Wake and Johnston counties, North Carolina, 1954–68. The regression equation of $y = 0.58 + 1.51x$, $r = 0.70$, $P < 0.01$ was calculated from data in Stephenson (1970).

Our conclusion was confirmed once in 1986 and again in 1987. On each occasion, as the hinged top was slowly and slightly lifted to determine if a female was on the nest, two females were observed in a struggle. In 1986, one female had the occipital area of her opponent's head in her grasp. The aggressor was the host female, more than one year of age, that had been incubating for three weeks. The intruder was an unbanded female (assumed to be a yearling). The "yearling" was about ready to lay an egg, as was apparent from the depressed lower abdomen. We placed the yearling in the vacant adjacent compartment, and when we returned half an hour later, an egg had been laid and the yearling was gone.

The scenario in 1987 was different. On May 26 two females were found in a nest compartment, one female with her mandibles clamped on the other's head. The aggressor was a yearling that had incubated this clutch for 21 days. The intruder was older; she had been banded as an incubating bird on June 4, 1986, and had been found in a nest house with no eggs on April 9, 1987. The intruding female had the skin removed from her skull and weighed only 461 grams (16.3 oz). When we returned on June 2 this bird was dead, but the eggs were warm. By June 10, 8 of the 13 eggs had hatched, but six dead ducklings remained in the nest compartment.

Besides head wounds and torn skin on the back of the neck, many of the contestants exhibited battered primaries. Often tail feathers were missing, and when we found deserted crushed eggs, there were body feathers indicating prior combat. In one case the dead female covered the eggs, but the living combatant deserted (desertion may have occurred more often had we not removed the dead females). Some survivors attempted to incubate their clutches even though a carcass covered a portion of the eggs.

The number of injuries and fatalities from conspecifics increased from their first observance in 1985 through 1987. In 1988, the population declined markedly and so did the degree of intraspecific strife. Evidence of intraspecific confrontations rose slightly in 1989 and 1990, concurrent with a rise in breeding pairs (Figure 80). During 1984–1987 the number of eggs dumped late by intruding females in nests being incubated by proprietor birds increased sixfold (Table 114), yet the number of dump nests increased only moderately. There was no significant correlation between the two. The number of wounded and killed incubating females, 1984–1990, appears correlated ($r = 0.82$, $P < 0.05$) with the proclivity of certain ducks to dump eggs in nests already under incubation. There also was a strong correlation ($r = 0.95$, $P < 0.001$) between the yearly increase in eggs dumped in incubated nests and eggs crushed and missing (Table 115).

The temporal distribution of several activities relating to intraspecific strife at Nauvoo Slough is presented in Table 115. The correlation matrix based on these data shows the degree of seasonal relationship between several activities (Table 117). Females injured or killed related most closely to the periods of egg loss, number of females laying, and number of eggs dumped in nests where incubation was underway. Egg losses were correlated largely with

At Nauvoo Slough, Illinois, from 1984 through 1990, breeding pairs of wood ducks reached densities of about 12 pairs per hectare (5/ac) in some years. These unusually high densities of breeding ducks probably contributed to intraspecific strife between female wood ducks during egg laying and incubation at some of the 80 available nest sites. Over the seven-year period, confrontations between host and intruding females resulted in 37 head injuries, 28 fatalities, 834 crushed eggs, and 649 eggs removed from nests. Torn crest feathers and skin removed from the area behind the eye represented common wounds (top). Wounds also occurred on top of the head, exposing the skull (center). Dead females usually were found next to an unscarred incubating hen (bottom). Most frequently, but not always, the intruding hen was a yearling and the surviving one was an adult. *Photos by Dan Holm; courtesy of the Illinois Natural History Survey.*

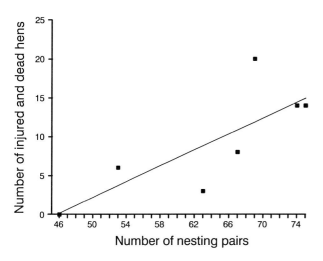

Figure 80. Effect of the number of nesting pairs of wood ducks on the number of injured and dead nesting hens at Nauvoo Slough, Illinois, 1984–90. The regression equation is: $y = -23.36 + 0.51x$, $r = 0.78$, $P < 0.05$.

Table 117. Correlation matrix for several wood duck activities/dump nest histories at Nauvoo Slough, Illinois, based on weekly changes in numbers during the breeding season, 1984–90, as shown in Table 115.

Parameter	Week of season	Number of females laying[a]	Number of dump nests[b]	Number of eggs Dumped late[c]	Lost[d]	Number of females injured or killed[e]
Week of season	1.00					
Females laying[a]	−0.65*	1.00				
Number of dump nests[b]	−0.73*	0.93*	1.00			
Eggs dumped late[c]	−0.49	0.91*	0.88*	1.00		
Eggs lost[d]	0.41	0.08	−0.08	0.17	1.00	
Females injured/killed[e]	−0.01	0.65*	0.43	0.51	0.49	1.00

[a] Minimum number of individual females laying during entire week.
[b] Nests that contained more than 16 eggs.
[c] After incubation had commenced by host female.
[d] Eggs crushed, cracked, or disappeared.
[e] Females killed or injured on nest by other female wood ducks.
* Significant at $P < 0.05$.

the week of the season. Eggs dumped in active incubated nests were correlated highly with the number of laying females and the number of dump nests initiated but were negatively correlated with weeks of the season. Initiation of dump nests was related to the week of season and number of females laying, but the strong negative coefficient indicated that dump nesting declined as the season progressed. The large negative coefficient for laying females indicated a pronounced decline in egg laying as the season progressed.

Among wounded birds (females with head wounds that were never found dead), 16 were adults and 21 were yearlings. In three cases, a yearling bird had been incubating for approximately 7 to 14 days when she tore the skin on the top of the head of an intruding yearling and exposed its skull. In other cases involving birds of known ages, one adult exposed the skull of another adult, one adult exposed the skull of a yearling, and a yearling exposed the skull of another yearling as the birds were laying prior to incubation. We were unable to document which birds inflicted injury in the remaining 31 cases.

We encountered injured females under a variety of circumstances: six birds acquired wounds after they started their incubation duties; six injured birds were observed sitting beside proprietor females (we found no injuries on the proprietor females); another injury apparently was sustained when two or more birds were laying eggs in the same nest; and 24 females already were injured when captured at the start of incubation.

All six females wounded after they had started incubating ultimately had successful hatches. In every case, eggs either were added to or disappeared from, or both, the clutches during the week that preceded the injuries. Mean clutch size and

nesting efficiency in these nests (n = 5; two birds apparently injured one another as they attempted to share incubation duties) were 22.2 ± 4.8 eggs and 59 percent, respectively.

In three of the six nests in which we observed an injured bird alongside a proprietor female, the clutches hatched successfully. In the successful nests, we encountered injured females 7–14 days after the start of incubation. The other three confrontations occurred during egg laying.

A female that showed no signs of head injuries was captured in a nest box that contained three eggs during the last week of April 1987. During a check of the same box eight days later, we found the same female incubating; this time, however, she had head wounds and was sitting on 19 eggs. In the succeeding weeks, the clutch size rose to 34 and then eventually dropped to 10 before the nest was deserted.

Of the 24 females that were wounded when captured during their first week of incubation, 15 had successful nests. A total of 355 eggs (average clutch size = 14.8 ± 7.4 eggs) were laid in 24 nests, but only 135 young were produced.

Overall, female wood ducks with head injuries were observed in 36 nests, 1986–1990. Nest success (64 percent) and nesting efficiency (38 percent) were surprisingly high in comparison with the nest success (47 percent) and nesting efficiency (28 percent) of the entire population, 1986–1990.

The fact that six proprietor females were wounded after they had begun incubation indicates that intruding females can be aggressive against birds in possession of the nest. In all cases, the wounds were minor; although proprietor females had feathers removed from their heads, the skin was not torn. We have no indication how the intruding birds fared during these encounters.

Some females inflicted wounds on other females when two or more birds contributed eggs to a clutch prior to incubation. In three cases, it appeared that one bird was aggressive while the other bird was submissive. In these instances, injuries were very severe and none of the wounded birds was ever found nesting again; however, another female that was wounded during egg laying lost only a narrow line of feathers that extended back from her eyes to the occiput. She returned to nest the following year.

The majority of wounded birds that we encountered (n = 24, 65 percent) were injured before they began incubating. An unknown proportion probably received their wounds when laying eggs in the nests they eventually incubated, whereas some birds undoubtedly were injured earlier in the nesting season when they attempted to dump eggs in the nests of other females.

Ten of 29 wounded birds (34 percent), 1986–1989, returned to Nauvoo Slough and established nests the year after their injuries. Eight of the 10 females had successful nests the year they were wounded, and six returned to the same nest site the following year. During the same period, females without injuries (n = 194) returned at a rate of 46 percent. There was no statistical difference (P > 0.05, chi-square = 0.7970) between the return rates of wounded and uninjured birds, 1986–1989.

Only 114 young were produced from 515 eggs (22-percent nesting efficiency) in the 26 nests where birds were killed, 1985–1990 (three females were killed in the same nest by the same proprietor). Thirteen nests were deserted and 13 hatched successfully. Undoubtedly, nest success (50 percent) and nesting efficiency would have been even lower had we not removed the dead birds.

Of the 28 fatalities, 22 were yearlings. In 17 instances, the survivors (the females that did the killing) were adults, 5 were yearlings, and 6 were unknown. All of the 17 adults appeared to be in possession of the nest sites that had been intruded on by 2 adults and 15 yearlings, all of which were killed. Two yearling proprietors killed intruding adult females. The yearlings had been incubating for 21–26 days when the adults were found dead. In two cases involving yearling survivors, no female was a true proprietor of the nest site, but yearlings killed yearlings in nests where egg laying was underway. In another case, however, a yearling proprietor killed an intruding yearling during the third week of incubation. Fatalities involving unknown-aged survivors also occurred in nests where incubation (n = 3) and egg laying (n = 2) were underway. In another instance, an adult bird that was in her fourth week of incubation was found dead; her

head wounds and battered wing and tail feathers indicated that she was killed by an intruding female. In summary, intruders rather than proprietors lost their lives in all cases except one.

Based on these data and our two observations of intruders in the grasp of the proprietors, intruders appear to be more submissive than proprietors. Oddly, despite severe wounds, several intruders made no effort to leave. Four yearlings observed with head wounds and incubating beside adult females were dead the following week.

Additional evidence suggested that several other females had attempted to share incubation of clutches with the original proprietors, but such states usually persisted less than a week. In 1989, however, two adult females incubated amicably, side by side, for at least 14 days until the nest hatched. Although this type of behavior is rare, Bellrose (1943) and Fuller and Bolen (1963) described similar cases in which two females showed tolerance of each other while simultaneously incubating a common clutch.

Of the 16 birds known to have killed other females, 1985–1989, six (38 percent) returned to nest at Nauvoo Slough the year after their confrontation. Although five of the six birds had successful nests, only one returned to the same site where she had nested the previous year.

We were able to follow the nesting histories of several birds involved in these confrontations. We captured a yearling female (#251) in 1986 during her first week of incubation. This bird had the skin torn and removed from the top of her head. She continued to incubate and successfully hatched the clutch. The following year, 1987, she returned to the same nest site (30-A); she was captured on April 9 and was injured again; this time she deserted. Nearly two months passed before we encountered #251 again. She entered the nest (2-A) of a yearling female (#348) that had been incubating for at least 21 days and was killed by #348. There was no tangible evidence that #251 attempted to defend herself.

In nest 20-B, we captured an injured yearling female (#238) as she began incubating in 1987; 20 eggs were laid over six days. Eggs were added to this nest throughout incubation. Bird #238 was found on the nest during the second and third weeks of incubation, but an injured female (#414), a three-year-old, was found incubating during the fourth week. Our next check was seven days later, and we found that nine eggs had been removed, #238 was back incubating, and #414 was dead. An additional seven days later, we checked the nest again and found it deserted; at least seven new eggs had been added during the intervening week, and 25 of 34 eggs were crushed. Although two or more

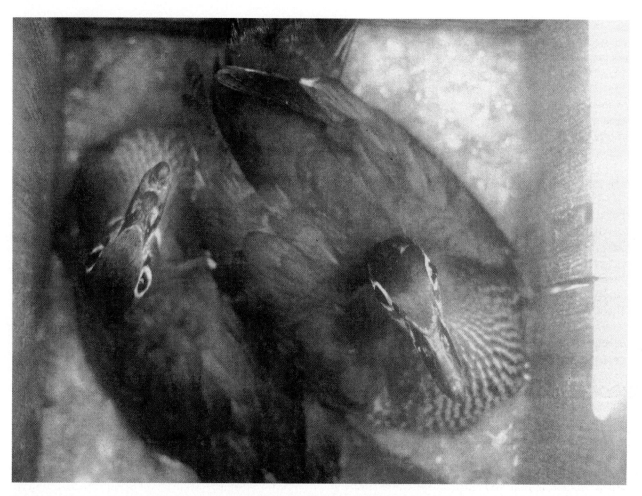

Rarely are two female wood ducks found incubating side by side in apparent complacency over many days to hatching. One such find was documented in Chillicothe, Illinois, in 1942, another in Nauvoo Slough, Illinois, in 1989. In both instances, the hens continued to incubate together for more than two weeks. Where one hen was marked, the two were shown to maintain the same relative positions on the nest until near hatching. The hens' clutches hatched in both years. *Photo by Dan Holm; courtesy of the Illinois Natural History Survey.*

females continued to lay eggs in this nest throughout incubation, #238 tried to maintain possession of the nest, but with continued strife she eventually gave up.

Female #357 (as a yearling) also had minor head wounds when we captured her in 1987 as she began incubating. She deserted the nest (10-B) during the third week of incubation when eight eggs disappeared and six of the remaining nine were crushed. In 1988, #357 returned to a different nest site (14-A) and successfully hatched a clutch of eggs. As far as we could tell, she had no confrontations with other females. In 1989, she returned to 14-A and was first captured on April 11; there were five eggs in the nest. Seven days later we found 15 eggs at this site. On April 25, #357 was incubating 18 eggs and a dead yearling female lay beside her; this nest was eventually deserted.

Unlike #357, who was wounded one year and apparently killed a conspecific female the following year, adult females #237 and #240 killed yearlings that entered their nests (boxes 23-B and 7-A, respectively) during incubation in 1987, but #237 and #240 were wounded by conspecifics the following year. The skull of #237 was exposed by another adult (#878); the confrontation occurred prior to incubation in box 24-B. In 1988, #240 received minor head wounds sometime before she began incubating. She returned to the same nest site (2-B) in 1989 and completed egg laying and incubation without any apparent signs of fighting.

Female #254 was banded as a yearling in 1986. Despite being wounded at the start of incubation, she had a successful hatch. The following year #254 returned to the same nest site (18-B) and was wounded by a conspecific during her last week of incubation, yet she had another successful nest. When she returned in 1988 and 1989, #254 had successful hatches in box 18-B, and we detected no signs of conspecific fighting.

In 1988, female #183 (as a yearling) hatched 15 of 26 eggs in box 1-B. The following year, 1989, she nested in box 1-A and hatched 13 of 15 eggs. We found no evidence that suggested that #183 engaged in conspecific fighting during 1988 and 1989. In 1990, however, #183 killed three yearling females that entered her nest (1-A) during the first, second, and fourth weeks of incubation, respectively.

Perhaps the most perplexing behavior of any female that was involved in these confrontations was displayed by #234. Her head was scarred when we captured her incubating in box 9-B on June 16, 1987. Nevertheless, she hatched 17 eggs later that month. The following year, she returned as a three-year-old to a different nest (5-A) and killed a yearling that preempted her incubation during the second week. In 1989, #234 returned to nest 9-B and began incubating sometime around the first of May. The following week we captured her and another adult female (#359) incubating the nest together; neither bird showed evidence of head wounds. Both continued to incubate the nest, without incident, until it hatched on May 29. Thus, #234 was injured by a conspecific, killed an intruding bird, and tolerated a female that preempted her incubation. Age-related behavioral differences or kinship are two factors that may have induced the extreme behaviors of #234.

Our observations of conspecific fighting by wood ducks at Nauvoo Slough revealed that females responded to attacks in a variety of ways. In some instances, when two or more females vied for possession of a common nest site during egg laying, neither appeared to be submissive and both parties inflicted severe injuries to the other. By contrast, females that preempted the incubation duties of other birds responded to attacks by exiting the nest before major injuries could be inflicted or by remaining submissive. Of the 37 females injured, 1984–1990, 24 were already wounded when captured at the start of incubation. Many of these females could have been injured when they entered a nest of a conspecific to dump eggs before they established nests of their own. Injuries were minor in 92 percent (n = 22) of the cases where birds were wounded at the start of incubation (some feathers were removed from the head but the skin was not torn), indicating that the injured females escaped before serious damage could be inflicted. By contrast, the 28 fatalities indicate that some females were unable or reluctant to leave the nest before being seriously injured. We found no evidence of injury on 22 females that were captured and examined within one week after they killed a conspecific. Thus, it appears that some females made little effort to defend themselves against attack.

The killing and mauling of conspecific females that has occurred at Nauvoo Slough are on a scale without precedent among birds. In all of our studies outside of Nauvoo Slough, we observed only two instances for which evidence indicated that incubating hens killed intruding females. An incubating female banded on May 11, 1961, was still on 15 eggs on May 23; next to her was a dead female with skull exposed. On April 29, 1963, we found two hens, one dead, in a nest house. The dead bird had been banded in a previous year; the incubating bird was on a clutch of nine eggs. Both clutches hatched.

Two other females with severe scalp wounds were observed incubating clutches—one on June 13, 1963, the other on June 8, 1964. At the time, we believed the wounds were from raccoons, but the fact that they continued to incubate without evidence of raccoons at the nest sites suggests, in retrospect, that they had been fighting with other females.

Leopold (1951) reported a dead hen alongside an incubating hen in a nest box on May 19. Incubation of the nest, in which eggs had been dumped, started April 24. Five eggs were under the dead bird, and 11 of the remaining 12 hatched on May 26.

Antagonistic behavior akin to that of the wood duck was observed by Schamel (1974) at an eider breeding colony in Alaska. He reported that pairs entered into physical combat to claim a specific nest site. Females in particular were aggressive in biting and pushing each other, whereas males were more prone to vocalize and make bluff charges at their opponents.

In his classic review of the effect of social behavior on animal population abundance, Wynne-Edwards (1962) made no mention of conspecific egg destruction and strife leading to mortality among breeding female birds. He did discuss the loss of eggs and juveniles from parental action. Such losses have been well documented in the white stork. Battles between nonbreeding storks, especially between those establishing nests for the first time, result in losses of eggs and young. Several species of birds, moreover, especially small passerines, are known to engage in adult infanticide (adults killing conspecific young) and intraspecific egg destruction (Mock 1984, Belles-Isles and Picman 1986, Goldstein et al. 1986, Romagnano et al. 1986).

A few cases of conspecific killing among nesting adult birds have been recorded. Tuck (1960) found severe fighting and occasional deaths among thick-billed murres nesting in dense colonies on cliffs of the Gulf of St. Lawrence. Clashes appeared to originate when birds brooding chicks objected to the presence of nonbreeding birds. Opponents gripped each other's beaks and twisted to the extent that some were torn off. Of six birds captured locked in combat, three were breeding and three were nonbreeding females. Loflin (1982) reported a male smooth-billed ani with a skull wound under a nest tree of an ani group in Dade County, Florida. Loflin concluded that it had been killed as its mate attempted to parasitize a nest. Lombardo (1986) found a dead female tree swallow in a nest house. From the female's head wounds, he attributed her death to another tree swallow. Belles-Isles and Picman (1987) found two dead male house wrens in nest boxes that were being defended by male wrens. They believed that the territorial wrens were responsible for the killings because the attacked birds were not eaten and had head and back injuries similar to those described by Lombardo (1986). Lombardo et al. (1989) captured starlings that had been wounded by conspecifics in nest boxes during the breeding season. They also found several male starlings—which had used nest boxes for night roosts during the nonbreeding season—dead as a result of conspecific fighting.

Why conspecific fighting occurs at Nauvoo Slough but apparently is largely absent on other wetlands where large numbers of nest boxes have built up dense populations of breeding wood ducks is puzzling. The proportion of nests at Nauvoo Slough that were dump nests is similar to or below levels found on several other wetlands (Table 107). Thus, female wood ducks that nested on these other wetlands probably entered nests to dump eggs and subjected themselves to potential attacks at least as frequently as females that nested at Nauvoo Slough; yet no other instances of fatal fighting among wood ducks have been documented. Perhaps one factor that contributed to the development of fatal fighting at Nauvoo Slough was the lack of extensive cover where woodies could seek isolation from conspecifics during the prelaying and laying periods. Outside of a few scattered locations where shrubs and trees grew along the Illinois shoreline, sparse growths of willows and residual herbaceous vegetation that formed a narrow strip on a 0.62-kilometer (1 mi) peninsula provided the only cover for wood ducks during March, April, and early May. By mid-May, about 12 hectares (30 ac) of additional cover became available as duck potato growth in the shallow waters surrounding the peninsula increased in density and height. An extensive bed of American lotus (more than 61 hectares: 150 ac) provided additional habitat as plants matured through June and July.

In addition to the limited amount of available concealing cover prior to and during egg laying, Nauvoo Slough was isolated from other suitable wood duck habitat by broad expanses of open water. The nearest large area of quality habitat was 6.4 kilometers (4 mi) upstream at the delta of Devil's Creek. Thus, wood ducks that nested on Nauvoo Slough, for the most part, remained there through the incubation period. Because paired wood ducks do not exclude conspecifics from a specific wetland area (see Chapter 6), woodies that nested at Nauvoo Slough were able to range over the limited habitat; aggressive encounters took place when conspecifics approached within 0.3–0.9 meters (1–3 ft). At low population densities there probably were few social encounters because pairs were able to avoid each other. As the population density increased, however, encounters with conspecifics probably became more common as pairs swam about looking for nest sites, food, and loafing areas. This increased frequency of aggressive encounters outside of the nest site—brought about by limited habitat and high breeding densities—may have contributed to behavioral changes that resulted in intense defense of nest sites by females.

Some features of conspecific fighting behavior by wood ducks at Nauvoo Slough suggest that its action on the breeding population was density-dependent. As shown in Table 117, the number of females engaged in fighting at the nest site was positively correlated to the number of females engaged in egg laying. The depressing effects of conspecific fighting on female survival may tend to inhibit population growth beyond a certain level. For example, the larger the population (the greater the density of breeding birds), the greater the number of females injured and killed as a result of conspecific fighting (Figure 80).

Fights between conspecifics that result in severe injury or death seldom occur for reasons other than reproduction; disputes over food and cover usually end before severe injuries are inflicted. Enquist and Leimar (1990: 1) reported that fatal fighting is most likely to evolve in species when "the value of a contested resource is similar to or greater than the value of the future." They noted that severe fights are common in some invertebrates (primarily arthropods) because a male's chances of mating successfully are limited and it will readily engage in dangerous fights to secure mating opportunities. By contrast, fatal fighting is uncommon in species that have relatively long reproductive lives. Nonetheless, a small proportion of the population of some species that have long reproductive life spans, such as some mammal groups—ungulates, primates, carnivores, and pinnipeds—is known to engage in contests that result in intraspecific fatalities (Geist 1966, 1971, Clutton-Brock et al. 1982, Huntingford and Turner 1987).

NEST SUCCESS

Probably 90-95 percent of the wood ducks in North America nest in natural cavities (Bellrose 1990). It is especially important, therefore, that nest success in and agents of destruction of natural cavities be examined as critically as possible. Unfortunately, most studies of nesting activities pertain to nest houses, which alter the role of predators and affect the evaluation of productivity.

Natural Cavities

The meager data for nest success in natural cavities are weighted for central Illinois (Mason County) (Table 118). Because of the provincial nature of the data, we are unable to obtain an adequate perspective of nest productivity and agents of nest destruction in natural cavities throughout the wood duck's range. Nonetheless, the available data (Table 118) indicate that between one-third and one-half of the wood ducks nesting in natural cavities are successful. Productivity, however, also is affected by other factors—renesting, double brood production, and brood survival.

We compared the density of natural cavities in 14 wooded tracts with nest success, 1958-1961, to evaluate the effect of cavity density on nest success. The wooded areas varied from 3.3 to 36.4 hectares (8.1-90 ac) and totaled 195.9 hectares (484 ac). A positive correlation was found between cavity density and nest success ($r = 0.62$, $P < 0.001$) over the four-year period. The fact that nest success increased as density of natural cavities increased is contrary to the expected density-dependent phenomenon in which nest success declines as population increases. We deduce that successful females returned to nest in "safer" woods and, in so doing, also attracted novice ducks to these woods. Woods that had a previous history of nest destruction and heavy predation would have fewer older ducks homing to its confines and, therefore, would attract fewer novice nesters. Thus, areas subject to heavy predation would have a lower breeding population the following year.

Further evidence of the important role homing plays in bringing ducks back to natural cavities that provided successful nests was given by Bellrose et al. (1964), who found that cavities that had housed successful nests were twice as likely to be used in subsequent years as were those that had housed unsuccessful nests. We were encouraged to find that, within the limits of the ranges in cavity densities we studied (0.04-0.20 per hectare: 0.1-0.5/ac),

an increase in breeding wood ducks did not result in greater nest losses. Homing back to successful nest sites, moreover, reduces the likelihood that wood ducks will nest in areas with high predator populations or that predators will exploit a learned food source. The dispersion of natural cavities at low to moderate densities makes accidental findings of wood duck nests on the part of predators a more likely scenario than the intentional seeking of nests.

Nest Houses

Nest houses are one of the most useful tools that wildlife biologists have for studying and managing wood ducks. One measure of the value of nest houses to wood duck management is shown by the large number of investigators that have used them to answer questions about wood duck nesting biology (Bellrose 1976).

Investigators of wood duck nest biology check houses at frequent intervals to ascertain nest histories: chronology of laying, clutch size, nest success, predation, egg hatchability, duckling departure, and other pertinent facts. Incubating hens usually do not flush, but when alarmed by a previous encounter with a raccoon at the nest site, they readily take flight. *Photo by Jack Dermid.*

Mason County complex, Illinois, 1939–1974. The nest success in board nest houses and causes of losses in our Mason County study, 1939–1974, are presented in Table 119. In the early years, nest success rates were similar in both nest houses and natural cavities (tables 118 and 119). In 1943, however, predation by fox squirrels and raccoons combined to push losses of nests in houses to such high levels that changes in design clearly were needed if nest houses were to be of value.

From 1944 through 1951, we worked on three designs for nest houses (Bellrose 1953). The first was a house with an entrance to exclude raccoons. The second was a metal-covered house with wooden sides and front and a pyramidal roof. The third was a metal cylinder body with a conical roof. The metal cylinder was first lined with Celotex, then with auto undercoat, and still later with a hardware cloth "ladder."

Thus, the escalating nest success data, 1944–1952 (Table 119), represented progress in the "predator-proof" designs of nest houses (see Chapter 19). Except for sporadic, explainable intrusions into nest houses, raccoon depredations all but ceased after 1948. Losses to fox squirrels became negligible after 1949. Losses to bull snakes seemed to occur by chance and only to large snakes.

Metal houses. In 1953, we erected 100 galvanized metal pipe houses with conical roofs in upland wooded tracts where earlier board houses had been placed. A few board houses (n = 14) with "coon-proof" 7.6- by 10.2-centimeter (3 by 4 in) elliptical entrances masking 10.2-centimeter (4 in) circular entrances were left in place. During the limited test period, the metal houses were more resistant to penetration by predators than were the board houses and appeared acceptable to wood ducks.

The largest losses in metal houses occurred in 1961, when yearling raccoons were relatively small because of delayed breeding by adult raccoons during the unusually cold spring of 1960 (see Chapter 11). March of 1960 was one of the coldest on record at Peoria, Illinois, where the daily average was 10.6 degrees Celsius (19°F) below normal. These small yearling raccoons had less difficulty entering nest houses in 1961.

Table 118. Wood duck nest success in natural cavities, and agents of nest destruction.

Years	Region	Number of nests	Percentage successful	Percentage of nest losses					
				Desertion	Squirrel[a]	Raccoon	Snake[b]	Bird[c]	Wind
1938–40	Central Illinois	118	49.2	16.1	24.7	4.2	4.2	0.0	1.7
1958–61	Central Illinois	158	39.9	5.7	18.3	29.1	1.9	3.2	
1964–65	Central Illinois	48	31.2	6.2	20.8	33.3	8.3	0.0	0.0
1967–68	Southeastern Minnesota	93	32.2						
1963–64	New Brunswick	24	50.0	4.2	12.5	33.3			
1966–70	Southeastern Missouri	10	10.0	20.0	0.0	20.0	30.0	10.0	0.0
1984–85	Central Georgia	9	44.4						
1984–85	Central Indiana	36	38.9			41.7			
1972–73	Eastern Alabama	16	62.5	12.5					
Total		512							
Weighted mean			40.5 ± 8.72						
Mean by item			39.8 ± 14.8						

[a] Fox squirrel in central Illinois; gray squirrel in New Brunswick.
[b] Bull snake in central Illinois; rat snake in southeastern Missouri.
[c] Woodpecker, probably red-headed, in central Illinois; starling in southeastern Missouri.

When incubating woodie hens feel secure, they rarely flush from their nests. Investigators usually need to remove the hen from her clutch, firmly but gently, to count the eggs and band or weigh the female. A cloth plug in the cavity entrance will prevent the hen from flushing and likely will prevent her from attempting to do so. Although a hen seldom deserts her clutch as a result of this activity, she occasionally flushes after being returned to the nest. When frightened, female wood ducks often defecate over their eggs or as they flee the nest cavity. *Photo by Jack Dermid.*

Table 118. (continued)

Percentage of nest losses		
Predator unknown	Percentage of all losses	Reference
	50.8	Bellrose et al. (1964)
	60.1	Bellrose et al. (1964)
	68.6	Shake (1967)
	67.7	Strom (1969)
	50.0	Prince (1965)
10.0	90.0	Hansen (1971)
	55.6	Almand (1965)
	61.1	Robb (1986)
25.0	37.5	Teels (1975)

We congratulated ourselves on achieving a practical, predator-proof nest house until 1962, when starlings unexpectedly invaded the nest houses. Not only did they use numerous unoccupied houses, but they also destroyed 17.9 percent of the wood duck nests by usurping these sites from incubating females (Table 119). Wood duck nest losses from starlings remained high through 1967, when they mysteriously declined until 1973.

A comparison of the relationships among the sources of wood duck nest losses in board houses in Mason County, 1939–1952, is revealing of predator interactions (Table 120). As the years progressed, losses from desertion, fox squirrels, and bull snakes all decreased as raccoon depredations increased. Oddly, desertion of nests declined as an item of loss as destruction by raccoons increased, but it increased as activities by fox squirrels and bull snakes increased. Losses from fox squirrels and bull snakes were negatively related to increased losses from raccoons.

For the period 1939–1952, a strong correlation was found between the percentage of successful nests one year and the percentage of house use the following year ($r = 0.70$, $P < 0.01$). For each 1 percent increase in nest success, house use increased a comparable amount (0.96 percent). The relationship between increased nest success and increased use of natural cavities was similar. During 1953–1974, however, no significant correlation ($r = -0.26$, $P > 0.05$) was found between nest success in board houses one year and house use the succeeding year.

Table 119. Wood duck nest histories in board and metal nest houses, Mason County, Illinois, 1939–74.

Year	Number of houses	Number used	Percentage		Percentage of nest losses		
			Used	Successful	Desertion	Fox squirrel	Raccoon
1939	349	181	51.9	45.9	5.5	18.8	21.5
1940	401	233	58.1	57.5	12.0	18.5	6.0
1941	376	243	64.6	49.4	6.1	34.2	7.4
1942	723	470	65.0	30.4	11.9	21.9	25.1
1943	559	279	49.9	15.8	9.3	34.8	33.3
1944	334	106	31.7	20.8	17.9	35.9	10.4
1945	476	67	14.1	41.8	9.0	31.3	16.4
1946	83	38	45.8	38.8	5.6	38.8	11.1
1947	66	37	56.1	33.5	6.3	3.1	40.6
1948	52	22	42.3	31.3	6.3	12.5	31.3
1949	33	7	21.2	25.0	0.0	75.0	0.0
1950	22	3	13.6	33.3	0.0	0.0	0.0
1951	22	5	22.7	60.0	0.0	0.0	20.0
1952	12	5	41.6	60.0	0.0	0.0	20.0
1953	114	11	9.6	81.8	9.1	0.0	9.1
1954	114	12	10.5	66.7	0.0	8.3	8.3
1955	126	9	7.1	100.0	0.0	0.0	0.0
1956	115	10	8.7	80.0	0.0	0.0	10.0
1957	161	20	12.4	65.5	0.0	0.5	20.0
1958	171	18	10.5	72.2	5.6	0.0	11.1
1959	160	22	13.8	86.4	4.5	0.0	4.5
1960	161	32	19.9	81.3	15.6	3.1	0.0
1961	185	55	29.3	55.5	20.0	0.0	25.0
1962	183	78	42.6	68.6	2.6	0.0	10.3
1963	171	85	49.7	56.4	1.2	2.3	12.9
1964	162	88	54.3	38.6	9.1	2.3	11.4
1965	163	59	36.2	62.7	11.9	0.0	0.0
1966	167	67	40.1	56.7	3.0	0.0	6.0
1967	113	35	31.0	68.5	5.7	0.0	0.0
1968	108	41	38.0	80.5	4.9	0.0	0.0
1969	106	44	41.5	86.4	6.8	0.0	0.0
1970	98	43	43.9	86.0	2.3	0.0	0.0
1971	87	38	43.7	86.8	5.3	0.0	0.0
1972	83	32	38.6	81.3	6.3	0.0	0.0
1973	63	28	44.4	71.4	10.7	0.0	0.0
1974	50	24	48.0	62.5	8.3	0.0	0.0
Total/weighted mean	6,369	2,547	40.0				
Mean by year			34.8	59.4	6.2	9.5	10.3
S.D.			17.3	21.7	5.2	16.9	11.0

Table 120. Correlation matrix between agents of destruction among wood duck nests in board houses, Mason County, Illinois, 1939–52.

	Year	Desertion	Raccoon	Fox squirrel	Bull snake
Year	1.00				
Desertion	−0.16	1.00			
Raccoon	0.46	−0.31	1.00		
Fox squirrel	−0.17	0.30	−0.60*	1.00	
Bull snake	−0.58*	0.77*	−0.42	0.19	1.00

*Significant at $P < 0.05$.

Table 119. (continued)

	Percentage of nest losses		
Bull snake	Woodpecker	Starling	Other agents
6.1	0.0	0.0	2.2
6.0	0.0	0.0	0.0
2.9	0.0	0.0	0.0
6.8	0.3	0.0	3.6
2.5	0.0	0.0	4.3
9.4	0.0	0.0	5.6
1.5	0.0	0.0	0.0
0.0	0.0	0.0	0.0
0.0	0.0	0.0	0.0
0.0	0.0	0.0	0.0
0.0	0.0	0.0	0.0
66.7	0.0	0.0	0.0
20.0	0.0	0.0	0.0
20.0	0.0	0.0	0.0
0.0	0.0	0.0	0.0
16.7	0.0	0.0	0.0
0.0	0.0	0.0	0.0
10.0	0.0	0.0	0.0
0.5	0.0	0.0	0.0
11.1	0.0	0.0	0.0
0.0	4.5	0.0	0.0
0.0	0.0	0.0	0.0
0.0	0.0	0.0	0.0
0.0	1.3	17.9	0.0
0.0	1.2	25.9	0.0
0.0	14.8	22.7	1.1
0.0	8.5	15.3	1.7
0.0	9.0	25.4	0.0
0.0	2.9	22.9	0.0
0.0	4.9	9.8	0.0
0.0	4.5	2.3	0.0
0.0	7.0	4.7	0.0
0.0	5.3	2.6	0.0
0.0	9.4	3.1	0.0
0.0	0.0	17.9	0.0
0.0	0.0	29.2	0.0
5.0	2.0	5.5	0.5
12.0	3.6	9.4	1.3

Throughout this 22-year period, nest success was high but nest house occupancy was low (Table 119). Apparently there was environmental resistance to brood survival. Only the loss of preflight young could account for prolonged high nest success without a comparable increase in the breeding population as reflected in the use of nest houses. This problem will be addressed in greater detail in Chapter 18.

Quiver Creek complex, Mason County, Illinois, 1956–1974. We began placing metal, predator-proof houses along Quiver Creek in 1953 but did not achieve a good coverage of the study area, especially the lower 8.9 kilometers (5.5 mi), until 1956. Table 121 presents data on the yearly number of wood duck nests, nest success, and factors responsible for nest failures, 1956–1974. From 1956 through 1973, wood duck nests increased greatly as high nest success usually (though not always) resulted in an increased number of nests the following year.

Table 122 shows that as the years progressed, 1956–1974, nest desertion and nest losses from raccoons and fox squirrels decreased, but losses from starlings and flickers increased. Desertion rates were negatively related to starling activity, probably because these birds appropriated appreciable numbers of nests deserted from other causes. Desertion correlated with losses from fox squirrels and flickers but not at all with losses from raccoons (Table 122). Starling destruction of wood duck nests was correlated with losses from flickers and raccoons but unrelated to squirrel-destroyed nests. Flicker destruction also was related to that caused by raccoons but not to that by fox squirrels. The varying yearly loss by different predators suggests a replacement of various sources of nest failure. A high rate of desertion not fully explained by predator activity is believed to have been caused by intraspecific strife among wood duck hens.

Nauvoo Slough unit, Hancock County, Illinois, 1983–1990. Nest houses in the Nauvoo Slough unit were placed on posts in a slough 1.4 kilometers (0.9 mi) long that was adjacent to the Keokuk Pool of the Mississippi River. Although George Arthur (retired) of the Illinois Department of Conservation had erected a variety of house types in the mid-1970s, we checked them only once a year in July from 1978 through 1982 and failed to determine the outcome of nests still under incubation. In 1983 we examined these houses on five occasions and determined the fate of all nests. From 1984 through 1990 we inspected the houses each week from early April into July.

We replaced the wide variety of houses provided by George Arthur with 40 duplex houses (80 nest sites) of cypress erected on 5.1-centimeter (2 in) pipes in March 1984. Occupancy of nest houses by wood ducks more than doubled from 1983 through 1986 but declined slightly in 1987 (Table 123). Although appreciable numbers of nest sites were unused, in three of the five years there were more nests than nest houses through the 90-day nest initiation season because new nests were created in houses that held previously destroyed or hatched nests.

Table 121. Wood duck nest histories in sheet metal nest houses, Quiver Creek, Illinois, 1956–74.

Year	Number of houses	Number used	Percentage		Percentage of nest losses	
			Used	Successful	Desertion	Fox squirrel
1956	79	22	27.8	72.7	22.7	4.5
1957	106	34	32.1	64.8	20.6	0.0
1958	118	40	33.9	82.5	10.0	2.5
1959	129	53	41.1	83.0	13.2	1.9
1960	120	73	60.8	78.1	21.9	0.0
1961	125	113	90.4	66.4	16.8	0.0
1962	139	126	90.6	75.4	2.4	0.0
1963	139	136	97.8	69.1	1.5	0.0
1964	153	163	106.5	56.4	5.5	0.6
1965	177	125	70.6	75.2	3.2	0.0
1966	179	184	102.8	73.9	6.5	0.0
1967	195	169	86.7	74.0	3.6	0.0
1968	197	158	80.2	88.6	4.4	0.0
1969	209	168	80.4	88.7	5.4	0.0
1970	209	179	85.6	91.1	5.2	0.0
1971	209	143	68.4	93.7	4.2	0.0
1972	209	190	90.1	90.0	5.8	0.0
1973	230	208	90.4	85.6	1.9	0.0
1974	226	172	76.1	84.3	2.3	
Total/weighted mean	3,148	2,456	78.0			
Mean (year)			74.3	78.6	8.3	0.5
S.D.			24.4	10.2	7.1	1.2

Table 122. Correlation matrix between agents of destruction among wood duck nests in metal houses, Quiver Creek, Illinois, 1956–74.

	Year	Desertion	Starling	Flicker	Raccoon	Fox squirrel
Year	1.00					
Desertion	−0.74*	1.00				
Starling	0.001	−0.42	1.00			
Flicker	0.07	0.26	0.41	1.00		
Raccoon	−0.20	0.00	0.49*	0.16	1.00	
Fox squirrel	−0.58*	0.50*	−0.31	−0.14	−0.23	1.00

* Significant at $P < 0.05$.

Table 123. Wood duck nest histories in nest houses on posts (duplex compartments in 1984 and subsequent years), Nauvoo Slough, Illinois, 1983–87.

Year	Number of houses	Number used	Percentage		Percentage of nest losses			
			Used	Success	Desertion	Flicker	Starling	Raccoon
1983	28	42	150.0	45.2	11.1	33.3	2.2	15.6
1984	81[a]	71	87.7	59.2	11.3	25.4	2.8	0.0
1985	80	73	91.3	58.9	13.7	20.5	5.5	0.0
1986	80	101	126.3	45.5	51.9	0.0	2.0	0.0
1987	80	85	106.3	42.4	54.8	2.4	1.2	0.0
Total/mean	349	372	112.3±26.0	50.2±8.1	28.6±22.7	16.3±14.6	2.7±1.6	3.1±7.0

[a] Includes one metal house equipped with a floating bottom for determining weight; this house was removed after the 1984 nesting season.

Table 121. (continued)

	Percentage of nest losses		
Raccoon	Flicker	Starling	Other agents
0.0	0.0	0.0	0.0
2.9	0.0	8.8	5.9
2.5	0.0	0.0	2.5
0.0	1.9	0.0	0.0
0.0	0.0	0.0	0.0
10.6	0.9	5.3	0.0
3.2	2.4	15.9	0.8
5.1	0.0	23.5	0.7
4.9	15.3	16.6	0.6
2.4	8.0	11.2	0.0
3.3	4.3	9.8	2.2
1.8	4.7	14.2	1.8
0.6	3.8	2.0	0.6
0.6	2.3	3.0	0.0
0.5	1.1	1.6	0.5
0.7	0.7	0.7	0.0
0.0	2.1	2.1	0.0
3.4	0.0	7.2	1.9
1.2	0.6	7.0	4.7
2.3	2.5	6.8	1.2
2.6	3.8	6.9	1.7

Mean nest success, 1983–1987, was 50.2 percent—lower than on our other study areas in Illinois. During the first three years, puncturing of eggs by flickers was responsible for most of the nest destruction. Nest desertion, induced largely by intraspecific strife among laying and incubating hens, increased greatly in 1986 and 1987 (Table 123). Other aspects of intraspecific strife were discussed under dump nesting. Several nests were destroyed in 1983 because some of the initial houses had circular entrances large enough to admit raccoons. Starlings evicted wood ducks from a mean of 2.7 percent of their nests, 1983–1987 (Table 123).

Table 124 presents a correlation matrix of the interrelationship among wood duck nest losses. Desertion of nests increased as losses to flickers, starlings, and raccoons declined. This rate of desertion occurred because greater numbers of intact nests were more likely to be subject to intraspecific strife. Losses to flickers were not significantly ($P > 0.05$) correlated with losses to starlings and raccoons.

Lake Chautauqua National Wildlife Refuge, Mason County, Illinois. Nest houses at the Chautauqua National Wildlife Refuge were placed in both bottomland and upland woods. During 1939–1945, the houses were made of cypress lumber, with 10.2-centimeter (4 in) circular entrances. Data for 1950–1962 and 1965–1986 were for cylindrical galvanized metal houses provided with conical tops and horizontal elliptical 10.2- by 7.6-centimeter (4 by 3 in) entrances. The use of these nest houses and the subsequent nest success (Table 125) are very close to the use and success in the units of the Mason County complex that we managed for wood ducks (Table 119).

Notwithstanding high nest success, 1950–1961, at the Chautauqua National Wildlife Refuge, use of nest houses was low, probably because of fewer breeders due to heavy losses to predators, particularly raccoons, in 1942 and 1943. The breeding population showed a recovery to 151 nests by 1970, but despite nest success of 60 percent, nests numbered only 48 in 1971. From that year through 1987, the number of nests in houses varied from 18 to 73, even with nest success ranging from 58 to 94 percent. There was no correlation between nest success one year and nest house use the following year ($r = 0.02$, $P > 0.05$).

As noted, these findings agree with those from nest houses in units of the Mason County complex (Table 119)—namely, some area of environmental resistance that developed after 1945 adversely affected the survival of woodie broods. Otherwise, the high nest success in houses at the Mason County complex and Lake Chautauqua National Wildlife Refuge would have resulted in an expanding breeding wood duck population, which in turn would have been reflected in the increased use of nest houses.

The environmental resistance to which we have referred appears to stem from a reduction in the food base and cover conducive to brood survival.

Table 124. Correlation matrix between agents of destruction among wood duck nests in houses, Nauvoo Slough, Illinois, 1983-87.

	Year	Desertion	Flicker	Starling	Raccoon
Year	1.00				
Desertion	0.89*	1.00			
Flicker	− 0.95*	− 0.98*	1.00		
Starling	− 0.27	− 0.54	0.38	1.00	
Raccoon	− 0.71	− 0.58	0.69	− 0.13	1.00

*Significant at $P < 0.05$.

Table 125. Wood duck nest house use and nest success, Lake Chautauqua National Wildlife Refuge, Illinois, 1939–87.

Year	Number of house-years	Number of nest-years	Percentage	
			Use	Success
1939–45[a]	1,422	753	53.0	27.1
1950–61[b]	1,561	185	11.9	62.2
1965–87[b]	3,853	1,480	38.4	77.0
Total/weighted mean	6,836	2,418	35.4	60.3

[a] Nest houses made of cypress with 10.2-centimeter (4 in) circular entrance.
[b] Nest houses of sheet-metal cylindrical body, conical top, and elliptical 10.2- by 7.6-centimeter (4 by 3 in) entrance.

During this period, Bellrose et al. (1979, 1983) documented the decline in aquatic and marsh plants at Lake Chautauqua and other lakes in the Illinois Valley. Increased sedimentation resulted in the degradation of aquatic and marsh vegetation through greater turbidity and bottom erosion directly caused by wave and fish activity, which suspended the fine silt and clay soils composing the unstable bottom.

Nest House Use and Nest Success by Regions of Flyways

Publications and theses on wood duck occupancy rates of nest houses and nest success provide a nationwide perspective (Table 126). Overall, wood duck use of houses was significantly higher ($P < 0.001$) than use of natural cavities (see Table 64). Nest success also was much better in nest houses than nest cavities ($P < 0.001$) (tables 118 and 126).

In the Atlantic Flyway, nest house use declined from north to south (Table 126). Nest success was highest in the northern states and lowest in the central states area. Wood duck house use greatly increased from north to south in the Mississippi Flyway; nest success was highest in the northern states and lowest in the central. Data for the Central Flyway were entirely from eastern Texas (Table 126) and showed a slightly lower rate of use but an above-average success rate. Use of nest houses by wood ducks and nest success also were above average in the Pacific Flyway states of Washington, Oregon, and California (Table 126).

Data obtained through questionnaires on wood duck use of nest boxes and the success of nesting efforts on national wildlife refuges in various regions of the nation were similar to those reported in published data and theses (Table 127). In both the Atlantic and Mississippi flyways, use of nest houses on refuges increased from north to south. With the exception of refuges in the southern states

Table 126. Wood duck nest house use and nest success in flyway regions, based on information from publications.[a]

Flyway	Region	Number of house-years	Number of nest-years	Percentage	
				Use	Nest success
Atlantic	North	20,272	9,906	48.9	80.2
	Central	27,052	10,035	37.1	44.4
	South	28,798	9,824	34.1	71.4
Mississippi	North	2,277	452	19.9	75.6
	Central	42,944	15,869	37.0	60.6
	South	7,651	5,120	66.9	63.4
Central	Eastern Texas	254	98	38.6	62.2
Pacific	All	2,560	1,484	58.0	63.6
Total/weighted mean by region		131,808	53,058	40.3	63.9
Mean				50.1 ± 33.1	67.4 ± 17.5

[a] See Appendix I for details.

Table 127. Wood duck nest house use and nest success on national wildlife refuges, based on information from respondents to questionnaire.[a]

Flyway	Region	Number of house-years	Number of nest-years	Percentage		Number of refuges responding
				Use	Nest success	
Atlantic	North	3,420	1,050	30.7	64.6	9
	Central	2,193	1,106	50.4	43.0	11
	South	3,416	1,856	54.3	82.4	12
Mississippi	North	1,156	94	8.1	78.6	6
	Central	7,407	3,173	42.8	75.4	10
	South	13,090	9,295	71.0	70.2	15
Central	All	1,159	158	13.6	82.4	5
Pacific	All	2,035	810	39.8	46.2	15
Total/weighted mean by region		33,876	17,542	51.8	68.1	
Mean				38.5 ± 29.8	69.7 ± 20.2	

[a] See Appendix J for details.

of the Atlantic Flyway, nest success was better in northern areas. Use of nest houses was low in refuges of the Central Flyway despite high nest success, suggesting high brood losses. Nest houses on refuges in the Pacific Flyway provided a degree of nest success only slightly below that of refuges in eastern states.

A third source of information on the use of nest houses and nest success by wood ducks is from unpublished reports (Table 128). Although these data are not as abundant as information from other sources, findings by regions are similar.

Findings from all data sources on wood duck occupancy of and nest success in nest houses embrace numerous types of houses erected by several different means. During the last two decades, almost all houses have had some method of deterring climbing predators. How various types of houses and their placement affect nest success is discussed in Chapter 19. We can safely generalize, however, that the nest houses constructed and erected by a number of investigators have been used at a higher rate than suitable natural cavities and have provided safer places to nest.

Table 128. Wood duck nest house use in flyway regions, based on information from unpublished reports.[a]

Flyway	Region	Number of house-years	Number of nest-years	Percentage	
				Use	Nest success
Atlantic	North	1,674	678	40.5	69.4
	South	70	33	47.1	
Mississippi	Manitoba	462	175	37.9	
	North	10,215	1,756	17.2	
	Central	5,673	2,077	36.6	
	South	910	586	64.4	68.7
Pacific	North	3,774	1,879	49.8	65.3
	South	3,140	2,975	94.7	68.4
Total/weighted mean by region		25,918	10,159	38.7	68.1
Mean				47.4 ± 21.7	68.0 ± 1.6

[a] See Appendix K for details.

UNCONVENTIONAL NEST SITES

On rare occasions, wood ducks abandon their traditional nest sites for sites that are quite bizarre. In 1938 we found a wood duck incubating eggs in a red-tailed hawk's nest; less than 61 meters (200 ft) away, we found another nesting in a cottage chimney. Audubon (1840–1844) found a nest in a rock fissure on the Kentucky River. A brood was observed at the base of a cliff by Carleton (1971), who assumed that the ducklings came from a hole three-fourths of the way up the escarpment.

Hugh Bateman, Louisiana Department of Conservation, discovered a number of wood ducks nesting in hollowed depressions at the top of river pilings, as well as one among the gables of a house. Sweet (1976) observed a wood duck nesting on a metal crossbar attached to a power line tower in the Oakwood Bottoms of southern Illinois.

At the Great Swamp National Wildlife Refuge, Zipko and Kennington (1977) found a wood duck nest on the ground in a grassy field 10 meters (32.8 ft) from a pond. The nest hatched. Mason and Dusi (1983) discovered a nest on a grass/alder hummock in a pond near the Auburn University campus. The nest failed to hatch, but evidence suggested that a wood duck had nested there the previous year. A wood duck nest was discovered on a muskrat house within the city limits of Antigo, Wisconsin, in May 1987 by McIlquham and Bacon (1989). It was destroyed by a predator. Roberts (1932) reported second-hand accounts of wood ducks nesting on the ground under clumps of prostrate rushes or in banks under overhanging willows in Jackson County, Minnesota. He also noted that, on rare occasions, wood ducks may nest in barns. Similarly, Forbush (1925), Phillips (1925), and Palmer (1949) reported several records of wood ducks entering barns and nesting in haylofts.

Hall (1969) found a wood duck nesting in an open leaf and stick nest placed in an oak tree. Todd (1979) knew of one case where a wood duck built a nest in a pine tree. In June 1985, Glen W. Bond, Jr., photographed a female wood duck incubating eggs in an abandoned squirrel or hawk nest composed of sticks. It was placed 10.7 meters (35 ft) above the ground in a loblolly pine, 4.6 meters (15 ft) from an arm of Lake Marion in Clarendon County, South Carolina.

Of all the unconventional nest sites used by wood ducks, the most common are those provided by chimneys of cottages in the country and houses in towns. Most of such reports that we receive note that hens entered chimneys and emerged through fireplaces or furnace ducts into rooms from which there was no escape. At the Crane Lake Duck Club near Bath, Illinois, Basil Taylor, former caretaker, inspected individual cabins of absentee members in March 1942 and found, in different residences, four female wood ducks dead and one pair still alive. In one instance, the female entered through a stove-pipe; in the others, the birds came through chimneys. We have a number of records of wood ducks entering homes in Havana, Illinois. These hens were either captured and released or died by flying against windows. In May 1986 a male wood duck entered, by way of a chimney, a blacksmith shop that was part of the Nauvoo, Illinois, Restoration by the Church of the Latter-day Saints.

Leopold (1951) reported that a neighbor in Burlington, Iowa, found a dead wood duck above the damper of his fireplace. Ray Cunningham noted that a hen wood duck was killed in a fireplace at New Brighton, Minnesota, in April 1968. Pettingill (1935) stated that Witmer Stone found a dead wood duck plugging the flue of a chimney near Philadelphia, Pennsylvania. According to Stewart (1971b), Milton B. Trautman told him of many dead wood ducks found in chimneys at Put-in-Bay, Ohio. Stewart (1957) reported on three nests in chimneys; at least one hatched and the young departed successfully. This chimney was only 1.68 meters (5.5 ft) deep. The successful nest that we observed in 1938 was built in a chimney on a raised bracket 2.5 meters (8.2 ft) deep.

Chimneys on the Crane Lake cottages and on numerous houses in Havana have been screened to prevent the entrance of wood ducks. Stewart (1971b) reported that entrance of wood ducks into chimneys was such a problem in parts of Michigan that many chimneys were screened.

SUMMARY

The biology of the wood duck is attuned to the habitat conditions and predators of the deciduous forest biome. In no other biome are predators as diverse and abundant; moreover, there is the problem of fluctuating water levels—daily, weekly, and seasonally—in riverine habitats. Wood ducks have evolved many strategies to combat the adversity of their habitat niche and exploit its assets. They have developed a long breeding season commensurate with the climate within their breeding range. Where conditions permit, appreciable numbers raise two broods per year. Apparently because of high duckling loss in the first week of life, more ducklings depart wood duck nests than do those of any other duck species (with the possible exception of the black-bellied whistling duck) in North America. Large departures of ducklings occur because of notably large normal clutches abetted by the addition of dumped eggs by other females. Intraspecific laying has proven to be advantageous to augmenting reproduction, or evolutionary forces would have eliminated it long ago.

Wood ducks probably moved from ground nesting sites to tree cavity sites to reduce predation. Such a shift in nest sites would gradually permeate through a population through greater nest success leading to greater tree cavity use. The strong contemporary homing by adults and young wood ducks to previous nest sites is illustrative of one mechanism that probably reinforced the nest site transformation.

Chapter 11

Competitors and Nest Predators

Whether in natural cavities or in nest houses, wood ducks are in competition with other species for nest sites and face destruction of their nests by cavity-seeking predators. In some instances, species that compete with wood ducks for nest sites also prey on the eggs; one predator—the raccoon—commonly kills the incubating female when she is captured in the nest cavity.

COMPETITION FOR NATURAL CAVITIES

Because of their range of size and degree of accessibility, natural cavities are used by a variety of species, from bees to raccoons. Most cavity dwellers occupy a site on a temporary, transient, or seasonal basis; rarely does an individual animal use the same cavity throughout the four seasons. Wood ducks may evict certain tenants and be evicted by others.

The relative use by other animals of natural cavities considered suitable for wood ducks is listed in Table 129. Fox and gray squirrels and raccoons are most likely to occupy these cavities during the season when woodies seek and use them. Opossums, flying squirrels, screech-owls, and barred owls are other relatively large species that occupy cavities. Numerous songbird species also use cavities for nest sites.

At Muscatatuck National Wildlife Refuge in Indiana, Robb (1986) found more evidence of use of suitable cavities by fox squirrels and raccoons than by wood ducks. He inspected cavities in winter (n = 122) and summer (n = 157) and found that raccoon use remained fairly constant at 10–20 percent during both seasons. Use by fox squirrels, however, dropped from 45 percent (winter) to 24 percent (summer), probably because they made greater use of leaf nests during summer.

On four occasions, we observed wood ducks dislodge fox squirrels from cavities that the squirrels had used through the winter. A number of visits by cavity-seeking wood ducks, with the females poking their heads through the entrances and presumably hissing at the squirrels, were required to dislodge the squirrels. A hen wood duck caused a squirrel to abandon a den site in 1981, but the following year the fox squirrel refused to budge, even though a pair of wood ducks continued their eviction efforts for several days.

Occasionally, the contest for nest sites between squirrels and wood ducks leads to fatal results for the latter. We found two dead hens, with head wounds and fox squirrel hair in their bills, in wooden nest houses. Ray Cunningham of St. Paul, Minnesota, found a freshly killed female in a nest house occupied by a gray squirrel and her young. The wood duck's head wounds indicated that death probably had occurred from the gray squirrel's bite. A fully formed egg was removed from her oviduct. Cunningham also has witnessed several gray squirrels with litters attack hens prospecting for nest sites, but the hens had not entered the nest houses.

Table 129. Percentage use of potential wood duck natural cavities during spring and early summer by various animals.

Region	Number of cavities	Fox and gray squirrel	Flying squirrel	Raccoon	Opossum
Central Illinois	251	0.4	0.0	4.4	0.8
	249	2.0	0.4	12.0	0.4
	110	3.3	0.9	8.0	0.5
Southeastern Missouri	109	45.0	0.0	25.7	0.0
Eastcentral Michigan	90	15.6	0.0	13.3	0.0
Southcentral Indiana	157	23.6	0.6		
Westcentral Mississippi	23	43.5	0.0	34.8	0.0
Westcentral Minnesota	411	21.0		15.0	

[a] Mostly barred owl.
[b] Pileated woodpecker.

After observing a hen perched in the entrance of a wood duck house for many minutes, Cunningham investigated to find three eggs where the day before there had been a gray squirrel litter. In the interim, the litter had been moved to another site. Breckenridge (1947) reported that an attacking red squirrel was repulsed by a female wood duck while perched on a limb near a nest cavity that she later occupied.

Tom Jones of Fulton, Illinois, observed in April 1992 a hen wood duck enter a nest house without preliminary inspection. The house, in his yard, was occupied by a fox squirrel, but it had been used by a wood duck the previous year. When the hen did not reappear, he examined the house later in the day. Jones found the wood duck dead, bitten through the neck, and the litter removed by the mother squirrel. It is assumed that the killed hen had nested there previously and, because of familiarity, did not take the customary precaution of first inspecting the interior of the house cavity.

Although squirrels and wood ducks may compete for the same sites, squirrels are nonetheless beneficial because they create and improve nest sites for wood ducks. Fox squirrels often create optimal entrances for wood ducks and make unusable cavities suitable by plugging hollow trunks and limbs and providing pathways to heartrot fungi (Baumgartner 1940, Weier 1966).

Raccoons prefer larger cavities, though they often use nest cavities suitable for wood ducks, especially in the South. Lowney (1987) found raccoons using 35 percent (n = 8) of the suitable wood duck cavities he discovered in Mississippi. In contrast, Robb (1986) suspected that use in Indiana probably was limited to raccoons foraging for duck eggs. On one occasion, we found evidence that a wood duck hen had been killed as she inspected a cavity occupied by a raccoon. As in the case of the fox squirrel episode, the hen's customary caution in peering into cavities numerous times before entering is entirely warranted.

Although starlings were not found nesting in the cavities studied by the investigators listed in Table 129, they have been found in smaller cavities. In a study of natural cavities in woodlots used by wood ducks, Shake (1967) found that every cavity

Gray squirrels (above) and fox squirrels compete with wood ducks for den sites but also create cavities, some sufficiently large for wood ducks to use as nest sites. Squirrels frequently gnaw holes through sapwood of trees to open hollows formed by decay in heartwood. They also keep cavities open by gnawing at holes closing in from seasonal cambium growth. *Photo by F. Eugene Hester.*

Table 129. (continued)

Owl[a]	Other birds	Bees	Reference
1.2	0.0	0.4	Johnson (1959)
3.2	0.0	0.4	Meyers (1962)
0.0	0.0	0.9	Shake (1967)
0.9	1.8[b]	0.0	Weier (1966)
0.0	0.0	0.0	Boyer (1975a)
0.0	1.9	0.0	Robb (1986)
0.0	17.4	4.3	Lowney (1987)
	4.0		Nagel (1969)

(n = 28) with an entrance smaller than 7.1 centimeters (2.8 in) was being used by starlings, but he found only wood ducks using cavities with entrances larger than 8.1 centimeters (3.2 in) in diameter. At another study area encompassing woods within a 4.8-kilometer (3 mi) radius of Macomb, Illinois, Shake (1967) found starlings using 48 percent of 102 cavities. The largest entrance used by starlings was 8.4 centimeters (3.3 in) in diameter; 13 cavities with larger entrances were not used.

A subsequent study of natural cavities and their use by starlings within the city limits of Macomb, Illinois, disclosed a broader acceptance of large entrances (Pace 1971). Pace found 23.4 percent of 141 cavities occupied by starlings, including 16.2 percent with entrances larger than 8.4 centimeters (3.3 in).

In breeding studies in westcentral Illinois, Baima (1971) reported that starlings selected nest sites in areas associated with human activity and where parklike habitats prevailed. Surprisingly, the development of foliage in a heavily wooded tract resulted in starlings deserting every nest.

Studies on the starling/wood duck relationship in central and westcentral Illinois make clear that where natural cavities with large entrances are available or where dense woods occur, starlings were not an important cavity competitor. Nevertheless, in optimum breeding habitats for starlings, compounded by a paucity of small cavities, starlings may be a competitor for natural cavities needed by wood ducks.

COMPETITION FOR NEST HOUSES

The use by other animals of wood duck nest houses is at quite different levels than is their use of natural cavities. Differences can be attributed to nest house visibility, density of placement, and the design or placement of nest houses to reduce availability to arboreal mammals.

Table 130 lists principal occupants of nest houses erected primarily for wood ducks. In the early studies by Brown and Bellrose (1943), Bryan (1945, 1946), Frank (1948), Klein (1955), and Lee (1953, 1954, 1956), nest houses were constructed of wood and were essentially as available to mammals and birds as were natural cavities. Fox and gray squirrels and raccoons utilized these houses as dens. More use was made of these houses in winter than during other seasons (Brown and Bellrose 1943). Fiedler (1967) reported that squirrels had winter dens in 70 percent of the nest boxes that he studied in Morrison County, Minnesota, yet only 10 percent were occupied during the wood duck nesting season. Because of the proclivity of squirrels to build leaf nests in these early wood duck houses, the annual removal of squirrel leaf nests prior to the wood duck nesting season was an important maintenance measure.

As the construction and erection of wood duck houses progressed, researchers and managers began making it more difficult for arboreal mammals to enter. In more recent times, therefore, the use of nest houses by squirrels and raccoons has diminished, as is evident in the metal houses that we employed on Quiver Creek and the duplex houses we placed on pipes at Nauvoo Slough, Illinois (Table 130).

Where apiaries are numerous, swarms of honey bees breaking away from their established hives may select wood duck houses to start new colonies. This is especially a problem in California because of that state's extensive apiary industry. Metal nest houses are less prone to attract bees than are wood houses. *Photo by James Leasch; courtesy of the California Waterfowl Association.*

Ecology and Management of the Wood Duck*

Table 130. Percentage use of wood duck nest houses by various animals during spring and early summer.

State	Years	Number of houses	Fox/gray/ flying squirrels	Raccoon/ opossum	Hooded merganser	Starling	Flicker	Tree swallow
Maine		2,081			22.7			
New Hampshire	1953-58	1,850	2.5	8.3	5.6	1.8	0.1	9.1
New York	1953	129	4.5	2.3		10.8		11.6
Connecticut	1944–46	197	51.5					
Michigan	1972–73	54		1.9		7.4		1.9
Minnesota	1964–75	668	10.0		6.3	8.5	0.7	
Wisconsin	1982–84	759	tr		10.9	46.5		12.0
Iowa	1967–87	2,875[a]	0.4	0.5	0.3	5.0	0.6	7.4
Ohio	1955–57	977	6.7	0.2	0.1	12.8		1.0
Illinois	1939–41	2,107[b]	2.7	0.6			0.2	
Central Illinois	1956–74	3,148[c]	0.1			11.5	0.4	
Western Illinois	1984–87	241[d]				31.5	1.2	
Mississippi	1968–69	309	1.3		10.0	5.8		
Alabama	1941–42	196	50.0	15.8				
	1961–69	657	16.4	8.4	0.1	1.1	3.0	
Louisiana	1951–61	1,229	5.3	0.6				
	1978–79	898	0.4		0.2			
Texas	1984–85	277	4.0					
California	1952–56	388					2.8	2.1

[a] Metal and plastic nest houses with elliptical entrances, on trees and pipes adjacent to water.
[b] Board nest houses with no predator devices.
[c] Metal houses with conical tops and elliptical entrances, on trees.
[d] Board duplex nest houses with elliptical entrances, on pipes.

A shortage of natural cavities is evident in many areas, and a number of cavity-nesting wildlife species are attracted to wood duck houses. Mammals commonly found denning in nest cavities and houses include fox, gray, and flying squirrels, raccoons, opossums, and deer mice. American kestrels, starlings, tree swallows, screech-owls (above), great crested flycatchers, flickers, grackles, red-winged blackbirds, and bluebirds are some of the birds most frequently reported to occupy wood duck houses. Screech-owls appear to be innocuous with respect to breeding wood ducks. Although they use nest houses extensively, nowhere are these owls abundant enough to reduce materially the availability of nest sites for woodies. *Photo by Frederic Leopold; courtesy of the Starr's Cave Nature Center (Burlington, Iowa).*

With the exception of a horizontal pipe house developed by McGilvrey and Uhler (1971), most houses do not inhibit use by birds (tables 130 and 131). Use of wood duck houses by tree swallows, great crested flycatchers, screech-owls, kestrels, and hooded mergansers is generally viewed favorably by wildlife managers. However, wood ducks have been known to evict all of these species from nest houses, except for some kestrels and hooded mergansers.

In a strange change from their customary nest sites, common grackles have been found nesting in wood duck houses. Several refuges, particularly in the northeastern states (Table 131) reported grackles occupying nest houses. Baker (1971), Lumpkin (1972), Nero (1957), and Spero and Pitts (1984) also found grackles nesting in wood duck houses. At Smith's Lake in Mason County, Illinois, in 1982, we found four red-winged blackbird nests in wood duck houses on posts in the water and six grackle nests in houses placed in adjacent shoreline trees.

Information in tables 130 and 131 points to the starling as the bird species that occupies substantial numbers of wood duck houses. Because of their aggressiveness, starlings can oust wood ducks from established nests. If the ducks are in the process of establishing nesting sites, starlings may harass nest-seeking females until they are driven to nest

Table 130. (continued)

Kestrel	Owls	Other birds	Source
			Spencer et al. (1980)
			Lee (1954–56)
			Lacaillade (1958)
1.6	3.9		Klein (1955)
	3.6		Frank (1948)
		7.4	Boyer (1975a)
6.3	0.6		Fiedler (1967)
tr			Soulliere (1985)
0.6	1.0	3.8	Glen Welp
0.2	9.2	1.3	Stewart (1957)
0.1	2.1	0.4	Brown and Bellrose (1943)
1.1	4.9		This study
			This study
0.3	0.6	21.0	Baker (1971)
	2.6		Bryan (1945, 1946)
	0.8	7.8	Beshears (1970)
0.3	1.9	0.8	M. M. Smith (1961)
	1.6	5.8	Moore (1981)
	1.4	6.9	May (1986)
7.0	26.5	2.3	Naylor (1960)

elsewhere. In these instances, wood ducks may be coerced to nest in natural cavities that are at higher risk from predation than are nests in houses.

Other cavity-nesting duck species include black-bellied whistling duck, bufflehead, Barrow's goldeneye, common goldeneye (left), common merganser, and hooded merganser (top right and bottom right). Only the latter provides some degree of competition for wood duck nest sites in natural cavities and nest houses. The other four species primarily nest north of the woodies' breeding range and select for somewhat different cavity characteristics than those preferred by woodies. The hooded merganser selects for essentially the same characteristics as does the wood duck but is not particularly abundant where the two species' breeding ranges overlap. Where competition occurs, it is not serious. Note, at bottom, the hen hooded merganser's approach to the nest house by a leap from water. This is a highly unusual maneuver for that species. *Left photo courtesy of the Wildlife Management Institute. Top right and bottom right photos by Don Helmeke.*

Table 131. Use of wood duck houses by various animals on national wildlife refuges.

State	Refuge	Years	Squirrel	Hooded merganser	Starling	Grackle	Woodpecker
Vermont	Missisquoi	1957–79		X[a]			
New York	Montezuma	1978–79			X	X	
	Iroquois	1979		X		X	
	Morton	1979			X		
Massachusetts	Great Meadows	1979–80					
	Parker River	1979			X		
Pennsylvania	Erie	1977–79			X	X	
	Tinicum	1979			X		
New Jersey	Great Swamp	1979			X		
Virginia	Presquille	1979			X		
	Chincoteague	1979			X		
	Back Bay	1979			X		
	Mackay Island	1970–78	X				
Maryland	Blackwater	1971–79			X		
	Eastern Neck	1970–75			X		
Delaware	Bombay Hook	1979			X		
North Carolina	Pungo	1979			X		
South Carolina	Santee	1979					
Georgia	Savannah	1977–78			X		
	Piedmont	1979		X			
Florida	St. Marks	1979	X				
	Lake Woodruff	1978–80					X
	Merritt Island	1977–80					
Alabama	Eufaula	1975–76			X		
Minnesota	Tamarac	1979	X				
	Fergus Falls	1979	X		X		
	Big Stone	1973–78		X			
Michigan	Seney	1974–79	X	X[a]	X		X
Wisconsin	Necedah	1979		X			
Iowa	Union Slough	1984–86	X	X	X	X	
	Mark Twain	1950–79	X	X			
Ohio	Ottawa	1979			X		
Illinois	Upper Miss.	1975–78	X	X			
	Mark Twain	1969–79	X		X		
	Chautauqua	1958–70			X		
	Meredosia	1978–79			X		
Indiana	Muscatatuck	1978–79			X		
Missouri	Mingo	1975–81		X			
Tennessee	Cross Creek	1979					
	Reelfoot Lake	1974–79					
	Hatchie	1967–79	X	X			
Mississippi	Hillside	1979			X		
Arkansas	White River	1970–80		X			
	Wapanocca	1979					
Louisiana	Catahoula	1979					
Montana	Lee Metcalf	1978–79			X		
Idaho	Grays Lake			X[a]			
	Kootenai	1979		X	X		
Washington	Ridgefield	1979			X		
	Willapa	1979			X		
	Conboy Lake	1979			X		
	Columbia	1977–80			X		
	Cold Spring	1969–72			X		
	Toppenish	1979					
Oregon	Finley	1968–79					
California	Klamath	1963–79		X			
	Sacramento	1978					
Nevada	Stillwater	1968–70		X			

[a] Includes common goldeneye nests.

Table 131. (continued)

Tree swallow	Screech-owl	Kestrel	Flicker	Wren
X				
	X			
	X			
X				
	X			
	X			
	X			
	X			
X		X		
	X			
X	X	X		
	X			
X	X			
	X			
	X			
	X		X	
			X	
				X
X				
		X		
		X	X	
		X		
		X		
		X		
	X			
	X			
	X	X	X	
	X	X		

Flickers occasionally nest in wood duck nest houses and may excavate additional entrance holes in wooden boxes. In at least one instance in California, a red-shafted flicker drilled a hole sufficiently large in the bottom of a nest house for all the wood duck eggs to fall out. *Photo by Greg R. Hubbard; nest house provided by Stephen Simmons.*

Starling Competition

Starlings occur throughout the breeding range of the wood duck and consequently are potential competitors everywhere for nest sites. When starlings take possession of nest sites from wood ducks, they may inflict tiny punctures in the eggshells that are much smaller than those made by woodpeckers. The wood duck eggs remain intact as the starling builds its bulky grass nest over them. The sheer volume of material placed over wood duck eggs by starlings during egg laying is sufficient cause for many hen wood ducks to desert. During incubation, woodie hens usually are not off their nests long enough for starlings to add a layer of material over the eggs. In most takeovers by starlings during laying, wood duck eggs are buried under 3–13 centimeters (1–5 in) of grass and other coarse materials; sometimes such nests include incubated clutches. We have never known starlings to consume any of the egg contents, as woodpeckers are prone to do.

As noted earlier, starlings do not pose a problem to wood ducks nesting in natural cavities. For the most part, starlings are content to seek small cavities that wood ducks are unable to use; however, starlings are attracted to wood duck houses.

Usurpation of wood duck nests by nesting starlings poses the greatest overall problem to the enhancement of wood duck breeding populations using nest houses. Because wood ducks are away from their nests for most of the day during the egg-laying period, starlings often succeed in building their large, bulky grass nests on top of woodie clutches. When this happens, wood ducks may stop laying in those cavities because starlings can be aggressive in guarding their nest sites. Starlings have fewer opportunities to build nests over woodie clutches that are being incubated because hen woodies remain on their nests for most of the day during incubation. *Photo by Dan Holm; courtesy of the Illinois Natural History Survey.*

The starling's penchant for these houses all too frequently results in the usurpation of occupied houses. Continued harassment by starlings causes wood ducks to desert nests from preincubation to near hatching.

The aggressiveness of individual starlings and wood ducks differs. At times, wood ducks have rebuffed the efforts of starlings to dislodge them. Indeed, occasionally we have found wood ducks that have taken over starling nests. Part of the variation in starling aggressiveness is explained by the phase of its breeding cycle. Kessel (1957) observed that early in the breeding season, starlings were aggressive in evicting other birds and in fighting among themselves for control of nest sites. However, once settled in its small territory—the entrance and a radius of 25–51 centimeters (10–20 in) around it—the starling becomes tolerant of other species and other conspecifics. Kessel (1957) cited three

observers: one reported three pairs of starlings, one red-headed woodpecker, and a kestrel nesting in the same tree; another found a starling, a red-headed woodpecker, and a flicker nesting in a single telephone pole; and the third recorded four woodpecker holes all within 1.8 meters (6 ft) in a dead tree containing the nests of two starlings, one house wren, and a kestrel. Thus, wood ducks may be able to oust starlings after the territorial establishment of the starlings has been resolved and they are in a phase of breeding activity with reduced aggressiveness.

Bellrose has watched starlings attack wood ducks numerous times in the trees about his home. Starlings customarily fly to a branch or to the top of a nest house where a wood duck female or pair is perched. They then jab with their rapierlike bills at the larger birds in an effort to displace them. If not successful, starlings may try hovering about the wood ducks, squawking shrill notes. When a female wood duck enters a nest site, a starling may follow, but we do not know what confrontations ensue. When starlings perch within nest houses with their heads out, most wood ducks do not attempt to enter.

Bellrose saw a starling come to blows with a female woodie that was on a short flight from an inspection perch to a natural cavity. In a flash, a starling that had been harassing the perched female flew to her back and pecked at her head with such rapidity that she plummeted 6 meters (20 ft) to the ground. The hen was obviously stunned, but first her tail waggled, then she stood erect, and moments later when a dog passed, she flew.

Occasionally, an aggressive wood duck hen evicts a starling from a nest house or uses a nest that a starling has abandoned. Above, a wood duck has used a former starling nest to cover her eggs prior to incubation; the paucity of down indicates either a dump nest or late-season nest. *Photo by Jack Dermid.*

Hartman (1972) reported a similar incident. A female flying from the water in front of a nest house toward the entrance was struck by two starlings, causing the hen to land, when she was struck a second time. The pair of starlings left along with a companion pair. Hartman also observed a starling pull feathers from a hen in flight to a nest house. Carpenter (1953) reported a starling attack on a perched hen in which the starling grabbed the hen's head, resulting in the flight of the hen when the antagonist persisted.

An aggressive starling, usually the male, is more than a match for the relatively docile wood duck. Our analysis, however, of starling/wood duck use of nest houses on the Quiver Creek study area, 1963–1974, showed that starlings selected vacant houses (45.5 percent, n = 879) over those already occupied by wood ducks (9.5 percent, n = 2,614, P < 0.001). This significant difference in selection by starlings suggests that they choose vacant sites when these are available rather than enter into conflicts with wood ducks.

An analysis of starling use of metal houses grouped in 13 units along Quiver Creek, 1959–1974, provided information on the starling's choice of nesting habitats (Table 132). Starlings occupied houses at statistically different rates on these units. A subjective arrangement based on tree density and distance to fields suggests three degrees of selectivity: (1) the lowest use by starlings (units 13 and 1) occurred where trees were densest and field borders farthest away; (2) the highest use (units 3, 4, and 6) occurred where trees were more open and

field borders nearer; and (3) the others fell in between in tree density, distance to the nearest fields, or both. Use of these units of houses by starlings indicates that the denser the woods and the greater the distance to open areas, the less likely that starlings will occupy nest houses. Units 2 and 3 had the highest densities of breeding wood ducks, but a considerable difference between them existed in terms of starling use.

Data from nest houses in Mason County, as reported by Shake (1967), disclosed starling occupancy as 90.6 percent (95-percent C.L. = 79.0–102.3) in open woods, compared with 40 percent (95-percent C.L. = 4.6–75.4) in closed woods. This is further evidence of the importance of tree density as a limiting factor to starling use of natural and artificial nest cavities. The high acceptance of nest houses by starlings poses one of the most pressing problems in the employment of nest houses in wood duck management.

Starling Nesting Chronology

Throughout most of the United States, there is an interval of about 70 days from the time of first nesting by starlings to the latest initiation of second nesting by those that produce two broods (Table 133) (Kessel 1957). A cline in the temporal pattern in initiation of egg laying begins March 15 in the South and progresses to May 15 in the North, where usually only one brood is reared.

Prior to nesting, the male starling takes possession of a potential nest site and brings in a small amount of nest material (Kessel 1957). His attachment to a particular site extends back to early autumn and includes roosting in the nest cavity after November (Kessel 1957, Lombardo et al. 1989). With the attraction of a female, nest building is begun at a leisurely pace until two to three days before laying, when large amounts of material are added.

Table 132. Use of metal wood duck houses by starlings on 13 units arranged by decreasing density of trees and decreasing distance to farm fields on the Quiver Creek area, Illinois, 1959–77.

Unit number	Number of house-years[a]	Percentage used	95% C.L.[b]
13	247	5.3	2.3–8.3
1	766	11.9	9.5–14.2
2	785	16.2	13.5–18.8
12	121	17.4	10.2–24.5
9	149	15.4	9.3–21.6
10	137	16.1	9.5–22.6
5	153	24.8	17.7–32.0
11	197	23.4	17.2–29.5
7	311	33.1	27.7–38.5
8	132	31.1	22.8–39.3
3	264	34.5	28.5–40.4
6	150	34.0	26.1–41.9
4	125	76.8	69.0–84.6

[a] Number of houses times the number of years available.
[b] $x^2 = 399$, P < 0.011
  linear regression: y = −0.63 + 3.83x, r = 0.84, P < 0.001

Table 133. Temporal nesting of starlings by latitude for first and second nestings in North America.[a]

Degrees latitude	First nesting	Second nesting
30–35	March 15–April 5	April 30–May 25
35–40	April 1–April 13	May 21–June 1
40–45	April 11–April 28	June 1–June 20
45–48	April 28–May 19	June 10–June 28
48–50	May 15–June 7	None
>50	June 15	None

[a] Data from Kessel (1957).

Because of their prolonged attachment to a cavity prior to laying, starlings may take over a wood duck house before the wood ducks start laying eggs. We found starling nests in wood duck houses from late March to late June (Figure 81). Over much of their range, nest building by starlings overlaps most of the period of egg laying by wood ducks.

Starling Nest Box Site Preference

We and other researchers have made numerous attempts to develop nest houses that would deter starlings, including altering house dimensions, adding windows or skylights, using dyed base materials, changing the axis of the nest house, and providing starling houses adjacent to wood duck houses. Our experiments with nest houses in three diameters—25, 30, and 36 centimeters (10, 12, and 14 in)—disclosed that starlings preferred the smaller sizes (Table 134).

Nault (1981) evaluated eight variables (seven of which concerned placement) as they affected starling use of wood duck houses on the Chautauqua National Wildlife Refuge. None of the placement variables had a significant influence on use of houses by starlings. Nault tested houses with three diameters—23, 25, and 30 centimeters (9, 10, and 12 in)—and found that starlings preferred ($P < 0.01$) 23-centimeter (9 in) diameter houses to the two larger sizes. Large entrances also deterred starlings (Shake 1967) but permitted raccoons to enter. Grice and Rogers (1965) reported that attaching tunnel guards as an extension to entrances of wood duck houses reduced raccoon depredation but increased starling use. We tested the preferences for cavity depths reported by Shake (1967) and found that starlings shunned cavities less than 25 centimeters (10 in) deep and preferred those 51–76 centimeters (20–30 in)—but so did wood ducks.

To determine if color affected use by starlings, we used sawdust dyed red, green, and blue as bases for wood duck nests. Houses with natural sawdust were used at a rate of 5.9 percent, red 19.6, green 21.4, and blue 40.9 percent ($P < 0.005$); the darker the color, the more desirable starlings found the substrate.

A radical change in the design of wood duck houses was submitted by McGilvrey and Uhler (1971) as a means to reduce use by starlings. Their house consisted of a horizontally mounted metal cylinder 30 centimeters (12 in) in diameter and 61 centimeters (24 in) long. Wooden ends filled one opening but only half covered the other, providing a large semicircular entrance. Starlings used only 5 percent of 944 house-years available; wood ducks

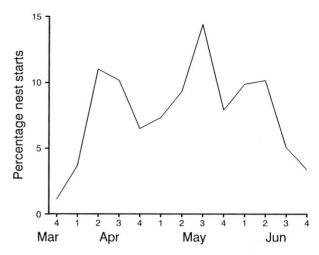

Figure 81. Temporal distribution of 354 starling nests in wood duck houses, 1959–67, Quiver Creek, Illinois.

used 33.4 percent. In standard vertical metal nest houses, starlings used 46 percent of 70 house-years; wood ducks used 38.6 percent.

Heusmann et al. (1977) tested horizontal cylinders against standard vertical wooden houses in Massachusetts. They found no starling nests in the horizontal cylinders. Wood duck use of 297 cylinder house-years was 31.6 percent; nest success was 73.4 percent. The use of 1,108 wooden vertical house-years by wood ducks was 48.5 percent; nest success was 77.1 percent. No statistical difference was found between wood duck use of the two structures. Heusmann et al. (1977) felt that some of the success of cylinder houses in Massachusetts might have been due to an expanding wood duck population with large numbers of pioneering yearlings. They noted that use of cylinders by wood ducks occurred later in the nesting season than did the use of board houses, an indication that substantial numbers of yearlings were involved.

A wood duck population at a lower density and reduced expansion rate may explain the comparatively lower use of cylinder nest houses in eastern Tennessee (Muncy and Burbank 1975). Horizontal

Table 134. Effect of house diameter on starling nest occupancy of metal cylindrical wood duck houses, central Illinois, 1962–77.

House diameter in centimeters (in)	Number	Percentage occupied	95% C.L.[a]
25.4 (10)	575	36.9	32.8–40.9
30.5 (12)	3,613	25.0	23.6–26.5
35.6 (14)	499	15.0	11.8–18.3

[a] $x^2 = 68.5$, $P < 0.005$.

cylinder houses were used by wood ducks at a rate of 11.3 percent, compared with 33.3 percent for board houses and 32.9 percent for vertical metal houses. Starlings occupied cylinder houses at a rate of 3 percent, compared with 39.5 for board houses and 30.5 percent for vertical metal houses.

Data from these three studies support the premise that starlings use horizontal cylinder houses at a lower rate compared with that for other types of wood duck nest houses. Cylinder houses, however, do not appear as acceptable to wood ducks as are the more standard types, especially where wood duck breeding densities are low or stable.

McGilvrey and Uhler (1971) speculated that starlings found horizontal cylinder houses less desirable because of the additional light that reached the nest area. Along with Heusmann and Bellville (1982), we followed up on this suggestion and incorporated windows in the more standard houses. Heusmann and Bellville (1982) used windows as skylights in the lids of board houses; they found 40 percent of the skylight houses occupied by starlings compared with 78 percent of those with solid lids (P<0.01). Wood ducks were not deterred by skylights; house use was similar to that of standard ones.

We experimented with windows of Plexiglas placed in the body of vertical metal houses, but this design failed to reduce nest house use by starlings appreciably. Wood ducks used these houses to the same degree as they used houses without windows.

On his farm near Amissville, Virginia, Captain William Keim found that wood duck use of 30 standard nest houses declined from 80 percent to 10

percent, 1984–1987. During this period, starlings occupied up to 89 percent of the nest houses. In an attempt to reduce the number of starlings nesting in the houses, Keim enlarged the opening of several wooden boxes to 10.6 centimeters (4 in) vertical and 28 centimeters (11 in) horizontal. Houses with an enlarged entrance were not used by starlings in 1988 and 1989; they received average use by wood ducks.

At Dulles International Airport in northern Virginia, just west of Washington, D.C., Richard C. Cullerton documented an increased use of wood duck nests in houses from 0 in 1983 to 82 in 1990; starlings occupied a substantial number of houses from 1985 to 1989 (Table 135). At the suggestion of William Keim, Cullerton enlarged the entrances in a similar fashion for a portion of his houses. Apparently because of greater starling breeding pressure, there was little reduction in starling occupancy of nest houses with rectangular entrances (Table 135). Arboreal predators were kept at bay in these houses with large entrances because they were attached to pipes and placed in ponds.

Grabill (1977) tried a different approach. He placed nest houses specifically designed for starlings adjacent to standard board houses on posts at Pungo National Wildlife Refuge in North Carolina. During 1973–1975, 39.9 percent of 317 standard houses were occupied by starlings, whereas they used only 20.7 percent of 82 wood duck houses with adjacent houses tailored for their nesting. Wood duck use was higher (64.6 percent) in houses with attached starling compartments than in conventional houses (40.4 percent), indicating that starling competition for wood duck nest houses was reduced. Of the 82 starling nest houses, 93.9 percent were occupied by that target species.

Table 135. Percentage use of conventional wood duck houses with two types of entrances at Dulles International Airport, northern Virginia.[a]

Year	Circular entrance				Large rectangular entrance[b]			
	Number of houses	Wood duck	Starling	Both species	Number of houses	Wood duck	Starling	Both species
1983	8							
1984	20							
1985	39	10.3	33.3					
1986	39	23.1	30.8					
1987	40	52.5	20.0					
1988	28	64.3	50.0	43.0	10	70.0	50.0	30.0
1989	21	80.9	52.4	54.5	17	70.6	41.2	41.2
1990	22	81.8	13.6	0.0	16	62.5	6.3	0.0
1988–90	71	75.7[c]	38.7[d]	48.8	43	67.7	32.5	23.7

[a] Data provided by Captain Richard C. Cullerton, Washington, D.C. Airport Authority.
[b] 10.16 centimeters (4 in) vertical and 30.48 centimeters (12 in) horizontal.
[c] Wood duck use circular versus rectangular: t=0.92>0.10.
[d] Starling use circular versus rectangular: t=0.677>0.10.

As pointed out by Heusmann and Bellville (1978), the periodic removal of active starling nests from wood duck houses may eventually reduce their occupation by starlings because the production of young is reduced. According to Kessel (1957), starlings return to nest at or close to the sites used the previous year. Because adult starlings experience a 50-percent annual mortality (Kessel 1957), the lack of production of young would rapidly diminish local breeding populations. Only pioneers nesting for the first time might invade sites where production previously had been curtailed, but unfortunately there seems to be a large "floating" population that periodically appears at sites of wood duck nest houses.

We found starlings to be very persistent rebuilders of discarded nests within a breeding season. After removing preincubation nests, we have observed starlings carrying in new nesting materials within five minutes. Nests that we removed at Nauvoo Slough were rebuilt the following week in the same or adjacent compartments. Nests that contained advanced incubated eggs or young, once removed, were more likely to be deserted than were less advanced nests that were removed. Late in the breeding season, sites were invariably deserted after nests had been removed.

NEST PREDATORS

Predation takes a heavy toll of wood duck nests in natural cavities (see Table 118). Raccoons, squirrels, and snakes are all important predators, but their impact varies from place to place. A review of the literature helped us to identify species and places where agents of destruction are an important factor (tables 136 and 137). In early studies—in some cases extending to the late 1950s—few houses were protected from predators other than those placed on posts in water. Since that time, wildlife managers have employed various devices to impede access to the nest cavity by climbing animals and to reduce cavity attractiveness to starlings. The data in Table 136 embrace findings from both periods. Although the predation of wood duck nests in houses has been reduced, data in tables 136 and 137 indicate that predation remains a problem. The effectiveness of various predator-inhibiting devices is discussed in chapters 10 and 19.

Table 136. Destruction of wood duck nests in houses by various predators.

State	Years	Total nests	Raccoon		Squirrels		Other mammals	Starlings		Woodpeckers	
New Hampshire	1953–58	568	75	(13.2)							
Connecticut	1953–62	4,102	69	(1.7)							
New York		30	6	(20.0)							
Pennsylvania	1953–56	95	35	(36.8)						9	(9.5)
New Jersey	1975–76	393	40	(10.2)				42	(10.7)		
Maryland	1963–72	50					tr				
North Carolina	1954–68	822	70	(8.5)	2	(0.24)		40	(4.9)		
South Carolina	1974–75	50									
Georgia	1969	60									
Minnesota	1964–75	265	13	(4.9)	8	(3.0)	1 (0.4)	1	(0.4)	3	(1.1)
Ohio	1956–57	44	1	(2.3)				3	(6.8)		
Illinois	1939–45	1,579	303	(19.2)	418	(26.5)	18 (1.2)			27	(1.7)
Missouri	1961–62	68	29	(42.6)						7	(5.9)
	1966–70	438	20	(4.6)				19	(4.3)		
	1970–71	235						41	(17.4)		
Kentucky	1970–71	8	3	(37.5)							
Mississippi	1966–68	496	3	(0.6)						65	(13.1)
	1968–69	126								3	(2.4)
	1969–73	1,747	89	(5.1)						219	(12.5)
	1976–77	159	51	(32.1)						106	(6.1)
Louisiana	1951–61	416	3	(0.7)						19	(4.6)
	1970–72	79	28	(35.4)	1	(1.3)					
	1976–77	419								2	(0.5)
	1978–79	761	3	(0.4)						20	(2.6)
Texas	1984–85	79									
Oregon	1965–67	202	15	(7.4)							

Raccoons

Throughout the wood duck's range, the raccoon has been most frequently identified as the predator having the greatest impact on egg clutches and incubating hens. In raiding 51 nests in natural cavities, raccoons killed six incubating birds (12 percent) (Bellrose et al. 1964); one additional bird was killed inspecting a cavity. Occasionally, a raccoon seeking entrance would excite the woodie female into attempting to flee and grab her by the head at the entrance but, unable to extract her body, leave it headless in the nest.

At Muscatatuck National Wildlife Refuge in Indiana, Robb (1986) reported that raccoons accounted for 68.1 percent (n = 15) of all wood duck nests destroyed in natural cavities; 13.6 percent (n = 3) of these also represented the loss of incubating females. Hansen (1971) found 2 of 10 nests in natural cavities destroyed by raccoons; one incubating female had been killed. Haramis (1975) reported that raccoon nest predation was common in tree cavities at the Montezuma National Wildlife Refuge in New York but absent from predator-proof nest houses.

Table 136. (continued)

Other birds		Snakes		Reference
				Lee (1953, 1954, 1955)
				Beckley (1965)
				Klein (1955)
				Decker (1959)
				Zipko (1979)
1	(2.0)	tr		McGilvrey (1975)
		31	(3.8)	Stephenson (1970)
		1	(2.0)	Luckett (1977)
		3	(5.0)	Odom (1970)
4	(1.5)			Fiedler (1967)
				Stewart (1957)
27	(1.7)	82	(5.2)	Bellrose et al. (1964)
		2	(2.9)	Hartowicz (1963)
		111	(25.3)	Hansen (1971)
		3	(1.3)	Clawson (1975a)
				Allen (1972)
		8	(1.6)	Cunningham (1968)
		4	(3.2)	Baker (1971)
		58	(3.3)	Strong (1973)
		28	(1.6)	Landin (1977)
		87	(20.9)	M. M. Smith (1961)
		15	(19.0)	Louisiana Tech Wildlife Club (1972)
		7	(1.7)	Davis (1978)
		25	(3.3)	Moore (1981)
1	(1.3)	17	(21.5)	May (1986)
				Morse and Wight (1969)

Raccoons killed 102 incubating hens in destroying 304 nests (33.6 percent) in unprotected board nest houses in central Illinois (Bellrose et al. 1964). As shown in Table 136 (excluding data from central Illinois), raccoons depredated 553 wood duck nests and killed 21 hens (3.8 percent) in the process. No other animal poses such a lethal threat to incubating wood ducks as does the raccoon.

Raccoons are among the most ingenious of all native mammals. In our early years of developing houses to exclude them, we consistently underestimated their capabilities and resourcefulness. By chewing, they enlarged entrances in wood houses that were too small for access. If bands of metal encircling tree trunks were too narrow or a break in the surface afforded a toe hole, they climbed over. If a shrub or vine or adjacent tree was close, they climbed it and jumped the hurdle. In 1983 at Nauvoo Slough we found a raccoon getting over conical guards around posts by using limber willow branches that bent with the animal's weight to place it either on or above the guards. We discovered that one raccoon apparently gained entrance to metal houses by shaking the conical tops so violently that some of the metal screws popped out. We could follow its behavior through a wooded tract as it endeavored to repeat, with varying results, its earlier success.

At Oquawka, Illinois, Delbert Koke reported that a raccoon killed an incubating female after unhooking the lid of a wood house with a standard elliptical entrance. The following year, Koke attached the lid with larger hooks and eyes that fit so tightly he had difficulty prying the hooks from the eyes; thereafter raccoons were unable to enter. A raccoon, however, frightened an incubating wood duck into attempting to leave and beheaded her at the entrance so that her torso fell back into the house. A year later, the scenario was repeated at another house. This time, the raccoon was live-trapped and removed, bringing to an end this modus operandi.

Ray Cunningham of St. Paul, Minnesota, lost three female wood ducks in one night (May 22, 1968), even though they were in houses with elliptical entrances. He deduced that raccoons reached in and grabbed the females, perhaps frightening them into attempting to flee. Fiedler (1967) noted that raccoons in central Minnesota entered 11 of 668 houses (1.6 percent) and killed three females; an additional two houses with nests were torn from trees by raccoons and destroyed. At Fort Lewis, Washington, Beall et al. (1984) found small raccoons entering houses with elliptical openings.

Raccoons follow the well-known Bergman's Rule, which stipulates that mammals increase in

Table 137. Principal losses of nests in wood duck houses on some national wildlife refuges.

State	Refuge	Years	Raccoon	Squirrel	Snake	Starling	Woodpecker	Flooding
Vermont	Missisquoi	1957–79						
New York	Montezuma	1978–79				X		
	Iroquois	1979						
	Morton	1979	X					
Massachusetts	Parker River	1979				X		
Pennsylvania	Erie	1977–79						
New Jersey	Great Swamp	1979				X		
Virginia	Presquille	1979				X		
	Chincoteague	1979			X	X		
	Mackay Island	1970–78						
Maryland	Blackwater	1971–79						
	Eastern Neck	1970–75	X					
Delaware	Bombay Hook	1979				X		
North Carolina	Pungo	1979			X	X		
South Carolina	Santee	1979						
	Carolina Sandhills	1980	X					
Georgia	Savannah	1977–78				X		
	Piedmont	1979						
Florida	Okefenokee	1983			X		X	
	St. Marks	1979			X			
	Lake Woodruff	1978–80						
	Merritt Island	1977–78						
Alabama	Eaufala	1975–76				X		
	Wheeler	1979						
Minnesota	Tamarac	1979	X					
	Fergus Falls	1979						
	Big Stone	1973–78						
Michigan	Seney	1974–79		X				
Iowa	Union Slough	1984–86						
Illinois	Mark Twain	1969–79						
	Chautauqua	1958–70	X			X		
	Meredosia	1978–79						
Indiana	Muscatatuck	1978–79	X					
Missouri	Mingo	1975–81	X	X	X			
Tennessee	Cross Creek	1979–80						X
	Reelfoot Lake	1974–79	X		X			
	Hatchie	1967–79					X	
Arkansas	White River	1970–80			X		X	
	Wapanocca	1979	X	X	X			

size from south to north. South of 38 degrees (southern Indiana) an increasing proportion of adult raccoons are smaller than 4.54 kilograms (10 lb). At Duck Creek Wildlife Management Area near Puxico, Missouri (36.95 degrees), Hartowicz (1963) reported that 46 percent of 75 raccoons captured during the wood duck breeding season weighed 4.54 kilograms (10 lb) or less. Females were smaller than males; 78 percent weighed less than 4.08 kilograms (9 lb), while only 27 percent of the males fell below that weight. At Quiver Creek, Illinois, in central Minnesota, and at Fort Lewis, Washington, adult raccoons larger than 4.54 kilograms (10 lb) should predominate; therefore, their entrance in 1961 into houses with elliptical entrances required further explanation (see Table 119).

North of 38 degrees, raccoon litters customarily are born between early March and mid-June—a mean of April 18 in central Illinois (Sanderson and Nalbandov 1973). Young born during this period normally weigh 4.54 kilograms (10 lb) or more by the following spring. The mean of 4,521 young females weighed in central Illinois during the 1955–1986 trapping seasons was 4.82 kilograms (10.63 lb); 5,119 young males weighed 5.19 kilograms (11.44 lb) (Sanderson 1987b). They would be even larger by spring. Small young are likely to occur when pseudopregnancy, abortion, or resorption of embryos is followed by ovulation and breeding 80–140 days later (Sanderson and Nalbandov 1973). In that event, late-born young would weigh less than 4.54 kilograms (10 lb) the following spring. Sanderson and Nalbandov (1973) reported that severe weather interfered with the raccoon's normal breeding cycle and resulted in late litters. North of 38 degrees latitude, this undoubtedly is the small proportion of

An entrance hole 12.7 centimeters (5 in) in diameter enabled a raccoon to use this slab-sided wood duck house for a den. A horizontal 7.6- by 10.2-centimeter (3 by 4 in) elliptical hole prevents most raccoons in the northern half of the United States from entering nest houses. Northern raccoons are larger than those in southern regions; consequently, most of those south of the Mason-Dixon line are not deterred from entering nest houses with elliptical entrances. *Photo by James S. Ayars; courtesy of the Illinois Natural History Survey.*

the raccoon population that is able to penetrate nest houses with elliptical entrances. According to Glen C. Sanderson, although most young of late-born litters do not survive the average northern Midwest winter, some survive average winters and even more live through mild winters.

High nest losses occurred in "raccoon-proof" houses in 1961 (see Table 119). Deep snow and unseasonably cold weather in Illinois throughout March 1960 probably resulted in a failure to breed and in the loss of embryos or litters, which in turn resulted in later breeding. The large number of small yearlings during the spring of 1961 entered an unprecedented number of wood duck houses with elliptical entrances. Fortunately, these raccoons were too inexperienced to kill incubating females; despite high losses of eggs, not one incubating bird was lost.

Because of mild temperatures, small raccoons might be expected in central California. However, over an 18-year period at Merced, California, Stephen Simmons has had no raccoons enter any of his 150-plus wood nest houses equipped with elliptical entrances. As shown by chewed entrances and claw marks, raccoons have tried scores of times to gain entrance but failed. Several wood duck hens have been killed by raccoons outside the nest cavity as they attempted to flee, but these losses have been few considering the 2,971 nest attempts and 1,988 successful nests (66.9 percent) as of 1991. Most of the nest destruction was caused by red-shafted flickers.

Raccoons not only compete with wood ducks for den sites, but more importantly, they consume eggs and kill incubating hens. Throughout the wood duck's range, the raccoon is by far the greatest menace to breeding wood ducks in natural cavities and nest houses. *Photo by F. Eugene Hester.*

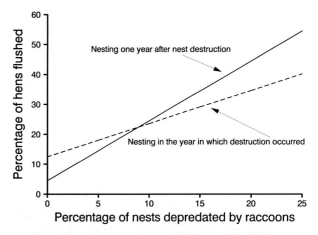

Figure 82. Flushing rate of incubating wood ducks for all nests in relation to the yearly percentage of nests destroyed by raccoons, 1939–65, based on 1,935 observations. Data summarized for each year for regression analysis: flushing rate in same year in which destruction occurred: $y = 12.50 + 1.11x$, $r = 0.33$, $P > 0.05$, $n = 14$; flushing rate in the year following nest destruction: $y = 4.50 + 2.00x$, $r = 0.61$, $P < 0.05$, $n = 13$.

Author Bellrose devised a 7.6- by 10.2-centimeter (3 by 4 in) elliptical entrance hole to prevent raccoons 4.54 kilograms (10 lbs) or larger from entering a wood duck nest house. Frustrated raccoons chew and claw the entrance in an effort to reach an incubating hen. Where this poses a problem with wood houses, a sheet-metal face plate can be placed over the upper fourth of the front. *Photo courtesy of the Illinois Natural History Survey.*

Raccoon intrusion versus wood duck flushing.
The behavior of nesting wood ducks makes clear that they are alarmed by raccoons more than any other nest predator. As early as 1938, we became aware that wood ducks nesting in cavities in bottomland woods usually flushed as we approached or climbed toward a nest cavity; those nesting in upland tracts were less likely to flush. At that time, raccoons were abundant in bottomland woods but not in upland areas.

Tallies were made from 1939 to 1965 of the flushing and nonflushing behavior of incubating hens. From 1,935 records, 17.1 percent of the birds flushed before we reached the nest site. The flushing rate was significantly correlated to the year following the year of nest destruction but was not significantly correlated with the same year in which the nests had been destroyed (Figure 82). We deduced that fright generated by raccoon nest invasion was carried over to the next year as shown by nest behavior of the surviving hens. Because about 50 percent of the hens survive (see Chapter 18), the increased flushing rates become even more meaningful, since 50 percent of the new nesting yearlings would not have been previously exposed to the threat of raccoons.

Wood ducks incubating in unprotected board houses, 1939–1943, flushed 65.7 percent (n = 204) in units subjected to raccoon depredations but only 37.8 percent (n = 148) in units free of raccoon predation. Only 4.1 percent (n = 1,303) of the incubating hens flushed from units with metal houses and elliptical entrances. Over eight years, 1958–1965, the number of hens flushing exhibited a steady decline (r = −0.82, y = 10.91 − 1.42x) as raccoon depredations declined (see Table 119). Wood ducks did not exhibit the high level of flushing following nest destruction by fox squirrels, starlings, woodpeckers, or bull snakes. Apparently wood ducks perceive the presence of a raccoon at a nest site as a potential threat to their survival and flee if they can. Predators of eggs alone—such as flickers, squirrels, and bull snakes—do not elicit an escape response; on the contrary, wood ducks often try to repel these predators as they attempt to invade a nest cavity.

Don Helmeke stated that where raccoons are active around nest sites in northwest Minneapolis, Minnesota, wood ducks become "paranoid," flushing at the slightest disturbance.

Raccoon population trends. When we began our study of wood ducks in spring of 1938, raccoons were in modest numbers and confined almost entirely to the bottomlands. We seldom found evidence that raccoons entered natural cavities or nest houses in upland woods not adjacent to water areas. In 1943, however, the highest flood of record occurred in the Illinois River Valley, and from that time on raccoons have made their presence apparent in upland areas.

Coupled with the flood that forced raccoons into upland areas was an inexplicable increase in their abundance. Sanderson (1951a) stated that in Missouri the large increase in raccoon numbers started with the 1943 breeding season. Similarly Sanderson (1951b) reported that numbers harvested in Iowa increased slightly from 1930 to 1942 but jumped in 1943 from 20,100 to 38,300 — a 90.5-percent gain, the largest percentage he recorded, 1930-1950. In Wisconsin, Woehler (1957) reported that raccoons had increased steadily since 1948. Again in Illinois, Sanderson and Hubert (1981) stated that raccoon harvest appeared to reflect population increases between the early and late 1940s, which followed significant changes in age and sex ratios and weight of females. According to Keefe (1953), low raccoon populations were reported by most states prior to 1941, but they greatly increased throughout the nation after 1942.

The incredible increase in raccoons is well illustrated by regressions of fur harvest records in several states and over the nation (Figure 83). Although high fur prices in the late 1970s and early 1980s may have heightened the take of raccoons, we believe that the harvest data provide an approximate indication of the increase in raccoon populations that began in 1943.

The current high raccoon populations pose an unmeasured threat to wood duck productivity. Because of a lack of studies in recent years on wood

ducks nesting in natural cavities, there are no proximate data on the extensiveness of impact of raccoons on wood duck nest success rates.

Raiding of wood duck nests by raccoons occurred at no particular time during the wood duck's laying and incubation period (Figure 84). The locating of wood duck nests by raccoons appeared unrelated to the length of time the female had been incubating. Hence, odor and activity at the nest site were not responsible for raccoons finding nests. If true, this hypothesis implies that they found most nests largely by chance while climbing about in trees inspecting cavities or seeking other food sources. No doubt memory plays a role in raccoons returning to nest sites that previously provided food.

Raccoon destruction of wood duck nests in unprotected board houses in Mason County, 1939–1947, followed a temporal pattern that lagged only slightly behind the availability of active nests (Figure 85). Hence, the seasonal rate of raccoon destruction of nests paralleled the rate of nesting activity.

In North Carolina, Stephenson (1970) reported a similar scenario in which, among 822 nesting attempts, raccoon depredations amounted to 1.2 percent of the nests in February–March, 8.8 percent during April–May, and 3.9 percent during June–August. The highest percentage of nest destruction coincided with the period of greatest use of wood duck houses.

Again, the data indicate a general methodical investigation by raccoons of cavities and nest houses. But obviously, if every suitable cavity and every accessible nest house were visited by raccoons at frequent intervals, the loss would be much greater than has been recorded.

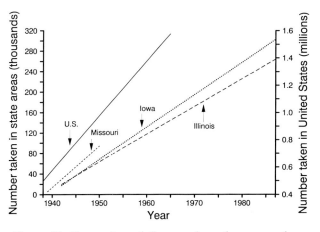

Figure 83. Regression of the number of raccoons harvested in several states and the United States for various years. The regression equations for Missouri, Iowa, Illinois, and the United States, respectively, are: $y = -10,450 + 8,060x$, $r = 0.93$, $n = 11$, $P < 0.001$; $y = -13,850 + 6,335x$, $r = 0.93$, $n = 33$, $P < 0.001$; $y = -7,000 + 5,430x$, $r = 0.75$, $n = 36$, $P < 0.001$; and $y = 458,400 + 40,060x$, $r = 0.76$, $n = 26$, $P < 0.001$. Data were obtained for the United States by Sanderson (1987a), for Missouri by Sanderson (1951a) and Keefe (1953), for Illinois by Mohr (1943) and Sanderson (1987b), and for Iowa by Sanderson (1951b) and Andrews and Judson (1987).

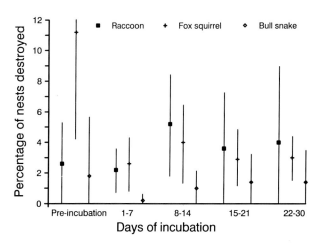

Figure 84. Predator destruction of wood duck nests in unprotected board houses at various stages from egg laying to hatching 1939–43. Vertical bars represent 95-percent confidence limits of mean.

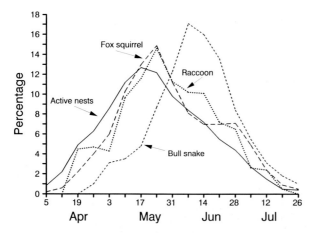

Figure 85. Chronology of wood duck nest destruction in wooden houses, Mason County, Illinois, by three predators, in relation to the proportion of active nests, 1939–47. Data are presented as a moving average of three.

Squirrels

Three species of squirrels—fox, gray, and pine (red)—are indicted in the predation of wood duck nests. The pine squirrel is small and occurs mainly in the North and in habitats of low value to wood ducks; therefore, it plays an insignificant role in wood duck nest losses.

The fox squirrel was an important predator in Mason County, Illinois, in unprotected nest houses (Table 136) and in natural cavities (see Table 118). Strom (1969) reported 60.7 percent mammalian predation, usually by fox squirrels and raccoons. He found that the fox squirrel was the principal pre-incubation predator. The only other reported fox squirrel loss was in Louisiana, where 1 of 79 (1.3 percent) nests was raided (Table 136).

Prince (1965) found that gray squirrels had predated 12.5 percent of wood duck nests in natura cavities in New Brunswick. Leopold (1966) observed gray squirrels in the Burlington, Iowa, yard where he had from 3 to 22 board nest houses for wood ducks, 1943–1965; however, he experienced no nest destruction by squirrels until 1957 when one nest was destroyed. Subsequently, eight other nests were lost; nevertheless, in 398 house-years, nest destruction by gray squirrels amounted to only 2.5 percent. Hester and Dermid (1973) reported that several gray squirrels constructed nests over clutches of wood duck eggs. In North Carolina, Stephenson (1970) observed that gray squirrels predated only 2 of 822 (0.24 percent) wood duck nests.

Even in Mason County, Illinois, where nest destruction by fox squirrels was high, it was not as bad as the data indicated (Table 136) because nearly half (46 percent) of all nests destroyed were destroyed

Because wood duck nest predators are rarely caught in the act or at the scene, the best clues are egg remains. Among the principal predators, woodpeckers leave puncture holes, rat and bull snakes take entire eggs, fox squirrels sever the shells cleanly at one end, and raccoons (above) crush the eggs inward. *Photo by Greg R. Hubbard; shell fragments provided by Stephen Simmons.*

during preincubation (Figure 84). Of all nests destroyed by raccoons, only 15 percent were destroyed during preincubation (Figure 84). The temporal distribution of nest destruction by fox squirrels coincides fairly closely with the availability of wood duck nests (Figure 85). Nest predation by squirrels appears unrelated to their nutritional needs; rather, it seems attributable to happenstance and availability.

In some places where squirrels have been exposed to dense numbers of nesting ducks over a long period, they appear to have developed a penchant for wood duck eggs. In the black oak woodlots of Mason County, both fox squirrels and wood ducks are abundant; apparently through long association, fox squirrels became acquainted with eggs as a food source and therefore developed into important predators.

Fox squirrels and gray squirrels (above) compete for den sites with wood ducks, and in some areas they actively consume the contents of wood duck eggs. The fox squirrel appears to be a greater threat to wood ducks than does the gray squirrel. *Photo by James Leasch; courtesy of the California Waterfowl Association.*

To prevent fox squirrels from entering wood duck nest houses to pilfer eggs, author Bellrose placed metal sides and flanges over the wood structures. The effort failed (above). Not until he developed a pyramidal roof with metal sides and front were fox squirrels excluded. This led to the development of a cylindrical sheet-metal house (formed from heating duct pipe) with a conical roof. *Photo by Frank Bellrose; courtesy of the Illinois Natural History Survey.*

Other Mammals

Wood ducks have nested in cavities in trees adjacent to the yard of Bellrose in Havana, Illinois, for 10 years, yet abundant fox squirrels have not destroyed a single nest. The 14 years that passed before Leopold (1966) found a nest destroyed in his yard by gray squirrels is further evidence that some populations of squirrels do not associate wood duck eggs with a source of food. The lack of reported instances of egg losses to squirrels by other researchers (Table 136) in areas where squirrels occur is further evidence that their trait of using eggs as food probably is highly localized. The data at hand indicate that none of the species of squirrels plays an important role as a predator of wood duck nests over the duck's entire breeding range.

Minks killed four incubating hens in our central Illinois nest houses, but all losses occurred during the same year in one area where leaning willow trees prevailed (Bellrose et al. 1964). Fiedler (1967) observed a mink feeding on a wood duck in a nest house in central Minnesota. Strong (1973) reported that a mink killed an incubating hen in a nest house in Mississippi. In Massachusetts, Grice and Rogers (1965) reported that minks occasionally took eggs from nests without destroying the entire clutch.

In the Merced, California, area, Stephen Simmons lost incubating wood duck hens to minks in 2 of 19 years. In one instance a mink killed 10 hens in a single group of houses; two years later only 2 incubating females were killed in this same unit of houses.

Opossums are a negligible predator of wood duck eggs. Although opossums are known for their consumption of eggs of ground-nesting birds, few wood duck nests were found during 50 years of research in Illinois that possibly were destroyed by them. In the few instances that an opossum was found in a destroyed wood duck nest, the animal may have been scavenging egg remnants left by a raccoon. *Photo by Chuck Scott; courtesy of the Illinois Natural History Survey.*

Although minks occur extensively in wooded bottomland habitats where wood ducks breed, they are never abundant. Our experience suggests that they can climb inclined trees with corrugated bark, such as the black willow, but their climbing ability is limited. Because of these circumstances, minks do not appear to have a significant impact on wood duck nest success over extensive areas of the duck's range.

At the Yazoo National Wildlife Refuge in Mississippi, bobcats killed 65 incubating wood ducks during the 1987 nesting season (Wilkins et al. 1990). The cats apparently jumped from the ground to the top of wood duck nest houses on pipes 1.2–2.0 meters (4–6 ft) above the ground. They appeared to reach in to pluck the incubating hens from their nests. The houses were along a footpath adjacent to a water area.

Three opossums suspected of killing incubating hens in central Illinois (Bellrose et al. 1964) may have been feeding on carcasses left by raccoons. No other records of this mammal preying on wood duck nests have been reported, and we conclude that it has little or no effect on nesting wood ducks.

Woodpeckers

Several species of woodpeckers puncture wood duck eggs to consume part of the contents. The puncture usually is prominent, with a diameter almost the size of a pencil. Woodpeckers are the only birds that make such large drilled openings.

Flickers also may make tiny holes in wood duck eggshells, apparently in an attempt to cause nest desertion. At Merced, California, Stephen Simmons captured several red-shafted flickers in wood duck nests where eggs in 10 houses all showed one or more minute holes. When red-shafted flickers were not present, wood duck eggs remained intact. We have noted similar small perforations in wood duck eggs by yellow-shafted flickers.

We first observed a red-headed woodpecker puncturing eggs in May 1942. It punctured a few eggs at a time, exiting the nest and wiping its bill. Hartowicz (1963) suspected red-headed woodpeckers of puncturing eggs in seven wood duck clutches at the Duck Creek Wildlife Management Area in Missouri. At the same area, Clawson (1975a) also recorded red-headed woodpeckers puncturing eggs in four nests during a two-week period. Decker (1959) suspected that either red-headed woodpeckers or starlings punctured eggs in nine wood duck houses in northwestern Pennsylvania. A red-bellied woodpecker was observed by Cunningham (1968) to peck holes in wood duck eggs of one nest, but the woodpecker did not consume the contents. Wilkins et al. (1990) found egg yolk in the esophagi of red-bellied woodpeckers collected leaving wood duck nests.

In our experience, however, and that of most other researchers, the flicker is the principal culprit among the woodpeckers. From 1939 to 1963, we noticed no appreciable loss of nests to woodpeckers (see tables 119 and 121). Commencing in 1964, flickers were observed entering or leaving large numbers of wood duck nest sites; since that time, clutch losses in Illinois from flickers have waxed and waned but have been appreciable.

Flickers were an especially important cause of egg loss at Nauvoo Slough, Illinois (see Table 123). There in a 1.4-kilometer (0.9 mi) string of 40 duplex houses, flickers wreaked havoc, 1983–1985. Two pairs of flickers in 1983 and 1984 ranged along the entire length of the nest house unit, even though most houses were in water 37–91 meters (40–100 yd) from trees. Both years, flickers nested in the house unit. One pair attempted to nest in 1985, none appeared in 1986, and a transient destroyed two nests in 1987.

Losses of wood duck nests to flickers and other woodpeckers may not be extensive. Reports from refuge managers (Table 137) indicate only scattered areas where these birds were important egg predators. However, where nest houses are close together, as at Nauvoo Slough, flickers may be formidable predators.

Several woodpeckers—notably red-headed and red-bellied woodpeckers, but flickers in particular (red-shafted flickers on the West Coast and yellow-shafted flickers east of the Mississippi River)—puncture the shells of wood duck eggs. Holes as large as the size of standard pencil erasers are made for the purpose of partially extracting the eggs' contents. *Top photo by Greg R. Hubbard; blown egg courtesy of Stephen Simmons. Bottom photo by Jack Dermid.*

Starlings

Starlings act more as competitors of the wood duck than as predators. Nevertheless, in evicting wood ducks from nests, starlings inadvertently cause egg loss from pre-incubation to hatch. Tables 119, 121, 123, and 130–137 document the role starlings play in the destruction of wood duck nests. At various times and places, starlings have been an important factor in reducing nest success. An indication of the threat they pose is illustrated by Heusmann and Bellville's (1982: 44) statement that "Starling competition nearly eliminated wood duck populations on several Massachusetts areas."

With respect to wood duck nesting, starlings are a problem that wildlife managers have to consider.

Other Birds

A hawk or owl rarely kills an incubating duck at the nest site. Wood duck feathers found May 1, 1958, on the ground at a nest site on Quiver Creek indicated a kill of the incubating hen by an unknown hawk. That same day, several miles away, Edward Nichols, then of the Chautauqua National Wildlife Refuge staff, observed a red-tailed hawk with a wood duck hen in its grasp. As he approached the hawk, it released the duck and both birds flew away.

According to Ernest L. Rauber, Assistant Manager of the Santee National Wildlife Refuge in South Carolina, a red-tailed hawk killed 13 incubating wood ducks during the spring of 1987. The hawk perched on plastic nest houses on posts and apparently captured the ducks when they fled. The houses were on posts placed along levees largely devoid of trees. Rapp (1941) witnessed a red-shouldered hawk eating a wood duck on April 6, 1940, along the Passaic River in New Jersey.

Snakes

Rat snakes. South of the 37-degree parallel, black and brown rat snakes become an increasing menace to nesting wood ducks. These long (up to 183 centimeters: 6 ft), slender snakes are agile tree climbers and have been found in nest houses more than 1.6 kilometers (1 mi) from land (Rogers 1955). They feed extensively on birds and their eggs, and with their tree-climbing and swimming abilities they are well adapted to life in southern swamps and overflow bottomland forests. Rat snakes occur throughout the wood duck's breeding range east of the Great Plains except in the extreme northern part of the United States (P. W. Smith 1961). They plundered an especially large proportion of nests in southeastearn Missouri (Hansen 1971), Louisiana (Louisiana Technical Wildlife Club 1972), South Carolina (Fendley 1980), and east Texas (May 1986) but were prominent nest predators throughout the South (Table 136). Over a 10-year period, M. M. Smith (1961) found that the rat snake was the most important predator of wood duck nests in various areas of Louisiana.

Rat snakes are very adept at getting over obstructions to reach nest cavities. Stanek (1970) studied rat snakes placed in an enclosure with nest houses on posts. He found that they crossed bands of axle grease of 61 centimeters (24 in) and got by a plastic skirt flared 91 centimeters (36 in) downward and outward 15 centimeters (6 in). They were unable to enter houses placed atop 2.5-centimeter (1 in) or 5.1-centimeter (2 in) galvanized pipes. Also, Davis (1978) found that boxes with conical metal guards in Louisiana were adequately protected against rat snakes. Landin (1977) reported that bands of grease around posts appeared to stop

all but the largest rat snakes from gaining access to houses. In South Carolina, Fendley (1978, 1980) found that rat snakes readily crossed a metal band 42 centimeters (16.5 in) wide placed around dead cypress trees 0.5 meter (20 in) below the nest houses.

Conflicting findings regarding the rat snake's ability to surmount obstacles may result from differences in snake size. Stanek (1970) reported that longer snakes more frequently climbed poles. Some of his confined snakes never attempted to climb posts within the enclosure.

Hansen (1971) marked black rat snakes found in nest houses and recaptured some of them later in the same houses. He concluded that certain snakes learn to seek eggs in houses. He found that nest houses in isolated trees in open areas were especially vulnerable to depredation by snakes.

At the Coulee Wildlife Refuge in Louisiana, Davis (1978) marked 11 rat snakes; 13 days to 10 months later he found 5 back in the same nest houses. He also found marked and unmarked snakes using the same nest house, including houses without a history of use by wood ducks.

Rat snakes, agile climbers and swimmers, are important predators of wood duck eggs. In many swamps in the southern states, rat snakes destroy a higher proportion of wood duck nests than do raccoons. These snakes have been found swimming over 1.6 kilometers (1 mi) from land, and they frequently use natural cavities as den sites in flooded swamps. *Photo by Frederic Leopold; courtesy of the Starr's Cave Nature Center (Burlington, Iowa).*

Wood duck egg membranes that were regurgitated by a black rat snake show that the shell and contents were completely digested but the tough membranes remained intact. Membranes of hatched eggs appear similar but are one-third shorter from loss of excised cap. *Photo by Jack Dermid.*

Apparently some snakes used cavities as temporary den sites, whereas others sought food there.

In most incidents of nest invasion, rat snakes do not jeopardize the life of the incubating bird; however, a rat snake occasionally will attack an adult bird. Hansen (1971) reported that black rat snakes apparently killed three incubating wood ducks at Mingo National Wildlife Refuge in Missouri. Hester and Dermid (1973) recorded finding two large rat snakes in a nest box with a dead hen. The wet, matted feathers of her head and neck provided evidence that one of the snakes had attempted to swallow her. Fendley (1980) also found three wood ducks and a hooded merganser killed on their nests by black rat snakes near North Augusta, South Carolina. Similarly, Stewart (1981) found evidence that a black rat snake had killed an incubating wood

Rat snakes—black and gray—are slender snakes that reach lengths of 1.5–2.1 meters (5–7 ft), enabling them to climb trees easily and rapidly by elevating their ventral scales for purchase. Because of their length, rat snakes are frequently able to circumvent metal shields (left) and guards (top right) placed below nest houses. When climbing trees, they are prone to inspect any natural cavities they encounter (bottom right). The rat snake, a constrictor, seldom kills incubating wood ducks but readily consumes their eggs. *Left photo by Richard Kaminski. Top right and bottom right photos by Steve Barry; courtesy of Mississippi State University.*

duck. All of the wood duck victims had twisted necks.

Bull snakes. In black oak tracts in the old sand dune area of Mason County, Illinois, we found bull snakes to be important predators of wood duck nests in natural cavities and board nesting houses (tables 119 and 136). They consumed eggs at various stages of incubation (Figure 84), which suggests that odor or prolonged activity by incubating birds at the nest site did not play a role in attracting snakes to the sites. Most bull snake depredations, unlike those of raccoons and fox squirrels, occurred in late May and early July—a time when the rate of wood duck nesting was rapidly declining (Figure 85). This temporal destruction by bull snakes may reflect their increased tree-climbing activity as a result of rising temperature.

We witnessed a wood duck striking at a bull snake entering a nest site. At each hit at the snake, the snake's body retreated an inch or two, but it

In areas where bull (gopher) snakes predominate over rat snakes, the former may be an important predator of wood duck eggs. Like the rat snake, the bull snake is an agile climber and a good swimmer. *Photo by Chuck Scott; courtesy of the Illinois Natural History Survey.*

continued its inexorable entrance. On another occasion (June 1, 1951) an incubating wood duck struck at a bull snake until it left the box and returned to the ground, where it was dispatched by the observer. An hour later, the resident of a home a few yards away heard a commotion in the nest house. A snake was seen partially exiting and then reentering the nest house. Further sounds of the wood duck calling and striking at the snake were heard, and then the female appeared at the entrance, struggling to get out. When she did, the snake was observed coiled around one leg. The female broke free, and the snake returned to the nest.

We have found wood ducks continuing to remain on their nests despite bull snakes consuming eggs from their clutches. On one occasion, a wood duck flushed from a box that we were about to check. Inside were two 127-centimeter (50 in) bull snakes, both engorged with eggs.

Although bull snakes readily climb trees and investigate each cavity they encounter, we found that very few entered metal nest houses (see Table 121) compared with the number that entered board nest houses (see Table 119) in Mason County, Illinois. Of 18 bull snakes collected in Mason County in 1940, one contained wood duck eggs and one had ingested ducklings (probably captured in a nest prior to departure).

The range of the bull snake is largely west of the wood duck's range (P. W. Smith 1961). It is restricted to localized areas in wood duck breeding habitats from Lake Michigan west through Wisconsin, Minnesota, western Illinois, Iowa, and northern and western Missouri. Because the bull snake's range does not coincide with areas in which wood ducks breed in abundance, it is a minor predator compared with rat snakes.

RECOGNITION OF POTENTIAL PREDATORS

At Nauvoo Slough in May 1985, we saw an unusual response by about 10 adult wood ducks to a large (51–61 centimeters long: 20–24 in) snapping turtle that was swimming in shallow water. The wood ducks converged on the turtle, flanking it and swimming along both sides for at least 20 meters (22 yd) until it swam out of our sight.

A similar response by wood ducks to a 1.5-meter (4.9 ft) long alligator was reported in Louisiana by Rothbart (1979). At the appearance of the alligator, all of the adult woodies in the area ceased activities and watched the reptile. After five minutes, approximately 35 ducks swam toward the alligator and formed a moving circle around it that lasted about two minutes until it exited through an opening in a willow thicket.

Apparently wood ducks feel more secure after they have identified the location of a known aquatic predator, and when it is visible they keep it under surveillance, much as blackbirds and starlings do with hawks.

PRINCIPAL PREDATORS AND NEST DENSITY

Over the entire breeding range of the wood duck, raccoons appear to be the principal predator north of the 37-degree parallel; to the south, the rat snake and the raccoon are both important nest predators. Of the many species of animals competing for nest houses, starlings provide the greatest threat to wood ducks.

Because of their uniform, conspicuous appearance, wood duck nest houses provide a signal to previously successful predators that a reward may follow inspection. According to Martin (1988), the intensity with which predators search increases as birds increase their occupancy of available nest sites. He found from experimentation that comparable nest densities among a single type of nest site experienced heavier predation than did a diversity of nest sites. Confined as they are to natural cavities or nest houses, wood ducks are potentially at increased risk to predation as their nest density increases.

Maps

Map 1. Current breeding range of the wood duck.

Map 2. Average density of wood duck harvest per square mile for each county in the United States, 1966–85.

Map 3. Relative density (number counted per 100 party hours) and distribution of wood ducks counted during Audubon Christmas Bird Censuses, 1979–80.

Map 4. Land use and physiographic features of the eastern United States.
  A.
  B.
  C.
  D.

Map 5. Current and pristine distribution and abundance of bottomland hardwood wetlands in the Lower Mississippi Alluvial Plain (from U.S. Fish and Wildlife Service 1988).

Map 6. Distribution and abundance of agricultural lands in drainage enterprises in the eastern United States, 1959 (U.S. Bureau of the Census 1959, U.S. Geological Survey 1970), and distribution and abundance of farm ponds, 1964 (U.S. Bureau of the Census 1964, U.S. Geological Survey 1970).

Map 7. Migration corridors of wood ducks banded in northcentral New York and southwestern Wisconsin.

Map 8. Migratory routes of wood ducks banded in northern regions of the Mississippi and Atlantic flyways.

MAP 1
Current breeding range of the wood duck

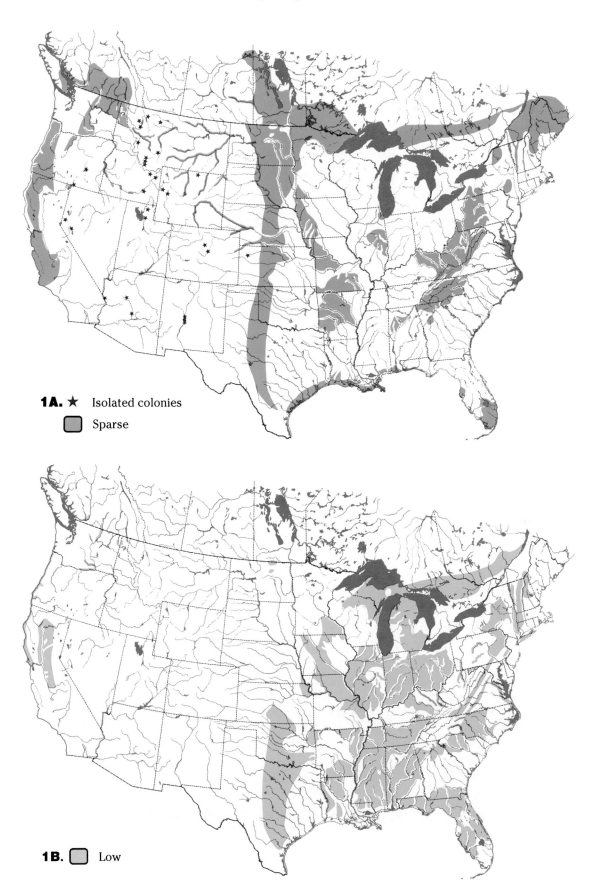

1A. ★ Isolated colonies

☐ Sparse

1B. ☐ Low

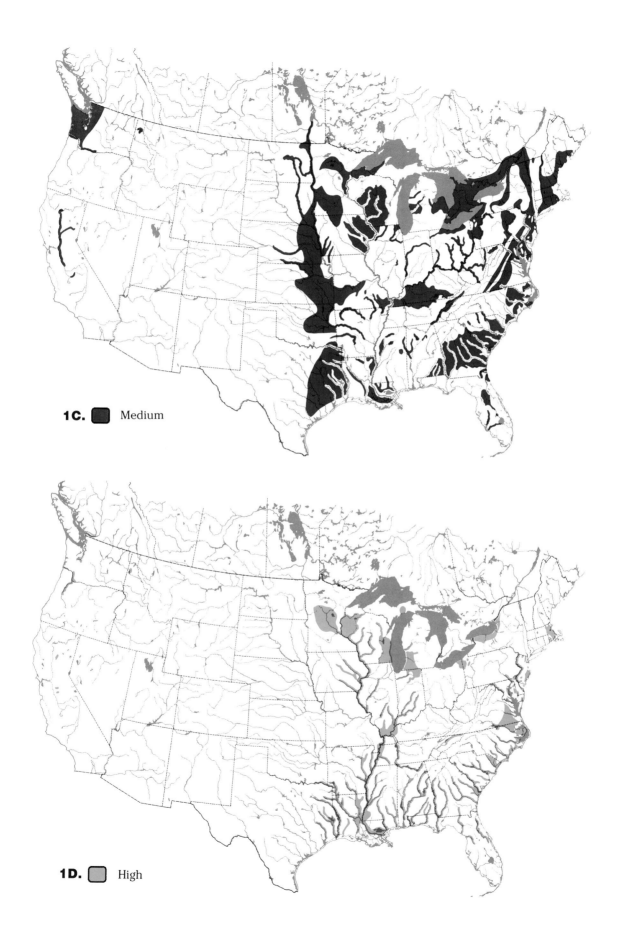

1C. ◼ Medium

1D. ▨ High

MAP 2

Average density of wood duck harvest per square mile
for each county in the United States, 1966-85

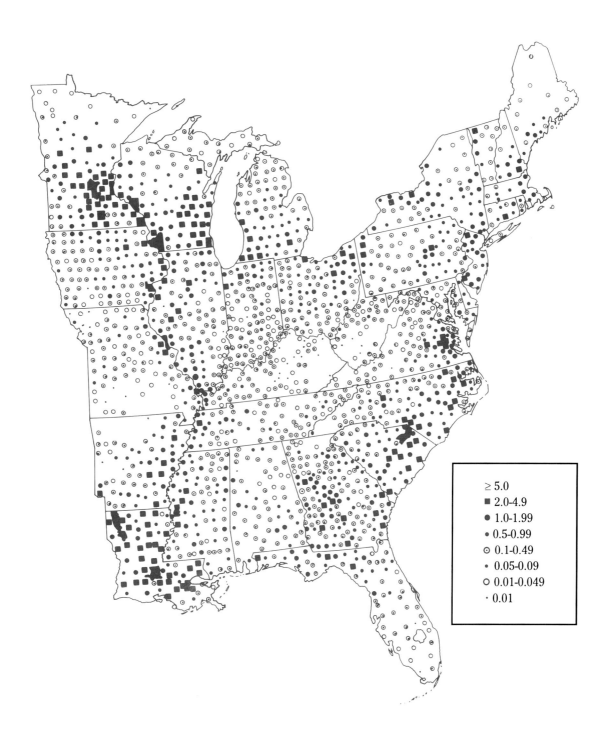

≥ 5.0	
■	2.0-4.9
●	1.0-1.99
•	0.5-0.99
⊙	0.1-0.49
·	0.05-0.09
○	0.01-0.049
·	0.01

MAP 3

Relative density (number counted per 100 party hours) and distribution of wood ducks counted during Audubon Christmas Bird Censuses, 1979-80

MAP 4
Land use and physiographic features of the eastern United States

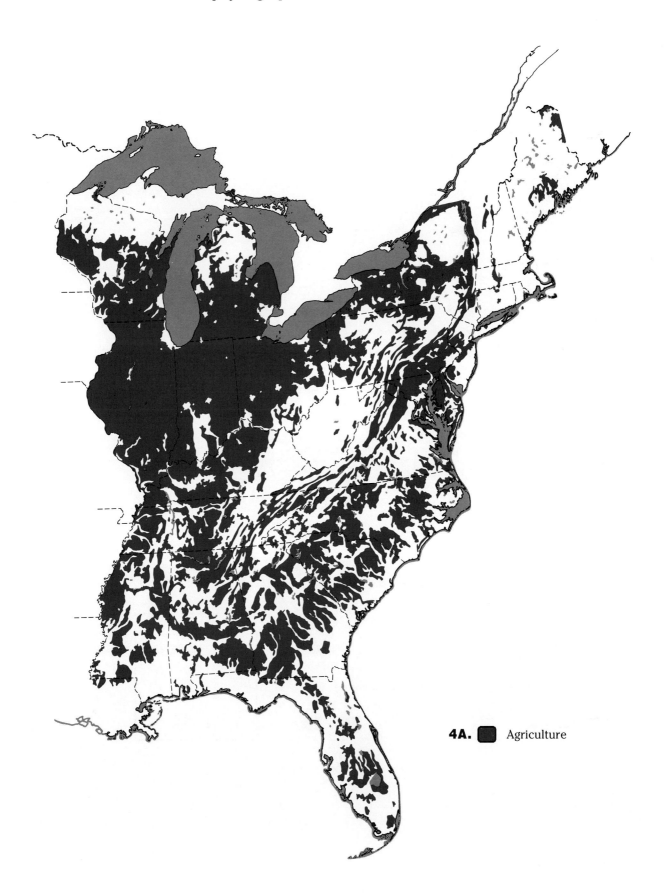

4A. Agriculture

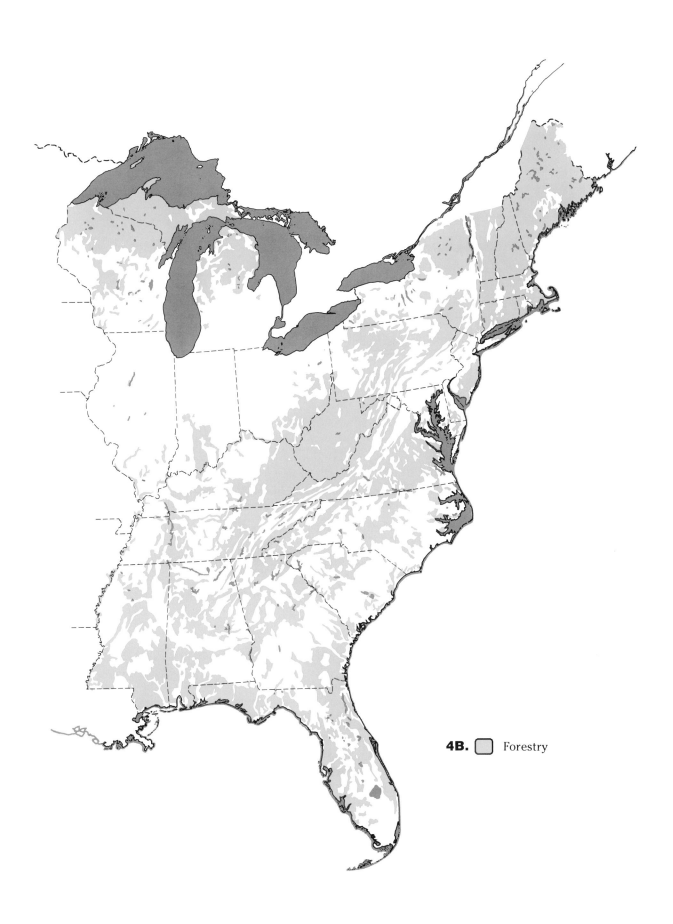

4B. Forestry

MAP 4
Continued

4C. Swampland
Marshland

4D. Metropolitan areas

MAP 5

Current and pristine distribution and abundance of bottomland hardwood wetlands in the Lower Mississippi Alluvial Plain (from U.S. Fish and Wildlife Service 1988)

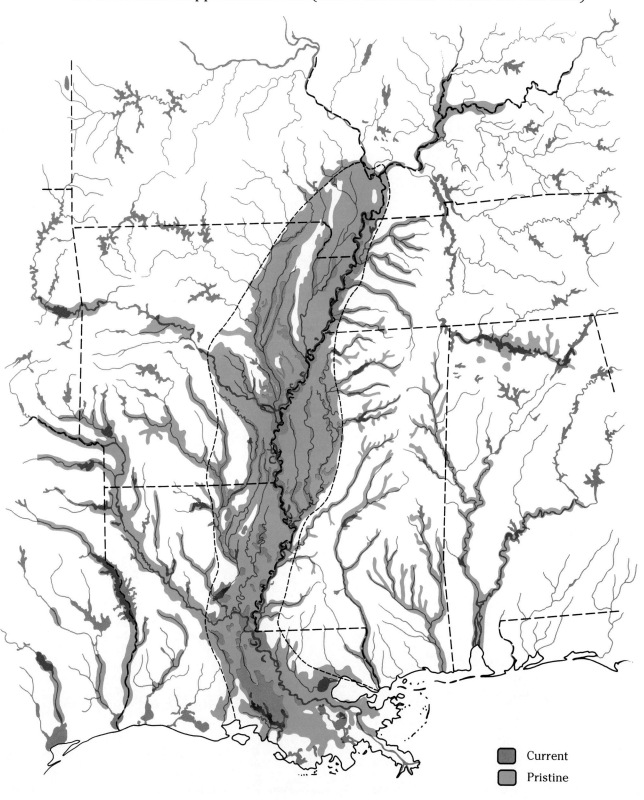

■ Current
■ Pristine

MAP 6

Distribution and abundance of agricultural lands in drainage enterprises in the eastern
United States, 1959 (U.S. Bureau of the Census 1959,
U.S. Geological Survey 1970), and distribution and abundance of farm ponds, 1964
(U.S. Bureau of the Census 1964, U.S. Geological Survey 1970)

Drainage enterprises - each dot represents
20,000 acres

Farm ponds - each dot represents 500 ponds,
including pits, reservoirs, and earthen tanks

MAP 7
Migration corridors of wood ducks banded in northcentral New York and southwestern Wisconsin

Mean
Standard deviation
Banding station

MAP 8
Migratory routes of wood ducks banded in northern regions of the Mississippi and Atlantic flyways

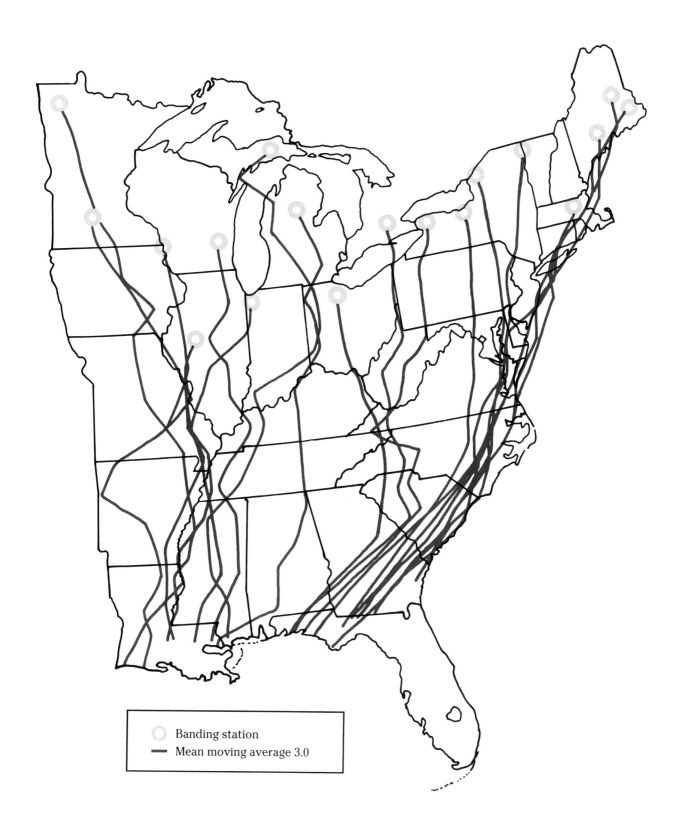

Banding station
— Mean moving average 3.0

Brood Behavior and Survival

Young wood ducks face many perils between the beginning of embryonic development and the achievement of flight. The major causes of death to developing embryos were discussed in chapters 10 and 11. A second critical period begins after the eggs hatch. Maternal females provide guidance and protection for their young throughout much of the preflight period, yet many ducklings succumb to accidents, diseases, predation, inclement weather, and other agents of mortality.

Wood duck hens care for their young by leading them to protective cover when danger threatens, diverting the attention of potential predators away from the brood, providing warmth and protection during adverse weather, and locating food. Although a young wood duck is never fed by its mother, it probably learns where to find and obtain certain foods by watching her actions.

Many of the innate behaviors on which young wood ducks rely for survival change as the ducklings mature. Dreis (1954) observed that ducklings less than one week old normally stay very close to their mothers and remain concealed in dense protective cover on land throughout much of the day. As wood ducks grow, they become more independent and tend to stray farther from their mothers. In addition, they no longer spend as much of the day hidden in terrestrial cover; nevertheless, older ducklings will, without hesitation, seek protection in upland vegetation when threatened by a predator.

For comparison of age and survival in the wild, young ducks have been grouped into classes based on body size and plumage development. Gollop and Marshall (1954) proposed that ducklings be classified as Class I through the natal down stage, Class II through development of contour body feathers, and Class III through final development of head, back, and flight feathers. Subdivisions of these classes (Ia, Ib, Ic, IIa, IIb, IIc, III) are less apparent but provide further information on the stage of development. The aspect criteria of woodie duckling age in relation to feather development and size compared with that of an adult female is presented in Table 138 and Figure 86.

BROODING

Because they are sensitive and particularly vulnerable to the effects of exposure, especially chilling, young woodies spend a lot of time out of the water on logs, on muskrat houses, and in cover along shorelines. They often huddle under their mothers to become dry and warm.

The amount of time hens devote to brooding after the young have left their nests is unknown. Age of brood and environmental conditions undoubtedly combine to influence frequency and duration of brooding periods. Wood ducks less than two weeks old frequently are brooded by females for varying lengths of time at dusk and during the evening and early morning hours. Moreover, hens often brood young ducklings during midday hours when rainy weather conditions, cold, or both merit such activity. We recorded an average air temperature of 15.6 degrees Celsius (range = 5.6–22.8 degrees Celsius) (60°F; range = 42–73°F) at the beginning of 13 diurnal brooding periods in central Illinois. The ducklings brooded most frequently belonged to age classes Ia (50 percent), Ib (29 percent), and Ic (14 percent).

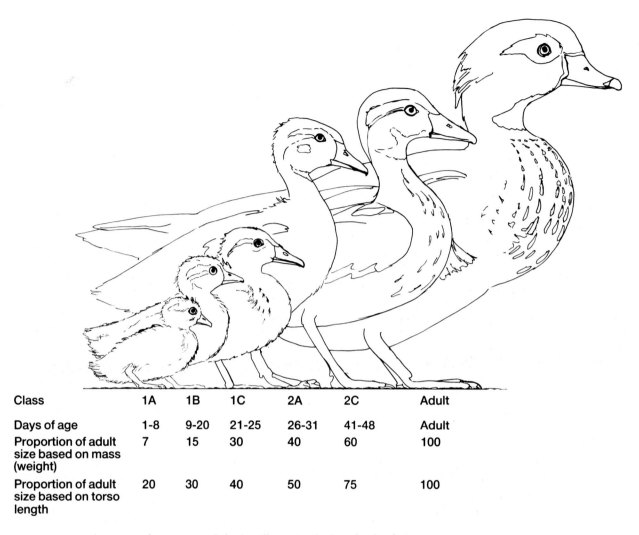

Class	1A	1B	1C	2A	2C	Adult
Days of age	1-8	9-20	21-25	26-31	41-48	Adult
Proportion of adult size based on mass (weight)	7	15	30	40	60	100
Proportion of adult size based on torso length	20	30	40	50	75	100

Figure 86. Development of young wood ducks. *Illustration by Beverley Sanderson.*

Table 138. Growth criteria of wood duck ducklings in relation to development.[a]

Age class	Age (days)	Plumage development[b]	Proportion of length to an adult female
Ia	1–6	Black-brown down on crown, back, and tail; pale sulphur down on cheeks, breast, and belly.	20
Ib	7–20	Down more brownish above and grayish below; body elongating.	40
Ic	18–24	Scapular and tail feathers appear and grow rapidly.	45
IIa	25–30	Contour feathers developing on sides.	50
IIb	31–36	Contour feathers fully developed on chest, breast, and belly; wing coverts complete; sheaths of flight feathers appear.	60
IIc	37–47	Down replaced by contour feathers on crown and cheek; male head markings apparent; sheaths of flight feathers one-half grown, vanes partly exposed.	75
III	48–60	Juvenile plumage complete except for some down on back; flight develops.	90

[a] Adapted from Gollop and Marshall (1954).
[b] Some plumage characteristics are difficult to see unless the birds are captured and examined.

As soon as day-old woodie ducklings are afloat, they begin to feed by pecking at floating objects and chasing insects. Although some nest sites are over water, most are over land; thus many hatchlings have to trek for hours overland before reaching water. On their initial journey to water, many ducklings—often entire broods—are lost along the way. Those that fail to reach water fall victim to predators, accidents, and insufficient energy to keep up with the fast-moving brood. Duckling wood ducks instinctively are attracted to minute moving food items, and they also seek overhead cover. When threatened with perceived danger, they dive, even using their wings to propel themselves below the surface a linear distance of about 4.6 meters (15 ft). *Photo by Jack Dermid.*

Although the female normally initiates brooding periods, ducklings may stimulate her under some circumstances to begin brooding. On several occasions we observed young wood ducks respond to calls given by the hen and subsequently move beneath her outstretched wings. We once observed, in contrast to that behavior, several ducklings approach a resting female and bury their heads beneath her breast feathers. After a few seconds the hen stood up, spread her wings, and began brooding the ducklings.

Apparently, some ducklings within a brood require more brooding than others do. In 29 percent of our brooding observations, hens brooded only a portion of their ducklings. Nonbrooded individuals generally remained in compact groups beside the females, but they often stretched and preened and sometimes swam or fed in close proximity to their brooding mothers.

Duckling age and weather conditions principally determine the extent of brooding by wood duck hens. The younger the ducklings, the more maternal attention they receive, and brooding periods are increased and/or extended by woodie hens during cold or wet weather. The above brood (Class Ib) has been reduced to seven, six of which huddle together while the other one presses against its mother to find warmth. *Photo courtesy of the Minnesota Department of Natural Resources.*

BROOD MOBILITY

Hester and Dermid (1973) reported that wood duck hens seldom use wetlands smaller than 4 hectares (10 ac) for brood rearing. This behavior may have developed because predators are more likely to eliminate entire broods when ducklings are confined to a limited area.

After the young leave the nest, they embark on a journey that sometimes lasts for several days. Some broods travel several kilometers through a series of wetlands before reaching one that provides the essential requirements of adequate size, abundant supplies of available plant and animal foods, and an interspersion of open water and emergent cover. In other cases, nest sites are located on or adjacent to acceptable rearing areas, and little travel is required.

Smith and Flake (1985) observed that some wood duck hens often departed or bypassed seemingly acceptable brood cover during their initial movements. They suggested that brood hens may preselect rearing areas. Ball (1971) followed the movements of several radio-tagged brood hens on the Chippewa National Forest in Minnesota. Each female that he monitored prior to hatching subsequently took her young to a wetland that she had previously visited. David (1986) also found that broods were moved to wetlands the mothers had frequented during incubation. He often could predict subsequent primary rearing sites by following the movements of radio-tagged hens during incubation.

In Ohio, Stewart (1958) found that, immediately after hatching, wood ducks moved their broods to the nearest water areas that provided concealing vegetation and remained there for about two weeks. In contrast, 75 percent of the brood hens monitored by Ball (1971) in Minnesota did not take their young to the wetlands nearest the nests, even when apparently suitable cover was available there. And although their nests were located over water, three (33 percent) of the brood hens monitored by Hepp and Hair (1977) moved their broods from small (less than 0.23 hectare: 0.57 ac), sparsely vegetated beaver ponds to larger (more than 3.25 hectares: 8.03 ac) ponds with more concealing cover. Each of these broods then remained on its respective wetland until the ducklings reached flight stage.

Most lengthy brood movements occur during the first two days after nest exodus. Hardister et al. (1962) and Farmer (1970) followed brood movements on the same study area in North Carolina and found that brood hens moved up to 2.4 and 4.1 kilometers (1.5 and 2.5 mi) shortly after they left their nests. Ball (1973), Rothbart (1979), and David (1986) stated that brood hens moved an average of 1.1, 0.6, and 1.3 kilometers (0.7, 0.4, and 0.8 mi) from nest sites to primary rearing areas. While studying brood movements along the Big Sioux River in eastern South Dakota, Smith and Flake (1985) found that brood hens traveled average distances of 4.8 and 2.5 kilometers (3.0 and 1.6 mi) during the first two days after nest exodus in 1980 and 1981. Drought conditions were thought to be responsible for the shorter travel distances in 1981. Of the broods monitored by Hepp and Hair (1977) in South Carolina, 67 percent moved an average distance of 2.1 ± 1.3 kilometers (1.3 ± 0.8 mi) during the first 48 hours after nest departure, even though their nests were located over water in beaver ponds. Where water and cover were close to nest sites at Muscatatuck National Wildlife Refuge in Indiana, Robb and Bookhout (1990) found that primary movements from nest site to brood-rearing habitat averaged 1.2 kilometers (0.7 mi). They concluded that lack of secondary movements reflected high-quality and dispersed brood habitats, which would reduce competition between broods and their resulting movements.

During these initial movements the rate of travel varies with the type of travel route, cover conditions, and number of disturbances. Leopold (1951) and Hardister et al. (1962) indicated that overland movements usually are direct and rapid unless the brood is disturbed. Farmer (1970) determined that wood duck broods traveled overland at an average speed of 4.2 meters per minute (13.8 ft/min) and a maximum speed of 22.3 meters per minute (73.2 ft/min). This speed contrasts with their more leisurely pace of 2.3 meters per minute (7.5 ft/min) on water. Hens commonly move broods directly to rearing areas. Ball (1973) indicated that broods traveled in a direct manner when they undertook major moves. In contrast, he observed that ducklings typically retraced their travel routes in the course of daily movements. DiGiulio (1978) observed one brood in Louisiana that traveled 4.3 kilometers (2.7 mi) in 12 hours.

It is advantageous for broods to reach quality rearing habitat as soon as possible and remain there until requirements change or conditions become unfavorable and necessitate another shift. Restricted mobility probably increases brood survival by allowing ducklings to become familiar with the location of escape routes, protective cover, and food resources (Hepp and Hair 1977).

Many broods are reared to flight stage on the wetlands reached by initial moves; however, some broods are very mobile and visit several wetlands during prefledge periods. Brood hens may under-

take secondary movements in response to predatory activity, deteriorating environmental conditions, increased competition for available resources, or when interim wetlands do not meet all of the requirements of brood rearing.

As ducklings grow older, their behavior and dietary needs change. Interim wetlands may provide the cover and food preferred by young ducklings but lack the habitat requirements of older ducklings. In northern Louisiana, Rothbart (1979) observed that six broods relied on the protective cover associated with the shoreline areas of two freshwater impoundments during their first two weeks of life. During their third week, four of the six broods moved into adjacent rice fields and remained there for the duration of the rearing period. In this case, the shift in brood habitat appeared associated with a change in diet from invertebrates to plant foods.

In 1985 four (57 percent) radio-tagged brood hens left Nauvoo Slough and swam nearly 6–7 kilometers (3.7–4.3 mi) to an alternate rearing area. These females had hatched their clutches in mid and late June; the radio-tagged brood hens (n = 3) that remained on the slough to raise their young had hatched their clutches during May. This delay in lengthy brood movements may indicate that the hens responded to high local brood densities by seeking alternate rearing habitat. One of the four broods apparently left Nauvoo Slough the day of nest exodus. Two broods remained for six days before they moved upriver. The fourth spent nearly 18 days on Nauvoo Slough before traveling to the alternate rearing area.

In 1987 five radio-monitored hens hatched nests on Nauvoo Slough. Each remained in the area until the hen/brood bond dissolved. Although the number of egg-laying hens increased by six between 1985 and 1987, hatched nests declined by 18 percent (eight clutches). Water levels also were considerably lower in 1987, creating more loafing sites.

Lawton L. Shurtleff observed that most late-hatched broods left his 3-hectare (7.4 ac) impoundments on a small tributary of the Russian River near Healdsburg, California. Most broods that hatched early remained on the impoundment, where artificially supplied food augmented natural foods. Here again, late-season brood departures appear more related to intolerance of density than to a limitation of food resources.

Thirty-nine percent of the hens monitored by David (1986) in northern Illinois moved an average of 1 kilometer (range = 0.5–1.8 kilometers) (0.6 mi: range = 0.3–1.1 mi) to new rearing areas after spending 6–28 days (average = 16 days) on the wetlands reached by their initial movements.

At several weeks of age, dietary emphasis for woodie ducklings shifts from invertebrates to plant foods. This, in turn, may necessitate a change of rearing habitats. Above, five Class IIb woodie ducklings (30 days old) have started to show independence from their mother as they feed actively in a dense bed of duckweed. Note the molt on the female's head; she evidently hatched her young late during the breeding season. *Photo by Stephen Kirkpatrick.*

In the Piedmont region of South Carolina, Hepp (1977) found that wood duck broods tended to space themselves throughout the available habitat. However, brood females were not territorial, and the ranges of different broods often overlapped (Farmer 1970, Rothbart 1979), particularly as brood densities increased.

HOME RANGE

By the second week after nest exodus, most wood duck broods have established relatively stable home ranges. The size of the home range varies greatly among broods and from one location to another. Brood age, wetland size and location, cover conditions, availability of food, and habitat preferences of individual hens are key factors that influence the size of brood ranges. On Nauvoo Slough, the minimum size of the home ranges of seven radio-tagged brood hens averaged 22.8 ± 17.3 hectares (56.3 ± 42.7 ac). Farmer (1970) found that home ranges varied from 2.2 to 3.9 hectares (5.4–9.6 ac) in a 10.5-hectare (25.9 ac) marsh and from 7.4 to 10.6 hectares (18.3–26.2 ac) in a 32.4-hectare (80.1

ac) millpond. In addition, two brood hens that utilized North Carolina's Little River as rearing habitat ranged as much as 2.4 kilometers (1.5 mi) along the waterway. In contrast, wood duck broods that used the Holston River in eastern Tennessee as a rearing site restricted their movements to a 0.7-kilometer (0.4 mi) segment of the river (Cottrell 1979a).

The minimum areas utilized by six brood hens in northern Louisiana were 3.9, 4.5, 24.5, 60.9, 69.7, and 71.0 hectares (9.6, 11.1, 60.5, 150.5, 172.2, and 175.4 ac) (Rothbart 1979). In South Carolina Hepp and Hair (1977) reported that home ranges of seven radio-tagged brood hens varied from 0.8 to 29.6 hectares (2.0–73.1 ac) (average = 12.5 ± 11.0 hectares: 30.9 ± 27.2 ac). These wood duck broods consistently utilized a large proportion (67 ± 11 percent) of the available wetland habitats.

Home range size seems to be influenced by amounts of usable vegetative cover. Hepp (1977) found that broods in wetlands with a limited amount of quality habitat restricted their movements by necessity to that habitat during the rearing period. In contrast, broods in close proximity to larger expanses of good cover generally were more mobile and subsequently had larger home ranges.

Daily Movement Patterns

Although wood duck broods are active throughout the day, they generally are considered to be less mobile during midday hours (Schreiner and Hendrickson 1951, Stewart 1958, Grice and Rogers 1965, McGilvrey 1969, Farmer 1970, Hepp and Hair 1977, Rothbart 1979), but there are exceptions to this pattern. Along the Holston River in Tennessee, Cottrell (1979a) documented brood activity at fixed observation points and found that wood duck broods were most active during midday and evening hours.

We made observations of the daily activity of wood duck broods on Smith Lake, a 4-hectare (10 ac) open body of water amid the agricultural lands of Mason County, Illinois, in July and August of 1980 and 1982. The lake was devoid of emergent cover, but about half of the shoreline contained a rim of large trees. A cattle feed lot was at one end.

Wood duck broods appeared on the lake twice a day—early morning and late afternoon. At other times they remained hidden in vegetation near shore or as far back as 30 meters (98.4 ft). From July 10 to August 6, 1980, feeding was active in the morning for 2.2 ± 0.4 hours. From July 10 to August 27, 1982, broods were active for 2.0 ± 0.8 hours in the morning and 1.1 ± 0.6 hours in the evening. Thus, they fed about twice as long in the morning as they did late in the day.

Because Dreis (1954) and Farmer (1970) repeatedly located individual broods in specific areas at different hours of the day, they felt that wood duck broods were fairly consistent in their daily movement patterns. Farmer (1970) found that the maximum activity period began about 15 minutes before sunrise and lasted until 10:00 a.m. By midmorning, broods generally began moving into dense cover where they remained loafing until late afternoon, when they again moved about more frequently.

Female Absence from Broods

Females of many duck species frequently leave their young unattended for periods of 15–75 minutes (Beard 1964). Stewart (1974) suggested that wood duck broods are left unattended because hens retain the same feeding patterns they established during incubation. He captured one wood duck hen feeding at a wetland 2.4 kilometers (1.5 mi) from where she temporarily left her Class I brood. In southcentral North Dakota, Talent et al. (1983) observed that mallard hens regularly left their broods to feed in grain fields; these feeding trips lasted up to two hours. The time female

woodies stay away from their young varies among individuals and with food availability, distance to the food source, and environmental conditions.

Carpenter (1953) and Ball (1971) also saw wood duck hens temporarily abandon their broods on several occasions. Ball observed no discernible temporal pattern to these absences. Because most hens moved their broods to other wetlands shortly after this activity was noted, Ball speculated that females temporarily abandoned their broods, at least in some cases, in order to search for more suitable rearing habitat.

At Nauvoo Slough, 1985–1987, we observed female wood ducks exhibit this type of behavior on 11 different occasions. Most absences lasted less than 30 minutes (average = 18 ± 8.4). Many females (64 percent) left ducklings that were less than two weeks old. Invariably, the hen left her brood while it rested at a loafing site; however, many broods moved off loafing areas and began feeding before the hens returned.

All of our observations of females temporarily abandoning broods occurred in either the early morning (5:04–6:10 a.m.) or evening (5:48–7:12 p.m.) hours. These times correspond to the feeding periods of incubating hens. Because we were unable to observe these females when they isolated themselves from their young, we could not document a reason for their departures. We surmise that they may have left in order to obtain food high in carbohydrates, in contrast to the ducklings' need for food high in protein.

BROOD HEN TOLERANCE

Wood duck females with broods usually tolerate the close approach of other adult ducks, regardless of species, so long as they show no aggressive behavior. Adults usually are allowed to encroach upon an occupied loafing site because they seldom make an attempt to dislodge brood hens. When other ducks approach a brood hen too closely, she may rush at them or simply remain stationary and lower her neck and head, with bill open, in a threat position to rebuff the intruders. At Nauvoo Slough, adult mallards and wood ducks occasionally were seen resting on logs within 0.5–1.0 meter (1.6–3.3 ft) of female wood ducks and their broods.

Although wood duck broods often feed and travel in close proximity to one another without noticeable aggression between adults or young, brood hens are intolerant of one another around loafing sites. As noted by Beard (1964), brood hens characteristically avoid loafing spots that are occupied by other broods.

On occasion, however, a female may try to dislodge another brood hen from her loafing spot. We observed a brood hen defend her loafing site from an intruding wood duck female and brood at Nauvoo Slough on May 23, 1985. The female in possession of the log was brooding six Class Ib ducklings. As another female with ducklings approached, the hen that occupied the log interrupted her brooding to chase them away. Ducklings from both broods intermixed while the adults engaged in a short skirmish. During the fight, four ducklings apparently became confused as to which hen was their parent, and the intruding hen swam away with her brood plus four ducklings that had belonged to the female occupying the loafing spot.

HEN/BROOD BOND

In contrast to the strong hen/brood bonds found in most dabbling ducks (Evans et al. 1952), wood duck hens have bonds of shorter duration. By the time young woodies reach five weeks of age, they often ignore or respond slowly to calls given by the hens attempting to gather and lead them (Beard 1964, Ball 1973). In contrast, Hochbaum (1944) observed that the females of most dabbling duck species attend their broods until the ducklings are able to fly.

Apparently the hen/brood bond in wood ducks dissolves slowly as the young ducklings grow and spend more and more time away from the female.

Brooding wood duck hens are extremely alert to potential threats to their young. Though generally tolerant of other ducks during most activity phases, a woodie hen can be quite aggressive toward other wood ducks that approach her brood's resting site, such as a log or loafing bar. *Photo by Dave Menke; courtesy of the U.S. Fish and Wildlife Service.*

Hepp (1977) pointed out that wood ducks less than one week old often act independently of their mothers. McGilvrey (1969), Farmer (1970), and Ball (1971) each indicated that ducklings sometimes leave hens rather than vice versa. In one brood intensively observed by Ball (1971), three of five young left the female when they were approximately four weeks old. Moreover, he noted that all of the ducklings abandoned the hen before she departed the rearing area. Although brood members generally begin to disperse shortly after the breakdown of the hen/brood bond (McGilvrey 1969), some individuals remain together in quasi-groups.

Fredrickson and Hansen (1983) noted that wood ducks in the southern portion of the species' breeding range commonly raise two broods per reproductive season. They found that females waited an average of 33 ± 1.8 (SE) days between hatching the first clutch and initiating the second. Thus, a brood-rearing interval of about five weeks appears adequate for most double-brooded hens in southeastern Missouri. The short hen/brood bond of wood ducks may have developed in response to environmental conditions under which young ducklings survive without prolonged parental protection from predators and adverse weather.

The wide variation in the duration of wood duck hen/brood bonds reported in the literature is not altogether unexpected, partially because of the highly variable levels of attentiveness individual hens exhibit toward their young. Although some of the brood hens that Ball (1973) observed were never known to abandon their young temporarily, others were so remiss in their attendance that Ball believed the hen/brood bond had been terminated prematurely.

Grice and Rogers (1965) reported that most hens nesting on Great Meadows National Wildlife Refuge in Massachusetts remained with their young for about 60 days, and suggested that late-nesting hens may leave their broods earlier. McGilvrey (1969) stated that hens hatching nests in Maryland after mid-June generally remained with

their young for only two or three weeks. Ball (1973) reported that early-nesting wood ducks (those hatching nests before June 23) in northcentral Minnesota remained with their young an average of 35.4 days, longer ($P<0.05$) than did late-nesting hens (23.6 days). Moreover, because the breeding season is compressed in the northern part of the breeding range, female woodies there may abandon their broods earlier than do hens in more southern latitudes because of the truncated time prior to autumn migration.

We found that the percentage of parentless broods on Nauvoo Slough increased for classes I and II as the season advanced (Table 139). Although this increase indicated that proportionally more broods were without a parent at earlier ages later in the season, most late-nesting females (77 percent) remained with their young for a minimum of six weeks (Table 139).

Bellrose (1953) stated that female woodies normally remain with their broods for about two months. Stewart (1958: 161), in discussing the dissolution of hen/brood bonds in Ohio, noted that, "While the females gave their broods less attention after about 6 weeks of age, they did not ordinarily completely abandon them at this time." Two wood duck hens that hatched their nests around June 10 on the Upper Peninsula of Michigan remained with their young for approximately five weeks (Beard 1964).

McGilvrey (1969) reported that the hen/brood bonds of five marked females in Maryland dissolved at 32, 35, 38, 44, and 47 days. On Montezuma National Wildlife Refuge in central New York, two marked females abandoned their broods before 50 days (Haramis 1975). Ball et al. (1975) found the average duration of hen/brood bonds in northcentral Minnesota to be 30.8 days. In contrast, Hepp (1977) determined that the average bond in South Carolina lasted nearly 40 days. Much of this variation in the duration of hen/brood bonds appears to stem primarily from differences in individual behavior and secondarily from latitude.

Table 139. Percentage of parentless wood duck broods on Nauvoo Slough, Illinois, 1983–87.

	Age class					
	I		II		III	
Sample interval	Percentage	Number[a]	Percentage	Number[a]	Percentage	Number[a]
May 5–25	2.5	81	0	3	0	0
May 26–June 15	3.1	287	8.7	69	0	0
June 16–July 6	2.3	130	11.7	163	72.7	11
July 7–27	5.9	85	14.6	151	56.5	62
July 28–August 17	12.5	8	22.5	40	57.1	42

[a] Total number of all brood observations.

The length of time that a wood duck hen broods her young is extremely variable. The woodie hen/brood bond may begin to dissolve in just a few weeks, usually at the initiation of the ducklings seeking independence. Only occasionally will a hen remain with her offspring until they fully fledge at about 60 days. More commonly, woodie ducklings are on their own by five to seven weeks of age. The ducklings above, still with their mother, represent an advanced Class IIc brood, about 48 days old. *Photo by F. Eugene Hester.*

Displaced Ducklings

It is not uncommon for young woodies to become separated from their brood mates. Individuals may become lost when they scatter too far while feeding and traveling, and some simply may not be strong enough to keep up with other members of the brood. Because ducklings sometimes scatter widely when attempting to escape predators, females may be unable on some occasions to relocate their entire broods. In some instances, ducklings are orphaned when their mothers are killed or desert them. If young wood ducks are unable to relocate their brood, they may form aggregations with other parentless broods (Stewart 1958), integrate into another cohesive brood (Beard 1964, Haramis 1975, McGilvrey 1969, Clawson 1975a), attempt to survive on their own, or possibly be adopted by a foster mother (Haramis 1975).

When very young ducklings are separated from their brood they often respond, seemingly without fear, to almost any sound or movement by following it. Stewart (1958) described how lost Class Ia ducklings approached and followed boats and land fishermen on the Scioto River in Ohio. In addition, Ball (1971) related how a day-old lost duckling followed a jeep for approximately 45 meters (148 ft) down an unpaved road. While inspecting nest boxes on Nauvoo Slough, we often found live woodie ducklings that were unable to exit the nest when the other members of their brood departed. Most of the young swam leisurely away after we released them, and some followed our canoe for several minutes. Stewart (1958) pointed out that this behavioral trait has survival value, particularly in areas with high brood densities, because lost woodie ducklings may increase their chances of joining another cohesive brood.

Ducklings left behind in nests when their siblings depart sometimes are able to leave on their own but probably never join their brood mates. We observed one duckling at Nauvoo Slough depart a nest box six hours after its mother had called her other young out. This duckling immediately began calling as it swam through the surrounding duck potato, as did most of the abandoned ducklings that we released from nest boxes.

Clawson (1975a) observed one young wood duck jump from a nest box six minutes after its mother stopped calling to it. By this time, the female and her brood were approximately 70 meters (230 ft) away. A second female with a brood of two two-day-old ducklings responded to the calls of the lost wood duck by giving several "kuk-kuk-kuk" (maternal) calls. The displaced duckling immediately swam over and joined her brood.

Beard (1964) noted that woodie brood hens are more willing to accept stray or orphaned young than are hens of most other duck species. She observed one female that even accepted and raised two hooded merganser ducklings in addition to her 14 woodie young.

Although wood duck brood hens are known to accept displaced ducklings into their broods (Stewart 1958, Beard 1964, Haramis 1975), the extent to which this occurs undoubtedly varies between individual hens and from one location to another. Hardister et al. (1962) used bait and drive traps to capture web-tagged broods in eastcentral North Carolina. They reported capturing three mixed-age broods. In two cases, ducklings apparently had joined younger broods. Because these older ducklings were never seen with the brood before they were trapped, Hardister could not ascertain whether the hen actually accepted them into her brood. McGilvrey (1969) observed an increased mixing of broods as wood ducks became more concentrated on his study area in Maryland. He noted that wood duck hens at Patuxent Wildlife Research Center readily accepted displaced young, even those of different ages.

In contrast, Haramis (1975) observed that female woodies on the Montezuma National Wildlife Refuge in central New York appeared to accept only stray ducklings that were the same age as their own young. Of 648 brood sightings we documented at Nauvoo Slough in 1985 and 1986, only three were of mixed-age broods.

By making almost daily observations of a marked (nasal saddle) brood hen at Nauvoo Slough, we were able to document changes in her brood size (Table 140). Within one week, two ducklings had joined her original brood of 11. She accepted two additional displaced ducklings the following week. Thus, a minimum of four orphaned young were integrated into her brood. Distinction in age could be observed between her original young and those that were accepted into the brood.

Table 140. Changes in the number of wood duck young comprising one cohesive brood on Nauvoo Slough, Illinois, 1985.

Date observed	Brood size	Estimated age (days)
May 28	11	3
May 31	13	6
June 6	15	12
June 18	14	24
June 19	12	25
July 1	11	36
July 3	8	38

The subsequent decrease in brood size may have occurred as a result of duckling mortality or in response to the gradual dissolution of the hen/brood bond.

Two of four patagial-tagged brood hens that Haramis (1975) observed accepted displaced young into their broods. In one instance, he observed a female attending to 16 ducklings 48 days after her original brood of 12 had left the nest. A second female that had an original brood of 13 young was later observed leading 15 ducklings.

Not all displaced young are accepted into intact broods. On several occasions, we have witnessed females with Class I broods chase away stray ducklings of similar ages. Moreover, brood hens typically repel stray ducklings that attempt to join a younger brood.

As the hen/brood bond weakens, however, females apparently become more tolerant of displaced ducklings. Haramis (1975) observed that females with Class II ducklings often allowed older young to tag along approximately 3 meters (10 ft) behind their brood.

On July 8, 1985, we observed a parentless brood of 10 Class Ia ducklings feeding and traveling together in a continuous backwater area of the Mississippi River. The ducklings were observed at this same location until July 17. On July 10, one Class Ib wood duck joined the brood. Two days later, the brood had diminished in size to six Class Ia and one Class Ib duckling. The behavior of this brood varied noticeably from broods that were attended by hens. The parentless ducklings were obviously less wary and allowed us to approach within 3–4 meters (9.8–13.1 ft) before they began swimming leisurely away from us. We elicited no noticeable fear as we moved about along the shoreline within 5–7 meters (16.4–23.0 ft) of them. Stewart (1958) reported that he followed one brood of young ducklings, which had become separated from their mother, at an approximate distance of 5 meters (16.4 ft) for more than an hour without eliciting escape behavior.

It is not uncommon for ducklings to become separated from their natural broods. Individual young tend to attempt to fend for themselves or attach to another like-age brood of woodies. Because woodie ducklings are not dependent on adults for food, and despite their vulnerability to predators (because of flightlessness and the absence of a brood hen's alerts to danger), some orphans survive to adulthood. *Photo by Stephen Kirkpatrick.*

ESCAPE BEHAVIORS OF FLIGHTLESS YOUNG

Wood duck brood hens are ever alert to potential danger. The types of evasive action that females and broods take when danger threatens vary with brood age, proximity to protective cover, and immediacy of the disturbance.

Woodie ducklings of all ages often dive when threatened at some distance from concealing cover. Stewart (1957) caused one individual that had just left its nest to dive. He noted that the duckling remained submerged for 7.5 seconds and swam underwater at a speed of slightly more than 0.6 meter per second (2 ft/sec). When Dreis (1954) pursued four- to five-week-old wood duck broods, he noted that they frequently dove, swam underwater, and subsequently emerged in protective cover or ran into terrestrial vegetation after surfacing near shore.

In late May 1958, William Starrett released two two-day-old wood ducks in a backwater area of the Illinois River. While calling almost continuously, they swam into and about a nearby brush pile. About 10 minutes after their release, an English setter approached one of the ducklings. The two-day-old wood duck immediately dove. The duckling continued to dive as the dog swam around looking for it. No less than 20–25 dives were made

during the 20-minute attack. During each dive, which lasted from 10 to 20 seconds, the duckling was able to propel itself approximately 3 meters (10 ft) underwater.

Hens with broods five weeks of age and older often abandon their young and simply fly away at the approach of danger, regardless of their proximity to protective cover (Ball 1971). Because of the evasive behavior of wood duck hens, older ducklings often are forced to avert predation attempts on their own. Depending on the intensity of pursuit, ducklings usually either swim to cover or dive and attempt to swim underwater to cover. Class III ducklings living on swift-flowing streams in the Ozark region of Missouri sometimes attempt to avoid predation by squatting motionless at the edge of gravel bars (Vance 1986).

When threatened from a relatively long distance, females with younger broods normally lead their ducklings, bunched tightly or in close single file, as quickly as possible into cover. If the ducklings are younger than four weeks, they often skitter across the surface of the water at a speed that is about 9.5 times faster than their normal swimming speed (Stewart 1957). Older ducklings rely less on skittering and more on rapid swimming when attempting to escape danger. As noted by McGilvrey (1969), the female often utters a danger call as she leads her young to concealing vegetation.

Hens with broods less than one week old seldom leave their young when disturbed. If pursued, they usually continue to lead the young and often double back around the predator (Ball 1971). Although hens with broods older than four weeks often fly away when disturbed (Ball 1971), they seldom leave broods less than four weeks old before finding cover for them. After leading two- to four-week-old ducklings into cover, however, they often flush and fly away. Ball (1971) noted that females in this situation usually uttered several "yeeeek" calls and appeared to fly away at a slower flight speed than normal. Hence, this behavior could be considered a form of tolling, in that the female attempts to divert attention from her brood by moving conspicuously away from it. After several minutes she generally circles back and, if the danger has passed, lands and swims into the cover where her brood is hidden or, less commonly, calls her brood out from the vegetation.

Brood hens that are forced out of cover or pursued in open water often feign injury while the ducklings scatter and seek cover. Ball (1971) speculated that either the call given by a hen when she begins her feigning display or her posture at this time cues the young to disperse and dive or swim to cover. The hen quickly moves away from her brood in an apparent effort to attract attention in her direction. When intensely pursued, a brood hen may continue to feign injury until she lures the predator more than 0.8 kilometer (0.5 mi) from her brood.

On a swamp in southern Connecticut, Saunders (1937: 202) observed a female wood duck feign injury and divert the attacks of a red-shouldered hawk away from her Class I brood: "The mother instantly extended her head and neck upon the water, turned on one side, flapped one wing in the air and paddled about in circles as though quite helpless. The hawk immediately turned and struck at her."

On a number of occasions, we have surprised brood females that subsequently performed similar feigning behavior. In all cases, the hens were observed to move away from their young in more or less straight lines. They usually made a sudden thrust forward, with head and neck outstretched, while flapping their wings on the water or land. Although females that engaged in this behavior on land generally continued to move away from us, hens on water often deviated from their course of travel, turning at some point to determine the immediacy of danger.

Prince (1965) observed a female wood duck feign injury and lead a mink approximately 60 meters (197 ft) across a stretch of open water before she flew off and returned to her Class I young. He

Hundreds of brood counts have revealed that the greatest loss of woodie ducklings occurs during the first two weeks of life, a time when their physiological growth rate is most rapid. Above, the hen's swimming posture and the surge of water around her chest as she escorts the four surviving members (Class Ib) of her brood indicate a rapid pace away from potential danger. *Photo by Jim Rathert; courtesy of the Missouri Department of Conservation.*

noted that the hen stopped several times and allowed the mink to catch up and approach within 1–2 meters (3.3–6.6 ft) before she continued her feigning display.

As noted by Ball (1971), the intensity of this display varies with the degree of pursuit. Females that are not actively pursued may flap their wings only a few times before taking flight. They usually land a short distance away but remain alert and call vociferously while swimming about.

SURVIVAL OF FLIGHTLESS YOUNG

Precocial birds usually experience their highest levels of mortality during the first week after hatching (Welty 1979). The wood duck is no exception, and broods may experience up to 90 percent of their total prefledge mortality during the first two weeks after leaving their nests (McGilvrey 1969). Factors responsible for initial losses include predation, chilling, disease, accidents, water impermanence, and a lack of suitable cover and food. Moreover, survival can be importantly influenced by nest location because broods that hatch far from rearing habitat normally suffer higher initial losses (Leopold 1951, Klein 1955, Odom 1970, Ball et al. 1975, Ridlehuber 1980) than those that hatch over water near good brood habitat (Grice and Rogers 1965, McGilvrey 1969, Baker 1971, Haramis 1975).

The relative importance of specific mortality factors has not been adequately determined. As a result, causes of prefledge mortality are poorly understood. The significance of a specific mortality factor varies from one area to another because of different environmental conditions. Drowning, for instance, can be a serious cause of duckling fatality on wetlands where extensive algae mats grow. Stewart (1967b) noted that young ducklings frequently attempt to evade danger by diving and swimming underwater. On several occasions he observed submerged ducklings become entangled and drown among filamentous algae.

Diseases can become a serious mortality factor when environmental conditions are favorable for their spread. On the Piedmont National Wildlife Refuge in Georgia, botulism outbreaks caused the death of many young wood ducks during the summers of 1968 and 1969 (Odom 1970). At various times from 1977 through 1989, we found woodie ducklings sick from a botulismlike disease along Quiver Creek.

Throughout the wood duck's breeding range, however, predation is presumed to be the principal cause of duckling loss. The same wetlands that woodies use for brood rearing are frequented by a diverse array of predators. Mammals are most likely to capture ducklings when broods travel overland or leave water to rest and feed along the shoreline.

Minks, raccoons, foxes, weasels, and domestic cats and dogs are chief mammalian predators. Most avian predators capture young woodies either by waiting in ambush or by attacking from the air. Great horned owls probably are the most dangerous avian threat to young wood ducks. Ducklings also are subject to attack from a variety of aquatic predators, particularly large predacious fishes (largemouth bass, bowfin, chain pickerel, and northern pike), water snakes, cottonmouth moccasins, snapping turtles, alligators, and bullfrogs (Table 141).

Mortality caused by predatory species varies from wetland to wetland and year to year because of changing environmental conditions and fluctuating predator and prey populations. Predators may limit duckling populations on certain wetlands but appear to have little influence on wood duck production beyond the local level. Ducklings probably are most vulnerable when stranded or concentrated in inferior habitat during years when low water levels reduce available food and cover.

A variety of sampling techniques has been used to assess survival and mortality rates of wood ducks during the prefledging period. Direct observations of marked brood hens provide reliable information, because the occurrence and extent of total brood mortality or the integration of displaced ducklings into cohesive broods can be determined.

Table 141. Predators known to have consumed or pursued young wood ducks.

Mammals	Birds	Fish	Reptiles	Amphibians	Source
	Red-shouldered hawk[a]				Saunders (1937)
			Water snake[a]		Gigstead (1938)
			Snapping turtle		Alexander (1943)
	Northern harrier				Wright (1954)
			Bull snake[b]		Bellrose (1953)
			Snapping turtle		Coulter (1957b)
Mink[a]					Beard (1964)
Raccoon	Great horned owl				Grice and Rogers (1965)
Mink					
Mink[a]	Black tern[a]				Prince (1965)
	Peregrine falcon				
				Bullfrog	Stewart (1967c)
	Red-tailed hawk[a]				Farmer (1970)
		Bowfin			Baker (1971)
		Bass			
			Snapping turtle		Odom (1970)
	Black-crowned night heron				DiGiulio (1978)
	Northern harrier				Rothbart (1979)
	Great horned owl				Haramis and Thompson (1984)
Mink			Snapping turtle		This study

[a] Observed pursuing ducklings.
[b] Ducklings were captured while in nest box.

The amount of loss of wood duck adults and broods to alligators is unknown, but it may be significant in habitats where both are numerous (top right). The same is true of snapping turtles (top left), which are particularly adept at taking flightless young. Adult wood ducks have been observed flanking and trailing both alligators and large snapping turtles. They apparently recognize these species as being dangerous to their survival but of limited mobility. By knowing where these predators are, the woodies reduce the possibility of a surprise attack. Cottonmouths (bottom) inhabit southern swamps and streams and, along with other water snakes, are considered to be predators of woodie ducklings, although their basic diet is fish and frogs. *Top right photo by Frank Bellrose; courtesy of the Illinois Natural History Survey; top left photo by F. Eugene Hester. Bottom photo by Jack Dermid.*

Several researchers have used the Lincoln/ Peterson mark/recapture sampling to determine duckling survival rates (Table 142). Although this method requires the recapture of marked ducklings, it is superior to brood observations because ducklings that leave broods or become separated and survive are included in the estimate. In many studies, however, survival has been determined by counting the number of young per brood, estimating their age, and calculating an overall average brood size (brood size counts). Although such counts frequently are used to determine survival rates, they may overestimate production levels because they do not account for loss of entire broods (Ball et al. 1975, David 1986). In addition, this method does not account for brood mixing and the oversight of ducklings in dense vegetation. Adequate sampling of brood sizes would minimize the effect of brood mixing on the entity of a brood by prorating ducklings among all brood hens.

Table 142. Wood duck brood survivalship from selected areas throughout their breeding range.

State	Average brood size at flight stage	Percentage of young raised to flight stage	Method of determining survivalship[a]	Source
New York	4.6	41	Brood size counts	Klein (1955)
Massachusetts			Return and recapture of one-year-old hens web-tagged as ducklings	Grice and Rogers (1965)
1952	5.7	53		
1953	5.8	42		
1954	5.8	48		
New Brunswick	8.3	59	Brood size counts	Prince (1965)
North Carolina	3.4	38	Grice and Rogers (1965) method	Holloman (1967)
Maryland				McGilvrey (1969)
1964	5.6	53	Brood size counts	
1965	5.2	50		
1966	5.3	59		
1967	4.9	53		
Mississippi				
1968	5.4	56	Grice and Rogers (1965) method	Baker (1971)
1969	5.6	52	Brood size counts	
Arkansas	6.0	52	Grice and Rogers (1965) method	Brown (1972a)
New York				
1972–73	6.5	59	Brood size counts	Haramis (1975)
1974	7.9	61		
		48	Grice and Rogers (1965) method	
South Carolina		68	Marked broods	Hepp (1977)
Tennessee	5.0	44	Brood size counts	Cottrell (1979a)
Louisiana	6.8	58	Marked broods	Rothbart (1979)
Illinois	4.5	40[b]	Marked broods	David (1986)
1983	6.2	56	Brood size counts	This study
1984	5.3	56		
1985	6.3	48		
1986	5.9	55		
1987	5.6	53		
Mean	5.7 ± 1.04	52.1 ± 7.24		

[a] No observations of broods older than six weeks are included when brood size counts were used.
[b] No observations of broods older than 35 days are included in the survivalship estimate.

On their northcentral Minnesota study area, Ball et al. (1975) determined that all ducklings were lost from 5 of 21 (23.8 percent) marked wood duck broods. If they had calculated survival rates based solely on brood size counts, production estimates might have been inflated by 38 percent. Similarly, David (1986) reported that 5 of 26 (19.2 percent) nesting hens marked at Max McGraw Wildlife Foundation in northern Illinois lost their entire broods. At Muscatatuck National Wildlife Refuge in Indiana, Robb and Bookhout (1990) found that all ducklings in 18 percent of the wood duck broods were lost. Overall, brood size counts would have inflated production estimates by about 20 percent. In addition, several researchers have indicated that production levels of mallard and American black duck broods were seriously overestimated when total brood losses were not accounted for (Ball et al. 1975, Reed 1975, Ringelman and Longcore 1982, Talent et al. 1983).

In most cases, observers have not determined whether the complete loss of all ducklings represented mortality or dissolution of the brood. Farmer (1970) and Fredrickson and Hansen (1983) indicated that some wood duck brood bonds dissolve as early as three weeks after hatching. Many researchers have noted the propensity of woodie ducklings to become separated from their brood or to mix with other broods. In addition, two broods may merge and be raised by one hen (Stewart 1958). The extent to which these events occur needs to be evaluated further. Nevertheless, the presence of a broodless hen does not necessarily indicate that all of her young died or were killed. In many instances, some of the ducklings may have survived to flight stage.

Don Dick observed parentless young wood ducks on a pond in Pratt, Kansas, for approximately three months. His observations began on May 9, 1986, when five one-day-old orphaned ducklings were discovered. Although another five young joined the initial ducklings on May 20, no maternal females were present. The parentless birds were observed at least once a week during May and June. Four of the 10 ducklings were still alive on June 24; one bird was noticeably larger than the others. These same individuals were seen again on July 29. Snapping turtles and a great horned owl were suspected predators.

Haramis (1975) also determined that wood duck ducklings can survive when separated from their mothers at a very early age. He found the remains of a patagial-tagged female three days after she called her brood of 15 from the nest. Despite being orphaned within several days after hatching, three of her ducklings were captured as flying juveniles later in the year. Such survival of motherless woodie ducklings indicates that some broods that lose their mothers are not necessarily or entirely lost from populations.

At the Patuxent Wildlife Research Center in Maryland, McGilvrey (1969) found that wood duck broods experienced little mortality after reaching five weeks of age. The average brood size of six-week-old ducklings was only 0.3 young less than that of four-week-old broods. On the Noxubee National Wildlife Refuge in Mississippi, broods also experienced an average mortality rate between four and six weeks of age of only 0.3 duckling per brood (Baker 1971).

The behavioral traits of young wood ducks preclude using brood size counts to assess duckling survival beyond six weeks of age. In many cases, counts that include Class III individuals seriously underestimate prefledge survival, because many of the ducklings that leave as the hen/brood bond dissolves live to flight stage. Moreover, some Class III broods have inflated sizes as a result of integrating displaced young and combining broods, as discussed earlier. Wright (1954) and Haramis (1975) found that Class III broods were larger than Class I and II broods.

Although brood mortality rates may vary widely among brood hens on the same wetland, from year to year, and between wetlands, studies of wood duck brood survival show that, on average, about half of the ducklings that leave a nest survive to flight stage (Table 142). Bellrose (1976) reported that an average of 11 young woodies depart a successful nest and that the mean sizes of Class I, II, and III broods are 6.9, 5.7, and 5.4 ducklings, respectively. Thus, brood size is reduced by about five ducklings (45 percent) between hatch and fledging.

McGilvrey (1969), Baker (1971), Ball et al. (1975), Hepp (1977), Rothbart (1979), David (1986), and Robb and Bookhout (1990) have reported that duckling mortality was most severe during the first two weeks following nest exodus—90 percent, 74 percent, 86 percent, 56 percent, 74 percent, 76 percent, and 79 percent, respectively. Although 83 percent of all prefledge mortality from 18 radio-tagged broods in eastcentral Texas occurred within the first 10 days, 63 percent occurred during the first two days (Ridlehuber 1980).

Wood ducks experience a much higher loss of young during the prefledging period than do representative prairie dabbling ducks (Table 143). Data in

The presence of 12 Class Ib brooded ducklings, about 35 days old, suggests an ideal rearing area, requiring limited daily movement to food and shelter, excellent protective cover, and few predators in the vicinity. There also is a probability, albeit small in this instance because of the uniform age of the young, that a number of the ducklings were "adopted" by the hen. *Photo by Ed Bry; courtesy of the North Dakota Game and Fish Department.*

Table 143. Comparative losses in broods among several species of ducks between hatching and Class II-developed ducklings.[a]

Species	Number of young			Percentage loss
	Hatching	Class I	Class II	
Wood duck	11.0	6.9	5.7	48.2
Mallard	8.4	6.6	6.1	27.4
Northern pintail	6.9	5.9	5.6	18.8
Northern shoveler	8.7	6.8	6.5	25.3
Blue-winged teal	9.5	8.4	7.9	16.8

[a] Based on data presented in Bellrose (1976).

Chapter 18 indicate that wood ducks also may experience a higher level of total brood mortality than do many prairie ducks. The food resources over all of the wood duck's range are not as favorable for broods as are the food resources for prairie duck broods when potholes are normal. In addition, the greater loss in wood duck broods probably stems from differences in predator pressure in the deciduous forest and prairie biomes. As shown by the list of predators in Table 141, woodie ducklings encounter a formidable array of animals—many of them abundant—that are a threat to their survival.

Because wood ducks have coexisted with heavy nest and brood predator populations since historic times, they have evolved strategies to prosper: (1) a large clutch size; (2) a long breeding season; (3) double brood production in the South, where predators are most abundant; and (4) brood hens that are more alert and attentive than those of other duck species.

Motherless Broods

Ducklings that are led by a female presumably have a better chance of survival than do parentless young. Hens not only lead ducklings to food sources and cover but also protect them from exposure and predators. In northcentral Minnesota, however, Ball et al. (1975) found no appreciable difference (P > 0.30) between the number of two- to four-week-old ducklings in broods led by females (average = 5.70) and those surviving on their own (average = 5.57). Because young wood ducks sometimes are left alone while the hen feeds away from them, and as a result of their independent behavior, Ball et al. (1975) suggested that the permanent absence of a hen may have little effect on brood survival. In support of this claim, they noted that parentless broods more than four weeks old averaged about the same number (P > 0.40) (5.13 ducklings per brood) as did younger parentless broods (5.14 ducklings per brood). Although the possibilities of

total brood mortality and ducklings merging into larger broods were not considered, the Ball et al. (1975) data indicated that young wood ducks, even when abandoned at a very early age, may suffer mortality rates similar to the rates experienced by broods that are led by hens.

From 1983 to 1987, we observed 27 parentless broods on Nauvoo Slough that were between two and four weeks old. The number of ducklings in these broods was compared with the number in similar-aged broods seen on the same days but attended by hens. Broods led by females were significantly larger (P < 0.01, t = 6.47) (average = 7.43) than were parentless broods of the same ages (average = 3.74). It is not surprising that the survival pattern of parentless broods studied by Ball et al. (1975) disagrees with our data, because variation in duckling survival rates from wetland to wetland may occur due to variations in food resources, cover, and kinds and abundance of predators.

Other Factors Affecting Brood Survival

Grice and Rogers (1965) found that duckling survival on Great Meadows National Wildlife Refuge in Massachusetts was related to time of hatching (Table 144). Sixty-six percent of the ducklings that hatched early survived to flight stage, whereas only 22 percent lived of those hatched late in the season. Grice and Rogers suggested that a combination of factors may have led to elevated late-season mortality: (1) travel in response to crowded rearing conditions; (2) early abandonment by the hen; (3) increased brood concentrations due to low water levels, thus higher susceptibility to predation and disease; (4) lower or less available food sources; and (5) inadequate time available for ducklings to mature before autumn migration. Rothbart (1979) also found that early-hatched broods in Louisiana had a higher survival rate (62.5 percent) than did late-season hatches (53.0 percent); the difference was not significant (P > 0.05).

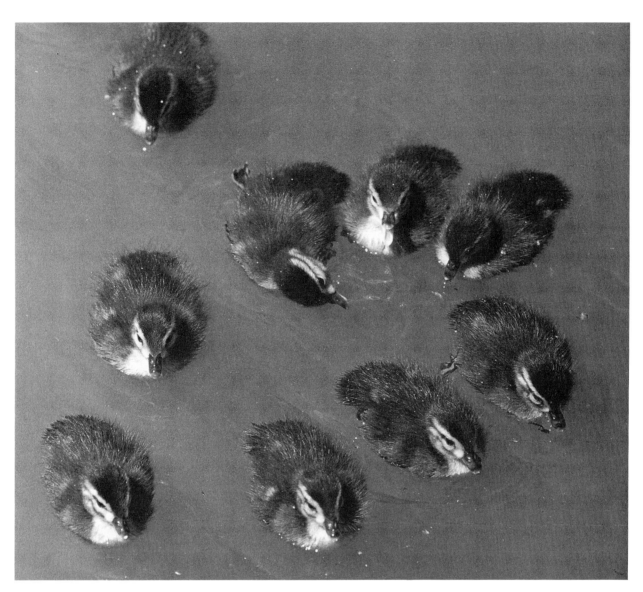

Wood duck broods abandoned or otherwise permanently separated from their mothers after the ducklings are several weeks old may experience mortality loss no greater than attended broods. Such survival, of course, depends on food availability, optimal weather conditions, and limited predation. Furthermore, the evidence of survival of motherless broods rarely factors in the losses of entire broods, so the actual rate of survival may be significantly less than for brooded woodies. Overall, brooded woodie ducklings are more likely to survive to flight age than are motherless young. *Photo by Jack Dermid.*

Table 144. Survival of wood duck broods hatched at Great Meadows National Wildlife Refuge, Massachusetts, in relation to time of hatching, 1952-54.[a]

Period hatched	Number of hatched nests	Average brood size at hatching	Brood size at flight
May 10–31	48	14.1	9.3
June 1–21	48	12.9	5.4
June 22–July 19	39	9.9	2.2

[a] From Grice and Rogers (1965).

In order to evaluate seasonal differences in brood mortality on Nauvoo Slough, 1984–1987, we divided the brood-rearing season into three arbitrary periods: May 1–June 4, June 5–July 2, and July 3–30. Estimates of brood survival did not differ ($P > 0.05$) throughout the four-year study (chi-square = 2.44). During each period, brood size was correlated ($P < 0.01$) with brood age. Average brood size declined by 1.12, 1.00, and 0.74 ducklings per brood per week during May, June, and July, respectively (Figure 87). Although brood size at hatching varied ($P < 0.01$) with seasonal advancement, no differences ($P > 0.05$) in mortality rates between time periods were evident.

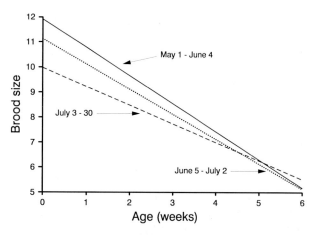

Figure 87. Seasonal differences in wood duck brood survival on Nauvoo Slough, Illinois, 1984–87. The regression equations for May, June, and July periods, respectively, are: y = 11.92 − 1.12x, r = −0.28, P < 0.01; y = 11.13 − 1.00x, r = −0.46, P < 0.01; and y = 9.98 − 0.74x, r = −0.44, P < 0.01.

The earliest hatched broods lost an average of 4.95 ducklings by the time they reached four weeks of age. Most of this mortality (94.5 percent) occurred during their first two weeks of life (Table 145). Broods that hatched in June and July lost an average of 5.19 and 2.76 ducklings, respectively, between nest exodus and fledging. July-hatched young incurred only 1.3 percent mortality during their first two weeks of life (Table 145). Early-hatched brood losses were probably high because of rain, cold temperatures, and lack of adequate brood-rearing cover. Initial losses of late-hatched broods probably were minimized because of improved food resources, weather, and rearing cover. Overall, initial losses were minimized because nest boxes on Nauvoo Slough were located over water in or adjacent to excellent brood-rearing habitat.

Survival rates of young wood ducks increase when they are hatched near or over water in good brood habitat. Prokop (1981) characterized most of Oklahoma's mud channel rivers as inferior wood duck brood-rearing areas because they contain little protective cover. He found duckling survival on these rivers to be only 19 percent. The highest survival rates that have been reported are by broods hatched and raised on relatively large impoundments (more than 2.5 hectares: 6.2 ac) with readily accessible cover.

No difference in survival of broods reared by adult or yearling females was found by Grice and Rogers (1965) in Massachusetts. Hens that were found nesting for the first time on the Max McGraw Wildlife Foundation in Illinois hatched larger broods (average = 11.6) than known adult hens (average = 10.9); however, yearlings raised significantly (P < 0.05) fewer (2.8 versus 5.6) ducklings to 35 days of age (David 1986).

Although it has been determined that, in some cases, ducklings from each clutch of double-brooded hens have survived, estimated mortality rates of ducklings from each brood have seldom been defined. By observing marked (nasal saddle) females, Rothbart (1979) was able to compute the survival rates of ducklings from two double-brooded hens in northern Louisiana. In one instance, the first brood of 15 ducklings (hatched April 19) had a prefledge survival rate of 60 percent, whereas 42 percent of the second brood of 12 young (hatched July 19) remained together as a cohesive group 26 days after hatching. A second female called 13 and 6 young from her nests on April 21 and July 18, respectively. Survival rates for these broods were 54 and 50 percent, respectively.

Heusmann (1972) found nearly equal recapture rates of ducklings hatched from dump nests (26.4

Table 145. Seasonal changes in wood duck brood sizes at Nauvoo Slough, Illinois, 1984–87.[a]

Mean brood size	Brood-rearing period								
	May 1–June 4			June 5–July 2			July 3–30		
	Number	Average	S.D.	Number	Average	S.D.	Number	Average	S.D.
Nest exodus	57	13.30	5.30	67	11.06	5.09	32	8.63	4.09
1 week	106	10.34	5.10	80	10.86	3.81	20	12.00	3.63
2 weeks	71	8.62	3.67	63	8.19	2.94	27	8.52	2.23
3 weeks	62	8.61	3.93	93	8.25	3.36	24	8.21	2.28
4 weeks	17	8.35	3.41	77	6.65	2.66	45	6.64	2.55
5 weeks	5	11.20	4.38	61	6.25	3.00	35	5.63	2.70
6 weeks				30	5.87	2.47	39	5.87	2.80
Total/mean by week	318	10.07 ± 1.95		471	8.16 ± 2.12		222	7.93 ± 2.19	

[a] Although our observations included broods that hatched from natural cavities, brood size at nest departure was obtained only for broods that hatched in nest boxes on the refuge.

percent) and normal nests (26.0 percent) in Massachusetts. Similarly, in Louisiana, Rothbart (1979) found no appreciable difference ($P > 0.05$) in survival rates of small (1–8 ducklings), moderate (9–15 ducklings), and large (more than 15 ducklings) broods. Thus, within limits, brood size appears to have little influence on the ability of female wood ducks to protect their ducklings from decimating factors. Hens that hatch larger clutches generally raise proportionally more young to flight stage.

Hepp (1977) suggested that the optimum survival of young wood ducks requires extended areas of quality brood habitat. In such situations, brood hens tend to disperse rather evenly throughout the area. As a result, predators normally capture fewer young. This theory is supported by the relatively low mortality rates of 32, 42, and 48 percent found on impoundments and in high-quality stream habitat where brood hens could disperse without the hazards of overland travel (Hepp 1977, Rothbart 1979, Baker 1971). In contrast, mortality rates of 92, 81, and 59 percent have been documented on poor-quality streams or small upland marshes by Ridlehuber (1980), Prokop (1981), and Klein (1955).

The crux of brood production is how many young survive to flight stage. This is difficult to ascertain because some females that lose early broods renest and other females raise two broods. And then there is the larger question of how many hens fail to hatch a brood. But based on brood survival data per se, it appears that the average successful nesting hen raises 4.6 young to flight stage (5.7 young minus 20 percent for entire brood losses).

The larger picture on productivity will be addressed in Chapter 18 through the examination of age ratios—the proportion of adults and juveniles in hunters' bags.

Chapter 13

Growth, Plumage, and Molt

GROWTH

When adequate supplies of cover and nutritious foods are available, young wood ducks grow rapidly. Ducklings require about 100 days to increase their hatching weight of approximately 25 grams (0.88 oz) to more than 600 grams (21.16 oz). Bellrose (1976) reported that during the autumn hunting season immature wood ducks weighed nearly as much as adult birds—immature males averaged 13 grams (0.46 oz) less than adult males, whereas immature females were about 59 grams (2.08 oz) lighter than adult hens.

At hatching, male and female wood ducks have essentially the same (P > 0.05) body mass (Luckett 1977, Hepp et al. 1987). Because wood duck eggs vary in size within and between clutches (see Chapter 10), it is not surprising that the weights of newly hatched young also vary (Table 146). According to Hepp et al. (1987) the heaviest ducklings hatch from the largest eggs. Average body mass measurements of one-day-old wood ducks vary slightly geographically (Table 147). Either genetic or nutritional factors, separately or in combination, appear responsible for the mostly subtle geographic differences in average weights of day-old wood ducks. Although both sexes grow at similar rates (P > 0.05) and reach mature (asymptotic) size within a day or two of one another (P > 0.05), males grow to slightly but significantly (P < 0.01) larger sizes than do females (Brisbin et al. 1987).

Posthatching growth can be dramatically affected by food quality, ambient temperatures, and activity of growing ducklings (Lightbody 1985). Obviously, dietary deficiencies can retard the development of growing birds. Johnson (1971) found a direct relationship between survival and growth and the level of protein ingested by juvenile wood ducks (Table 148). His data revealed that low protein intake can retard development of plumage, body mass, and tarsus length. Dietary protein restrictions at 5- and 10-percent levels markedly reduced these parameters of growth.

According to David Grice (in Johnson 1971), the average age at which young wood ducks reached flight stage on Great Meadows National Wildlife Refuge in Massachusetts varied from 60 days in 1952–1954 to 73 days in 1964. Grice attributed the slower plumage development during 1964 to diminished aquatic invertebrate populations that provide high-protein foods.

Captive-reared wood ducks are traditionally fed optimum diets, so they have the potential to exhibit maximum growth rates. Because wild wood ducks grow under a wide range of environmental conditions, individuals within and among populations undoubtedly follow different growth curves. Haramis (1975) used a logistic model to determine a growth curve for known-age wild wood ducks of both sexes (n = 103) (Figure 88). He determined that wood ducks on the Montezuma National Wildlife Refuge in New York reached 608 grams (21.45 oz) at approximately 126 days of age. At hatching, ducklings weighed only 4.13 percent of their mature weight. Their greatest percentage of weight gain occurred during the first and second weeks, when

Table 146. Average body mass of day-old wood duck ducklings captured in nest boxes on Quiver Creek, central Illinois.

Date	Number weighed in clutch	Weight[a]					
		Mean		S.E.		Range	
June 15	9	25.64	(0.904)	0.18	(0.006)	24.9–26.4	(0.878–0.931)
June 27	8	25.71	(0.907)	0.22	(0.008)	24.8–26.5	(0.875–0.935)
July 1	7	25.81	(0.910)	0.26	(0.009)	24.8–26.8	(0.875–0.945)
July 2	10	25.46	(0.898)	0.28	(0.010)	24.0–26.4	(0.847–0.931)
July 5	9	24.53	(0.865)	0.29	(0.010)	23.5–26.0	(0.829–0.917)
July 6	6	25.52	(0.900)	0.21	(0.007)	24.6–26.2	(0.868–0.924)
July 13	7	24.84	(0.876)	0.35	(0.012)	23.6–26.3	(0.832–0.928)
July 20	7	24.79	(0.874)	0.25	(0.009)	23.8–25.9	(0.840–0.914)
July 24	7	24.67	(0.870)	0.35	(0.012)	23.3–25.9	(0.822–0.914)
July 29	6	24.45	(0.862)	0.25	(0.009)	23.7–25.2	(0.836–0.889)
Total/mean	76	25.14	(0.887)	0.10	(0.004)	23.3–26.8	(0.822–0.945)

[a] In grams (oz).

Table 147. Average body mass (grams) of day-old wood duck ducklings from various locations throughout the species' breeding range.

State	Male			Female			Both sexes combined			Source
	n	Mean	S.D.	n	Mean	S.D.	n	Mean	S.D.	
Ohio							5	24.7		Stewart (1957)
New York							320	27.8	0.095	Haramis (1975)
South Carolina										Fendley and Brisbin (1977)
Site 1	22	24.3	1.6±2[a]	28	24.2	1.2±2[a]	50	24.2		
Site 2	10	25.1	1.7±2[a]	10	26.5	1.7±2[a]	20	25.8		
Site 3[b]	28	24.9	1.2±2[a]	25	24.5	1.4±2[a]	53	24.7		
South Carolina	92	27.1	0.11	96	26.4	0.11	188	26.8	0.13	Luckett (1977)
South Carolina							43	23.7	0.35	Hepp et al. (1987)
Illinois							76	25.1	0.10	This study
Total/weighted mean	152	26.2		159	25.7		755	26.5		

[a] ±2 standard errors.
[b] Study area was contaminated with nuclear reactor effluents.

Table 148. Relationship between levels of dietary protein to survival and primary development of growing wood ducks.[a]

Percentage of protein in diet	Survival to 60 days		Age (days) at which primaries appeared
	Percentage	n	
5	11	6	>59
10	25	9	50
15	53	25	43
20	63	24	39

[a] From Johnson (1971).

ducklings daily gained 5.5 and 5.7 percent of their existing weights. As they grew older this percentage steadily declined, presumably because more energy was needed for maintenance of tissues. By week 10, wood ducks added only 0.7 percent of

their weight daily. The highest percentage of their mature weight gain occurred during week six, when 14 percent of their final weight was added (Figure 89).

Growth rates also can vary during the course of a brood-rearing season because aquatic invertebrates often are less abundant later in summer (Hubert and Krull 1973, Haramis 1975, Drobney and Fredrickson 1979). Haramis (1975) showed that ducklings from late-hatched wood duck broods on the Montezuma National Wildlife Refuge in New York experienced retarded growth rates of primary feathers. He estimated that primary feather development on two 78-day-old late-hatched ducklings was delayed by as much as 20 and 28 days. In addition to extending the flightless period, protein deficiencies undoubtedly diminish the health of growing ducklings, potentially increasing their susceptibility to predators and disease.

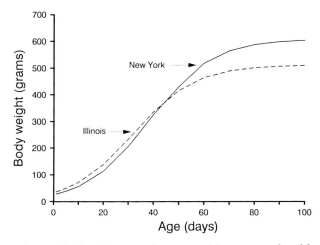

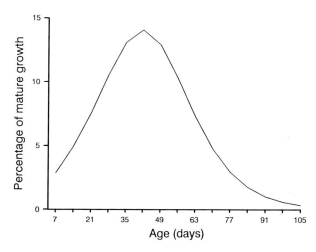

Figure 88. Logistic growth curve of known-aged wild wood ducks (n = 103) captured on Montezuma National Wildlife Refuge, New York (Haramis 1975), and wood ducks (n = 237 data sets) raised at the Van Norman Aviary, Illinois.

Figure 89. Cumulative percentage of mature (asymptotic) weight gained by young wood ducks during the first 14 weeks of life (from Haramis 1975).

Day-old woodie ducklings weigh about 25 grams (0.9 oz). At three days of age (top left) they weigh about 28.4 grams (1 oz). For the first 40–45 days their growth is very rapid, so that when they reach that age, they weigh about 400 grams (14 oz). At 22 days old (top right), woodie ducklings weigh about 175 grams (6 oz). Juvenile feathers are replacing down on the breast, belly, and sides. At 28 days of age (bottom) they weigh about 200 grams (7 oz), which is approximately one-third of their eventual mature weight. Juvenile feathers are just beginning to supplant down on the cheeks. *Top left photo by Jack Dermid. Top right photo by David McEwen. Bottom photo by Ed Bry; courtesy of the North Dakota Game and Fish Department.*

Growth Characteristics

Woodie ducklings may lose 4–5 grams (0.14–0.18 oz) of their hatching weight before they leave the nest. Roughly 2–4 grams (0.07–0.14 oz) of water are evaporated as the down feathers dry. Stewart (1957) found that five wood ducks lost an average of 0.8 gram (0.03 oz) between drying and nest departure.

The duckling's highest percentage of weight gain occurs during its first two weeks of life, when nearly all metabolizable energy can be used for tissue production. As more and more tissue is produced, proportionally more energy is needed for its maintenance. In addition, feather development begins in earnest at 25–30 days, diverting energy to new channels. These needs mean that less energy is available for production of new tissue as body mass increases. Thus, the proportion of weight gained per day decreases with increasing weight.

Brisbin et al. (1986) analyzed growth characteristics of wild captive-reared wood ducks from South Carolina and Georgia (breeding locations were separated by approximately 220 kilometers [137 mi]). They reported that mature size was the only growth parameter that varied significantly among sexes and populations. There were no significant differences in total growing time and shape of growth curves. Males from each location grew to larger (P < 0.01) mature sizes than did females, and both sexes grew to larger sizes from eggs obtained in South Carolina. Because nutritional and environmental conditions were similar, this growth pattern supports the presumption that genetic factors may influence growth of wood ducks. However, when Thul (1979) collected various morphometric measurements from wood ducks throughout the Atlantic Flyway, he found no conclusive evidence that size could be used to distinguish birds from the northern and southern regions.

The ducks that Brisbin et al. (1987) studied reached maximum growth rates at approximately three weeks of age. Males from South Carolina and Georgia required 55.4 and 57.8 days to attain mature weights of 520 and 469.7 grams (18.34 and 16.57 oz), respectively. Similarly, females from South Carolina and Georgia reached mature weights of 443.6 and 469.7 grams (15.62 and 16.57 oz) in 56.6 and 57.4 days, respectively. When all birds from both locations were grouped together, shape of the growth curve (m = 1.33) was found to be intermediate between the Gompertz and logistic sigmoid models. We utilized a method presented by Ricklefs (1967) to determine the type of model that best described the growth of game farm wood ducks (five males and two females) raised in captivity at the Van Norman Aviary in Hanna City, Illinois. Their growth best fit the logistic model (Figure 88). Our captive wood ducks required 58.9 days to grow from 10 to 90 percent of mature size (544 grams: 19.19 oz). Fledging occurred when ducklings were 55–59 days old, at weights of 415–450 grams (14.64–15.87 oz).

In Massachusetts, many wild wood duck juveniles began flying at 60 days, and all but the most retarded by 70 days (Grice and Rogers 1965). Seventy percent of 33 wild juveniles were able to fly in North Carolina between 70 and 77 days of age (Benfield 1970). Apparently nutrition and photoperiod play important roles in determining the age of flight. Latitude, of course, affects the photoperiod.

Fendley (1978) found varying patterns of growth between the offspring of captive and wild-reared wood ducks. Young from females reared in captivity grew approximately 1.12 times slower than offspring of wild-reared birds. The former group required two additional days to reach their maximum growth rates.

Although mature males weigh on the average about 9 percent more than females, there can be considerable overlap during the growth period between light males and heavy females (Table 149). Moreover, individuals of the same sex often show extreme variance in growth between and within broods. We found a nearly 50-gram (1.76 oz) difference in the average weights of 12-day-old male ducklings from two different broods. This difference reached a maximum around day 54, when the average weight of male ducklings from Brood C was over 100 grams (3.53 oz) more than that of Brood A (Table 149). By day 75, however, only 56 grams (1.98 oz) separated their mean weights. Because both broods were exposed to similar environmental conditions, most if not all of the variance may be attributed to differences that might operate through protein food demand and its assimilation.

Benfield (1970) also found a marked difference in the growth rate of wild young wood ducks within a brood and among individual broods. Variations among individuals were so pronounced that he was unable to make valid comparisons of development related to brood areas, years, and sexes.

Age-related Changes in Body Composition

Clay et al. (1979) described age-related changes in the major body components of wild captive-reared wood ducks. At hatching, lipid reserves comprised 24.6 percent of the duckling's weight. These reserves were rapidly utilized during the first

Table 149. Mean weights (grams) and standard error of wood duck weights from captive-reared wood ducks in central Illinois.

| Age (days) | Brood A[a] | | | | Brood C[b] | |
| | Male | | Female | | Male | |
	Mean	S.E.	Mean	S.E.	Mean	S.E.
5	30.56	1.94	31.80	3.90	35.47	1.47
12	62.20	6.02	62.00	12.80	110.07	1.25
19	108.08	6.69	122.05	33.65	169.63	12.34
26	179.04	9.82	204.85	41.35	235.47	35.81
33	231.42	11.20	265.40	48.70	306.97	60.70
39					379.40	65.08
40	242.82	11.08	301.75	23.55		
46	322.28	8.09	352.75	38.65		
47					490.90	63.12
54	390.52	14.46	404.00	48.00	538.50	44.25
61	450.72	9.91	460.20	39.80	554.77	53.42
75	522.32	21.89	525.60	4.90	578.27	55.58

[a] Brood A hatched on June 7 and contained five males and two females.
[b] Brood C hatched on June 14 and contained three males.

week and reached a minimum level between weeks two and three. When ducklings were approximately 2.5 weeks old, they started to again accumulate lipid reserves. The maximum level of stored fat was reached at 49 days of age. Thereafter, lipid reserves steadily diminished as energy demands for plumage growth increased.

Weller (1965) observed that during the period of most rapid growth of the large flight feathers, some juvenile redheads lost about 50 grams (1.76 oz). In wood ducks, rapid development of the large flight feathers usually occurs at 6–8 weeks of age. Thus, it is not surprising that energy reserves begin declining at this time (Clay et al. 1979).

No significant (P > 0.05) changes were detected in ash indices (grams of ash per gram of lean dry weight) or the caloric values of lean dry and ash-free lean dry biomass during the growing period (Clay et al. 1979). However, the caloric values of live weights varied significantly (P < 0.01) with age, following the same growth patterns as the fat indices.

There was a rapid increase in the water content of ducklings during the first week posthatching, arriving at a maximum index value (grams of water per gram of lean dry weight) during week one (Clay et al. 1979). This posthatching hydration was thought to be related to the development and maturation of body tissues. A general decline in body water followed, reaching a minimum value shortly after juvenile wood ducks attained 99 percent of their mature weight.

Tarsus, Culmen, and Wing Growth

Hepp et al. (1987) reported the average lengths of tarsus, culmen, and wing from 43 one-day-old wood ducks as 18.2 ± 0.78 millimeters (0.72 ± 0.03 in), 15.3 ± 0.63 millimeters (0.60 ± 0.02 in), and 15.5 ± 0.70 millimeters (0.61 ± 0.03 in), respectively. The lengths of fully developed tarsus, culmen, and folded wing for age and sex classes of adult wood ducks are given in Table 150. Carney (1964) recorded folded wing lengths from notch to tip of primaries. He found that 69 percent of adult males were 222 millimeters (8.74 in) or greater; 70 percent of juvenile males were less than 222 millimeters (8.74 in); 66 percent of adult females were 215 millimeters (8.46 in) or greater; and 68 percent of juvenile females were less than 215 millimeters (8.46 in).

Tarsus, culmen, and folded wing length growth curves of wood ducks raised in captivity at the Van Norman Aviary are presented in figures 90 and 91. No appreciable differences in growth rates of these body parts occurred between sexes. The tarsus and culmen of males grew to slightly larger sizes than did those of females (Figure 90). In both sexes, the tarsus grew faster than the culmen. Culmen length averaged 91 percent of adult size by the time wood ducks weighed 395 grams (13.93 oz)—at approximately 47 days (Figure 90). Adult tarsus length was attained 31 days after hatching, at 245 grams (8.64 oz). In contrast to the culmen and tarsus lengths, folded wing sizes were similar for males and fe-

Table 150. Tarsus, culmen, and folded wing (in millimeters) lengths in mature age and sex classes of wood ducks.

Body part	Adult[a]		Juvenile[a]	
	Male	Female	Male	Female
Tarsus	36.0[b] (12)	34.5[b] (12)	39.1±0.85 (4)	38.8±0.84 (5)
Culmen	34.7[b] (12)	33.5[b] (12)	34.0±1.0 (5)	32.0±1.0 (5)
Folded wing	225.3±0.48 (27)	216.2±0.63 (16)	215.0±0.58 (32)	216.0±0.93 (37)

[a] Number of birds in parentheses.
[b] Data from Palmer (1976).

males (Figure 91). When young males were at approximately 420 grams (14.81 oz), their folded wing was 71.1 percent that of an adult male and 71.8 percent that of an adult female. They continued to grow to reach 215 millimeters (8.46 in) at maturity, 98 percent of an adult's folded wing.

Growth, plumage development, and survival of ducklings can be ascertained by recapturing known-aged young, such as the bait-trapped 74-day-old male wood duck (above) previously banded with a web tag during its first day of life. An important aspect of population dynamics, obtained through the return of web-tagged ducklings to nest sites in subsequent years, is the proportion that homes to natal areas, as compared with those that pioneer new nesting areas. *Photo by Jack Dermid.*

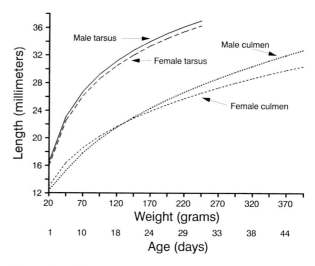

Figure 90. Culmen and tarsus growth of wood ducks raised at the Van Norman Aviary, Illinois, 1981. The regression equations for male and female culmen and tarsus growth, respectively, are: $y=3.99(x^{0.35})$, $r=0.97$, $P<0.001$, $n=88$; $y=5.52(x^{0.29})$, $r=0.91$, $P<0.001$, $n=58$; $y=-8.19+8.23$ (log x), $r=0.98$, $P<0.001$, $n=57$; and $y=-8.48+8.15$ (log x), $r=0.95$, $P<0.001$, $n=34$.

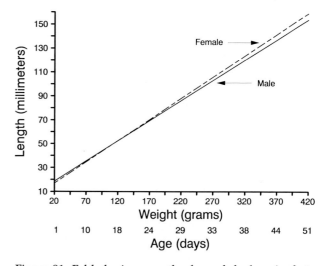

Figure 91. Folded wing growth of wood ducks raised at the Van Norman Aviary, Illinois, 1981. The regression equations for males ($n=102$) and females ($n=75$) are: $y=11.86+0.34x$, $r=0.97$, $P<0.001$; and $y=9.76+0.36x$, $r=0.86$, $P<0.001$, respectively.

MOLTS AND PLUMAGES

The molt of feathers leading to a variety of plumages is more complex in the wood duck than previously realized. Different feather tracts molt at different ages, and in some instances only part of a specific tract is molted. Molting is influenced by both endogenous and exogenous changes. Age, sex, breeding activities, nutrition, and latitude are factors that have been identified with the timing of molts in ducks.

The appearance of contour feathers in different tracts varies with age and condition of woodie ducklings. The influence of these two parameters on the rate of development of several feather tracts in captive and wild wood ducks is given in Table 151. It is apparent that growth, as measured by weight, although important, is considerably less a factor than is age in determining the rate of plumage development.

Although duckling age was the most important factor affecting plumage development, weight also affected the rate at which feathers grew. Weight appeared to be a more important variable in the wild, where diets are more diverse and protein often is less available than under aviary conditions. Even so, up to a 10-day difference was noted in the plumage development of our captive wild and aviary wood ducks. The span of development of various feather tracts represents an average among observed individuals.

Terminology for the sequence of plumage changes in birds was outlined by Humphrey and Parkes (1959) to replace terms that failed to adequately address cyclical feather replacement. Their primary thesis was that each molt and attendant plumage in a cycle (one year in ducks) should be labeled sequentially regardless of physiology, season of year, and plumage color. They proposed that the first plumage following the juvenile plumage would be the first basic (basic I), acquired by the prebasic molt; the first alternate (nuptial) plumage (alternate I) would follow the prealternate molt. Entering the second cycle (second year of life in ducks), the second prebasic molt would produce the definitive basic (eclipse) plumage, which in turn would be replaced during the second prealternate molt by the definitive alternate (nuptial) plumage.

Contemporary students of molting ducks have followed the basic tenets proposed by Humphrey and Parkes (1959) in describing cyclical changes in plumages (Billard and Humphrey 1972, Palmer 1976, Weller 1976, Paulus 1984, Heitmeyer 1985, Wishart 1985, Miller 1986, Lovvorn and Barzen 1988). The alternate plumage is considered analogous to the bright breeding (nuptial) plumage of adult male ducks. The definitive basic plumage is the dull midsummer (eclipse) plumage in which males resemble juveniles or females.

The focal point of the problem of linking plumage changes in wood ducks is the basic I or immature plumage, which follows the juvenile plumage and precedes the alternate I (nuptial) plumage. According to Weller (1976), the basic I plumage has been considered homologous to the nonbreeding (eclipse) plumage of adults. Weller (1976) considered that basic I plumage in male ducks varies from partial renewal of head feathers and several body feathers in the mallard to nearly complete and long-lived plumage in the blue-winged teal.

Table 151. Multiple correlation of weight and age of ducklings in relation to the development of various plumage tracts in captive and wild wood ducks.

Origin of sample	Plumage tract	Time span (days)	Coefficients			Times greater	Intercept
			r	Weight	Age		
Aviary	Cheek	40–150	0.89	0.09	1.27	14.5	−49.07
Aviary	Breast/chest	50–125	0.82	0.004	0.98	245.0	39.10
Wild	Breast/chest	10–8/12–10	0.56	0.40	0.56	1.4	−98.11
Wild	Back/rump	10–8/12–10	0.60	0.03	0.34	11.3	1.53
Aviary	Primary	25–110	0.95	0.18	1.91	10.6	−99.49
Aviary	Rectrices	6–190	0.85	0.05	1.80	33.3	−140.28
Wild	Second set rectrices	10–8/12–10	0.39	0.22	0.35	1.6	−77.21

Feather Characteristics of Plumage Tracts

Because we needed to evaluate the temporal pattern of incoming contour feathers in the numerous plumage tracts relative to the mature characteristics of feathers in each tract, we counted, measured, and weighed feathers from an adult male wood duck (tables 152 and 153). The plumage tracts were delineated as depicted in Figure 92. Except where feathers were small and of similar size, such as on the cheek and belly, they were individually counted and measured. To determine an average length and weight of small feathers, large samples were measured to within 1 millimeter and weighed to 0.0001 gram. We tallied 8,216 feathers on this adult male—4,486 on the head, 2,634 on the body, and 1,096 on both wings (tables 152 and 153).

Our results are similar to the findings of Eric Hopps, who at our suggestion studied the feather composition of 10 wood ducks. He tallied a mean of 8,602 (n=2) and 8,064 (n=3) feathers on adult and juvenile drakes and 8,342 (n=2) and 8,498 (n=3)

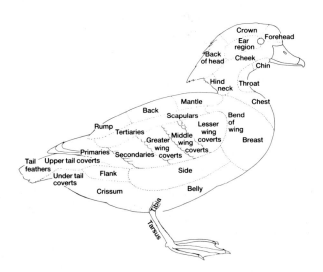

Figure 92. Topography of a wood duck, delineating the specific tracts of feathers followed during changes in plumage. *Illustration by and courtesy of Beverley Sanderson.*

Table 152. Number, size, weight, and calculated dietary protein necessary to synthesize feathers in various nuptial (definitive alternate) plumage tracts of an adult male wood duck.

| Feather tract | Number of feathers | Feather length (millimeters) | | | | Feather tract weight[a] | Individual feather weight[b] | Protein requirements for feather growth[c] |
		Mean	S.D.	C.V.	Range			
Head								
Crown	1,056	14.5	6.19	42.7	4–25	0.5505	0.521	0.9608
Crest	278	35.4	9.77	27.6	17–58	0.4502	1.619	0.7857
Cheek, ear	1,985	9.8	3.02	30.8	4–16	0.6243	0.315	1.0896
Chin, throat	816	9.1	4.14	45.5	3–15	0.2219	0.272	0.3873
Hindneck	351	18.9	6.35	33.6	5–39	0.7570	2.157	1.3212
Subtotal	4,486					2.6039	0.580	4.5446
Body								
Chest	310	24.3	2.82	11.6	9–35	1.3297	4.289	2.3207
Breast	203	39.1	2.91	7.4	33–46	2.2754	11.209	3.9712
Belly	1,118	32.9	4.52	13.7	27–40	8.1330	7.275	14.1944
Crissum	41	37.5	5.72	15.3	26–45	0.3682	8.980	0.6426
Side	223	46.2	13.91	30.1	16–94	3.4254	15.361	5.9783
Vertical side bars	102	42.4	3.33	7.9	35–50	1.1379	11.156	1.9860
Flank	106	41.5	5.71	13.8	26–55	0.9982	9.417	1.7421
Lower tail coverts	14	57.4	7.15	12.5	47–71	0.2672	19.086	0.4663
Upper tail coverts	14	76.1	10.63	14.0	65–97	0.5540	39.571	0.9669
Tail	14	113.9	6.94	6.1	100–122	1.8021	128.721	3.1452
Mantle	106	38.0	5.15	13.6	18–49	0.7924	7.475	1.3830
Scapular	110	52.0	25.56	49.2	17–110	2.0263	18.421	3.5365
Back	164	31.1	6.09	19.6	25–39	0.7943	4.843	1.3863
Rump	109	40.4	6.48	16.0	28–52	0.8659	7.944	1.5112
Subtotal	2,634					24.770	9.404	43.230
Total	7,120					27.374		47.775

[a] Weight in grams of all feathers in designated tract on the head and body.
[b] Mean single feather weight in milligrams.
[c] Amount of dietary protein (in grams) necessary to synthesize feathers in the designated plumage tract. Calculations are based on 96.0-percent protein content of feathers—see Papadopoulas et al. (1986) and Williams et al. (1991)—times 55.0-percent (times 1.818) efficiency of conversion (Heitmeyer 1988).

feathers on adult and juvenile females, all only slightly different from our count of 8,216 feathers on an adult drake. Several ornithologists have been intrigued by the question of how many feathers cover a bird. The first comparative study was made by Wetmore (1936), who recorded the number of contour feathers in 79 species of small birds. He found that feathers varied in number by species, individuals, and season.

Feathers counted on other waterfowl species provide a basis for comparison with the number we found on the wood duck: green-winged teal 11,450 (Brodkorb 1951); mallard 11,903 (Knappen 1932); northern pintail 14,914 (Brodkorb 1951); and whistling swan 25,216 (Ammann 1937). The relationship of number of feathers to body mass on these waterfowl does not agree as well as does that of small birds.

Table 153. Number, size, weight, and calculated dietary protein necessary to synthesize feathers in various plumage tracts of the wing of an adult male wood duck.

Feather tract	Number of feathers (one wing)	Feather length (millimeters)				Feather tract weight[a]	Individual feather weight[b]	Protein requirements for feather growth[c]
		Mean	S.D.	C.V.	Range			
Flight								
Primaries	10	154.8	25.03	16.6	118–184	4.3716	218.58	7.6297
Secondaries	10	110.0	4.35	4.0	104–116	1.7876	89.38	3.1199
Tertials	3	99.7	7.02	7.0	93–107	0.5518	91.97	0.9630
Alula	4	46.6	19.42	41.7	21–71	0.2356	29.45	0.4112
Subtotal	27					6.9466		12.1238
Upper coverts								
Greater								
primaries	10	65.4	8.10	12.4	58–77	0.5904	29.52	1.0304
secondaries	10	62.6	6.70	10.7	51–70	0.4840	24.20	0.8447
tertials	3	43.3	3.51	8.1	40–47	0.0989	16.48	0.1726
Middle								
secondaries	7	43.1	4.60	10.7	36–50	0.1539	10.99	0.2686
tertials	3	30.3	3.51	11.6	27–34	0.0462	7.70	0.0806
Anterior rows								
first	10	29.2	8.40	28.8	19–43	0.0672	3.36	0.1173
second	9	18.9	6.33	33.5	10–29	0.0394	2.19	0.0688
third	9	25.0	3.71	14.8	20–29	0.0520	2.89	0.0908
fourth	10	22.5	2.18	9.7	19–26	0.0518	2.59	0.0904
Lesser								
primaries	44	11.8	4.96	42.0	7–23	0.1204	1.37	0.2101
secondaries	159	14.3	4.56	31.9	7–27	0.4746	1.49	0.8283
tertials	5	62.0	10.95	17.7	43–71	0.2098	20.98	0.3662
Subtotal	279					2.3886		4.1688
Underwing coverts								
Axillars	4	75.0	12.25	16.3	61–88	0.1620	20.25	0.2827
Greater								
primaries	10	60.2	8.61	14.3	40–68	0.3024	15.12	0.5278
secondaries	11	80.3	5.01	6.2	73–88	0.4965	22.57	0.8665
Middle								
primaries	6	32.5	5.01	15.4	58–77	0.1002	8.35	0.1749
secondaries	22	34.1	7.35	21.6	36–50	0.3866	8.79	0.6747
tertials	3	33.7	8.14	24.2	27–34	0.0516	8.60	0.0901
Lesser								
primaries	73	14.9	8.59	57.6	5–23	0.3198	2.19	0.5581
secondaries	113	14.4	3.34	23.2	3–25	0.4024	1.78	0.7023
Subtotal	242					2.2215		3.8771
Total	548 (x2) = 1,096					11.5567		20.1697

[a] Weight in grams of feathers on both wings in designated tract.
[b] Mean single feather weight in milligrams.
[c] Amount of dietary protein (in grams) necessary to synthesize feathers on both wings in the designated plumage tract. Calculations are based on 96.0-percent protein content of feathers—see Papadopoulas et al. (1986) and Williams et al. (1991)—times 55.0-percent (times 1.818) efficiency of conversion (Heitmeyer 1988).

A comprehensive study by Turček (1966) of 91 bird species revealed a close correlation between body size and plumage weights. Large birds had a smaller proportion of total weight in plumage than small species, and water birds had lower proportions of plumage mass than terrestrial species. In general, for each 1 percent increase in body weight, plumage weight increased 0.95 percent.

Turček (1966) made his comparison of body mass and plumage relationships on the basis of the plucked bird without stomach contents. For all 91 species, average plumage mass amounted to 6 percent of body mass. A similar comparison (with stomach contents) for the wood duck showed that 5 percent of its body mass was plumage. In domestic poultry, feathers represent 5 to 7 percent of the bird's total weight (Williams et al. 1991).

On the wood duck, feather density increased as feather size decreased (tables 152 and 153). The smallest feathers covered the cheek, chin, and throat tracts and formed the lesser coverts adjacent to the leading edge of the wing. The largest feathers were the remiges (primaries) and the rectrices (tail feathers); the latter were 50 percent longer than the upper tail coverts. Some scapulars were 101–110 millimeters (3.98–4.33 in) long, but smaller feathers

at and in proximity to the base of the tract reduced their mean size to 52 millimeters (2.05 in).

There were 278 feathers in the crest alone; some were as long as 60 millimeters (2.36 in), but numerous short ones reduced the mean size to 35.4 millimeters (1.39 in). The nine (one side) bronze, black-and-white-barred side feathers were unusually large for body feathers, averaging 77.1 millimeters (3.04 in). The vertical black and white side bars (anterior to the wing), forming a fingerlike projection, were 51 in number (one side) and averaged 42.4 millimeters (1.67 in).

The most extensive tract of feathers occurred on the belly and was composed of 1,118 feathers that averaged 32.9 millimeters (1.30 in) in length. Although the cheek areas had more feathers—1,985—their minute size covered only a small area. The 203 burgundy and white breast feathers were slightly longer than the average belly feather, but the 310 chest feathers were slightly shorter (Table 152).

The number of new body feathers that we tallied at weekly intervals through the first prebasic and first prealternate molts on juvenile wood ducks were, for most tracts, a fraction of the total number typical of the tract (Table 154). The combined weekly counts in plumage tracts where incoming

Table 154. Comparison of mean number of sheathed feathers counted on five juvenile male wood ducks during their first prealternate molt, and the number of feathers counted on an adult male wood duck that had acquired his definitive alternate plumage.

Feather tract	Adult male — Number of feathers[a]	Juvenile male — Mean number of sheathed feathers[b]	Juvenile male — Percentage of total feather complement[c]	Mean span of molt development (days)[d]	Estimated number of incoming feathers per week required to obtain a complete set of alternate feathers[e]
Hindneck	351	52 ± 35.4	14.8	29	12.5
Mantle	106	25 ± 7.7	23.6	39	20.5
Scapulars	110	26 ± 5.5	23.6	60	15.4
Back	164	4 ± 4.9			
Rump	109	30 ± 10.7	27.5	52	18.2
Upper tail coverts	14	29 ± 10.6	207.1	44	2.3
Lower tail coverts	14	31 ± 6.5	221.4	38	2.8
Tail	14	27 ± 4.3	193.0	70	1.7
Chest/breast	310/203	150 ± 18.2	29.2	25–27	18.3
Side	223	55 ± 29.5	24.6	60	28.9
Flank	106	37 ± 12.9	34.9	40	21.2
Belly	1,118	161 ± 24.3	14.4	25	279.5
Crissum	41	25 ± 13.9	61.0	34	10.3
Vertical side bars	102	14 ± 4.3	13.7	32	19.3

[a] From Table 152.

[b] Mean and standard deviation of the number of incoming sheathed feathers observed on five male wood ducks during their first prealternate molt.

[c] Percentage of total number of adult male wood duck's feathers that were observed developing in selected plumage tracts of five juvenile male wood ducks.

[d] From Table 160.

[e] The average number of feathers that would have been expected per week to match the number of feathers on the adult male wood duck. Based on duration of molt to total number of feathers in plumage tract.

feathers were fewer than those found in comparable tracts of the adult male indicate those tracts where feathers developed in less than one week. Obviously we viewed only those feathers that were developing in sheaths at that particular moment. Because we observed only 24–25 percent of the mantle, scapular, and side feathers in sheaths, 75–76 percent must have matured in the period between our weekly visits. On the other hand, the percentage tallied over the designated number in a plumage tract indicated that the same feather was in a sheath condition for more than one week (Table 154). Upper and lower tail covert feathers were counted more than twice and tail feathers about twice.

Our observations imply that individual head feathers (except the crest) and many body feathers (except the tail, tail coverts, and black-and-white-barred side feathers) matured in one to three days. However, the sequence of molt filling in a particular plumage tract was protracted and could be followed weekly for 4 to 8 weeks (Table 154).

SEQUENTIAL MOLT

In describing the molt of wood duck plumages, Humphrey and Clark (1964: 179) stated: "First year males begin to assume the first alternate plumage, which is very similar to older birds, early in the fall. There is apparently no record of a first basic plumage in young males." On the other hand, Palmer (1972, 1976) described male and female wood ducks as molting from the juvenile plumage to a basic I prior to alternate I plumage acquisition.

In our plumage studies of developing wood duck juveniles, prior to Palmer's (1972) analyses, we saw no evidence of a basic I plumage, and neither did Grice and Rogers (1965). Our subsequent studies over several years (1982, 1983, 1988, 1990, 1991) involved tracking plumages dyed with Rhodamine B on three occasions and with undyed plumages at other times, particularly 1990. Color photographs and notes were taken weekly in all years, and in 1990 the sheathed feathers were counted as they appeared in the various body plumage tracts (Table 154). Most plumage development was followed from downy ducklings through alternate I (nuptial)—up to ages of 170 days. A few individuals were monitored at intervals of several weeks through winter into spring in 1982–1983 and 1988–1989.

Our studies revealed that except for certain plumage tracts on the head, juvenile body feathers were replaced with nuptial (breeding) plumage. Because such development places a sequential arrangement out of synchrony, we classify nuptial

plumage as alternate I—although in sequence much of it really is basic I. Perhaps more important than semantics is understanding of periodicity of the molt and development of various plumage tracts.

An overview of age-related molts resulting in plumage changes of the various feather tracts in juvenile male wood ducks is presented in Figure 93. The molts of female wood ducks appeared similar to males except for the cheek area.

After the 150 days it takes juveniles to achieve the alternate I (nuptial) plumage, they begin to develop a scattering of new feathers identical to others in that particular tract (Table 155). The appearance of limited numbers of new feathers of similar characteristics extended from December to mid-April. We are uncertain as to the degree that this protracted molt replaced feathers of the specific tracts involved. In most cases, the new feathers appear to represent only a partial molting of the tract feathers.

This pattern of partial molt also seemed to be the case in the belly feathers of incubating yearling and adult wood ducks that we followed from April through June at Nauvoo Slough (Table 156). About one-third of the yearling and adult females exhibited light to heavy definitive basic (eclipse) plumage; two-thirds retained their white nuptial plumage to mid-June.

We periodically inspected the Rhodamine B-dyed plumages of juvenile woodies (five males and four females) between November 11, 1982, and February 8, 1983, when floodwaters ended the observations. Two females had molted most of their alternate breast feathers between January 21 and February 8; dyed belly feathers remained intact. A

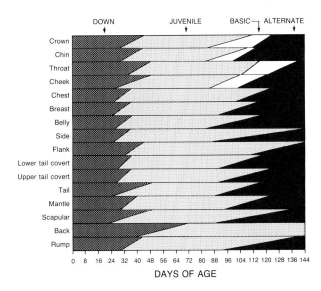

Figure 93. Overview of the molt cycle in captive, wild-hatched, juvenile male wood ducks studied July 4 through November 28, 1990.

Table 155. Appearance of new feather sheaths among juvenile male and female wood ducks at the Van Norman Aviary, Illinois. Numbers in feather tracts pertain to the number of individual feathers that were currently molting in one or more areas, 1988–89.

Date	Sex	Number examined	Number molting	Percentage molting	Chest/ breast	Belly	Side	Flank	Rump
Dec 13	Male	12	7	58					
Jan 9	Male	11	6	55	1		1		
Jan 30	Male	10	4	40		1			
Feb 7	Male	2	2	100			2		
Feb 27	Male	10	3	30					
Apr 16	Male	14	4	29		1			
Total/weighted mean		59	26	44	1	2	3	0	0
Dec 13	Female	7	4	57			1		
Jan 9	Female	8	5	63		3			
Jan 30	Female	9	4	44		2			
Feb 7	Female	2	2	100					
Feb 27	Female	6	6	100		4			
Apr 16	Female	5	4	80		1			
Total/weighted mean		37	25	68	0	10	1	0	0

dyed juvenile drake that we observed for 310 days up to April 6, 1989, lost only a few nuptial belly feathers, which were replaced by feathers with the same white color. Among the juvenile ducks that we observed between December 13, 1988, and April 16, 1989, the belly, upper tail coverts, tail, and scapulars were areas where molt of similar feathers—none basic in color—was particularly pronounced (Table 155). Among this sample, females were more prone than males to develop new belly feathers.

At Mississippi State University, Richard M. Kaminski and Scott C. Barras examined 18 wood ducks with clipped scapular, flank, and tail tracts for feather loss at weekly intervals from December 21, 1990, through March 21, 1991; they added breast, belly, crown, and mantle tracts to their December 21, 1991–March 21, 1992, study. In three adult males, they found no new feathers in any of three tracts (Table 157), but both yearling and adult females showed a moderate level of feather replacement during the three-month winter period. Nuptial feather replacement by similar-colored feathers was more evident in yearling than adult females, and most apparent in breast and belly feathers.

Table 156. Percentage of incubating wood duck hens at Nauvoo Slough, Illinois that displayed some evidence of basic plumage on the belly. Females were captured on nests and examined at approximately weekly intervals, April 8 through June 19, 1990 and 1991.

Date[a]	Number of incubating females	Percentage of incubating females that showed a degree of basic plumage on the belly			Percentage of incubating females with evidence of basic plumage
		Light	Medium	Heavy	
April 8, 10	7	28.6			28.6
April 16, 17	13	23.1	7.7		30.8
April 23, 24	28	14.3			14.3
April 30, May 1	36	5.6	16.7	5.6	27.9
May 8	52	17.3	15.4	5.8	38.5
May 15	69	20.3	11.6	4.3	36.2
May 22	64	15.6	10.9	6.3	32.8
May 29, 30	55	12.7	14.5	5.5	32.7
June 5	56	14.3	12.5	7.1	33.9
June 12	42	16.7	16.7	4.8	38.2
June 17, 19	23	26.1	4.3	4.3	34.7
Total/weighted mean	445	16.2	11.9	4.9	33.0

[a] Birds were examined in 1990 and 1991. When two dates are listed, the second date indicates 1991.

Table 155. (continued)

		Feather tracts		
Upper tail coverts	Back	Tail	Scapulars	Tertials
1		2	4	
2		3	1	2
1		2	1	3
	2			
3		1		
3		1		
10	2	9	6	5
1		4		
1		3		
2		2		2
	2	1	1	
5		3	2	
2		4	1	
11	2	17	4	2

Our evidence, too, indicates that more females than males molt feathers between autumn and spring. New, growing feathers were especially prevalent in the belly, tail, and upper tail coverts. Except in the belly area of some females, all of the new feathers were similar to the alternate plumage typical of each tract at that time. The approximately one-third of the incubating hens at Nauvoo Slough, April to June, with traces of definitive basic belly plumage suggests that there is a slight early prebasic molt in both yearling and adult hens at that latitude (Table 156). However, all of the males and most of the females showed no evidence of prebasic molt until late in May (see Chapter 14).

Molts between autumn and the breeding season appear to be present in diverse species of ducks—greater scaup (Billard and Humphrey 1972), gadwall (Paulus 1984), American wigeon (Wishart 1985), northern pintail (Miller 1986), mallard (Heitmeyer 1987), and canvasback (Lovvorn and Barzen 1988). Investigators have classified winter-spring molts as prebasic, leading to at least a partial basic plumage prior to the breeding season.

CHRONOLOGY OF PLUMAGE CHANGE FROM DOWNY TO JUVENILE

In an amazingly brief period, the wood duck's downy plumage of head and body was replaced by contour feathers (Table 158). The tips of contour tail and scapular feathers first began to push down feathers out of their follicles at 19–24 days. A few days later, at 22–26 days, contour feathers began to appear in chest, breast, belly, and crissum plumage tracts. Juvenile feathers began to appear on the head a week later. The last vestiges of the down plumage were on the back of head, hind neck, back, and tibia. In most areas of the body, juvenile plumage had replaced down by 35 days and head tracts by 50 days of age; the back was much later, not completing development until ducklings were 56–70 days of age (Table 158).

As indicated by the minimum and maximum spans of days for individuals to develop particular juvenile head and body feather tracts, feather growth and coverage was rapid. Because of their large size, tail feathers required the longest time among body feathers to reach maturity: 25–31 days.

Table 157. Number and percentage of captive wood ducks studied at Mississippi State University that showed evidence of winter molt (loss of clipped-marked feathers or presence of sheathed feathers) in various plumage regions, December 21, 1990 to March 21, 1991, and seven plumage regions, December 21, 1991 to March 21, 1992.[a]

Feather region	Yearling female			Adult female			Adult male
	Number examined (number that molted)			Number examined (number that molted)			Number examined (number that molted)
	1990	1991	Percentage	1990	1991	Percentage	1990
Scapulars	7 (2)	8 (3)	33.3	8 (2)	7 (3)	33.3	3 (0)
Flank	7 (3)	8 (5)	53.3	8 (4)	7 (0)	26.7	3 (0)
Tail	7 (7)	8 (0)	46.6	8 (3)	7 (0)	20.0	3 (0)
Belly		8 (7)	87.5		7 (3)	42.9	
Breast		8 (5)	62.5		7 (4)	57.1	
Crown		8 (1)	12.5		7 (0)	0.0	
Mantle		8 (0)	0.0		7 (0)	0.0	

[a] Data from Richard M. Kaminski and Scott C. Barras.

Table 158. Age (days) of seven wood duck ducklings when juvenile plumage replaced the downy plumage in various feather tracts of the head and body, July through August 1990.[a]

Feather tract	Percentage of feather replacement			Span of feather development	
	1–50	51–90	91–100	Minimum	Maximum
Crown	29–35	36–39	40–45	11	16
Cheek	29–36	37–45	46–50	17	21
Chin and throat	25–34	35–39	40–45	15	20
Hindneck	40–45	46–49	50–55	10	15
Chest	22–26	27–30	31–35	9	13
Breast	22–26	27–30	31–35	9	13
Belly	22–26	27–30	31–35	9	13
Crissum	22–26	27–30	31–35	9	13
Side	22–26	27–30	31–35	9	13
Flank	29–35	36–40	41–45	12	16
Lower tail coverts	24–29	30–32	33–35	9	11
Upper tail coverts	24–29	30–32	33–35	9	11
Tail	19–24	25–43	44–50	25	31
Mantle	26–32	33–38	39–43	13	17
Scapulars	16–32	33–43	44–50	28	34
Back	32–43	44–55	56–70	24	38
Rump	26–30	31–38	39–43	13	17

[a] Subject birds were wild-hatched and raised in captivity by Eric Hopps in central Illinois.

With a few exceptions, feathers in each delineated tract initiated and developed at concurrent rates. This uniform growth was especially evident in the tail and lower and upper tail coverts. It was least uniform on the head and back.

At 35–40 days of age a woodie duckling is able to survive quite well on its own. The loss of down on the rump and back, lack of flight feather development, bill length, and head markings help in determining its age and that of other ducklings. *Photo by David McEwen.*

CHRONOLOGY OF PLUMAGE CHANGE FROM JUVENILE TO ALTERNATE

Head

Plumage on the head of wood ducks has posed an enigma to us and has caused much concern despite several years of study. Almost all head plumage tracts of dyed feathers, 1983 and 1988, appeared to molt directly from juvenile to nuptial plumage except for the crown and ear regions, where basic plumage prevailed from 100 to 120 days before being replaced by nuptial feathers.

However, photographs of non-dyed ducks taken at weekly intervals in 1990 and at more frequent intervals during critical molting in 1991 appear to show a brief basic plumage in most head tracts of males. Shortly before the juvenile head plumage is replaced by nuptial, tract feathers exhibit a ruffled appearance as new feathers push out old. The gray cheek feathers then become tan, and scattered tan feathers appear in the previous immaculate white U-prong tract that embraces the cheek. The margins of the white U, once sharply delineated, become clouded with light tan feathers. The white throat feathers exhibit a ruffled appearance.

Unlike plumages on the body of the wood duck where there is a substantial interval of time between molts of most feather tracts, the head plumage appears to be in a constant molt from juvenile to nuptial (alternate). We feel confident that the crown and ear region tracts have an interim basic plumage, but we are less confident about the apparent interim tan feathers of the forehead and cheek regions. Because photographs of an adult male in prealternate molt show similar transitional tan feathers on the forehead and cheek between full basic and alternate plumages, it is possible that this color change in juvenile woodies stems from feathers changing color as they are pushed from their follicles by incoming nuptial feathers and do not represent a new generation. The tiny feathers in these tracts—some as small as 3 millimeters (0.12 in)—develop so rapidly as to complicate evaluating their place in the molt cycle.

Chin and throat. The sulfur-white chin and throat of the downy plumage is replaced by immaculate white juvenile plumage when ducklings are 30–60 days of age (Table 159). The juvenile white chin is molted between 80 and 100 days into a similar white; the throat molts later at ages of 100–115 days. A continuous molt into another white is suggested by additional new white feathers appearing up to 140 days of age.

Forehead. The area between the bill and the eye remains in juvenile plumage until 100–115 days, when slightly tannish feathers replace gray ones before black feathers begin to appear at 105 days. They completely envelop the tract by 120–125 days (Table 159).

Crown. The juvenile feathers of the crown are green until 90 days, when brown feathers begin to replace them. When completely brown at 100–105 days, a brilliant green starts to form in the center of the crown in males. This green streak develops anteriorly, posteriorly, and, last, laterally to encompass the crown area by 115–120 days. There are thus three sets of contour feathers in the crown tract within 30 days (Table 159).

Back of head. Down is retained longer in the back of the head tract (nape) than in other head tracts (Table 159). In the nape area, juvenile feathers replace down at 40–55 days in males and at 38–56 days in females. During the later stages of molt, a tuft of feathers becomes apparent in the posterior area of the tract. We are unsure whether this is replaced by a second set of feathers at 90–105 days prior to the development of the nuptial feathered crest. Our photographs suggest that there is a brief replacement by similar feathers. The prominent nuptial crest develops at 110–140 days in males and 115–135 days in females in an area at the back of the head that is anterior to the juvenile/basic tuft, which is molted. The crest ultimately reaches a length of 42 millimeters (1.67 in) in males and 30.5 millimeters (1.20 in) in females.

Ear region. The ear tract extends from behind the eye to the back of the head. Dyed juvenile feathers began to be replaced by basic at 60–115 days of age in males, and by 100 days only a trace of juvenile plumage remained (Table 159). Black nuptial plumage began to appear at 115 days and was complete by 140 days in the males. The white wedge-shaped mark posterior to the eye in females continued to elongate to 150 days.

Cheek. Juvenile plumage in the cheek tract prevailed to 100 days of age, when tan-colored feathers appeared among the gray (Table 159). By 110 days, they enveloped the cheek area, but meanwhile dark nuptial feathers appeared, and they completed tract coverage by 120–125 days.

Female head. Except for minor areas, the female's head plumage changes in sequence with that of males, although the changes occur much more subtly. Occasionally in the juvenile plumage of females, a white U extends dorsally from the white throat. Among eight females in 1990, this male characteristic was evident in four juveniles—two faint, two marked—and not apparent in the other four. When present, the U mark disappeared with the alternate molt at 90–100 days. In females, a white margin developed around the bill at 65–75 days. At 95 days, the white wedge posterior to the

Table 159. Age (days) of wood duck ducklings (males and females) during head plumage development, 1990.

	Tentative acquisition of plumages[a]					
	Juvenile		Basic I		Alternate I	
Feather tract	Male	Female	Male	Female	Male	Female
Crown	29–45	29–45	90–105	90–105	105–120	100–125
Back of head (crest)	40–55	38–56	90–105	90–105	110–140	115–135
Ear region	35–43	35–45	60–115	65–120	115–140	115–150
Cheek	30–100	30–100	100–110	100–110	108–120	110–125
Forehead	25–40	25–40	100–115	100–115	105–120	110–125
Chin	30–45	30–45	80–100	80–100	100–110	100–110
Throat	45–60	45–60	100–115	100–115	115–140	115–140

[a] Tentative because we are unsure of basic I presence in all head tracts.

The juvenile male wood duck (above) mirrors hand-reared ducklings about 40 days old. Down still is present on the nape and hindneck, and the primary wing feathers are sheathed, with the tips of the vanes just emerging. The white U facial markings have just developed to the point of determining sex; in game farm ducklings, these develop between 35 and 38 days. *Photo by F. Eugene Hester.*

eye appeared and slowly increased through an age of 150 days or more. This sequence appears to be the last change from basic to alternate plumage among females.

Body

As far as we could ascertain in the first 150 days, body feathers (with possibly small areas of exceptions to be detailed later) molted directly from juvenile to nuptial plumage (Table 160).

Belly. At about 77 days, the speckled belly was the first area to show several white nuptial feathers (Table 160). Some woodies had an entirely white belly by 89 days of age, while others took as long as 125 days; the mean of 10 birds was 86 ± 5.5 days for early stages of the molt to 103 ± 9.6 days for its apparent completion. However, substantial numbers of new feathers in sheaths were noted up to 118 days in most wood ducks, a number of days beyond their white plumage aspect. This observation suggests that the nuptial belly plumage was composed of more feathers than the juvenile ones that they replaced.

The bellies of juveniles of both sexes were delineated by a gray-tan spotted plumage. As the white plumage developed it increased in coverage about 10 percent anteriorly into what was formerly the posterior area of the breast. It also encroached dorsally into areas previously occupied by juvenile side feathers.

As the juvenile plumage in the anterior 10 percent of the belly and posterior 15 percent of the breast began to molt, spotted tan-gray feathers appeared among the white in the posterior and the burgundy in the anterior areas of these plumage tracts. The spotted tan-gray feathers were most pronounced at 96–120 days before being largely replaced by white. The cycle of feathers in this region is particularly vexing as to classification, but it appears that in this limited area there are three cycles of molt. From the appearance of a red-dyed juvenile male, there was little change in this particular area between 120 days and 310 days when last photographed.

Table 160. Age (days) of five male wood duck ducklings when nuptial plumage replaced juvenile plumage in various feather tracts of the body, based on observations and interpretation of Kodacolor photos of plumage taken weekly, 1990.[a]

Feather tract	Percentage of feather replacement			Span of feather development
	1–40	41–90	91–100	
Hindneck	109–116	117–123	124–138	29
Chest	100–110	111–116	117–125	25
Breast	90–103	104–110	111–115	25
Belly	77–89	90–100	101–105	28
Crissum	86–93	94–102	103–120	34
Side	90–95	96–110	111–145	55
Vertical side bars	103–114	115–125	126–135	32
Flank	105–110	111–134	135–145	40
Lower tail coverts	80–95	96–110	111–118	38
Upper tail coverts	80–103	104–118	119–124	44
Tail	80–97	98–124	125–150	70
Mantle	86–104	105–120	121–125	39
Scapulars	80–95	96–118	119–140	60
Back		slight		
Rump	80–98	99–115	116–138	58

[a] Subject birds were wild-hatched and raised in captivity by Eric Hopps in central Illinois.

Breast/chest. Tan juvenile breast feathers began to be replaced by white, gray, and burgundy feathers when males were about 90 days old (Table 160). The molt progressed anteriorly, reaching the chest area at the age of 100 days; 10–16 days later the nuptial burgundy of the breast/chest tracts was complete. Females followed a similar chronology, but a few new feathers appeared as late as 131 days (Table 161).

Males had a narrow band of gray between the streaked tan juvenile chest plumage and the white throat. At about 110 days of age, brownish feathers replaced the gray for a brief period of 5–10 days before giving way to a narrow black ring at 118–125 days. Thus, three generations of feathers occurred in this tiny area within 15 days.

Crissum. This tract lies between the vent and the lower tail coverts. The spotted gray-tan feathers of the juvenile male plumage began to be replaced by black feathers at 86 days, and the molt was completed by 120 days (Table 160). This color change is comparable to the time frame that new sheathed feathers were encountered (Table 161). The crissum area of females changed from spotted gray-tan feathers to white at ages similar to those of males.

Side. Nuptial side feathers first appeared at 90 days (Table 160). They continued to replace juvenile feathers in both sexes over the next 55 days. The molt started in the anterior and ventral areas of the tract and proceeded posteriorly. Last to develop in males were the eight or nine (on one side) large dorsal feathers tipped with black and white bars; they appeared first in the posterior tract area at about 120 days and progressively developed anteriorly for the next 20 days. These feathers overlap lower wing areas when birds are at rest—a view evident in most paintings and photographs of resting wood ducks. New incoming sheathed feathers appeared in the side tract of ducklings between 80 and 138 days of age (Table 161).

A group of feathers that form black and white vertical bars anterior to the base of the wing in males, between the bronze side feathers and the burgundy breast, began to develop at 103 days. These two bars gradually lengthened from dorsal to ventral, terminating at the white belly by 135 days. Whether these bars displace burgundy and bronze feathers or replace those in the area of development is unknown. However, in this limited area we found a large number of sheathed feathers developing over an extended period, making us suspicious that all three generations of feathers were involved in this particular area. We also observed a large number of incoming feathers on females in this same area, suggesting that a brief basic plumage developed there prior to appearance of nuptial feathers.

Flank. Feather development in this small tract, anterior to the tail and posterior to the side, began later than on the side (tables 160 and 161). In the male, these feathers are dark burgundy; two to four spectacular burnt-orange feathers that arise between the flank and rump and droop over the flank were the last to appear. They developed at 130–145 days and signaled completion of the nuptial plumage. Sheaths of incoming flank feathers were documented at 86–138 days (Table 161).

Table 161. Mean number of feathers in sheaths enumerated in plumage tracts of 10 juvenile wood ducks (five males and five females) during their 74- to 145-day periods of growth, 1990.[a]

Feather tract	Sex	Age (days)										
		74	80	86	96	103	110	118	124	131	138	145
Hindneck	Male	0	0	1	3	5	18	18	14	10	7	0
	Female	0	4	3	7	7	13	10	11	10	0	0
Chest and breast	Male	9	13	31	23	28	33	15	0	0	0	0
	Female	0	21	21	22	26	24	23	8	2	0	0
Belly	Male	13	39	49	27	18	13	2	0	0	0	0
	Female	0	29	32	35	15	26	19	2	0	0	0
Crissum	Male	0	0	0	14	9	8	2	0	0	0	0
	Female	0	0	0	0	11	11	6	1	0	0	0
Side	Male	0	1	10	17	6	10	12	7	4	0	0
	Female	0	1	3	6	5	5	8	7	4	1	0
Flank	Male	0	0	2	5	5	11	8	6	5	1	0
	Female	0	0	0	5	4	3	6	2	1	0	0
Lower tail coverts	Male	3	4	7	8	3	3	1	0	0	0	0
	Female	2	5	7	8	9	4	3	0	0	0	0
Upper tail coverts	Male	2	2	1	3	5	9	6	6	0	1	0
	Female	0	4	2	5	4	3	2	1	0	0	0
Tail	Male	0	3	4	7	7	5	4	2	1	0	1
	Female	0	3	3	6	4	3	4	3	0	0	1
Mantle	Male	0	2	5	2	3	10	3	1	1	1	0
	Female	0	2	5	6	5	5	6	2	2	0	0
Scapulars	Male	0	1	1	2	2	5	4	3	0	0	0
	Female	0	0	1	2	2	2	1	1	1	1	0
Back	Male	0	0	1	1	0	1	1	0	0	0	0
	Female	0	1	0	1	1	1	1	1	0	0	0
Rump	Male	1	3	5	2	2	4	0	0	0	0	0
	Female	1	3	5	4	6	4	2	2	0	0	0

[a] Subject birds were wild-hatched from three different broods and raised in captivity by Eric Hopps in central Illinois.

Hindneck. New feathers began to replace the juvenile plumage at 80–86 days (Table 161), but the narrow black band marking the nuptial hindneck did not become apparent until about 109 days because of relatively few feathers molted at the onset. New feathers appeared in increasing numbers for the next 30–40 days, becoming completely nuptial by 138 days.

Mantle. Nuptial mantle feathers appeared as early as 86 days and continued to replace juvenile feathers for the next 39 days (Table 160). New sheathed feathers were identified at 80–131 days but were few in number after ducklings reached 118 days of age (Table 161).

Scapulars. Up to 150 days of age, woodie ducklings had two sets of scapulars. The second set was acquired as replacement for the juvenile set when ducklings were 80–138 days of age (Table 160). Incoming feathers were also noted over the same time frame (Table 161).

Back. As noted earlier, juvenile back feathers were the last to replace the downy plumage, at about 70 days of age (Table 158). For the next 80 days, we observed that only a few scattered feathers appeared in the tract (Table 161). Many juvenile back feathers that were dyed on July 7, 1989, still were present 11 months later, but new feathers had replaced about half of the juvenile back. On February 7, in a different group of four juveniles of both sexes, each had 1–5 (mean = 2.5 ± 1.7) sheathed feathers in the back area—about 1.5 percent of the feathers present. Thus, for the first 150 days there appears to be only one plumage—the juvenile. Later there is a prolonged molt of the back feathers that may be partial or complete by the prebasic molt in early summer.

Rump. The wood duck's rump contains more than 100 feathers (Table 152). From acquisition of the juvenile plumage at 43 days of age, there was a hiatus of approximately 40 days before the next generation began to appear (tables 160 and 161). By the time the woodie ducklings were 138 days old, this tract had completed its second generation of development.

Tail coverts. About 14 new feathers gradually began to replace the juvenile upper tail coverts when the ducklings were 70–80 days old (tables 160 and 161). The second generation of upper tail coverts completed development during the next 44 days. Lower tail coverts were similar in chronology of development to the upper tail coverts but completed growth a week earlier.

Tail

The juvenile tail usually was fully developed by 50 days and remained intact for 5–15 days before the next generation commenced to push some of the juvenile feathers out of the center of the tail. Some feathers were lost before nuptial feathers appeared, and the remaining juvenile feathers presented a brown, ragged appearance. Their replacement was a slow process, with one to three juvenile rectrices still present on some wood ducks up to 100 days; one was still present at 110 days. Although juvenile rectrices may be absent, the growth of new feathers from all follicles may not be completed until duck-lings are 125–135 days of age. During the later stages of the molt, individuals showed juvenile and adult feathers and gaps where feathers had been lost; seldom was there the normal complement of 14 feathers until woodies reached 125 days of age.

The growth rate of individual tail feathers that we measured averaged 6.5 millimeters (0.26 in) per day. Attached rectrices averaged 110 millimeters (4.3 in) in length; thus, it took about 17 days for the growth of a mature remex. Since the molt of tail feathers extended for approximately 60 days, there was a protracted period of time over which follicles developed feathers. The synchrony so evident in the development of juvenile rectrices was most uneven in the second generation.

Wing Feather Development

Wings contain both the largest and some of the smallest feathers composing the plumage of wood ducks (Table 153). In waterfowl, three groups of flight feathers customarily are delineated: primaries, secondaries, and tertials. In songbirds and some other groups of birds, only primaries and secondaries are recognized. Miller (1925) studied flight feathers of woodies and mandarin ducks. By grouping secondaries and tertials, he enumerated 15 secondaries in the former and 16 secondaries in

the latter species. Because wood duck tertials are different in size and shape from secondaries, and because there are two generations of tertials – in contrast to the one generation of other remiges – it is useful to have distinctive terminology for this group of feathers.

There were 10 primaries, 10 secondaries, and 4 tertials in most of the wood duck wings that we examined, but numbers varied, especially in juveniles (Table 162). Often one small proximal tertial (22 millimeters: 0.87 in long) was missing and not considered in our analysis of color intensity; both it and the next proximal tertial – number 4 (62 millimeters: 2.44 in long) – were not measured for growth analysis.

The tertial feathers appeared first, as protruding sheaths at 25 days (slightly later than their coverts). Secondaries appeared a few days later, followed at 30 days by primary sheaths. At first the tertial feathers grew the most rapidly, but the faster-growing primaries reached and then surpassed the tertials at about 40 days (Figure 94). The shorter secondaries grew at a slower rate, but all flight feathers achieved maturity at about the same time – 75–85 days – when the primaries, secondaries, and tertials averaged 136 millimeters (5.35 in), 76–83 millimeters (2.99–3.27 in), and 73–90 millimeters (2.87–3.54 in), respectively.

Among wild wood ducks in Massachusetts, Grice and Rogers (1965) reported the length of primaries as 102 millimeters (4 in) at 60 days and 127–133 millimeters (5.0–5.25 in) at 70 days. In North Carolina, the tenth primary of juveniles reached 109 millimeters (4.29 in) between 70 and 77 days (Benfield 1970).

As a sheath grows distally, the vane starts to break free at the tip. In proportion to its length, the vanes of the tertials were the most exposed, followed by those of secondary feathers and lastly by primaries (Figure 95). We speculate that the varying degree of vane exposure in the three feather tracts is related to the relative vulnerability of the growing feather to damage. Tertials are the closest to the

Table 162. Percentage of wood ducks, by age and sex class, with various numbers of secondaries.

| Age | Sex | \multicolumn{8}{c}{Number of secondaries} | | | | | | | |
		8 n	8 Percentage	9 n	9 Percentage	10 n	10 Percentage	11 n	11 Percentage
Adult	Male	0		1	4.2	21	87.5	2	8.3
Adult	Female	0		1	7.1	13	92.9	0	
Juvenile	Male	2	3.5	5	8.8	49	86.0	1	1.7
Juvenile	Female	2	7.7	10	38.5	14	53.8	0	

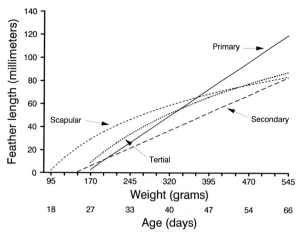

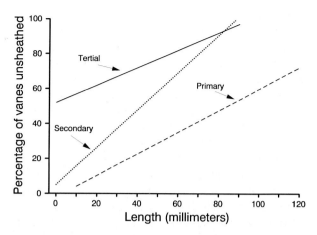

Figure 94. Development of wing feathers (ninth primary, n = 117; fifth secondary, n = 114; most distal tertial, n = 117; and longest scapular, n = 62) of juvenile wood ducks (males and females) raised at the Van Norman Aviary, Illinois, 1981. Regression equations for the indicated primary, secondary, tertial, and scapular feathers, respectively, are: $y = -50.16 + 0.31x$, $r = 0.81$, $P < 0.001$; $y = -28.82 + 0.21x$, $r = 0.78$, $P < 0.001$; $y = -337.99 + 67.53$ (log x), $r = 0.78$, $P < 0.001$; and $y = -209.31 + 46.47$ (log x), $r = 0.90$, $P < 0.001$.

Figure 95. Percentage protrusion of feather vanes above their sheaths for three flight feathers as they grow in length on juvenile wood ducks. The regression equations for tertial, secondary, and primary feather growth, respectively, are: $y = 52.1 + 0.50x$, $r = 0.69$, $P < 0.001$; $y = 5.2 + 1.07x$, $r = 0.75$, $P < 0.001$; and $y = -2.0 + 0.62x$, $r = 0.80$, $P < 0.001$.

body, and therefore more protected than the secondaries and distal primaries from abrasion during the critical maturation period.

Not all wing feather tracts have the same number of feathers. We have found wings with 9 primaries rather than the standard 10. Secondaries especially appeared to vary in number (Table 162); some juveniles had as few as 8, a moderate number had 9, and one bird had 11. Ten secondaries were more common in adult woodies than in juveniles, but one adult male had 9, two had 11, and one female had 9. A white terminal mark, usually absent on the tenth secondary (most proximal), was more prevalent in adult males than in adult females or in juveniles of both sexes.

Wing Coverts

A row of long feathers—the greater coverts—overlaps the flight feathers; they are labeled by the particular flight feathers they partially cover. The tertial greater coverts and lesser coverts were the first covert feathers to appear, at 20 days of age, followed by the secondary coverts at 23 days and the primary coverts at 30 days. The tertial and secondary coverts completed growth by 40 days, and the primary coverts completed growth by 60 days.

Anterior to the greater coverts is a row of shorter feathers—the middle coverts. These feathers developed concomitantly with the greater coverts. Four to five rows of small feathers between the middle coverts and the wing's leading edge make up the lesser coverts. They appeared at 20

Juvenile feathers completely replace downy plumage on young wood ducks by the time these birds are 70 days old. Above, about one-third of the base of primary and secondary feathers of a 77-day-old female (in North Carolina) still are enclosed in sheaths. Because of day length, the farther north a woodie duckling hatches, the more rapid its development. *Photo by Jack Dermid.*

days and were mature at 35 days.

With the exception of the tertial coverts, all covert feathers remain about one year until late in the second prebasic molt—after the flight feathers have been shed—thus making them the last feathers lost prior to acquisition of a new plumage.

The tertials and their coverts are the only wing feathers molted at least twice in a year, making them unique from the adjacent once-molted secondaries and their coverts. The tertials and their coverts molt from natal down to juvenile to alternate I, while other wing feather tracts molt only from natal down to juvenile plumage. We classify the second generation of tertials as alternate I because they are almost identical to definitive alternate of the adult.

The first generation of tertials and their coverts provides one of the clues to distinguishing adult from juvenile wings (Carney 1964). Other clues are provided by the greater, middle, and lesser secondary coverts.

Until juvenile tertials and their coverts are molted, they are distinctive from definitive alternate tertials of adults. Carney (1964) described juvenile tertials of both sexes as pointed with frayed tips and bronze in color; alternate tertials in juvenile and adult males are square-tipped and dark iridescent blue-black in color; alternate tertials in juvenile and adult females are bronze in color, with smooth, rounded tips.

Development of three prominent tertials was measured weekly (September through November) in confined wild-trapped wood ducks. The growth rate was similar for all sex and age classes, but these feathers commenced growing about 12 days earlier in adult males; tertials continued to lengthen among adults through November and among juveniles to mid-December.

The last alternate I tertial to appear in males is the most distal, readily identified by its square, white-banded tip. It is one-third broader than the adjacent tenth secondary and longer at full growth than the second tertial.

The change from juvenile to nuptial plumage in wood ducks is rapid between 100 and 130 days of age. Body feathers molt from juvenile to nuptial, but certain feather tracts on the head (crown, cheeks, and throat) molt from juvenile to basic to nuptial within a two-week span. *Opposite column top photo of male 100 days old by Charles and Elizabeth Schwartz. Center photo of male about 110 days of age (note the gray-tan basic plumage in the white facial marking, which is white in the juvenile and nuptial plumage stages) by Stephen Kirkpatrick. Bottom photo of drake approximately 115 days old by Scott Nielsen.*

DETERMINING SEX AND AGE

Presence or absence of a penis from day one can be used to determine wood duck sex. With age, the penis becomes increasingly adultlike, so that by early winter this character becomes unreliable for distinguishing juveniles from adults. The depth of the bursa of Fabricius and the open/closed opening of the oviduct in the cloaca appear to be viable indicators of age in females until early January.

The white horn-shaped U mark on the cheek area becomes visible in young males at 35–38 days, enabling the sex of most wood ducks to be distinguished by plumage from that age forward. The white terminal edgings of secondary feathers are the most prominent wing markings for distinguishing the sexes. Male wings show a narrow white band across the terminal edge of the secondaries; females have a broader tear-shaped white spot that is largely confined to the outer part of the vane. Although there is a small proportion of wood ducks with markings that do not conform to this customary sexual dimorphism, more than 95 percent of the woodies we examined could be distinguished on this basis.

When the white marking on secondaries is not adequately defined for sexual determination, the most proximal secondary may be employed. This usually dark-tipped feather has a purplish green (oil drop) sheen on the outer vane in the male and a black stripe in the female, according to Sam Carney. The white-tipped secondaries usually become sufficiently exposed from their sheaths by 40–45 days to use as a sex character.

An inverted V notch occurs in juvenile tail feathers, marking the site of the detached down feather. As long as a brownish, ragged, or notched tail feather persists, it can be used to separate juveniles from adults. One or more juvenile tail feathers are likely to persist up to 110 days. The comparative development of nuptial rectrices on wild wood ducks from southern and central Illinois is presented in Figure 96.

The dark juvenile bill of drake woodies begins to show a trace of pink at 55–65 days. With increasing age, the red margins enlarge to encircle the base of the bill, and the red becomes brighter. An adultlike bill is evident from 95 to 115 days. An orange cere starts to develop around the upper mandible of males at 90 days and is complete by 120 days.

The male's iris begins to show pink-orange at 50 days and becomes progressively darker red at 110–125 days. A yellow eyelid appears as early as 60 days, deepens to orange by 100 days, and becomes red—matching the iris—by 150 days.

Many yearling females can be distinguished from adults during autumn and the subsequent breeding season by the length of the white mark posterior to the eye. On females we examined in October, the white dash extended back from the eye an average of 15.9 ± 5.38 millimeters (0.63 ± 0.21 in) in juveniles and 23.2 ± 2.49 millimeters (0.91 ± 0.10 in) in adults. On incubating females from central Illinois, this mark averaged 17.3 ± 1.44 millimeters (0.68 ± 0.06 in) for yearlings and 19.1 ± 0.88 millimeters (0.75 ± 0.03 in) for adults. Adult hens probably had slightly smaller white marks in spring than in autumn as a result of early prebasic molt in some birds. Although there was an overlap, 60 percent ($n = 43$) of incubating hens with less than an 18-millimeter (0.71 in) mark were yearlings.

By the time juvenile female wood ducks are 96 days old, sexual dimorphism is distinct. The pronounced white eye ring has prevailed from 60 days of age. Male woodie ducklings begin to have a white-margined cheek at 40 days. *Photo by Stephen Kirkpatrick.*

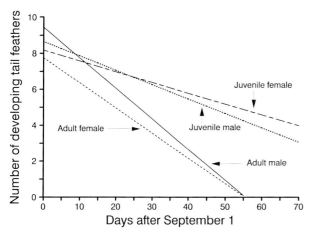

Figure 96. Number of tail feathers (n = 14) in sheaths after September 1, 1981 through 1983 on wild wood ducks from central and southern Illinois. The regression equations for adult males, adult females, juvenile males, and juvenile females, respectively, are: $y = 9.45 + -0.17x$, $r = -0.75$, $P < 0.001$, $n = 65$; $y = 7.76 + -0.14x$, $r = -0.56$, $P < 0.01$, $n = 24$; $y = 8.66 + -0.08x$, $r = -0.52$, $P < 0.001$, $n = 152$; and $y = 8.18 + -0.06x$, $r = -0.41$, $P < 0.001$, $n = 96$.

Wing Plumage

After the first molt, tertials and their coverts in juveniles are fully developed and very similar in color to those of adults. To assist in using color of the greater middle and lesser coverts for age identification, we subjectively classified the color intensity of each feather in these tracts for all sex and age groups (figures 97 and 98). Each feather was examined with magnification under bright fluorescent light and compared with the color of a selected set of adult covert feathers. Bellrose and Nanette Trudeau rated color shades of each feather independently and obtained similar results.

We found that the greatest difference in color between juveniles and adults occurred in females, especially in the first row (greater) of the secondary coverts. In males, the second-row (middle) and third-row (lesser) secondary coverts had the greatest difference in color intensity between juveniles and adults.

Testing by U.S. Fish and Wildlife Service personnel examining wings from wood ducks that were aged on the basis of cloacal examination, disclosed that a sizable proportion of male wings were improperly identified as to age. The major error was recording adult males as juveniles. Evidently even experienced biologists had difficulty distinguishing between color intensities of the different age groups of males. Fortunately, the error rate was appreciably lower in females, probably because of the greater differences in the color of the wing coverts (figures 97 and 98).

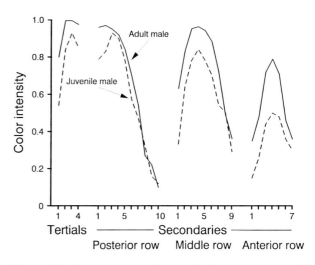

Figure 97. Color intensity of covert feathers in adult and juvenile male wood ducks. Feathers arranged by rows posterior to anterior and, in each row, from proximal to distal and by 0.1 degree of color intensity. The shades of color intensity are: purple = 1.0; blue to blue-green = 0.5; blue-green to brown = 0.

Zicus (1982) and Harvey et al. (1989a) found differences in the lengths and widths of primaries, secondaries, and secondary coverts that enabled yearling females to be distinguished from adults. They used discriminate function analyses of measurements of these feathers to demonstrate that there were statistical differences between yearling and adult females. In primaries and secondaries that we measured, these feathers were smaller in yearlings than in adults, but there were no significant differences in the tertials (Table 163). We

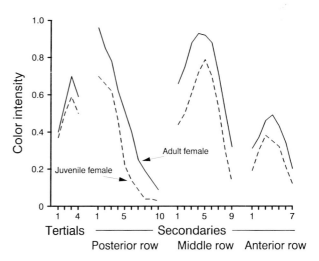

Figure 98. Color intensity of covert feathers in adult and juvenile female wood ducks. Feathers arranged by rows posterior to anterior and, in each row, from proximal to distal and by 0.1 degree of color intensity. The shades of color intensity are: purple = 1.0; blue to blue-green = 0.5; blue-green to brown = 0.

Table 163. Length (millimeters) of the ninth primary, center secondary, and three tertials (proximal to distal) in wing feather tracts of wild wood ducks, by age and sex classes.

Feather tract	Adult		Mature juvenile	
	Males (n = 11)	Females (n = 13)	Males (n = 24)	Females (n = 23)
Primary	143.3 ± 6.25	142.5 ± 4.50	136.3 ± 6.00	136.7 ± 6.41
Secondary	81.8 ± 2.22	85.8 ± 7.58	76.3 ± 5.17	83.2 ± 6.84
Tertial				
Proximal 1	85.4 ± 7.55	79.9 ± 6.32	85.8 ± 9.34	73.0 ± 6.95
Central 2	69.8 ± 5.95	85.4 ± 8.71	72.5 ± 7.07	80.7 ± 8.16
Distal 3	83.7 ± 7.42	91.8 ± 7.26	85.0 ± 6.98	90.0 ± 6.35

have noticed that in females the two most proximal greater secondary coverts protrude beyond the neat row formed by the remaining secondary coverts and are slow to develop in juveniles. Harvey et al. (1989a) found that even at maturity the first proximal secondary covert was smaller in yearlings than in adults (Table 164). Of the several parameters Harvey et al. (1989a) measured of this covert feather, the relative difference between yearlings and adults was greater for the covert feather than for either the primary or secondary feathers, which they also included in age evaluation.

Thus, the findings of Harvey et al. (1989a) and our color observations suggest that to differentiate juvenile/yearling females from adult females attention should be focused primarily on the degree of color intensity and size of the first two greater secondary covert feathers.

On the underwing surface, the wing lining (composed of feathers analogous to the coverts) developed on a similar growth schedule. Posterior to the leading edge are five or six rows of small, silvery feathers barred with gray-brown, followed by a terminal row of silvery feathers. Under the primaries, this particular row is similar in length to the greater coverts. Under the secondaries, however, these feathers are appreciably longer than the greater coverts, and they successively increase in length from distal to proximal. A small group of long feathers at the base of the underwing makes up the axillars.

ADULT MOLTS

Both in the wild and in captivity, many adult male wood ducks in central Illinois began to lose their definitive alternate (nuptial) plumage late in May (see Chapter 14). The first nuptial feathers molted were the bronze side feathers; they were replaced rapidly by a streaked brown-tan definitive basic (eclipse) plumage. This feather change appeared at least one week in advance of the prealternate molt in other feather tracts.

The breast/belly plumage of both sexes was the next area to show new feathers, as the alternate white was gradually partially replaced by gray-tan feathers, creating a dappled appearance. Within a two-week period, 30 to 100 percent of the formerly immaculate white became spotted or brownish and remained in this state for the next 70 days. Then the definitive prealternate molt began to produce pure white feathers that in one to two weeks completely covered the breast/belly area and formed part of the nuptial plumage.

The definitive alternate burgundy male chest began to be replaced by the definitive basic brown and tan streaked feathers a week after feathers were replaced in the white breast/belly area (Figure 99). Within two weeks, a drab basic plumage had replaced the brilliant burgundy alternate plumage of the chest. This definitive basic plumage persisted for 50–60 days before the definitive prealternate

Table 164. Difference in measurements of most proximal greater secondary coverts of known-aged female wood ducks during the breeding season in South Carolina.[a]

	Yearling		Adult		t-test P	Percentage difference
	Mean	S.E.	Mean	S.E.		
Mass	7.3	0.3	9.7	0.3	<0.01	24.74
Length	33.0	0.5	35.7	0.5	<0.01	7.56
Total width	8.1	0.2	10.2	0.1	<0.01	20.59
Mean width	14.9	0.2	16.7	0.2	<0.01	10.78

[a] Adapted from Harvey et al. (1989a).

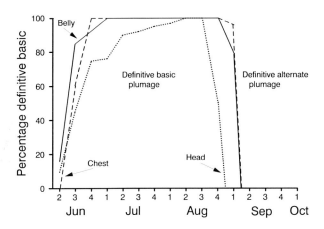

Figure 99. Time frame of the prebasic molt to the definitive basic (eclipse) plumage of two adult male wood ducks—leading into the definitive alternate plumage.

molt began to produce nuptial burgundy feathers—a transformation that took three to four weeks to complete.

Early in the prebasic molt of the head, the crest was lost in both sexes; the brilliant colors on the drake's head were rapidly replaced until about 75 percent became gray in 14 days. Thereafter, the molt of the head slowed so that 30–40 more days were required to complete the eclipse plumage (Figure 99). Full basic plumage on the head was maintained only briefly before it was gradually replaced in four

The onset of the prebasic molt in the adult wood duck drake gives only slight indication that, within a month's time, the brilliantly colored bird will resemble the woodie hen and experience a subsequent loss (replacement) of all flight feathers. Note that with the loss of variegated bronze side feathers, except for the white eye ring the plumage of the adult above is similar to that of a 120-day-old juvenile wood duck drake. The adult drake's eye ring persists through the basic (eclipse) plumage and is more pronounced than in the juvenile, where it usually is replaced by nuptial feathers by 115 days of age. *Photo courtesy of the Denver Museum of Natural History.*

to five weeks by the nuptial plumage. The crest began to grow as the first alternate feathers appeared on the drake's head and continued for a month beyond completion of the definitive alternate cheek plumage. Full development of the adult crest (50–60 millimeters: 1.96–2.36 in) was reached October 10–30 in central Illinois, at least 8 millimeters (0.31 in) longer than that of juveniles.

As the eclipse head molt progressed, the male's bright red iris and red bill base began to fade; these body parts assumed their former red color about midway through the basic plumage. There is, however, considerable variation among individuals. We have observed some males that retained their red eyes and bills throughout the molt period.

As indicated in Chapter 14, the prebasic molt in most adult females commences later than in males because of incubating and brooding activities. In females that fail to breed the prebasic molt may begin as early as in males.

Although not as apparent in females as in males, the side feathers probably were the first alternate plumage molted, followed by replacement of white throat/belly feathers with mottled white-gray feathers that produced a spotted appearance. We have noted that about one-third of incubating wood ducks in central Illinois have varying intensities of spotted breast/belly area (Table 156); none had lost its crest. The molt of the alternate streaked brown-tan chest feathers to basic plumage—dark gray flecked with white—lags several days behind the molt of breast/belly feathers.

From early April to mid-June, about a third of incubating woodie hens at Nauvoo Slough, Illinois, exhibit basic plumage on the belly. Other hens have the customary white belly of the nuptial (definitive) plumage. Note the pronounced white eye mark that, early in the prebasic molt, has yet to diminish in size. *Photo by Dan Holm; courtesy of the Illinois Natural History Survey.*

In the advanced basic molt stage, the adult wood duck hen loses her crest and part of her white eye mark, and her normally white belly is clouded with brown feathers. At that molt stage the hen (above), resting with her three surviving ducklings that are about 18 days old, probably will lose her flight feathers before the young can fly six weeks later. *Photo by David McEwen.*

On females, the crest was lost shortly after side feathers entered prebasic molt. The white dash behind the eye diminished in length; in some females it almost disappeared. The crown changed from black-green to brown. We have observed a few females with white horns on the cheeks (also noted in several juvenile females), as reported by Palmer (1976), during the definitive basic plumage.

Early in the prebasic molt, the upper and lower tail coverts began to be replaced; this occurred a few days in advance of similar replacements in the tail feathers (Table 165).

Table 165. Number of new rump, upper tail coverts (UTC), and tail feathers appearing on adult wood ducks raised at the Van Norman Aviary, Illinois, 1983.

| | Nonbreeders | | | | | | Breeding males | | | | | | | | |
| | Male | | | Female | | | #287 | | | #427 | | | #434 | | |
Date	Rump	UTC	Tail	Rump	UTC	Tail	Rump	UTC	Tail	Rump	UTC	Tail	Rump	UTC	Tail
June 13	0	6	2	4	8	1	0	0	0	0	0	0	0	0	0
June 20	10	0	8	0	0	1	7	8	0	5	10	1	0	10	1
June 27	0	3	2	10	0	2	0	4	0	1	2	1	0	1	9
July 5	0	0	6	1	0	4	0	0	0	0	2	0	0	0	0
July 11	0	0	4	0	1	0	0	0	4	3	0	2	0	0	0
July 22	0	0	0	10	3	0	5	0	2	4	1	3	4	0	0
July 27	4	0	0	0	0	5	2	0	6	0	0	0	0	0	0
August 3	7	0	3	2	0	1	4	0	0	0	0	6	0	0	1
August 10	3	0	7	1	0	0	0	0	0	0	0	0	0	0	3
August 17	0	4	0	0	0	0	3	0	0	0	0	0	0	0	5
August 29	8	2	0	6	5	2	4	0	5	3	0	2	0	4	0
September 9	0	1	0	0	0	5	0	9	3	0	10	4	5	0	0
September 15	0	0	4	0	0	2	0	3	0	3	0	0	4	1	0
September 22	0	2	0	0	3	0	0	0	2	0	0	0	0	2	0
October 4	0	0	2	0	4	0	0	0	2	0	0	3	0	0	6
October 10	0	0	0	3	0	3	0	2	0	0	6	0	3	1	0
October 17	0	0	0	0	0	0	0	1	0	1	0	0	0	0	0
October 26	0	0	0	0	1	2	0	0	0	0	0	0	0	3	1
October 31	0	0	0	0	1	2	0	0	0	0	1	0	0	2	0
Total	32	18	38	37	26	30	25	27	24	20	32	24	16	24	26

Tail Coverts and Tail

The temporal correlation between new incoming upper and lower tail coverts was $r = 0.75$, $P < 0.001$, indicating that both developed over a similar time frame. The temporal pattern of new incoming upper tail coverts, as discerned by the protrusion of sheathed vanes, is shown for five adult wood ducks in Table 165. During a 140-day period—June 13 through October 31—we enumerated a minimum of 18–32 new tail covert feathers per individual, suggesting that adults had two sets of upper tail coverts. Because replacement feathers also appeared in two sequences in the lower tail coverts and the tail, it was evident that, starting with the prebasic molt, adults developed two sets of both tail coverts and tail feathers—one for the definitive basic plumage and the other for the definitive alternate plumage. Customarily, there are 14 feathers in each feather tract when tail feathers and their coverts are fully developed, but numbers vary slightly in individuals, perhaps because of the latent development of feather follicles in some birds. The seasonal development of rectrices in trapped wild wood ducks is shown in Figure 96.

Rump

Rump feathers number 109 (Table 152), but we counted only 16–37 new incoming feathers on five adult wood ducks (Table 165). Apparently because of their short length, many feathers appeared and matured during the week interval between inspections. There appeared to be two periods of feather production—one in late June and another from July 29 to August 29. This sequence of feather growth suggests that the early activity represented the prebasic molt and the later feather development represented the prealternate molt.

Scapulars

There were 55 scapular feathers on one side of an adult wood duck (Table 152), but only about 12 were impressively long. Scattered incoming sheathed feathers were noted from mid-June through October (Table 166), but we were unsure whether that represented a protracted molt of one plumage or two cycles of feather replacement. Several incoming scapulars were found through winter

Table 166. Number of new (in sheath) scapular and back feathers appearing on adult wood ducks raised at the Van Norman Aviary, Illinois, 1983.

| | Nonbreeders | | | | Breeding males | | | | | |
| | Male | | Female | | #287 | | #427 | | #434 | |
Date	Scapular	Back	Scapular	Back	Scapular	Back	Scapular	Back	Scapular	Back
June 13	0	15	4	10	0	0	0	0	0	0
June 20	0	15	1	20	4	4	10	0	0	4
June 27	0	20	0	10	0	0	0	2	1	0
July 5	8	0	3	0	0	0	0	2	0	2
July 11	0	0	3	5	0	0	2	0	0	0
July 22	0	0	5	0	4	25	0	0	1	0
July 27	1	3	0	2	0	0	3	5	0	3
August 3	0	5	0	9	0	5	1	0	0	0
August 10	1	0	0	0	1	0	1	1	1	0
August 17	0	0	0	3	4	10	6	0	0	0
August 29	2	0	1	1	1	0	0	0	7	25
September 9	1	0	0	1	2	1	0	0	0	0
September 15	2	0	4	0	1	1	4	0	0	0
September 22	0	0	0	2	0	0	1	0	0	0
October 4	0	1	5	1	3	3	2	1	6	2
October 10	0	0	0	0	1	0	1	0	0	0
October 17	0	0	2	0	0	0	0	0	0	0
October 26	0		2		0	0	0		0	
October 31	0	0	2	0	0	0	0	0	0	0
Total	15	59	32	64	21	49	31	11	16	36

and as late as April 16 (Table 155), suggesting that there are two molts spread over a prolonged period.

Back

We enumerated 164 back feathers in an adult wood duck (Table 152). Over a 140-day period, 11–59 new feathers (mean = 41.8 ± 19.2) were observed. Because back feathers were relatively small, many matured between weekly inspections. The appearance of new feathers sporadically over a long period of time makes it difficult to ascertain if more than one molt occurred.

Wing

In the five adult wood ducks that we studied, there was considerable difference in the stage of body molt when the wing feathers were shed (Table 167). In one unmated yearling male, primaries were shed 18 days after the body molt started; in one breeding adult shedding of the primaries was delayed for 69 days; shedding of the primaries in two others started at 30 days and in another at 38 days after the body molt had begun. The loss of secondaries occurred either on the same day as or a day later than the loss of primaries (Table 167).

The growth of these flight feathers was quite rapid for the first 90 percent of their total increment: primaries averaged 3.2 millimeters (0.13 in) per day and secondaries averaged 2.2 millimeters (0.09 in) per day (Figure 100). After 90 percent of the ultimate growth of primaries and secondaries had been achieved in 35 days, their growth rate slowed nota-

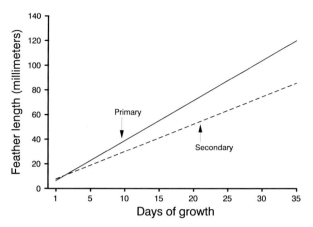

Figure 100. Growth rate of primary and secondary feathers in adult wood ducks during the prealternate molt. The regression equations for primary and secondary feather growth rate are: $y = 6.54 + 3.24x$, $r = 0.96$, $P < 0.001$; and $y = 7.82 + 2.22x$, $r = 0.93$, $P < 0.001$, respectively.

bly. Adult woodies probably are able to resume flight by the time their flight feathers have reached the 90-percent size at a mean of 33 ± 2.92 days. The daily growth rate of adult primaries and secondaries was 3.24 millimeters (0.13 in) and 2.22 millimeters (0.09 in) respectively. Juvenile primary and secondary daily growth rates were slightly lower— 2.95 millimeters (0.12 in) for primaries and 2 millimeters (0.08 in) for secondaries.

After regaining flight feathers, the five adults took an additional 26–70 days to achieve body plumage that approached 90 percent of their ultimate development. Thus, the time span from the beginning of the prebasic molt to 90-percent completion of the prealternate molt was 108–125 days (mean = 119 ± 6.5 days) (Table 167).

Table 167. Development of primary and secondary wing feathers in relation to the beginning of definitive prebasic molt and completion of definitive prealternate molt in adult wood ducks, Van Norman Aviary, Illinois, 1983.

Specimen	Date prebasic 90-percent started[a]	Primaries		Secondaries		Prealternate molt 90-percent complete	
		Lost	90-percent regained[b]	Lost	90-percent regained[b]	Date	Days[c]
Adult male, unmated	5–27	6–14	7–20	6–15	7–11	9–12	108
Adult male, mated	6–1	7–1	7–30	7–2	7–26	10–4	125
Adult male, mated	6–5	7–5	8–9	7–5	8–2	10–4	121
Adult male, mated	6–10	8–18	9–18	8–18	9–14	10–10	122
Adult female, unmated	6–8	7–16	8–19	7–16	8–16	10–4	118
Mean span (days)			33.0 ± 2.92		27.2 ± 2.59		

[a] Estimated based on stage of molt when observed on June 13.
[b] Based on growth to 90 percent of total length when birds have no difficulty in flying.
[c] Completed on head, chest, breast, belly, back, and rump, but only partially completed on side, flank, tail coverts, tail, and second set of scapulars.

NUTRITION AND MOLT

Molting requires protein and lipid energy. It is evident that, to reduce taxing their energy reserves, ducks have staggered the molt of plumage tracts — and of feathers within a specific tract — to accommodate these demands. Greatest development of juvenile plumage and renewal of adult alternate plumage occur during summer, when food and weather are most favorable. At other times of the year, however, the availability of food may prolong or eliminate a molt.

Nutritional Costs

Feathers are composed of about 96 percent protein (Papadopoulas et al. 1986, Williams et al. 1991). Using Heitmeyer's (1988) calculated dietary protein efficiency for mallards at 55 percent, a wood duck growing a complete set of wing and nuptial body contour feathers probably would need to synthesize 37.4 grams (1.32 oz) of protein as derived from 67.9 grams (2.40 oz) of ingested protein (tables 152 and 153).

Besides contour feathers, a considerable amount of down feathers insulates the bodies of ducks. Eric Hopps determined that in the wood duck, down composed an additional 10.8 percent of the feather mass of five males and 14.25 percent of five females. Considering the additional protein required to produce the sheaths of contour feathers plus the down feather mass, we calculate that 49.86 grams (1.76 oz) of protein are used in feather synthesis. This would require the ingestion of 90.65 grams (3.2 oz) of protein by an adult drake wood duck to acquire its down and nuptial plumage contour feathers. At the beginning of the basic molt, the areas around roosting logs are littered with plucked down feathers. Apparently most down feathers are lost at this time, so we assume that a new complement of down develops concurrently with the woodie's nuptial plumage.

Heitmeyer (1988) reported that the basic plumage mass of an adult female mallard was 72.7 grams (2.56 oz), whereas that of an adult male wood duck was 38.9 grams (1.37 oz). An adult female mallard weighs about 1.6 times more than an adult male wood duck, yet the mallard's plumage mass was 1.87 times greater than that of the wood duck. The

Molting is the replacement of worn feathers. The timing of the molting cycle in wood ducks is dictated primarily by genetics, photoperiod, age, and nutrition. Although molting occurs primarily in summer months, not all woodies molt through the various stages simultaneously. In theory, the fact that all birds of the species in an area are not flightless at the same time (or to the same degree) may be a survival mechanism. More likely, it reflects physiological variations among individuals. That the birds molt when habitat vegetation is at maximum green-up, therefore most concealing, almost certainly is a survival (antipredator) adaptation. The wood duck drake achieves its resplendent full nuptial plumage after three to three and a half months of molting, in time to be most impressive for autumn courting and sustained migration flight. *Photo by Charles and Elizabeth Schwartz.*

difference in plumage mass may be due to the more northern distribution of the mallard resulting in a denser covering of feathers.

In addition to the protein component of a mature feather, protein is needed to form the sheath that initially enclosed the shaft and vane. Murphy and King (1986) determined that in white-crowned sparrows, sheath mass accounted for an additional 18–20 percent of the protein required for feather production. Recognizing this additional protein need would account for 73.9 grams (2.61 oz) of dietary protein necessary for complete feather production in the wood duck.

Although the head of the wood duck has a larger number of feathers than does any other body region, the feathers are so small (except for the crest) that the ingested protein requirement for their growth is only 4.54 grams (0.16 oz), compared with 43.23 grams (1.52 oz) needed for production of body feathers and 20.17 grams (0.71 oz) needed for production of wing feathers (tables 152 and 153). If these calculations are reasonably correct, they indicate that the wood duck's nutritional requirements for molting are substantial. Because of the juvenile's rapid, synchronous molt of body tracts, the protein demand is greatest per day during development of the juvenile plumage. Development of alternate plumages is spread over much longer periods (tables 158 and 160), thereby reducing the daily intake of protein necessary to produce these plumages. One of the most demanding molt activities is that of remigial development, which requires 11.71 grams (0.41 oz) over 30–40 days in both juveniles and adults.

Pehrsson (1987) found that mallard body condition, as indicated by lipid deposits, declined during the flightless period. We observed that wood duck weights also declined during this time frame (see Chapter 9). Because lipids rather than protein seem to be the cause of weight loss, Pehrsson (1987) speculated that the decline is due to an adaptive strategy rather than to the stress of molting: by weighing less, ducks are able to fly at an earlier stage of flight feather development—a temporary asset to survival. However, low-protein diets during the molting period did reduce wing length in mallards, especially in males. A reduction in wing surface would require the expenditure of more energy on long migration flights later in life.

Winter Molts

In wild mallards, Heitmeyer (1987) observed that female adults molted earlier in the winter when winter precipitation improved habitat conditions.

Miller (1986) came to a similar conclusion after studying the winter molting of northern pintails in California. From a series of nutrition experiments with captive mallards, Richardson (1989) concluded that the onset of prebasic molt in female mallards during winter was related to the nutrition of the food available. He found that reduced availability of food or corn diets in mallards resulted in delayed initiation of the prebasic molt.

Despite the necessity for female ducks to build up their lipid reserves for egg laying and incubation (see Chapter 9), female wood ducks, along with northern pintails (Miller 1986), American wigeons (Wishart 1985), gadwalls (Paulus 1984), and canvasbacks (Lovvorn and Barzen 1988), all molt more extensively through winter and early spring than do males of these species.

Through winter and early spring, most female prairie ducks undergo at least a partial prebasic molt, resulting in a more drab appearance. Wood duck females, on the other hand, usually replace molted feathers with those of similar color. The difference in the color aspect changes brought by the winter molt between wood ducks and prairie-nesting species is logical. Female prairie-nesting ducks are under heavy jeopardy from ground predators (Sargeant et al. 1984). Therefore, it is advantageous for the incubating hen's plumage to provide maximum camouflage. Apparently, the part of the prebasic molt prior to the nesting season in females of prairie-nesting species furthers this need. Studies of the prebreeding prebasic molt in female mallards (Heitmeyer 1987), American wigeons (Wishart 1985), northern pintails (Miller 1986), gadwalls (Paulus 1984), and canvasbacks (Lovvorn and Barzen 1988) suggest that color changes brought about by the early phase of prebasic molt may make these species less visible to predators at a time of greatest risk.

What useful purpose the winter molt serves female wood ducks is conjectural. The molt appears centered in the breast/belly, tail coverts, and tail plumage areas. Improving the feather coverage of these areas may be an asset during incubation when feather abrasion is maximized by friction with cavity entrances, entering and leaving cavities, and turning and incubating eggs. The prebreeding portion of the wood duck's molt includes little of the dorsal plumage, where concealing coloration is so important to prairie ducks.

Because female wood ducks nest in cavities, they do not require the concealing coloration important to prairie ducks. Perhaps female wood ducks do not have an extensive prebasic molt prior to the breeding season because it would not be an asset at that time to their survival. Later, during the brood and wing molt seasons, the female's plumage is at its maximum drabness—a time of greatest need to avoid detection.

Genetics, nutrition, photoperiod, and temperature are factors that appear to control the rate of development and molting chronology of juvenile wood ducks. Therefore, the temporal pattern of molt that we described is an amalgamation of feather changes observed over a period of years in central Illinois. Elsewhere, we would anticipate differences in the temporal change of the various plumage tracts.

Chapter 14

Postbreeding Activities

For most individual wood ducks, postbreeding activity extends from the cessation of breeding to the southward migration. These are halcyon days for woodies. Temperatures are mild, food is abundant in the right places, and escape cover is readily available. When the flightless period of the molt is behind them, energy demands are low and rather easily met. Woodies then spend an inordinate amount of time loafing on logs, banks, and muskrat houses, barely stirring for hours. No longer do mated males fret about the intrusion of other males seeking their mates. No longer do they feel compelled to follow their mates seeking nest sites or remain close by while the hens are laying or incubating eggs. For females with broods, this respite period must await the maturity of their charges.

The first birds to enter this period of changed activity are the nonbreeding woodies, presumably yearlings. At the Van Norman Aviary in Illinois, yearlings that failed to mate were the first wood ducks to enter the prebasic molt (see Chapter 13). Among breeding ducks at Nauvoo Slough, the first males to abandon reproductive activities were those that deserted early-incubating hens. For a few males, this time was as early as mid-April. Males associated with late-nesting or renesting females that failed to hatch successfully remained paired longer—a few until late July (figures 101 to 104).

As shown by sporadic courtship activity that extends into June, some unmated males delay entering the postbreeding period until female breeding activity is on the wane. Hens with early-hatched broods shed their maternal responsibilities in late June; those with late broods do not begin their postbreeding activities until mid to late August. The initiation of postbreeding activities, therefore, varies among individuals by as much as two months.

FLOCK FORMATION

All through the breeding season at Nauvoo Slough, unmated males—at times up to 19—remained in loose flocks that became most apparent when they formed a courting party in pursuit of a mate-seeking female. Members of the unmated male group displayed varying degrees of attachment, separating and coming together at varying times of the day. As males deserted their mates, their numbers loafing on logs increased, and during May and June little coteries of adult males were forming at favored loafing sites.

At Nauvoo Slough, the first flying juveniles began to appear in late June. Early in July, distinct groupings could be seen as a few juveniles fed together or loafed together on logs. These may have been brood mates that had kept some filial attachment. Small flocks increased as the summer progressed. These juvenile flocks contained birds of both sexes, in contrast to some of the adult flocks that were entirely of one sex. There were more males than females in most flocks, but occasionally the reverse was true.

Nonbreeding adult males remained in clusters through June—the month in which other males, deserting their mates, began to form small flocks. Associations of two and three males were common after mid-May and into early August, but few flocks were larger than five, apparently because some males departed from the area as flocks developed.

Adult females formed larger and more numerous flocks than those formed by adult males. Many flocks of adult females remained as distinct entities until mid-August. Flocks composed of 7–13 females were numerous.

For the most part, early summer flocks contained a large proportion of juveniles. According to

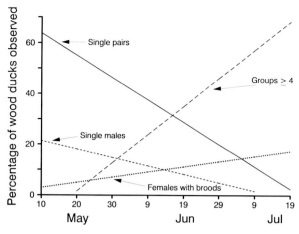

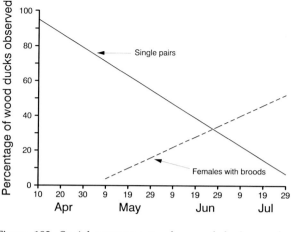

Figure 101. Social components of a wood duck population during breeding and postbreeding periods at Nauvoo Slough, Illinois, 1983. Regression equations for single pairs, single males, females with broods, and groups of four or more, respectively, are: $y = 68.5 - 0.878x$, $r = -0.86$, $P < 0.001$; $y = 23.2 - 0.331x$, $r = -0.87$, $P < 0.001$; $y = 2.1 + 0.205x$, $r = 0.75$, $P < 0.01$; and $y = -15.1 + 1.114x$, $r = 0.88$, $P < 0.001$.

Figure 102. Social components of a wood duck population during breeding and postbreeding periods at Nauvoo Slough, Illinois, 1984. The regression equations for single pairs and females with broods are: $y = 92.5 - 0.805x$, $r = -0.85$, $P < 0.01$; and $y = -14.1 + 0.604x$, $r = 0.86$, $P < 0.01$, respectively.

Grice and Rogers (1965) the first flocks in Massachusetts were juveniles, with adult males joining as the season progressed, followed by increasing numbers of adult females. They observed premigratory flocks forming during the second week in July.

Beshears (1974) reported that summer flocks of wood ducks in Alabama became increasingly numerous in August. Based on trapping, he surmised that the first flocks were largely juveniles with adults progressively augmenting their ranks through the month, after which large numbers left the region.

As the breeding season draws to a close, wood duck males and females that failed to produce broods begin to gather on logs to spend many hours resting and preening. The farthest male is just beginning to molt its head feathers for basic (eclipse) ones. If there is a golden season for woodies, this is it. Food is abundant, temperatures are warm, days are long, and there is no breeding activity that requires energy. *Left photo by David McEwen. Right photo by Dave Menke; courtesy of the U.S. Fish and Wildlife Service.*

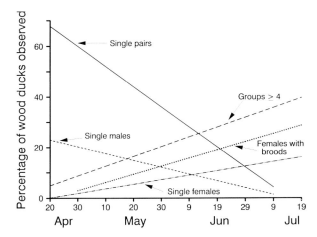

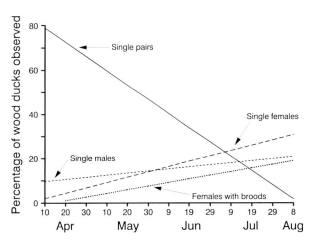

Figure 103. Social components of a wood duck population during breeding and postbreeding periods at Nauvoo Slough, Illinois, 1985. The regression equations for single pairs, single males, females with broods, groups of four or more, and single females, respectively, are: $y = 72.2 - 0.796x$, $r = -0.84$, $P < 0.001$; $y = 24.1 - 0.270x$, $r = -0.53$, $P < 0.05$; $y = -1.7 + 0.322x$, $r = 0.58$, $P < 0.05$; $y = 2.9 + 0.387x$, $r = 0.58$, $P < 0.05$; and $y = -0.8 + 0.179x$, $r = 0.66$, $P < 0.01$.

Figure 104. Social components of a wood duck population during breeding and postbreeding periods at Nauvoo Slough, Illinois, 1986. The regression equations for single pairs, single males, females with broods, and single females, respectively, are: $y = 78.8 - 1.56x$, $r = -0.87$, $P < 0.001$; $y = 9.4 + 0.12x$, $r = 0.48$, $P < 0.05$; $y = -1.0 + 0.166x$, $r = 0.81$, $P < 0.001$; and $y = -1.9 + 0.242x$, $r = 0.48$, $P < 0.05$.

Decker (1959) noted that young woodies in northwestern Pennsylvania were all flying by late August and that several broods combined to form small flocks. At the Oakwood Bottoms in southern Illinois, Sweet (1976) found postbrood congregations in late July, with populations increasing to 1,200 by mid-September.

In Ohio, Tolle (1973) reported that wood ducks captured on roosts were largely juveniles in September, but nearly equal numbers of juveniles and adults were caught in October.

It is apparent that some individuals do not join flocks prior to autumn migration (Table 168). These are paired birds and duos of either sex. On airboat trips through an American lotus bed at Nauvoo

After the breeding season, groups of unmated wood duck males are joined by drakes that have abandoned their mates late in the incubating period. The group size tends to remain small due to attrition by members departing to other areas to molt. *Photo by David McEwen.*

Table 168. Percentage distribution of postbreeding and autumn wood ducks observed flying in the Nauvoo Slough area, Illinois, 1983.

	Percentage by observation period or date			
Number	August 2–September 1 (n = 1,287)[a]	September 16 (n = 476)	September 28 (n = 593)	October 18 (n = 1,030)
1	1.9	3.2	7.1	1.0
2	4.0	2.9	18.2	2.5
3	1.6	3.2	8.6	2.3
4	3.1	5.0	11.5	2.3
5	5.4	9.5	4.2	2.4
6	3.3	2.5	8.1	1.2
7	4.4	2.9	2.4	0.7
8	7.5	10.1	1.4	3.1
9	2.1	1.9	3.0	1.8
10	4.7	4.2	6.8	1.9
11	6.0	5.5[b]	2.6[b]	4.9[c]
12	4.7	5.5	2.6	4.9
13	13.1	5.5	2.6	4.9
14	2.2	5.5	2.6	4.9
15	3.5	5.5	2.6	4.9
16	3.7	1.5[d]	3.0[d]	4.9
17	6.6	1.5	3.0	4.9
18	5.6	1.5	3.0	4.9
19	1.5	1.5	3.0	4.9
20	4.7	1.5	3.0	4.9
21	0	1.1[e]	3.0	4.9
22	0	1.1		4.9
23	1.8	1.1		4.9
24	0	1.1		4.9
25	0	1.1		4.9
>25	9.0	14.3		30.4

[a] Number of wood ducks counted.
[b] Prorated among flocks recorded as 11–15 ducks.
[c] Prorated among flocks recorded as 11–25 ducks.
[d] Prorated among flocks recorded as 16–20 ducks.
[e] Prorated among flocks recorded as 21–25 ducks.

Slough on October 18, 1983, and September 8, 1986, we found woodies in a variety of numerical associations (Table 169).

In two years at Nauvoo Slough, 1983 and 1985 (figures 101 and 103), flocks containing four or more birds rapidly increased linearly as a component of the population. During 1984 and 1986 flocks formed, but the number of flocks failed to show a progressive linear increase. We assume that as new flocks formed, a similar proportion of previously formed flocks left the area.

Weekly counts of flying and loafing wood ducks in 1983 (Table 168) revealed that individuals prorated their attachments rather evenly among assemblages up to 20. As shown by analysis of flock sizes entering and leaving nocturnal roosts (figures 103–105), flocks vary in size from day to day and between evening arrivals and dawn departures. Because of the considerable variation in flock size, many groupings appear to have been extemporaneous; individuals become attracted to a flock only to leave it moments, hours, or perhaps days later.

Table 169. Size and composition of wood duck groups flushed by airboat from American lotus beds near Nauvoo Slough, Illinois.

	Percentage of total ducks flushed										
Date	Total number	1 male	1 female	Pair	2 males	2 females	Pair and 1 male	3 males	4	5–12	Total
September 8, 1986	186	33.9	38.7	14.0				1.6	2.1	9.7	100
October 18, 1983	512	11.5	12.5	17.6	7.0	5.9	16.4	11.1	3.1	15.0	100

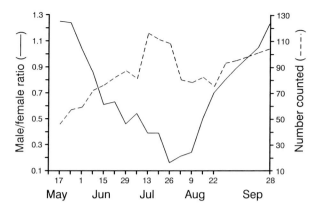

Figure 105. Ratio of male to female wood ducks during the postbreeding period in the area of Nauvoo Slough, Illinois, 1983.

Nevertheless, the frequency of small flocks suggests a core group with a semblance of affinity. Radio-telemetry findings by Kirby (1990a) and Kirby et al. (1988) support this contention. They documented movements of ducks in relatively cohesive flocks that stayed together throughout the migratory period despite the presence of other flocks. However, data obtained by Kirby (1976) also indicated that when many flocks used a single area, some individuals moved from one flock to another.

At Nauvoo Slough, the number of adult woodies gradually increased from mid-May to mid-June (Figure 105) and then leveled off, but the proportion of males steadily declined until early August. A few drakes molted on the area, but the majority departed before molting in all years, 1983–1987. The high proportion of females observed through August 1983 (Figure 105) suggests that most females remained on the area for the wing molt. The six hens telemetered with operational transmitters in 1984 stayed in the area during the period of wing molt; one was recovered on September 10 with the primaries about half grown.

Juveniles appeared to remain in the same general area, but many apparently moved 6–7 kilometers (3.7–4.3 mi) north to the delta of Devil's Creek, 8 kilometers (5 mi) south of Fort Madison, Iowa. Surveys there during August revealed 100 to 500 wood ducks concentrated on banks along narrow, wooded cutoff channels. Because of a lack of nest sites, few broods ever were found there; these birds had apparently moved in from elsewhere.

In Minnesota, Kirby (1976) found from telemetry that juvenile wood ducks were still within a radius of 10–11 kilometers (6–7 mi) of brood marshes in late September. Limited dispersal of postbreeding birds also was reported by Thompson and Baldassarre (1988, 1989), who observed that postbreeding woodies seldom left the Wheeler

National Wildlife Refuge in northern Alabama — a refuge of 13,808 hectares (34,120 ac) — until after November 1.

MOLTING

This section addresses the temporal pattern of molt among sex and age classes in wood duck populations. This temporal pattern exhibits changes in the gross appearance of ducks in the field, not the intricate changes in plumage tracts that were discussed in Chapter 13. Some subtle tracts of plumage change extend beyond the time frame of obvious acquisition of new feathers.

Adult Males

By May 20 in central Illinois, a few male wood ducks begin to show evidence of the prebasic molt — patches of gray appear in the bronze side, and the black and white "finger" projection disappears. Within 10 days, the sides have turned completely gray, head plumes are partly lost, and the cheeks and breast are mottled with gray or brown. Within the following two weeks, the entire bird assumes a drab brown appearance; except for losing the wing feathers, the male is in full basic plumage.

The proportion of adult males showing basic (eclipse) plumage replacing alternate (nuptial) plumage increases linearly from mid-May to late July (Figure 106). Shortly thereafter, early molting

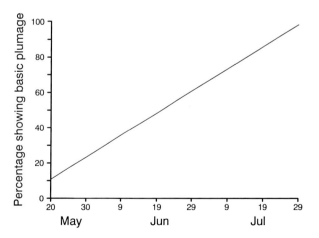

Figure 106. Proportion of adult male wood ducks observed in the Nauvoo Slough area of Illinois showing evidence of basic (eclipse) plumage, in comparison with those with alternate (nuptial) plumage, 1983–86. Based on 570 ducks recorded in 35 episodes. The regression equation is: $y = -14.28 + 1.25x$, $r = 0.69$, $P < 0.001$.

drakes begin to appear with new wing feathers, their bodies showing traces of definitive alternate feathers. The acquisition of nuptial plumage progresses in a linear fashion from early August through October, by which time almost all adult males are in full plumage (Figure 107).

Many males remained on Nauvoo Slough until their body plumage was about half in basic (Table 170)—a mean date of June 25. Thereafter, males increasingly left the area to complete their body and wing molts elsewhere.

Adult Females

Adult females usually have a late prebasic molt because they are delayed by broods, especially late ones. Some females enter the prebasic molt concurrently with males, but these are apparently nonbreeding females, presumed to be mostly yearlings. Gilmer (1971) found that one pair and four females—about 20 percent of the hens tracked—failed to establish nests; ducks such as these have the potential to molt first.

Some of the earliest incubating females in April 1990 at Nauvoo Slough showed brown feathers scattereded among the white belly feathers—an indication of a slight degree of prebasic molt. Of 223 birds examined (75 individuals examined an average of three times each) during the period April 10–July 10, 32.3 percent showed various degrees of spotted belly feathers: 17.5 percent slight, 10.8 percent moderate, and 4.0 percent heavy. A linear regression (r = 0.83, P < 0.01) indicated that the proportion of birds with brown belly spots increased from 14 percent on April 17 to 45 percent by June 19. Of those showing some basic plumage, 44 percent were yearlings and 56 percent were adult hens. The incubating birds were composed of 51 percent yearlings. After May 1, most females began to molt the white mark around and posterior to the eyes. Late in May, the crest on several females became ragged as feathers were being lost.

On June 15, 1988, we examined by scope 15 females and 17 males reposing on stumps and logs

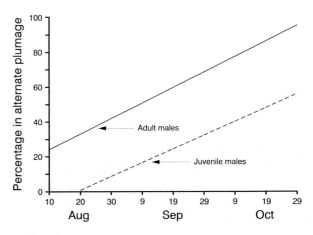

Figure 107. Proportion of male wood ducks trapped or shot in central Illinois that had obtained full alternate (nuptial) plumage, compared with those that exhibited some basic (eclipse or juvenile) plumage. The regression equations for adult males and juvenile males are: y = 15.25 + 0.89x, r = 0.50, P < 0.001; and y = −15.00 + 0.79x, r = 0.66, P < 0.001, respectively.

at Nauvoo Slough. All 15 females had lost their crests, and mottled brown feathers appeared in 12 amid the grayish breast and side feathers. Two of the 17 males still were in full alternate plumage, but the sides of the others were in basic plumage; nine had lost their crests. Of 14 incubating hens examined, none had diminished crests. On June 22, of six hens still incubating, two had ragged crests, four had brown spots amid the white bellies, five had molted feathers around the eyes, and one was still in full plumage.

On June 19, 1983, we observed 68 loafing females. All had lost their crests and appeared to be in the same stage of molt as nearby males. Seven paired birds were still 90 percent or more in their alternate plumage. It was apparent that the wing molt was delayed in females with later broods; those individuals entered the wing molt in late August or early September. At Nauvoo Slough, we observed two females with Class IIc broods as late as August 30. Perhaps late broods explain why Grice and Rogers (1965) found some adult females trapped in September that still wore old plumages.

Table 170. Percentage of basic (eclipse) plumage among adult male wood ducks observed at Nauvoo Slough, Illinois, 1984–87.

	Percentage			
	1–25	26–50	51–75	76–100
Number	66	178	16	12
Mean	June 17	June 25	July 4	July 22
S.D.	June 7–27	June 13–July 7	June 16–July 22	July 11–August 2
Range	May 21–July 5	May 28–August 1	June 11–August 6	July 3–August 3

As wood ducks complete their prenuptial (alternate) molt in late summer, they begin to form small flocks of both sexes. Above, more than a dozen males are in full nuptial plumage, while nearly a dozen females—with narrow white eye rings—still are acquiring the nuptial head plumage. The hens' lag in the molt cycle attests that they were delayed by brood rearing. *Photo by George Kammerer; courtesy of the California Waterfowl Association.*

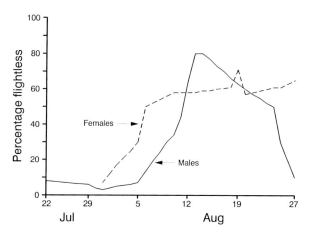

Figure 108. Percentage of flightless and flighted adult male and female wood ducks per trapping episode at Green Island, Iowa, 1980. Data plotted on a moving average of 5. A total of 30 males and 41 females were trapped. Data contributed by Robert Sheets and James L. Hansen, Iowa Conservation Commission.

Wing Molt

About one month after the prebasic molt starts, males begin to be flightless because they have lost all primaries and secondaries within a few days; this places the first flightless wood ducks in Illinois by mid-June. An early molting drake at the Van Norman Aviary also shed its flight feathers by mid-June. Gilmer et al. (1977) found that early molting drakes in Minnesota also became flightless in mid-June. At the Van Norman Aviary, five birds required an average of 35 days to grow primaries of sufficient length to sustain flight. Generally, wild wood ducks were flightless for about three weeks in Massachusetts (Grice and Rogers 1965).

Unfortunately, trapping data on flightless adults are available to us only after mid-July. At Missouri's Duck Creek Wildlife Management Area, Harriet Wedger reported that, in 1982, 11 flightless adult drakes were trapped August 4–31 and 18 flightless adult hens were trapped August 3–30. At Green Island, Iowa, the largest proportion of flightless males occurred between August 10 and 24 and of flightless females between August 5 and 27 (Figure 108). Near Ventura, Iowa, James L. Hansen found the wing molt completed in 24 adult males and 18 females trapped between August 15 and September 11; during that period, 1 male and 25 females still were flightless.

At Quiver Creek in 1964, we captured 18 flightless adult hens and no drakes between July 22 and August 28. Fourteen flightless adult drakes and 8 hens were trapped between August 25 and September 29, 1968.

In northcentral Minnesota, Gilmer et al. (1977) reported the first flightless hens in mid-July; 5 of 23 did not begin the wing molt until after September 1, and 1 still had old flight feathers on September 10.

Juveniles

Latitude has only a slight influence on the hatching date of late broods. As discussed under the temporal influence on nest initiation (see Chapter 9), last broods over most of the wood duck's range are hatched between mid-July and August. However, latitude does have a profound effect on when first broods hatch—from late February in the South to mid-May in the North.

One result of the broad spread in hatching among wood ducks is that young ducks obtain their juvenile plumage over a more extended period in the South than in the North. Ultimately, a similar spread in achieving alternate (nuptial) plumage can be observed.

Trapping young wood ducks at Quiver Creek provided data on the time of population changes from juvenile to alternate plumages (Figure 107). The linear expression for plumage turnover reflects the temporal distribution of the trapped population as a whole. Individual variation encompasses extremes of six weeks on each side of the trend line.

Latitude and Temporal Activity

Latitude also appears to have only a slight effect on the temporal phase of postbreeding behavior. According to Beshears (1974), wood duck drakes in Alabama began to assemble in flocks by June 1. By mid-June they entered into the prebasic molt, and by mid-July they were flightless.

In northcentral Minnesota, roughly 1,600 kilometers (1,000 mi) to the north, Gilmer et al. (1977) reported that wood duck drakes deserted their mates from mid-May to late June, left the area from May 25 to July 10, and were flightless from mid-June into early August. Unsuccessful hens left the area during the same period as did the drakes, with successful hens leaving from early July into September; they were flightless from mid-July into October. Gilmer et al. (1977) found that a minimum of 59 percent of all hens and 48 percent of all drakes remained on the breeding areas through the flightless period. The large percentage of drakes that remained there may have resulted from the location in the extreme northern part of the wood duck's breeding range.

While the adult wood ducks are changing plumages during the summer from nuptial (alternate) to eclipse (basic) and back to nuptial, young woodies are changing too—from juvenile to nuptial. The juveniles' habits emulate those of adults, with much time devoted to bathing, resting, and preening. Note how the 105-day-old juvenile male (top left) has raised his chest and wing covert feathers to facilitate their drying following bathing. Dressing feathers is an important ritual of wood ducks, as evidenced below by the same juvenile drake. Feather lice and debris are removed, separated feather vanes realigned, and feathers waterproofed by oil from the uropygial gland. *Photos by Charles and Elizabeth Schwartz.*

NORTHWARD MOVEMENTS

As with other studies of postbreeding activities, we did not locate the destination of drake wood ducks that left our study areas for the wing molt. Bandings of adult wood ducks from mid-July through August on areas extending northward from central Illinois to Ontario (Table 171) show an extraordinarily large proportion of males in northern areas. In contrast, among 3,065 adult wood ducks trapped in Alabama during late spring and summer, only 59.1 percent were males (Hayden and Pollock 1990). The high proportion of adult drakes captured on northern marshes suggests that the great disparity between the sexes observed there resulted from a summer ingress of males from more southern areas (Table 171).

Some population elements of southern breeding wood ducks inevitably move north. At a time when habitat quality is at a minimum because of low water in streams and in bottomland hardwoods south of a line from Omaha, Nebraska, to New York City, northern lakes and marshes are at their optimum for ducks. Marshes and lakes are abundant in northcentral Iowa, the Lake States, Ontario, and Quebec. Aquatic plants and invertebrates—more plentiful in marshes than in other habitats—produce a rich food base, and emergent marsh vegetation—cattails, bulrushes, whitetop, reeds, and waterlilies—provides an abundance of cover. These areas may not furnish good breeding conditions because of a brief nesting season or a shortage of nest sites, but they offer quality habitats that enhance the premigratory energy requirements for molting ducks. By taking advantage of these underused aquatic resources, wood ducks appear to have evolved postbreeding movements that have the potential to improve population survival.

The role these northern wetlands play in the postbreeding activity of wood ducks has been reported by several investigators. Wood ducks were not known to breed at Round Lake, near Ruthven, Iowa, at the time that Errington (1937) observed an appreciable influx of this species in late summer; when numbers peaked in September 1936, he estimated 2,000 wood ducks on 15.8 hectares (39 ac). Gilmer et al. (1977) reported that the Agassiz National Wildlife Refuge in northwestern Minnesota (an area without breeding wood ducks) receives a large influx of molters during June and July. In southwestern Minnesota, Lac Qui Parle Wildlife Area is known for its concentration of molting woodies, with birds arriving from as far as Missouri (Gilmer et al. 1977). At the Netley-Libau marshes in Manitoba, June to July 1980, Elmer E. Mowbray, Jr., observed 3,000 wood ducks, of which 90 percent were males. During July 1988, Robert E. Ingstad observed many male wood ducks molting in sloughs near Valley City and Woodworth, North Dakota. On July 19, he walked the shore of Lake Louise, a 243-hectare (600 ac) wetland 12 kilometers (7.5 mi) southeast of Woodworth, and counted 117 male wood ducks. He also observed 2 to 9 males on 8 of 23 ponds on nearby wetlands. At Adams Slough, 10 kilometers (6.5 mi) northeast of Valley City, Ingstad observed 17 male wood ducks on July 20.

Leo Kirsch saw more wood ducks during July and August 1988 in the Woodworth area of North Dakota than in any of the previous 25 years. On August 28 he noted a minimum of 300 woodies, most if not all males, feeding in a wheat stubble field.

The unexpectedly large number of male wood ducks molting in North Dakota in 1988 may have occurred because of unusually low water levels in streams and wetlands throughout the Midwest. Leo Kirsch noted that one year later appreciably fewer wood ducks were observed in central North Dakota.

Woodie drakes also concentrate on certain western marshes for the wing molt. At the Cheyenne

Table 171. Proportion of males among adult wood ducks banded during 10-day periods in late July and August in the upper Midwest and Ontario.

Period	Number (percentage)				
	Illinois	Iowa	Minnesota	Wisconsin	Ontario
July					
11–20	58 (39.7)	1 (0.0)		19 (84.2)	2 (0.0)
21–31	92 (43.5)	45 (57.8)	5 (20.0)	18 (72.2)	6 (33.3)
August					
1–10	162 (70.3)	64 (53.1)	17 (88.2)	104 (89.4)	38 (92.1)
11–20	260 (56.2)	278 (71.2)	133 (92.5)	366 (86.6)	75 (85.3)
21–30	288 (45.8)	316 (62.7)	338 (86.7)	542 (81.0)	88 (85.2)
Total	860 (52.9)	704 (64.9)	493 (87.9)	1,049 (83.7)	209 (83.9)

Late summer concentrations of wood duck drakes on northern and western lakes and marshes, but particularly in the Lake States, reveal the dispersal of drakes from nesting area wetlands, usually farther south. Southern shallow nesting wetlands tend to lose water as summer progresses and are occupied as well by developing broods. Some northern habitats, though offering inadequate nesting sites, provide abundant and diverse foods essential for the woodies to fulfill molting and premigratory energy needs. *Photo by Scott Nielsen.*

Bottoms Wildlife Area in central Kansas, Karl Grover observed as many as several hundred wood ducks when marsh habitat was favorable.

Lakes and marshes in the deciduous wooded areas of the Lake States and adjacent prairie regions probably provide a molting refuge for postbreeding wood ducks from distant areas. The broadened food base and escape cover appear to enhance survival of the population.

Band Recoveries

Direct recoveries of banded wood ducks provide additional information on their northward postbreeding movements, but that evaluation is hindered by the interval between banding and the hunting season. Wood ducks may migrate north after the wing molt and remain, or they may move north for the wing molt only to return south prior to the hunting season. Thus, band recoveries north of banding sites are relevant to early autumn hunting seasons—a time when migration movements are developing.

Despite their limitations, recoveries reveal that limited numbers of all ages and both sexes of wood ducks move north from their banding locations in Alabama, Illinois, and even more northern sites (Table 172). Except for Alabama bandings, few differences were noted between rates of recovery from adult males and females; Alabama differences were statistically weak.

Table 172. Proportion of direct wood duck recoveries in latitudes north of banding sites in comparison with direct recoveries for all latitudes by age and sex classes.[a]

Banding location	Adult males			Adult females			Juvenile males
	Total recoveries	Percentage north	95% C.L.	Total recoveries	Percentage north	95% C.L.	Total recoveries
31–35° N 85–88° W	126	16.7	9.8–23.6	89	10.1	3.3–16.9	1,813
40–41° N 89–90° W	45	0.0		40	0.0		277
43–44° N 89–93° W	401	0.8	0.2–1.8	108	0.9	1.3–3.1	426
43–44° N 78–85° W	112	0.0		18	0.0		128
43–44° N 69–75° W	437	9.2	6.2–12.0	221	7.2	3.6–10.8	982
Combined	1,121	5.7	4.3–7.1	476	5.5	3.3–7.7	3,626

[a] Data provided by David C. Hayden and Kenneth H. Pollock.

No statistical difference in the rate of northward recoveries was found between adults and juveniles for banding sites north of Alabama. Significantly more adults than juveniles in Alabama moved north (Table 172). Data from all banding stations combined revealed a significantly greater movement north by juvenile males than by juvenile females. After reviewing several papers that analyzed wood duck band recoveries, Stewart (1979) concluded that summer dispersal movements were independent of age and sex.

The closeness in proportions of postbreeding band recoveries among adult males, adult females, and juveniles north of their banding sites suggests a northward movement by some adult females after the wing molt in addition to their earlier, limited northward flight beforehand.

Only in late summer are juveniles capable of extensive flight. Kirby et al. (1988), using radiotelemetry, reported that first flights of juvenile woodies from their brood marshes occurred during their third week of flight. Although juvenile males departed five days later than juvenile females, these males moved farther afield. This differential movement may explain observed differences in the proportion of juvenile males and juvenile females found north of summer banding sites. Because females weigh less than males of the same age and have relatively less energy for sustained flight, they may be less likely than males to participate in northward movements.

After considering the northward movement of juveniles, we speculate that they accompany adult males or females rather than heading for distant destinations on their own. Their timing appears synchronous with the postmolt development of flight by large numbers of adults. Their disposition to emigrate, however, may differ among individuals because of varying genetic inheritance.

The farther south breeding occurs, the greater distance wood ducks move north in both the Atlantic and Mississippi flyways (tables 173 and 174). From southern banding sites, small numbers moved more than 1,609 kilometers (1,000 mi) north in both flyways; woodies banded at midlatitudes showed up 966–1,287 kilometers (600–800 mi) to the north, and ducks banded at northern sites appeared as far as 644–805 kilometers (400–500 mi) farther north. At all banding sites, wood ducks were most likely to limit their northward excursions to one or two degrees of latitude (109–220 kilometers: 68–137 mi). Once they were one or two degrees north of their natal sites, wood ducks from southern sites were prone to move north of a line between New York City and Omaha, Nebraska.

Although the northward egress is the most spectacular of postbreeding movements, limited lateral dispersion occurs as well. Stewart (1958) found that wood ducks leaving late summer concentrations in Ohio scattered in all directions. His

Table 172. (continued)

Juvenile males		Juvenile females		
Percentage north	95% C.L.	Total recoveries	Percentage north	95% C.L.
5.4	4.3–6.5	130	2.4	0.6–
2.2	0.3–4.1	208	0.5	0.7–1.7
1.7	0.4–3.0	542	2.2	0.9–3.5
1.6	1.0–4.2	70	0.0	
9.1	7.3–10.9	948	6.2	4.6–7.8
5.6	4.8–6.4	1,898	4.0	3.1–4.9

Table 173. Percentage of direct recoveries from wood ducks killed north of their banding sites in the Atlantic Flyway. Banding sites grouped by five degrees of latitude.

Degrees north of banding site[a]	Latitude of banding site		
	30–35°	36–40°	41–45°
1	5.21	1.34	3.92
2	1.53	0.62	0.38
3	0.92	0.38	0.08
4	0.41	0.24	0.02
5	0.20	0.10	0.00
6	0.20	0.29	0.05
7	0.61	0.05	0.02
8	0.71	0.00	
9	0.82	0.05	
10	0.92		
11	0.61		
12	0.41		
13	0.31		
14	0.61		
15	0.10		
16	0.10		
Total	13.67	3.07	4.47
Number of recoveries[b]	134/980	64/2,087	276/6,276

[a] One degree of latitude is 110 kilometers (68 mi).
[b] Number of recoveries north compared with total recoveries.

Table 174. Percentage of direct recoveries from wood ducks killed north of their banding sites in the Mississippi Flyway. Banding sites grouped by five degrees of latitude.

Degrees north of banding site[a]	Latitude of banding site		
	30–35°	36–40°	41–45°
1	8.36	3.59	2.46
2	1.66	0.32	0.37
3	0.55	0.39	0.09
4	0.18	0.47	0.11
5	0.25	0.37	0.00
6	0.31	0.28	0.00
7	0.43	0.22	0.01
8	0.74	0.19	
9	0.68	0.04	
10	0.74	0.02	
11	0.86	0.02	
12	0.55	0.02	
13	0.25		
14	0.06		
15	0.18		
Total	15.80	5.93	3.04
Number of recoveries[b]	257/1,627	318/5,371	269/8,825

[a] One degree of latitude is 110 kilometers (68 mi).
[b] Number of recoveries north compared with total recoveries.

later analyses of wood duck bandings in other states (Stewart 1977a, 1977b, 1977c) showed that dispersals were more limited in lateral egress.

Direct recoveries from extensive Alabama bandings (Hayden and Pollock 1990) displayed pronounced lateral and northward dispersals (Table 175). Slightly more than half of the weighted direct band recoveries of adult and immature females occurred in Alabama; however, only 38.9 percent of the adult band recoveries of males and 35.5 percent of those from immatures occurred within the state. The proportion of recoveries taken in the northern region of the Atlantic and Mississippi flyways suggests that both adult and immature males moved farther afield than did females of both age groups. All age and sex groups moved laterally from Alabama to other southern states of the Atlantic, Mississippi, and Central flyways. Adult females, in particular, flew to Florida and states east of Alabama, whereas immatures of both sexes tended to migrate to southern states west of Alabama. Of all the postbreeding season dispersals from Alabama banding sites, by far the greatest was laterally to other states in the southern zone. Direct band recoveries from wood ducks that nested on Wheeler National Wildlife Refuge and Swan Creek Wildlife Management

After the breeding season, as determined by band recoveries, a significant percentage of the wood duck population migrates somewhat farther north (some, particularly in the South, move laterally), usually before wing molt. Nest counts and other earlier indices of local (latitudinal) abundance do not accurately reflect woodie concentrations during the autumn migrations within the established flyways. *Photo courtesy of the Illinois Department of Conservation.*

Table 175. Weighted percentage of postbreeding season recoveries by age and sex classes of wood ducks banded in Alabama and shot their first autumn in other regions of the Atlantic, Mississippi, and Central flyways.[a]

Flyway/region	Adult		Immature	
	Male	Female	Male	Female
Atlantic				
North	0.135	0.000	0.193	0.037
Central	0.135	0.096	0.039	0.148
South[b]	1.952	2.382	1.101	1.036
Mississippi				
North	0.942	0.477	0.831	0.185
Central	0.201	0.096	0.251	0.074
South[b]	1.682	0.762	2.492	2.111
Central (entire)	0.135	0.192	0.289	0.074
All regions[b]	5.182	4.005	5.466	3.665
Alabama	3.298	4.479	3.014	4.815

[a] Data provided by David C. Hayden and Kenneth H. Pollock and weighted to recovery level of immature males for each region.
[b] Outside of Alabama.

Area in northern Alabama revealed that the birds moved predominantly southwesterly after November 1, although a few birds were recovered southeast of their banding sites (Thompson and Baldassarre 1989).

Lateral dispersion appears most pronounced where riverine conditions prevail. Where marshes, swamps, natural lakes, or stable impoundments occur, postbreeding dispersal is less extensive. Thus, habitat quality and proximity to brood-rearing areas appear to play important roles in the distance and direction of postbreeding flights.

LOCAL DEVELOPMENT

The high proportion of direct band recoveries within the degree-block of banding suggests that the wood duck is one of the most provincial of all ducks (Table 176). The proportion of recoveries reflects the comparative amount of time that wood ducks remain in the vicinity of the banding station during the hunting season versus the time they are outside this indigenous zone.

Because of migration, wood ducks in the northern zone are exposed to more days of hunting than are those in the central zone. In turn, ducks in the central zone are exposed to more days of hunting than are woodies in the southern zone. Thus, the expectation is for the local proportion among all direct recoveries to decline from north to south. However, the proportion of local recoveries was significantly higher in the northern zone ($P < 0.001$) than in the central zone. Due to more limited movement, local recoveries were significantly higher in

Table 176. Proportion of direct band recoveries from wood ducks that occurred within one degree of latitude and of longitude of banding sites grouped by blocks of five degrees of longitude and latitude.

	Latitude of banding sites								
	31–35°			36–40°			41–45°		
Longitude of banding sites	Total recoveries	Percentage[a]	95% C.L.	Total recoveries	Percentage[a]	95% C.L.	Total recoveries	Percentage[a]	95% C.L.
66–70°	750	45.20	48.83–41.57						
71–75°	3,228	46.87A***	48.61–45.13	179	34.64D**	41.88–27.39			
76–80°	1,690	53.49A***	55.90–51.08	534	24.16D**	27.88–20.44	486	59.67G**	64.13–55.21
81–85°	1,241	47.86	50.68–45.04	1,325	43.70E***	46.41–40.99	883	51.30G**	54.65–47.95
86–90°	2,826	46.71B***	48.57–44.85	4,351	37.55E**	42.22–32.88	922	24.73H***	27.57–21.89
91–95°	5,875	55.06B***	56.34–53.78	201	40.69	47.73–33.65	316	50.63H***	56.30–44.96
Total[a]	15,610	50.64C***	51.43–49.85	6,590	39.52C,F***	40.71–38.33	2,607	43.38F***	45.30–41.46

[a] Values followed by the same letters are compared.
  D + D compared with E + E***
  G + G compared with H + H***
  ** = P < 0.01
  *** = P < 0.001

the southern zone (P < 0.001) than in zones to the north (Table 175).

Folley (1979) evaluated the proportion of direct recovery rates in the banding area for five locations in Wisconsin. This proportion varied locally from 68.5 percent at the Mead Wildlife Area to 22.7 percent at Crex Meadows Wildlife Area. Others were at national wildlife refuges: Upper Mississippi 56.6, Horicon 37.2, and Necedah 31.1 percent.

Barden (1968) found that 57 percent of 191 direct recoveries in Maine from wood ducks banded before September 1 were made in the same 10-minute block of latitude and longitude as banded. Thirty-six percent were made in an adjacent 10-minute block, and only 9 percent were made elsewhere in Maine. About 52 percent of all band recoveries occurred in Maine. According to John Fulton, nearly one-half of all recoveries from wood ducks banded at the Yazoo National Wildlife Refuge in Mississippi were within 29 kilometers (18 mi) of the banding sites, with females closer than males.

Despite the propensity of many wood ducks to move north in the postbreeding season, most woodies remain in or return to areas within about 56 kilometers (35 mi) of their nesting areas. This is indicated by the high percentage of direct band returns from areas in close proximity to their breeding ground origins. *Photo by Jack Dermid.*

In Massachusetts, Heusmann and Bellville (1982) reported that 59 percent of all direct recoveries in 1962–1968 and 58 percent in 1969–1978 occurred within the state. They also analyzed bandings elsewhere and found that the direct recoveries within political geographic areas were New Brunswick 59.0 percent, Maine 50.6 percent, New Hampshire 46.1 percent, Vermont 50.4 percent, Massachusetts 50.6 percent, and Connecticut/Rhode Island 22.0 percent. Heusmann and Bellville concluded that during autumn, wood ducks remained in the general summering area until hunting pressure or weather induced them to leave.

The propensity for a large proportion of wood ducks to remain in the vicinity of their breeding grounds and rearing areas well into the hunting season is pertinent to their local management—a point that will be elaborated on in Chapter 18.

SURVIVAL

The survival of young wood ducks from fledging to autumn migration was studied by Kirby (1990b) via radio-telemetry. He found that in north-central Minnesota, survival between August 2 and September 30 was 91 percent for females and 89 percent for males. Survival from fledging to autumn migration on or near the breeding grounds, including the first 14 days of the hunting season, was 43 percent for females and 59 percent for males—a statistically significant difference.

Once juveniles are awing, their losses appear to be minor until the hunting season. Losses may be especially acute on opening and subsequent days of the hunting season before juveniles have learned by experience to avoid decoys, blinds, and humans. Kirby et al. (1988) reported a 33-percent harvest (n = 6) of the locally reared young wood ducks that remained on their study area during the hunting seasons, 1972–1974.

NOCTURNAL ROOSTS

A prominent activity of the postbreeding period is the formation of nocturnal roosts. These roosts develop in midsummer at specific locations where cover and shallow water provide favorable habitat. In many cases sites are traditional and may exist for a decade or more. In other instances they are impromptu, arising from a temporary combination of adequate food, stable water levels, and dense cover. The number of wood ducks using nocturnal roosts varies from a score to congregations of several thousand.

Because nocturnal roosts occur at all seasons of the year, this aspect of postbreeding behavior is discussed further in the following chapter.

AUTUMN INSPECTION

Ray Cunningham has observed both male and female wood ducks enter nest houses during autumn in Minnesota. On October 16, 1987, between 6:30 and 6:50 a.m., we saw 10 pairs of wood ducks on top of 9 of the 40 duplex nest houses at Nauvoo Slough, Illinois. In previous autumns, we have seen one or two wood duck pairs on these nest houses on a single visit to the area. Immature hooded mergansers and Barrow's goldeneyes also have been observed inspecting nest houses in early summer (Bellrose 1976). They apparently engage in this behavior to remain familiar with the location and characteristics of nest sites.

Nocturnal Roosts

There are several periods during the course of a year when wood ducks engage in nocturnal activity. Oftentimes woodies initiate a migratory journey at dusk or after nightfall and continue flying throughout the night. Brood hens are known to move ducklings from one wetland to another in darkness and engage in nocturnal foraging excursions with their young. On some moonlit autumn nights, the female's stentorian hauk and coquette calls and the male's soft whistles emanate from roosts, revealing nighttime activity. For the most part, however, wood ducks remain inactive from about one hour after sunset to one hour before sunrise.

Woodies normally spend the night roosting on water in habitat that provides a protective low canopy of dense cover. During the nesting season, most pairs roost by themselves or in small groups at scattered locations. As birds enter the postbreeding period, however, many individuals participate in evening roosting flights that terminate at traditional sites where the birds gather at common roosts. Although certain segments of local populations engage in social roosting during all seasons of the year, many roosts that develop during the breeding season and early summer are relatively small and often temporary.

Some wood duck roosts are used by several species of waterfowl on a transitory basis. In Iowa, Hein and Haugen (1966a) observed a few blue-winged teal flying to autumn roosts along with wood ducks. Perry (1977) reported that approximately 97 percent of the waterfowl arriving at four roosts in North Carolina (September–March) were wood ducks. Occasionally, he observed a flock of hooded mergansers or mallards flying into swamp roosts with wood ducks. In southern Illinois, Parr and Scott (1978) observed large numbers of wood ducks, mallards, American black ducks, American wigeons, green-winged teal, and Canada geese coming to a roost on the Union County Wildlife Refuge. In fact, so many waterfowl used the roost that accurate counts of wood ducks were impossible to obtain.

Wood ducks that concentrate at specific roost sites normally disperse throughout surrounding wetlands during the day, returning to the roost shortly after their late afternoon feeding activities. They seldom fly more than 8 kilometers (5 mi) to roost, but distances vary markedly depending on the characteristics of the habitat and the availability of food. In southern Illinois, Parr et al. (1979) found that most wood ducks stayed within 2 kilometers (1.2 mi) of their roosts. Nonetheless, two birds were observed to make roosting flights of 10 kilometers (6.2 mi). Hein and Haugen (1966a) reported that the farthest roosting flight in northeastern Iowa was 12.9 kilometers (8 mi).

Immediately preceding or soon after the onset of autumn migration, many roosts in the central and southern portions of the eastern United States contain their peak numbers of wood ducks, often in excess of 1,000 birds, with densities greater than 494 individuals per hectare (200/ac) of water (Hein and Haugen 1966a, Hester and Dermid 1973).

Because roost flight counts are one of a limited number of methods that yield information on wood duck numbers, researchers have scrutinized the woodies' roosting habits for more than three decades to determine the reliability of flight counts as an index to population levels. Unfortunately, variability brought about by environmental and behavioral factors precludes the use of roost counts as a means of population assessment in most areas (Tabberer et al. 1971, Parr and Scott 1978).

Chapter 15

PROBABLE FUNCTIONS OF ROOSTING

Conspecifics of many bird species come together, forming aggregations of various types at some time during the year. These groupings vary widely in size, organization, and purpose. Enormous numbers of birds often come together in breeding colonies, in postbreeding flocks, and at nocturnal roosts. Because the formation of aggregations in birds is so common, such groups undoubtedly have important survival value.

Although wood ducks associate for different reasons in small groups throughout much of the year, their gregariousness increases in summer and throughout autumn, when spectacular numbers of birds congregate at nocturnal roosts. The number of wood ducks that use a particular roost varies as populations change dramatically in response to environmental conditions and seasonal advancement. Nonetheless, at some point during autumn most roosts contain hundreds of wood ducks, and counts of 1,000–3,000 wood ducks at a single roost site are commonly reported.

In areas where roosting habitat is scarce, wood ducks must rely on isolated wetlands that provide suitable cover. Such a situation exists along a 169-kilometer (105 mi) reach of the upper French Broad River, which flows through mountainous terrain in western North Carolina (Cottrell 1979b). In areas where extensive roosting habitat exists, however, woodies still concentrate at specific sites (Hein and Haugen 1966b, Hester 1966, Parr et al. 1979). Thus, wood duck roosting aggregations are not necessarily formed because of an attraction to a limited resource, but rather as the result of social needs (Hein and Haugen 1966a). The predisposition to join roosting aggregations ultimately must center around increased survival. Presumably, important mortality factors are lessened and life-perpetuating elements are increased as a result of communal roosting.

Several theories have been proposed to explain the value of roosting concentrations to birds. Wynne-Edwards (1962) presented a strong case in favor of communal roosting as a type of postbreeding dispersionary adaptation. He reviewed roosting behaviors of representative species from many orders of birds and found four features common to all roosting populations. Briefly, local populations of birds that feed and live in a given area utilize the same roost; roost sites normally persist from year to year; collective displays, vocalizations, or both are performed after members assemble at a roost; and communal roosting usually is restricted to the postbreeding season, but on occasion it undoubtedly

overlaps into the breeding period. Outside of the breeding season, population densities essentially are regulated by emigration and immigration rates. Social displays and vocalizations are believed to peak during migration, and resident birds are signaled to move southward as migrants from the north move into an area. Wynne-Edwards (1962: 298) concluded that, "in the face of the constant drift of transients, the roost appears capable of acting as a continuous regulator of population-density in its own neighborhood and feeding the migrants through the region in an orderly progression."

Features of wood duck roosts basically conform to the dispersal theory presented by Wynne-Edwards (1962). The synchronized, unremitting calling of female and male wood ducks around dusk at autumn roosts that occurs during the period of migration may serve to inform resident woodies that they should depart southward. Thus, one function of roost formation in wood ducks may be regulation of local population densities during autumn migration.

The importance of autumn roosts to the pairing process of wood ducks is discussed in Chapter 6. It is noted there that courtship displays and vocalizations regularly are performed by wood ducks at roost sites. Obviously, many birds are brought into close contact at these gatherings and are presented with seemingly unlimited opportunities for encounters. At the same time, they are repeatedly required to defend established pair bonds. Moreover, young woodies can readily observe the courtship displays of adults, possibly allowing yearlings to become acquainted with courtship techniques and refine their courting performances.

Kirby (1976) also speculated that young wood ducks benefited from their association with adult birds at nocturnal roosts. He surmised that by following adults about during the day, young woodies might become familiar with preferred feeding and loafing areas and other roost sites.

Another function of roost formation may relate to the efficient detection of food (Brown 1975). Where food sources are patchy, individuals can observe other birds and more readily locate food. This association undoubtedly benefits transient wood ducks that use nocturnal roosts. During autumn evenings in central Illinois, we often have seen flock after flock of wood ducks leave a roost and fly to the same agricultural field to feed. Recent migrants from the north undoubtedly locate food sources by following the flights of resident birds.

Whether birds increase their chances of survival by sleeping in large aggregations is subject to debate; in any case, such chances must vary with predator densities and habitat conditions. In areas where densities of nocturnal predators are high, birds in roosting aggregations may be more easily preyed on than are those that exhibit scattered roosting (Wynne-Edwards 1962). In some cases, however, the clumped distribution brought about by groups of roosting birds may act to lessen predation because conspecific predators tend to space

Throughout much of the year, but particularly from late summer into late winter, wood ducks fly to nocturnal roosts, where shallow water and low overhead cover provide a "safe" retreat from predators. As singles and pairs and in small flocks, most birds arrive at roost sites from half an hour before sunset to half an hour after. Upon arrival, woodies usually land in open water and swim to and under overhanging cover. They depart for feeding areas at daybreak, in a much briefer time span than that of their arrival. *Photo by Stephen Kirkpatrick.*

themselves (Brown 1975). Thus, wood ducks at a communal roost may have to contend with fewer predators in the aggregate than if the birds roosted in scattered locations. Moreover, a large number of sentinels are available to detect predators when woodies form roosting aggregations. In any event, the habit of roosting under dense emergent vegetation, in itself, would seem to protect wood ducks from many avian nocturnal predators.

ROOST SITE CHARACTERISTICS

Researchers have long recognized that the habitat characteristics and other environmental features of a site selected as a roost by wood ducks are not necessarily restricted to that given location; similar habitat often extends throughout the surrounding landscape (Hein and Haugen 1966a, Parr et al. 1979). Similar to the observations made by Hein and Haugen (1966a) in Iowa, we often have observed wood ducks flying over several miles of apparently suitable roosting habitat in order to reach a traditional roost site. As long as conditions remain favorable, wood ducks generally return to the same roost night after night and year after year. Use of permanent, often well-defined roosting areas by wood ducks is a trait seldom seen in other waterfowl species.

Frequency of human disturbances, presence of suitable habitat, and availability of food are important factors that influence local distributions of roost sites. Along a 161-kilometer (100 mi) segment of the Mississippi River in northern Iowa, Hein and Haugen (1966a) found that wood duck roosts were separated by an average of 10.5 kilometers (6.5 mi). Numerous small swamps and millponds scattered throughout the Piedmont and upper Coastal Plain of North Carolina provide roosting habitat. Here wood ducks often establish roosts within 1.6 kilometers (1 mi) of one another, but each roost seldom supports more than 170 birds (Hester 1966). Conversely, in the Illinois River Valley we have observed more than 3,000 wood ducks gathering at roosts that were isolated from other sites by several miles. In Iowa, Hein and Haugen (1966a) saw little relationship between the distribution of roosts and the number of wood ducks that congregated at specific sites.

Woodies prefer roosts with open water in which to land, but they will descend through overstory branches when no adequate openings exist. Typical roost sites contain small areas of open water with adjacent dense growths of woody and/or herbaceous emergent plant species. Although the dominant vegetation types at roost sites often vary with seasonal advancement and from wetland to wetland, they characteristically provide low overhead cover but have a growth form that allows birds to swim about freely (Hein 1966, Tabberer et al. 1971).

From observations made at 44 roosts scattered throughout the state of Louisiana, Tabberer (1971) concluded that dense stands of buttonbush, water-elm, and swamp privet were preferred roosting habitat vegetation types. Thompson and Baldassarre (1988) found that wood ducks in northern Alabama preferred to roost in American lotus during August and September. However, as water conditions became unfavorable and the lotus senesced, wood ducks chose wooded swamps as roost sites. On Union County Refuge in southern Illinois, roosting wood ducks selected shrub swamps dominated by buttonbush more frequently than inundated forest habitat (Parr et al. 1979). Sixty percent of one roost site was covered by buttonbush, with the other 40 percent open water. Just 14 kilometers (8.7 mi) north of Union County Refuge, wood ducks used two roost sites where the dominant plant species were American lotus and swamp loosestrife. Tolle (1973) found that wood ducks in northeastern Ohio roosted among buttonbush whenever it was present. In the absence of buttonbush, they chose to roost in whichever vegetation types provided the most concealment. In northeastern Iowa

wood ducks roosted exclusively in emergent vegetation, but the species of vegetation seemed not to be a determining factor (Hein and Haugen 1966a). In central Illinois we found that the most important roosting habitats for wood ducks were buttonbush-fringed backwater lakes and wetlands supporting a mixture of buttonbush and black willows. Other important habitat types were thickets of sapling black willows, beds of American lotus, beds of duck potato, and beds of marsh smartweed.

Although the boundaries of some roosts are well defined, roost sites in many cases are simply a portion of an extensive vegetated area. As expected, wood ducks exhibit great latitude in the types and sizes of water areas on which they roost. Farm ponds, lakes, river backwaters, swamps, marshes, oxbows, sloughs, ditches, beaver ponds, and flooded bottomlands are some of the aquatic habitats where wood duck roosts commonly are found. Roost area can vary from less than 0.4 hectare (1 ac) to more than several hundred hectares.

Because of the woodies' requirements for unimpeded swimming mobility and overhead cover, water depths at most active roosts are similar. Generally, the average water depth at roost sites ranges between 0.3 and 1.2 meters (1–4 ft). At this range, wood ducks seek overhead canopy of dense cover approximately 0.3–0.6 meter (1–2 ft) high.

At some times of the year many wood ducks are active at night, usually in relation to brood feeding or flight in migration. Generally, however, woodies fly to a common roosting area just after sunset and remain in situ until just before sunrise. Several thousand woodies have been observed together at a single roost, which characteristically has overstory vegetation and dense emergent vegetation adjacent to at least a small open-water area. *Photo by Scott Nielsen.*

The numbers of wood ducks using roosts vary seasonally and yearly depending on the physiological phase of activity, population abundance, water levels, food resources, and hunting disturbance. The traditional nocturnal roost site, used year after year, is composed of limited open water and inundated overhanging woody cover. Since herbaceous cover— lotus, waterlilies, bulrushes, duck potato, smartweeds, etc.—varies in yearly occurrence, roosts in these vegetative types are likely to be more transitory. *Photos by Dan Holm; courtesy of the Illinois Natural History Survey.*

Changes in water levels and an assortment of other environmental factors may cause traditional roosts to be abandoned or result in decreased usage. In Louisiana, Smith (1958) and Tabberer et al. (1971) found that as the water level increased at a particular roost site, fewer wood ducks used the roost. We have observed a number of roosts that were deserted when water levels rose to heights that eliminated overhead cover. In South Carolina, McGilvrey (1966a) estimated that 10,000 wood ducks were roosting in the Rimini Swamp at the beginning of December 1961. He noted that the roost was abandoned shortly thereafter because of a 1.2-meter (4 ft) rise in water level.

Drought and drainage are other important causes of roost abandonment. Drought also may concentrate wood ducks at roost sites that retain adequate water, resulting in increased use during years with low rainfall. Alternations in the successional stages of aquatic plant communities often make roost sites uninhabitable for wood ducks. Human disturbances, such as hunting and trapping, at roost sites (Tabberer et al. 1971, Tolle 1973, Lingle 1978) may cause wood ducks to forgo or diminish use of a particular roost. Finally, roost populations may disband when food supplies are reduced or disappear.

Hein and Haugen (1966a) observed that when wood ducks in Iowa forsake traditional roost sites because of unfavorable environmental conditions, they usually establish another roost at a nearby location. In cases where drought or flooding occurs over an extensive area, woodies may be forced to move farther away from their traditional roost, and roost populations may disperse. Wood ducks losing roosting sites in the Mississippi River bottoms formed new roosts rather than join conspecifics at existing roosts. Hein and Haugen (1966a) felt that familiarity with a previous site played an important part in selection of a new roost.

SEASONAL PATTERN OF ROOST FORMATION

Wood ducks are gregarious throughout the year, including the breeding season. Groups of two to six pairs commonly search for nest sites together. Unpaired males associate and often compete against one another in courting parties. During the nesting season, small groups of unpaired males commonly are seen resting and preening on the same log, and mated pairs frequently are observed sitting within several meters of one another and of unpaired males. As mentioned earlier (see Chapter 6), woodies do not establish and defend territories,

and breeding pairs usually allow conspecifics to approach within 1–2 meters (3.3–6.6 ft).

The behavioral traits of wood ducks, unlike those of many other species of birds, permit the formation of communal roosts during the breeding season. The juxtaposition of nesting, feeding, and roosting habitat seems to influence whether spring roosting aggregations develop. Moreover, spring roosting groups probably are more likely to develop in wetland complexes that support large breeding populations of woodies. In areas with moderate breeding densities and ample roosting cover near feeding sites and nesting habitat, breeding wood ducks often roost in pairs or small groups at scattered locations. On the other hand, as Hansen (1971) found on Mingo National Wildlife Refuge in Missouri, 40–45 mated pairs of wood ducks commonly join together at communal roosts.

As spring advances and pair bonds dissolve, drakes and nonbreeding wood ducks fly to communal roosts (Hartowicz 1965, Bellrose 1976). These late spring to early summer roosting flights are made up primarily of birds that gather before they begin the eclipse molt. The flights may or may not involve large numbers of wood ducks, depending on local population levels and habitat conditions. In central Illinois, roost congregations of postbreeding and nonbreeding wood ducks begin to develop during May (Bellrose 1976).

Eric Hopps documented the seasonal pattern of usage received by one wood duck roost in the Illinois River Valley during 1986 (Figure 109). He observed 72 wood ducks enter the roost on the last day of May. During the first half of June, the population fluctuated between 44 and 109 birds. Approximately 30 wood ducks used the roost from mid-June to mid-July. Roost use increased dramatically

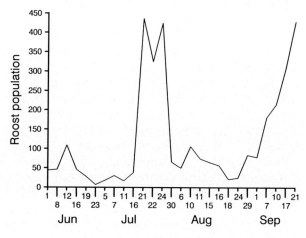

Figure 109. Seasonal changes in wood duck use of Hopps Pond roost, central Illinois, 1986. Data collected by Eric Hopps.

during the last half of July, when 300–450 wood ducks arrived at the site. During August, a time of prebasic molt, counts declined and remained relatively constant, fluctuating between 20 and 106 birds, and then steadily increased through September as more birds achieved flight.

Hartowicz (1965) also documented a spring through early autumn roosting pattern at a site in southeastern Missouri. He counted 78 woodies arriving at the roost on May 29, 1962. On June 12, 902 wood ducks arrived at the roost. Shortly thereafter, the population experienced a marked decline, but at least 200 birds continued to use the roost throughout June and July, and by August 500 wood ducks were congregating at the site.

Environmental and behavioral factors probably interact to bring about abrupt day-to-day fluctuations in the number of birds that engage in roosting flights during the spring and summer. The degree of fidelity that wood ducks exhibit toward any one roost site at this time of the year is unknown. However, in view of the fact that many adults undertake premolting movements that result in the dispersal of local breeding populations, it seems improbable that the same group of birds would continue to use a particular roost site throughout the premolt period. Hence, some of the variability of counts recorded at spring and summer roosts may be attributed to the dispersal movements of postbreeding and nonbreeding wood ducks. As is the case with autumn roosts, changes in daily flight patterns and habitat conditions undoubtedly contribute to fluctuations in late spring roost flight counts.

The number of birds flying to roosts often declines to a low level as wood ducks enter the prebasic molt and become flightless. Nevertheless, because of varying molting chronologies and the addition of young-of-the-year birds to roosting flights, some roosts receive continued use throughout the summer (Hartowicz 1965) (Figure 109).

Postbreeding flocking behavior, molting chronology, and dispersal movements are important factors that influence roost usage and the age and sex ratios of flocks engaging in evening flights during summer and early autumn. Flocks made up principally of adults or juveniles are common during mid to late summer months (see Chapter 14). Many drakes and broodless hens undergoing prebasic molt move away from the immediate area where they spent the breeding season. Males that remain on their respective breeding areas to molt usually enter into the flightless period before most brood hens do. Thus, in many areas adult females and juveniles of both sexes often account for a substantial proportion of roosting flights during July and August.

Eric Hopps observed 16 wood duck flocks arriving at a July roost in the central Illinois River Valley. Hopps was able to distinguish sex and age composition, and he found that only 3 groups (18.8 percent) contained adult males, whereas 10 groups (62.5 percent) contained adult females. Adult males, adult females, and juveniles accounted for 11.5, 38.5, and 50 percent, respectively, of the identified wood ducks. Hansen (1971) believed that most of the 62 wood ducks that arrived at a late August roost on Mingo National Wildlife Refuge, Missouri, were adult females. Of 15 woodies that were clearly observed, 13 were females.

Although the proportion of adult and immature woodies in the continental population varies from year to year, there are usually about 20 percent more juveniles than adults during late summer and autumn (see Chapter 18). Because some adults (both males and females) depart breeding areas and others are unable to participate in evening flights because of their temporary flightless condition, it should not be surprising that young-of-the-year birds often are more abundant than adults at mid- to late summer roosts. Nonetheless, juveniles must locate traditional roost sites by following the movements of at least a few adult birds.

In the central and northern portions of the eastern United States, counts of wood ducks that engage in evening roost flights often exhibit tremendous increases during the latter half of August and early September (Hartowicz 1965, Hein and Haugen 1966a, Tolle 1973, Lingle 1978) (figures 109 and 110). Late summer enlargements of roost populations apparently result partly from an increased level of gregariousness. The larger numbers also reflect proportional increases in numbers of flying juveniles and adults that have completed wing molt. They also may represent adult males that migrated earlier for the wing molt and have returned to their breeding area. Hein and Haugen (1966a) believed that all wood ducks on their study area in Iowa flew to communal roosts after mid-September. Some roost sites support their highest yearly populations at this time (Grice and Rogers 1965, Hein and Haugen 1966a, Parr and Scott 1978), whereas other roosts experience peak numbers of wood ducks during autumn migration (Hein 1961, Luckett and Hair 1979) (Figure 110).

Evening flight counts made in Michigan (Lingle 1978), Iowa (Hein 1961), Illinois (Parr and Scott 1978) (Figure 110), and Missouri (Hartowicz 1965) often show marked declines in the number of wood ducks flying to roosts in late September. Presumably, roost populations regress at this time because some adults and juveniles undertake dispersal movements (see Chapter 14). Whether these birds

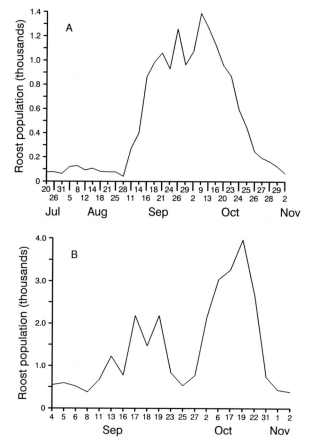

Figure 110. Pattern of roost usage by wood ducks at two backwater lakes in the central Illinois River Valley (A = Rat Lake, 1985; B = Anderson Lake, 1984). Rat Lake data collected by Eric Hopps.

join other roost populations as they travel to and arrive at new areas is unknown.

Wood ducks continue to gather at communal roosts throughout autumn and winter. In North Carolina, Hester and Quay (1961) documented peak populations at roosts in late October and early November as wood ducks migrated through the state. Costanzo et al. (1983) observed wood ducks using large communal roosts in South Carolina during winter. They believed that most of the wood ducks that gathered at common roost sites were transient birds.

Tabberer et al. (1971) found that the number of wood ducks arriving at roosts in Louisiana steadily increased from mid-July until the onset of waterfowl hunting in mid-November. Counts made at roosts following the opening of the waterfowl season were 75–80 percent below those made prior to hunting activity. Roost usage remained low throughout the hunting season but increased by about 65 percent shortly after season closure. Large numbers of woodies continued to gather at roosts in Louisiana until the end of February.

We have noted that many of the same sites that are used for roosting by wood ducks during autumn in central Illinois are used again in spring as the birds migrate north through the state. Although the number of birds that engage in communal roosting varies dramatically during the course of a year, it is evident that segments of many local populations gather at common roosts year-round.

CHARACTERISTICS OF ROOSTING FLIGHTS

During autumn, the form and duration of morning and evening flights differ appreciably. Morning flight departures often are decidedly more compressed than evening flight arrivals; woodies usually leave morning roosts in several waves, whereas flights to early autumn evening roosts usually occur over extended periods as small groups of birds arrive at the site. Hence, more accurate counts usually can be made of populations as they enter evening roosts.

Figure 111 presents an example of differences in wood duck flock sizes arriving and departing a roost site on Anderson Lake in central Illinois. Nearly 70 percent of the birds that departed the roost left in groups of 11 or more, whereas only a third of the evening arrivals were in flocks greater than 10 birds.

Researchers generally agree that both morning and evening flights occur over progressively shorter periods and under lower light levels as the autumn season advances (Martin and Haugen 1960, Hein 1961, Hester and Quay 1961, Hein and Haugen 1966b, Hansen 1971, Tabberer et al. 1973, Perry 1977,

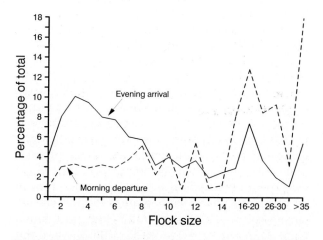

Figure 111. Percentage of wood ducks in various-sized flocks entering and leaving a roost in the northeastern part of Anderson Lake, Illinois, September 4 through October 9, 1984.

Lingle 1978, Scott and Parr 1978, Luckett and Hair 1979). However, interpretations of data collected at different roost sites have led to varying conclusions concerning the influences of selected environmental factors on roost flight behavior.

Although wood ducks do not use a constant illumination level as a signal to depart morning roosts or begin evening flights, light intensity along with physiological and social stimuli combine to influence when periods of flight activity occur. Hein and Haugen (1966b) noted that wood ducks probably are stimulated to leave morning roosts because of metabolic needs (primarily hunger). In South Carolina, Luckett and Hair (1979) determined that most woodies exited roosts (September–November) at an average light intensity of 0.67 ± 0.74 foot-candle. Hein and Haugen (1966b) found that wood ducks in Iowa (August–November) required at least 0.50 foot-candle of light to trigger morning flight departures. On clear days, these levels of illumination often are evident around 30 minutes before sunrise.

Researchers in Iowa (Martin and Haugen 1960, Hein 1961, Hein and Haugen 1966b) and South Carolina (Luckett and Hair 1979) have determined that the time wood ducks spend roosting has important implications on the timing and duration of morning departures. As summer and autumn advance and daylight hours shorten, woodies spend more and more time at nocturnal roosts. Consequently, a hunger stimulus builds up over longer intervals, and the level of light required to initiate morning flights gradually decreases as the season progresses.

Martin and Haugen (1960) observed that wood ducks departed an August roost in Iowa from approximately 20 minutes before sunrise to 15 minutes after sunrise, with the peak departure occurring 5–10 minutes before sunrise. In contrast, October roost departures were completed by sunrise, with the peak flight period occurring 25–30 minutes before sunrise. Similarly, Luckett and Hair (1979) noted that wood ducks in South Carolina left the roost at successively lower light intensities relative to seasonal advancement (September–November).

For each 10-day period that passed from August through October, Martin and Haugen (1960) found that wood ducks left their roosts an average of four minutes earlier in relation to sunrise. Hein and Haugen (1966b) recorded a similar chronology of morning departures by wood ducks from a number of different roosts in Iowa. The Hein and Haugen results indicated that for each 10-day period that passed from mid-August through early November, the last woodie left the roost 3.6 minutes earlier relative to sunrise. Mid-August morning depar-

tures often spanned 25 minutes. By early November, wood ducks exited most roosts in less than 5 minutes, usually in one or two waves, approximately 30 minutes before sunrise.

Hein and Haugen (1966b) speculated that wood ducks returned to roosts in the evening because of social needs. The trigger that governs the timing of evening roost flights was thought to be decreasing light levels. Although a few wood ducks may return to autumn roost sites throughout the day, most birds engage in evening roosting flights sometime during the 45 minutes preceding and following sunset.

Like morning flight departures, autumn evening arrival flights are triggered by lower light values relative to seasonal advancement. In southern Illinois, Scott and Parr (1978) found a high correlation ($r = 0.91$, $P < 0.01$) between the level of light intensity that triggered evening flights and declining day length. The average time that the first bird was observed to arrive at roosts in September, October, and November was 53 minutes before sunset, 36 minutes before sunset, and 1 minute after sunset, respectively. Hence, wood ducks initiated evening flights under lower light levels concurrent with lengthening nocturnal periods. This response probably is a result of less time (fewer daylight hours) for social stimuli to reach the level necessary to initiate roosting flights (Hein and Haugen 1966b).

In Iowa, Martin and Haugen (1960) reported that August evening flights began 25–30 minutes before sunset and lasted for approximately 45 minutes; the peak arrival time occurred 10–15 minutes before sunset. In September and October, peak numbers of wood ducks arrived between 0–5 and 20–25 minutes after sunset, respectively. Other researchers have found similar seasonal changes in evening flights (Hein 1961, Hester and Quay 1961, Hein and Haugen 1966b, Hansen 1971, Tabberer et al. 1971, Perry 1977, Scott and Parr 1978, Luckett and Hair 1979). In general, August evening flights may last from about an hour before sunset to 10–30 minutes after sunset. By November, wood ducks seldom are seen arriving at roosts until after sunset, and flights may last for only 15–20 minutes.

Although illumination levels at the initiation of evening roost flights vary markedly with seasonal advancement, termination of evening flights in relation to sunset remains relatively constant throughout summer, autumn, and winter (Hein and Haugen 1966b, Tabberer et al. 1973). In Iowa, Hein and Haugen (1966b) found that for each 10-day period from mid-August through early November, roost flights started, peaked, and terminated an average of 4.7, 2, and 1 minutes later, respectively, relative to sunset.

In southern Illinois, Scott and Parr (1978) found that for each 10-day period, September 2–November 30, the first wood ducks arrived at roosts an average of 6 minutes closer to sunset. Conversely, the end of evening flights was delayed by an average of only 1.9 minutes later relative to sunset. From mid-August through November, last arrivals appeared at relatively constant light intensities that fluctuated between 5 and 10 foot-candles.

Little is known about the flight patterns of roosting wood ducks from the winter solstice to the vernal equinox. Hester and Dermid (1973) stated that wood ducks arrive at winter roosts progressively later as the season advances. They suggested that roost flights may be delayed because food resources diminish and become degraded throughout autumn and winter, thereby causing woodies to invest more time in the search for food. However, the regression models that Tabberer et al. (1973) calculated from data collected in Louisiana revealed little relationship between arrival time and increasing day length; the first birds continued to arrive 5–10 minutes after sunset during January and February. In North Carolina, Perry (1977) found that more than 90 percent of the wood ducks that engaged in evening flights, December through January, arrived after sunset. As winter advanced, however, progressively larger proportions of evening flights arrived before sunset (concurrent with an increase in daylight hours). By March, nearly 40 percent of the birds involved in roosting flights arrived before sunset.

Spring Flight Behavior

Spring roost flight counts have been used to obtain a breeding pair index (Hein 1966, Hansen 1971); however, spring evening flight counts probably are useful only in areas where roosting and nesting habitat are separated by some distance. Along the Mississippi River in northeastern Iowa, breeding wood ducks often spend the day in tributary valleys. Hein (1966) was able to obtain consistent daily counts as birds returned each evening to scattered roosts in the Mississippi River bottoms. He believed that spring flight counts were a reliable estimator of the number of wood ducks that nested in tributary valleys. Similarly, Hansen (1971) argued that spring flight counts provided a useful index of breeding wood ducks in the area he studied on Mingo National Wildlife Refuge in Missouri.

Besides documenting the number of birds in evening flights, investigators have collected little information on the characteristics of spring roost flights. In fact, there is no information on morning departure from common spring roosts. Based on the dynamic changes in late summer and autumn flight patterns in relation to population characteristics and seasonal advancement, prominent differences probably exist between spring and autumn roosting behavior.

Eric Hopps observed evening flight patterns from March 22 through June 27, 1989, at a spring roost in central Illinois. Although 1,000–1,500 wood ducks often congregated at this site in autumn, the peak spring count was only 112 (Table 177). Moreover, a limited number of observations revealed that morning departures are extended during spring. On April 15, at least 54 wood ducks arrived at the roost during the evening (Table 177), but only 15 wood ducks were observed leaving the roost the following morning. Many of the remaining birds engaged in courtship activities, and some flew into the surrounding timber in search of nest sites. Although some birds appeared to remain at the roost all day, others left in late afternoon to feed in agricultural fields. In March and the first week of April, flocks with more than five birds were probably migrants.

We documented the relationship between evening wood duck flight activity and sunset throughout spring at Nauvoo Slough in westcentral Illinois, 1985–1986 (Table 178). As spring advanced, proportionally more wood ducks engaged in roosting flights under increased light levels. Sixty percent, 35 percent, and 28 percent of evening woodie flight activity occurred after sunset in April, May, and June, respectively.

Although sex identification was impossible in most cases, the percentage of birds flying in groups of two decreased from 68 percent during April to 51 percent in May and 29 percent in June (Figure 112). Hence, the relative proportion of breeding pairs involved in evening flights decreased as the breeding season advanced and an increasing number of females turned to incubation.

Prior to incubation, females must spend a large proportion of their day acquiring nutrients (Drobney 1980). Consequently, evening flights probably occur later with respect to sunset in early spring because hens require larger investments of time to satisfy their nutritional needs.

Nonbreeding birds and males whose pair bonds have ended probably account for most roosting flights in May and June. The proportion of woodies arriving in small flocks (1–10 birds) at a backwater roost along the Illinois River remained relatively constant throughout spring (Table 177). By contrast, flock size increased at Nauvoo Slough throughout the observation period (Figure 112)—a finding that suggests that additional postbreeding

Table 177. Spring evening roost flight characteristics of wood ducks arriving at Matthews Bay, central Illinois, 1989.[a]

Date	Total that arrived	Percentage of flight arriving in groups of						
		1	2	3	4	5	6–10	11+
March 22	101	3.0	35.6		31.7	5.0	24.7	
March 27	69	7.2	66.7		17.4		8.7	
April 9	112	6.3	37.5	13.4	7.1	4.5	21.4	9.8
April 15	54	9.3	74.1	5.6			11.1	
April 17	27	18.5	81.5					
April 23	20	15.0	70.0	15.0				
April 30	30	20.0	60.0	20.0				
May 8	54	16.7	48.1	5.6	7.4	9.3	13.0	
May 17	46	23.9	43.5	32.6				
May 30	59	20.3	27.1	10.2	13.6	8.5		20.3
June 7	75	21.3	37.3	16.0	10.7	6.7	8.0	
June 13	15	60.0	40.0					
June 27	8	25.0	75.0					

[a] All observations were started before evening flights began and continued until at least one-half hour after sunset. Data collected by Eric Hopps.

birds were coming on line as their breeding activities ceased. Because postbreeding birds need less energy than do breeding or brood females, their daily nutritional needs can be acquired in less time. As a result, the stimulus to come together has more time to develop, and peak evening flight activity subsequently appears to begin under increased light levels as spring advances (Table 178).

Influence of Weather

Wood ducks may alter some aspects of their roost flights in response to overcast skies and other

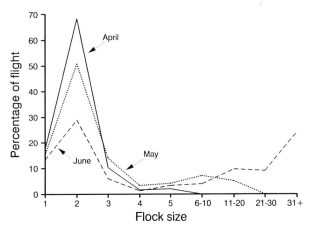

Figure 112. Percentage of wood ducks in various-sized flocks during spring roost flights at Nauvoo Slough, Illinois, 1985–86.

Table 178. Proportion of wood ducks in evening roosting flights at Nauvoo Slough, Illinois, 1985–86.[a]

Minutes from sunset	April (6)[b]		May (5)		June (4)	
	Percentage	S.D.	Percentage	S.D.	Percentage	S.D.
−40 to −30	8.7	4.3	12.0	7.0	20.5	7.9
−30 to −20	6.2	4.2	13.4	5.5	10.0	7.1
−20 to −10	10.3	5.7	20.4	17.3	14.8	11.2
−10 to sunset	14.8	6.7	18.8	10.8	27.5	20.9
Sunset to +10	27.3	14.6	18.4	13.6	20.5	19.7
+10 to +20	26.5	19.1	13.0	4.3	7.0	14.0
+20 to +30	6.5	12.1	4.0	5.3	0.0	0.0

[a] A total of 234, 236, and 298 birds were enumerated in April, May, and June, respectively.
[b] ( ) = number of counts.

weather-related variables. Apparently roost flights on days with reduced light intensity (brought about by storms, fog, or haze) are initiated at illumination levels similar to those that prevail on clear days (Hein and Haugen 1966b). Thus, morning departures are delayed and evening flights are somewhat advanced on days when weather conditions reduce visibility (Hester and Quay 1961, Hein and Haugen 1966b, Hansen 1971, Tabberer et al. 1971, Scott and Parr 1978).

In Louisiana, Tabberer et al. (1971) found that wood ducks arrived at roosts earlier as cloud cover increased. They noted that peak arrivals on clear, partly cloudy, and cloudy days were 22, 17.5, and 12 minutes after sunset, respectively. Although Scott and Parr (1978) found that mean arrival times of the first bird were earlier on cloudy days (40.2 minutes before sunset) in comparison with clear days (34 minutes before sunset), the difference was not significant (P>0.10). They concluded that cloudy weather had little influence on the arrival of the first wood ducks at roosts in southern Illinois, because no limiting low level of illumination was reached on cloudy days during their study.

Hein and Haugen (1966b) believed that morning flights were compressed in time on stormy days, and that evening flights were prolonged because they began considerably earlier but peaked and ended only slightly ahead of flights that occurred on clear days. Conversely, Scott and Parr (1978) found that the mean arrival times of last birds differed significantly (P<0.10) between cloudy (17.8 minutes after sunset) and clear (25.3 minutes after sunset) days. Their results indicated that a larger percentage of the roosting population arrived before sunset on cloudy days than on clear days.

The presence or absence of rainfall influenced the time of arrival of wood ducks at roosts in Louisiana. On rainy days, mean arrival times for first and last wood ducks were 2.2 and 6 minutes earlier, respectively, than on days with no rain (Tabberer et al. 1971).

No relationship (P>0.05) between temperature and the number of wood ducks arriving at roosts was detected by Tabberer et al. (1971) or Scott and Parr (1978). Moreover, Scott and Parr (1978) found no relationship (P>0.01) between temperature and the percentage of the wood duck flight arriving before sunset.

In Louisiana, counts of wood ducks arriving at roosts were not noticeably influenced by changes in wind direction, wind velocity, barometric pressure, or relative humidity (Tabberer et al. 1971). Hein (1961, 1965) also found no single weather-related factor correlated with changes in roosting flight counts.

Flock Sizes

Wood ducks arrive at roosts as singles and pairs and in a large assortment of flock sizes. Groups of one to five birds are the most common flock sizes that arrive at summer and autumn roosts (Hester and Quay 1961, Hansen 1971) (Figure 113). Some groups land without hesitation, whereas others circle the roost once or twice before alighting. Although many birds descend into the roost proper, others land along the periphery. Some birds usually can be seen swimming about, feeding and preening, until darkness.

Large groups of birds often disband into a number of smaller flocks as they approach and land at a roost. Moreover, we have seen duos and trios arrive at roosts only to separate and land 100 meters (328 ft) or more apart. This sort of behavior indicates that groups or single birds may temporarily join other wood ducks during the evening flight to a roost; separation on arrival indicates no lasting attachment.

Flock sizes arriving at roosts are influenced by environmental and behavioral factors. Location and availability of food probably have important impact on flock sizes. When food is widely distributed, the likelihood of flock augmentation is reduced because birds must scatter to feed in a number of sites. Larger flocks are more common at roosts that support large numbers of birds and where localized food resources funnel birds together.

Flock size of evening flights in relation to seasonal advancement was documented at three roosts in the Illinois River Valley (Figure 113). Peak counts at the Anderson Lake, Rat Lake, and Hopps Pond roosts were 3,975, 1,391, and 1,771, respectively. More than 80 percent of the wood ducks that engaged in evening flights during July and August arrived at the roosts in groups of 10 or fewer (Figure 113). Although flocks of 20 or more birds were common at the Anderson Lake roost, July–November, no sizable groups were observed arriving at Rat Lake or Hopps Pond roosts until September. Beginning in early September, an occasional flock of 30 or more birds arrived at roosts, but small flocks continued to be the predominant component of evening flights until the time of migration departure in early November.

Hester and Quay (1961) observed 814 flocks arrive at three roosts in North Carolina from October to January. Peak populations did not exceed 170 birds. Groups of two were the most common flock size, representing 35.5 percent of all observations. Fewer than 4 percent of all flocks contained more than 10 birds, and no flocks in excess of 20 wood ducks were observed.

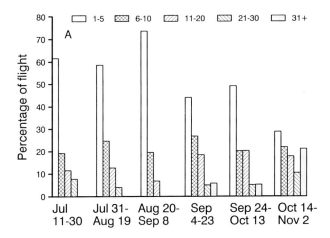

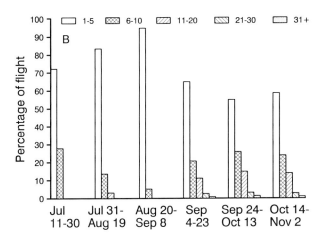

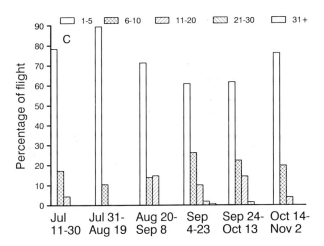

Figure 113. Proportion of wood ducks arriving in various-sized flocks at three roosts in central Illinois, 1984–86 (A = Anderson Lake, 1984–85; B = Rat Lake, 1985–86; C = Hopps Pond, 1985–86). Rat Lake and Hopps Pond data collected by Eric Hopps.

In southeastern Missouri, Hansen (1971) observed 579 flocks arriving at roosts from August through October. Peak counts numbered around 1,000 birds at some roosts. Single birds (23 percent) and pairs (24 percent) accounted for nearly half of the flights arriving at the roosts. Twelve percent of the flocks contained more than 10 birds, and 4 percent contained over 20. The largest flock contained 48 wood ducks.

Although single birds are a common component of late summer and early autumn evening flights, most single wood ducks either form pair bonds or join flocks as autumn advances (see Chapter 6). More than 30 percent of wood ducks flying to some September roosts in Illinois (Eric Hopps), Louisiana (Tabberer et al. 1971), North Carolina (Perry 1977), and South Carolina (Luckett and Hair 1979) arrived as singles. In the South, single birds seldom comprise more than 10 percent of evening flights, October–February (Tabberer et al. 1971, Perry 1977).

INDIVIDUAL VARIATIONS IN ROOSTING BEHAVIOR

Radio-telemetry studies conducted by Kirby (1976), Parr and Scott (1978), and Costanzo et al. (1983) have provided insight into the roosting habits of individual wood ducks during autumn and winter. As individuals, wood ducks exhibit a high degree of variability in roosting behavior. Not all birds conform to the pattern of departing roosts at daybreak and returning in the evening. Whereas some individuals may never leave a roost, others often depart and return throughout the day. Thus, flight counts seldom reflect the true number of birds that constitute a roost population.

Eric Hopps found that a significant proportion of some summer roost populations were birds that did not participate in morning and evening flights. Instead the birds remained at the roost throughout the day or swam and walked to the site from adjacent wetlands. On several July evenings, Hopps observed 70–130 wood ducks fly into a roost on Rat Lake in central Illinois. Another 40–80 birds, representing both sexes and age classes (primary feathers were visible on many adult birds), swam approximately 200 meters (656 ft) across the open water of an adjacent wetland, walked over a low levee, and swam another 200 meters (656 ft) into the roost on Rat Lake. Many of the wood ducks that swam into the marsh at dusk reversed their swimming route at daybreak, dispersing throughout the adjacent wetland where they spent the day feeding and loafing. A similar arrival and departure pattern of roosting

As autumn advances, wood duck roosts become larger and more woodies associate in flocks. Roosting flocks vary in size from evening to evening, suggesting that they represent only transitory groupings. At autumn roosts, wood duck hens utter their piercing coquette calls, apparently in an effort to attract males. *Photo by Stephen Kirkpatrick.*

wood ducks was observed at a second backwater roost along the Illinois River.

At autumn roosts (August 20–November 30) in southern Illinois, Parr and Scott (1978) determined that 54 percent of the time radio-tagged wood ducks failed to engage in morning departures or leave roosts at any hour of the day. Likewise, Hankla and Smith (1963) found wood ducks at roosts in the Coastal Plain of South Carolina and Georgia throughout the day and suggested that the roost sites were being used for daytime feeding as well as nocturnal roosting.

Individual birds sometimes use several roosts within a local geographical area. In Minnesota, Kirby (1976) reported that radio-tagged wood ducks used the same roost sites only 20 percent of the time during any 10-day period (August–September). Tolle (1973) observed one wood duck in Ohio that moved 1.9 kilometers (1.2 mi) to a second roost site. Hein and Haugen (1966a) believed that one roost population in northeastern Iowa moved back and forth between two locations that were separated by about 1.6 kilometers (1 mi). Similarly, Hein and

Haugen (1966a) observed that wood ducks at Union Slough National Wildlife Refuge in northcentral Iowa shifted between three roost sites that were located approximately 3.2 kilometers (2 mi) apart. Parr and Scott (1978), however, found that movements between established roosts in southern Illinois were uncommon; radio-monitored birds were located at specific roosts 97 percent of the time. Similarly, Costanzo et al. (1983) found that radio-tagged wood ducks in South Carolina tended to roost at the same location night after night.

Parr and Scott (1978) noted that wood ducks occasionally failed to return to their roosts after leaving in the morning. On these rare occasions, the birds either remained at their diurnal habitat or failed to return to the roost proper. Costanzo et al. (1983) also observed that some wood ducks in South Carolina failed to join other birds at previous roosting congregations.

Wood ducks have developed a strong nocturnal roosting tradition for two apparent reasons: (1) to reduce losses to predators and (2) to aid in the formation of pairs and flocks. Most other species of waterfowl leave marshes or agricultural fields late in the day and fly to extensive sheets of water to roost. By roosting on broad open waters, most waterfowl species reduce potential contact with nocturnal predators. In contrast, wood ducks seek roost sites where overhead cover minimizes the threat of predation. Obviously wood ducks are at greater potential risk from barred and great horned owls, minks, bobcats, alligators, and other predators of wooded wetlands than are ducks that roost on open water far from shore. Because wood ducks begin to pair and form small flocks late in summer, their roosting habit enables birds that are in similar physiological states to form liaisons. Therefore, the unique roosting sites selected by wood ducks play an important role in their survival and social organization.

Chapter 16

Feeding Behavior and Food Habits

Wood ducks are omnivores and opportunistic feeders. Their diet is influenced by abundance, availability, distribution, and seasonal occurrence of localized food sources. The diet of a wood duck also is influenced by the bird's age and physiological condition and by time of day. Of course, morphological and physiological adaptations impose constraints on the types of food that wood ducks locate, secure, consume, and digest. Woodies not only feed on vegetable matter and invertebrates in aquatic habitats but often forage for mast, insects, fruits (fleshy and dry), and cultivated foods on dry land (Brakhage 1966, Bellrose 1976, Bateman 1977, Milbert 1984). Some nutrients that occur in low levels in plants or are absent from them are contained in animals. Thus, it should not be surprising that wood ducks consume animal matter (primarily aquatic and terrestrial invertebrates) throughout the year. Animals are an especially important source of protein to breeding females and ducklings.

Wood ducks are mainly seed eaters during autumn and winter. According to Bellrose (1976:194), "Acorns are the favored foods of more wood ducks in more places than any other plant food—from New Hampshire to South Carolina to Mississippi to Wisconsin." In areas where acorns are scarce, woodies turn to other desirable foods, such as seeds of baldcypress, hickory, bulrush, arrowarum, and burreed.

HISTORICAL ACCOUNTS OF DIETARY DIVERSITY

Although many early reports on the feeding habits of wood ducks indicated that acorns were a favorite autumn food, ornithologists recognized that woodies are general feeders, consuming a wide variety of plant and animal matter. Wilson and Bonaparte (1831) stated that acorns, seeds of wild oats, and insects were principal foods of the wood duck. Peabody (1838) reported that wood ducks in Massachusetts fed on grapes, berries, nuts, tadpoles, and water insects. In Kansas, Goss (1891) stated that wood ducks consumed insect life, shoots and seeds of aquatic plants, grains, wild grapes, and acorns. Grinnell and Bryant (1915) indicated that the diet of wood ducks in California consisted of aquatic plants and insects, corn, wheat (after harvest), wild grapes, and acorns. Spiker (1931) noted that at the Peterboro Swamp of New York, wood ducks and American black ducks had similar feeding habits; both species obtained much of their plant and animal food in shallow water and on shore. He also reported that woodies fed on insects, chestnuts, acorns, and beechnuts that they found on the forest floor.

Several early accounts of the wood duck's feeding habits indicated that rice was a principal food in some regions. Beckman (1909) reported that wood ducks consumed a large amount of newly sown rice and continued to feed on rice plants until the shoots were about 5 centimeters (2 in) high. Lett (1883) and Kumlien and Hollister (1903) stated that wood ducks fed extensively on wild rice during autumn. Mabbott (1920) reported that a wood duck shot at Point Pelee, Ontario, contained at least 1,200 wild rice seeds in its esophagus and gizzard. He noted that a wood duck collected in August at Sand Point, Michigan, had consumed about 400 flowers of this plant.

Additional reports emphasized the importance of other plants, attesting to the highly adaptive feeding habits of wood ducks. Ingalls (1881) stated that fruits and seeds of winterberry accounted for a considerable proportion of the autumn diet of some wood ducks in Massachusetts. McAtee (1915) wrote that the seeds of swamp privet were consumed by many wood ducks in the South. Alexander (1915) flushed several hundred feeding wood ducks from a wetland in South Carolina and found thousands of arrowarum seed coats floating on the water. He shot two of the birds and found that their esophagi were full of arrowarum seeds. McAtee (1908) reported that several wood ducks shot on Delaware Lake, Wisconsin, had consumed only smartweed seeds. Norton (1909) wrote that wood ducks are particularly fond of duck potato tubers. Roosevelt (1884) stated that wood ducks consumed unripe American lotus seeds, frequently visiting marshes to feed on them in early autumn.

According to Martin et al. (1951), wood ducks consume more seeds of cowlily, waterlily, and watershield than any other duck. Schoffman (1946) found that cowlily seeds comprised 68 percent of the food ingested by wood ducks on Reelfoot Lake in Tennessee. Mabbott (1920) found up to 380 watershield and 577 white waterlily seeds in the upper digestive tracts of wood ducks.

Martin et al. (1951) reported that beetles (adults and larvae), true bugs, spiders, and ants and other Hymenoptera comprised the principal animal foods of wood ducks. Mabbott (1920: 48) wrote that "The wood duck's taste for spiders is quite marked. Several full stomachs from southern localities contained remains of from 20 to 40 spiders." He reported that insects constituted nearly two-thirds of the animal matter consumed by 399 wood ducks. Dragonflies and damselflies (adults and nymphs), grasshoppers, crickets, and flies (adults and larvae) are other commonly consumed insects. Wood ducks also readily eat emerging aquatic insects, such as caddis flies, mayflies, midges, and stoneflies. The synchronous hatching and swarming behaviors of some short-lived insect species result in an abundant food source for both adult and immature woodies. Each summer on Nauvoo Slough, Illinois, 1984–1987, literally thousands of mayflies covered the emergent vegetation and water surface

for one to two weeks, during which time many wood ducks were observed gorging themselves with this food source.

Wood ducks occasionally capture tadpoles, small frogs, salamanders, and fish (Bent 1923, Hester and Dermid 1973). Mabbott (1920) found fish and frog remains in about 2 percent of the 399 wood duck gizzards he examined. Siegler (1950) reported that 2 of 72 wood ducks (2.8 percent) collected in New Hampshire during the hunting seasons, 1946–1948 (October–December), had ingested frogs. On many occasions in 1983, we observed wood ducks exploiting a localized, concentrated source of small fish in a continuous backwater area of Nauvoo Slough. Scheider (1957) also observed wood ducks feeding on fish, and Rawls (1954) found fish remains in one wood duck that was collected in Tennessee during autumn.

Because wood ducks consume a wide variety of food, they are able to utilize many different types of habitat. They readily locate and exploit temporary food sources. We have observed 10–12 pairs feeding on Diptera larvae in small, isolated, wooded areas along the Illinois and Mississippi rivers shortly after these rivers had been inundated with spring rains and runoff. Moreover, we have seen paired wood ducks in April feeding along a state highway on scattered corn and wheat that had spilled from grain trucks. Later, in the same area, wood ducks were observed feeding on the fruit of fallen black cherries. Because wood ducks consume such a broad range of foods and readily exploit locally abundant food sources, they can occur on almost any type of wetland that provides some overhanging cover. Their food habits are one of several factors that enable the species to occupy an extensive breeding range.

Wood ducks consume a wide variety of foods. Consumption seems to depend primarily on the availability of preferred foods, seasonal nutritional demands, and characteristics of the feeding site. Their ability to consume and utilize many food sources affords the species an extensive breeding range. *Photo by Eric Hopps.*

MANNER OF FEEDING

Wood ducks do not establish and defend feeding territories. Although they feed throughout all daylight hours, they feed more intensely late in the afternoon and during the early morning hours, before and after the inactive nocturnal period. They commonly feed in small groups and may cover sizable areas during their search for food. Apparently wood ducks prefer to forage in flooded woody vegetation and adjacent open water habitat when sufficient food is available there. However, in areas where flooded timber habitat is limited or food resources are low, woodies commonly feed in marshes and agricultural fields.

In most areas and during all seasons, wood ducks spend a much higher proportion of their time foraging for food by swimming about on the water surface than by walking on land. Woodies feed by sight and touch, but most of the food they ingest occurs on or near the surface of the water. Throughout spring, wood ducks often forage for insects and windrowed plant matter, such as the fruits of maple and elm, found along shorelines. In floodplain areas characterized by rising and falling water levels, woodies tend to follow the changing, inundated shoreline to exploit newly available food. As spring advances, floating duckweed and submerged aquatic plants develop in shallow areas of open water, and wood ducks often feed on these plants and the associated invertebrates.

Although wood ducks frequently submerse their heads and necks to obtain food in shallow water, only occasionally do they "tip up" or dive for food. Unlike many dabbling ducks that are efficient at straining solid particles from the water and bottom mud, the relatively narrow bill (with poorly developed lamellae) of wood ducks limits their ability to filter food. Thus, wood ducks characteristically feed by pecking at individual food particles. They "dabble" more than do other ducks collectively termed dabblers, such as the mallard, northern pintail, American wigeon, gadwall, teal, and northern shoveler.

A "dabbling" duck, the woodie feeds most often in shallow waters with only its bill immersed, probing for seeds, aquatic vegetation, and invertebrate animals. Wood ducks also feed extensively in upland oak groves, nut orchards, and harvested grain fields. *Photos by David McEwen.*

Wood ducks will, under certain circumstances, repeatedly dive and "tip up" for food. Kear and Johnsgard (1968) reported that wood ducks occasionally engaged in foraging dives, with females diving more frequently than males. Scheider (1957) observed one female capture and consume two fish during five dives in water that was about 2 meters (6.6 ft) deep on the Seneca River, New York. In Arkansas, Briggs (1978) observed both male and female wood ducks diving for pin oak acorns in water that averaged 1 meter (3 ft) deep. He noted that blue jays were gathering acorns from the tree branches and frequently dropped them into the water below. Wood ducks would attempt to catch dropped acorns by "tipping up" or diving for them. W. Bray observed a similar situation in South Carolina (Kistler 1939), but in this instance squirrels were feeding on water oak acorns, and whenever an acorn was dropped into the water, one of a small group of wood ducks would consume it. We have observed male and female wood ducks repeatedly (three to four times in succession) "tip up" to obtain fish and other food on Nauvoo Slough during early spring. Arthur Hawkins observed wood ducks diving for corn in April 1990 and 1991 in water 0.5–1.0 meter (1.6–3.3 ft) deep.

When foods are too deep to reach by immersing their bills or putting their heads below the water surface, wood ducks "tip up." In the left scene, the tipped-up drake is on water covered with floating duckweed, which is high in protein and readily consumed by woodies. It is likely that the drake was seeking a carbohydrate-rich food. Woodies can remain in this upside-down position for quite a while by treading with their feet, but they rarely remain submerged for more than 5–10 seconds. The generally short tip-up duration may reflect the woodie's ability to secure its food items quickly, relatively limited lung capacity, and/or innate wariness. *Top photo by Irene Vandermolen. Bottom photo by Stephen Kirkpatrick.*

Drobney (1977) indicated that 66 percent and 55 percent of the wood ducks that he collected during spring (n = 115) and autumn (n = 40), respectively, were feeding by pecking at the water surface. Between 20 and 38 percent of the birds were feeding by surface dabbling—the second most common feeding method. Only five individuals (4 percent) were bottom feeding. No apparent differences (P > 0.05) in the modes of feeding occurred between sexes and seasons.

Because the bill of wood ducks is not adapted for crushing, food generally is swallowed whole. Wood ducks are extremely proficient at maneuvering food items prior to swallowing. We have noticed that pin oak acorns are positioned with the apex pointing upward as they descend the esophagus and proventriculus. Other types of acorns probably are swallowed in a similar manner, effectively reducing the chance of lacerating the esophageal lining with the acute end of an acorn.

In some instances, wood ducks will nibble and tear items that are too large to be swallowed whole. We have frequently seen wood ducks spend 5–10 minutes nibbling off pieces from large duck potato tubers before swallowing remnants of the item. Drobney (1977) observed that wood ducks usually removed the coats of maple and elm seeds before swallowing the seeds. Similarly, Sweet (1976) reported that wood ducks severed the wing of ash samaras before ingesting the seed. Wood ducks commonly tear off the shoots and leafy parts of some plants, such as arrowarum and banana waterlily.

With its hooked and narrow bill, the wood duck is able to excise bits of food from items too large to swallow, such as tubers from uprooted banana waterlilies (above). At Nauvoo Slough, Illinois, woodies have been observed to bite off small pieces from golfball-sized tubers of duck potato. *Photo by Stephen Kirkpatrick.*

Unlike most other dabblers but similar to certain diving ducks, the woodie cants, or cocks its head to the side, to find foods that are underwater (left). Observations have shown that woodies can detect food items such as corn and acorns as much as 1.5 meters (5 ft) or more below the water surface. To reach such foods, woodies may dive. Though not common, but more so than among other dabblers, diving by wood ducks is accomplished by a leap or lurch up and forward, propelled by the feet, into a tight arc (right). The woodie's head is outstretched and its wings are drawn close to the body, streamlining the bird, which reduces entry and underwater resistance. *Left photo by David McEwen. Right photo by F. Eugene Hester.*

The woodies's bill is ideally adapted to grasping solid food particles (left). Acorns invariably are maneuvered once picked up so that the sharp apex faces outward (right). Therefore, when an acorn is swallowed whole, its apex is positioned safely upward as the food descends the esophagus and proventriculus. *Photos by Jennifer A. Loomis.*

Importance of the Esophagus

The wood duck's esophagus (or gullet) is quite distensible, allowing consumption and storage of several relatively large or many small foods. Including the proventriculus (glandular stomach), the upper digestive tract is about 210 millimeters (8.3 in) long—the esophagus is 155 (6.1 in) and the proventriculus 55 millimeters (2.2 in). The esophagus without contents varies from 7 to 10 millimeters (0.28–0.39 in) in diameter and the proventriculus 10–15 millimeters (0.39–0.59 in). Yet within this relatively small space, wood ducks are able to cram an astounding amount of large-sized items. Dixon (1924) stated that wood ducks in California consumed large quantities of California white oak acorns and noted that these slim, conical acorns often grow to 5.7 centimeters (2.25 in) in length and 1.9 centimeters (0.75 in) in diameter. Zahm et al. (1987) indicated that wood ducks in Oklahoma stored an average of five to eight commercial pecans in their esophagi. These oblong fruits attain lengths of 2.5–6.4 centimeters (1.0–2.5 in).

We have found up to seven pin oak acorns in the esophagi of wood ducks shot in central Illinois. Mabbott (1920) found 15 entire pin oak acorns in the esophagus and gizzard of one wood duck shot in Arkansas. Tolle (1973) reported that six wood ducks trapped in Ohio, October 14 to November 1, 1972, contained an average of 18.2 (range = 2–30) small acorns (probably pin oak) in their esophagi. In addition, the esophagi of 26 birds contained an average of 6.7 (range = 1–20) large acorns (probably

swamp white oak). Hall (1962) found up to 13 cherrybark oak, 10 water oak, and 5 willow oak acorns in the esophagi and gizzards of wood ducks collected in Mississippi. Scott Barras of Mississippi State University observed a captive wood duck hen swallow 11 willow oak acorns in 30 seconds.

As many as seven pin oak acorns have been found in an adult wood duck's 210-millimeter-long (8.27 in) esophagus and proventriculus (half shown). Without food, the esophagus is 7–10 millimeters (0.28–0.39 in) in diameter. The pin oak acorns above, with point up (as found in the esophagus), measured a combined 90 millimeters (3.54 in) in length, with a mean of 12.6 millimeters (0.50 in), and had a mean width of 17.5 millimeters (0.69 in). Larger items, such as commercial pecans and bur oak acorns, are sometimes ingested, demonstrating the tremendous elasticity of the wood duck's esophagus. Scott Barras, at Mississippi State University, observed a wood duck ingest 11 willow oak acorns in 30 seconds. Moreover, the acorns selected were amid cherrybark, water, and willow oak acorns placed in clear water 10.2 centimeters (4 in) deep. The mean size of 420 willow oak acorns was 11.6 by 11.7 millimeters (0.457 by 0.461 in). The 11 acorns would have filled 127.6 millimeters (5.02 in)—61 percent—of the esophagus and proventriculus. *Photo by Frank Bellrose; courtesy of the Illinois Natural History Survey.*

Nelson (1944) reported that a wood duck from Ohio swallowed a white-footed mouse. He noted that the tail protruded from the gizzard and that the mouse was apparently swallowed whole.

Mabbott (1920) found the following numbers of seeds in the gizzards and distended esophagi of wood ducks: 3,000–5,000 bulrush (*Scirpus cubensis*), 1,200 wild rice, 10,000 meadow grass, 1,100 smartweed (*Polygonum opelousanum*), 51 arrowarum, 157 swamp privet, and nearly 10,000 lizardtail.

The fully distended esophagus of a wood duck can easily accommodate more than 100 kernels of corn, roughly 40 grams (1.4 oz). Stewart (1967a) removed up to 190 grains of corn (98.9 grams: 3.5 oz) from one wood duck (136 kernels were from the esophagus and proventriculus). He noted that corn may swell after being in the esophagus for some time and wood ducks with fully distended esophagi often disgorge some kernels for lack of storage space. Stewart (1967a) estimated that a fully distended wood duck esophagus could accommodate 158 kernels of corn.

After withholding food from a captive adult wood duck hen for 48 hours, we observed that she consumed 21 corn kernels (7 grams: 0.25 oz) within 15 minutes before she temporarily stopped feeding. Because we could detect no kernels in the gullet, the kernels that were ingested apparently filled the gizzard and proventriculus. On the basis of weight changes, it was determined that a gullet could accommodate 126 corn kernels (42 grams: 1.48 oz).

Stewart (1967a) reported that wild wood ducks trapped during the evening and held captive overnight moved approximately 24 kernels of corn from the esophagus into the proventriculus and gizzard. The high-energy plant foods that are consumed around dusk undoubtedly provide needed nourishment through the nocturnal hours and into the following day. Because wood ducks may remain at roost sites throughout the day—departing in the evening to obtain food—it appears that some birds can obtain sufficient nutrition while feeding only once a day.

UPLAND FEEDING SITES

When desirable natural foods become depleted or where they occur at low levels, woodies often venture into upland areas in search of food. They search the forest floor for fruits and seeds of woodland plants, agricultural fields for cereal grains, and mast orchards for nuts. Woodies shy away from potential upland feeding sites where rank vegetative growth precludes efficient detection of foods and probably increases vulnerability to predation.

We have flushed wood ducks apparently foraging for acorns from black oak woodlots in autumn. In South Carolina, woodies search the forest floor for beechnuts, acorns, and the fruits of dogwood, black gum, grape, and ash (Hester and Dermid 1973).

The wood duck's penchant for feeding on the dry forest floor has attracted much attention from researchers over the years. Anderson (1907: 173) wrote that "The wood duck is remarkable for its habit of frequently alighting in trees and also for foraging the timber, feeding largely on acorns at certain seasons." Lett (1883: 56–57) often observed wood ducks on land "acres away from water" searching for acorns and beechnuts. In describing the feeding habits of the wood duck, Mabbott (1920: 37) noted, ". . . it not only feeds upon the seeds and other parts of the plants which grow in or near the water, but it often wanders far out into the drier parts of the woods to pick up acorns, nuts, grapes, and berries, and the seeds of various trees and shrubs." Bent (1923: 166) concurred: "The wood duck is particularly fond of acorns, chestnuts, and beechnuts, which it picks up on the ground in the woods, turning over the fallen leaves to find them."

The fruits of many trees and shrubs provide food for wood ducks, including the flowering dogwood (top), a common small tree found throughout the eastern United States. Woodies frequently leave wetlands to glean fruit from the forest floor. Several trees and shrubs in swamps or bordering wetlands furnish fruit for wood ducks, most notably the black tupelo, or black gum (bottom), and swamp privet. *Photos by Jack Dermid.*

Wood ducks readily consume commercial nuts, especially when orchards occur within several kilometers of water. On January 14, 1970, Zahm et al. (1987) counted 2,000 wood ducks arriving at a 30-hectare (74 ac) pecan grove in southern Oklahoma. In the Pacific Flyway, wood ducks frequent filbert and hazelnut orchards that occur from British Columbia south to northwestern Oregon and almond groves in California (Bartonek et al. 1990).

In certain areas wood ducks rely on cereal grains to supplement their diet. Long (1879) and Grinnell and Bryant (1915) reported wood ducks feeding on waste corn and wheat left in fields after harvest. Soybeans, rice, sorghum, and oats are other commercial crops commonly consumed by wood ducks.

We have observed wood ducks feeding in agricultural fields during all seasons of the year in central Illinois. Corn appears to be a particularly important source of energy to wood ducks migrating through the Illinois River Valley, especially in years when low water levels prevent woodies from easily obtaining many natural plant foods.

Waste corn continues to be an important food for resident wood ducks throughout spring and summer and into autumn. Because corn has a relatively high carbohydrate and fat content, it is an especially important source of energy for females during the prelaying period, when lipid deposition is rapid, and throughout incubation.

Mechanical corn pickers and combines were first widely used to harvest grain from fields in the central Illinois River Valley during autumn 1937. With the combining of the first grain in August 1938, wood ducks were observed to flock to the stubble fields until they had consumed most of the grain or until the stubble was plowed under. A similar situation occurred in harvested cornfields. Hawkins and Bellrose (1940) estimated that 3,000 wood ducks were feeding on scattered wheat kernels in one field adjacent to the Illinois River. They also reported that approximately 8,000 wood ducks were feeding in the wheat fields of one drainage and levee district. Later nearly 2,000 woodies were observed feeding in a harvested cornfield. Both migrating and resident wood ducks have continued to

exploit the readily available high-energy grain from these fields ever since.

In central Illinois, wood ducks travel to agricultural fields from river backwaters individually or in groups of 2–150, but mostly in groups of 2–20 (Table 179). Wood ducks usually make two feeding flights a day, the first commencing at daybreak and the second normally peaking shortly before sunset. Flight patterns may change during the hunting season, when wood ducks often engage in only one feeding flight per day, usually in the evening. Resident birds travel to fields in small flocks during the spring and summer, and single wood ducks are more commonly observed flying to agricultural fields at this time of the year than at any other time.

During autumn 1987, we observed the evening feeding flights of a group of 1,000–3,000 wood ducks from October 23 to December 1. The birds that we observed spent the day in an extensive area of flooded willows on Chautauqua National Wildlife Refuge in Illinois and flew approximately 3.2 kilometers (2 mi) to feed on waste corn in a drainage district south of the refuge. The peak flight normally began about 20–30 minutes prior to sunset and continued until 20 minutes after sunset. The increasingly later exodus from the roost (Table 180) appeared to result from shooting about 400 meters (437 yd) from the departure area. The earliest departures (October 23) were prior to the hunting season. As the hunting season progressed, an increasing number of flocks climbed higher to surmount the optimum range of shotguns. Late in the hunting season, wood ducks descended from heights of 60–100 meters (65–109 yd) when they arrived at their feeding destination.

Field feeding by wood ducks certainly is not restricted to Illinois. Stewart (1957) stated that corn was a preferred food of wood ducks in Ohio during August and September. Harold Burgess observed that wood ducks on Union Slough National Wildlife Refuge in Iowa began field feeding in oat stubble shortly after fields were harvested in early August. He indicated that field feeding became especially evident after the corn harvest (harvest for both ear-corn silage and for grain) began in mid-September. In addition to Illinois (Anderson 1959, Havera

Table 179. Percentage of wood ducks in central Illinois flying to agricultural fields in flocks of various sizes, 1987.[a]

Flock size	Oct 28 (2,319)	Nov 4 (2,651)	Nov 5 (1,104)	Nov 6 (1,626)	Nov 9 (1,570)	Nov 11 (1,935)	Nov 28 (700)	Nov 30 (945)	Dec 1 (1,234)
1–10	54.9	21.4	49.1	64.7	42.5	55.3	40.4	40.1	8.8
11–20	18.4	12.5	13.7	15.9	33.4	24.2	28.0	29.7	7.4
21–35	3.1	19.8	21.7	8.0	15.5	11.5	6.3	21.2	13.9
36+	23.6	46.3	15.5	11.4	8.6	9.0	25.3	9.0	69.9

[a] ( ) = number of birds that left the Chautauqua National Wildlife Refuge during observations.

Table 180. Percentage of wood ducks departing on evening feeding flights from Chautauqua National Wildlife Refuge, Illinois, 1987, in relation to sunset.[a]

Minutes from sunset	Oct 23 (1,923)	Oct 28 (2,319)	Nov 4 (2,651)	Nov 5 (1,104)	Nov 6 (1,626)	Nov 9 (1,570)	Nov 11 (1,935)	Nov 28 (700)	Nov 30 (945)	Dec 1 (1,234)
−50 to −40	17.8									
−40 to −30	5.7						1.8			
−30 to −20	32.8	17.1	1.4		28.2	6.3	37.9	18.7	8.0	0.6
−20 to −10	38.3	36.7	26.6	41.8	13.9	27.8	20.1	3.4	31.7	0.0
−10 to sunset	2.0	4.4	52.1	58.2	12.2	34.5	10.5	33.9	51.4	3.4
Sunset to +10	2.6	5.9	19.9		28.5	4.8	19.7	25.0	8.8	77.3
+10 to +20	0.8	35.8			15.4	23.1	10.0	18.0		18.6
+20 to +30					1.7	3.5		1.0		

[a] ( ) = number of birds that left the refuge during observations.

1985), researchers in New York (Foley and Taber 1951), New Hampshire (Siegler 1950), Missouri (Korschgen 1955), Tennessee (Rawls 1954), South Carolina (McGilvrey 1966a, 1966b, Kerwin and Webb 1971, Landers et al. 1976), and Mississippi (Delnicki and Reinecke 1986) have found that agricultural crops formed an important part of the autumn and winter diets of wood ducks in those states.

Wood ducks usually move hurriedly about when prospecting for food on land. They act particularly skittish when field feeding in flocks, frequently assuming alert postures and running and flying in front of one another—creating a rapidly

Waste corn is a preferred food of wood ducks and an important source of energy. Although corn is low in protein and most minerals (especially calcium) and, like acorns, provides only a small proportion of requirements, it has a low fiber content and is high in carbohydrates, fat, and nitrogen-free extract. Because corn normally occurs abundantly and provides concentrated sources of high energy, it is readily sought and consumed by woodies. In areas where seeds of natural foods are scarce, corn can be a valuable source of food for woodie hens during the prelaying period, when lipid deposition is accelerated. Incubating hens also may consume corn that is readily available because nest attentiveness reduces the time available for seeking and consuming food. Corn and abundant low-fiber natural foods, such as elm and maple seeds, provide a high amount of energy per unit of food item consumed. In many areas, corn also is an important supplement in wood ducks' autumn and winter diets. Other grain crops readily consumed by wood ducks are wheat, soybeans, rice, sorghum, and oats. Development of mechanical cultivating and harvesting equipment increased the amount of land sown for commercial crops and the expedience of harvest. Although this technology provided woodies with new and bountiful food sources in the form of waste grains, agricultural advancements often occurred at the expense of wetlands and their natural plant foods. Corn and other commercial grains have been used to entice waterfowl, including wood ducks, to preserves (above), rehabilitated habitats, and, illegally, gunning sites. *Photo courtesy of the National Archives.*

moving rolling line—during the search for grain. Zahm et al. (1987) observed a similar feeding behavior of wood ducks foraging in commercial pecan groves. He stated that wood ducks often flew over birds in front of them to reach open feeding sites. In spring, single pairs commonly are seen flying to and feeding in harvested agricultural fields. Their manner of feeding often appears decidedly less hurried than that of birds feeding in flocks, with the female often searching for grain while the male remains alert and follows along.

The time woodies spend feeding in forest stands and fields is dependent on a number of factors, foremost of which are disturbances from hunting activities and the availability of food. Zahm et al. (1987) reported that wood ducks spent about 10 minutes in pecan groves while ingesting five to eight pecans, probably the maximum number that their esophagi could accommodate. The researchers observed that the necks were noticeably swollen as the ducks departed in small flocks. Similarly, Richard D. Bauer observed that wood ducks required 5–15 minutes to fill their crops with filberts at an orchard in Oregon. He estimated that there were 10–20 nuts per square meter (0.9–1.9/ft²) on the bare ground. The wood ducks were selective in choosing which nuts to ingest; some birds picked up and dropped up to 10 nuts before swallowing one that apparently was of suitable size and shape. Stewart (1957) stated that wood ducks required 10–30 minutes to fill their esophagi with corn when an abundant supply was available.

Natural foods undoubtedly form the major staple of the wood duck's diet when they occur in abundance and are readily available to the birds. Only 4 of the 155 wood ducks (2.6 percent) that Drobney and Fredrickson (1979) collected on Duck Creek Wildlife Management Area in Missouri contained cultivated foods in their esophagi and gizzards. Soybeans were the only agricultural food consumed, and they constituted a small fraction of the total volume. This feeding behavior occurred despite the fact that agricultural fields were located within 0.5 kilometer (0.3 mi) of where many of the birds were collected. In contrast, Delnicki and Reinecke (1986) reported that soybeans made up 23.4 percent (dry weight) of the food consumed by wood ducks wintering in westcentral Mississippi. In Illinois corn comprised 48.4 percent and 57.4 percent, respectively, according to Anderson (1959) and Havera (1985), of the food found in the gizzards of wood ducks shot during hunting seasons. In areas with an abundance of natural food, commercial crops probably become more important to wood ducks late in the year, after natural foods have begun to degrade or become depleted.

NUTRITION AND FOOD SELECTION

Staple foods of the wood duck change from one region to another, and a wide range of dietary patterns results (Table 181). The relative occurrence and proportion of food items in the upper digestive tracts of wood ducks are by themselves unreliable estimators of food value. In areas where preferred foods are scarce or absent, wood ducks may, by necessity, consume large quantities of food that has little nutritional value. Additionally, intense shooting pressure on popular hunting areas may preclude eating of preferred food (Stoudt 1944), thereby forcing wood ducks to feed at locations that provide food of lower quality.

Plants with high fiber content generally are poor sources of nutrients because waterfowl are unable to digest cellulose (Mattocks 1971, Miller 1974). Moreover, the fibrous covering of some seeds resists breakdown in wood duck gizzards and passes through the digestive tract without yielding much nutrition to the bird. Seeds from wild water pepper constituted the third most important plant material (in terms of aggregate percentage) consumed by wood ducks on Duck Creek Wildlife Management Area in southeastern Missouri during autumn, 1975–1976 (Drobney and Fredrickson 1979). However, many of these seeds remained intact after passing through the gizzard, consequently reducing the nutritional value of the plant. These hard seeds probably served as abrasive material, breaking apart food in the gizzard and thus aiding the digestive process.

Because foods vary widely in their chemical and structural makeup, wood ducks derive different amounts of nutrients and metabolizable energy from individual items. The chemical compositions of some major foods consumed by wood ducks are presented in Table 182. Plants generally contain higher levels of fiber and nitrogen-free extract (sugar and starch) than do invertebrate foods. Conversely, invertebrates contain markedly higher levels of protein (and essential amino acids) and calcium (Table 182).

Because nutritional needs change during the course of a year, wood ducks exhibit variation in the amounts of plant and animal matter that they ingest. Holm and Scott (1954) reported that mallards require a diet that contains at least 18.6 percent protein for normal egg production and hatchability. Most plants have less than that level of protein (Table 182). Moreover, plants high in protein generally contain low ratios of amino acid compared with the protein found in woodie eggs (Drobney 1977).

Scott (1973) suggested that calcium should range from 2.5 to 3.5 percent of the diet of birds that

Table 181. Staple autumn plants in the diet of wood ducks as reported from selected food habit studies.

Location	Sample size[a]	Food item	Percentage volume	Percentage occurrence	Reference
Wisconsin	22	Acorns	65.0	41.0	Stollberg (1950)
		Greater burreed	16.0	45.0	
		Rice cutgrass	6.0	9.0	
		Coontail	4.0	23.0	
		Bulrush	3.0	64.0	
Tennessee	36	Baldcypress	50.0	66.7	Rawls (1954)
		Acorns	32.8	38.9	
		Corn	2.8	2.8	
		Hickory	2.6	8.3	
		Grasses	1.7	2.8	
Missouri	38	Acorns	42.4	50.0	Korschgen (1955)
		Buckwheat	28.2	10.5	
		Corn	7.9	5.3	
		Grapes	3.8	23.7	
		Buttonbush	2.8	15.8	
Maine	54[b]	Wild rice	15.0	20.4	Coulter (1957a)
		Pondweeds	12.5	48.1	
		Burreeds	12.0	53.7	
		Bulrush	11.0	20.4	
		Acorns	9.0	11.1	
South Carolina	134	Acorns	19.9	11.9	Kerwin and Webb (1971)
		Corn	15.6	4.5	
		Bulrush	9.1	44.0	
		Arrowarum	8.5	26.1	
		Beakrush	6.4	41.8	
Texas	35[c]	Acorns	77.7	66.0[d]	Allen (1980)
		Buckwheat	5.9	26.0	
		Hammock sedge	4.9	51.0	
		Sweetgum	4.9	23.0	
Illinois	265	Corn	57.4	53.2	Havera (1985)
		Acorns	4.4	5.3	
		Waterhemp	3.8	7.9	
		Dogwood	2.3	15.1	
		Foxtail	2.0	4.5	
Mississippi	94[e]	Acorns	74.3	33.0[d]	Delnicki and Reinecke (1986)
		Soybeans	23.4	34.0	
		Beggarticks	1.4	7.4	

[a] Number of gizzards examined.
[b] Crop, proventriculus, and gizzard contents examined.
[c] Esophagus and gizzard contents examined.
[d] Minimum values.
[e] Only esophagus contents examined.

produce large numbers of eggs. Krapu and Swanson (1975) reported that plants consumed by breeding northern pintails in North Dakota contained calcium levels far below those recommended for breeding waterfowl. Landers et al. (1977) reported the average calcium levels of major plant and animal foods consumed by wood ducks in South Carolina as 0.59 percent and 5.2 percent, respectively. Five plants contained calcium levels over 1 percent,

but no species met the minimum recommendations proposed by Scott (1973). Consequently, invertebrates would be expected to account for a higher proportion of the female wood duck's diet during the spring egg-laying period than in other seasons.

Plants are important to wood ducks during periods of lipid deposition and when energy demands are high. Plants probably comprise more than 70 percent of the food ingested by adult wood

Table 182. Nutrient composition of some major plant and animal foods ingested by breeding wood ducks.

Item	Percentage dry weight						
	Protein	Fat	NFE[a]	Ash	Fiber	Calcium	Water
Plant foods							
Barnyard grass[b]	14.2	0.5	46.6	7.3	31.3	<0.05	
Wheat[b]	18.2	1.7	75.8	2.0	2.4	<0.03	
Buttonbush seeds[c]	8.9	6.7	34.2	3.3	46.9		7.2
Elm seeds[c]	23.8	5.2	44.6	8.8	17.4		7.7
Maple seeds[c]	29.2	5.9	45.4	5.7	13.8		7.4
Watershield seeds[c]	6.2	1.3	44.9	2.8	44.8		7.7
Pin oak acorns[c]	5.6	6.7	57.8	2.6	27.5		4.8
Water oak acorns[d]	3.8	14.6	48.7	1.6	17.2	0.40	
Asiatic dayflower[d]	21.3	0.5	49.0	8.1	10.8	0.30	
Rice cutgrass[d]	13.8	1.9	57.8	7.6	9.3	0.35	
Duckweed[e]	25.4	3.2	54.8	11.0	5.6		
Smartweed achenes[e]	8.9	1.7	65.3	2.3	21.8		
Duck potato tubers[e]	18.6	3.2	70.4	4.7	3.1		
Wild rice[e]	13.5	1.0	72.8	2.5	10.2		
Corn[f]	9.7	5.0	79.7	1.9	3.6	0.06	
Animal foods							
Midge larvae[b]	66.4	5.8	14.9	13.1		0.50	
Snail[bg]	58.9	<0.1	21.9	18.4	0.7	4.20	
Adult beetles[ch]	63.9						65.0
Larval beetles[ch]	71.0						82.4
Isopods[c]	40.3						83.0
Dragonfly (nymph)[e]	66.7	8.2	8.4	5.6	11.1		
Mayfly (nymph)[e]	51.2	14.5	16.2	13.2	4.9		
Water-boatman[e]	71.1	5.0	0.8	4.7	18.4		
Whirligig beetle[e]	45.6	27.6	5.2	2.1	19.5		

[a] NFE = Nitrogen-free extract.
[b] From Krapu and Swanson (1975).
[c] From Drobney (1977), results reported as crude protein, crude fiber, and crude fat.
[d] From Landers et al. (1977), results reported as crude protein and crude fiber.
[e] From Reinecke and Owen (1980), results reported as crude protein, ether extract, and crude fiber.
[f] From Baldassarre et al. (1983), results reported as crude protein, crude fiber, and crude fat.
[g] Without shell.
[h] Analyzed adult water scavenger beetles and larval predacious diving beetles.

ducks during all periods except when females are producing eggs. Ricklefs (1974) reported that carbohydrates and lipids are more efficient substrates for fat synthesis than is protein. Because plants generally are low in water and contain high starch and sugar levels in comparison with invertebrates (Table 182), they provide relatively more concentrated sources of energy-yielding nutrients. Of course, the relative proportion of nitrogen-free extract and fiber in a particular food serves as a measure of its nutritional quality to wood ducks.

Acorns or corn normally constitutes one of the principal foods consumed by wood ducks during autumn and winter (Table 181). Both are important to wood ducks because they occur abundantly and, being low in fiber and high in nitrogen-free extract, provide readily available sources of high energy. Yet by themselves these staple foods contain a relatively small proportion of the total nutrients required for normal body maintenance.

Acorns of the black oak group are readily consumed by wood ducks. Because of their relatively greater levels of tannin, acorns from black oaks—including cherrybark, pin, Nuttall, water, willow (above), red, live, black, and blackjack oak—are thought to be less palatable to wildlife than are white oak acorns. However, trees of the black oak group are more characteristic of the moist bottomlands where the wood duck generally resides, and it readily partakes of these foods. *Photo by Jack Dermid.*

Baldassarre et al. (1983) compared the chemical makeup of corn with nine types of native plants commonly consumed by waterfowl on the southern high plains of Texas. Although corn was higher in carbohydrates, it contained markedly low levels of protein (including some essential amino acids) and most minerals compared with the nine native plants, which contained average protein and calcium levels that were 37 percent and 867 percent higher, respectively, than the levels for corn.

Although calcium levels in acorns (Short and Epps 1976, Landers et al. 1977) are much higher than those in corn (Baldassarre et al. 1983), acorns are relatively deficient in protein and especially poor sources of phosphorus (Short and Epps 1976). Of the 28 plant species analyzed by Landers et al. (1977), acorns contained the lowest levels of crude protein. Six of 11 types of acorns analyzed by Short and Epps (1976) contained calcium/phosphorus ratios that were considered inadequate for normal animal metabolism. Thus, as expected, normal body maintenance would be inhibited by a diet based solely on corn or acorns.

Martin et al. (1951) stated that because of their greater tannin levels, acorns of the black oak group were less palatable to wildlife species than were those of the white oak. Nevertheless, wood ducks frequently consume acorns that belong to the black oak group (cherrybark oak, pin oak, Nuttall oak, water oak, willow oak, red oak, live oak, black oak, and blackjack oak). Many of these trees grow in moist bottomland soils where the acorns are readily available to wood ducks. Acorns from both black oak and white oak groups appear palatable to wood ducks, and each type probably is eaten in relation to its availability.

Food habit studies indicate that wood ducks have highly diversified diets, as previously noted. Drobney (1977) pointed out that the wood duck's habit of consuming a wide range of foods is behaviorally analogous to selecting a balanced diet. He determined that paired wood ducks were more likely (P < 0.005) to ingest a variety of foods than they were to eat foods that were similar. Although breeding females consumed a significantly greater (P < 0.005) diversity of animal food than did males, both sexes ingested a similar quantity of plant foods. The diversified animal diet of females increases the likelihood that they will obtain the required levels of essential amino acids needed for oviduct maturation and egg production. Both sexes ingested a similar number of plants and animals in autumn (Drobney 1977). A diversified diet helps to ensure that adequate levels of essential nutrients are obtained and that the detrimental effects of nutritional deficiencies are offset.

Egg-laying wood duck hens need protein for egg production and therefore pursue food items, such as insects, that are rich in this source of nutrition. Insects often are found on woody stems and the bottoms of leafy vegetation overgrowing water. Woodie hens are alert to such prospects for food, while males — not in need of additional protein — are less inclined to direct their attention off the water. Not infrequently, a hen will leap up from the water to pluck a food morsel from woody stems, while an accompanying male pays little heed. *Photo by Ed Bry; courtesy of the North Dakota Game and Fish Department.*

CONSUMPTION OF GRIT

Like most seed-eating birds, woodies consume bits of gravel and other abrasive materials (grit) to aid in grinding their food. Contractions of the gizzard cause these abrasive particles to grind against ingested foods, which are subsequently broken into smaller pieces more suitable for digestion.

Wood ducks periodically ingest grit because old particles eventually dissolve in the acidic gizzard. Diet and structural composition of a particular grit particle influence grit retention time. Anderson (1959) believed that the grit demands of waterfowl were relatively low. Captive mallards provided with an abundant supply of granite grit ingested less than one piece per day over a 14.5-month period. Even though adequate amounts of grit were readily available, some birds retained grit particles in their gizzards for as long as 7.5 months.

Because certain types of grit contain calcium and other mineral elements, they undoubtedly provide nutrients to wood ducks. Anderson (1959) reported that limestone and rough, jagged pieces of quartz and chert made up the grit material found in waterfowl gizzards collected during the autumn hunting seasons, 1938–1940, in Illinois. Although most grit particles from wood duck gizzards were under 2 millimeters (0.08 in) in width, a few pebbles ranged up to 12 millimeters (0.47 in).

According to Uhler (1964), waterfowl often substitute hard seeds for mineral grit; the seeds serve as both abrasive and nutrient material. It is logical to assume that, when a variety of food enters the gizzard, normal contractions cause harder foods to break down softer material. Moreover, the pressure of one large seed pushing against another large seed may result in their breakdown. Stoddard (1942) reported that bobwhite quail ingested very little grit when they fed on hard seeds. Similarly, Bump et al. (1947) noted that ruffed grouse tended to consume more grit when they fed on soft food items than when they consumed hard food. Thus, the amount of grit found in the gizzard of a wood duck may vary with availability and diet.

Anderson (1959) determined that the average capacity of a wood duck gizzard during autumn in Illinois was 9 cubic centimeters (0.55 in³). He indicated that grit occupied an average of 21.22 percent (1.91 cubic centimeters: 0.12 in³) of the capacity of the wood duck's gizzard during autumn. Although corn and acorns were the staple foods of the wood ducks that Anderson (1959) examined, the birds ingested more than 20 types of plants.

Conrad (1965a) measured the volume of grit in 18 wood duck gizzards that were collected by hunters in South Carolina during November and December 1964. These gizzards contained an average of 3.3 cubic centimeters (0.2 in³) of grit—73 percent more than the amount found by Anderson (1959) in Illinois. Staple foods of the South Carolina birds included fruits and seeds of arrowarum, oaks, and cypress. Anderson (1959) found that each of eight plants constituted at least 1 percent of the food volume consumed by wood ducks in Illinois; conversely, only three plants formed 1 percent or more of the food eaten by wood ducks in South Carolina (Conrad 1965a).

Grit may make up a considerable proportion of the material in a wood duck's gizzard during autumn. In their Illinois studies, Anderson (1959) and Havera (1985) reported that grit comprised 29 percent and 43.5 percent of the total contents from 26 and 265 gizzards, respectively. Similarly, Kerwin and Webb (1971) found that grit formed 33.3 percent of the contents of gizzards collected from 134 wood ducks in South Carolina.

In contrast to the above studies, Cronan and Halla (1968) noted that grit formed only 8.6 percent of the gizzard contents from eight wood ducks collected in Rhode Island, 1954–1957. As expected, these wood ducks consumed many types of hard seeds that apparently assisted in breaking down other foods.

FOOD HABIT STUDIES

One of the first extensive food habit studies that attempted to quantify the importance of particular foods consumed by wood ducks was undertaken by the U.S. Bureau of Biological Survey (now the U.S. Fish and Wildlife Service) in the early 1900s. Mabbott (1920) reported the contents of 399 wood duck stomachs collected in 24 states and the District of Columbia during the months of August through December and February through April. Plant matter comprised 90.19 percent of the examined food. With each of 15 different plant groups accounting for more than 1 percent of the ingested vegetable matter, no one food dominated the woodies' diet.

The principal types of plants consumed by these 399 birds in descending order of importance (by volume) were duckweeds (10.35 percent), cypress cones and galls (9.25 percent), sedge seeds and tubers (9.14 percent), grasses and their seeds (8.17 percent), pondweed foliage and seeds (6.53 percent), acorns and beechnuts (6.28 percent), waterlily seeds and leaves of watershield (5.95 percent), seeds of waterelm and its allies (4.75 percent), smartweed and dock seeds (4.74 percent), coontail seeds (2.86 percent), arrowarum and skunkcabbage seeds (2.42 percent), seeds from various composites

(2.38 percent), seeds from buttonbush and its allies (2.25 percent), burreed seeds (1.96 percent), wild-celery and frogbit (1.31 percent), bitter pecans (0.91 percent), wild grape seeds (0.82 percent), and seeds from swamp privet and ash (0.72 percent).

Mabbott (1920) also found that wood ducks consumed a wide variety of animal food. At least 15 families of beetles (Coleoptera) and 17 families of other insects (Heteroptera and Homoptera) were ingested by the 399 birds. Dragonflies and damselflies constituted 2.54 percent of the food volume. Beetles (1.02 percent) and other insects (1.56 percent) were the only other invertebrate groups that accounted for 1 percent or more.

Many food habit studies have been conducted subsequently to determine the types and amounts of food consumed by adult wood ducks, including Mendall and Gashwiler (1940), Siegler (1950), Stollberg (1950), Rawls (1954), Coulter (1955, 1957a), Korschgen (1955), Anderson (1959), Hall (1962), Conrad (1965b), McGilvrey (1966a, 1966b), Cronan and Halla (1968), Kerwin and Webb (1971), Landers et al. (1976, 1977), Drobney and Fredrickson (1979), Allen (1980), Perry and Uhler (1981), and Delnicki and Reinecke (1986). Palmer (1976) reviewed unpublished reports on woodie food habits. We have included information from several other unpublished manuscripts in the following discussion.

Food habit studies on other species of waterfowl indicate that dietary requirements may vary widely between sexes (Perret 1962, Bartonek and Hickey 1969, Dirschl 1969, Swanson and Nelson 1970), especially during the breeding season. Only in recent years have researchers reported dietary patterns of the wood duck in relation to physiological condition, sex, or both (Landers et al. 1977, Drobney and Fredrickson 1979, Delnicki and Reinecke 1986). Because many early food habit studies involved birds that were not actively feeding, and disregarded post-mortem digestion and the differential breakdown of foods between esophagus and gizzard samples, they undoubtedly inflated the importance of hard seeds in the diet of wood ducks (Dillery 1965, Swanson and Bartonek 1970).

Swanson and Bartonek (1970) demonstrated that soft food is broken down within several minutes after ingestion, whereas hard seeds may be retained for days. They found that most food passed through the esophagus and proventriculus and into the gizzard of blue-winged teal within 10 minutes after consumption. Many of the soft-bodied invertebrates were digested beyond distinction by this time. Moreover, no invertebrates were found in the gizzard 20 minutes after ingestion. This finding illustrates the importance of collecting and immediately preserving the contents of the esophagi of actively feeding birds and, of course, recording the results according to sex and physiological condition. The relative proportion of invertebrates and soft plants in the diet of wood ducks was likely underestimated in studies where only gizzards were analyzed and where birds were shot without prior investigator knowledge of feeding activity, or without the immediate preservation of the contents of the esophagi.

Although Delnicki and Reinecke (1986) suggested that feeding habits may change during the course of a day, this aspect of the wood duck's feeding ecology has not been adequately studied. Landers et al. (1977), Drobney and Fredrickson (1979), and Allen (1980) collected actively feeding wood ducks. In most other studies, birds either had been shot by hunters or collected without prior knowledge of feeding activity. Several authors (Coulter 1955, 1957a, Hall 1962, Conrad 1965b, Sweet 1976, Landers et al. 1976, 1977, Drobney and Fredrickson 1979, Allen 1980, Louisiana Department of Wildlife and Fisheries 1981, Delnicki and Reinecke 1986) examined parts of or the entire esophagus for ingested food.

Variations in the relative importance of a particular food may occur between studies because of different collection techniques and types of laboratory analysis. Researchers have used both aggregate volume and aggregate percentage methods as measures of food consumption. The aggregate volume method gives equal weight to each item consumed by every bird; the aggregate percentage method evaluates each bird independently. Martin et al. (1946) stated that because of the large number of uncontrollable variables associated with food habit studies, differences between aggregate percentage and aggregate volume results were inconsequential. However, studies that used wet volumes to determine food consumption reflected higher proportions of invertebrates in the diet than did studies that used dry weights or dry volumes (Drobney and Fredrickson 1979, Delnicki and Reinecke 1986). Direct comparisons among studies using different collection and analytical techniques must be made with caution.

EFFECT OF SEASON ON FOOD HABITS

The following discussion of seasonal food habits must be read in light of biases that are brought about by various sampling, processing, and laboratory techniques that have been noted in the preceding discussion.

Breeding Season or Spring Diet

Invertebrates (primarily insects) are an important component in the spring diet of wood ducks. Drobney and Fredrickson (1979) found that insects constituted 46 percent and 25 percent (wet volume) of the diet of breeding females and males, respectively, in southeastern Missouri. Although many types of insects were consumed, beetles and flies ranked highest in frequency of occurrence and volume.

Mabbott (1920) recognized that animal food comprised a higher proportion of the wood duck's diet during spring than in other seasons. He reported that damselflies and dragonflies together constituted 8.75 and 10.44 percent of the food volume in the esophagi of wood ducks (males and females combined) collected during March (n = 16) and April (n = 9), respectively. These animal foods represented a much smaller proportion of the diet during other months.

Mabbott (1920) and Landers et al. (1977) suggested that increased invertebrate consumption during spring might be related to an increase in availability. However, Drobney and Fredrickson (1979) found that breeding males consumed proportionally less (P < 0.0005) (34 percent) animal matter than did breeding females (58 percent) collected at the same feeding site. Consequently, seasonal dietary adjustments probably occur in response to changing physiological requirements (an increased need for protein) and not solely as the result of increases in abundance of invertebrates.

In addition to consuming insects, breeding wood ducks readily eat the fruits, seeds, and foliage of certain plants. Grice and Rogers (1965) noted that the spadix of skunkcabbage was a preferred food of breeding wood ducks on Great Meadows National Wildlife Refuge in Massachusetts. Similarly, Haramis (1975) reported that wood ducks on Montezuma National Wildlife Refuge in New York consumed the spathe, spadix, and leaves of skunkcabbage and the foliage of arrowarum. Duckweeds, water fern, and the floating fruits of arrowarum, maple, and elm are important spring foods to wood ducks because of their chemical composition, wide geographical range, and abundant supply. Although acorns provide nourishment for wood ducks throughout the year (Sweet 1976, Drobney and Fredrickson 1979), their availability to breeding wood ducks largely depends on the previous year's production.

Because of the relatively low numbers of wood ducks in the continental population prior to the 1960s, researchers were reluctant to collect woodies during the breeding season. Investigators in Maine

circumvented this problem by studying the food habits of wood ducks (n = 39) that were inadvertently caught in muskrat traps (Coulter 1955). Unfortunately, many of the birds remained in the traps for hours after their capture, allowing for the digestion of recently consumed food. In addition, food from the esophagi and gizzards of both sexes was combined in this study.

Coulter (1955) reported that insects constituted 9.2 percent of the food eaten by breeding wood ducks in Maine. Mayflies, beetles, flies, tree hoppers, grasshoppers, stoneflies, whirligig beetles, water striders, and moths were the principal insects consumed. Hard seeds formed the bulk of the

Wood ducks consume a variety of invertebrates to meet their nutritional needs for growth, reproduction, and molting. Many types of terrestrial insects, including burrowing mayflies (above), have adult stages that live near wetlands and immature stages that live in water. Certain species of these insects live as adults for only several hours; others live a day to a week or more. Some species of mayflies, chironomids, and caddis flies swarm in enormous numbers, forming dense clouds. Wood ducks capture adults that cling to emergent vegetation and individuals near death and floating on the surface. Unlike the adults, immature-stage insects are available to wood ducks for relatively long periods. Some species have a single generation per year, some have two or more generations per year, and others have a two- or three-year life cycle. Although the immature stages of some species live on the bottom of water basins and are largely unavailable to woodies, many live near the surface in association with aquatic plants and provide wood ducks with a critical source of high-protein food. *Photo by Dan Holm; courtesy of the Illinois Natural History Survey.*

spring diet; sedges and burreed each made up 36 percent of the food volume. Other important plant foods included wild rose, dogwood, wildcelery, and duck potato.

Landers et al. (1977) collected esophageal and proventricular samples from breeding wood ducks in South Carolina. They found that from mid-January through early April females consumed significantly (P<0.05) more invertebrates than did breeding males. No difference in invertebrate consumption rates was detected outside of this late winter to early spring period. Because their results were reported on a monthly basis rather than by physiological condition, the relationship between dietary change and breeding status cannot be fully determined.

Crayfish and snails were important animal foods for breeding wood ducks in South Carolina: 12 and 5 percent (dry volume), respectively, of the food consumed in March. Landers et al. (1977) found temporal variations in the importance of major insect taxa to the diet of breeding woodies. Trichoptera (caddis flies), Hymenoptera (ants, bees, and wasps), Odonata (damselflies and dragonflies), and Hemiptera (true bugs) were the major insect groups consumed during January, February, March, and May. Important plant foods ingested during the breeding season included seeds from Asiatic dayflower, panic grasses, slough grass, and smartweeds.

Drobney and Fredrickson (1979) collected 55 male and 60 female wood ducks during spring, 1975–1976, on Duck Creek Wildlife Management Area in southeastern Missouri. Esophagus and proventriculus contents were examined and results evaluated by wood duck sex and reproductive status. The diet of breeding females was influenced by their reproductive condition (Figure 114). Although invertebrates accounted for 79 percent (wet volume) of the food consumed by egg-laying hens, animal matter accounted for only 54 and 43 percent of the food ingested by prelaying and postlaying females, respectively. In contrast, invertebrates formed about one-third of the volume of food consumed by breeding males.

Maple seeds were consumed in the greatest volume (25 percent) and occurred in 19 (35 percent) of 55 drakes collected by Drobney and Fredrickson (1979). The seeds from watershield were the second most important food to breeding males, constituting 10 percent of the food found in the 55 birds. Elm seeds were consumed by 13 males (24 percent) and constituted 8 percent of the ingested food. Although the seeds from buttonbush formed only 3 percent of the volume, they had the highest rate of occurrence (40 percent). Each of five other plants

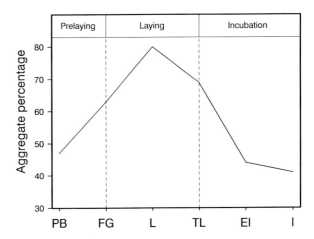

Figure 114. Changes in invertebrate consumption levels by breeding wood duck hens in relation to physiological condition (from Drobney 1977): PB = prebreeding; FG = follicle growth; L = laying; TL = terminal laying; EI = early incubation; I = incubation.

(soybeans, duckweeds, acorns, sassafras, and viburnum) accounted for 2 percent or more of the volume.

Of the 34 percent animal matter consumed by breeding male wood ducks in southern Missouri, flies were the most common food and occurred in 25 (46 percent) of the birds (Drobney and Fredrickson 1979). Collectively, flies and beetles formed 15 percent of the volume. Isopods, snails, damselflies and dragonflies, spiders, and moths each comprised 2 percent or more of the food eaten by breeding males.

Beetles and flies constituted more than half of the animal food consumed by breeding females on Duck Creek Wildlife Management Area (Drobney and Fredrickson 1979). Adult water scavenger beetles and their egg cases, along with the larvae of predacious diving beetles, were the most frequently eaten coleopterans. Similarly, adult midges and the larval forms of crane flies and horse flies were the most important dipterans consumed.

Moths, flies, and beetles comprised 36 percent of the food consumed by prelaying hens (Drobney and Fredrickson 1979). Other principal animal foods were snails, isopods, true bugs, and unidentified pupae. The most important plant materials consumed by prelaying females were watershield and maple seeds, which together formed 23 percent of the volume. Although half (n = 10) of the prelaying hens had consumed buttonbush seeds, this plant material constituted only 3 percent of the contents. Five other plants (swamp privet, soybeans, sweetgum, acorns, and grapes) each formed 2 percent or more of the volume.

404   •   *Ecology and Management of the Wood Duck*

The principal animal foods consumed by egg-laying females were beetles (32 percent), flies (10 percent), isopods (10 percent), lacewings (6 percent), and snails (5 percent) (Drobney and Fredrickson 1979). Plant matter constituted 21 percent of the food consumed by the egg-laying woodies. Maple, watershield, and elm seeds collectively made up 17 percent of the volume.

Plant material dominated the diet of postlaying females. Drobney and Fredrickson (1979) reported that incubating females in southeastern Missouri consumed a diet of 57 percent plant food. Maple seeds were consumed in the greatest volume (44 percent) and occurrence (65 percent). Elm seeds were consumed by four birds (20 percent) and constituted 5 percent of the food eaten by incubating females. Beetles remained an important animal food, forming 33 percent of the volume.

Corn is an important plant food for incubating wood ducks in Illinois. We frequently have observed females leave their nests and fly to agricultural fields in search of food. These fields often had corn, soybeans, or wheat growing in them; in all cases, however, the previous year's waste corn was scattered over the soil. We also have observed wood ducks regularly feeding in a hog lot along Quiver Creek and eating corn in a cattle feed lot at Smith's Lake, near Mason City, Illinois. Stewart (1957) also reported that incubating wood ducks in Ohio obtained corn by feeding in hog lots.

In 1987 we placed radio transmitters on five female woodies that were incubating on Nauvoo Slough. Each left the refuge and flew to agricultural fields during some of their incubation recesses. After leaving their nests, they normally flew to areas where a number of wood ducks were resting and preening on logs. Within several minutes of landing, a hen would depart the refuge either by herself or with a small group of loafing birds. We located several of these marked females with groups of 50–60 other wood ducks feeding on waste grain in a cornfield where the plants were about 0.61 meter (2 ft) high.

Wood ducks that nest on and around Chautauqua National Wildlife Refuge in central Illinois also exhibit this type of feeding behavior. We observed single pairs and small groups of 3–10 birds fly into a wheat field from April 19 through May 5, 1987, to feed on corn that had been left from the previous autumn. On April 22, 54 wood ducks flew into the field between 5:11 and 6:35 p.m. CST.

We also documented the occurrence of corn in the esophagus of incubating wood ducks that were captured during our nest box inspections on Nauvoo Slough, 1985–1987, and on Quiver Creek, 1961–1985 (Table 183). At least 48, 41, and 39 percent of the incubating females on Quiver Creek consumed corn during incubation recesses in April, May, and June, respectively. Although proportionally fewer incubating hens on Nauvoo Slough ingested corn during summer months, occurrence levels indicated that, nevertheless, corn was an important food. We also have noticed that incubating hens in Illinois readily consume ripe mulberries.

Table 183. Occurrence of corn in the gullets of incubating wood duck females captured on the nest, Nauvoo Slough (1985–87), and Quiver Creek (1961–85), Illinois.

Period of capture		Nauvoo Slough		Quiver Creek	
Month	Week	Number of females captured	Percentage containing corn	Number of females captured	Percentage containing corn
April	1			12	58.3
	2	6	16.7	20	65.0
	3	8	12.5	65	52.3
	4	18	38.9	94	40.4
	5	32	34.4	8	50.0
May	1	18	11.1	80	54.1
	2	25	24.0	52	35.1
	3	47	29.8	149	37.6
	4	41	34.1	122	32.8
	5			45	60.0
June	1	45	42.2	83	37.3
	2	30	33.3	102	35.3
	3	26	46.2	39	43.6
	4	22	36.4	21	42.9
	5			6	66.7

Late Summer Diet

Relatively little is known about the feeding habits of postbreeding wood ducks between the time of pair-bond dissolution and autumn courtship. During this period, many females are engaged in brood-rearing activities and both sexes undergo prebasic and prealternate molts. Contour feather replacement is calculated to cost 66.6 grams (2.35 oz) of protein (see Chapter 13). Because large flight feathers develop over 30 days and require more protein than do small contour feathers, there is considerable variation in protein requirements during the 100-day period when wood ducks develop their basic (eclipse) and alternate (breeding) plumages.

Marsh and moist-soil plants are used extensively by wood ducks during this season of the year. Duckweeds and water fern undoubtedly are preferred foods of wood ducks during this late summer and early autumn period. These small succulent plants not only have a high protein content but also occur abundantly throughout much of the wood duck's range. Mabbott (1920: 38) wrote, "Whenever present in the feeding grounds of the wood duck, duckweeds probably are its favorite food."

As mentioned previously, wood ducks in many areas begin to feed on commercial grain immediately after grain fields are harvested. On August 12, 1986, we observed 85 wood ducks feeding on wheat kernels in an unharvested, recently mowed wheat field. At least 180 wood ducks were observed feeding on the waste grain the following evening. By August 17, nearly 600 woodies were exploiting this abundant and readily available food.

Hester and Dermid (1973) reported that wood ducks seek out the fruits of arrowarum in late summer. They reported that the foliage of pondweeds, the seeds of wild rice, spatterdock, watershield, dogwood, elm, and pondweeds, and the fruits of nightshade are important summer foods of wood ducks in South Carolina.

Several species of duckweed are readily consumed by growing young and adult wood ducks because the small plants are widely distributed, occur abundantly, and provide high levels of energy and protein. These tiny plants float on the surface of placid water areas where decomposing organic matter provides them with nutrients; they often completely cover the water surface of wooded sloughs and ponds. The less abundant water fern, a floating plant with a thicker thallus, also provides a high level of protein for wood duck diets and, where abundant, often is preferred to duckweed. *Photo of author Bellrose in the 1950s, by Chuck Scott; courtesy of the Illinois Natural History Survey.*

Beyer et al. (1907) noted that American lotus was an important food for wood ducks in Louisiana. Roosevelt (1884) reported that wood ducks in Florida fed heavily on unripe lotus seeds in early autumn. We have noted that wood ducks in Illinois begin to feed on immature seeds of American lotus in August. Woodies apparently tear open the seed pods with their bills. In 1983 we determined the number of lotus seeds that wood ducks consumed from 59 partially eaten seed heads on Nauvoo Slough. Of 1,222 seeds initially available in the 59 seed heads, wood ducks removed 753, or 61.6 percent. Wood ducks continue to consume lotus seeds after the seeds mature and harden (Anderson 1959). We removed three intact lotus seeds and the remains of several others from the esophagus and gizzard of a wood duck that was shot in late September along the Mississippi River in southeastern Iowa.

Early in summer wood ducks find cover and insects for brood rearing in beds of American lotus that often cover hundreds of hectares (bottom). When lotus seeds begin to mature in late summer (late August and September), wood ducks leap out of the water to tear at the seed heads to extract the marble-shaped, soft-coated seeds (top left). The woodie's hook-tipped bill is used to good advantage in tearing apart the seed receptacles. As seed coats mature to rocklike hardness, however, their palatability diminishes. Mats of duckweed cover the water in many lotus beds. Similar (except for the seeds) and closely related plants include spatterdock or cowlily, white waterlily, banana waterlily, and watershield. *Photos by Dan Holm; courtesy of the Illinois Natural History Survey.*

Gigstead (1938) reported that wood ducks in central Illinois fed on chufa, wild millet, and smartweeds during August. Wood ducks in Michigan feed during August on pondweed tubers and seeds, wild rice, dogwood, bulrush, sedge, yellow waterlily seeds, and insects (Pirnie 1935). Mabbott (1920) reported that one wood duck collected on Rush Lake, Michigan, in August contained about 350 pondweed tubers in its esophagus and gizzard.

Because flightless wood ducks seldom venture far from dense emergent vegetation, most if not all of the food consumed during the flightless period of about 30–36 days (see chapter 13) is associated with aquatic habitats. Landers et al. (1977) collected 4 females in July and 10 in August on the Savannah River Plant in South Carolina. Animal matter (primarily beetles) constituted roughly 6–9 percent (dry volume) of the food in the esophagi and proventriculi of these birds. Males (n = 16) collected during the same period exhibited similar feeding habits. Pondweeds, duckweeds, barnyardgrass, white waterlily, smartweeds, and watershield were the most important plants consumed there by woodies during July and August.

Autumn and Winter Diet

Most of the information on wood duck feeding habits comes from studies that were conducted during autumn and winter. Researchers are in general agreement that outside of the breeding season, male and female wood ducks consume relatively equal amounts of invertebrates (Landers et al. 1977, Drobney and Fredrickson 1979, Delnicki and Reinecke 1986). Moreover, animal foods constitute less than 10 percent (dry weight) of the food consumed by wood ducks during this postbreeding and wintering period.

Siegler (1950) analyzed the contents of 72 wood duck gizzards that were collected during the 1946, 1947, and 1948 waterfowl hunting seasons (October–December) in New Hampshire. He reported that woodies consumed 39 different plant and 10 different animal foods. Acorns were consumed in the greatest volume (36.8 percent) but occurred in only 13 gizzards (18 percent). Black alder and arrowarum seeds each made up 8.9 percent of the volume. Burreed seeds were the most prevalent food, occurring in 40 gizzards (55 percent) and constituting 7.8 percent of the food eaten by the 72 wood ducks. Other principal plant foods that made up 1 percent or more of the volume included wild cherry (5.9 percent), white pine (5.2 percent), dogwood (3.1 percent), grape (2.8 percent), blue beech (2.6 percent), unidentified grasses (2.1 percent), duck

potato (2.1 percent), pickerelweed (2 percent), corn (1.8 percent), and pondweed (1.3 percent). Insects were the most common type of animal food consumed, occurring in 11 gizzards (15 percent). Snails, crustaceans, and frog remains were found in four (5.6 percent), three (4.2 percent), and two (2.8 percent) gizzards, respectively. Collectively, animal matter formed 4.8 percent of the food found in the 72 gizzards.

Stollberg (1950) reported the food habits of 22 wood ducks that were collected on Horicon Marsh in Wisconsin during the hunting season. Acorns comprised 65 percent of the volume consumed. Although the species of many acorns could not be identified, the mast of swamp white oak was an important food. Greater (giant) burreed, rice cutgrass, and coontail constituted 16 percent, 6 percent, and 4 percent, respectively, of the food eaten. Animal matter (insects) represented only 1 percent of the food found in the 22 birds.

Contents of 36 wood duck gizzards collected during the 1950–1954 hunting seasons around the Reelfoot Lake area of Tennessee were analyzed by Rawls (1954), who reported that plant material constituted 98.5 percent (dry volume) of the food consumed. Remains from baldcypress cones and seeds ranked first in importance, comprising 50 percent of the volume and occurring in 66.7 percent of the gizzards. Acorns, corn, hickory nuts, grass seeds, and smartweed seeds accounted for 32.8 percent, 2.8 percent, 2.6 percent, 1.7 percent, and 1.4 percent, respectively, of the food consumed by the 36 wood ducks. Of these foods, acorns were the only food that was consumed by more than five birds.

The 1 to 20 seeds enclosed in each cone scale of the baldcypress provide food for wood ducks in southern swamps, where only remnants of the once abundant tree remain. *Photo by Jack Dermid.*

Fishes (0.83 percent) and insects (0.69 percent) were the only animal foods consumed in quantities large enough to measure. Insect parts were found in seven (19.4 percent) gizzards.

Korschgen (1955) examined 38 wood duck gizzards collected during the hunting seasons of 1940 and 1946–1952 (October 26–December 13) in Missouri. Acorns were a prevalent food, occurring in 50 percent of the gizzards and totaling 42.4 percent (dry volume) of the food found in the 38 birds. Acorns from red oaks ranked first in importance (by volume) (19.6 percent), followed by unclassified oaks (10.4 percent), pin oaks (7.2 percent), and white oaks (5.2 percent). Of the identified oak species, pin oak acorns were consumed more frequently (15.8 percent) than red oak acorns (10.5 percent) or white oak acorns (2.6 percent). Other plant foods that constituted a considerable proportion of the diet included buckwheat (28.2 percent), corn (7.9 percent), grapes (3.8 percent), buttonbush (2.8 percent), wild millets (2.1 percent), and beggarticks (2.1 percent). Although smartweed seeds were consumed more frequently than any other type of plant material (55.3 percent), they comprised only 2.1 percent of the volume. Animal foods occasionally were found in the gizzards and made up 2.5 percent of the volume. At least 24 types of animal foods were consumed by the 38 birds. Stink bugs, plant bugs, spiders, ground beetles, grasshoppers, squash bugs, leaf hoppers, tree hoppers, snout beetles, and water striders were the principal types of ingested animal matter.

Coulter (1957a) reported the types of food found in the esophagi and gizzards of 54 wood ducks collected in Maine during autumn (September and October), 1938–1953. With each of eight plants accounting for more than 4 percent of the food eaten, no one plant food dominated the autumn diet. Wild rice (15 percent), pondweeds (12.5 percent), burreeds (12 percent), bulrush (11 percent), acorns (9 percent), pickerelweed (5 percent), dogwood (5 percent), and duck potato (4.5 percent) formed a majority percentage (74) of the diet. Coulter (1957a) listed 19 other plant species that together made up 14.5 percent of the volume. He indicated that 16 of the wood ducks had ingested insects, which collectively formed 5 percent of the food eaten by all birds.

Wild rice thrives where waters are shallow and clear, particularly in the Lake States and east to New England, and wood ducks find the seeds available from late summer into autumn (left). The burlike clusters of seeds of the greater (giant) burreed, a marsh plant, are utilized by wood ducks wherever it is common in wetlands of northern and central states. *Photos by Jack Dermid.*

Anderson (1959) documented the types and amounts of food found in wood duck gizzards (n = 26) collected by hunters in Illinois during autumn (October–December), 1938–1940. Plant matter constituted 99.9 percent of the volume. Corn was the principal food, occurring in 11 gizzards (42.3 percent) and comprising 48.4 percent of the food eaten by woodies. Acorns ranked second in order of importance (15 percent), followed by wild millets (12.1 percent), coontail (6.5 percent), buttonbush (4.3 percent), pondweed (4.3 percent), rice cutgrass (3.8 percent), and grapes (2.1 percent). The remains in two of the three gizzards that contained acorns were listed as unclassified, and the third gizzard contained pin oak acorns. Arthropods were the only type of animal food consumed and constituted only 0.15 percent of the volume.

Esophagus and gizzard contents of seven wood ducks that were collected during November and December from green-tree reservoirs on the Noxubee National Wildlife Refuge in Mississippi, 1960–1962, were analyzed by Hall (1962). He reported that these woodies had ingested an average of 5.33 acorns per bird. Although cherrybark oaks produce fewer acorns than do willow oaks or water oaks, wood ducks consumed more cherrybark oak acorns (average = 3.66 per bird) than water oak (average = 1.11 per bird) or willow oak (average = 0.55 per bird) acorns. Smartweed seeds were the only other type of plant material consumed. These wood ducks ingested few invertebrates; only one leaf hopper was found in the food.

Conrad (1965a) examined the contents of 18 wood duck gizzards (including six esophagi) that were collected by waterfowl hunters on the Lower Pee Dee and Waccamaw rivers in South Carolina, 1964, during November and December. Plant matter constituted 99.9 percent (dry volume) of the food eaten by these wood ducks. Arrowarum was the most important food, totaling 60.9 percent of the volume and found in 71 percent of the gizzards. Only about one-third of the woodies had ingested acorns, which constituted a similar 31.9 percent of the consumed food. The cone scales and seeds of cypress along with smartweed seeds were other principal plant foods ingested. Dipterans (flies) were the only type of animal matter that had been ingested, but they accounted for merely a trace of the food eaten by these wood ducks.

Hunters contributed gizzards from 108 wood ducks that had been shot between November 29 and December 6 on Lake Marion, South Carolina, in 1961 (McGilvrey 1966a). Gizzards of males comprised 68 percent of the sample. Acorns were one of the principal foods eaten and constituted 58.2 percent of the volume. Of the identified acorns, those

from water oak were eaten more frequently than those from pin oak (31 percent versus 21.3 percent), and water oak acorns constituted a larger proportion of the ingested food than pin oak acorns (26.8 percent versus 20.9 percent). Seventy-four (68.5 percent) of the birds had consumed baldcypress cones and seeds, and this plant matter represented 20.4 percent of the volume. Other important plants included sweetgum (10.3 percent), water hickory (5.5 percent), and corn (4.2 percent). McGilvrey (1966a) noted that buttonbush was very abundant and had produced large amounts of seeds, yet only six birds had consumed small amounts of this plant. No animal matter was found.

McGilvrey (1966b) examined the gizzard contents of 62 wood ducks collected in 1961 by hunters near Santee Refuge, Lake Marion, South Carolina. Acorns were the principal food consumed, occurring in 40 gizzards (64.5 percent) and constituting 57.9 percent of the ingested material. The cone scales and seeds of cypress ranked second in volume (11.8 percent) and frequency of occurrence (35.5 percent). Other plants forming an important portion of the diet included corn (6.9 percent), green hawthorn (5.8 percent), sweetgum (3.7 percent), and Asiatic dayflower (1.5 percent). Two (3.2 percent) wood ducks consumed bryozoa statoblasts, the only animal matter found in the gizzards.

Cronan and Halla (1968) reported on the contents of eight wood duck gizzards collected by hunters in Rhode Island during hunting seasons (November–January), 1954–1957. Five (62.5 percent) of the birds had ingested burreed seeds, making these seeds the most common food found in the gizzards. However, burreed constituted only 1 percent of the food. Although only one wood duck (12.5 percent) had consumed acorns, acorns made up 92.3 percent of the volume.

At least 90 different types of plant food were found in the gizzards of 134 wood ducks wintering in South Carolina, 1965–1967 (Kerwin and Webb 1971). Plant matter represented 99.5 percent of their food. Pin oak acorns had been consumed in greatest volume (19.9 percent) but occurred in only 16 gizzards (11.9 percent). Similarly, corn ranked second in volume (15.6 percent), but only six individuals had ingested this food. It was eaten less frequently but in larger amounts than many native plants. Seeds from softstem bulrush were the most common food found in the gizzards (44-percent occurrence) and constituted 9.1 percent of the volume. Six other plant species (arrowarum, beakrush, spikerush, mermaidweed, tupelo, and bayberry) each made up 2 percent or more of the gizzard contents.

Sweet (1976) examined the gullets of 102 wood ducks that were harvested by hunters in the Oakwood Bottoms Greentree Reservoir in Illinois during the 1972 and 1973 hunting seasons. A total of 21 plant taxa and 38 animal taxa were removed from the esophagi of these birds. Although 94 wood ducks (92.2 percent) had recently consumed plants, only 45 individuals (44.1 percent) had animal matter in their esophagi. Plant material constituted 98.5 percent (dry weight) of the contents. Acorns formed 91.3 percent of all food consumed and were found in 68.6 percent of all samples. Pin oak acorns were consumed by 64 wood ducks (62.8 percent) and made up 88.2 percent of their food. Pecans made up 6.4 percent of the food, but only three wood ducks (2.9 percent) had ingested this item. Cherrybark oak acorns were consumed by five wood ducks and constituted 2.5 percent of the esophageal contents. No other plant food accounted for more than 1 percent of the ingested food. Although animal matter formed only 1.5 percent of the dry weight of all consumed food, the high diversity and percentage occurrence of invertebrates in the diet of these wood ducks indicated that animal food probably was important. Terrestrial and aquatic insects formed 1.1 percent and 0.3 percent, respectively, of the woodies' ingested food. The mast of trees was the only plant food that comprised a larger proportion of the ingested material than did terrestrial insects. Adult spittle bugs, rat-tailed maggots, and bush crickets were the most important animal foods consumed; one wood duck had recently consumed 77 rat-tailed maggots.

Foods from 32 wood duck esophagi and gizzards collected by hunters on managed tidal impoundments in South Carolina were reported by Landers et al. (1976). Animal matter comprised less than 1 percent (by volume) of the foods eaten by these birds. Acorns (57.2 percent) and corn (16 percent) constituted nearly 75 percent of the volume. Arrowarum, foxtail, bulrush, and wild millets each made up around 5 percent of the food. Smartweed and panic grass seeds each accounted for at least 1 percent of the volume.

Landers et al. (1977) examined the esophageal and gizzard contents of 200 wood ducks that had been collected during all months of the year at the Savannah River Plant, South Carolina, 1973–1975. They reported that wood ducks consumed over 95 types of plant food during the study. Acorns comprised 40.4 percent (dry volume) of the winter diet in 1973. Smartweed and Asiatic dayflower seeds were other principal winter foods. Only trace amounts of animal matter were found in the digestive tracts of wood ducks during November and December.

The autumn (September and October) feeding habits (esophagus and proventriculus contents) of 20 male and 20 female wood ducks from Duck Creek Wildlife Management Area in Missouri, 1975–1976, were reported by Drobney and Fredrickson (1979). Animal matter formed 36 percent and 33 percent (wet volume) of the diet of males and females, respectively. Insects were the primary animal food consumed, with Lepidoptera (moths) comprising 21 and 13 percent of the food ingested by males and females, respectively. In addition to being the most prevalent plant material consumed (70–75 percent occurrence), watershield seeds constituted 28–29 percent of the volume. Acorns accounted for 16 percent of the food consumed by both sexes. Acorns from water oaks were consumed most frequently (12.5 percent), followed by pin oak acorns (7.5 percent) and post oak acorns (5 percent).

The contents of 35 wood duck esophagi and gizzards collected from green-tree reservoirs in eastern Texas during the 1972–1974 hunting seasons (November–January) were analyzed by Allen (1980). At least 25 different types of plants had been consumed. Acorns constituted 77.7 percent of the volume. Water and white oak acorns had been selected over willow oak acorns. Although sweetgum formed only 4.9 percent of the volume, it represented 40 percent of the wood ducks' diet in November of 1974. Animal matter was found in 17 birds (49 percent) and comprised 2.9 percent of the food.

The food from 255 wood duck crops and gizzards that were collected from birds shot at roosting sites in Louisiana, August–February, 1975–1976, was analyzed by the Louisiana Department of Wildlife and Fisheries (1981). Food consumption patterns were presented for each of seven months and as a composite for the entire study. At least 50 plant and 16 animal groups were identified. As expected, seasonal availability influenced utilization rates of some items. Water oak acorns were a staple throughout all months. Duckweeds contributed a major proportion of the diet in August. Although only traces of duckweed were consumed in September and October, duckweed constituted at least 2.5, 3.2, and 6.4 percent of the volume in November, December, and February, respectively. Snowbell was an important food throughout the study, especially in September and January. Fruits of bitter pecan, sweet pecan, and Nuttall oak were heavily utilized when they became available. Overall, acorns constituted 46.2 percent of the food eaten. Snowbell and pecans made up 16.6 percent and 12.1 percent, respectively, of the volume. Animal matter accounted for only 0.5 percent of the ingested food.

Perry and Uhler (1981) analyzed the gizzards of eight wood ducks that were collected in Virginia during the 1973 and 1975 hunting seasons. At least 24 plant species were consumed by the eight birds; the investigators indicated that arrowarum was the most important food, constituting 35 percent of the volume. Shell remains from a small Asiatic clam represented the only animal matter found.

Gizzard contents of 265 wood ducks collected by hunters in Illinois, 1978–1983, were presented by Havera (1985). Plant material formed 98.7 percent (dry volume) of the ingested food. Corn was the principal item, constituting 57.4 percent of the volume and occurring in 141 gizzards (53 percent). Pin oak acorns—uncommon in occurrence—were eaten less frequently (5.3 percent) than many other foods. Seeds from gray dogwood (15.1 percent), rice cutgrass (11.3 percent), and waterhemp (7.9 percent) were consumed more frequently than acorns, and each item formed at least 1.8 percent of the food eaten by the 265 birds. Other plant foods that each constituted 1 percent or more of the volume included giant foxtail, duck potato, smartweeds, buckwheat, burreed, and hackberry.

Delnicki and Reinecke (1986) examined the esophageal contents of 94 wood ducks that were collected in Mississippi, 1979–1982, during December and January. They reported that animal matter made up about 1 percent (dry weight) of the food consumed. Only 8 (8.5 percent) of the 94 wood ducks had recently ingested animal food. Twenty-six types of plants had been consumed. Acorns made up 74.3 percent of the food eaten. Nuttall oak acorns were consumed in the greatest amount (48.3 percent) and frequency (33 percent); nevertheless, both water oak (18.7 percent) and willow oak (6.1 percent) acorns formed a substantial proportion of the ingested food. Soybeans ranked second, totaling 23.4 percent of the esophageal contents.

Although they found few invertebrates in the esophageal samples, Delnicki and Reinecke (1986) still believed that animal matter was an important part of the wood duck's diet in winter. They suggested that wood ducks consume small numbers of invertebrates throughout the day to offset nutritional deficiencies associated with certain plant foods. During the evening hours prior to roosting, when many birds are collected for food habit studies, wood ducks feed almost exclusively on high-energy plant foods.

 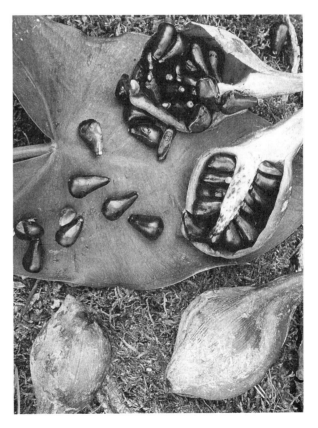

Arrowarum in the foreground and pickerelweed with flowering spikes in the background are two herbaceous swamp-edge plants that often grow along muddy shorelines (left). Their seeds, especially those of arrowarum, are relished by wood ducks. Arrowarum has a spathe containing brown berries, each with one to three seeds surrounded by gelatinous material (right). Arrowarum is thinly but extensively distributed over much of the eastern United States. *Left photo by Frank Bellrose; courtesy of the Illinois Natural History Survey. Right photo by Jack Dermid.*

Wood ducks are second only to mallards in their ability to utilize a wide variety of plant and animal foods. Undoubtedly, before humans affected swamps and overflow bottomland forests, woodies relied primarily on acorns and other mast for their diet from autumn into spring. The loss of much of this food resource to drainage and land clearing was mitigated by supplementing these basic food items with corn, wheat, and other cereal crops. *Photo by Jennifer A. Loomis.*

The foods consumed by wood ducks reflect: (1) availability, (2) palatability, and (3) nutrition. The abundance of a particular seed, fruit, or invertebrate in relation to its availability on dry land or in water provides one set of parameters determining use. The palatability of some foods may limit use because of hard seed coats inhibiting digestion or because of unpleasant flavors. For example, the limited use of buttonbush seeds—an abundant food in habitats frequented by wood ducks—suggests that these seeds contain too much indigestible fiber (Table 182).

According to Martin et al. (1951), acorns of the black oak group are less palatable to wildlife than acorns of the white oak group because their high tannin content produces a bitter flavor. Yet most of the acorns consumed by wood ducks belong to species in the black oak group. Food habit studies generally have placed cherrybark oak first, followed by water oak, pin oak, Nuttall oak, and willow oak. Use of acorns from species in the white oak group has trailed. However, only a few species of the

white oak group occur in bottomland areas—most notably the overcup oak, swamp white oak, and basket oak.

In a lengthy test of acorn selection, Scott Barras of Mississippi State University found that among cherrybark, Nuttall, willow, and water acorns, captive wood ducks preferred willow oak by a wide margin. Among these four species of oaks, willow oak acorns are the smallest and have the thinnest seed coat, perhaps the reasons for their selection.

Short and Epps (1976) found that the crude fiber contents of black and white oak acorns were essentially the same but that black oak acorns contain significantly ($P < 0.01$) more crude fat (17.9 percent dry weight) than do white oak acorns (4.3 percent dry weight); thus, black oak acorns yielded more digestible energy. Moreover, black oak acorns remain available for longer periods during autumn and winter than do white oak acorns, which germinate shortly after dropping in autumn. Thus, nutrition qualities and availability appear to account for the kind of acorns utilized by wood ducks.

Acorns are the mainstay of the wood duck's diet from late summer through spring. These are provided largely by bottomland oaks of various species—cherrybark (top row), overcup, pin, swamp white, water (center row), willow (bottom row), and others. At least one study (in Mississippi) has indicated that willow oak acorns are preferred over most other oak species, including Nuttall oak. The willow oak acorn's relatively small size and thin shaft may contribute to its preference by woodies. *Photo by Richard Kaminski; courtesy of Mississippi State University.*

FEEDING BEHAVIOR AND DIET OF DUCKLINGS

Like adults, young woodies exhibit wide variation in the foods they consume. A variety of plant and animal matter is readily ingested. This behavior increases the likelihood of balanced amounts of dietary protein, carbohydrates, lipids, minerals, and vitamins. Although morphological and physiological adaptations impose constraints on the types of food that ducklings can locate, secure, swallow, and derive nutrients from, ducklings consume both aquatic and terrestrial material. The young woodie's diet changes with age and is influenced by availability and abundance of local foods.

Time and Manner of Feeding

Because ducklings require large amounts of metabolizable energy for growth, feather production, and tissue maintenance, they spend large amounts of time looking for and consuming food. Stewart (1957) reported that preflight wood ducks feed at all times of the day. Young wood ducks feed most intensely, however, during early morning,

evening, and nighttime hours.

The time ducklings allocate to feeding during the day undoubtedly is influenced by environmental conditions and probably varies among broods and with age. Beard (1964) reported that wood duck broods at Seney National Wildlife Refuge in Michigan spent 70 percent of the morning hours (5:30–10:30 a.m.) feeding. The average duration of morning feeding bouts was 105 minutes (range = 15–210).

Between feeding periods, wood duck broods spend most of their time preening and resting. Beard (1964) observed that broods usually slept only once during the morning observation period. Morning sleeping bouts lasted an average of 48 minutes (range = 45–60).

Farmer (1970) observed that many brood hens terminated evening feeding bouts 15 minutes after sunset. However, like many prairie-nesting ducklings, which follow their mothers into open water to feed at night (Swanson and Sargeant 1972), some wood duck broods become very active at night; many spend appreciable time feeding during nocturnal hours (Ball 1973). This is further substantiated by the notable increase in broods found on nocturnal surveys of rivers (Minser and Dabney 1973, Cottrell 1979a).

Although young wood ducks primarily forage for food in aquatic habitats, they will venture onto shore in their search for invertebrates and plant matter. In describing the foraging behavior of young wood ducks, Blanchan (1898: 113) noted that the mother leads "the ducklings about on land and water in quest of seeds of plants, wild oats or rice, roots of aquatic vegetables, acorns, and numerous kinds of insects." We have noted that brood hens seldom lead their young on terrestrial foraging excursions more than 9.1–18.3 meters (10–20 yd) from the shoreline.

Because the relative importance of a particular food varies among wetlands and localized feeding sites within wetlands, ducklings show considerable variation in their feeding modes. Even though young woodies are capable of diving, they seldom obtain food from below the surface of the water. Young wood ducks of all ages feed by pecking at insects, feeding on the surface, and dabbling. In general, Class Ia (see Chapter 12) ducklings primarily consume flying insects and invertebrates that cling to emergent substrates, along with those that live on the water surface. These young ducklings occasionally consume duckweeds and the foliage and seeds of plants by dabbling at the surface. As they grow older, ducklings consume proportionally more plant matter and obtain most of their food by dabbling and surface feeding.

Collias and Collias (1963) observed that captive woodie ducklings fed primarily by pecking at invertebrates. Young woodies seldom fed by straining food from water because their relatively narrow bills and lack of well-developed lamellae precluded efficient capture of planktonic organisms.

Young wood ducks are confronted with many of the same obstacles that adult birds face when attempting to procure food. They cannot crush food with their bills and therefore must swallow their food whole. Insects and fruits, such as those from maple and elm, are picked up one at a time and swallowed, whereas small seeds often are extracted from the seed head in large quantities. In describing how Class Ic to Class III ducklings obtained reed canarygrass seeds, Strom (1969: 25) wrote that "The duckling would grasp the stem of the plant and slip the stem through its bill and the ripe seeds then fell off in its bill." Ducklings of all ages consume the foliage of some plants (Stewart 1957, Hocutt and Dimmick 1971) by cutting, tearing, pulling, or biting off small pieces of the vegetation before ingesting them.

Probably more frequently than any other duck species, young wood ducks jump out of the water to capture insects that are flying or clinging to emergent vegetation. In addition, they frequently dart and skitter along the water surface chasing insects. As ducklings grow older, they feed more frequently by surface feeding. However, Beard (1964) observed young wood ducks that were almost able to leap 20–25 centimeters (8–10 in) out of the water in an effort to capture insects on emergent vegetation.

Female wood ducks normally lead their broods when they travel to and from feeding sites. Woodies less than two weeks old usually follow close behind the hen in a compact group. Occasionally, one or several members will break away from the formation to pursue insects; however, only a few seconds are spent chasing or capturing the prey before the strayers typically rejoin their brood mates. As ducklings grow older, they tend to spread out and roam farther from the hen when moving from one location to another and while feeding.

After they reach a feeding site, brood members usually spread out on both sides of the female and move along slightly ahead of her. Although the hen frequently interrupts her feeding to watch for signs of danger, the ducklings generally feed without pausing.

Woodie ducklings spend much of their daily time and energy seeking and consuming food that is necessary for rapid growth, feather production, and tissue maintenance. Ducklings feed at all times of the day and often at night, but the most intense feeding periods are in early morning and evening. Very young ducklings (Class Ia) feed primarily by dabbling for duckweed, seeds, and other palatable vegetation on the surface, by snatching flying insects, and by pecking at invertebrates on the water and emergent vegetation. *Photo by Jack Dermid.*

The feeding opportunities of young wood ducks are limited by their inability to fly. They must meet all of their nutritional needs in areas that can be safely reached by walking or swimming, which underscores the importance of adequate water levels until ducklings reach flight stage. Thus, abundance and availability necessarily influence the types of food consumed by young wood ducks.

Duckling Nutrition and Diet

Low-fiber plant food and high-protein animal food are readily consumed by ducklings. Invertebrates provide most of the nutritional requirements of wood ducks less than one week old. Indeed, Strom (1969) and Hocutt and Dimmick (1971) reported that animal matter constituted more than 70 percent of the food consumed by wood ducks during their first week of life. Ducklings belonging to classes Ib, Ic, and IIa are opportunistic feeders, consuming whatever types of food (plant or animal) are most available in their immediate surroundings. Although plant material is the major dietary component of ducklings six weeks of age and older, some invertebrates must be ingested to satisfy nutritional demands.

Several researchers have examined the types of food consumed by young wood ducks. Coulter (1957a) analyzed the esophageal and gizzard contents of eight ducklings collected in Maine. The wood ducks ranged in age from four days to seven weeks. Contents were presented separately for each bird and measured by volumetric displacement. Strom (1969) collected 45 actively feeding ducklings on the Upper Mississippi River Wildlife and Fish Refuge in Wisconsin and Minnesota. The food contents of their esophagi and gizzards were preserved immediately after collection to prevent post-mortem digestion, and visual estimates were made of the percentage of foods. Hocutt and Dimmick (1971) presented the types and amounts of food found in the proventriculi of 45 actively feeding ducklings from John Sevier Lake in Tennessee. Baker (1971) collected 37 ducklings on the Noxubee National Wildlife Refuge in Mississippi during the morning hours after they had finished feeding. He removed and preserved the esophagus contents immediately after the birds were collected. Hocutt and Dimmick (1971) and Baker (1971) measured the amount of food consumed by volumetric displacement.

As previously stated, the dietary intake of ducklings is restricted by the types of food that occur on and around the wetland where they live. Because the food chronology changes throughout the summer, a particular food may be available only to early or late-hatched broods. Thus, the importance of an individual food to similar-age ducklings not only varies from one locality to another but also throughout the brood-rearing period.

Coulter (1957a) noted that the esophagi and gizzards of eight young wood ducks from Maine contained at least 22 types of insects and nine species of plants. Frequently consumed invertebrates included dragonflies, damselflies, water-boatmen, water striders, leaf bugs, leaf beetles, and snout beetles. The most important plant foods were seeds of mannagrass and sedges. One seven-week-old duckling had approximately 150 unripened wild rice seeds in its esophagus and gizzard.

Of the 37 wood ducks collected by Baker (1971), 16 were less than two weeks of age, 15 were two to four weeks old, and 6 were four to six weeks of age. These birds consumed at least 29 types of animal foods and five species of plants. Although only four birds (10.8 percent) consumed mayfly nymphs, this insect accounted for 34.7 percent of the volume ingested by all 37 ducklings. Dragonfly nymphs constituted 19.3 percent of the volume and were consumed by 10 ducklings (27 percent). Water striders were consumed more frequently (83.7 percent) than any other food and comprised 7.7 percent of the food. Damselflies and water treaders each constituted about 5 percent of the food eaten by these ducklings. At least 14 birds (37.8 percent) ingested small fishes, which made up 15.5 percent of the volume.

Stewart (1957) collected a five- to six-week-old duckling in Ohio and found 800 spikerush, 44 smartweed, and 8 bulrush seeds in its esophagus. He reported that another five- to six-week-old wood duck contained 26 avens seeds in its esophagus.

Although Strom (1969) was unable to identify the family of many of the animal foods captured by Class Ia ducklings (n = 8) on the Upper Mississippi River Wildlife and Fish Refuge, he noted that beetles and flies were the most important animal foods consumed, followed by snails, mayflies, mosquitoes, and water striders. The major types of plant material consumed were pondweeds, duckweeds, and seeds of sedges and reed canarygrass. On Noxubee National Wildlife Refuge in Mississippi, Baker (1971) found that water striders, damselflies, and water treaders were a major component of the diet of ducklings (n = 16) less than 15 days old. Hocutt and Dimmick (1971) determined that adult and immature flies (midges, black flies, stable flies, and flesh flies) comprised 50 percent of all food consumed by Class Ia ducklings (n = 6) on the Holston River in eastern Tennessee. Other principal animal foods were adult forms of dragonflies and damselflies (6.8 percent), beetles (5.8 percent), moths (3.4 percent), true bugs (2.7 percent), and ants (0.2 percent). The only types of plant matter found in the esophagi of Class Ia ducklings were tubers from uprooted sago pondweed and the foliage of curlyleaf pondweed. The pondweed tubers and foliage constituted 21.2 and 8.4 percent, respectively, of all food eaten by these one- to seven-day-old wood ducks.

Plant food comprised 72 percent and 69 percent of the total volume ingested by two- to three-week-old ducklings on the Holston River (n = 9) and the Upper Mississippi River Refuge (n = 17), respectively (Strom 1969, Hocutt and Dimmick 1971). Strom (1969) found that Class IIa ducklings consumed more invertebrates (66 percent) than either Ib (51 percent) or Ic (22 percent) ducklings. Hocutt and Dimmick (1971) noted that ducklings 27–36 days of age (n = 5) had ingested more animal foods (59 percent) than plant foods (41 percent). Because of the small sample size, however, the results for this age group may be misrepresented.

Apparently young wood ducks between the ages of 13 and 36 days readily feed on both plant and animal matter, consuming whichever is most available. Coulter (1957a) collected two five-week-old ducklings and found that one had consumed mainly plant matter (81 percent) and the other had ingested primarily animal food (71 percent). Strom (1969) also found a high degree of variance between food types consumed by individual birds from this age group (Table 184). Although some Class Ib, Ic, and IIa ducklings were found to contain more than 7,000 reed canarygrass or 100 elm seeds in their esophagi, others fed almost exclusively on beetles, flies, and cankerworm larvae. Strom (1969) noted that individuals that contained primarily animal food in their esophagi were collected from areas where little plant food was available.

Although Hocutt and Dimmick (1971) collected only five individuals, which were four to five weeks old, their results support the contention that ducklings in this age group are opportunistic feeders.

Table 184. Estimated percentage of animal matter consumed by young wood ducks on the Upper Mississippi River Wildlife and Fish Refuge, Minnesota and Wisconsin.[a]

Age class	Sample size	Mean	Range	S.D.
Ia	8	75.5	40–100	27.6
Ib	5	51.0	20–95	34.0
Ic	12	22.3	0–70	26.5
IIa	8	65.9	0–99	39.6
IIb	6	3.2	0–15	5.8
IIc	1	5.0		
III	5	4.8	0–20	8.6

[a] Compiled from data presented in Strom (1969).

One individual ingested enough cutworm larvae and pupae to rank the cutworm first in overall volume of animal food consumed by all ducklings during their study. In contrast, only one of the remaining four individuals consumed leaves from buttercup. However, buttercup ranked first (16.1 percent volume) among plant food consumed by members of this age class. Pondweed tubers were consumed by three birds (60 percent) and made up 14.1 percent of the volume. Two ducklings (40 percent) consumed pondweed foliage, which comprised 10.3 percent of the food eaten by these ducklings. Adult flies and beetles were consumed by three ducklings (60 percent), and each formed about 6 percent of the volume.

Ducklings older than five weeks occasionally feed on animal matter but apparently select for plant food (Table 184). Hocutt and Dimmick (1971) and Strom (1969) found that invertebrates comprised only 4 percent and 4.8 percent, respectively, of food ingested by ducklings six weeks of age and older. Major plant foods, listed in order of relative importance (by volume), consumed by Class IIc and older woodie ducklings in Tennessee (n = 25) were tubers from uprooted sago pondweed (43.7 percent), foliage of curlyleaf pondweed (19.4 percent), leaves from water stargrass, and drupes, pits, or both of wild black cherry (12.6 percent). Important animal foods were the adult forms of dragonflies, flies, beetles, and moths (Hocutt and Dimmick 1971).

On the Upper Mississippi River Refuge, seeds from rice cutgrass and foliage of duck potato, curlyleaf pondweed, and sago pondweed were the major types of plant material ingested by Class IIb, IIc, and III ducklings (Strom 1969). Beetles, spiders, and water striders comprised most of the animal food captured by these older ducklings.

We have made several casual observations on the feeding habits of young wood ducks along Quiver Creek and the Chautauqua National Wildlife Refuge in Illinois. In one instance, a brood of eight Class IIc ducklings was observed avidly pursuing and consuming top minnows. On another occasion, a hen and her three Class III young were observed swimming along the shoreline of Quiver Creek. Whenever they came to a mulberry tree, the female and young left the water, ran up the stream bank to below its canopy, and began searching for mulberries or insects associated with the fruit. Another brood of Class IIa ducklings followed its mother up the bank and immediately began tossing old leaves aside in a hunt for terrestrial insects. The birds pursued this endeavor for 23 meters (75 ft) until the dense woody vegetation obstructed their path and necessitated their return to the creek.

While conducting nest box inspections on Nauvoo Slough during summer 1985, we found a Class IIa duckling that had recently been "surgically" decapitated by a snapping turtle. Examination of its esophagus and proventriculus revealed that the duckling had consumed a large quantity of duckweed. Judd (1900) reported a "third grown" (one-third mature) wood duck with the legs of a small frog extruding from its bill.

These food habit data show that young wood ducks, like adults of the species, have adaptable feeding habits and consume quite a diversified diet. Invertebrates provide substantial sustenance for ducklings throughout the preflight period, and the amount of animal matter eaten varies with availability and duckling age. Just about any type of insect that lives on or near or flies over the water surface may be consumed by woodie ducklings. Small fishes also are readily eaten by some individual woodie ducklings. Fruits, seeds, and the foliage of some marsh plants are foods favored by young wood ducks. Succulent fruits, such as mulberries and wild cherries, and the dry fruits of maple and elm also provide important sources of nourishment to growing ducklings.

Young wood ducks began consuming whole corn kernels as early as 30 days—the youngest age of 2,000 woodies that we captured in banding traps. From 30 days on, increasing numbers were captured as they matured, suggesting that protein became less important and carbohydrates more important in their diet.

Wood ducks have an uncanny ability to exploit fortuitous food sources. We have observed wood ducks (and have reliable reports of others) finding secluded pools occupied by thriving, temporary populations of Diptera larvae; locating wheat fields where grain was made available by weather destruction; discovering waste corn turned up by spring plowing; searching urban lawns for fallen maple seeds; searching oak groves and pecan and filbert orchards for fallen nuts; picking up mulberries, wild grapes, and bird cherries as they ripened; tearing the maturing seed pods of American lotus to obtain embedded seeds; and finding sporadic inundated moist-soil plant beds and mast in flooded bottomland forest. Because of its ability to locate and use a wide variety of plant and animal foods, the wood duck has a claim to possessing one of the most diverse food habits of any North American waterfowl. Such diversity is of course an advantage in the struggle for survival. As it is for other animal populations, food is one of the most important factors regulating wood duck abundance. *Photo by Jennifer A. Loomis.*

Chapter 17

Parasites and Diseases

Wood ducks are plagued by a number of animal parasites and a wide variety of bacterial, fungal, and viral infections. Many parasites must live on (ectoparasites) or in (endoparasites) other living organisms in order to survive. They derive nutrients and, in many cases, protection from their host. Wobeser (1981) defined waterfowl diseases as impairments that alter the performance of normal body functions in response to environmental factors, infectious agents, and inherent or congenital defects. Under this broad definition, a parasite that modifies the behavior or physiological functioning of a wood duck is considered a disease. Rothschild and Clay (1957) emphasized that all parasites are potentially harmful to their hosts. Subtle behavioral changes in the host wood duck—such as a relative lack of vitality or decreased wariness—that are brought about by parasitism are not easily recognized, but they may lead to cumulative debilitating infections which, in turn, make the bird more vulnerable to predation. Thus, in the following discussion, all animal parasites, pathogenic microorganisms, and environmental contaminants that are known to impair the wood duck's health are considered potential disease-causing agents that may lead to mortality.

Survival of wood ducks is slightly below that of mallards and northern pintails and on a par with other duck species (see Table 206). As a result of nonhunting-related losses and hunting mortality, roughly 54 percent of immature woodies and 47 percent of adults alive in September will die before the following September (see Chapter 18). Direct and indirect losses from hunting account for one-third to one-half of the woodies' annual mortality, indicating that accidents, predation, and diseases account for half or more of the annual losses.

A wood duck can become seriously impaired when infected by lethal organisms or toxins or when subject to exceptionally large numbers of parasites. Injuries, overcrowding, inclement weather, and poor nutrition are among the factors that allow disease organisms to gain access and increase in density.

In most cases, mortalities from diseases are restricted to a small number of wood ducks at a given locality. Although spectacular mass die-offs have not been reported, wood ducks are susceptible to epizootic diseases (Bellrose et al. 1945, Forrester et al. 1980). Woodies probably are most vulnerable to epizootic diseases during autumn and winter months, when they congregate at nocturnal roosts or when pathogenic organisms are associated with a concentrated, readily available food source.

The methods by which diseases are transmitted to wood ducks vary greatly. Many ectoparasites are transmitted directly from bird to bird. Some ducklings probably acquire ectoparasites from their mothers while in the nest or during brooding periods. Consumption of contaminated foods provides a means for toxins to enter the wood duck's system. Many endoparasites are ingested with or injected by natural vectors. Other organisms may gain access through the respiratory system or through external lesions. Still others enter by actively penetrating the skin.

Some wood ducks undoubtedly are killed during storms with high winds, heavy rains, or both. Others succumb to miscellaneous accidents, such as colliding with inanimate objects or females becoming trapped in cavities and chimneys during their searches for nest sites (see Chapter 10).

Many diseases such as coccidiosis, tumors, uremic poisoning, avian tuberculosis, pesticide poisoning, algal and fungal toxins, and various genetic functional and morphological abnormalities are not included in the following discussion because of the paucity of information pertaining to wood ducks.

The inherent complexity surrounding the subject of wood duck diseases and the lack of knowledge about concurrent infections involving sublethal agents preclude mention of all known and suspected wood duck mortality factors. Nevertheless, many of the recognized disease-causing agents of wood ducks are reviewed in the following pages.

VIRAL INFECTIONS

Wood ducks are known to be susceptible to duck virus enteritis (DVE) and Newcastle disease. Although there is no evidence that wild wood ducks have died from viral diseases, DVE—also known as "duck plague"—is highly contagious and potentially epizootic among captive and wild waterfowl (Wobeser 1981).

Duck Virus Enteritis

To date, only one major epizootic caused by DVE in wild waterfowl has been documented. The outbreak occurred at Lake Andes National Wildlife Refuge in South Dakota during January and February 1973 (Friend and Pearson 1973). An estimated 43,000 ducks (mainly mallards) and 350 Canada geese died during the epizootic. No wood duck mortality was reported, but it is unlikely that wood ducks were on the refuge at the time.

DVE apparently is transferred through contact with infected birds, contaminated water, or both. Death is rather rapid (about three to seven days), and birds usually die in good weight (Bellrose 1976). Infected birds may exhibit nonspecific symptoms, but sick birds often undergo a series of convulsions immediately preceding death (Wobeser 1981).

Interspecific differences in susceptibility to DVE have been noted. Behavioral differences between mallards and Canada geese were thought responsible for differential mortality rates of these species during the 1973 DVE outbreak in South Dakota (Friend and Pearson 1973). Spieker (1978) infected several waterfowl species with the Lake Andes strain of DVE. He reported that the wood duck, redhead, Muscovy, gadwall, mallard, and Canada goose were moderately susceptible, that blue-winged teal were the most susceptible of the species examined, and that northern pintails were the least susceptible.

Burgess et al. (1979) noted that wood ducks and other species of waterfowl infected experimentally with the Lake Andes DVE virus acted as carriers and shed the virus for at least one year after infection. Friend and Pearson (1973) noted that DVE

outbreaks have been reported in captive waterfowl from all flyways. Conceivably, DVE could cause a high mortality among wood ducks if conditions were favorable for its spread.

Newcastle Disease

Webster et al. (1976) isolated a paramyxovirus from wood ducks, mallards, and gadwalls shot during the 1974–1975 hunting season in Arkansas. The Newcastle disease virus also was isolated from wood ducks, mallards, and a Canada goose shot in Wisconsin during autumn of 1975 (Slemons and Easterday 1975). Although many species of waterfowl apparently are commonly infected with this virus (Wobeser 1981), the available evidence indicates that the Newcastle disease viral strains infecting wild waterfowl are not highly pathogenic.

BACTERIAL INFECTIONS

Bacteria and, in some instances, the toxins they produce are responsible for a variety of diseases that wood ducks may contract. The most prominent bacterial diseases are botulism and avian cholera, but *Salmonella* infections also have received much attention from waterfowl researchers. Stout and Cornwell (1976) surveyed nonhunting mortality of wild waterfowl, 1930–1964, and found that more waterfowl died from botulism than from all other natural losses combined. Besides botulism, hailstorms were the only nonhunting mortality factor that surpassed avian cholera as a decimating agent of wild waterfowl. Large losses of wood ducks to either botulism or avian cholera have not been documented. However, as with other diseases, most wood duck deaths from botulism or avian cholera go unnoticed.

Botulism

The anaerobic bacterium *Clostridium botulinum*—type C in most cases—is the agent responsible for botulism in waterfowl. Spores from this organism can be found in the soil throughout the wood duck's range (Wobeser 1981). The spores apparently are ingested by invertebrates, and when conditions are favorable the bacterium germinates, reproduces, and synthesizes toxin (the result of metabolic activities) within the invertebrate host. Botulism bacteria do not invade the tissues of birds that ingest infected insects; rather, toxins released by the bacteria through autolysis are absorbed in the duck's digestive system, resulting in a paralytic condition that is progressive in nature and varies with the amount of ingested toxin (Wobeser 1981).

The toxin in dead bird carcasses apparently remains very stable. Friend (1987: 89, 92) stated that "preformed toxin can be taken in by invertebrates, remain free in bottom sediments, or become suspended in the water column where it can serve as the source of winter and spring botulism outbreaks when ingested by feeding birds." Graham et al. (1978) noted that winter and spring (cold-weather) botulism may result from ingestion of invertebrates in which the toxin formed during an earlier warm period.

Hunter et al. (1970) and Friend (1987) reviewed conditions responsible for botulism outbreaks. Most botulism outbreaks occur in late summer and early autumn (July through September). The botulism bacterium grows best at temperatures of 25–30 degrees Celsius (77–86° F), and the optimal temperature for toxin production is 28 degrees Celsius (82° F) (Rosen 1971). Environmental factors such as flooding and drought that accompany hot weather and result in the death of invertebrates often provide the base from which a botulism epizootic begins. The bacterium continues to multiply and produce toxins in the carcasses of dead birds. Although fly larvae and other insects that feed on these carcasses ingest botulism bacteria, they are not killed by the toxin (Hunter et al. 1970). However, when ducks consume carrion-feeding insects and ingest the toxin, the birds usually die. Their carcasses serve, in turn, as substrates for additional fly larvae, effectively perpetuating an outbreak.

Although we lack conclusive evidence, botulism appears to have been responsible for the deaths of many wood ducks along Quiver Creek in Illinois (Table 185). Most of the sick birds exhibited the syndrome of botulism-poisoned wood ducks. Unfortunately, the symptoms are nonspecific. In a few instances, we apprehended sick birds and shipped them to the National Wildlife Health Laboratory in Madison, Wisconsin. Regrettably, our handling of the moribund wood ducks (providing drinking water, which may have diluted the toxin) precluded accurate testing. No pathogens were found in these specimens of good weight, suggesting that a toxin was the causative agent. There is a strong probability that botulism toxin is lethal at a lower level in wood ducks than in prairie-nesting ducks. Waterfowl that nest on the prairies have been exposed to the botulism bacteria over the millennia and therefore have had more time than wood ducks to evolve resistance to the disease.

In central Illinois, sick adult females were observed three times more frequently than were sick adult males (Table 185). In early spring, this sex-linked difference probably occurred because the spring breeding season diet of females is comprised principally of animal foods, whereas the diet of breeding males is dominated by plant matter. Because many males leave Quiver Creek after the dissolution of pair bonds to molt on nearby backwater lakes or undergo a molt migration, we were more likely to observe sick females than sick males throughout the summer months. Thus, the presence of proportionally more sick females in June, July, August, and September probably reflects variations in behavioral patterns rather than differences in food habits.

Regardless of the specific decimating agent(s), we know that since 1977 production and survival of wood ducks along Quiver Creek have been curtailed by disease. During the course of our field operations in 1977, 67 sick wood ducks were observed.

Within the last decade, conditions apparently have become favorable for the occurrence of a botulismlike disease along Quiver Creek. Without our constant surveillance and monitoring of the breeding population there would have been no indication of a disease problem. None of the landowners we know reported seeing sick or dead wood ducks on their property. As Bellrose (1976) indicated, sick ducks usually seek concealment in dense cover and their deaths go unnoticed; exceptions occur during epizootics. Although the behavior of diseased birds precludes precise mortality estimates, it appears that a proportion of the annual natural mortality experienced by wood ducks on Quiver Creek can be attributed to both direct and indirect effects of botulism.

Odom (1970) reported that botulism outbreaks occurred at the Piedmont National Wildlife Refuge in Georgia during the summers of 1968 and 1969 and that a number of young wood ducks succumbed to this disease. The opportunistic feeding on flies and their larvae by ducklings would seem to make them especially susceptible to poisoning during botulism outbreaks.

Forrester et al. (1980) reported that at least 26 wood ducks succumbed to a botulism epizootic during May and June 1979 in northern Florida. The esophagi and gizzards of three dead females discovered in artificial nest boxes and one drake found floating in shallow water all contained a large number of maggots. Apparently the birds were feeding on maggots that had become dislodged from decaying carcasses. As previously noted, female wood ducks are especially vulnerable to botulism during spring outbreaks because animal matter constitutes a considerable proportion of their diet at this time of

Table 185. Seasonal occurrence of sick male and female wood ducks observed along Quiver Creek, Illinois, 1977–89.

Year	Number of adults[a]															
	Mar		Apr		May		Jun		Jul		Aug		Sep		Oct	
	M	F	M	F	M	F	M	F	M	F	M	F	M	F	M	F
1977[b]																
1978										7	3	9	6	11		
1979[c]																
1980			3	3	1	2										
1981 (25)[d]					3	2	1	1				2		2		
1982 (7)				1	1	2	2	3	2	4		4		1		
1983 (8)		1	1	1	1	4	1	4		1						
1984		2	1	3		2										
1985[c]																
1986[c]																
1987 (6)	1	2	1	4	2	4	1	4		2		1				1
1988 (5)			2	3	4	6	3	4		2		4	1	4		1
1989 (11)						3	1	1								1
Total	1	5	8	15	12	25	9	17	2	16	3	20	7	18	0	3

[a] M = male; F = female.
[b] A total of 67 sick wood ducks was observed in 1977.
[c] No sick wood ducks were observed.
[d] Numbers in parentheses represent sick juvenile wood ducks.

the year (Drobney and Fredrickson 1979). However, botulism outbreaks usually occur in midsummer and early autumn (Hunter et al. 1970), when vegetable matter is the main component in the wood duck's diet.

We collected 28 wood ducks that had died of botulism at Rice Pond near Chillicothe, Illinois, from October 3 to 10, 1974. Gary Pearson used the mouse toxicity test to confirm that botulism poisoning was the cause of death. In this instance, wood ducks ingested toxic maggots that were feeding on carcasses of decaying fish. A total of 2,075 dead and moribund ducks were collected, of which 1.3 percent were wood ducks.

Another known incidence of botulism involving wood ducks occurred in late August 1981. Dying wood ducks were found in shallow backwater areas of the Illinois River near Banner, Illinois. Personnel at the National Wildlife Health Laboratory in Wisconsin determined that two of four moribund wood ducks tested positive for botulism.

An article that appeared in the Burlington, Iowa, *Daily Hawk-Eye Gazette* on July 29, 1939, informed the public that more than 100 wood ducks had been found dead on an island in the Mississippi River. The report suggested that the wood ducks had ingested botulism toxin when they consumed dead mayflies.

Because only a few reports confirm the deaths of wood ducks as a result of botulism, the importance of this disease as a natural mortality factor of wood ducks is difficult to estimate. Certainly the threat of botulism is most severe in the Pacific Flyway, where documented outbreaks have been prevalent. However, most of the wood duck population occurs within the Mississippi and Atlantic flyways, and it is likely that more wood ducks are lost to botulism in the eastern United States than throughout the Pacific Coast states.

Avian Cholera

Most species of birds, including waterfowl, are highly susceptible to avian cholera infections. This disease can spread rapidly through local populations, and large outbreaks frequently occur among waterfowl. However, only a few cases are known of wood ducks succumbing to avian cholera (Vaught et al. 1967, Rosen 1971). Apparently interspecific variations in susceptibility to avian cholera exist, but the degree of vulnerability can change from year to year (Rosen 1969). In general, all waterfowl are highly susceptible to this disease (Wobeser 1981).

Transmission of avian cholera occurs through contact between birds, ingestion of contaminated food or water, and possibly through inhaling bacteria in the aerosol created during landing and takeoff (Friend 1987). After the bacterium gains entrance, death can occur quickly (6–12 hours after exposure) and probably results from the release of endotoxins (Wobeser 1981, Friend 1987). The avian cholera bacterium, *Pasteurella multocida*, invades the circulatory system and infects the body organs of its host. Most avian cholera outbreaks have occurred in winter (Stout and Cornwell 1976), but losses occur at any time of the year.

New outbreaks of avian cholera can occur for months after an initial die-off. Friend (1987) referenced studies where researchers found this bacterium surviving in pond water three weeks after dead birds had been collected and in soil after four months. He also noted that avian cholera bacteria can live in dead bird carcasses for at least three months.

Vaught et al. (1967) believed that 48 wood ducks died as a result of avian cholera at Squaw Creek National Wildlife Refuge in Missouri in 1964. In addition to the wood ducks, 5,615 mallards, 23 American black ducks, 23 American wigeons, 38 green-winged teal, 1 northern pintail, and 1 canvasback were picked up. It was noted that 1,110 lesser snow and blue geese died overnight during the outbreak. Wobeser (1981) suggested that behavioral differences between species and population densities may result in varying degrees of exposure to the avian cholera bacterium. He also noted that avian cholera mortality can occur sporadically rather than as epizootics. At present there is little evidence to indicate that avian cholera has been a serious disease of wood ducks, but future avian cholera outbreaks could involve larger numbers of wood ducks.

Salmonellosis

Salmonellosis refers to infections caused by any of the microorganisms that belong to the genus *Salmonella*. These bacteria are commonly found in waterfowl but apparently seldom cause mortality (Wobeser 1981). All members of the genus (in excess of 1,200 serotypes) are considered potential pathogens. They generally infect the intestinal tract and may cause enteritis, diarrhea, septicemia, and death or simply live as commensals (Steele and Galton 1971).

Paratyphoid organisms (motile forms of salmonella that infect birds) can cause a serious disease in wild wood ducks that are raised under confined conditions in captivity (Levine and Graham 1942). Grice (1963) found that young woodie ducklings in Massachusetts occasionally were infected with *Salmonella* bacteria that caused omphalitis and paratyphoid.

Omphalitis may occur when the duckling's yolk sac is not completely absorbed prior to hatching, providing a site for infection by salmonella bacteria. Ducklings that contract omphalitis usually die within a few days after leaving the nest (Heusmann and Bellville 1982). Paratyphoid infections in young wood ducks can occur when bacteria are transmitted from the hen's ovaries (Heusmann and Bellville 1982) or when the bacteria are ingested (Levine and Graham 1942). In Massachusetts, Grice (1963) determined that the incidence of omphalitis and paratyphoid in wild wood ducks was minimal.

FUNGAL INFECTIONS

Aspergillosis is a well-known infectious, often pathogenic, fungal disease of waterfowl. The causative fungus, *Aspergillus fumigatus*, occurs ubiquitously in the soil (Bellrose 1976). Most waterfowl acquire aspergillosis when feeding on moldy grain. Spores, or conidia, are inhaled during feeding and the fungi subsequently colonize and attack the trachea and lungs of susceptible hosts.

Wobeser (1981) reported that aspergillosis generally is recognized as a sporadic disease of waterfowl. Because mortality often occurs at low levels, many deaths go unnoticed. Epizootics may appear when large numbers of birds feed on or near moldy grain. Bellrose et al. (1945) documented an outbreak of aspergillosis among wood ducks in Illinois. They found 89 dead wood ducks and estimated that

100–200 birds died after inhaling *Aspergillus* spores while feeding on moldy corn that had spilled from a storage bin. Duckling mortality from aspergillosis can occur when moldy straw is used as a base material in nest boxes (Friend 1987).

Davidson and Nettles (1977) found that an adult male wood duck collected in Louisiana on January 19, 1976, was infected with rhinosporidiosis. This fungal disease is caused by *Rhinosporidium seeberi* and usually occurs as an inflammatory nasal polyp (Wobeser 1981). Rhinosporidiosis is considered a rare disease in the United States, and based on reported cases few wood ducks are affected by it.

PARASITIC INFESTATIONS

Parasites are found in and on most wild animals, and the thorough examination of wood ducks probably would reveal one or several types of parasites. All of the 215 wood ducks collected from representative areas throughout the Atlantic Flyway by Thul et al. (1985) were infested with at least one species (average = 5.1 species per bird) of parasitic helminth (roundworms and flatworms). Moreover, 71 percent of these birds were infested with ectoparasites (mites, lice, or both) (Thul 1985). The mean number of parasitic species found on each wood

Table 186. Variation in the frequency of occurrence of hematozoal parasites in wood ducks from different geographical regions.

Area	Sample size	Prevalence	Percentage infested		
			Leucocytozoon	*Haemoproteus*	*Plasmodium*
Maritime provinces of Canada	51	29	14	20	6
Massachusetts	730	87	33	94	15
Maine	77	87	59	64	0
Maine	422	85	62	67	0
Wisconsin[a]	40		8		
Iowa	168[b]	46		46	
	68[c]	0			
Maine	13		69	85	0
Massachusetts	230		0.4	38	8
Vermont[d]	128[e]		0	14	2
Vermont[f]	198		0	24	1
New York	157		0	8	0
Ohio	35		3	43	0
Maryland	114		0	11	0
Maine	24	96	83	83	21
Vermont	10	30	0	20	0
Massachusetts	12	67	0	67	0
New York	12	50	0	50	0
New Jersey	12	58	0	58	0
Northwestern Pennsylvania	7	57	14	57	0
Southeastern Pennsylvania	3	100	0	100	0
Maryland	11	45	9	45	9
West Virginia	5	20	0	20	0
Virginia	12	33	0	33	0
Northeastern North Carolina	14	0	0	0	0
Westcentral North Carolina	12	0	0	0	0
South Carolina	17	0	0	0	0
Florida	62	2	0	0	0

[a] Only *L. simondi* recorded.
[b] Samples were collected from the Upper Mississippi River Wildlife and Fish Refuge, northeastern Iowa.
[c] Samples were collected from Union Slough National Wildlife Refuge, northcentral Iowa.
[d] For 1952.
[e] Trypanosomes were found in 1 percent of the birds.
[f] For 1953.

duck was 6.9 (Thul 1979). Ogburn-Cahoon (1979) reported that only 3 of the 235 wood ducks (1.3 percent) she examined from Louisiana contained no endoparasitic helminths. Age, sex, diet, habitat quality, population density, time of year, and geographical distribution are factors that influence the occurrence, type, intensity, and severity of parasitic infestations in or on individual wood ducks.

Wobeser (1981) noted that parasite infestations on waterfowl are so common as to be considered almost normal. Although some disease-causing organisms, by themselves or in combinations, are capable of causing death to wood ducks, most birds remain healthy throughout much of their lives despite being parasitized. Wood ducks commonly harbor between 25 and 50 intestinal helminths and remain in apparent good health (Drobney et al. 1983, Thul et al. 1985). Presumably the results of parasitism range from unapparent disease symptoms to rapid death. The wood duck's age and condition and the types and numbers of organisms infesting the bird dictate its fate.

Hematozoa

The wood duck is host to a variety of blood parasites. Its close association with shallow water and both woody and herbaceous vegetation brings it into contact with numerous potential vectors. Bennett et al. (1974) reported that wood ducks in Massachusetts experienced a significantly higher rate of hematozoal infestations than did American black ducks, mallards, blue-winged teal, and green-winged teal.

Numerous studies have determined the occurrence and types of blood parasites in wood ducks (Nelson and Gashwiler 1941, Mielcarek 1954, O'Meara 1956, Trainer et al. 1962, Roslien and Haugen 1964, Herman et al. 1971, Bennett et al. 1974, 1975, Thul et al. 1980). Three genera of protozoans (*Leucocytozoon*, *Haemoproteus*, and *Plasmodium*) and microfilarial nematodes are common inhabitants in the blood of many wood ducks (Table 186). Only a few cases of *Trypanosoma* (a protozoan) parasitism have been reported (Herman et al. 1971, Bennett et al. 1975).

The life cycles of the major protozoan blood parasites are basically similar. Each group of protozoans lives in the wood duck's tissues and blood cells and is transmitted by an arthropod vector. The parasites undergo sexual reproduction (sporogony) within an insect vector and multiply by asexual reproduction (schizogony) after being injected into a wood duck.

Adult birds are less likely than young ducklings to succumb to hematozoal infestations (O'Roke 1934), but any wood duck that survives an initial attack will become a chronic carrier. Herman (1968) reported that adult carrier ducks enter a latent period during which the parasites are restricted to internal organs; few of these parasites, if any, are found in the blood. However, some birds experience a relapse, and parasites from the initial infestation may again appear in the blood. In Massachusetts, Bennett et al. (1974) found that most infested wood ducks had entered a latent period by October and that relapses usually occurred before the ornithophilic black fly vectors emerged in spring.

Table 186. (continued)

Percentage infested

Microfilaria	Reference
2	Bennett et al. (1975)
7	Bennett et al. (1974)
38	Nelson and Gashwiler (1941)
22	O'Meara (1956)
	Trainer et al. (1962)
	Roslien and Haugen (1964)
0	Herman et al. (1971)
0	
0	
0	
0	
0	
0	
46	Thul et al. (1980)
20	
0	
0	
8	
43	
0	
9	
20	
0	
0	
0	
0	
2	

The prevalence rates (percentage of birds infested) of hematozoal infections within local wood duck populations are subject to complex sets of environmental interactions. The proportion of wood ducks from any geographical region that becomes infested with blood parasites depends on the presence of the parasite, the occurrence and density of suitable vectors, and the local density of wood ducks and other host species. Each factor is subject to seasonal and annual changes. Thul et al. (1980) found only 1 of 105 wood ducks infested with blood parasites in samples collected from North Carolina southward to Florida. In contrast, 58 percent (n = 63) of the wood ducks sampled from Virginia northward to Maine contained hematozoa. Thul et al. (1980) noted that some birds from every northern collection site contained hematozoa. Differences in temporal or geographical distribution or in numbers of appropriate vectors were believed to account for the differential infestation rates of wood ducks throughout the Atlantic Flyway.

Blood protozoans, primarily *Leucocytozoon simondi*, are an important cause of disease and mortality in young wood ducks in eastern Canada and the northcentral and northeastern United States. Thul et al. (1980) suggested that *L. simondi* probably limits production in Atlantic Flyway wood duck populations that occur north of 42 degrees north latitude. In Massachusetts, Bennett et al. (1974) came to a similar conclusion and suggested that hematozoa act as a potential limiting factor of waterfowl populations in areas where prevalence of infestations reaches at least 80 percent.

Although *L. simondi* can cause mortality in waterfowl, the significance of *Haemoproteus* and *Plasmodium* infestations is poorly understood. No information is available on the detrimental effects of multiple infestations. Thul et al. (1980) found immature wood ducks much more likely than adults to harbor two or more species of blood parasites.

Leucocytozoonosis. Birds are the only animals that are known to be susceptible to leucocytozoonosis (Cook 1971). The *Leucocytozoon* found in wood ducks *(L. simondi)* is transmitted by ornithophilic black flies (O'Roke 1934, Wobeser 1981), most notably *Simulium rugglesi* and *S. anatium* (Fallis et al. 1956, Barrow et al. 1968), and is believed to be the most pathogenic of the blood parasites infesting wood ducks (Bennett et al. 1974). Black flies acquire the infestation from birds that have survived the disease and continue to harbor the parasite. Infested black flies subsequently pass on the parasite when they draw blood from healthy wood ducks. Bennett et al. (1974) found that the prevalence of leucocytozoonosis in Massachusetts was bimodal—peaking in May and again in June.

The wood duck's age and condition influence the pathogenicity of leucocytozoonosis. Mortality is most likely to occur in young ducklings (O'Roke 1934, Fallis and Bennett 1966), and losses of adult birds are rare. The course of leucocytozoonosis in young ducklings is fairly rapid; birds that appear healthy one day may be dead the next (O'Roke 1934).

Wobeser (1981) presented a detailed review of the life cycle of *L. simondi*. Briefly, the sexual stages occur primarily in the bird's young red blood cells that are ingested by black flies. The protozoans subsequently reproduce within the fly's stomach, and resulting zygotes undergo a series of developmental changes terminating in motile sporozoites. Sporozoites eventually move to the salivary glands of an infested fly and subsequently are injected into a wood duck. Sporozoites multiply by schizogony within certain organs (primarily the spleen) and reticuloendothelial cells. After a one- to two-week period, merozoites escape into the bloodstream, penetrate red blood cells, and mature into male and female parasites. Destruction of red blood cells often results in anemia, the most obvious pathologic feature.

Leucocytozoonosis appears to be a fairly common disease of wood ducks in areas where habitat allows the black fly vector and the wood duck to come into contact. Obviously the range of transmission is controlled by distribution of the black fly. Wood ducks that nest in the New England states, especially Maine, are most likely to contract leucocytozoonosis (Table 186).

Haemoproteus. *Haemoproteus* sp. is known to parasitize birds and reptiles. *H. nettionis* is the most commonly found blood parasite infesting wood ducks (Table 186) and other species of North American waterfowl (Wobeser 1981). Biting midges (*Culicoides* sp.) are the only organisms known to transmit *H. nettionis* to waterfowl (Fallis and Wood 1957). Normally 14–21 days pass after a wood duck is bitten before *Haemoproteus* parasites occur in the blood (Wobeser 1981). Although this protozoan invades tissues and red blood cells, no known losses of wild waterfowl have been attributed to *Haemoproteus* parasitism (Wobeser 1981). Nevertheless, Thul (1979) considered *Haemoproteus* a potential pathogen of wood ducks because infections are known to cause mortality in other species of birds (Herman 1963).

Plasmodium. Similar to malaria transmission in humans, *Plasmodium* protozoans are transmitted to birds by mosquitoes. The most common species found parasitizing wood ducks are *P. circumflexum* and *P. relictum* (Mielcarek 1954, Herman et al. 1971, Bennett et al. 1974, Thul et al. 1980). Mosquitoes that belong to the genus *Culiseta*, primarily *C. morsi-*

tans, are known vectors of malaria to waterfowl (Meyer et al. 1974).

Little information is available on the effects of *Plasmodium* sp. on populations of wild waterfowl. Although *Plasmodium* is a relatively rare parasite of wood ducks, the prevalence rates found by Bennett et al. (1974) and Thul et al. (1980) suggest that *Plasmodium* protozoans may be important disease organisms in certain areas of the wood duck's range (Table 186). Thul (1979) suggested that, where prevalent, *Plasmodium* parasitism may limit the size of wood duck populations.

Filarial Worms

Blood-sucking insects are required to complete the life cycle of nematodes that are classified as filarial worms. Young of adult filarial worms are termed "microfilarial" and often are found in the peripheral blood of wood ducks that harbor adult filarial nematodes.

Filarial worms inhabit a variety of tissues and can cause varying degrees of damage. However, Wobeser (1981) reported that only a single species of filarial worm, *Sarconema eurycerca*, is known to be pathogenic to waterfowl. Seegar et al. (1976) discovered that a feather louse served as an intermediate host for this pathogenic filarial heartworm. *S. eurycerca* was found in 2.6 percent (n = 6) of the wood ducks examined by Ogburn-Cahoon (1979) in Louisiana.

A number of types of microfilaria have been found in the blood of wood ducks (Nelson and Gashwiler 1941, Anderson 1954). Microfilaria prevalence rates of 20–46 percent are common in wood ducks from New England states (Table 186). The lack of microfilaria from wood ducks in southern states suggests that appropriate vectors are absent (Thul et al. 1980). Bennett et al. (1975) believed that the microfilaria found in wood ducks from eastern Canada were transmitted by black flies. Although there is no indication that microfilaria harm their host per se, little is known about the significance of multiple hematozoal infections.

Sarcosporidiosis

Sarcocystis sp. are parasitic protozoans that produce muscle cysts in intermediate hosts such as waterfowl. Hunters often notice the wormlike macroscopic forms of these cysts in pectoral muscles of harvested waterfowl. The cysts form parallel to muscle fibers and resemble rice grains in appearance.

Sarcosporidiosis is a relatively common disease of dabbling ducks that belong to the genus *Anas* (the wood duck belongs to the genus *Aix*). Transmission of macroscopic *Sarcocystis* is believed to occur when waterfowl ingest eggs (oocysts) that were shed in the feces of definitive hosts (carnivores) (Friend 1987). Concentrations of birds that feed on land or in shallow water presumably have an increased chance of contracting this disease (Wobeser 1981).

Prevalence rates in adult dabbling ducks vary among species but generally are around 10 percent (Cornwell 1963, Hoppe 1976). Visible sarcocysts are rarely found in wood ducks, diving ducks, and juvenile dabbling ducks. Thul (1979) examined 215 wood ducks and detected no macroscopic sarcocysts. In-house reports by Bump (1939) and Cheatum (1952) of the New York State Conservation Department (now the New York Department of Environmental Conservation) documented the occurrence of sarcosporidiosis in wood ducks. We know of no other verified cases involving wood ducks.

There is little evidence to indicate that sarcosporidiosis directly causes mortality in waterfowl. However, heavy infestations are thought to weaken the host, making it more susceptible to other decimating agents (Bellrose 1976). Humans are not believed to be final hosts of the *Sarcocystis* parasites that infect waterfowl (Wobeser 1981, Friend 1987).

Ectoparasites

Like all other waterfowl, wood ducks are hosts to parasites on their feathers and body surface. Not every individual is infested, and the types of external parasites found on wood ducks vary with the bird's age, health, behavior, geographic location, and in some cases the time of year. Normal preening and bathing probably serve to remove and control ectoparasites. We suspect that a secondary function of mutual preening (allopreening) is the removal of bothersome ectoparasites. Molting also may reduce the number of ectoparasites on birds (Boyd 1951). Because waterfowl in good condition generally have few external parasites, Wobeser (1981) believed that other factors must act to weaken a bird before ectoparasite populations would increase. Large numbers of ectoparasites, however, lower the vitality of their host and may serve as indicators of poor health, and as vitality is lowered—by poor nutrition for example—ectoparasites increase.

In discussing external parasites of birds, Peters (1936: 10) wrote: "I believe it is possible for every kind of bird to have at least three kinds of lice, one or two hippoboscids (bird flies), and several mites, and that those birds feeding or alighting on the ground may carry one or more kinds of ticks." Mites (Acari) and biting lice (Mallophaga) are common inhabitants of the skin and plumage of wood ducks (Thul 1985). Insects such as black flies, mosquitoes, and biting midges that remain on wood ducks only long enough to obtain a blood meal are ectoparasites because they derive essential nutrients from a living host (Welty 1979, Wobeser 1981). Many of these blood-sucking insects serve as vectors of infectious diseases. Other important ectoparasites that probably occur incidentally on woodies include fleas, ticks, chiggers, and leeches.

At least seven genera (representing 10 species) of lice are known to occur on wood ducks (Table 187). Biting lice normally live their entire lives on the host and are usually found clinging to feathers (Boyd 1951). Although feather lice are not considered to be effective vectors of disease organisms, one species, *Trinoton anserinum*, acts as an intermediate host for a pathogenic nematode heartworm found in wood ducks (Seegar et al. 1976, Ogburn-Cahoon 1979). Most lice are transmitted to new hosts when wood ducks come into contact with one another.

Although little if any harm results when biting lice are few in number, severe effects may result from heavy infestations. The mouth parts of Mallophagan parasites are adapted for chewing on pieces of epithelial material (Beer 1970). Most species of biting lice eat feather fragments, the protective sheaths of growing feathers, down feathers, scabs, pieces of epidermal material, and, on rare occasions, blood. A louse species, *Trinoton querquedulae*, that regularly feeds on blood was recovered from 10 percent (n = 21) of the wood ducks examined by Thul (1979). He indicated that heavy infestations may result in irritation or bare patches of skin and anemia.

Thul (1985) found five species of mites living on wood ducks that were collected from areas dispersed throughout the Atlantic Flyway (Table 187). Four of the five species occurred on the plumage, and one species (*Rhinonyssus rhinolethrum*) inhabited the nasal cavity. Wobeser (1981) noted that nasal mites are potentially pathogenic to waterfowl. Similar to biting lice, feather mites probably spend their entire life cycle on the wood duck and are transmitted by contact.

Populations of mites and lice on wood ducks are variable and little affected by seasonal changes. Thul (1985) found no ectoparasites on 29 percent (n = 62) of the 215 woodies he examined. From one to five species (average = 2) of mites and lice occurred on the remaining 153 birds (71 percent). Lice occurred on 54 percent (n = 116) and mites on 46 percent (n = 99) of the 215 wood ducks. Sixty birds (28 percent) served as hosts for mites and lice.

Immature wood ducks apparently are more susceptible to biting lice and mite parasitism than are adult birds. Mites and lice were found on 50 percent and 71 percent, respectively, of the immature wood ducks (n = 100) examined by Thul (1985). In contrast, only 30 percent and 50 percent, respectively, of adult birds (n = 115) were infested. Male and female woodies of each age class were parasitized at similar rates.

Table 187. External parasites that have been found on wood ducks.

Group	Reference
Mallophaga (biting lice)	
Anaticola crassicornis	Stewart (1957), Thul (1985)
A. lepidotus	Malcomson (1960)
Anatoecus dentatus	Peters (1936), Malcomson (1960), Thul (1985)
Esthiopterum crassicorne	Peters (1936)
Holomenopon clauseni	Thul (1985)
H. loomisii	Peters (1936)
Menacanthus sp.	Stewart (1957)
Menopon gallinae	Stewart (1957)
Trinoton querquedulae	Thul (1985)
Acari (mites)	
Chenophila sp.	Johnston and Kethley (1973)
Haemophysalis choredelis	Keirans (1967)
Ingrassia sp.	Thul (1985)
Rhinonyssus rhinolethrum	Pence (1972), Thul (1985)
Freyana largifolia	Thul (1985)
Bdellorhynchus sp.	Thul (1985)
Rectijanua sp.	Thul (1985)

The wood duck's association with woodland habitats brings it into contact with a variety of other ectoparasites. The occurrence of fleas and ticks on other species of waterfowl (Wobeser 1981) suggests that wood ducks may be susceptible to parasitism by these organisms. Benton and Shatrau (1965) reported that bird fleas commonly are found in the nests of hole-nesting species. Moreover, fleas are common ectoparasites of squirrels and frequently are found in their nests and dens (Allen 1943). Because many of the fleas that are associated with mammal nests usually are found infesting birds that use similar nesting sites (Turner 1971), some female woodies undoubtedly are parasitized by fleas during the nesting season.

Helminths

A wide assortment of trematodes (flukes), cestodes (tapeworms), and nematodes (roundworms) and a few acanthocephalans (thorny-headed worms) have been recovered from wood ducks (tables 188–190). Thul (1979) presented a detailed list that included historical records of known wood duck helminth parasites. Many of the species were recovered from birds that had died in foreign zoological parks and are not included in tables 188–190. Although some species of parasitic helminths are transmitted directly from one wood duck to another, others require one or more alternate hosts to complete their development. Several helminth species have larvae that actively infest wood ducks by penetrating the skin of their feet or legs. However, most wood ducks acquire parasitic worms when they ingest eggs or larvae that occur on vegetation or inside intermediate (usually invertebrate) hosts.

In comparison with many other waterfowl species, wood ducks harbor, on average, a relatively low number of parasitic helminths. Thul et al. (1985) recorded a relative density (mean number of parasites per host examined) of 47.9 helminths from 215 wood ducks collected throughout the Atlantic Flyway. In southeastern Missouri, Drobney et al. (1983) found an average density of 14 helminths among 155 wood ducks. In contrast, Crichton and Welch (1972) reported helminth densities of 191 for mallards and 80 for northern pintails collected from the Delta Marsh in Manitoba. Apparently the wood duck's food habits, feeding behavior, and association with woodland habitats reduce its chances of becoming parasitized by helminths (Drobney et al. 1983).

In general, small numbers of parasitic worms do not appear to harm their hosts, but large numbers often cause emaciation and may lead to death. Cornwell and Cowan (1963), however, pointed out that relatively small numbers of those helminths that destroy tissue can cause direct mortality in waterfowl.

Intestinal worms often are pathogenic, causing enteritis and diarrhea. Schistosomes (blood flukes) commonly cause chronic enteritis and ureteritis because their eggs must pass through blood vessels and then the walls of either the urinary or digestive tract before reaching the lumen (Wobeser 1981). Inflammation of other body organs often results when they are attacked by parasitic helminths or when blood flow is obscured by the presence of adult worms, helminth eggs, or both in capillaries and other blood vessels.

Many factors, of course, interact to determine the numbers and types of parasitic worms that occur in a given wood duck. The bird's age and sex, along with the size of the initial infestation, occurrence of other parasite species, occurrence and density of host species, climatic conditions, presence of suitable intermediate hosts, nutrition, and geographic location are some variables that regulate the prevalence and intensity of helminth infestations. Hence, the helminth community within a given wood duck and throughout local populations of woodies changes with time and location.

Three detailed studies have been made of the helminth communities in wood ducks: Ogburn-Cahoon (1979) examined 235 wood ducks collected in Louisiana, August–February; Drobney et al. (1983) documented the intestinal helminth fauna of 155 wood ducks collected during spring (March–May) and autumn (September–October) courtship periods in southeastern Missouri; and Thul et al. (1985) determined regional differences among helminth communities in 215 wood ducks collected throughout the Atlantic Flyway, May–October. Little is known about the helminth communities in wood ducks from northern parts of the Mississippi Flyway and throughout the entire Pacific and Central flyways.

In Louisiana, Ogburn-Cahoon (1979) recorded 33 species of helminths (12 trematodes, 4 cestodes, and 17 nematodes) from wood ducks collected during autumn and winter. Parasitic helminths were recovered from 98.7 percent (n = 232) of 235 examined birds. The mean level of infestation by specific helminths was similar to the level Drobney et al. (1983) found and ranged from 1 to 55.8 worms per bird.

Seven species of cestodes and four species of trematodes were recovered from the wood ducks examined by Drobney et al. (1983). The prevalence of infestation (percentage of birds infected) was

Table 188. Nematodes that have been found parasitizing wood ducks.

Species	Location in host[a]	Prevalence[b]	Intensity of infestation		Reference[b]
			Mean	Range	
Acuaria uncinata					A
Alifilaria pseudolabiata	6	2(D)	1.2	1–2	D
Amidostomum acutum	7	84(C)	5.7	1–47	B, C, D
		79(D)	8.7	1–56	
A. anseris	7				B
Aproctella stoddardi	5, 8	<1(C)	1.5	1–2	C, D
		4(D)	2.0	1–6	
Capillaria anatis	2, 3	2(C)	1.4	1–2	B, C, D
		5(D)	1.8	1–4	
C. contorta	9	21(C)	3.7	1–19	C, D
		14(D)	2.9	1–34	
C. exilis	2				B
C. longifila	2				B
C. obsignata	2	3(C)	1.3	1–2	C
C. spinulosa	2, 3	1(C)	1.3	1–2	C, D
		7(D)	2.4	1–6	
Contracaecum spiculigerum	2	2(D)	1.2	1–2	D
Cyathostoma bronchialis	10	1(D)	2.0	1–3	D
Echinuria uncinata	1	2(D)	6.5	3–9	D
Epomidiostomum uncinatum	7	1(D)	1.5	1–2	D
Hadjelia sp.	7	<1(C)	1.0		C
H. neglecta	1, 7	7(D)	1.8	1–6	D
Heterakis caudata					A
H. circumvalata					A
H. dispar					A
Hystrichis tricolor	7	<1(D)	1.0		D
Ingliseria sp.	7	<1(C)	1.0		C
Porrocaecum crassum	2	<1(C)	1.0		B, C
Sarconema eurycerca	8, 11	3(C)	1.5	1–2	C
Splendidofilaria sp.	8	<1(C)	1.0		C
Streptocara sp.	7	<1(C)	1.0		C, D
		1(D)	1.0		
S. crassicauda	7	<1(D)	1.0		D
Strongyloides sp.	2, 3, 4	2(C)	5.8	2–8	C, D
		7(D)	6.7	1–21	
Synhimantus sp.	7	<1(C)	3.0		C
Tetrameres crami	1				B
T. fissispina	1	1(C)	1.0		C, D, E
		8(D)	2.7	1–8	
T. galericulata	1	26(C)	5.6	1–55	C, D, E
		20(D)	10.3	1–128	
T. ryjikovi	1	6(D)	2.1	1–8	D, E
T. sponsae	1	41(C)	6.4	1–95	C, D, E
		63(D)	8.5	1–66	
T. striata	1	<1(D)	36.0		D

[a] Location in host: 1 = proventriculus; 2 = intestine; 3 = cecum; 4 = liver; 5 = body cavity; 6 = subcutaneous; 7 = gizzard; 8 = air sacs; 9 = esophagus; 10 = trachea; 11 = heart.

[b] Reported by: A = Lapage (1961); B = McDonald (1969); C = Ogburn-Cahoon (1979); D = Thul et al. (1985); E = Mollhagen (1976).

relatively low, with intestinal parasites occurring in only 37 percent (n = 57) of 155 birds. If tissues in addition to the alimentary tract had been examined, the prevalence would undoubtedly have been higher (Ogburn-Cahoon 1979, Thul et al. 1985). Although infested birds harbored up to seven parasite species, most of the birds contained only one (57 percent) or two (19 percent) species. The mean intensity (mean number of parasites per infested host) of infestation by each parasite ranged from 1.2 to 59.6 worms per wood duck.

Thul et al. (1985) recovered 42 helminth species (15 trematodes, 6 cestodes, 20 nematodes, and 1 acanthocephalan) from wood ducks collected in 12 states of the Atlantic Flyway. The prevalence of infestation—100 percent—was similar to that found by

Table 189. Trematodes that have been found parasitizing wood ducks.

Species	Location in host[a]	Prevalence[b]	Intensity of infestation		Reference[b]
			Mean	Range	
Apatemon gracilis	2	29(E)	6.0	1–27	E, F, G
		27(F)	8.2	1–72	
Amphimerus speciosus	4	1(E)	7.0	4–10	E
Dendritobilharzia pulverulenta	5	6(E)	1.2	1–2	E, F
		5(F)	1.8	1–3	
Distomum delicatulum					B
Echinoparyphium recurvatum	2	6(A)	26.0		A, C, E, F
		8(E)	6.4	1–60	
		9(F)	12.2	1–92	
Echinostoma revolutum	2	3(A)	2.0		A, C, E, F
		9(E)	2.5	1–10	
		13(F)	5.1	1–44	
Eucotyle warreni	8	1(F)	3.0	2–4	F
Maritrema sp.	2	2(F)	3.4	1–9	F
Notocotylus attenuatus	2	6(A)	3.7		A, C
N. imbricatus	3				C
N. urbanesis	2, 3	22(E)	12.8	1–110	B, E, F
		33(F)	22.8	1–519	
Prosthogonimus cuneatus	2	18(D)		15–55	D
P. ovatus	6, 7, 9	6(E)	1.5	1–6	E, F
Psilochasmus oxyurus	2	15(F)	6.0	1–23	
Psilotrema simillimum	2	<1(F)	1.0		F
Psilostomum sp.	2	7(E)	24.6	1–93	E
		2(E)	55.8	1–182	E, F
Ribeiroia ondantrae	1, 2	13(F)	11.4	1–93	
		<1(E)	9.0		E, F
Sphaeridiotrema globulus	2	10(F)	26.3	1–133	
Stephanoprora denticulata	2	2(F)	54.2	1–194	F
Trichobilharzia sp.	5				C
T. ocellata	5	48(F)	19.5	1–292	F
Typhlocoelum cucumerinum	10	20(E)		1–250 +	E
Zygocotyle lunata	3	1(F)	5.7	1–15	F
		3(A)	1.5		A, D, E, F
		11(E)	1.5	1–3	
		24(F)	2.7	1–8	

[a] Location in host: 1 = proventriculus; 2 = intestine; 3 = cecum; 4 = liver; 5 = blood vessels; 6 = bursa of Fabricius; 7 = oviduct; 8 = kidneys; 9 = cloaca; 10 = body cavity.
[b] Reported by: A = Drobney et al. (1983); B = Lapage (1961); C = McDonald (1969); D = McLaughlin and Burt (1979); E = Ogburn-Cahoon (1979); F = Thul et al. (1985); G = Palmieri (1973).

Ogburn-Cahoon (1979) in Louisiana. Wood ducks harbored from 1 to 14 species of helminths. Most birds (88 percent) contained multiple infestations of two to seven helminth species, with an average of five species per bird. Helminths occurred at mean intensities that ranged from 1 to 542 and averaged 47.9.

Substantial differences in the composition of endoparasite fauna of wood ducks collected from the northern (Maine through Virginia) and southern (North Carolina through Florida) portions of the Atlantic Flyway were found by Thul et al. (1985). Birds from the northern portion harbored 44 species of helminths—10 more than the number of species recovered from southern birds. Although northern wood ducks contained a higher average number of helminth species in comparison with southern birds (5.8 versus 4.5), slightly higher relative densities were recovered from the southern wood ducks (46.7 versus 49.2 worms per bird).

Nematodes (roundworms). Nematode parasites are the most common helminths infesting wood ducks. Adult roundworms often inhabit specific areas of the digestive tract but may be found in almost any body organ (Table 188). Wood ducks are known hosts to at least 35 species of nematodes (Table 188).

Nematode prevalence rates of 94 percent recorded by Ogburn-Cahoon (1979) and 96 percent by Thul et al. (1985) indicated that nearly every wood duck from the investigators' respective study areas was infected with roundworms. In Louisiana, wood

Table 190. Cestodes that have been found parasitizing wood ducks.

Species	Location in host[a]	Prevalence[b]	Intensity of infestation		Reference[b]
			Mean	Range	
Cloacotaenia megalops	3	2(D)	1.2	1–2	D
Diorchis bulbodes	1	3(A)	20.6		A, C, D, E
		3(C)	5.0	2–8	
		15(D)	6.0	1–53	
Dicranotaenia sp.	1	16(A)	1.8		A
D. coronula	1	9(C)	4.5	1–29	C
Fimbriaria fasciolaris	1, 2	12(A)	59.6		A, B, D
		1(D)	2.7	1–6	
Hymenolepis anceps					E
H. hopkinsi	1	9(B)	53.0		B
H. mayhewi					E
H. sp.	2	12(D)	1.9	1–10	D, E
Microsomacanthus paracompressa	1	12(C)	2.8	1–16	C
M. sp.	1	3(A)	4.2		A, D
		7(D)	3.8	1–18	
Nadejdolepis sp.	1	10(A)	4.7		A
Sobolevicanthus sp.	1	3(A)	10.4		A, C, D
		5(C)	4.3	1–9	
		17(D)	16.4	1–206	
S. gracilis	1	27(B)		1–3	B

[a] Location in host: 1 = intestine; 2 = cecum; 3 = cloaca.
[b] Reported by: A = Drobney et al. (1983); B = McLaughlin and Burt (1979); C = Ogburn-Cahoon (1979); D = Thul et al. (1985); E = Schiller (1951).

ducks harbored an average of 2 (range = 1–6) species and exhibited a mean intensity of 5.4 (range = 1–95) worms per bird (Ogburn-Cahoon 1979). Thul et al. (1985) found that wood ducks in the Atlantic Flyway were infested with an average of 2.6 (range = 1–7) nematode species and harbored a mean intensity of 16.9 (range = 1–128) individual roundworms.

Trematodes (flukes). Trematodes are encountered in wood ducks almost as often as nematodes and usually at higher intensities. More than 20 species of trematodes have been recovered from wood ducks (Table 189). Ogburn-Cahoon (1979) and Thul et al. (1985) reported prevalences of trematode infestation in wood ducks as 69 percent and 88 percent, respectively. Parasitized wood ducks contained an average of approximately two trematode species (Ogburn-Cahoon 1979, Thul et al. 1985)—a number similar to that of nematode species in woodies. A mean intensity of 9.6 (range = 1–250 +) and 31.2 (range = 1–519) individual flukes were recovered from the wood ducks examined by Ogburn-Cahoon (1979) and Thul et al. (1985), respectively.

Cestodes (tapeworms). Cestodes generally occur at low prevalences and mean intensities in wood ducks (Table 190). Most tapeworms are found in the small intestine, and they seldom attack other tissues. Ogburn-Cahoon (1979) found that parasitized wood ducks in Louisiana harbored an average of 1.1 (range = 1–2) tapeworm species and contained a mean of 3.9 (range = 1–29) individual cestodes. As with nematode and trematode infestations, wood ducks collected from the Atlantic Flyway by Thul et al. (1985) harbored greater cestode burdens than did those woodies collected in Louisiana. Wood ducks from the Atlantic Flyway contained a mean of 1.3 (range = 1–4) tapeworm species per infested bird. The mean intensity of infestation ranged from 1 to 206 and averaged 9.2 cestodes per bird (Thul et al. 1985).

Acanthocephalans (thorny-headed worms). Apparently acanthocephalans are rare parasites of wood ducks. No thorny-headed worms were recovered from the 235 wood ducks examined by Ogburn-Cahoon (1979). Thul et al. (1985) encountered only one species, *Polymorphus minutus*, in 1.4 percent of the wood ducks they collected. Adult worms were found in the small intestine. Infested wood ducks contained an average of 3.7 worms per bird. The thornlike hooks that occur on the proboscis of these worms cause damage to the host's intestinal epithelium.

Effects of Age and Sex

In general, relatively few differences in the helminth faunas of male and female wood ducks occur outside of the spring breeding season. Of the 33 species of helminths recovered by Ogburn-Cahoon (1979), only five exhibited a significantly greater (P<0.05) prevalence in one sex. Just one of the 42 species of helminths found by Thul et al. (1985) displayed a significantly different (P<0.05) prevalence between sexes. Similarly, Ogburn-Cahoon (1979) and Thul et al. (1985) reported that only one and three helminth species, respectively, occurred at significantly higher (P<0.05) intensities in one sex. However, in southeastern Missouri, Drobney et al. (1983) found significantly greater (P<0.05) prevalences and relative densities of helminth infections in female wood ducks than in males. They recovered intestinal parasites from 49 percent (n=39) of the examined females, and each bird harbored an average of 20.9 helminths. In comparison, only 31 percent (n=23) of the males contained intestinal parasites, and each bird harbored an average of 1.1 worms per bird. The varying diets of breeding males and females may have been responsible for the sex-related differences in helminth infestations.

The fact that most parasitic helminths recovered from wood ducks during the postbreeding season are found in a similar proportion of male and female birds and occur in similar intensities within their hosts suggests that both hen and drake woodies consume essentially the same foods, frequent similar habitats, and probably exhibit little immunological difference.

Although a few helminth species occasionally are found more often, at higher densities, or both within specific age classes of wood ducks, adult and immature woodies generally harbor similar helminth faunas (Ogburn-Cahoon 1979, Thul et al. 1985). In certain cases, adults may exhibit a higher prevalence of infestation because the major period of exposure to parasitic larvae occurs before many ducklings hatch. Morphological, immunological, and dietary differences may account for some of the other minor variations of helminth infestations that occur between age groups.

Effects of Season

Substantial variations in the helminth communities of local and regional wood duck populations occur over time (Ogburn-Cahoon 1979, Drobney et al. 1983). Physiological changes in the wood duck, the stress of migration, changes in diet and feeding behavior, variations in the seasonal occurrence of intermediate hosts, and the loss of short-lived adult parasites are factors that may contribute to the natural loss of helminths (Buscher 1965, McLaughlin and Burt 1973).

In Missouri, Drobney et al. (1983) found that the prevalence and relative density of helminth infestations in male and female wood ducks were significantly higher (P<0.05) during the spring breeding season than during the autumn courtship period. Whereas 58 percent of all females and 38 percent of all males examined during spring contained intestinal helminths, only 20 percent of the females and 10 percent of the males examined during autumn were found to be parasitized. Similarly, the relative density of helminths in females and males decreased from 26.2 to 5.2 and from 1.2 to 0.2, respectively, between spring and autumn.

Because breeding female wood ducks consume considerably more invertebrates than males do (Drobney and Fredrickson 1979), hens are believed to have an increased chance of ingesting infested intermediate hosts. Similarly, the dietary shift from predominantly animal foods to predominantly plant foods by postbreeding females tends to reduce their chances of consuming parasitic larvae and results in autumn parasitism rates lower than those of spring.

Although drakes exhibit little seasonal variation in the amounts of plant and animal matter that they ingest (Drobney and Fredrickson 1979), Drobney et al. (1983) determined that the relative density and prevalence of helminth infestations in males were significantly greater (P<0.01) in spring than in autumn. Drakes consume primarily aquatic and aquatic-associated invertebrates during spring and terrestrial insects during autumn. Apparently, most of the helminths that parasitize wood ducks use aquatic invertebrates as intermediate hosts (McDonald 1969), hence the increased parasitism of drakes in spring.

The helminth community of breeding females varies dramatically in relation to their physiological condition. Drobney et al. (1983) noted that the prevalence (20 percent versus 80 percent) and relative density (<1 to 59) of helminths increased significantly (P<0.005) between the prelaying and laying periods. The increased level occurred concurrently with a dietary shift to principally animal foods by laying woodie hens. No differences (P>0.05) in the prevalence and relative density of helminth infestations occurred from laying to incubating hens. Interestingly, most of the intestinal parasites acquired by breeding females were lost by the time autumn courtship was initiated. The relative density and prevalence of infestation were essentially unchanged between autumn courtship and prelaying, indicating that few new infestations occurred during winter. The diet of postbreeding and prebreeding females (primarily plant foods) apparently reduces the chances of incurring new helminth infestations and assists in eliminating old infestations.

METALLIC POISONING

Lead, mercury, copper, zinc, cadmium, and vanadium are recognized as environmental contaminants and as toxicants for waterfowl (Wobeser 1981). Although these metals occur naturally, industrial, recreational, and agricultural activities often expose plants and animals to abnormally high concentrations. Mine wastes, industrial plant discharges, hunting activity, and agricultural seeds treated with metal-based dressings are major sources of metallic poisoning. A few wood ducks probably die each year because they ingest foods that are contaminated with poisonous metal. However, consumption of spent lead-shot pellets has been by far the most significant factor in the metallic poisoning of wood ducks.

Lead poisoning has caused the deaths of millions of waterfowl during this century. Spent lead-shot pellets are deposited by hunters and other shooters in many of the favored wetland feeding areas of waterfowl. Waterfowl ingest this shot along with seeds and benthic organisms during feeding activities.

Digestive juices, along with abrasive grit, combine to dissolve and erode lead pellets that enter the gizzard, resulting in the formation of soluble lead salts. These salts pass into the digestive tract and are subsequently absorbed into the bloodstream, where they produce an anemic condition in waterfowl (Bellrose 1975).

Food habits and feeding behaviors influence the susceptibility of a waterfowl species to lead poisoning. The bird's size, age, and sex, along with the number of ingested shot pellets and the volume and types of foods consumed, are important factors that regulate the severity of lead toxicity (Bellrose 1964a).

Although a single lead pellet can be fatal, waterfowl that ingest only one or two pellets usually live (Bellrose 1959, Sanderson and Bellrose 1986). Of the wood duck gizzards examined by Bellrose (1959) that contained ingested shot, none contained more than two pellets. Because wood ducks primarily consume food that is located on or above the water surface (Drobney and Fredrickson 1979), they are less likely to ingest lead pellets than are species such as the mallard and northern pintail, which

feed by sifting through the bottom mud.

As expected, wood ducks exhibit a relatively low shot ingestion rate in comparison with many other North American waterfowl species. Bellrose (1959) determined that 1.6 percent of 379 wood ducks collected during hunting seasons had ingested shot. This low rate contrasted markedly with ingestion levels for mallards (6.8 percent), American black ducks (8.3 percent), northern pintails (8.9 percent), redheads (13.6 percent), ring-necked ducks (14.2 percent), canvasbacks (11.8 percent), lesser scaups (13.1 percent), and ruddy ducks (5.4 percent). Sanderson and Bellrose (1986) reviewed accounts of lead poisoning reported between 1973 and 1984 and noted that the ingestion rate of lead and steel pellets in wood ducks ranged from 0 to 4.5 percent, with an average of 2.2 percent. The results of these recent studies supported the earlier findings of Bellrose (1959) and indicated that during the hunting season, wood ducks exhibited one of the lowest rates of ingested shot of all North American waterfowl.

Researchers, however, must recognize that considerably more than 2–4 percent of the continental wood duck population ingests lead pellets during the course of a year. Each bird that consumes a lead pellet will either die, excrete the pellet, or erode it to an undetectable particle within 20 days after ingestion (Sanderson and Bellrose 1986). Thus, throughout much of autumn and winter, approximately 2–4 percent of the wood duck population ingests lead pellets every 20 days. Like other species of waterfowl, wood ducks continue to consume lead-shot pellets after the hunting season ends. Because most of the wood duck's breeding grounds are in areas that receive heavy hunting pressure, woodies are exposed to lead poisoning for a longer period than are waterfowl that spend six months on northern wetlands where hunting is light.

SUMMARY

Parasites and diseases are important mortality factors of wood ducks. Generally, the vitality of an infected wood duck declines as its parasite fauna increases. Before an individual woodie succumbs to parasites and/or diseases, a predator usually strikes, removing all evidence of the diseased bird.

The large number of sick wood ducks that we observed on Quiver Creek were almost all sufficiently viable to escape our efforts at capture; yet none were found dead and only a few were found in a helpless state. Apparently as the sick woodies became more moribund, predators captured and consumed them. If their moribund state had continued toward termination, there should have been a point of helplessness permitting us to capture more specimens or find carcasses.

Unless there is a large local die-off, most wood ducks whose vitality is decreased by disease become victims of predation. Finding a duck carcass in the wild is a rarity except where large local losses occur and victims die at a rate faster than predators and scavengers can consume them. From the large natural losses that ensue in wood duck populations during the course of a year (see Chapter 18), it is evident that disease—from parasites and viral and bacterial infections—provides the agent that so methodically operates at such a high level of mortality.

Population Dynamics

The abundance of wood ducks over an extensive region is largely determined by the relationship between the production of flying young and the mortality that occurs after fledging. In addition, local breeding populations are affected by immigration and emigration, as a large proportion of males and a modest proportion of juvenile females may shift to new breeding habitats (see Chapter 4). But only a few wood ducks, largely males, emigrate so far as to leave one flyway for another. Therefore, we are most concerned with the effect of changes in annual recruitment and survival rates on the subsequent size of local or regional breeding populations of wood ducks.

Female wood ducks typically begin nesting when one year old. Because many yearling females return to nest near their natal areas, those hatched locally become the primary source of new breeders for that area. One way to evaluate the effect of recruitment on local population size is to measure yearly change in the size of breeding populations. The size of a discrete population theoretically decreases when the previous year's recruitment is too low to offset mortality associated with that spatial and temporal parameter. On the other hand, when nest success and brood survival are more than adequate, a discrete population theoretically increases to the limit imposed by the food base and the availability of nest sites.

In our earlier discussions of the changing status of the wood duck (see Chapter 5), evidence was presented that autumn numbers in both eastern flyways increased dramatically from 1959 through 1985. During the last 10 years, however, the rate of increase appears to be slowing. The overall population growth during this period provides convincing evidence that regional reproductive rates have more than offset mortality rates. Nevertheless, the rate of increase has varied from year to year. Annual changes in recruitment and survival relate to changes in habitat quality, variations in weather and water levels, and losses due to hunting. By evaluating annual changes in recruitment and survival rates, we may be able to ascertain their effect in determining annual populations. Our recruitment rates were derived from an analysis of age ratios of wings that were solicited by mail from randomly selected hunters and submitted to the U.S. Fish and Wildlife Service. Species, sex, and age (i.e., adult or immature) of ducks are identified by biologists who examine the wings at annual "wing bees" held in January in each of the four flyways. Survival estimates were obtained from an analysis of banding and recovery data tapes supplied by the Bird Banding Laboratory, U.S. Fish and Wildlife Service.

EFFECT OF REPRODUCTIVE RATES

Recruitment rate, as measured by the ratio of immatures to adults in autumn wood duck populations, is dependent on nest success and brood survival during the previous summer. Unfortunately, there is very little information on nest success in natural cavities, where perhaps 90 percent or more of the wood ducks nest (Bellrose 1990). Data on success rates in nest houses are not applicable per se to regional or flyway reproductive rates because density and predator-deterrent devices alter the fate of nests. Nevertheless, nest success in artificial nest houses provides the only long-term data obtainable for indirectly evaluating the recruitment rate of young to the status of the subsequent breeding population.

Since 1961, "wing bees" have been held annually in each flyway, coordinated by the U.S. Fish and Wildlife Service as part of its Waterfowl Harvest Survey. Each year before the hunting season, a random selection of licensed waterfowl hunters throughout the United States is asked to send in a wing from each duck and tail feathers from each goose they harvest. Hunters also report when and where each bird was harvested. Technicians at each of four collection sites separate the submitted wings by species and record the time and location of harvest. At the wing bees in late winter, state and federal biologists examine a sample of about 77,000 duck wings and 13,000 goose tails from the four flyways to determine the sex and age of waterfowl harvested by the Survey participants. These data then are collated with geographic and chronologic information, which together provide estimates on total harvest. Since 1980, waterfowl hunters participating in the Survey have sent in wings from about 8,000 wood ducks annually, of which 85 percent were harvested in the Atlantic and Mississippi flyways. Hunters in the Survey have harvested wood ducks in all states except Alaska and Hawaii. Nationwide, the wood duck harvest, as a percentage of the total duck harvest, has increased from about 6 percent in the 1960s to about 11 percent in the 1980s. The supervising biologist (standing) in the photo is Sam Carney of the U.S. Fish and Wildlife Service, who pioneered the use of wing markings to identify the species, sex, and age of ducks. *Photo by David Dolton; courtesy of the U.S. Fish and Wildlife Service.*

In order to appraise the effect of recruitment on populations, we examined (1) the level of nest success that is necessary to maintain several discrete breeding populations and (2) the rate of change in breeding abundance that followed a change in nest success rates. We therefore compared the rate of nest success one year with the change in proportion of newly banded incubating birds the following year (Figure 115). In addition, for a different data set, we compared the rate of nest success with the percentage change in nest house use the following year (figures 116 and 117, Table 191).

Table 191. Relationship between wood duck nest success in nest houses and nest house use the following year during three periods at the Chautauqua National Wildlife Refuge in Mason County, Illinois. The coefficient of determination and slope within each period also are given.

Period	Number of nests per year	Percentage successful		Percentage of nest house use the following year				
		Mean	S.E.	Mean	S.E.	r^2	b^a	P^b
1939–45	102	33.9	0.52	48.8	0.75	0.563	2.34	<0.001
1950–61	15	68.6	1.78	10.8	0.60	0.017	0.01	>0.10
1965–87	64	79.1	0.26	39.0	0.62	0.0001	0.07	>0.10

[a] b = average change in population size given a 1-percent change in nesting success the previous year.
[b] b ≠ 0.

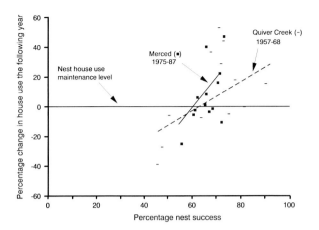

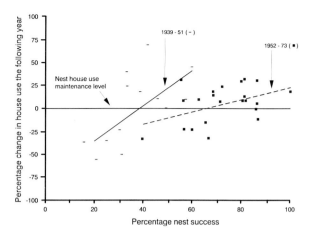

Figure 115. Effect of nest success in nest houses in a given year on the percentage of change in female wood ducks incubating the following year in nest houses at Merced, California, 1974–88, and at Quiver Creek, Illinois, 1957–68. The regression equations are: Merced, California, $r^2 = 0.27$, $P < 0.05$, $y = -121.5 + 1.94x$, S.E. = 0.188; Quiver Creek, Illinois, $r^2 = 0.64$, $P < 0.01$, $y = -78.3 + 1.37x$, S.E. = 0.104.

Figure 116. Effect of wood duck nest success in nest houses in a given year on the percentage of change in use of nest houses the following year during two time periods at Mason County, Illinois. The regression equations are: for 1939–51, $r^2 = 0.45$, $P < 0.05$, $y = -74.8 + 1.94x$, S.E. = 0.153; and for 1952–73, $r^2 = 0.21$, $P < 0.05$, $y = -42.3 + 0.66x$, S.E. = 0.168.

Another factor besides survival that affects the rate of recruitment in a specific area is the influence of nesting density on the pioneering rate of yearlings (see Chapter 4). Evidence suggests that as the density of breeding birds increases, the rate of pioneering increases. At Quiver Creek, Illinois, we found that as nest house use increased, proportionately fewer yearlings returned. Grice and Rogers (1965) reported similar findings at Great Meadows National Wildlife Refuge, Massachusetts. In his 1-hectare (2.5 ac) yard, Frederic Leopold achieved a nesting density of 17 by the eighth year, 1951. Yet, despite surplus nest houses and a phenomenal hatching success of 73.2 percent of all eggs laid, there was an average of 14 ± 4.2 nests annually in the next 27 years and never more than 20. Pioneering elsewhere by yearling females apparently occurred on a large scale because of the small size and isolation of Leopold's urban residential study area.

Although pioneering of yearlings was a factor in the following case histories of nest success versus recruitment, our evaluation points to habitat factors as the probable cause for appreciable differences. In the meager water areas around Merced, California, Stephen Simmons, who studied nesting in wood duck houses, 1974–1988, found that use declined in 6 of 15 years, but only in 1 year was the decline severe (Figure 115). A nest success of 62.6 percent was required to maintain a constant level of nest house use. An increase of 5 percent in nest success resulted in a subsequent 9.7-percent increase in nest house use.

Data from Quiver Creek, 1957–1968, indicated that a nest success rate of at least 57.3 percent was required to maintain a constant breeding population of wood ducks (Figure 115). A 5-percent change in nest success resulted in a change the following year of 6.9 percent in the number of breeding females.

Nest houses placed in the Mason County study area were immediately accepted by pioneering wood ducks in 1939. During the early years of 1939–1951, when the breeding population was rapidly expanding, a nest success rate of only 38.4

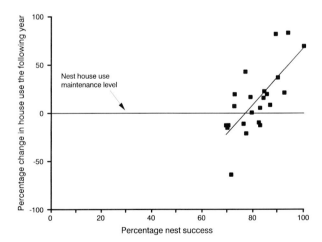

Figure 117. Effect of wood duck nest success in nest houses in a given year on the percentage of change in use of nest houses the following year at Union Slough National Wildlife Refuge, Iowa, 1966–89. The regression equation is: $r^2 = 0.42$, $P < 0.001$, $y = -272.7 + 3.64x$, S.E. = 0.118.

percent was required to maintain a stable nesting population. A change of 5 percent in this level of success resulted in a corresponding increase or decrease of 9.7 percent in the number of nests (Figure 116) initiated the following year. As population levels increased, a higher percentage of nest box use was required to maintain a stable population; for 1952–1973, it was 64.1 percent. Moreover, there was a lower population response to changes in nest success; a 5-percent increase in nest success resulted in only a 3.3-percent increase in the number of nests the subsequent year.

Because of the size (1,816 hectares: 4,488 ac) and integral habitat of Chautauqua National Wildlife Refuge, we have separated refuge data from that for the rest of Mason County, Illinois. We compared the percentage of successful wood duck nests with subsequent percentages of nest house use for three periods (Table 191). Nest house use was highest in the first period when nest success was the lowest, and the correlation between nest success and subsequent use also was highest. Despite high nest success in the second and third periods, the use of nest houses in subsequent years was lower; there were insignificant correlations between nest success one year and the rate of house use the following year.

We believe that the drastic decline in breeding wood ducks at the Chautauqua National Wildlife Refuge occurred despite high nest success because of reduced recruitment attributed to a high loss in ducklings and broods stemming from the disappearance of aquatic and marsh plants (Bellrose et al. 1979). Both aquatic and marsh plant beds began to disappear from the lakes following the disastrous floods of 1943 and 1944. The progressive loss of American lotus, marsh smartweed, and river bulrush beds greatly reduced brood cover and food by eliminating insect populations affiliated with these plants. Submergent beds of sago and longleaf pondweed and coontail disappeared from the open waters of these lakes; so did the rich source of aquatic insects they harbored (see Krull 1970). Sedimentation from the 1943, 1944, and subsequent smaller floods was principally responsible for the reduction of aquatic and emergent plant life in Lake Chautauqua and other bottomland lakes in the Illinois Valley (Bellrose et al. 1979, 1983).

The loss of these food and cover resources for wood duck broods in the lakes of the Illinois Valley was responsible for an excessively large loss of ducklings, and this loss accounted for the high nest success necessary to maintain even a low breeding population.

Breeding populations of wood ducks at the Union Slough National Wildlife Refuge in Iowa in-

creased steadily from one nest in 1962 to 251 in 1987 to 326 in 1990. This refuge is a traditional breeding home for blue-winged teal and mallards, and not until nest houses were erected in the early 1950s did the first wood ducks breed there. Houses provided previously unavailable nest sites, and the 445 hectares (1,100 ac) of open water and marsh provided exceptional brood habitat. For every 10 ducklings hatched, 1962–1986, there was a phenomenal gain of 1.2 nests the following year ($R^2 = 0.94$, $P < 0.001$).

Of the areas analyzed for influence of nest success on subsequent gains in nest house use, Union Slough had the highest rate—18.2 percent for every 5-percent increase in nest success (Figure 117, cf. figures 115 and 116). Because of the high rate of gain in response to nest success, it is apparent that brood survival was much better there than at other areas studied. That high survival rate, in turn, suggests that the food base and cover provided by marsh habitat were highly advantageous to increasing brood survival in the wood duck.

In order to maintain high levels of discrete populations as a result of nest site enhancement, nest success has had to reach levels of 39–75 percent, depending on brood habitat quality and breeding density.

Brood survival is prominently involved with nest success in determining the rate of recruitment. From all of our studies and from data analyses of nest histories on other study areas, we deduce that recruitment may decline not only from reduced nest success but also apparently from a decline in brood survival.

The pattern observed in every long-term nesting study—with one notable exception—is for breeding populations to increase rapidly during the first few years after the erection of nest houses and then to level off or partially decline. When the local breeding populations stabilize or decline while experiencing favorable nest success, the cause must primarily lie in low brood survival or increased yearling pioneering. In most instances that we have studied, declines in brood survival appear to be responsible rather than variations in pioneering (see Chapter 4). Even with high nest success, wood duck breeding abundance failed to respond to reduced population levels in Mason County, Lake Chautauqua National Wildlife Refuge, Quiver Creek (all in Illinois), and Merced, California. At Merced, wood duck nests increased from six in 1974 to 254 by 1980 and peaked at 279 in 1983 before declining for the next five years. Because nest success was better the last five years (70.6 ± 7.96) than during the first 10 years (65.7 ± 5.30), we attribute the decline to reduced recruitment rather than to pioneering.

In all of these long-term studies, if reduced recruitment had been due to reduced pioneering from outside the study areas because of population density, then the lowered populations should have increased the natal homing rates by yearlings. Because that failed to occur, we conclude that loss of broods was mainly responsible for the reduced recruitment.

The one notable exception to the traditional decline in nest house use a few years after their placement occurred at Union Slough National Wildlife Refuge, Iowa. The interspersion of marsh cover and aquatic plants there provided a bonanza for broods and permitted continuing high survival of young (at least until 1991), as indicated by the ever-increasing number of breeding wood ducks.

Variations in brood survival appear to be responsible for area and yearly differences in the nest success rate required to maintain a local breeding population. Changes in the status of local breeding populations reflect in part the density-dependent response of nest success and brood survival to existing population size in relation to carrying capacity of the habitat. At lower population densities, more space, cover, and food are available for each brood, thereby reducing the rate of brood losses because of reduced competition for habitat resources. Conversely, as populations grow, the mortality of immature birds can increase because of heightened competition for limited habitat. Thus, nest house use can increase when the population has room to expand and decrease when the population approaches the capacity of the habitat to support broods. Clearly reproduction can act as a compensatory mechanism to help regulate local population sizes.

In contrast to the high nest success rate necessary to maintain some local wood duck breeding populations, prairie-nesting ducks are calculated to maintain their breeding levels at considerably lower nest success rates—15 percent for mallards and northern pintails and 20 percent for other species (Cowardin et al. 1985, Klett et al. 1988). Renesting enables mallards and northern pintails to maintain breeding populations with low nest success rates. Wood ducks have a longer breeding season than do prairie ducks and also a high propensity to renest (see Chapter 10) that may equal or exceed that of prairie-nesting ducks. Thus, wood ducks probably have comparable or greater potential to maintain high recruitment via nesting activities than do prairie nesters.

The difference in nest success rates required to maintain populations of wood ducks and prairie-nesting species suggests that brood survival of prairie-nesting ducks is much higher than that of

wood ducks (see Table 143). Wood duck broods suffered a 48-percent loss from hatching to Class II ducklings. Major species of prairie duck broods declined from 18 to 27 percent during the same growth period. The large loss in wood duck broods implies a high loss (which escapes detection) of entire broods. Table 192 provides modeled recruitment parameters that further evaluate differences between the prairie-nesting mallard and the wood duck (from Johnson et al. 1992). Nest success was by far the most important factor affecting recruitment in the mallard. In the wood duck, nest success and brood survival were equally important in determining the production of flying young. Again, evidence points to the quality of wood duck brood habitat—as defined by the food base and cover—as playing an important role in brood survival.

MEASUREMENT OF PRODUCTION

The net result of the breeding season is a variable addition of flying young to the population at the end of summer. The magnitude of the juvenile cohort as a part of the autumn population has been measured by the ratio between adults and immatures in the bag of hunters over the wood duck's range. These data originate from the wing bee sessions described earlier.

Data from hunters are biased by differences in the shooting vulnerability of age and sex classes of ducks (Bellrose et al. 1961). These biases can be corrected to approximate ratios existing in nature; band recovery rates for each age and sex class can be used to adjust for intentional or unintentional selection by the hunter of a particular duck, occasioned by prevalence, degree of wariness, or plumage (Table 193). To evaluate yearly and regional variations in potential recruitment, we have analyzed the "age ratios" of wood ducks, corrected for hunter-biased samples, for 26 years in northern states and 24 years in southern states of the Atlantic and Mississippi flyways.

Table 192. Factors affecting recruitment in mallards and wood ducks.[a]

Factor	Mallard	Wood duck
Dump nesting	0.00	0.14
Breeding incidence	0.28	0.38
Renesting	0.13	0.20
Clutch size	0.09	0.19
Nest success	0.76	0.53
Egg survival	0.05	0.35
Brood survival	0.40	0.54

[a] Aadapted from Johnson et al. (1992).

Table 193. Relative vulnerability of immature and mature wood ducks in regions of the Atlantic and Mississippi flyways. Based on direct band recovery ratios (mean number of immatures to 1.0 adult[a]), 1960–85 in northern and central regions, and 1962–85 in southern regions.

Flyway/region	Number of years	Male			Female			t-statistic males/females
		Mean number of immatures per adult	S.E.	Percentage immature	Mean number of immatures per adult	S.E.	Percentage immature	
Atlantic								
Northern	26	1.399	0.0565	58.32	1.646	0.0804	62.21	0.287[b]
Southern	24	1.280	0.1099	56.14	1.175	0.0796	54.02	0.148[b]
Mississippi								
Northern	26	1.606	0.0692	61.63	1.574	0.0857	61.15	0.035[b]
Central	26	1.502	0.0802	60.03	1.504	0.0616	60.06	0.002[b]
Southern	24	1.045	0.0583	51.10	1.305	0.0941	56.62	0.384[b]

[a] Based on collation of actual yearly recovery rates distinct from estimated contrived rates obtained in population-survival analyses.
[b] Not significant: $P > 0.20$.

Gender is easy to identify in the wood duck, but determining whether a woodie is an adult or immature is more difficult, especially among drakes. When examining wings for age separation, key characteristics are the color and shape of coverts and tertials. Wood duck age ratios provide pertinent data on regional and yearly changes in productivity. *Photo by David Dolton; courtesy of the U.S. Fish and Wildlife Service.*

Recruitment as Determined by Age Ratios

Hunter recoveries of banded ducks suggest that immature wood ducks are more vulnerable to hunting losses than are adults (Table 193). This conclusion is consistent with the view that vulnerability to hunting decreases with age-related experience. Also, vulnerability of immatures decreases from north to south. And immature females are only slightly more vulnerable to hunting than are immature males.

In appraising recruitment deduced by age ratios, only the ratio of immature females per adult female was used, because of possible errors in classifying the age of male wood duck wings. We found no detectable difference in the ratio of immature to adult females between the north and south regions of the Atlantic Flyway (Table 194), with a mean age ratio of 1.54 immature females per adult female (60.6 percent) over a 20-year period. In the Mississippi Flyway we found no statistical difference in immatures per adult female in the northern and central zones, but the ratio in the southern region was significantly lower than those farther north (Table 194). The mean for all three regions (1.40 immatures per adult female), 58.3 percent, was lower but not significantly so than that in the Atlantic Flyway.

As the years progressed (1966–1985), there were significant increases in the proportion of immature females per adult female (Figure 118) in all regions of the Mississippi Flyway. The general increase in recruitment in these regions of the Mississippi Flyway corresponds with the steady increase in autumn populations during this period (see Chapter 5).

Table 194. Immature wood duck females per adult female in nature as determined by correcting wing samples for hunter selectivity. Data derived from classification of age and sex of wings submitted by hunters to the U.S. Fish and Wildlife Service and processed at annual "wing bees," 1966–85.

Flyway/region	Mean number of immatures per adult	S.E.	Percentage immature	Regions tested	t-statistic
Atlantic					
Northern (N[1])	1.51	0.080	60.16	N[1] and S[1]	0.31, 18df, P>0.20
Southern (S[1])	1.56	0.178	60.94		
Mean[a]	1.54		60.63		
Mississippi					
Northern (N[2])	1.48	0.163	59.68	N[2] and C	0.12, 18df, P>0.20
Central (C)	1.51	0.181	60.16		
Southern (S[2])	1.21	0.114	54.75	C and S[2]	1.74, 18df, P<0.10
Mean[a]	1.40		58.33		

[a] t-statistic: 0.15, 18df, P>0.20.

In the final analysis, the bottom line is the number of young per female that reach flight stage. The proportion of young females per adult female, as derived from hunter bag analysis corrected for hunter bias that includes young males, gives estimates of 3.33 during autumn in the Atlantic Flyway and 3.03 in the Mississippi Flyway.

Evidence presented at the end of Chapter 12 suggested that 20 percent of breeding woodie females lose their entire broods before flight. Oddly, we also found that about 20 percent of the wood ducks at Nauvoo Slough, 1983–1987, still were paired at the end of June—an indication that those pairs failed to raise a brood. Assuming that the average brood numbers 5.7 at flight (see Table 142) and prorating a 20-percent loss of entire broods, we

estimate that 4.6 young per female may reach the flight stage of life. Yet age ratios provide estimates of 3.33 immatures per adult hen in the Atlantic Flyway and 3.03 in the Mississippi Flyway. On this basis, 58 percent of the female wood ducks in the Atlantic Flyway and 53 percent of those in the Mississippi Flyway were successful in raising 5.7 ducklings to flight. At the theorized level of 4.6 ducklings per adult female, 72 percent of the hens in the Atlantic Flyway and 66 percent in the Mississippi Flyway would be successful. The difference—14 and 13 percent—between these two speculative data sets may roughly represent hens that never had a successful hatch or did not breed.

Sex Ratios

Every game duck population contains an excess of males, and the wood duck is no exception. The higher the proportion of males, the greater the proportion of unproductive individuals that must be considered in evaluating the status of a population.

For example, in computing the wood duck breeding population it would be convenient to consider that the number of breeding pairs is half of the calculated population. Unfortunately, the number of breeding pairs is somewhat less than half of the total population, and the known sex ratios do not provide an exact number, merely an approximation.

Waterfowl sex ratios may be obtained from three sources: (1) visual counts; (2) records of birds trapped for banding; and (3) examination of birds or their wings from hunters' bags (Bellrose et al. 1961). Unfortunately, visual sex ratios of wood ducks have not been obtained in significant numbers because of the dispersed nature of their populations in wooded habitats. Data from trapped samples may

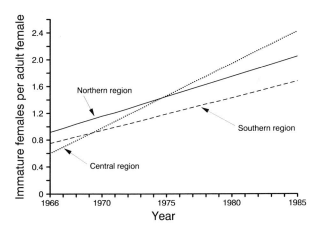

Figure 118. Number of immature females per adult female wood duck, 1966–85, in regions of the Mississippi Flyway. The regression equations are: northern region, $r^2=0.23$, P<0.05, y=0.86+0.060x, S.E. = 0.172; central region, $r^2=0.49$, P<0.001, y=0.50+0.10x, S.E. = 0.114; and southern region, $r^2=0.32$, P<0.01, y=0.70+0.05x, S.E. = 0.152.

be meaningful, especially from night lighting, but baited traps may give biased samples where competition for bait is keen. Currently the most valid data on wood duck sex ratios are derived from hunters' bags corrected by band data for the intentional or unknown selectivity by hunters. Band recovery rates indicate that hunters take males more frequently than female woodies (Table 195). The greater vulnerability of wood duck males to hunting losses increased from north to south and was statistically similar in both adult and immature age classes.

Wood duck sex ratios of all ages combined obtained from hunters' bags and corrected for vulnerability to hunting reveal a surplus of males in autumn populations (Table 196). The excess proportion of males is remarkably similar in the several regions of the Atlantic and Mississippi flyways.

A small proportion of extra drakes would appear to serve a useful reproductive function, because females are able to select the male with the most vitality and dominance to replace a mate lost through death or, if necessary, to find a replacement mate for renesting. At what level surplus males become unnecessary to population productivity or its well-being is difficult to ascertain.

Most duck species have a greater excess of males than do wood ducks. Bay-diving and sea ducks, for example, usually have 60 percent or more males (Bellrose 1976). Species with the lowest disparity in sex ratios are the American black duck, mallard, and wood duck. The mallard is noted for its fecundity, as is the wood duck.

The proportion of excess males most advantageous to the welfare of a particular species is clouded through the eons of evolution. It may have evolved as a deterrent to a species wasting energy in futile reproductive efforts due to habitat limitations. Evolution of unbalanced sex ratios may have been nature's answer to production of more young than necessary to maintain the population within the species' food resources.

Contemporary wood duck sex ratios probably are more balanced than those in centuries past. Because hunters take proportionately more males than females (Table 195), they reduce the number of males prior to the rigors of winter. Unfortunately, no data are available from which we can compare mortality by sex during the winter. Logically, however, the larger, more aggressive males would survive better than females. The numbers of extra drakes observed in the spring, forming trios and engaged in courtship, suggest a moderate surplus of males—more than needed to maximize immediate production. However, supernumerary males may prove genetically beneficial over the long term through female selection of the most viable drake.

Surplus drakes accrue under natural conditions from hatching through sexual maturity. At fertilization, the sex ratio in wood duck eggs is nearly equal. Fifty-one percent of 574 fertile eggs hatched or with near-term embryos were males (Bellrose et al. 1961). Among the 85 eggs with advanced dead embryos, 48 percent were males. Of 1,112 ducklings that were sexed, 49.3 percent (not statistically significant from 50 percent) were males.

Various types and sizes of traps have been devised to capture wood ducks for banding, an important tool in research. Band recovery data are employed to determine annual and regional mortality rates and the proportion of annual losses due to hunting. A comparison of productivity information from age ratios with mortality data provides a means of determining the "mechanics" of population dynamics. *Photo by Jack Dermid.*

Table 195. Hunter selection of male to female wood ducks in regions of the Atlantic and Mississippi flyways. Based on direct band recovery ratios (mean number of females to 1.0 male[a]), 1960–85 in northern and central regions, and 1962–85 in southern regions.

Flyway/region	Number of years	Adult			Immature		
		Females per male	S.E.	Percentage females	Females per male	S.E.	Percentage females
Atlantic							
Northern	26	0.859	0.0327	46.21	0.955	0.0298	48.85
Southern	24	0.784	0.0405	43.95	0.774	0.0257	43.63
Mississippi							
Northern	26	0.956	0.0381	48.88	0.878	0.0362	46.75
Central	26	0.847	0.0399	45.86	0.907	0.0320	47.56
Southern	24	0.637	0.0450	38.91	0.788	0.0392	44.07

[a] Based on collation of yearly data.

Table 196. Sex ratio (mean number of males to 1.0 female[a]) of autumn wood duck populations in several regions of the Atlantic and Mississippi flyways, 1966–85. Based on adult and immature sex ratios combined from "wing bee" classification corrected for hunter bias.

Flyway/region	Mean number of males per female	S.E.	Percentage males
Atlantic			
Northern	1.246	0.0417	55.48
Southern	1.266	0.0600	55.87
Mean[b]	1.256		55.68
Mississippi			
Northern	1.150	0.0425	53.49
Central	1.067	0.0610	51.62
Southern	1.252	0.0629	55.60
Mean[b]	1.156		53.62

[a] Collated on a yearly basis, with equal weight for adult and immature age classes.
[b] Mean unweighted by sample size.

The sex ratios of young wood ducks can be appraised two to five months after hatching, when birds are trapped for banding (Table 197). These data show an excess of 2.6–5.4 percent males, depending on the region, but the ratios for the northern and central regions of the Mississippi Flyway may be inflated by a postbreeding influx of more immature males than females (see Chapter 14). Omitting from consideration the two regions most suspect, excess males then amount to 2.6–4.3 percent. Sex ratios obtained during the hunting season for combined age groups show an excess by flyway of 3.6–5.7 percent in males (Table 196). This slight gain in males probably is caused by the greater disparity in sex ratios of the adult class—again, a characteristic of most game ducks (Bellrose et al. 1961). As discussed later, greater yearly mortality occurs in females than in males, occasioned by greater exposure to predators during incubation and brood rearing. The older the adult component of a wood duck population, the greater the proportion of males because recruitment of immatures—with their more balanced sex ratios—is diminished (Bellrose et al. 1961).

Table 197. Sex ratio (mean males to 1.0 female) of immature wood ducks trapped for banding during late summer, 1959–1978, in several regions of the Atlantic and Mississippi flyways.

Flyway/region	Number of years	Mean number of males per female	S.E.	Percentage males
Atlantic				
Northern	30	1.13	0.005	53.05
Southern	13	1.19	0.011	54.33
Weighted mean		1.16		53.70
Mississippi				
Northern	19	1.24	0.021	55.36
Central	19	1.14	0.009	53.27
Southern	19	1.11	0.007	52.61
Weighted mean		1.16		53.75

SURVIVAL AND BAND RECOVERY RATES

Band recovery rates provide a mechanism by which survival and harvest rates of several species of waterfowl have been computed. The fundamentals of modern survival analyses from band recovery rates were developed by Jolly (1965) and Robson and Youngs (1971) and expanded by Brownie et al. (1985). Anderson (1975) was the first to use these models in his extensive study of mallard survival in relation to harvest rates.

We used 445,378 bandings and 46,344 recoveries provided by the Bird Banding Laboratory of the

U.S. Fish and Wildlife Service to evaluate survival and recovery rates in the wood duck during various periods, 1950–1985.

Survival Rates

Age classes. Mean annual survival and recovery rates are given by age and sex classes for two regions of the Atlantic Flyway and three regions of the Mississippi Flyway (Table 198). Annual survival of adult males ranged from 59 percent in the south to 51 percent in the north; adult females ranged from 59 percent in the south to 46 percent in the

Table 198. Summary of mean annual recovery and survival rates for adult and immature male and female wood ducks in regions of the Atlantic and Mississippi flyways for the years of available banding and recovery data.[a]

Flyway/region	Sex	Period	Survival rate				Recovery rate			
			Adult	S.E.	Immature	S.E.	Adult	S.E.	Immature	S.E.
Atlantic										
Northern	M	1950–85	50.8	0.90	34.3	1.32	6.1	0.17	8.3	0.17
	F		46.1	1.89	35.8	2.14	4.9	0.23	7.7	0.17
Southern	M	1962–85	58.4	2.60	65.2	4.95	4.1	0.19	4.8	0.19
	F		49.0	1.98	52.9	4.67	3.2	0.19	3.6	0.18
Mississippi										
Northern	M	1960–85	54.3	0.73	41.1	1.41	5.2	0.10	8.5	0.17
	F		47.2	1.62	39.8	2.17	5.0	0.19	7.4	0.18
Central	M	1960–85	55.5	1.07	44.5	1.58	4.9	0.14	6.7	0.10
	F		49.2	1.18	41.7	1.71	4.0	0.13	5.9	0.10
Southern	M	1962–85	58.5	1.50	58.7	2.62	4.0	0.16	3.9	0.12
	F		59.1	2.92	57.0	4.39	2.4	0.13	3.0	0.12

[a] All estimates from model H1 of Brownie et al. (1985).

Table 199. Summary of results of hypothesis tests regarding differences between adult and immature wood ducks in regions of the Atlantic and Mississippi flyways. Significance levels for all tests: *P<0.10; **P<0.05; ***P<0.01.

Flyway/region	Sex	Period	df	Survival and recovery rate[a]		Survival rate[b]			
				X^2	P	S–S'	se(S–S')	Z	P
Atlantic									
Northern	M	1950–85	71	424.0***	0.000	0.165	0.0024	11.05***	0.000
	F		71	271.9***	0.000	0.104	0.0029	4.06***	0.000
Southern	M	1962–85	47	50.9	0.322	−0.068	0.0027	−1.61	0.107
	F		47	37.7	0.831	−0.039	0.0026	−0.84	0.403
Mississippi									
Northern	M	1960–85	51	485.2***	0.000	0.133	0.0020	8.68***	0.000
	F		51	230.7***	0.000	0.074	0.0026	2.96***	0.003
Central	M	1960–85	51	318.0***	0.000	0.110	0.0018	6.64***	0.000
	F		51	256.9***	0.000	0.075	0.0017	3.94***	0.000
Southern	M	1962–85	47	56.4	0.163	−0.003	0.0020	−0.10	0.919
	F		47	57.5	0.141	0.020	0.0017	0.49	0.625

[a] Results of a test of hypothesis (model H0 versus H1) that survival and recovery rates are identical for adult and immature age classes (Brownie et al. 1985).
[b] Results of a z-test of the null hypothesis that mean annual survival or recovery rate is the same for adult and immature age classes.

north. Immature survival was lower and more variable: survival of males ranged from 65 percent in the south to 34 percent in the north; females ranged from 57 percent in the south to 36 percent in the north. The difference in survival rates between adults and immatures was statistically significant for all regions except those of the southern Atlantic and Mississippi flyways (Table 199), for which data sets were comparatively sparse.

Sex classes. In all but one instance, adult males survived at a higher annual rate than did adult females (Table 198). Although survival rates favored immature males over immature females, differences were smaller. And in only one region (southern Atlantic) was male survival significantly higher than that of females (Table 200).

These survival data generally support the sex ratio data that suggested that young males survived at a slightly higher rate than did females. As inferred from sex ratio data, higher adult male survival accounts for most of the disparity in overall sex ratios.

Recovery Rates

Band recovery rates reflect the relative age and sex proportion of the population taken by hunters. (The proportion of bands not reported by hunters will be addressed later.)

Age classes. Recovery rates were significantly higher for immature males and females than for adults of both sexes in all but 2 of 10 data sets (Table 198), and those cases lacked statistical significance

Table 199. (continued)

	Recovery rate[b]		
f–f′	se(f–f′)	Z	P
− 0.022	0.0024	− 9.29***	0.000
− 0.027	0.0029	− 9.50***	0.000
− 0.007	0.0027	− 2.72***	0.006
− 0.004	0.0026	− 1.59	0.111
− 0.039	0.0020	− 16.69***	0.000
− 0.024	0.0026	− 8.94***	0.000
− 0.018	0.0018	− 10.07***	0.000
− 0.018	0.0016	− 11.15***	0.000
0.001	0.0020	0.60	0.546
− 0.006	0.0017	− 3.20***	0.001

(Table 199). As noted earlier, the greater vulnerability of immatures to hunting results in proportionately more losses; nonhunting losses also appear to be greater among juveniles.

Sex classes. Males in both adult and immature classes experienced slightly greater recovery rates than did females (Table 198). Because of lower points for a bagged drake, its brighter plumage (easier identification), or behavioral difference (males are seen alone more frequently than females, and single birds are more apt to decoy), hunters generally select wood duck males over females. Despite their higher hunting losses, males have a higher annual survival rate than do female wood ducks. This higher rate reflects higher losses incurred by females during the breeding season when they are exposed to predation more frequently than males. During incubation, female wood ducks suffer severe mortality from raccoons (see Chapter 11). Mortality linked to stress on the maternal female—from egg laying and brood raising followed by the wing molt—has not been quantified but may play a further role in their reduced survival.

Data from the recovery of bands of flightless young wood ducks will provide mortality data and information on the eventual movement of the ducks from their natal wetlands. Those that return to nest in houses on or near their natal areas can be identified and the degree of homing calculated. Comparisons of information on marked and unmarked breeding yearlings suggest that about 43 percent of surviving females return to their natal areas and 57 percent move to new breeding sites. *Photo by Jack Dermid.*

Table 200. Summary of results of hypothesis tests regarding differences between survival and recovery rates in male and female wood ducks in regions of the Atlantic and Mississippi flyways. In all tests, the null hypothesis was no difference between males and females. Significance levels for all tests: *P<0.10; **P<0.05; ***P<0.01.

Flyway/region	Period	Survival and recovery rate[a]			Adult survival rate			
		df	X²	P	$S_m - S_f$	S.E.	Z	P
Atlantic								
Northern	1950–84	71	127.4***	0.000	0.0468	0.0210	2.24**	0.025
Southern	1962–84	47	59.6	0.102	0.0937	0.0327	2.87***	0.004
Mississippi								
Northern	1960–84	49	88.3**	0.002	0.0712	0.0178	4.01***	0.000
Central	1960–84	51	146.5***	0.000	0.0635	0.0159	3.98***	0.000
Southern	1962–84	47	153.2***	0.000	−0.0061	0.0329	−0.19	0.853
					Adult recovery rate			
					$f_m - f_f$	S.E.	Z	P
Atlantic								
Northern	1950–85				0.0113	0.0028	3.98***	0.000
Southern	1962–85				0.0092	0.0027	3.47***	0.001
Mississippi								
Northern	1960–85				0.0018	0.0022	0.82	0.412
Central	1960–85				0.0089	0.0019	4.68***	0.000
Southern	1962–85				0.0157	0.0021	7.60***	0.000

[a] Results of a chi-square contingency table test (Brownie et al. 1985).

Wood duck harvest has increased steadily in the Atlantic and Mississippi flyways from 1950 through 1980 (see Chapter 5), but recovery and survival rates do not consistently mirror the trend in increased harvest. Although adult survival declined during 1980–1985, compared with 1970–1979 in four of five regions for males; in all five regions for females (Table 201), the decline was significant

Table 201. Summary of mean annual survival and recovery rates of male and female wood ducks by decade, 1950–85.[a]

Sex	Flyway/region	Years	Survival rate				Recovery rate			
			Adult	S.E.	Immature	S.E.	Adult	S.E.	Immature	S.E.
Male	Atlantic									
	Northern	1950–59	46.8	2.49	30.4	3.03	7.0	0.47	8.8	0.42
		1960–69	51.9	1.34	34.9	1.97	6.3	0.24	8.3	0.28
		1970–79	52.9	1.35	35.3	2.26	5.7	0.24	7.9	0.27
		1980–85	52.6	2.93	39.0	3.53	5.0	0.27	7.9	0.29
	Southern	1960–69	60.1	4.71	73.7	9.87	3.8	0.30	4.5	0.33
		1970–79	56.4	3.75	60.5	6.33	4.3	0.33	4.4	0.30
		1980–85	59.5	7.46	60.8	10.44	4.2	0.35	6.1	0.36
	Mississippi									
	Northern	1960–69	55.7	1.18	41.5	1.77	5.3	0.16	8.5	0.23
		1970–79	54.8	1.11	43.3	2.52	5.0	0.16	8.8	0.32
		1980–85	50.4	2.59	35.8	3.45	5.2	0.21	7.9	0.34
	Central	1960–69	55.1	1.47	46.5	2.06	4.9	0.20	6.5	0.16
		1970–79	57.4	1.57	43.2	2.40	4.9	0.23	6.6	0.17
		1980–85	52.7	4.06	43.3	4.73	4.9	0.35	7.3	0.24
	Southern	1960–69	58.3	3.05	54.0	3.99	4.7	0.37	4.5	0.24
		1970–79	61.3	1.92	62.0	4.20	3.5	0.20	3.4	0.19
		1980–85	53.0	4.13	59.8	5.86	3.9	0.25	3.9	0.22

[a] All estimates are from model H1 of Brownie et al. (1985).

Table 200. (continued)

	Immature survival rate		
$S'_m - S'_f$	S.E.	Z	P
−0.0146	0.0251	−0.58	0.561
0.1232	0.0681	1.81*	0.070
0.0125	0.0259	0.48	0.630
0.0280	0.0233	1.20	0.229
0.0172	0.0511	0.33	0.737

	Immature recovery rate		
$f'_m - f'_f$	S.E.	Z	P
0.0060	0.0024	2.52**	0.012
0.0124	0.0026	4.69***	0.000
0.0112	0.0025	4.55***	0.000
0.0084	0.0015	5.68***	0.000
0.0089	0.0017	5.29***	0.000

only for adult females in the central region of the Mississippi Flyway. Immature survival declined over the same periods in two of five regions for males and four of five regions for females, but the

loss was significant only for females in the northern and southern regions of the Mississippi Flyway.

Linear trends in survival over the entire period, 1950–1985, show a significant downward tendency only among adult males and immature females in the northern region of the Mississippi Flyway (Table 202 [tests A and B]). In two regions survival actually increased for both adults and immatures. However, the general downward trend (although nonsignificant in a number of regions) gives cause for concern.

To examine the relationship of band recovery rates to survival, we randomly partitioned the data into two parts, following the method used by Trost (1990), to obtain statistically independent estimates of band recovery and survival rates. Pearson correlation coefficients were determined for the four age and sex classes of wood ducks in each of the five eastern regions of the United States (Table 203) in order to evaluate the significance of the relationship between band recovery rates and survival rates. In 16 of 20 cases, a negative correlation was found between recovery and survival rates, but only six were significant (Table 203). Thus, the upward trend in wood duck harvest did not occur at the expense of the population but as a result of a growing woodie population.

Individual test results were pooled (Table 204). The combined result indicated that there was an overall relationship between harvest and survival rates.

Table 201. (continued)

Sex	Flyway/region	Years	Survival rate				Recovery rate			
			Adult	S.E.	Immature	S.E.	Adult	S.E.	Immature	S.E.
Female	Atlantic									
	Northern	1950–59	43.0	5.71	39.5	5.58	5.1	0.59	7.8	0.43
		1960–69	46.2	2.51	33.0	2.80	5.8	0.39	7.8	0.29
		1970–79	49.3	2.37	36.0	3.46	4.7	0.36	7.8	0.28
		1980–85	45.9	3.88	33.5	4.52	3.8	0.37	6.9	0.29
	Southern	1960–69	57.8	5.13	58.8	8.57	2.8	0.30	3.4	0.30
		1970–79	44.4	2.74	55.6	7.34	3.2	0.30	3.4	0.31
		1980–85	44.1	5.32	37.9	7.57	3.7	0.38	4.2	0.33
	Mississippi									
	Northern	1960–69	45.3	2.13	44.8	3.17	4.5	0.29	7.7	0.24
		1970–79	48.7	2.53	41.5	3.86	5.4	0.34	7.3	0.32
		1980–85	48.1	5.47	26.4	4.28	5.2	0.39	6.9	0.38
	Central	1960–69	47.0	1.85	41.6	2.27	4.3	0.20	5.6	0.16
		1970–79	53.0	1.56	41.5	2.55	3.8	0.19	6.1	0.17
		1980–85	45.9	4.18	42.6	5.16	4.2	0.32	6.2	0.25
	Southern	1960–69	62.2	5.65	61.7	6.33	2.7	0.28	3.4	0.20
		1970–79	60.5	4.62	60.4	8.21	2.0	0.16	2.6	0.18
		1980–85	51.0	5.13	42.9	5.91	2.9	0.23	3.2	0.23

Table 202. Differences in survival and recovery rates between sex and age classes of wood ducks for specified groups of years, 1950–85, in regions of the Atlantic and Mississippi flyways. Significance levels: *$P < 0.10$; **$P < 0.05$; ***$P < 0.01$.

Test	Sex	Flyway/region	df	Adult survival rate			Immature survival rate		
				$S_1 - S_2$	X^2	$P > X^2$	$S_1 - S_2$	X^2	$P > X^2$
A[a]	M	Atlantic							
		Northern	3		4.47	0.18		5.57	0.13
		Southern	2		3.21	0.20		2.00	0.37
		Mississippi							
		Northern	2		3.47	0.18		3.14	0.21
		Central	2		1.49	0.47		1.20	0.55
		Southern	2		0.35	0.83		1.36	0.51
	F	Atlantic							
		Northern	3		1.54	0.67		1.33	0.72
		Southern	2		4.48	0.11		4.12	0.12
		Mississippi							
		Northern	2		1.00	0.61		12.49***	0.00
		Central	2		6.16**	0.05		0.04	0.98
		Southern	2		2.64	0.27		5.59**	0.06
B[b]	M	Atlantic							
		Northern	1	0.0029	15.07***	0.00	0.0032	8.07***	0.00
		Southern	1	−0.0013	0.55	0.46	−0.0070	2.06	0.15
		Mississippi							
		Northern	1	−0.0021	6.25**	0.01	−0.0014	0.62	0.43
		Central	1	−0.0002	0.03	0.86	−0.0009	0.23	0.63
		Southern	1	−0.0019	1.52	0.22	0.0065	3.34*	0.07
	F	Atlantic							
		Northern	1	0.0058	31.99***	0.00	0.0017	0.87	0.35
		Southern	1	−0.0025	1.33	0.25	−0.0051	0.94	0.33
		Mississippi							
		Northern	1	−0.0001	0.00	0.96	−0.0089	13.62***	0.00
		Central	1	0.0087	0.55	0.46	−0.0023	1.23	0.27
		Southern	1	−0.0025	1.33	0.25	−0.0051	0.94	0.33
C[c]	M	Mississippi							
		Northern	1	0.066	3.91**	0.05	0.063	1.84	0.18
		Central	1	0.050	0.75	0.39	0.012	0.04	0.84
		Southern	1	0.078	1.84	0.17	0.029	0.13	0.72
	F	Mississippi							
		Northern	1	0.004	0.00	0.96	0.133	4.28**	0.04
		Central	1	0.019	0.11	0.75	−0.060	0.79	0.37
		Southern	1	0.138	3.12*	0.08	0.175	2.72*	0.10
D[d]	M	Mississippi							
		Northern	1	0.090	3.33*	0.07	0.144	7.78***	0.01
		Central	1	0.092	1.34	0.25	0.087	2.24	0.13
		Southern	1	0.236	5.66**	0.12	0.182	3.10*	0.08
	F	Mississippi							
		Northern	1	0.106	1.19	0.27	0.177	4.63**	0.04
		Central	1	0.001	0.00	0.99	−0.030	0.32	0.57
		Southern	1	0.170	0.68	0.41	0.392	2.35	0.13

[a] By decades: 1950s versus 1960s versus 1970s versus 1980s. Comparison of mean annual rates among decades for years of available data.

[b] By linear trends over years. Test of H0: no linear trend in rates for available years. $S_1 - S_2$ is an estimate of b, the mean annual rate of increase (+) or decrease (−).

[c] By pre-early season years versus current early season years. Comparison of years before (1970–80) and during (1981–1984) initiation of early wood duck seasons in Iowa (1982), Kentucky (1981), and Tennessee (1981).

[d] By wet versus dry years. Comparison of wet winters (1961, 1972, 1973, and 1978) versus dry winters (1962, 1965, 1976, and 1980). Classification of winters from Nichols et al. (1983).

Table 202. (continued)

Adult recovery rate			Immature recovery rate		
S_1-S_2	X^2	$P>X^2$	S_1-S_2	X^2	$P>X^2$
	11.81***	0.01		3.03	0.38
	8.77**	0.01		13.83***	0.00
	5.73*	0.06		1.50	0.47
	0.99	0.61		17.55***	0.00
	4.42	0.11		22.29***	0.00
	12.13***	0.01		3.02	0.39
	7.54**	0.02		10.93***	0.00
	5.96*	0.05		1.35	0.51
	4.31	0.11		5.58*	0.06
14.00***	0.00		9.86***	0.01	
−0.0055	12.49***	0.00	−0.0002	1.81	0.18
0.0006	5.39**	0.02	0.0007	7.92***	0.00
0.0002	1.96	0.16	0.0003	1.57	0.21
0.0002	1.13	0.29	0.0004	5.94	0.15
−0.0001	0.06	0.80	−0.0005	8.14***	0.00
−0.0005	7.26***	0.01	−0.0002	1.26	0.26
0.0011	0.55	0.46	0.0008	12.27***	0.01
0.0009	13.68***	0.00	0.0000	0.00	1.00
−0.0005	7.95***	0.01	0.0002	2.02	0.16
0.0002	1.14	0.29	−0.0003	3.01*	0.08
−0.010	9.94***	0.00	0.00	1.50	0.22
−0.006	1.51	0.21	−0.01	9.63***	0.00
−0.007	3.12*	0.07	−0.00	2.10	0.15
−0.006	0.92	0.34	−0.00	1.58	0.21
−0.004	0.98	0.32	−0.00	0.28	0.60
−0.012	12.93***	0.00	−0.00	5.70**	0.02
−0.017	25.79***	0.00	−0.015	5.38**	0.02
−0.010	4.39**	0.04	−0.004	1.52	0.21
−0.012	4.34**	0.04	−0.011	7.30***	0.01
−0.014	4.93**	0.03	−0.015	5.38**	0.02
−0.011	5.39**	0.02	−0.005	2.15	0.14
−0.010	3.70*	0.05	0.003	0.73	0.39

Our findings and those by Trost (1990) suggest that harvest rates influence survival. Therefore, harvest mortality is not completely compensated by a corresponding reduction in other sources of mortality. Evidence that hunter mortality is additive to the overall mortality in the wood duck is at variance with the preponderance of evidence that harvest rates during the last two decades have been compensatory (nonadditive) in mallards (Anderson 1975, Anderson and Burnham 1976, Nichols et al. 1984). Although Trost (1987) found evidence of a negative effect of harvest rates on adult and immature survival in mallards, he later concluded that survival studies generally have tended to demonstrate that harvest rates of mallards operate in a compensatory manner (Trost 1990). However, in the 1979–88 appraisal of hunting and mallard survival, Smith and Reynolds (1992) concluded that under certain conditions, curtailing harvest increased survival rates in the mallard. At any rate, mallards illustrate compensatory mortality adjustments to hunting losses to a greater degree than do woodies.

Geographic Variation in Survival and Recovery Rates

Regional survival rates compared by paired north/south differences in the two eastern flyways (Table 205) showed that in every case, wood duck males, females, adults, and immatures experienced lower survival rates in the northernmost regions— 11 of 16 differences were significant. North/south regional differences in survival were more apparent in adult females than in males and in immatures than in adults of both sexes.

Nichols and Johnson (1990) also analyzed the effect of migration distance on survival of wood ducks. They concluded that the shorter the migration distance, the higher the rate of survival. The farther-migrating immature males had significantly lower survival rates than did adult males. Perhaps because of mitigation by adult breeding mortality, differences in the effect of migration distance on survival between adult and yearling females were not as evident.

Band recovery rates were higher in the north than in the south in all 16 regional categories, and the differences were significant in 15 comparisons. As might be expected, the farther north a wood duck breeds, the more exposed it is to hunting losses. Nichols and Johnson (1990) reached a similar conclusion in their analyses of band recoveries versus distance of migration.

Wood ducks survived less well in the Atlantic

Table 203. Pearson correlation coefficients (r) between estimated recovery and survival rates of wood ducks in regions of the Atlantic and Mississippi flyways. Survival and recovery rates were independently estimated by dividing the data into two parts; all parameters estimated using Model H1 of Brownie et al. (1985). Significance levels: *P<0.10; **P<0.05.

		Estimated correlation coefficient and result of test of null hypothesis that S and f are uncorrelated			
		Male			
		Adult		Immature	
Flyway/region	Period	r	P<r	r	P<r
Atlantic					
Northern	1966–84	−0.22	0.18	−0.31	0.10*
Southern	1966–84[a]	−0.45	0.01**	0.35	0.88
Mississippi					
Northern	1966–84	−0.45	0.03**	−0.30	0.11
Central	1966–84	0.21	0.80	0.29	0.88
Southern	1966–84	−0.33	0.08*	−0.49	0.01**

[a] Males = 1972–84; females = 1966–84.

Flyway than in the Mississippi Flyway, but in only three of eight categories were differences large enough to be significant. Recovery rates were higher in six of eight categories in the Atlantic Flyway, four of which were significant (Table 205). Thus, regional survival rates were generally inverse to band recovery rates.

Effect of Special Seasons

Beginning in 1977, the U.S. Fish and Wildlife Service permitted certain states to have early hunting seasons for wood ducks. The early season was first used by Virginia and North Carolina in 1977, Georgia in 1980, South Carolina, Kentucky, and Tennessee in 1981, and Iowa in 1979. The liberalized regulations continued through 1989 in all states except Iowa, which terminated its early season on wood ducks in 1984.

Because early seasons have the potential to increase the harvest of wood ducks with possible adverse effects on survival rates, they have been evaluated in numerous studies. The first, by Johnson et al. (1986), analyzed the impact of the early seasons in the Atlantic Flyway. They found little evidence of increased mortality over extensive regional areas of the flyway as a result of changes in harvest rates, but they recognized that the effect on local populations was unknown.

Heusmann (1990) made a more detailed examination of the effect of liberalized regulations on harvest of wood ducks in Virginia, North and South Carolina, and Georgia. As measured by direct band recovery rates, the rate of harvest increased by 25 percent in North Carolina, 31 percent in South Carolina, and 124 percent in Georgia. A lack of banding in Virginia prior to the liberalized regulations prevented a similar comparison, but the component of wood ducks in Virginia's waterfowl

Table 204. Summary tests of null hypothesis that wood duck recovery and survival rates are uncorrelated, versus the alternative that they are negatively correlated, 1966–84. Significance levels: *P<0.05; **P<0.01; ***P<0.001.

Age	Sex	Number of regions	Z[a]	P<Z
Adult	M	5	−2.15	0.017*
Adult	F	5	−2.38	0.009**
Immature	M	5	−0.80	0.210
Immature	F	5	−1.22	0.111
Age and sex combined		20	−3.28	0.001***

[a] Individual tests in Table 203 were pooled into overall test of Ho: S and f are uncorrelated. When Ho is true, P values in Table 203 are uniformly distributed with theoretical mean 0.5 and theoretical variance 1/12. Pooled tests were calculated as Z = (P−0.5) divided by 1/12n.

Table 203. (continued)

Estimated correlation coefficient and result of test of null hypothesis that S and f are uncorrelated			
Female			
Adult		Immature	
r	P < r	r	P < r
−0.19	0.22	0.27	0.87
−0.02	0.47	−0.30	0.11
−0.30	0.11	−0.27	0.13
−0.38	0.06*	−0.22	0.19
−0.30	0.10	−0.05	0.42

bag rose from an average 7.2 percent before the expanded season to 24.7 percent during the years of the special seasons. The impact of the increased kill of wood ducks on their survival in those states remains unresolved, because bandings were not of sufficient size to permit adequate analysis of survival rates.

The effect of special September seasons on wood duck harvest and survival in Tennessee and Kentucky was studied by Sauer et al. (1990). Tennessee bandings indicated that survival in males decreased from 59.4 percent prior to the liberalized regulations to 46.8 percent, and that band recoveries increased from 3.7 to 4.6 percent. Survival rates among females decreased from 58 to 37.3 percent, and recovery rates increased from 2.3 to 4.1 percent. For six years preceding and six years during the liberalized wood duck seasons, the harvest in Tennessee increased from an annual mean of 9,652 to 29,265 — a gain of 303 percent.

Data from Kentucky bandings suggested that increased recovery rates followed the addition of an early hunting season on wood ducks. Sample sizes were small, however, and none of the results was large enough to be statistically significant. Nevertheless, the harvest increased from about 5,000 to 18,000 per year, and the correlation between increased harvest rates and reduced survival rates must be viewed with concern (Sauer et al. 1990).

From 1979 through 1984, Iowa was permitted to have part of its split duck season in September rather than in early October. Although intended to focus on blue-winged teal, the early season also enabled hunters to harvest wood ducks by virtue of the birds' increased availability. Prior to the Sep-

tember season, the survival rate of adult males, 1972–1978, was 55.1 percent; after the September season was in place, the survival rate was 52.4 percent. For adult females, the corresponding respective percentages were 43.6 and 45.6; for immature males, 48.3 and 34.6; and for immature females, 39.1 and 26.3 (Kienzler and Hansen 1990). Band recovery rates increased slightly during the years of the September season for all age and sex classes.

Despite the apparent depressing effect of harvest rates on survival in three of the four age and sex classes, the average annual harvest of wood ducks in Iowa was practically the same during the two periods: 32,800 during 1972–1978 and 31,000 during 1979–1984. Based on low significance of differences between survival and harvest rates and the failure of the kill to increase, Kienzler and Hansen (1990) concluded that the early season had little effect on wood duck populations in Iowa. Although there was no September season in Illinois or Wisconsin, wood duck survival in both states also declined from 1972–1978 compared with 1979–1983 in all age and sex classes except young females in Illinois (Kienzler and Hansen 1990). Although most differences in survival rates were of low or negligible significance, there appeared to be a trend toward lower survival rates in all three states, 1979–1983. These lower survival rates appeared unrelated to the September season in Iowa.

Bartelt and Trost (1990) examined survival and recovery rates for Minnesota, Wisconsin, and Michigan to determine their relationship to an expanding wood duck population. With minor exceptions, survival rates were similar during 1967–1984 (or 1969–1983) in all three states. Bartelt and Trost compared survival rates for sex and age classes in years of low harvest rates with years of high harvest rates; despite meaningful differences in recovery rates, they found no significant difference in survival rates among years.

To determine the effect of special seasons on wood duck survival, we separated Mississippi Flyway regional banding results into two components: those banded in years prior to early seasons in Kentucky, Tennessee, and Iowa and those banded during the years of early seasons (Table 202 [Test C]). Survival rates were slightly higher in the years prior to the early seasons, and recovery rates were inversely higher during seasons with early openings in all but one instance; 5 of 12 comparisons were significant (Table 202 [Test C]). In these analyses, there was evidence of increased harvest rates resulting from the early seasons in several states, and these increased harvest rates had a slight depressing effect on regional survival rates in the Mississippi Flyway.

Table 205. Results of z tests regarding geographic variation in mean annual survival and recovery rates of wood ducks.[a] Significance levels: *P<0.10; **P<0.05; ***P<0.01.

comparison	Sex	Period	Adult survival rate			
			S_1-S_2	S.E.	z	P
Atlantic						
Northern–Southern	M	1962–84	−0.0555	0.0275	−2.02***	0.044
	F		−0.0261	0.0239	−1.09	0.274
Mississippi						
Northern–Central	M	1960–84	−0.0122	0.0130	−0.94	0.348
	F		−0.0199	0.0200	−0.99	0.320
Northern–Southern	M	1962–84	−0.0451	0.0166	−2.71***	0.007
	F		−0.1054	0.0336	−3.14***	0.002
Central–Southern	M		−0.0365	0.0184	−1.98**	0.048
	F		−0.0884	0.0315	−2.80***	0.005
Northern Atlantic– Northern Mississippi	M	1960–84	−0.0192	0.0115	−1.67	0.094
	F		0.0019	0.0217	0.09	0.930
Southern Atlantic– Southern Mississippi	M	1960–84	−0.0011	0.0300	−0.04	0.972
	F	1962–84	−0.1009	0.0353	−2.86***	0.004

	Sex	Period	Adult recovery rate			
			f^1-f^2	S.E.	z	P
Atlantic						
Northern–Southern	M	1962–85	0.0159	0.0024	6.60***	0.000
	F		0.0156	0.0029	5.37***	0.000
Mississippi						
Northern–Central	M	1960–85	0.0027	0.0017	1.53	0.126
	F		0.0098	0.0023	4.22***	0.000
Northern–Southern	M	1962–85	0.0127	0.0019	6.68***	0.000
	F		0.0271	0.0023	11.59***	0.000
Central–Southern	M		0.0097	0.0022	4.48***	0.000
	F		0.0165	0.0018	9.09***	0.000
Northern Atlantic– Northern Mississippi	M	1960–85	0.0056	0.0018	3.17***	0.002
	F		−0.0012	0.0029	−0.40	0.692
Southern Atlantic– Southern Mississippi	M	1962–85	0.0010	0.0025	0.42	0.676
	F		0.0075	0.0023	3.32***	0.001

[a] Differences in mean survival and recovery rates are the first minus the second region in the comparison.

A comparison of survival and recovery rates in relation to years of low and high precipitation during the period wood ducks are on wintering grounds in the Mississippi Flyway is important in evaluating wintering habitat resources (Table 202 [Test D]). During years when higher water prevailed, wood ducks in 11 of 12 age, sex, and regional banding categories showed higher survival than in years of lower water levels; 5 groups were significantly different. Harvest rates estimated from band recoveries showed the opposite—they decreased during years of high precipitation on the wintering grounds (Table 202 [Test D]). In 11 of 12 sex, age, and regional banding categories (9 of which were significant), recoveries indicated that hunters harvested fewer ducks when waters were high. An increase in natural mortality may occur under low water conditions, because of reduced food resources and greater exposure to predators.

Especially on the wood duck's principal wintering grounds—the Mississippi Alluvial Plain—flooding of bottomland hardwoods results in a dispersal

Table 205. (continued)

Immature survival rate			
$S'_1-S'_2$	S.E.	z	P
−0.2891	0.0516	−5.60***	0.000
−0.1875	0.0510	−3.68***	0.000
−0.0345	0.0212	−1.63	0.103
−0.0190	0.0276	−0.69	0.491
−0.1814	0.0301	−6.03***	0.000
−0.1856	0.0489	−3.79***	0.000
−0.1517	0.0308	−4.93***	0.000
−0.1493	0.0473	−3.16***	0.002
−0.0519	0.0198	−2.62***	0.009
−0.0553	0.0295	−1.87*	0.061
0.0643	0.0560	1.15	0.251
−0.0417	0.0641	−0.65	0.515

Immature recovery rate			
$f'_1-f'_2$	S.E.	z	P
0.0329	0.0025	13.07***	0.000
0.0395	0.0025	15.76***	0.000
0.0179	0.0020	8.94***	0.000
0.0150	0.0021	7.31***	0.000
0.0476	0.0022	21.91***	0.000
0.0445	0.0022	20.33***	0.000
0.0286	0.0016	17.66***	0.000
0.0292	0.0016	18.77***	0.000
−0.0040	0.0024	−1.71*	0.087
0.0025	0.0024	1.02	0.306
0.0096	0.0023	4.24***	0.000
0.0061	0.0022	2.83***	0.005

percent of the hunting mortality is additive, but this level is difficult to establish with precision because of the many variables induced by local conditions. Each subpopulation is subject to varying hunting and natural losses, and either of these two factors may have different levels of importance in the matrix of mortality. Moreover, the additive component may vary with sex and age classes, time, and geography. But unlike mallards, wood ducks show that harvest rates can have a depressing effect on survival. Thus, hunting losses play a more important role in the population dynamics of the wood duck than they do in the mallard, a species that apparently has more flexible compensatory population capabilities. Regardless of the additive effects of hunting on annual mortality, wood duck populations have increased over much of their range (see Chapter 5).

To illustrate the length of time required for wood duck populations to disappear as a result of hunting and natural mortality, we constructed graphs based on age-specific estimates of survival from hunter recoveries and from the return of nesting females to Quiver Creek, Illinois (Figure 119).

At Quiver Creek, we recorded the return of 1,389 hens that nested in years following banding. These nesting females showed a slightly higher survival, based on a hyperbolic curve of recovery data, than did populations of females in the central region of the Mississippi Flyway; these data were determined from the shrinkage of band recovery cohorts reported by hunters (Figure 119). The rate of population loss was very similar to that derived by two very dissimilar methods of evaluating survival.

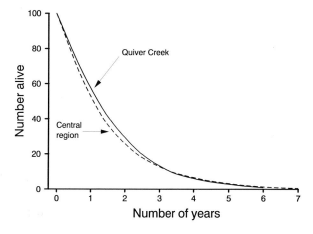

Figure 119. Disappearance rate of 1,389 adult female wood ducks nesting at Quiver Creek, Illinois, and as ascertained from 1,211 band recoveries in the central region of the Mississippi Flyway (from data in Table 198). Quiver Creek data plotted on basis of hyperbolic curve, $r^2 = 0.98$.

to new and more extensive feeding areas (see Chapter 16). As water levels fluctuate, wood ducks alter their feeding habits and locations to find optimum food resources. During flooding, wood ducks are able to disperse to more areas, thereby reducing contact with hunters. Flooding also results in improved survival rates because of increased food resources and improved nutrition.

There is little evidence to indicate when and under what conditions harvest rates become additive to mortality. Our data suggest that less than 80

As derived from age-specific estimates of survival (Table 198), the disappearance of male and female components of wood duck populations in eastern United States is plotted in Figure 120. As the population aged, the ratio of males to females gradually increased from 1.07:1 the first year to 1.99:1 the seventh year. Few wood ducks lived beyond the seventh year. As calculated from these data, a population embracing the survivors of all seven year classes in their proper yearly proportion of survival would be composed of 54.3 percent males (1.19 males per female)—very similar to the proportion of males determined from hunter bag inspection data (Table 196).

SPECIES COMPARISON

A comparison of survival rates and mean life spans of the wood duck with those rates of five other species shows adult male woodies with a lower survival rate, females with a rate about average, and immatures with a rate slightly above all species but mallard and northern pintail (Table 206). If the mean of all age and sex classes is given equal weight, survival of the wood duck is on a par with all but the mallard and northern pintail—species with the highest survival rates.

The mean life span of the several species presented in Table 206 is proportional to their survival rates as adults but differs slightly in immatures, because the survival rate relates only to the first year

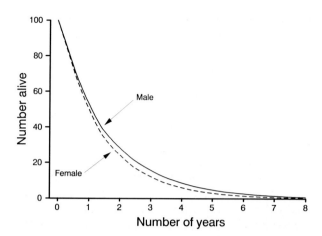

Figure 120. Disappearance of 100 immature male and female wood ducks, with time based on survival data summarized for all regions of the Atlantic and Mississippi flyways (from data in Table 198).

of life. Higher survival rates in adults of some species, therefore, will ultimately be reflected in longer life spans of immatures.

NATURAL MORTALITY VERSUS HUNTING MORTALITY

Overall mortality among wood ducks can be separated into losses from natural causes and losses from hunting. The rate of hunting losses can be determined from band recovery rates (adjusted for

Table 206. Comparative annual survival rates (SR) and mean life span (MLS) in years for sex and age classes of six duck species. All survival estimates are based on recovery ratios using models of Brownie et al. (1985).[a] Life span equations in Anderson (1975) from Seber (1973).[b]

	Adult				Immature			
	Male		Female		Male		Female	
Species	SR	MLS	SR	MLS	SR	MLS[d]	SR	MLS[d]
Wood duck	56	1.72	50	1.44	49	1.56	45	1.34
Mallard	62	2.09	54	1.62	48	1.72	46	1.44
American black duck	63	2.16	47	1.32	48	1.23	38	0.93
Northern pintail	72	3.04	60	1.96	56	2.46	51	1.73
Blue-winged teal	59	1.90	52	1.53	44	1.52	32	1.09
Ring-necked duck	70	2.80	47	1.32	41	1.12	33	1.04
Mean	64 ± 6		52 ± 5		48 ± 5		41 ± 8	

[a] Adapted from Johnson et al. (1992).

[b] Adults: $\dfrac{1}{-\ln S_A}$; S_A = average annual survival of adults, used as a decimal in hundreds.

Immatures: $\dfrac{1}{-\ln(S_Y)} + \dfrac{S_Y}{-\ln(S_A)} + \dfrac{S_Y}{\ln(S_Y)}$; S_Y = average annual survival of young; ln = natural log of S_A, S_Y.

[c] Mean for each species based on arithmetical average of equal weight for each age and sex class.

[d] Immature species, mean life spans are inconsistent with their survival rates because of species variations in life spans beyond one year in which higher adult survival rates prevail and thereby affect total life span.

nonreported bands) plus the calculated loss from crippling of 20 percent. Rates of hunting mortality were deducted from total mortality rates (derived from survival rates of Table 198) to obtain the magnitude of natural mortality.

Reward band findings for mallards by the U.S. Fish and Wildlife Service up to midsummer 1989 focus on a reporting rate of about 32 percent of the bands recovered (3.125 times correction factor), largely from hunters (Nichols et al. 1991). Nonreporting rates for wood ducks are believed to be similar to those for mallards (Geis and Atwood 1961). An adjustment for the nonreporting rate—a correcting factor of 3.125 times the band recovery rate—provides hunter-harvest rates. Because unretrieved cripples are an added loss from hunting, they have been computed at the standard rate of 20 percent (1.25 times the harvest rate).

Comparative natural mortality and hunting losses as the two components of overall mortality are shown by sex and age classes for five regions of eastern North America (figures 121 and 122). For all wood duck age and sex classes, the northern region of the Atlantic Flyway had the highest mortality, and in four of five regions, also the highest hunting loss. The northern region of the Mississippi Flyway followed with the next highest overall mortality and hunting loss. The central region of the Mississippi Flyway was lower for both categories. The lowest overall mortality and hunting loss for the four sex and age classes were found in the southern regions of the Atlantic and Mississippi flyways.

Table 206. (continued)

	Mean[c]	
SR	MLS	Source
50	1.52	Table 198
53	1.72	Anderson (1975)
49	1.41	Krementz et al. (1987)
60	2.30	Reinecker (1987)
47	1.51	Schroeder (unpublished)
48	1.57	Conroy and Eberhardt (1983)

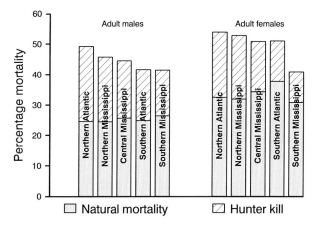

Figure 121. Proportion of natural mortality and hunter kill of adult wood ducks in eastern North America. Data from Table 198; band recovery rates were corrected (x 3.125) for unreported bands.

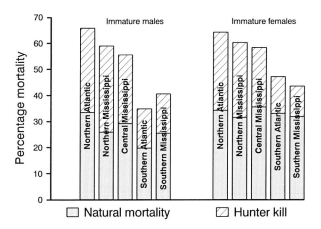

Figure 122. Proportion of natural mortality and hunter kill of immature wood ducks in eastern North America. Data from Table 198; band recovery rates were corrected (x 3.125) for unreported bands.

Hunting loss accounted for one-third to one-half of all annual mortality, depending on the age and sex class (Figure 123). Hunting loss was lowest in females of both age classes and lower in adults than immatures. The proportion of mortality attributable to hunting was highest in the north and lowest in the south of both flyways (Table 198).

Anderson (1975) estimated the percentage of annual hunting loss as part of total mortality in mallards by age and sex groups: adult males 55.3; adult females 41.6; immature males 50.7; and immature females 45.9. The estimated percentage of hunting loss to overall mortality in wood ducks for age and sex classes is: adult males 45.3; adult females 32.5; immature males 47.4; and immature females 38.3. Thus, for all age and sex classes, the proportion of annual mortality from hunting was greater in mallards than in wood ducks.

As previously noted, hunting loss ceases at some threshold to be compensatory and becomes additive. By separating natural mortality and hunting loss components of total annual mortality, the mortality role of hunting is defined more clearly (Figure 123). Unequal, incremental rises in both natural mortality and hunting losses are factors that affect increases in overall mortality rates (Figure 123). As total mortality rates rose at the rate of 1 percent, losses from hunting formed an ever greater component, increasing at the rate of 0.67 percent, while natural mortality rose at the rate of 0.33 percent. At the highest annual rate of mortality—60 percent—hunting losses accounted for 27 percent and natural mortality for 33 percent; at the lowest annual rate—35 percent—hunting losses accounted for 11 percent and natural mortality for 25 percent. Natural mortality apparently is more fixed than hunting loss, which becomes increasingly additive to the total mortality rate as it rises.

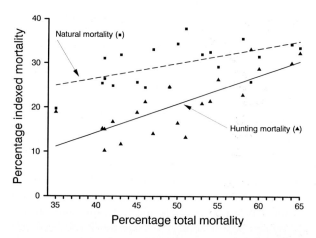

Figure 123. Relationship of natural and hunting mortality to all mortality of wood ducks, based on variations between five regions of the Atlantic and Mississippi flyways and four sex and age classes. The regression equations for natural mortality and hunting mortality are: $r^2 = 0.35$, $P < 0.01$, $y = 13.4 + 0.33x$, S.E. $= 0.145$; and $r^2 = 0.64$, $P < 0.001$, $y = -11.25 + 0.64x$, S.E. $= 0.080$, respectively.

East of the Great Plains in recent years (1990–1991 and 1991–1992), wood ducks composed about 19 percent of the total duck harvest, 23 percent in the Atlantic Flyway and 17 percent in the Mississippi Flyway. Woodies customarily are hunted from blinds, but in certain areas, especially in the Atlantic Flyway, jump shooting from a boat or by walking shores of streams and beaver ponds is a favorite tactic. *Photo by F. Eugene Hester.*

RECRUITMENT VERSUS SURVIVAL

In keeping with our findings that wood duck populations have increased over the last 20 years, our assumption that recruitment exceeded mortality during this period appears well founded. Comparison of female recruitment and mortality rates provides an approximation of the influence of recruitment on population status in regions of the two eastern flyways (Table 207).

The calculated differences in female recruitment and mortality rates are slightly lower than the annual gains in the autumn population, as derived from harvest and band data (see Chapter 5). Autumn populations embrace both males and females, whereas the recruitment and mortality data used here pertain only to females. But considering the tens of thousands of data sets that were compiled over extensive areas, we are surprised that these data from different sources are in general agreement. Northern areas had the lowest net gains in population; southern areas had the highest. Because there were few or no significant differences in the proportion of immatures in regional populations, lower mortality rates in both southern regions appear to have been responsible for the greater rate of population gains (Table 207).

The degree of population enhancement through recruitment levels above mortality levels results in a proportion of yearlings pioneering into new habitats (see Chapter 5). This expansion further fuels the ability of wood ducks to raise their

Table 207. Comparison of percentage of recruitment with percentage of mortality among wood duck females in regions of the Atlantic and Mississippi flyways, 1966–85.

Flyway/region	Females		Percentage difference in recruitment and mortality	Percentage of annual population gain[c]
	Percentage immatures[a]	Percentage mortality[b]		
Atlantic				
Northern	60.2	60.5	− 0.3	7.1
Southern	61.0	48.6	+ 12.4	8.7
Mississippi				
Northern	59.7	57.2	+ 2.5	9.2
Central	60.2	53.3	+ 6.9	12.1
Southern	54.8	42.1	+ 12.7	15.7

[a] From Table 194.
[b] Weighted for varying proportion of immature females in female population.
[c] From Chapter 5, figures 28–31.

recruitment capacity. Without recruitment rates above mortality rates, there would be no subsequent large-scale pioneering, and an existing population would sustain itself by incorporating a higher proportion of yearlings.

The number of breeders combined with the young they produce (recruitment) determines the autumn population. To arrive at the breeding population, we rely here on the previous season's survival of females combined with the calculated number of young females per adult female in the autumn population. As used here, the proportion of young among the female wood ducks examined at wing bees has been corrected for the increased vulnerability of young to hunting (as determined by banding data). Mortality rates (the reciprocal of survival rates) suggest that to maintain a stable population a female would need to produce 1.05 flying female young and 0.96 flying male young as of September 1.

Wood duck populations rise and fall as a result of yearly changes in survival and recruitment rates. To evaluate the relative interaction of these two factors on populations the following year, we analyzed the three variables by multiple regression, 1966–1985, for regions of the Atlantic and Mississippi flyways.

Survival and recruitment rates played different roles in the two flyways (Table 208). In the Atlantic Flyway, yearly survival rates were several times more important than recruitment rates in influencing the size of autumn populations. In the Mississippi Flyway, however, annual recruitment rates were 1.6 times more important than survival rates.

The greater importance of survival rates in the Atlantic Flyway may stem from the lower mean rates of survival that prevailed there from 1966 through 1985 (Table 198). In a similar corollary, the lower mean rates of wood duck recruitment in the

Table 208. Partial regression coefficients of the relative importance of annual survival versus annual recruitment in affecting the calculated annual autumn populations of female wood ducks in regions of the Atlantic and Mississippi flyways, 1966–85.

Flyway/region	R^2	P	a_0[a]	a_1[b]	a_2[c]
Atlantic					
Northern	0.21	<0.05	− 143.3	11.23	4.09
Southern	0.14	<0.10	453.6	5.87	0.50
Combined	0.24	<0.01	168.0	9.42	1.21
Mississippi					
Northern	0.38	<0.01	− 363.1	12.58	17.50
Central	0.46	<0.01	− 249.2	5.80	16.54
Southern	0.27	<0.05	− 226.1	− 10.45	60.56
Combined	0.15	<0.05	− 818.4	16.86	28.71

[a] Point of intercept.
[b] Regression coefficients of importance of survival.
[c] Regression coefficients of importance of recruitment.

Mississippi Flyway (see Table 194) may result in the yearly recruitment rates having the greater influence on yearly population size.

Wood duck populations have risen over the last 30 years as recruitment rates have exceeded mortality rates. An expansion of breeding birds into vacant or underpopulated habitats has provided a mechanism fostering population growth. Both of these rates are subject to change from year to year as various forces alter the wood duck's ability to survive and reproduce. Annual variations in recruitment probably relate to changes in temperature, intensity of precipitation, and timing in flooding of riverine habitats. Variation in yearly mortality rates stem at least in part from hunting harvest levels. Unlike mallard populations, which have an ability (within limits) to compensate for increases in harvest rates by a reduction in natural mortality rates, wood ducks experience a more additive effect of harvest rates on annual mortality rates.

Chapter 19

Nest Houses

Management programs often are designed to correct habitat deficiencies that limit population growth. After the mature forest was cleared in the eastern United States, wood duck production on wetlands with sufficient food and cover was curtailed because suitable nest sites were scarce. A lack of natural cavities was indicated by numerous reports of wood ducks nesting in house chimneys and other unusual places (Forbush 1925, Bellrose 1953, Stewart 1957).

The use of nest houses (or boxes) to improve wood duck nesting habitat was suggested by Forbush in 1912. In 1937, the U.S. Biological Survey (now the U.S. Fish and Wildlife Service) placed 486 bark-covered slab wood boxes (probably designed by Gill Gigstead and Milford Smith) on the Chautauqua National Wildlife Refuge in central Illinois. Over the next two years, the Illinois Natural History Survey erected approximately 700 rough-cut cypress board houses (designed by Arthur Hawkins and Frank Bellrose) in various parts of the state. Hawkins and Bellrose (1940) inspected many of these houses and found that more than half were used by wood ducks. They concluded that the provision of nest houses could be valuable in the management of this species.

NEST HOUSE DESIGN

Bellrose (1990), in his summary of nest house development, noted that the first nest houses built for wood ducks were used in aviaries. These structures usually were equipped with inclined walkways to large, round entrances (15 centimeters: 6 in) that were located only 5–10 centimeters (2–4 in)

above the floor of the house. In their pamphlet "Homes for Birds," Kalmbach and McAtee (1930) published a nest house design that resembled these aviary houses. They recommended the following measurements for wood duck nest houses: floor—25 by 46 centimeters (10 by 18 in); depth—25 to 38 centimeters (10–15 in); and entrance—7.6 centimeters (3 in) above the floor and 15 centimeters (6 in) in diameter.

Since the first attempt to improve wood duck nesting habitat with bark-covered slab boxes in the 1930s, a great deal of effort has been directed toward developing and testing new types of nest boxes. Major goals were to reduce predation, cost, and competition from other wildlife while increasing durability and ease of construction, placement, and maintenance (Bellrose 1953). Because of regional differences in habitats, predators, competitors, and climate, designs found effective locally often proved unsuccessful at other locations (M. M. Smith 1961, Strange et al. 1971, Grabill 1977, Soulliere 1985, Hartley and Hill 1990). The following descriptions of the more popular designs and predator guards include their dimensions, histories, major benefits, and negative aspects.

Slab Houses

Slab houses varied in size, but inside measurements averaged 23 by 23 by 61 centimeters (9 by 9 by 24 in), with the lowest point of the entrance 25.4–40.6 centimeters (10–16 in) above the house bottom. The round entrances averaged about 12.7 centimeters (5 in) in diameter. Like nearly all of the early styles, slab houses were erected on trees.

461

The first nest houses developed for use in game farms had large entrances, shallow depths, large receptacles, and usually an inclined walkway from the ground to the entrance. Those first extensively erected in the wild were relatively shallow slab-wood structures with large entrances that proved more attractive as raccoon dens. Only a small proportion were used by wood ducks. *Photo by James S. Ayars; courtesy of the Illinois Natural History Survey.*

Problems with this prototype included excessive weight, short life (only one-third remained functional five years after placement), and inability to exclude predators. Only 12 percent of these houses were used by wood ducks (Bellrose 1953).

Board Houses

The succeeding board house design was made from rough-cut lumber and had inside dimensions of 25 by 25 by 58 centimeters (10 by 10 by 23 in). This enclosure size—derived from information gained by measuring 28 natural cavities occupied by wood ducks in 1938 (Bellrose 1953)—was well accepted by wood ducks. An entrance of 10 centimeters (4 in) in diameter was placed 41 centimeters (16 in) above the floor. If smooth lumber was used instead of rough-cut lumber, a 5-centimeter (2 in) wide strip of 0.32- to 0.64-centimeter (0.13–0.25 in) mesh hardware cloth was attached to the inside from the bottom of the entrance hole to the floor so that the ducklings could climb out.

Using measurements based on those of natural cavities, 700 nest houses of rough-cut cypress boards were constructed and placed in numerous locations in Illinois by the Illinois Natural History Survey in 1939–1940. In the first year, acceptance by wood ducks was high, indicating that a shortage of natural cavities limited nesting opportunities. A horizontal perching bar or batten placed below the entrances of some early nest houses proved unnecessary; the proportional use of houses with and without the bar was similar. *Photo by Robert E. Hesselschwerdt; courtesy of the Illinois Natural History Survey.*

Board houses were far easier to erect and more durable than slab houses, and they could be built at a moderate cost, depending on type and source of lumber and cost of labor. Early board houses had 49-percent wood duck use (four times the use of slab houses), but nest predation was high; only 36.4 percent of the nests proved successful during 1939–1945 (Bellrose 1953).

Raccoons are an important predator in natural cavities (Bellrose et al. 1964, Prince 1965, Shake 1967) as well as in unprotected nest houses, and they often kill the female when destroying her nest (see Chapter 11). If smaller openings could be used, raccoon predation might be reduced. An experiment initiated in 1941 used captive raccoons and nest houses with entrances of various sizes and shapes to demonstrate that rarely was a raccoon of

4.5 kilograms (10 lb) or larger able to pass through an elliptical opening 10.2 by 7.6 centimeters (4 by 3 in) (Bellrose 1953). Although these dimensions were smaller than the head of a medium to large raccoon, field tests demonstrated that wood ducks could readily pass through entrances of that size and shape. Nest success increased dramatically after the installation of houses with "raccoon-proof" entrances. At northeastern Pennsylvania's Conneant Marsh, nest success more than doubled the year after houses with elliptical entrances were erected (Decker 1959).

In an effort to reduce cost and weight of wooden houses, Don Helmeke designed a cedar nest box with inside dimensions of 20.3 by 19.7 centimeters (8 by 7.75 in). On his study areas in Minnesota, wood ducks readily accepted this design with a small cavity. Helmeke now is experimenting with a box that has 20.3- by 16.5-centimeter (8 by 6.5 in) inside dimensions and measures about 25.4 centimeters (10 in) diagonally. He has found a number of successful nests and observed one wood duck hen that hatched 22 of 23 eggs in this small box.

The basic tree-mounted wood house design with a raccoon-proof entrance has continued to be the style most often employed (Figure 124). It is inexpensive, simple to construct, and natural in appearance. The entrance, however, must be a true ellipse and exactly 10.2 centimeters (4 in) horizontal by 7.6 centimeters (3 in) vertical. Any deviation will either permit the entry of larger raccoons or exclude increasing numbers of wood ducks.

Most of the early wood duck nest houses had large square (left) or circular (top right) entrances. Both the size and shape did little to discourage raccoon predation. Author Bellrose devised an elliptical entrance based on the size and shape of an adult wood duck body. At 10.2 by 7.6 centimeters (4 by 3 in), the holes permitted entry by wood ducks but not by most adult northern raccoons, whose skulls are too large. A few small yearling raccoons in the North and most adult raccoons in the South (particularly females) can wiggle through the prescribed elliptical hole (bottom right), but entrances larger or smaller in nest houses throughout the woodies' range have been shown to either increase predator access or reduce wood duck use. *Left photo by Clark Webster. Top right photo by Jack Dermid. Bottom right photo courtesy of the Michigan Department of Natural Resources.*

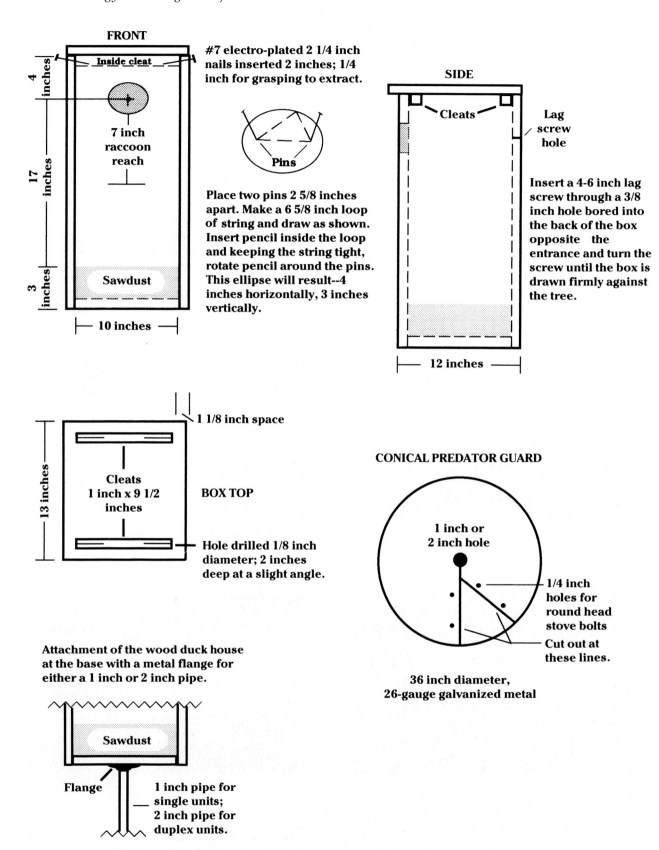

FRONT

Inside cleat

7 inch raccoon reach

Sawdust

10 inches

4 inches

17 inches

3 inches

#7 electro-plated 2 1/4 inch nails inserted 2 inches; 1/4 inch for grasping to extract.

Pins

Place two pins 2 5/8 inches apart. Make a 6 5/8 inch loop of string and draw as shown. Insert pencil inside the loop and keeping the string tight, rotate pencil around the pins. This ellipse will result--4 inches horizontally, 3 inches vertically.

SIDE

Cleats

Lag screw hole

Insert a 4-6 inch lag screw through a 3/8 inch hole bored into the back of the box opposite the entrance and turn the screw until the box is drawn firmly against the tree.

12 inches

13 inches

Cleats 1 inch x 9 1/2 inches

BOX TOP

1 1/8 inch space

Hole drilled 1/8 inch diameter; 2 inches deep at a slight angle.

CONICAL PREDATOR GUARD

1 inch or 2 inch hole

1/4 inch holes for round head stove bolts

Cut out at these lines.

36 inch diameter, 26-gauge galvanized metal

Attachment of the wood duck house at the base with a metal flange for either a 1 inch or 2 inch pipe.

Sawdust

Flange

1 inch pipe for single units; 2 inch pipe for duplex units.

Figure 124. Construction plan for a standard wooden nest house with a "raccoon-proof" entrance; measurements are in inches (1 inch = 2.54 centimeters) (from Bellrose 1976). Types of wood most often used include pine, cypress, and fir. If lumber is not rough-cut, the inside (from bottom of the entrance to the floor) must be thoroughly roughened or wire mesh must be added to provide a foothold for ducklings to climb out. A preservative should be applied on soft woods.

Elliptical entrances should be used in all wood duck nest houses wherever raccoons occur. At latitudes north of 38 degrees, almost all raccoons are too large to pass through an elliptical entrance of the dimensions given above; occasional late-born yearlings are an exception (see Chapter 11). As latitude decreases, however, an increasing number of raccoons are able to enter elliptical entrances (Figure 125). Raccoons become smaller with decreasing latitude, and south of 35 degrees latitude (the northern border of Tennessee/North Carolina), adult raccoons of average size can pass through elliptical entrances. Even in the deep South, however, some raccoons 4.5 kilograms (10 lb) or larger are excluded by elliptical entrances. For example, in eastcentral Alabama, about one-fourth of the adult male raccoons are excluded, but females are sufficiently small in spring to enter (calculated from data in A. S. Johnson 1970a).

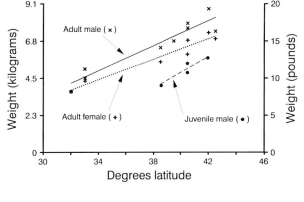

Figure 125. Average autumn weight of raccoons by sex and age in relation to degrees of latitude. Raccoon weights are slightly lower in spring. The regression equations for adult male, adult female, and juvenile male, respectively, are: $r = 0.95$, $P < 0.001$, $y = -17.50 + 0.84x$; $r = 0.97$, $P < 0.01$, $y = -13.56 + 0.69x$; and $r = 0.98$, $P < 0.01$, $y = -32.19 + 1.07x$.

Raccoons are tenacious predators of nesting wood ducks. When stymied from access to wood duck houses, some will attempt to enlarge the entry hole by clawing or chewing (top left). They also will reach into nest houses to claw at woodie hens inside (top right). The forelegs (including claws) and reach of adult raccoons are 22.9–30.5 centimeters (9–12 in). On about 10.2 centimeters (4 in) of nest material and eggs, woodie hens incubate at a head height of approximately 22.9 centimeters (9 in) above the nest bottom. Therefore, nest house depths below the bottom of the entrance should be a minimum of 45.7 centimeters (18 in). Damaged entrances or those wrongly shaped or too large can be "masked" by overlaying a board with a 10.2- by 7.6-centimeter (4 by 3 in) elliptical hole (bottom left). A sheet-metal face plate (bottom right) can prevent raccoons from enlarging nest house entrances. *Top photos by Greg Hubbard; houses provided by Stephen Simmons. Bottom photos by William E. Clark; courtesy of the Illinois Natural History Survey.*

Board variations and support guards. Other means of predator deterrence were tested about the same time as the elliptical entrance. In Massachusetts, Johnson (1947) found that houses erected on poles surrounded by open water were rarely pilfered by raccoons. At Yazoo National Wildlife Refuge in westcentral Mississippi, Strange et al. (1971) found only 10-percent raccoon predation of houses positioned over water, compared with 42 percent over land. Johnson (1947) deduced that wood ducks preferred marsh and pond edges because use decreased in houses farther from shore, but Grice and Rogers (1965) found that use was high when pole-mounted houses were placed in large open marshes in Massachusetts.

Raccoon predation was reduced with tunnel predator guards 25 centimeters (10 in) long and 10 centimeters (4 in) square that extended from house entrances. This design, developed by the Massachusetts Division of Fish and Game, prevented raccoon predation in that northern state (McLaughlin and Grice 1952) but proved ineffective in areas with smaller raccoons (Webster 1958). Additionally, Cronan (1957) found that when female wood ducks in Rhode Island had a choice, they selected houses without tunnel guards.

Because of variable success in developing predator-proof houses, designers began to investigate the use of support guards. These included wrapping trees with 0.6- to 0.9-meter (2–3 ft) bands of sheet metal, newspaper print aluminum or fiberglass fabric (Don Helmeke), or applying Tanglefoot® (a gummy substance used to prevent moth larvae from reaching forest canopies). When these barriers were placed 0.6 meter (2 ft) below and 1.2 meters (4 ft) above houses, and no adjacent tree or branch allowed a squirrel or raccoon to jump to the house or tree trunk between bands, nests escaped destruction (Bellrose 1953). Because of these requirements and because Tanglefoot® must be replaced yearly and sheet metal may need frequent adjustment with tree growth, these barriers proved of limited value. A strange occurrence was reported

Wood duck nest houses erected on poles or pipes in open water are not often disturbed by raccoons. Winter ice conditions provide opportune times to erect nest houses in appropriate shallow water areas and to repair and otherwise maintain existing overwater houses. *Photo by Jack Dermid.*

Effective use of wraparound sheet metal or nylon mesh bands between a nest house and the ground is a means of reducing nest destruction by arboreal, climbing predators. If trees are too close, squirrels (and sometimes raccoons) can gain access by leaping from one canopy to another. Also, the wrap must be wide enough or high enough above the ground to prevent squirrels, raccoons, and minks from leaping over it. *Photo by Frank Bellrose; courtesy of the Illinois Natural History Survey.*

in southeastern Missouri, where Clawson (1975b) found that cavity-seeking hens became trapped when investigating the space at the top of ill-fitting sheet metal guards wrapped around baldcypress trunks; these guards were responsible for the death of 20 hens.

When applied to wood posts or metal pipes, Tanglefoot® and axle grease can impede access to nest boxes by arboreal predators, but raccoons, squirrels, and snakes have been known to pass through these barriers (Bellrose 1953, Lowney 1987, Henne 1989). Applications of Tanglefoot® and axle grease must be inspected each year; if these substances become too dry, the hardened surface may permit predators to reach the nest box.

In eastern Texas, Ridlehuber (1980) observed fire ant predation on newly hatched woodie ducklings and pipped eggs. He found that by applying Tangletrap—a substance made by the Tanglefoot® company—to poles that supported nest boxes, fire ants could be prevented from reaching nest sites.

The shield design most frequently used today is the inverted cone. After a circle has been cut and riveted (or bolted) into a cone shape, it can be mounted on a wooden post with wooden mounting

Wood duck nest houses placed on posts or pipes on dry land have been used in a number of locations in the South. These duplex houses on 10- by 10-centimeter (4 by 4 in) posts are protected from arboreal predators by inverted cones. This house is on the Cross Creeks National Wildlife Refuge in Tennessee. *Photo by Glen C. Sanderson; courtesy of the Illinois Natural History Survey.*

blocks and galvanized nails or with metal support brackets and screws. When constructed to the proper dimensions and *snugly fitted*, cone shields provide the best available protection against pole-climbing predators. Strange et al. (1971) reported that inverted cones were ineffective against raccoons in Mississippi because many houses lost guards that were either inadequately mounted or poorly maintained. Lowney (1987) found that raccoon predation of nest boxes on Yazoo National Wildlife Refuge in Mississippi was reduced by about 85 percent where lithium grease was applied to metal poles that were protected with cone guards. When houses are placed on posts on land, some mammalian predators have reached nests by jumping above the guards (Henne 1989).

Snakes often are a significant predator of nests in the South, but their importance decreases at northern latitudes. In the Illinois River Valley, bull snakes were responsible for only 8 percent of all unsuccessful nests during 1939–1945 (Bellrose 1953). In Louisiana, however, rat snakes have been the most important cause of nest loss (M. M. Smith 1961, Bateman 1977). In a southeastern Missouri study, black rat snakes were the primary predator, destroying 33 percent of all nests (Hansen 1968). Rat snakes have been found in houses on poles more than 1.6 kilometers (1 mi) from land (Rogers 1955), and large snakes are able to circumvent predator guards (see Chapter 11).

The use of tightly fitted cone shields of adequate dimensions provides the best-known method of protecting wood duck nests where this predator is abundant, primarily in the deep South. Hansen and Fredrickson (1990) suggested that houses should be visually isolated from one another in habitats where rat snakes occur and not placed in areas known to support high populations of rat snakes. Application of a material similar to the pine resin that protects the nest cavities of red-cockaded woodpeckers from rat snakes (Jackson 1974, Rudolph et al. 1990) on wood duck cavity trees or house support structures probably would reduce snake predation (Hansen and Fredrickson 1990).

Fox squirrels were responsible for consistently high losses of wood duck nests in early tree-mounted board houses (Bellrose 1953), and experimentation to prohibit their entrance was undertaken. Houses with sheet metal flanges and houses totally wrapped in sheet metal with pyramidal roofs were evaluated. Squirrels were able to bypass flanges, often by hanging from them to secure a foothold at the entrance. Metal-wrapped wood houses performed better but were relatively expensive and time-consuming to construct (Bellrose 1953).

Metal Houses

In 1950, at the suggestion of Louis Ellebrecht, then manager of the Chautauqua National Wildlife Refuge, we used a galvanized cold-air pipe of 26-gauge metal, 30.5 centimeters (12 in) in diameter and 61 centimeters (24 in) long, to form the body of a new house design (Figure 126) (Bellrose 1953). An

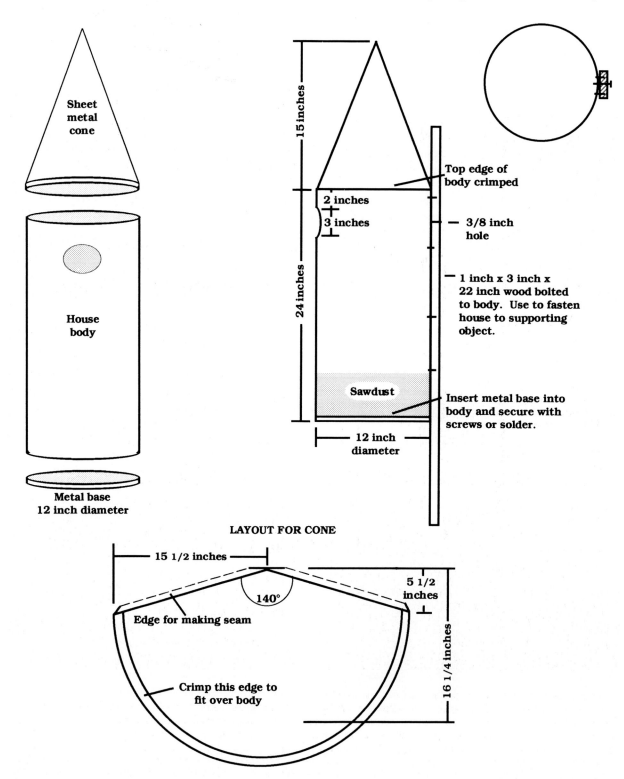

Figure 126. Construction plan for a metal ("rocket") house; measurements are in inches (1 inch = 2.54 centimeters) (from Bellrose 1976). These houses are easily constructed and the most predator-proof of all tree-mounted designs. Wood floors often are used, especially in colder climates.

elliptical, raccoon-proof entrance was cut with its upper edge 5–8 centimeters (2–3 in) from the upper end of the pipe section. An inverted, galvanized metal cone 38 centimeters (15 in) high was used for the roof; this design invited the nicknames "rocket house," "torpedo," and "tin-whistle." Three metal screws, which could be easily removed during inspections, attached the roof. The bottom was a circular piece of galvanized metal soldered to the pipe section.

Sheet-metal nest houses for wood ducks were developed to reduce nest predation, particularly by squirrels and starlings. Cylinders are 61.0 by 25.4 centimeters (24 by 10 in), with the conical top 38.1 centimeters (15 in) high. Combined with an elliptical entrance, they materially reduced nest losses, except from rat snakes and small raccoons in the South and starlings and flickers everywhere. Note the hen departing the house in the left photo. That house was experimentally enlarged to a 30.5-centimeter (12 in) diameter, with a circular entrance 12.7 centimeters (5 in) in diameter, to evaluate use by starlings and woodies. Although starling use of this model was less than smaller sizes, so was wood duck occupancy. These reductions and the increased construction cost warranted abandonment of this nest house prototype. Also, only the house in the top right photo has a properly shaped and sized entrance. *Left photo by Wilmer Zehr; courtesy of the Illinois Natural History Survey. Top right photo courtesy of the Illinois Natural History Survey. Bottom right photo by Clark Webster.*

The interior walls of early metal houses were brushed or sprayed with a tarlike auto undercoating that darkened the interior, roughened the walls, and provided ducklings a foothold to use in climbing out. An alternative was the attachment of hardware cloth below the entrance for a simpler, less expensive means of enabling ducklings to exit. On the Illinois River, wood duck use was compared in metal houses of two diameters and in houses with hardware cloth versus undercoated interiors. Use of houses with larger diameters was lower (P < 0.01, t-test) at one study area (Table 209), but interior design appeared to make little difference. Further investigation at Chautauqua National Wildlife Refuge during 1969–1971 revealed higher (P < 0.05, t-test) wood duck use of 30- and 25-centimeter (12 and 10 in) houses compared with the use of houses 20 centimeters (8 in) in diameter; percentage use was 41.2 (n = 318), 43.1 (n = 174), and 27.3 (n = 399), respectively. During 1975–1981, wood duck use at Chautauqua National Wildlife Refuge was 62.6 percent (n = 214), 71.4 percent (n = 56), and 52.5 percent (n = 183) for 30-centimeter (12 in), 25-centimeter (10 in), and 23-centimeter (9 in) houses, respectively, according to a report by Julia Nault. John Lakowski also reported that wood ducks at Moraine Hills State Park, northwest of Chicago, selected 30-centimeter (12 in) diameter houses more frequently (P < 0.05, t-test) than they selected 23-centimeter (9 in) houses. During 1977–1984, percentage use averaged 90 (n = 60) for the larger diameter and 54 (n = 135) for the smaller.

Nest house diameters varying between 23 and 36 centimeters (9–14 in) had only slight effect on clutch size in central Illinois (Figure 127). Oddly, the largest size had the smallest clutches, but this may relate to reduced dump nesting in large-diameter houses that are less attractive to woodies.

There has been little evidence that squirrels or other predatory mammals are able to enter a properly erected metal "rocket" house. The entry of small raccoons has been documented, but such occurrence can be reduced by mounting houses to

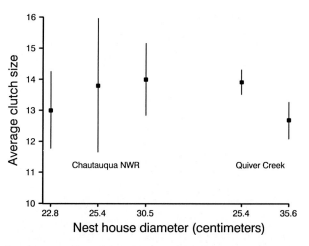

Figure 127. Effect of nest house diameter on wood ducks' mean clutch size at Chautauqua National Wildlife Refuge and Quiver Creek, Illinois. The lines extending from the means are standard deviations.

wooden posts with predator shields or attaching houses directly to pipes or metal brackets without the use of a mounting board (Webster 1958).

Metal houses with raccoon-proof entrances have had far greater nest success than did the early wood houses (Bellrose 1953). Metal houses are simple to construct, lightweight, and durable. They can be painted natural colors to make them esthetically more acceptable. Compared with wood houses, they are slightly more expensive to construct and, in some cases, initially used less frequently by wood ducks (Bellrose et al. 1964).

Standard wood houses that have 10.2- by 7.6-centimeter (4 by 3 in) elliptical entrances and are attached to trees have become the most commonly used design, but wood houses on poles—often with predator guards—and metal houses also have been widely deployed. These three house types make up about 85 percent of the houses that have been erected since 1937. Other wood, metal, and synthetic styles, including wood duplex and multibox, horizontal metal, plastic, paper, and nailkeg houses, also have been deployed and account for the remaining 15 percent.

Table 209. Percentage of wood duck use of metal nest houses with different interiors (undercoat spray versus hardware cloth) and diameters (30 versus 36 centimeters: 11.8 vs. 14.2 in) at two study areas on the Illinois River, 1968–74.[a]

Area	With undercoat spray		With hardware cloth	
	30 centimeters	36 centimeters	30 centimeters	36 centimeters
Duck Island	48.9 (45)[b]	24.4 (45)	44.7 (47)	15.7 (51)
Upper river	52.0 (75)	50.0 (44)	46.9 (49)	54.5 (33)
Mean (total)	50.5 (120)	37.2 (89)	45.8 (96)	35.1 (84)

[a] Undercoat spray versus hardware cloth interiors: t = 1.21, P > 0.10. Thirty-centimeter diameter versus 36-centimeter diameter: t = 2.56, P < 0.01.
[b] Number of house-years (number of houses times years available) are given in parentheses.

Raccoons are not only skillful climbers, but those 4.5 kilograms (10 lbs) and under can squeeze through even a 10.2- by 7.6-centimeter (4 by 3 in) elliptical opening. If nest houses are mounted on top of pipes, small raccoons have difficulty reaching the entrances. Moreover, a 38.1-centimeter (15 in) high conical top will inhibit most small raccoons from reaching the entrance while clinging to the peak with their hind paws. Raccoons that occur in the South are naturally smaller in size than northern raccoons and therefore pose a greater threat to woodies nesting in houses with elliptical entrances. Note that without the mounting board above, which was unnecessary, the raccoon likely could not have climbed onto the house or reached the entrance. *Photos by Clark Webster.*

A hen leaving a sheet-metal house illustrates the snug fit of a 10.2- by 7.6-centimeter (4 by 3 in) elliptical entrance. Nonetheless, in hundreds of nest houses with elliptical entrances examined periodically over many years, few were known to exclude wood duck females. Better a snug fit than a dead duck or eggs consumed by a raccoon. *Photo by Robert Hagar; courtesy of the Illinois Department of Conservation.*

Duplex Houses

In an effort to reduce cost of wood duck house construction, Webster (1958) suggested placing more than one house per pole and predator shield. The practice of placing "duplex" houses made of two abutting wood compartments with the same backboard on a single galvanized metal pole developed in Louisiana (Bateman 1977). Because its support mounting is in the center of the floor, a duplex is fairly predator proof even without a shield. The elliptical entrance excludes large raccoons, and smaller ones usually are unable to gain a foothold from under the house after scaling the pole. Base-mounted houses require less support material to achieve the standard entrance height—a slight economic advantage over other pipe mountings.

Barry (1992) found no significant difference in the success of wood duck dump nests in houses attached one or two per pole at the Yazoo National Wildlife Refuge, 1987–1991.

With the help of the Illinois Department of Conservation, we erected and studied 40 duplex houses (80 compartments) on a 1.4-kilometer (0.9 mi) continuous backwater area in the Mississippi River at Nauvoo, Illinois. Within three years (1984–1986), most of these houses were used by wood ducks, and the area developed the densest known population of breeding wood ducks in North America (see Chapter 10).

Authors Frank Bellrose (left) and Dan Holm check one of 40 duplex houses at Nauvoo Slough, Illinois. These houses were placed approximately 36.6 meters (40 yd) apart in a 1.6-kilometer (1 mi) long, 6-hectare (15 ac) slough adjacent to the Mississippi River. Although as many as 75 hens nested in the 40 houses, much intraspecific strife resulted; incubating hens attacked, injured, and killed intruding hens bent on laying eggs or incubating. *Photo by Mike Beno.*

Colonial Houses

The use of colonial structures or wood duck "apartments" with 18, 36, and 72 standard wood boxes was investigated at Coulee Wildlife Refuge in northeastern Louisiana (Moore 1981). This design was potentially more economical per compartment to construct and maintain, but Moore found that as the number of apartments increased, the proportion of nests completed decreased, as did the production (ducklings hatched per eggs laid) in each compartment. He observed that females may have become confused by the large number of boxes and could not consistently identify their nest sites. A lack of site attachment might have led to indiscriminate laying, nest abandonment, and a waste of eggs. Although ducklings were produced in 110 percent of the available duplex houses (many had more than one nest annually), production progressively declined from 42 percent to 21 percent to 15 percent in 18-, 36-, and 72-box structures, respectively. Earlier, Webster and Uhler (1964) had recommended that no more than six compartments be included in a structure, because they too suspected that hens might become confused and abandon nests. At Union Slough National Wildlife Refuge in Iowa, where groups of two to four (mostly four) boxes were spaced approximately 0.76-meter (2.5 ft)

apart and mounted on pipe support structures, Fleskes et al. (1990) found a 77-percent occupancy rate. However, we recommend that support structures have no more nest sites than the two provided by duplex compartments.

Placing an array of wood duck nest houses on a common pole or otherwise clustering them in close proximity reduces the construction cost and placement difficulty, and it simplifies inspection. However, such consolidations may increase dump nesting, intraspecific strife, and confusion among nesting hens, resulting in more negative than positive productivity. *Top left photo by Lloyd Poissenot; courtesy of the Louisiana Department of Wildlife and Fisheries. Bottom left photo by Barbara Myers; courtesy of the Union Slough National Wildlife Refuge. Right photo by Glen Stanley.*

Horizontal and Companion Houses

Starlings occur throughout the wood duck's range and often invade houses. On our Quiver Creek study area near Havana, Illinois, starlings not only used houses for nesting but also destroyed wood duck nests by harassing incubating hens until the hens deserted. In 1963, starlings usurped 24 percent of the nests in which woodies were either laying or incubating.

At the Patuxent Research Center in Laurel, Maryland, McGilvrey and Uhler (1971) designed a horizontal cylindrical house that was erected on posts. Wood ducks accepted this house but starlings rarely used it. The house consisted of a 61-centimeter (24 in) section of 30-centimeter (12 in) diameter galvanized furnace pipe. The lower two-thirds of one end was closed with a wood panel 2.5 centimeters (1 in) thick, leaving a 10- by 30-centimeter (4 by 11.5 in) entrance. Compared with wood ducks, starlings prefer less light in their nest sites—a conclusion indicated by the clear preference of starlings for the darker compartments of houses with tunnel predator guards (Grice and Rogers 1965), black-stained interiors, smaller entrances (Lumsden 1976), deeper cavities, and smaller diameters (see Chapter 11).

McGilvrey and Uhler (1971) found that although vertical metal houses had 39-percent use by wood ducks and 46-percent use by starlings, horizontal houses had only 5-percent use by starlings and 33-percent wood duck occupancy. On the Holston River in eastern Tennessee, Muncy and Burbank (1975) compared the use of wood, rocket (vertical metal), and horizontal metal designs. Starling use during 1971–1975 averaged 31 percent in rocket houses and 40 percent in wood houses but only 3 percent in horizontal houses. Wood duck use averaged 33 percent in wood and rocket houses and 11 percent in horizontal houses. During the five-year study, wood duck use of houses of horizontal design increased from 0 to 23 percent, while starling use increased from 0 to 6 percent. Muncy and Burbank (1975) concluded that horizontal houses reduced interspecific strife between starlings and wood ducks for nest sites.

In Massachusetts, 1970–1975, Heusmann et al. (1977) evaluated wood duck use of horizontal metal cylinders and conventional wood houses. Nest use in horizontal cylinders was 31.6 percent compared to 48.5 percent in wood boxes—a difference that lacked statistical significance. Nest success was 73.4 percent in the cylinders and 77.1 percent in the board boxes, again a statistically insignificant difference. Although starlings did not attempt to use the horizontal cylinders for nesting, grackles be-

came a problem in some units by usurping these nest sites.

Fiedler et al. (1990) compared wood duck use of horizontal cylinders and conventional wood houses along the Columbia River in central Washington, 1983–1987. In this region of sparse wood duck nesting populations, 5 and 51 percent of the cylinder and wood nest houses, respectively, were used by wood ducks. Fiedler et al. (1990) stated that blackening the interior of horizontal metal cylinders increased their use by wood ducks. Only one starling nest was recorded in the horizontal cylinders, but starling use of wood houses varied yearly from 8 to 45 percent. By covering entrances of wood houses until April 20, they reduced starling use from 45 to 8–16 percent. The earliest recorded wood duck nest was April 23, two to three weeks later than the earliest recorded starling nest.

A horizontal sheet-metal tube, 30.5 by 61.0 centimeters (12 by 24 in) with a 10.2- by 27.9-centimeter (4 by 11 in) semicircular entrance, has proven to be the most effective wood duck nest house developed for deterring use by starlings. Where wood duck nesting density is sufficient, substantial use is made of these houses, although somewhat less than of vertical houses. One way to put this type of nest house to effective use for wood ducks is to develop a nesting "colony" with vertical houses and then gradually substitute horizontal ones. *Photo by F. C. Schmid; courtesy of the U.S. Fish and Wildlife Service.*

In central Wisconsin, horizontal houses were not used by wood ducks, according to A. E. Geiger. We found that only 5 percent were used by wood ducks at Nauvoo, Illinois, 1978–1982, whereas average use of three other designs (wood, metal rocket, and plastic Tom Tubbs®) ranged from 74 to 98 percent during 1978–1982. Horizontals also met with little success at Pungo National Wildlife Refuge in eastern North Carolina (Grabill 1977).

Heusmann et al. (1977) suggested that the degree of horizontal cylinder acceptance by wood ducks appeared related to nesting population pressure. Where conventional nest sites were at a premium, an increasing number of wood ducks utilized metal cylinders. Subsequent findings further substantiated this hypothesis. Where starlings are a problem, Heusmann et al. (1977) suggested gradually shifting from vertical to horizontal nest structures over a five-year period.

Grabill (1977) recorded good results with a "piggyback" design. After attaching small wood houses to one side of wood duck houses of standard wood design, he found that starling use decreased in the larger houses. The small houses were 15 by 15 by 41 centimeters (6 by 6 by 16 in), with an entrance 5 centimeters (2 in) in diameter. In the third year of his investigation, starling use was 13 percent in the large houses and 93 percent in the small adjoining compartments. Starlings and wood ducks each used 31 percent of the conventional houses, whereas wood ducks occupied 62 percent of the units with small houses attached. Because the compartments were preferred by starlings and because these birds are territorial, nesting pairs prevented other starlings from using the attached wood duck houses. Starlings often harass wood ducks entering their territories, but Grabill (1977) did not find this to be a concern at Pungo; the average desertion rate of wood duck nests was similar in piggyback and conventional houses. Grabill's design has not received much recognition and its use has been primarily in North Carolina.

William Keim reduced starling use of wood duck houses in Virginia by enlarging the entrances of standard wood houses to 10.2 centimeters (4 in) vertical and 28 centimeters (11 in) horizontal. However, at Dulles International Airport in northern Virginia, Richard C. Cullerton still found moderate starling use and high wood duck use of the large entrance proposed by Keim (see Chapter 11). This design provides another means of reducing starling use, but its value may depend on the abundance of breeding starlings. Guards are necessary because the enlarged entrance allows unlimited access to arboreal predators.

Although starlings readily use houses placed in open, parklike settings, they rarely use houses placed in dense woods (see Chapter 11). Locating houses in heavily wooded areas so that no house is visible from an adjacent house not only helps to reduce use by starlings but also curtails predation and intraspecific competition among female wood ducks (Haramis and Thompson 1985, Semel et al. 1988, Henne 1989, Hansen and Fredrickson 1990).

Experimental designs to reduce starling competition for use of wood duck nests included large-diameter (35.6 centimeters: 14 in) vertical metal houses with a 12.7-centimeter (5 in) entrance (left) and a standard elliptical entry with additional light holes (right). Both somewhat deterred starling occupation, but also that of woodies. *Photos by Wilmer Zehr; courtesy of the Illinois Natural History Survey.*

Plastic Houses

The Tom Tubbs® wood duck nest house was commercially produced by the Minnesota Waterfowl Association, but is no longer available. This house is made of a durable plastic and mounted on either a horizontal pipe attached to a tree or a vertical pipe over water or land. The egg-shaped body is 28 centimeters (11 in) in diameter at the widest point, and the floor is about 38 centimeters (15 in) below the bottom of the 8- by 10-centimeter (3 by 4 in) elliptical entrance.

In central Wisconsin, Soulliere (1985) found that wood duck use of Tom Tubbs® houses compared favorably with five other commonly used designs; only wood houses had more use. However, Hartley and Hill (1990) found only 14 percent use of 1,150 Tom Tubbs® nest boxes placed along the Tennessee-Tombigbee Waterway in eastern Mississippi and westcentral Alabama. They discovered that heat buildup in boxes exposed to full sunlight can kill developing wood duck embryos. Consequently, in the southern half of the wood duck's range, Tom Tubbs® and similar single-walled plastic boxes should be placed only in areas that receive full shade.

Another type of plastic house was manufactured for Ducks Unlimited (1988–1991) and for Cattail Products, Inc., by Custom-Pak of Clinton, Iowa. The front and back portions of this house are molded separately and hinged for easy maintenance. The elliptical entrance is located 43.2 centimeters (17 in) above the floor and the body is 22.9 centimeters (9 in) in diameter. This design can be bolted to a pipe or nailed directly to a tree. Its light color, ventilation slots, and double-walled construction reduce heat buildup, which should not be a problem. At Riverside, California, Fred Pedley reported successful nests in these houses mounted on pipes in open areas.

In the deep South ambient temperature during the breeding season reaches levels that impact the nest success of wood ducks in houses composed of plastic and certain other materials. Hartley and Hill (1990) reported that in a single-walled plastic (Tom Tubbs®) nest house in full sun, placed over water with the entrance facing east in central Mississippi, maximum temperature exceeded lethal levels for egg viability—41.5 degrees Celsius (107°F)—and incubating hens—47 degrees Celsius (117°F)—for April, May, and June.

James Byrns of Custom-Pak at Clinton, Iowa, evaluated the effect of ambient temperatures on the interior temperatures of nest houses composed of different materials (Table 210). Unfortunately, only one day in 1992, August 24, did temperatures reach a high of 32.2 degrees Celsius (90° F) with a bright sun and no wind. Under those conditions, a cypress wood house was the coolest while a single-walled plastic and a metal canister house were the warmest (Table 210). A vented, light-colored, double-walled plastic house was next to the cypress box in temperature control.

The ambient shade necessary to protect the interior of wood duck houses from excessive heat buildup depends on latitude, house material, thickness, outside color, and air vents. Where temperatures are above 32 degrees Celsius (90° F) during

Table 210. Interior temperatures of wood duck nest houses composed of different materials, thicknesses, and colors, in relation to ambient temperature.[a]

Construction material	Thickness[b]		Temperature[c]							
			10:00 a.m.		12:00 noon		2:00 p.m.		4:00 p.m.	
[Ambient air]			31.1	(88)	32.2	(90)	31.7	(89)	30.0	(86)
Cypress wood	2.54–3.18	(1.0–1.25)							33.9	(93)
Particle board	0.95	(0.375)	35.6	(96)	36.1	(97)	36.7	(98)		
Single-walled plastic	0.48	(0.188)	37.8	(100)	38.3	(101)	37.2	(99)		
Single-walled plastic	0.32	(0.125)	38.9	(102)	40.6	(105)	40.0	(104)		
Metal canister	0.16	(0.625)	38.7	(102)	40.6	(105)	40.0	(104)		
Double-walled plastic (dark)	1.27	(0.5)	35.6	(96)	37.8	(100)	37.8	(100)		
Double-walled plastic (light)	1.27	(0.5)	35.0	(95)	36.7	(98)	36.7	(98)		
Double-walled plastic (light, vented)	1.27	(0.5)	34.4	(94)	35.6	(96)	35.6	(96)	33.3	(92)

[a] Recorded August 24, 1992 by James Byrns, Custom-Pak, Clinton, Iowa. August 24, 1992: full sun; no clouds or wind; facing south; thermometer in center of house; 10.2–15.2 centimeters (4–6 in) above bottom covered with 10.2 centimeters (4 in) of sawdust.
[b] In centimeters (inches).
[c] In degrees Celsius (Fahrenheit).

any appreciable part of the breeding season, nest houses should be placed in the shade or at least shaded from afternoon sunlight.

To determine use rates and learn of potential problems of the Custom-Pak house, a questionnaire was distributed following the first nesting season in which Ducks Unlimited boxes were available. Forty-one responses contained sufficient information to be used (Table 211). Use rates of 42 percent for the Mississippi Flyway and 43 percent for the Atlantic Flyway compared favorably with reports for other box designs (Bellrose 1976) (tables 211 and 212).

One problem observed with tree-mounted, plastic Tom Tubbs® and Custom-Pak houses is their use by squirrels that chew and enlarge the entrances. Enlarged entrances also admit excessive precipitation and provide easy access for raccoons that otherwise would be unable to enter. A metal ring currently provided with the Custom-Pak-produced houses can be attached around the elliptical entrance with rivets to reduce squirrel damage. Plans call for this metal ring to be attached to all houses at the factory.

The plastic "bucket house" is a homemade design formed with two standard 19-liter (5 gal) buckets (Meier 1983) or a single bucket with a wood top (Griffith and Fendley 1981). The two-bucket model, which was developed in Wisconsin, is mounted on a pipe; pipe flanges can be bolted to either the floor or the side of the bucket. The single-bucket design, developed in South Carolina, is mounted directly on trees. The developers of both designs predicted long house life, but the two-bucket design — tree-mounted on horizontal pipes — had significantly fewer (P < 0.05) usable houses four to six years after placement than did five other designs in Wisconsin (Soulliere 1985). Short life makes even cheaply constructed houses, such as the "bucket" types, inefficient (Heusmann and Early 1988).

Only one type of plastic wood duck house is currently being manufactured — by Custom-Pak of Clinton, Iowa. It is distributed by Cattails Inc. of Fulton, Illinois. Corrected for problems with heat buildup and squirrel damage, these houses are durable, reasonably priced, and easily and efficiently maintained. *Bottom photo by Dan Holm; courtesy of the Illinois Natural History Survey. Top photo by Robert A. Montgomery; courtesy of the Max McGraw Wildlife Foundation.*

Table 211. First-year use of Ducks Unlimited, Inc. nest houses (determined from a questionnaire survey), 1988.

Flyway/region	Number of replies	Number of houses	Number of houses used	Percentage of houses used
Mississippi				
North	11	100	48	48.0
Central	11	123	11	8.9
South	4	114	82	71.9
Subtotal	26	337	141	41.8
Atlantic				
North	11	205	89	43.4
Central	4	34	14	41.2
Subtotal	15	239	103	43.1
Total	41	576	244	42.4

Table 212. Average percentage of nest house use by wood ducks from studies with multiple designs available concurrently.

Location (area name)	Period	Designs on poles over water				Designs on trees over land	
		Wood	Metal	Horizontal metal	Tom Tubbs®	Wood	Metal
Central Wisconsin (Mead)	1982–84	0.0 (41)[a]				16.5 (128)	9.3 (343)
Westcentral Washington (Fort Lewis)	1984	82.5 (63)			30.4 (23)	60.1 (138)	
Northeastern Illinois (Max McGraw)[b]	1967–81	28.8 (52)		48.2 (108)	85.7 (7)		66.6 (632)
Westcentral Illinois (Nauvoo)	1978–83	78.4 (88)	88.3 (60)	5.6 (18)	74.1 (27)		
Northeastern Illinois (Moraine Hills)	1976–84	82.1 (28)		0.0 (2)		61.4 (176)	65.1 (195)
Central Illinois (Spring Lake)	1971–74					83.3 (36)	47.2 (36)
Western Tennessee (Bear Creek)	1977	15.2 (33)	26.5 (34)				
Northeastern Tennessee (Holston River)[b]	1971–75					33.3 (129)	32.9 (164)
Southeastern Missouri (Duck Creek)	1966–74	112.5[e] (48)				152.1 (194)	146.0 (441)
Central Maryland (Eastern Neck)	1970	47.4 (19)	14.3 (14)	17.2 (29)			

[a] Number of house-years (number of houses times years available) in parentheses.
[b] Some house styles were mounted on either poles or trees, and data were categorized by the majority mounting site. This study did not break down use rates by mount design.
[c] Unpublished data from Illinois Department of Conservation.
[d] Commercially produced design of plastic material similar to Tom Tubbs®.
[e] Percentages over 100 indicate multiple use of houses by wood ducks during the same year.

Other House Designs

A variety of materials have been used for still more designs, but none of these has been widely deployed. Less popular designs include metal wastebaskets (Montgomery et al. 1982), plastic detergent containers (J. D. Kason), wood ammunition boxes or cases (Stewart 1957, Almand 1965, Prevost 1983, Spero et al. 1983), polyvinyl chloride (PVC) pipe (Moore 1981), auto tires (Teague 1971, Moore 1981), fiberglass "rocket" (Bednarik 1984), salvaged fiberglass aerial radar pods (R. S. Sullivan), fiberboard (T. Z. Atkenson and S. K. Joyner), aluminum cylinders (Strom 1969), sheet aluminum (Warren 1969), steel grease pails and drums (J. C. Appel and G. L. Clawson), steel machine-gun belt canisters (R. Toltzman), and gas barrels and wing tanks (Hansen 1971). Among the welter of unusual materials, two types of nest houses stand out: one fashioned from PVC pipe, the other made of two freon canisters. Moore (1981) reported that houses constructed of 20.3-centimeter (8 in) PVC pipe were used as frequently and successfully as similarly erected wood houses. George Wellenkotter of Edgerton, Wisconsin, has had excellent use of 20.3-centimeter (8 in) PVC pipe nest houses left white but with black spots of spray paint to imitate white birch trees.

Two freon canisters were combined by Glen L. Welp, at Union Slough National Wildlife Refuge, Iowa, to make a sturdy, inexpensive nest house. From 1979 to 1987, 77 percent of these canister houses at Union Slough were occupied, compared with 78 percent of the metal rocket houses, 83 percent of fiberboard houses, and 58 percent of those made from tires (Fleskes et al. 1990).

Standard wood houses also have been treated with preservative (Warren 1969) and painted various colors (Morse and Wight 1969) in an effort to detect a preference by wood ducks. Uses of treated and untreated houses were similar. During 1968–1970, we tested variously colored bedding sawdust in nest houses in central Illinois to determine if wood ducks had a preference. Use of houses with uncolored sawdust was highest (84.7 percent, n = 544), followed by houses with red (57.6 percent, n = 92), green (21.4 percent, n = 28), and blue (11.4 percent, n = 44) sawdust.

Table 212. (continued)

Designs on trees over land			
Horizontal metal	Tom Tubbs®	Source	
	14.8 (50)	Soulliere (1985)	
	0.0 (6)	Beall et al. (1984)	
		Montgomery et al. (1982)	
		This study	
		J. I. Laskowski[c]	
	50.0[d] (18)	This study	
0.0 (7)		Goetz and Sharp (1981)	
11.3 (133)		Muncy and Burbank (1975)	
		Clawson (1975a)	
		McGilvrey and Uhler (1971)	

The most important ingredient in a wood duck nest site is security from predators. Nest houses have been successfully fashioned from old tires that are suspended by wires, reducing access to arboreal mammals and snakes. The use of such an unorthodox nest structure indicates the wide range of adaptability that woodies have to nest sites. *Photo by Lloyd Poissenot; courtesy of the Louisiana Department of Wildlife and Fisheries.*

Sections of PVC pipe have been successfully converted to wood duck nest houses (left) by George Wellenkotter of Edgerton, Wisconsin. Both 20.3-centimeter (8 in) and 25.4-centimeter (10 in) diameter PVC pipe have been used, but the former is preferred for commercial distribution because of lower cost and weight. Incubating hens may be relatively uncomfortable in the smaller diameter, but more than two-thirds of such nest houses have been used by woodies, attesting to its acceptability. *Photo by George Wellenkotter.*

IMPLEMENTING A NEST BOX PROGRAM

Nest house programs are started for a number of reasons—to increase local populations, conduct research, or satisfy a personal interest. To avoid the frustration of erecting many houses at an apparently good location, only to discover later that few are being used by wood ducks, programs should start small. A general rule is to add houses when a use rate of 50–80 percent is achieved; however, only as many houses as can be maintained should be added. Areas lacking the food and cover necessary for hens and broods are poor places to erect houses.

Wood ducks are not particularly critical of house designs or erection methods in most areas. In the deep South, for example, they appear to nest in practically any containerlike object on a tree or pole located near brood habitat. Moore (1981) found wood ducks in northeastern Louisiana using 41 percent of the houses constructed from auto tires and 134 percent (many houses had more than one nest annually) of houses made from polyvinyl chloride pipe. At Illinois' Max McGraw Wildlife Refuge, Dillon (1970) and Montgomery et al. (1982) found wood ducks using 70–90 percent of the houses made of wastebaskets placed on trees or poles.

Box Placement

Nest boxes can be placed in a variety of habitats where some dense herbaceous and shrub cover is available—marshes, swamps, woodland streams, overflow bottomlands, lakes, beaver ponds, farm ponds, and stock ponds. Wood duck houses are of most value in areas where wetland habitats provide sufficient food and cover but hardwood trees are too small or too few to provide a reasonable number of cavities.

Our subjective interpretation of the value of houses in selected habitats is shown in Figure 128. Marsh habitats generally have sufficient cover and food resources to support wood duck populations but lack cavity nest sites. Thus, they are ideal places to locate nest houses. Open swamps and bottomland forests generally support larger populations of wood ducks and have higher nest box occupancy rates than do the linear habitats provided by streams (Brown 1972a, Heitmeyer and Fredrickson 1990).

Farm ponds that provide dense herbaceous or woody cover and occur near streams also are of value to wood ducks, according to Ace Baxter, Richard C. Cullerton, and William Keim; however, boxes should be used sparingly. Ace Baxter achieved an

For a wood duck nest box program, three important rules of thumb are: (1) erect only the number of houses that can be maintained, (2) do not add more houses until 50 to 80 percent of those erected on a site are in use, and (3) allow a minimum of 46 meters (50 yd) between nest house structures. *Photo by Jack Dermid.*

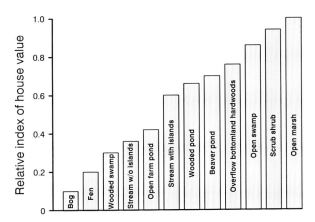

Figure 128. Subjective rating of the relative value of various types of aquatic habitats for the use of nest houses by wood ducks east of the Great Plains.

excellent occupancy rate on small ponds of 0.04–0.08 hectare (0.1–0.2 ac) located 2.8 kilometers (1.75 mi) from the Mississippi River in westcentral Illinois. Early in Ohio's wood duck nest house program, Handley (1955) reported that 17 percent of nearly 2,000 houses on farm ponds were used. On three 0.4-hectare (1 ac) ponds, 14 of 19 houses (74 percent) were occupied by wood ducks. According to a 1959 report on the use of houses placed on ponds in the Delaware Reservoir Area of Ohio, 49 percent of 100 houses had wood duck nests (Handley 1962). Karl Bednarik reported that farm ponds in Ohio are about equally distributed in pastures and wooded areas.

On farm pond-type wetlands in central New York, Klein (1955) found 34.4 percent of 64 board houses used by wood ducks. Fourteen areas varied in size from 0.61 to 5.46 hectares (1.5–13.5 ac). A low correlation of pond size in relation to wood duck nest house use indicated that within the parameters studied, pond size had little effect on use; however, cover characteristics did have an influence on use. Only 18 percent of the small wetlands that contained less than one-seventh cover produced ducks, but woodies were successful in 76 percent of the ponds where cover occurred over one-fourth or more of the area.

Harrigal (1990) reported nest house use by wetland type in South Carolina (Table 213). Except for high use of nest houses on lakes of 4–40 hectares (10–100 ac), there was no significant difference in use among wetland types. Farm ponds and beaver ponds were of comparable value for placement of wood duck houses, suggesting that most farm ponds were in wooded areas.

Nest houses for wood ducks have been erected in trees over water, such as snags and cypresses, and in upland woods 1.6 kilometers (1 mi) and farther from water. Because the trek to water exposes the hen and her brood to additional predation, the nearer the nest house to water the better. The above photograph features a backwater pond area with almost ideal site characteristics for wood duck nesting and brooding. *Photo by Jack Dermid.*

Table 213. Percentage of wood duck use of wood nest houses in various wetland types in South Carolina, 1989.[a]

Habitat type	Number of houses	Percentage of houses used	t-test
Bottomland hardwoods			
Seasonally flooded	67	46.3	1.92 P>0.05
Permanently flooded	501	58.7	
Farm wetlands			
Ponds (<4 hectares: 10 ac)	1,355	63.9	3.08 P<0.01
Lakes (4–40 hectares: 10–100 ac)	304	73.3	
Beaver ponds	130	64.6	
Hydroelectric reservoirs	21	57.1	
Managed impoundments			
Inland	580	58.5	1.17 P>0.10
Coastal	198	63.1	
Riverine	16	0.0	

[a] Data from Harrigal (1990).

In Maine, Allen et al. (1990) evaluated wood duck nest house use in five wetland habitat types: shallow marsh, deep marsh, open marsh, scrub/shrub, and wooded swamp. They found the highest use in shallow and open marshes; lowest use was in wooded swamps. In all habitats, however, variation in wood duck nest house use was small—44 to 65 percent—and nest success was remarkably similar.

Our survey of wood duck occupancy rates in various wetland habitats at national wildlife refuges revealed that houses in open swamps had the most use, followed by houses in marsh/swamps and marshes, impoundments, and riverine habitats (Table 214). Most of the swamp habitats in our survey were located in the Lower Mississippi River Valley, and all were in the southern two-thirds of the Mississippi and Atlantic flyways, where house use generally is high because of low cavity densities (see Chapter 7).

An example of occupancy rates in closed swamp habitat was provided by Norman L. Brunswig, manager of the Francis Beidler Forest (Four Holes Swamp) in Harleyville, South Carolina. Over a three-year period, 1983–1985, he found a 25.7-percent use rate of houses for 35 house-years (i.e., the number of houses multiplied by the number of years they were available) placed in mature cypress/tupelo forest that had never been cut. During the same period, wood ducks used houses (35 house-years) at a rate of 42.9 percent in a portion of the swamp that had been clearcut in the mid-1960s. These data indicate that house value in mature, closed swamp may be limited and support the contention that houses normally are used at higher rates in habitats lacking adequate nest sites.

Where water level fluctuations are minimal, such as in farm ponds, placing nest houses on posts and pipes in water is desirable; this practice eliminates predation by squirrels and reduces predation by raccoons. Goose and duck decoys have no apparent effect on attracting or discouraging a woodie to nest nearby. *Photo by Eric Hopps.*

Table 214. Percentage of wood duck use of nest houses in various wetland habitats at national wildlife refuges.[a]

Habitat type	Average	S.D.	Weighted average[b]	Number of refuges referenced
Open swamp	56.0	33.5	68.7	17
Marsh/swamp	46.2	30.6	39.3	6
Marsh	38.9	32.4	50.2	26
Brackish marsh	26.0	19.2	34.1	5
Impoundment	31.2	20.7	29.1	12
Riverine	27.4	26.3	34.1	15

[a] See Appendix H for more information.
[b] Averages determined with report means weighted for number of house-years (number of houses times years available).

In areas not subject to extreme flooding, nest boxes can be placed in water on wooden posts or galvanized pipes with predator shields. By placing boxes in shallow (0.3–0.9 meter: 1–3 ft) open water away from the shoreline, predation by raccoons is reduced and use by squirrels eliminated. Wood duck dump nests in houses on posts over water were 30-percent successful, compared with 19.2 percent on posts over land at the Yazoo National Wildlife Refuge, 1987–91 (Barry 1992). If nesting boxes are used in areas where water levels fluctuate appreciably, boxes should be placed on living trees. Morse (1969) found that the diameter of a support tree made little difference in the selection of houses in Oregon. Boxes must be attached securely, however, and the entrance hole cannot be obstructed by a canopy of branches (Table 215).

When houses are erected over land, the nearer they are to water the better—up to 0.8 kilometer (0.5 mi) is suitable, and 1.6 kilometers (1 mi) appears to approach the maximum distance. Comparable percentages of houses were used at distances exceeding 0.8 kilometer (0.5 mi) from water in the Illinois River Valley (Table 216). More ducklings are lost, however, when nest sites are far from water (see Chapter 3). We therefore recommend that nest boxes not be placed farther than 805 meters (880 yd) from the nearest permanent water.

As mentioned earlier, wood houses on trees and poles and metal rocket houses are used most commonly. When houses are placed for personal enjoyment, the design, number used, and method of erection should suit the implementor and the setting, but local predators should be considered in selecting a design. Varying circumstances make it difficult to recommend a particular design, but if wood ducks successfully use any house style, local populations usually increase along with occupancy rate.

Bellrose et al. (1964) found that natural cavities higher in trees (up to 18.3 meters: 60 ft) receive more use and have greater success rates than do natural cavities at lower heights. Therefore, height of placement should be considered when erecting houses in areas where wood ducks nest naturally. A northcentral Minnesota study found that 54 percent of the tree cavities used by wood ducks were at least 9.1 meters (30 ft) above the ground (Gilmer et al. 1978). Near Brainerd, Minnesota, Keran (1978) studied occupancy of wood houses placed on trees at various heights; use ranged from 62 percent (9.1 meters: 30 ft) to 33 percent (6.1 meters: 20 ft) to 5 percent (3 meters: 10 ft).

Although height of placement appears important in the northern portion of the Mississippi Flyway, this preference was not found in central and

Table 215. Wood duck use of nest houses in four categories of vegetational obstruction on the alluvial flats of Benton County, Oregon, 1968.[a]

Visibility index	Before April 20[b]			After April 20		
	Number of houses	Number (percentage) of houses used	Use index	Number of houses	Number (percentage) of houses used	Use index
75–100	38	11 (28.9)	0.57	14	6 (42.9)	0.50
50–74	30	5 (16.7)	0.33	28	7 (25.0)	0.29
25–49	19	1 (5.3)	0.10	38	7 (18.4)	0.21
0–24	8	0 (0.0)	0.00	22	0 (0.0)	0.00

[a] From Morse (1969).
[b] Mean day of leafout.

Table 216. Wood duck use of nest houses at various distances from water in the Illinois River Valley, 1939–56.

Distance from water, in meters (yd)	Number of houses[a]	Number of houses used	Percentage of houses used[b]
0–23 (0–25)	443	176	39.7
24–46 (26–50)	193	100	51.8
47–91 (51–100)	2,747	1,027	37.4
92–183 (101–200)	237	146	61.6
184–366 (201–400)	118	23	19.5
367–823 (401–900)	185	80	43.2
824–1,280 (901–1,400)	317	163	51.4
Total	4,240	1,715	40.4

[a] Numbers represent house-years (number of houses times years available).
[b] The lack of correlation between house use and distance from water ($r = 0.10$, $P > 0.10$) indicates that other environmental factors were of greater importance. Variation in predation rates in the numerous wooded tracts, rather than distance from water, appears largely responsible for the variation in house use.

southern states. In central Illinois, occupancy of houses at 4.6 meters (15 ft) above the ground was 51.5 percent ($n = 489$); for those at 7.3 meters (24 ft) the rate was 42.6 percent ($n = 469$). Wood ducks in northern Alabama also selected low boxes at a high rate; use ranged from 54 percent (2 meters: 6.5 ft) to

Wood duck nest houses erected over land are most likely to be used when they approximate the usual height of the vicinity's natural cavities. As a rule of thumb, the higher the nest house, the lesser the likelihood of predation. However, utilization may drop dramatically for nest houses higher than about 6.1 meters (20 ft). *Photo by Larry Stone.*

24 percent (3.8 meters: 12.5 ft) to 22 percent (5.6 meters: 18.4 ft) (Bowers and Atkins 1990). Nest houses only 1–2 meters (3.3–6.5 ft) above water or land had an 84-percent occupancy rate at the Yazoo National Wildlife Refuge, 1987–1991 (Barry 1992). Houses were placed on posts in open and wooded areas. Variations in height of nest sites selected by wood ducks probably stem from their previous experience in locating safe nest sites.

We observed an unusual wood duck nesting situation near Oquawka, Illinois, 1989–1991. Richard N. Lee placed an old wooden house that needed repairs on the bench of a picnic table located approximately 9.1 meters (10 yd) from his home. A female wood duck began laying eggs in the box while it sat unattached 51 centimeters (20 in) off the ground; the nest hatched successfully. In April 1990, the house again was placed on top of the picnic table with no means of attachment. For the second straight year, a female nested in the unattached box located only a few feet above the ground and a few yards from a residential dwelling. Later, in June 1990, a second clutch of eggs was deposited in the same box. The house again was occupied in April 1991.

Initially, wood ducks are most likely to locate nest houses in woods where they previously nested and at heights where they customarily found natural cavities. Yearlings follow experienced adult hens to these general locations and are influenced to nest in similar situations (see Chapter 4). Therefore, to attract wood ducks initially, nest houses should be as visible as possible and grouped in the better habitats for natural sites, such as open, parklike woods.

We suggest spacing boxes 50–100 meters (55–110 yd) apart and, ideally, 2–3 per hectare (1/ac). Maximum densities may be deduced by the following episodes: Frederic Leopold (Iowa) erected 26 nest houses per hectare (10 houses/ac) and found a maximum of 20 nests; Harvey Nelson (Minnesota) increased nesting populations from one pair in 1981 to 24 pairs in 1991 by adding nest houses each year—reaching 27 houses in 1991—on a linear tract of land about 0.4 hectare (1 ac) in size; Don Helmeke (Minnesota) erected 20 nest houses per 0.4 hectare (1 ac) and found a maximum of 20 nests; we documented 76 breeding pairs of wood ducks at Nauvoo Slough, Illinois, where nest houses occurred at a density of 12.4 per hectare (5/ac). Unless experience dictates otherwise, dense placements should be avoided.

However, Barry (1992) found no significant difference in wood duck dump nest success in sparsely or densely spaced houses at Yazoo National Wildlife Refuge, 1987–91. Dense houses were placed at 10 meters (32.8 ft) apart for one per pole and 20 meters (65.6 ft) for two per pole; sparse houses were separated by 100 meters (328.1 ft).

Where the food base is ample, grouped boxes may result in breeding numbers expanding to form colonies, the sizes and densities of which are governed by nest success and brood survival. Unfortunately, in most instances expansion stops within 5–10 years, because predation and intraspecific strife among local females reduce recruitment and the food base apparently fails to support more broods to flight stage.

When groups of nest houses demonstrate by reduced nest success that they are too visible and too dense to maintain a "healthy" breeding population, houses should be moved to more dispersed and concealed sites. Such a change in strategy is warranted, as the following studies indicate. Local nesting colonies in the Sacramento Valley, California (Jones and Leopold 1967), the Montezuma National Wildlife Refuge in New York (Haramis and Thompson 1985), and Nauvoo Slough, Illinois (this study) have experienced substantially reduced nest success as a result of intraspecific strife. Houses were mounted on trees in open marsh and flooded timber (for high visibility) and at densities of one house per 0.7 hectare (1.7/ac) in California, one house per 3.2 hectares (7.9/ac) in New York, and one house per 0.1 hectare (0.2/ac) in Illinois. Populations increased to such an extent that in a few years, dump nesting (i.e., multiple hens laying in one house), nest destruction, and reduced hatching lowered nesting efficiency (ducklings exiting houses divided by the number of eggs laid, multiplied by 100) to 25 percent in California, 22 percent in New York, and 24 percent in Illinois.

Haramis and Thompson (1985) reported that intraspecific strife could be reduced and production increased if boxes were spaced at low densities similar to natural cavities. Subsequent studies by Semel et al. (1988, 1990) and Henne (1989) showed that placing single boxes in obscured locations reduces the frequency of dump nesting and increases productivity.

We examined the level of dump nesting that occurred in open and dense forest stands on Quiver Creek, Illinois, 1960–1970. Dump nests made up 36.3 percent of 259 nests in open woods. In comparison, dump nests accounted for only 19 percent of 126 nests in densely wooded areas; the difference was significant ($P < 0.001$, $t = 3.60$). Thus, our Quiver Creek data support the contention of Haramis and Thompson (1985), Semel et al. (1988, 1990), and Henne (1989) that nest boxes widely scattered and/or hidden from one another reduce the rate of dump nesting.

Although Barry (1992) also found that wood duck dump nests occurred more often in houses highly visible in open settings over water at the Yazoo National Wildlife Refuge, 1987–1991, these nests surprisingly had higher nest success rates and lower costs per duckling produced than did houses that were less visible.

Optimal productivity may be achieved from wood duck houses by spacing at intervals of 50–100 meters (55–110 yd) and at densities of 2–3 per hectare (1/ac). Higher concentrations of nest houses, regardless of predation safeguards, can foster intraspecific strife and dump nesting. The inverted cone shields along with metal wrap on the posts (above) may effectively prevent raccoon predation, but not all rat snakes are deterred, and squirrels could leap from shore to the houses. But the principal long-term constraint on wood duck production from these closely spaced nest houses would be breeding density. *Photo by Ralph A. Lloyd.*

Nevertheless, when the number of wood ducks using a particular group of nest boxes increases, additional boxes should be deployed in less visible locations. Eventually groups of highly visible boxes may have to be separated to curtail high levels of nest abandonment and poor hatching rates (Semel et al. 1988, 1990, Henne 1989).

Allen et al. (1990) and Fleskes et al. (1990) minimized nesting interference on wetlands where nest boxes were located in the open and encouraged high wood duck populations by adding additional boxes in areas with high levels of dump nesting and moving unused boxes to more suitable locations. Allen et al. (1990) recommended adding boxes when occupancy exceeded 80 percent. However, we believe that at most locations it would be more beneficial to attempt to reduce dump nesting by adding boxes when occupancy is at a lower level (50–75 percent).

Maintaining Nest Houses

The number of houses successfully used by wood ducks each year ultimately determines the value of a program. Programs cannot rest with the initial installation of houses but must provide maintenance that is both adequate and continuing (Naylor 1960). Houses must be in a condition acceptable to the birds at the beginning of each nesting season. Because woodies do not carry nest material to the nest site, 8–10 centimeters (3–4 in) of sawdust, wood shavings, or other wood-based nest material must be added to houses. Starlings are more prone to remove wood shavings than sawdust, and for that reason we suggest sawdust. Starlings bring in grass for their nests, and subsequent nesting wood ducks use this grass. Houses without base material are seldom used by wood ducks (Bellrose and Crompton 1972).

Nest house inspection is necessary at least once a year and always prior to the nesting season to collect previous use and nest success information, to remove debris left by past occupants (e.g., bird eggs and nests, squirrel nests, beehives), because such remains may prevent use by wood ducks, and to check houses (and predator guards) for deterioration and defects. Although Keran (1978) found similar use (23 and 30 percent) of cleaned and uncleaned houses in Crow Wing County, Minnesota, large amounts of material left in houses can prevent subsequent use. For the most accurate wood duck house-use data, units should be inspected immediately after the nesting season, because other species may remove evidence of prior nests (see Chapter 10).

For ease of maintenance, houses at wildlife areas often are erected on poles or trees along levees or on poles strung out across impoundments or along marsh canals. This placement allows systematic maintenance and can improve the efficiency (cost per duckling) of large programs, as long as houses continue to have high use. Where water levels fluctuate and flooding necessitates high placement, houses may be checked with the help of a boat-mounted ladder-stand developed by Brown (1972b).

Researchers check nest houses periodically throughout the nesting period to determine the rate of nest house use, nest success, and causes of nest destruction; to band and weigh incubating hens; and, in a few studies, to web-tag hatched ducklings. Wildlife managers and others who erect wood duck nest houses should inspect them at least twice a year—once at the end of the nesting season to determine wood duck use and nest success, and once before the nesting season to add new sawdust and repair those that need rehabilitation. The large bowl-shaped predator shield below the nest box above, in a cypress swamp, helps to deter rat snakes as well as raccoons. Note, too, the pileated woodpecker nest hole in the dead snag directly above and behind the biologist. *Photo courtesy of the U.S. Fish and Wildlife Service.*

ESTIMATES OF HOUSE NUMBERS

To estimate the number of houses currently available and determine their usage, we distributed a questionnaire to national wildlife refuges in 1980 and to state wildlife agencies in 1984 (Bellrose 1990). In addition to their own programs, the state agencies were asked to provide information for all known wood duck nest house programs within their states, including programs on nonrefuge federal lands and private programs. Responses indicated that a minimum of 35,670 and 58,192 nest houses were available then in the Atlantic and Mississippi flyways, respectively (Bellrose 1990).

Following our initial inventory of nest houses, three large nest house programs were initiated. The South Carolina Wildlife and Marine Resources Department made 10,826 wood nest houses available to private cooperators, 1982–1989 (Harrigal 1990). According to Tom Jones, Ducks Unlimited, Inc., through its Fulton, Illinois, Chapter, sold 26,000 plastic houses manufactured by Custom-Pak, 1988–90. As of 1991, Chesapeake Wildlife Heritage has placed more than 3,000 nest houses in Maryland, with a goal of 1,000 more in 1992.

In 1988, under the aegis of Stephen Simmons, the California Waterfowl Association began urging members and wetland owners to erect nest houses for wood ducks. A committee was formed in 1991 to place more emphasis on this program. By 1992, about 3,100 houses had been placed at scattered locations throughout the state (Table 217). Brian Davin and collaborators monitored 2,295 nest houses in 1992. They recorded a rate of occupancy by wood ducks of 50.3 percent, of which 73.3 percent of the nests were successful, producing 9,103

ducklings that departed the structures (Table 217). The Association's goal is to have 7,500 nest houses in place by 1995.

Wood Ducks Now of Harrods Creek, Kentucky, made several thousand wood duck houses of wood, 1988–1989, that were largely distributed in the southeastern United States. In addition to these large nest house distribution programs, there undoubtedly were numerous programs conducted on a smaller scale. For example, in the late 1970s Don Helmeke of Maple Grove, Minnesota, marketed 6,000 polypropylene plastic wood duck houses. Since that time, he has distributed 350 metal wood duck houses of his own design.

The number of houses erected by state and federal agencies is about one-third of the total placed by other parties, such as private individuals and county and municipal park boards. Between 5 and 10 percent are on national wildlife refuges, and about 25 percent have been placed through efforts of state wildlife agencies.

Among states, South Carolina and Minnesota have comparably strong nest house programs, each with about 10,000 (5,500 in Minnesota are maintained by the USDA Forest Service). The Ohio Department of Natural Resources has had the most consistent program, maintaining about 3,200 houses, 1970–90. Other substantial programs by state wildlife agencies include Texas, Wisconsin, Illinois, New York, Maine, and Arkansas, each with 1,500–2,700 houses. The largest national wildlife refuge programs are located at Wheeler (Alabama), Great Swamp (New Jersey), White River (Arkansas), Iroquois (New York), Reelfoot (Tennessee), Santee (South Carolina), Yazoo (Mississippi), and Union Slough (Iowa), each with 280–540 houses.

Table 217. Use, nest success, and ducklings departed from wood duck nest houses monitored in 1992 in California.[a]

Region	Number of houses	Percentage of houses used	Percentage successful	Ducklings departed
Southern California	172	24.4	83.3	353
American Basin	68	50.0	82.4	327
Butte Basin	724	37.3	70.0	1,714
Colusa Basin	29	72.4	95.2	219
Yolo Basin	159	15.7	68.0	145
Sacramento-San Joaquin Delta	391	61.4	61.3	1,825
San Joaquin Basin	484	89.0	77.5	3,828
Northern Tulare Basin	21	0.0		
City of Sacramento	24	4.2	100.0	6
Northeastern California	68	27.9	73.7	153
Coastal Foothills	26	15.4	75.0	26
Northern Foothills	1	100.0	100.0	9
Sierra Foothills	128	50.0	85.9	498
Total/weighted mean	2,295	50.3	73.3	9,103
Mean		42.1 ± 31.8	80.9 ± 12.5	

[a] Data compiled by Brian Davis, California Waterfowl Association.

HOUSE OCCUPANCY TRENDS

In an attempt to discern trends in the wood duck's use of nest houses, we studied a number of reports. House use was determined at the national, flyway (Atlantic, Mississippi, and Pacific), and flyway regional (northern, central, and southern) levels. Averages were determined from three sources: publications (including professional reports); a questionnaire distributed to national wildlife refuges; and unpublished reports and memos from state wildlife agencies and individuals or groups with regularly maintained programs. The number of house-years (houses available multiplied by nesting seasons evaluated) totaled 131,808 for publications, 33,876 for refuges, and 26,249 for unpublished reports—a combined 191,933 house-years (tables 218 and 219 and appendices I, J, and K).

Published studies conducted nationwide revealed an average occupancy rate of 50.1 percent. Data from the percentage house-use questionnaire sent to the national wildlife refuges yielded an average of 39.3 percent, and the comparable figure for unpublished reports was 37.8 percent. When house-use data from each study or report were given equal weight for number of house-years, average percentage use was 40.3 (publications), 51.8 (refuge questionnaire), and 38.7 (other reports). The combined average house use from the three sources was 42 percent for both unweighted and weighted data (Table 218). Which house-use figure source is most representative of the national average is difficult to determine. Published reports included a larger total data set, but the national wildlife refuges are more widely and uniformly distributed, so their data may be more representative.

House use was similar among flyways but generally higher in the southern regions of the Mississippi, Atlantic, and Pacific flyways (Table 219). In the Mississippi Flyway, a marked increase in use rate was discernible from north to south. Nevertheless, houses were used at relatively high rates in portions of the northern Mississippi Flyway, especially areas that lacked natural nest sites and were close to suitable wetland habitat (Zicus and Hennes 1988, Hawkins et al. 1990). Zicus and Hennes (1988) reported a use rate of 34.2 percent from 298 houses located throughout the Minnesota River Valley and a 50-percent use rate from 18 boxes located in the Grantsburg landscape region of eastcentral Minnesota.

Increased house use from north to south, primarily in the Mississippi Flyway, might be caused by a number of factors. Among these are: (1) lower nest success in natural cavities in the South and more opportunities for renesting; (2) lower survival and return of northern hens to breeding areas and associated nest sites; and (3) a paucity of suitable tree cavities commensurate with the high food base in areas of the overflow bottomland hardwood forests in the South.

Lower nest success in natural cavities is related to the increased variety and density of nest predators at lower latitudes. Lower nest success, in turn, tends to cause renesting. Longer nesting seasons in the South also allow more nesting attempts, and wood ducks there frequently produce two broods per year (see Chapter 10). Because unsuccessful hens normally move to other nest sites, each attempt to use a house increases the house-use rate.

Regional dissimilarity in house use also may be explained in part by variable survival rates. Wood ducks that nest farther north suffer higher mortality because of the increased number of states and hunting seasons traversed during migration (see Chapter 18). With each migration, southbound hens dilute local populations, thus relieving local hunting pressure on their neighbors to the south (see Chapter 4). Native birds account for only 40 percent of the wood duck harvest in southern states (Bowers 1977) (see Chapter 20). A smaller proportion of

Table 218. Average wood duck use of nest houses determined from three information sources.[a]

Source	Period	Number referenced	Total house-years[b]	Wood duck use		
				Mean	S.D.	Weighted mean[c]
Publications	1939–90	124	131,808	50.1	38.3	40.3
National wildlife refuges	1950–85	83	33,876	39.3	30.5	51.8
Unpublished reports	1950–90	32	26,249	37.8	23.6	38.7
Total/mean		239	191,933	42.4		42.1[d]

[a] See appendices I, J, and K for more information.
[b] Number of houses times number of years studied.
[c] Means determined with report means weighted for number of house-years.
[d] Total number of houses used (80,759) divided by total house-years from all sources (191,933).

Table 219. Percentage of wood duck use of nest houses in flyway regions determined from publications, unpublished reports, and a questionnaire distributed to national wildlife refuges.[a]

Source	Atlantic Flyway			Mississippi Flyway			Pacific Flyway	
	Northern	Central	Southern	Northern	Central	Southern	Northern	Southern
Publications								
Mean	39.9	42.1	48.3	17.5	40.6	76.5	55.5	65.5
Standard deviation	24.0	27.8	29.7	14.0	29.4	56.8	19.3	30.8
Weighted mean[b]	48.9	38.1	34.1	19.9	37.0	66.9	56.2	62.2
Number of reports	21	10	15	6	31	27	8	4
National wildlife refuges								
Mean	26.5	41.2	52.9	12.2	36.2	60.0	29.3	47.5
Standard deviation	25.0	26.7	30.5	14.2	31.7	36.4	25.1	32.8
Weighted mean	30.7	50.4	54.3	8.1	42.8	71.0	38.0	51.5
Number of reports	9	11	12	6	10	15	12	3
Unpublished reports								
Mean	41.4		47.1	22.3	33.9	64.4	41.6	61.9
Standard deviation				12.6	20.6		27.7	31.4
Weighted mean				16.7	36.6		49.8	94.7
Number of reports	2		1	10	7	1	5	5

[a] See appendices I, J, and K for more information.
[b] Means weighted for amount of data (number of house-years) in each report.

northern woodie hens survive to return to their breeding areas, whereas those staying in the South to breed are able to home at a higher rate. Natural hazards encountered during migration also may reduce the return rate of wood duck hens to northern breeding areas.

A lack of suitable tree cavities can be the basis for high use of houses, especially where a high-quality food base results in an expanding wood duck population. At a regional level, natural nest sites can be less available because of the lack of juxtaposition of hardwoods and wetlands. The central states of the Mississippi Flyway (Iowa, Missouri, Illinois, and Ohio), for example, have 7 percent of the flyway's wetlands important to waterfowl (Shaw and Fredine 1956), but only 17 percent of that land is covered with hardwood forest (U.S. Forest Service 1978). Houses generally receive higher use by the denser wood duck populations found on this relatively small wetland area in central states of the Mississippi Flyway. When houses are erected on wetlands with a good food base and without proximate hardwood forests, such as a marsh, a few breeding pairs can develop into a dense colony.

In comparison, the northern states (Minnesota, Wisconsin, and Michigan) contain 41 percent of the important wetlands in the Mississippi Flyway; 31 percent of these lands are covered in hardwoods. With far more breeding habitat available to them and generally lower survival and homing rates, wood ducks returning to the northern Mississippi Flyway are less concentrated. As a result, dense wood duck colonies rarely develop and situations with high (greater than 50 percent) house use were seldom reported in the literature or through state and federal questionnaires.

Although the northern and southern thirds of the flyway have a similar abundance of wetlands and hardwoods, the northern region is made up of a mosaic of woodlands, lakes, and other riparian systems; Wisconsin alone has 14,900 lakes scattered throughout more than 6.1 million hectares (15 million ac) of forest land (U.S. Forest Service 1978). The southern third of the flyway is generally more uniform, with large expanses of contiguous wetlands and forest. The placement of houses on southern lakes and swamps, where they are highly visible to wood ducks and where natural cavities are scarce, results in high wood duck use, according to Edward Hill, Mississippi State University. Use of houses in southern swamps also may be high because of the variety of predator and competitor species that use tree cavities, making those cavities unsafe or unavailable to wood ducks.

Some of the factors that influence house use in the Mississippi Flyway also may be responsible for the variable use rates found in regions of the Atlantic Flyway. Survival and homing of hens breeding farther north are lower, as is the availability of wetlands in relation to hardwood forest. The percentage of hardwood coverage in the three regions of the Atlantic Flyway is similar, but the proportion of flyway wetlands increases from north to south

(Shaw and Fredine 1956). Thus, houses placed on relatively limited productive wetland areas in the North are more likely to be found and used by pioneering females concentrated there, even though survival rates are lower.

With only 2–3 percent hardwood coverage in both the northern and southern halves of the Pacific Flyway (U.S. Forest Service 1978), houses placed on wetlands with adequate food and cover generally have high use. Additionally, nesting seasons are relatively long in West Coast states, allowing greater renesting possibilities for wood ducks even in Oregon and Washington.

Wetlands in the Central Valley of California have a potentially high-quality food base for wood ducks, resulting from shallow, fertile, clear water with favorable temperatures and sunshine. A dearth of natural nest sites is indicated by an exceptionally high use of nest houses in the few locations where they have been erected. This region offers a great opportunity for increasing wood duck populations through sound nest house programs.

IMPACT OF NEST HOUSES ON LOCAL POPULATIONS

The ability of nest house programs to establish or greatly increase local populations has been well documented (Bellrose et al. 1964, Grice and Rogers 1965, Cunningham 1968, Clawson 1975a, Strader 1978, Zipko 1979, Haramis and Thompson 1985). Once wood ducks begin using houses, the homing of hens and their daughters usually causes an increase in local house use (Cunningham 1967, Baker 1971, Hansen 1971, Brown 1972a, Clawson et al. 1979, see also Chapter 4). Northcentral Iowa's Union Slough National Wildlife Refuge probably is the best example of a local population increasing as a result of nest houses. Few wood ducks were produced on this marsh habitat until houses were erected in the early 1950s. In 1986—35 years and more than 200 houses later—the area produced more than 2,400 ducklings (Fleskes et al. 1990).

On minuscule wetlands in the vicinity of Merced, California, Stephen Simmons established a thriving population of breeding wood ducks. With an average of 136 nest houses available per year, 1974–1988, he found an annual average of 158 nests (116-percent house use) with 104 successful nests (65.8 percent). When Bellrose visited the area, he was amazed at the small size of the wetlands, most of which would not have supported wood ducks east of the Great Plains. Food base attributes and nest houses were equally responsible for this high local breeding population.

Urban Wood Ducks

Wood ducks nest in hundreds of villages, towns, and cities in eastern North America. Usually these communities are adjacent to streams or wetlands, but in instances such as Lincoln, Illinois, Starkville, Mississippi, and Manhattan, Kansas (see Chapter 10), they are at a distance.

Where wood ducks have established active breeding within a community, people often become interested in erecting nest houses. Our data on results of these programs are fragmentary, and they show varying degrees of success. In some cases, nest houses may not be used simply because of chance, especially where wood duck breeding populations are sparse and natural cavities are adequate. In areas where only a few nest houses are available, it is difficult to develop a sufficient base of breeding birds to maintain population continuity in the face of unexpected adult and/or duckling mortality. In compensation for a general annual mortality rate of 50 percent, a high level of nest success is necessary so that females return in sufficient numbers to equal or add breeders to a local population (see chapters 4 and 18). Recruitment depends not only on nest success but also on food and cover resources. Nest house use will decline when females are lost from a population at a greater rate than they are replaced by recruitment.

Of all the urban wood duck management programs we know of, the greatest success has occurred in areas peripheral to Minneapolis-St. Paul, Minnesota. According to Hawkins et al. (1990), hundreds of nest houses have been erected in this area at residential locations, nature centers, wildlife refuges, and even along freeways. Although many individuals who live near the Minneapolis-St. Paul metropolitan area have placed wood duck houses on their property, five people in particular have been recognized for large nest house programs: Ray Cunningham, Shoreview; Arthur Hawkins, Hugo; Don Helmeke, Brooklyn Center; Lyle Bradley, Anoka; and Harvey Nelson, Bloomington. Each individual has increased local populations from zero to two nests at the start to 10–30 nests by 1991. A high use of nest houses by wood ducks in suburban areas that practically encircle the Twin Cities is shown in Table 220. The consistent high use of nest houses reflects high nest success and brood survival.

Frederic Leopold was responsible for inspiring many people in Burlington, Iowa, to erect wood duck nest houses. He started in 1943 with three nest houses and maintained 20–26 into the late 1980s. As far back as 1965, Leopold (1966) estimated that more than 100 wood duck nest houses had

Table 220. Wood duck nest house programs in suburban areas of Minneapolis-St. Paul, Minnesota.

Town	Program duration	House-years[a]	Percentage of wood duck use	Source
Bloomington	1980–91	139	82.0	H. K. Nelson
Brooklyn Center	1975–91	183	91.3	D. Helmeke
Champlin	1989–91	9	100.0	D. Helmeke
Edina	1988–91	25	104.0	D. Helmeke
Hopkins	1989–91	9	75.0	D. Helmeke
Minnetonka	1989–91	30	76.7	D. Helmeke
North Oaks	1977–91	69	95.7	D. Helmeke
Robbinsdale	1975–80	48	91.7	D. Helmeke
Hugo	1984–91	360	46.9	A. S. Hawkins

[a] Number of houses times number of years studied.

been placed in and around Burlington; in later years, residents have added many more houses to this program.

Proportion of Autumn Population Produced from Nest Houses

Bellrose (1990) determined that enough wood duck houses had been deployed by the early 1980s to have a positive influence on production. He estimated that approximately 150,000 wood ducks become part of the autumn population east of the Great Plains each year as a result of production from houses.

Nest houses for wood ducks are of value only if they increase nest success above that found in natural cavities. This increase in nest success can be achieved by making houses more resistant to the entrance of predators (see Chapter 11).

Acceptance of nest boxes by wood ducks offers wildlife biologists an excellent opportunity to study and manage this species. Use of well-placed predator-deterrent houses in habitats where a shortage of natural cavities limits wood duck production is an economical and effective management practice. Managers should consider using nest houses where suitable cover and food resources are not fully utilized because of a lack of proximate nest sites or where excessive predator pressure on nests in natural cavities results in low production. We have observed scores of wetlands with obvious cover and food resources for breeding wood ducks, but in our estimation an absence of nest sites curtailed their use. There surely must be thousands of similar wetlands in the United States. Doubtless, too, there are thousands of suitable cavities that are not in juxtaposition to wetlands, but it is more difficult to bring the wetlands—except by tens of thousands of small artificial impoundments—to the mature upland forest than it is to bring nest houses to the wetlands.

It has been estimated that nest house production east of the Great Plains contributes 150,000 wood ducks annually to the autumn population—a not insignificant 4–5 percent of the autumn juvenile component. Nest house programs have helped to offset the drastic reduction of pristine bottomland nesting habitat. They also have availed expansion of the species to areas without sufficient natural cavities but otherwise suitable for brood development. Increasingly, private citizens, especially landowners with or near forested wetlands, are initiating wood duck nest house ventures. Many are rewarded by dramatic views of nesting woodies and by the knowledge that they are assisting one of the continent's few duck species that has shown population increase over recent decades. *Photo by Frederic Leopold; courtesy of the Starr's Cave Nature Center (Burlington, Iowa).*

SUMMARY OF NEST HOUSE MANAGEMENT

During the past 50 years, numerous researchers have investigated wood duck response to nest house programs and determined management techniques that characterize success or failure. Although local conditions influence the type and number of houses and the method of placement best suited to a particular area, a number of basic management principles will help to ensure success.

- Scores of studies throughout the breadth of the wood duck's range indicate that wherever local habitat conditions warrant, nest houses can provide a potential means of enhancing production of young.
- Wood duck nest houses can be too small or too large for optimum use. Although wood ducks have used houses as small as 20.3 centimeters (8 in) in diameter, the best diameter appears to be 25.4 centimeters (10 in). Diameters larger than 30.5 centimeters (12 in) are less used. The depth should place the lower lip of the entrance 38.1–48.3 centimeters (15–19 in) above the inside bottom of the house. The deeper the cavity, the less likely a raccoon can reach an incubating hen or her eggs. Where smooth wood, metal, or plastic is used, a "ladder" is necessary for the ducklings to reach the entrance. A strip of hardware cloth 10.2 centimeters (4 in) wide securely affixed inside the house from the entrance to the bottom is the most commonly used method. However, automotive undercoat 5 millimeters (0.2 in) thick is as good or slightly better.
- Boxes made of wood, metal, or durable plastic are recommended. Rough-cut lumber, especially cypress, is best for wood houses; if smooth wood is used, an 8/10-centimeter (¾ in) strip of 0.32- to 0.64-centimeter (0.13–0.25 in) mesh hardware cloth should be firmly attached inside the box from the base of the entrance to the floor of the box to assist ducklings in leaving the nest. The inside of vertical metal houses should be sprayed with auto undercoating or provided with a hardware cloth ladder to allow ducklings to exit. In the South, certain plastic houses should be placed only in areas that receive full shade.
- The floor of every nest house should be covered with 8–10 centimeters (3–4 in) of sawdust, wood shavings, or wood chips, because wood ducks do not carry in nest material. Houses without material for a nest base and for covering eggs are seldom used.
- Houses must be protected against predators.

Entrances should be elliptical if houses are to be located where raccoons occur. Houses placed on galvanized pipe in 30–91 centimeters (1–3 ft) of open water farther than 4.9 meters (16 ft) from the shoreline have lower mammalian predation rates than do houses placed over land. Cone-shaped guards provide the best available protection against arboreal predators. Application of Tanglefoot® or axle grease to post supports reduces predation rates, but this material must not be allowed to harden, because a dry, roughened surface allows predators relatively easy access to a nest box.

- In areas where starlings are a serious problem and water levels remain relatively stable, horizontal-cylindrical houses or wooden houses with enlarged entrances protected by predator guards and placed on posts in wetlands are recommended. If flooding prevents the use of post supports to reduce starling nesting, boxes should be placed several feet above normal flood levels on trees in dense woods; the entrance must be kept free of obstructions such as overhanging branches.
- The entrance should face an open area, and passage to it should not be impeded by branches or other obstructions. The importance of easy flight access to the entrance cannot be overemphasized; this is the most common mistake that we have observed in many nest house programs.
- Because of hazards associated with overland travel by broods having left their nests, houses placed in upland woods away from water generally produce fewer fledged ducklings than do houses located over water. Erecting boxes in upland areas farther than 0.8 kilometer (0.5 mi) from water is not recommended. Houses should be attached to trees with straight, clean trunks at heights of 3.8–6.1 meters (12–20 ft) above the ground. Bands of fiberglass wrap, sheet metal, newspaper print aluminum, or Tanglefoot® 0.6–0.9 meter (2–3 ft) wide should be placed 0.6 meter (2 ft) below and 1.2 meters (4 ft) above houses where no adjacent trees or branches allow predators to jump to the house or tree trunk between bands; this generally prevents predation by climbing predators. Bands of sheet metal often require adjustment as trees grow, and Tanglefoot® must be replaced yearly.
- House programs should begin small. Initially, no more than 10 houses should be placed at densities no greater than 4.9 per hectare (2/ac)—the approximate size of a football field.

The success of nest house programs anywhere depends on a variety of fairly precise logistical considerations and adaptation to local conditions. Even under the best of circumstances, woodies may not pioneer new nest sites quickly or at all. If wood ducks occur regularly in an area, they likely will eventually inspect nest houses erected for their use. Program operators should not be discouraged by unoccupied nests. After several years of vacancy, houses can be moved, even if only vertically, to encourage use. A common cause of unoccupied nest houses is positioning of the structures in a direction that causes flight approach to be impeded by branches. *Photo by Scott Nielsen.*

To encourage occupancy by wood ducks during the initial phase of a house project, boxes should be placed in open areas of high visibility. As house use increases to 50–80 percent, additional boxes can be placed in concealed locations at approximate densities of one per hectare (0.4/ac). Fifty houses per hectare (20/ ac) would result in saturating even the most favorable habitats. Only as many houses as can be adequately maintained should be placed. Eventually, groups of highly visible houses may have to be dispersed to curtail intraspecific strife.

- Breeding "colonies" of woodies reaching a plateau of productivity as a result of population strife or food resource limitations still contribute up to 50 percent of their productivity as yearlings that pioneer new nest sites.
- An initial lack of wood duck nest house use may stem from low wood duck breeding numbers; a paucity of pioneering hens; houses placed in areas not traditionally searched for nest sites; and houses hidden too completely from the view of nest-site-searching birds.
- Local populations that have developed around a small nest house base are especially vulnerable to wide fluctuations in numbers. The annual return of breeders is small, and local populations are especially subject to divergence from the normal 50-percent survival rate. Without sufficient recruitment to compensate for unusual mortality in certain years and places, local populations may decline to the point of disappearance. Therefore, the more extensive a local nest house program, the greater the likelihood of continued wood duck use since there will be a sufficient base of breeding birds to withstand adversity.
- Prior to the nesting season nest houses should be inspected for damage and refurbished as necessary; usually new sawdust is required for an optimum nest base.

Chapter 20

Habitat and Population Management

The management of wood ducks is both art and science. It is art because of the complex and dynamic variables that prevent exact answers to many questions. It is science because fundamental information from research provides a logical framework for improving habitat and managing populations. The art of managing wood ducks combines scientific tenets with the provincial expertise that comes from observation over many years. Thus, wildlife managers familiar with the habits of wood ducks can draw on their observations and experiences to improve wood duck habitat. Similarly, they can use production and mortality data to evaluate the details of harvest regulations that may be most appropriate for current population levels. Obviously, local populations always will respond to changing productivity and hunting pressures that, at times, may be so temporary and/or local as to limit the usefulness of broad findings. Even on wider scales, however, scientific data do not enable fine-tuning of hunting regulations so that the maximum number of wood ducks can be harvested without the danger of local overharvests, because of yearly variables in weather, food resources, water levels, and interrelationships of the kill with the harvest of other species. Thus, even under the umbrella of an extensive data base on the wood duck, the art of management must continue to guide the future of this bird.

In the ensuing discussion of management of wood duck habitat and populations, we have relied primarily on scientific findings. Where these are wanting, however, we have taken the liberty of relying on unreported observations and experience.

HABITAT MANAGEMENT

Management philosophies and practices have changed over the years in response to changes in wood duck population levels and increased knowledge about the species' ecology and management. Wood ducks fared well prior to the late 1800s; quality habitat abounded and hunters were comparatively few and equipped with primitive firearms. Unfortunately, tens of thousands of suitable nest cavities were lost as mature hardwood forests were logged, cut, or burned between 1850 and 1920. At the same time that the forests were being destroyed, many wetlands were being drained and firearm manufacturers were developing more efficient ammunition and guns. As a result of habitat destruction and unregulated overharvest by gunners, most regional wood duck populations waned to alarmingly low levels during the early 1900s (see Chapter 5).

Habitat management for waterfowl in North America evolved in the 1930s after the detrimental effects of habitat reduction and poorly regulated harvest became apparent. Government agencies and private organizations began establishing refuges primarily to preserve waterfowl habitat. As biologists acquired knowledge about waterfowl ecology and habitat requirements, management goals were expanded to include practices that enhanced the quality of existing habitats. Because of the tremendous amount of wetland habitat lost over the years as a result of human activities (see Chapter 3), acquisition or control of remaining high-quality wetlands by conservation agencies has become imperative. Techniques for altering water levels provide a means of enhancing wetland values for wood ducks and other waterfowl. In this way, some of the loss in quantity of wetlands can be compensated by improvement in quality.

The three fundamentals of wood duck habitat management include food base, nest sites, and cover. Because wood ducks are capable of improvising under a variety of cover situations, cover is of secondary importance in management strategy. Because production of young is the most important key to a robust population, we are particularly concerned with the relationship between the food base during the breeding season and the availability of nest sites. Both are equally essential in devising a strategy to manage habitat.

The more marsh a wetland contains or the more marshlike it is, the more likely it is to have a food base conducive to brood survival. The denser a mature swamp, the more likely it will provide adequate nest sites but the less likely it will offer a good food base. The availability of nest sites in marshlike wetlands usually is not commensurate with the quality of the food base that prevails there.

Riverine habitats provide the most extensive breeding areas in the nation, but their linearity limits opportunities for management. The food base of rivers and streams varies tremendously because of water quality and velocity and bank cover. Depending on the size and age of stream-side timber, nest cavities may be adequate or scarce. Where streams have side channels or cut-off channels forming islands, their value doubles for breeding wood ducks compared with those reaches with only customary linear banks (see Chapter 3). Oxbows and other isolated floodplain wetlands further increase stream values.

Beaver ponds provide a moderate to high food base depending on water pH and nutrients. The availability of natural cavities may be consistent with the food base or in short supply, depending on the nature of adjacent timber.

Farm ponds provide a largely unrealized potential for increasing wood duck productivity. Their nutrient levels vary widely depending on soil type, erosion, drainage, animal pollution, and fertilizer leaching. Nevertheless, a large proportion of farm ponds are productive of aquatic and emergent plants. Their value for wood ducks improves geometrically with the presence of a complex of ponds, wooded tracts, and a permanent stream. Unless nest cavities are available in nearby woods, only the provision of nest houses will provide the necessary component to make farm ponds of optimum value for wood ducks.

The three fundamental elements of wood duck prosperity, and the cornerstones of woodie management, are adequate foods, nest sites, and cover. Although these elements apply to virtually all wildlife species, their importance is paramount for the wood duck, whose adaptability is great but whose requirements are relatively unique and specific. *Photo by Jack Dermid.*

Food Base

No matter how many wood duck nest houses are erected, the food base ultimately determines the size of a local breeding population. The critical food base for egg production and early brood survival is invertebrates—largely aquatic and terrestrial insects. These foods are usually gleaned from the foliage of floating aquatic and marsh plants and from wooded vegetation that grows along the shoreline of lakes, ponds, marshes, and streams. The aquatic food base is dependent on the clarity, depth, and quality of water, including pH level and available nitrogen and phosphorus.

To illustrate the importance of the food base to the breeding potential of wood ducks, we discuss three scenarios—Holston River, Nauvoo Slough, and Union Slough.

Holston River. The importance of the food base to breeding wood ducks is most evident along the Holston River in eastern Tennessee. Young and Dennis (1983) determined that the annual net primary productivity of aquatic plants on the upper Holston exceeded that reported for any other aquatic system in temperate North America. Of all streams surveyed by biologists for wood duck brood production, the upper Holston River consistently ranked first in number of broods seen per kilometer surveyed (see Chapter 3).

The upper Holston River is enriched by nutrients from the discharge of municipal sewage at Kingsport, Tennessee. Luxuriant beds of aquatic plants grow in the river as far downstream as the John Sevier impoundment. Aquatic vegetation is relatively sparse, however, above Kingsport and on the lower Holston River below Cherokee Lake, according to William Minser III. Many nutrients are progressively lost as the flow moves downstream from Kingsport (see Chapter 3).

Young and Dennis (1983) reported that aquatic plants covered 70 percent of a 31-kilometer (19 mi) section of the upper Holston River. Sago pondweed was most abundant, comprising 44 percent of total plant biomass. Its highly dissected leaves allow the colonization of large invertebrate communities (Krull 1970). In contrast, aquatic plants covered about 34 percent of the lower Holston River, and sago pondweed occurred only in scattered locations (Schacher and Minser 1988).

Muncy and Burbank (1975) placed 92 nest boxes on a 20.1-kilometer (12.5 mi) segment of the upper Holston River in 1971. They found an increase in use of these boxes from 6 percent in 1971 to 44 percent in 1975. It indicated that sufficient food and cover were available, allowing for population expansion with the provision of nest houses.

When Schacher and Minser (1988) placed 190 wood duck boxes on the lower Holston and French Broad rivers, they found a use rate of only 1.3 percent during a four-year period (1976–1979). They also found that brood densities ranged from 0.42 to 0.68 brood per kilometer (0.68–1.1/mi). During the same time, 2.0 wood duck broods per kilometer (3.2/mi) were observed on the upper Holston. Schacher and Minser (1988) believed that the marginal food base on the lower Holston and French Broad rivers limited wood duck production.

Nauvoo Slough. A dearth of nest sites was found on Nauvoo Slough, a marshlike, 6.1-hectare (15 ac) backwater area of the Mississippi River. Trees in the town of Nauvoo and along the wooded bluff below the slough provided a sprinkling of cavities. George Arthur, former waterfowl biologist with the Illinois Department of Conservation, erected about 30 nest houses in the mid-1970s. We inspected those nest boxes from 1979 to 1983 and found that 10–20 nests hatched successfully each year.

In 1984, we increased the number of nest sites to 81. The number of breeding pairs increased dramatically from 28 in 1983 to 46, 60, and 73 in 1984, 1985, and 1986, respectively. Our time-budget studies in 1986 revealed that females allocated about 23 percent of their time to feeding (see Chapter 8). This percentage was less than half that of many female dabbling ducks feeding on prairie breeding grounds (Dwyer 1975, Afton 1979, Kaminski and Prince 1981). Because wood ducks spent appreciably less time feeding at Nauvoo Slough than did species of prairie ducks, the data are indicative of a substantial food base in the slough.

By July, Nauvoo Slough is almost completely covered by duck potato and American lotus, with an understory of duckweed. Prior to development of the overstory, water stargrass, sago pondweed, and coontail compose the submergent plants of the slough. Because the slough had previously received the sewage effluent from the town of Nauvoo (population 1,200), soils of the slough are extremely fertile; duck potato, for example, commonly grows to heights of 0.9–1.2 meters (3–4 ft), much higher than normal.

Piest and Sowls (1985) studied breeding ducks at a lake that received sewage effluent from Show Low, Arizona, and found that the consequent abundance of invertebrates resulted in an extraordinary production of young ducks. In 1982, they reported 17.1 broods and 148.4 ducklings per hectare (6.9 broods and 60.1 ducklings/ac) of water surface. The highest density of ducklings they found reported in the literature was 7.1 broods per hectare (2.9/ac) in Alberta (Smith 1971) and 37 ducklings per hectare (15/ac) in Utah (Wingfield and Low 1955). These,

State, federal, and private waterfowl refuges are important to the continued welfare of the wood duck because of the life requirements those areas provide. The pair above, perched on a tree swallow house, could not have known the sign below proclaims Nauvoo Flat a state waterfowl refuge in Illinois, but they surely recognized the nest houses and food resources that the area affords. The single most important region vital to wood duck prosperity is the Mississippi Alluvial Plain, extending from Cairo, Illinois, to Baton Rouge, Louisiana, where, as of 1992, slightly more than 405,000 hectares (1 million ac) were in state and federal ownership. *Photo by Dan Holm; courtesy of the Illinois Natural History Survey.*

too, represented a variety of species. At Nauvoo Slough, an average of 6.5 broods and 72 wood duck ducklings per hectare (2.6 broods and 29.1 young/ac) left nest houses, 1984–1989. The high production of young is attributed to the excellent food base brought about by the earlier discharge of sewage effluent and the use of nest houses. The combination of nest houses and food base created the most productive wetland for wood ducks on record.

Union Slough. This 445-hectare (1,100 ac) slough in an 890-hectare (2,200 ac) national wildlife refuge receives the runoff from fertile, intensively farmed land in northcentral Iowa. The fertile soil and shallow water in six water-control units create a luxuriant interspersion of emergent and aquatic plant communities. Because of the scarcity of natural cavities in the 150 hectares (370 ac) of riparian woods, production was limited to fewer than 40 broods, 1945–1963 (Fleskes et al. 1990). One nest house was used in 1962; by 1990, 326 nests were recorded in 406 houses, according to Glen L. Welp.

Thus, a steady increase in the number of nest houses, combined with a food base typical of a good prairie marsh, provided the ingredients that have made Union Slough a showcase for wood duck management.

Riverine Habitats

Over much of the wood duck's range, the species' breeding potential is regulated by riverine habitats where water levels influence the food base. Floods inundate adjacent bottomland hardwoods, whereas low water is apt to leave barren banks.

The best way to manage most riverine habitats is to let nature do it. Instead, stream channels often are enlarged, realigned, and cleared of obstructions for flood control. Channelization includes removing all vegetation on either side of the stream and deepening and straightening the channel; in essence, the stream is transformed into a straight ditch. Changes in invertebrate communities often occur in channelized streams because straightening and widening the stream bed reduce habitat diversity and result in increased water velocity. In addition, channelization eliminates islands, cut-off sloughs, natural meanders, potential nest trees, and woody bank cover. Indirect effects of channelization include the likelihood of floodplain wetland drainage and tree removal, increased downstream flooding, reduction of groundwater levels, and accelerated bank erosion (Schneberger and Funk 1971).

An example of the effect of stream channelization on wood duck production was provided by Minser 1993. In 1991, he surveyed 61 kilometers (38.1 mi) of channelized and natural streams in west Tennessee. Not a single wood duck brood was found on the channelized streams, whereas 0.15 brood/kilometer (0.24/mi) was observed on unchannelized streams.

The unchannelized Hatchie River had more wooded cover, more large trees, and shallower banks than the channelized Obion and Forked Deer rivers. Steep banks with little vegetative cover characterized channelized rivers, and large sections of their banks frequently showed evidence of sloughing into the stream bed.

Informed opposition to channelization projects and other activities that destroy or degrade wetlands is needed to preserve critical habitat for all fish and wildlife species that use wetlands. An estimated 321,860 kilometers (200,000 mi) of stream channels in the U.S. have been modified in some manner (Wesche 1985). Fortunately, as a result of public involvement and concern, federal funding

An estimated 321,860 kilometers (200,000 mi) of streams in the United States have been channelized, leading to extensive losses of cover, nest sites, and food resources for wood ducks and other wildlife. Channelization also degrades fish habitat, increases downstream flooding, and accelerates bank erosion. Public awareness of these egregious activities has done much to eliminate channelization in favor of stream renovation practices that achieve desired hydrologic results without destroying natural values. *Photo by Chester A. McConnell.*

for channelization projects has decreased in recent years (U.S. Fish and Wildlife Service 1988).

Woods along the borders of streams should be kept intact to maintain water quality and benefit wildlife. Areas where timber has been removed at the edge of a stream by channelization or to increase arable farmland should be identified and protected from further degradation by reforestation. The amount of soil eroded along nonwooded stream banks is enormous and a major contributor to downstream sedimentation.

Overflow Hardwood Flats

Open swamps and extensive overflow bottomland hardwood flats are of greater value to wood ducks than are riverine habitats because they generally provide a better food base and a greater selection of natural cavities for nest sites (Heitmeyer and Fredrickson 1990). However, the extent of these swamps and flats is limited and declining rapidly, especially in the Mississippi Alluvial Plain (also known as the Mississippi Delta). The Mississippi Alluvial Plain, stretching from the mouth of the Ohio River to Baton Rouge, Louisiana, originally contained 9.7 million hectares (24 million ac) of bottomland forests. By 1979, the overflow bottomlands had been reduced to about 2 million hectares (5 million ac), primarily as a result of timber clearing

for agriculture (see Table 28). As recently as the early 1980s, an estimated 48,560 hectares (120,000 ac) of bottomland hardwoods in the Mississippi Delta were being destroyed annually (Blue Ribbon Panel for the Bottomland Hardwoods 1984). Because remnants of this once vast bottomland forest are important breeding and wintering areas for wood ducks (and are the single most important habitat for wintering mallards in North America), an all-out effort needs to be made by conservation agencies to protect what is left.

Areas of federal and state waterfowl and national forest lands in the Mississippi Delta are shown in Table 221. The nearly 415,000 hectares (1,025,000 ac) in public ownership represents about 5 percent of the original bottomland hardwood forest and about 20 percent of what remained extant in 1979. Thus, a small part of the remaining bottomland forest in the Mississippi Alluvial Plain is secured for posterity; the rest is privately owned and subject to further clearing for crop production.

Creators of the Lower Mississippi Valley Joint Venture–part of the North American Waterfowl Management Plan–expect to acquire an additional 121,407 hectares (300,000 ac) of forested wetlands and improve other public and private forested lands for waterfowl through water control. This program is essential to prevent the potential creation of more farmlands at the expense of overflow bottomland hardwoods.

Table 221. Amount and location of federal and state areas of bottomland forest in waterfowl and national forest reserves in the Mississippi Alluvial Plain, as of June 1, 1991.[a]

	Area					
	Federal		State		Combined	
Location	hectares	(ac)	hectares	(ac)	hectares	(ac)
Missouri	8,801	(21,747)	14,028	(34,664)	22,829	(56,411)
Tennessee	19,699	(48,677)	4,795	(11,848)	24,494	(60,525)
Arkansas	97,788[b]	(241,637)	66,315	(163,866)	164,103	(405,503)
Mississippi	51,280[c]	(126,715)	417	(1,030)	51,697	(127,745)
Lousiana	52,308	(129,254)	99,031	(244,708)	151,339	(373,962)
Total	229,876	(568,030)	184,586	(456,116)	414,462	(1,024,146)

[a] State data provided by: Dale Humburg, Missouri; Joe Hopper, Tennessee; Timothy Moser, Arkansas; Richard Wells, Mississippi; and Robert Love, Louisiana. Federal refuge data from "Annual Report of Lands Under Control of the U.S. Fish and Wildlife Service as of September 30, 1990."
[b] Includes the 8,477-hectare (20,946 ac) St. Francis National Forest.
[c] Includes the 24,079-hectare (59,500 ac) Delta National Forest.

Overflow bottomland hardwoods constitute the single largest habitat type used by wood ducks. The greatest block of these forests occurs on the Mississippi Alluvial Plain, or Delta. Where there once were 9.7 million hectares (24 million ac) of bottomland hardwoods, there are now only 2 million hectares (5 million ac). Above, a bottomland forest along the Obion River in west Tennessee has been cleared and ditched to reduce flooding. The effort merely displaces and compounds flooding elsewhere, and it effectively eliminates breeding habitat for wood ducks and winter habitat for mallards and wood ducks. *Photo by Chester A. McConnell.*

Impoundments for Human Purposes

The effect of impoundments on wood ducks ranges from highly detrimental to highly beneficial. Factors that affect their value to wood ducks include size, depth, shape of basin, period and degree of water fluctuation, water clarity, shoreline cover, and amount and type of woods in juxtaposition to the impoundment. Impoundments can be categorized by their primary purpose as power, flood control, water supply, navigation, recreation, or wildlife.

Usually, the larger the impoundment and the more open the water, the less its value to breeding wood ducks. The more V-shaped the basin, the lower the proportion of shallow water and the lower the food base. Generally, low water during the breeding season is undesirable; flooding, on the other hand, usually is advantageous because it makes more cover and food available, especially in areas with extensive flats. In overflow bottomland hardwood flats, a slight change in water level may make an enormous difference in the area flooded.

Stable water levels, however, contain less silt, and the clearer the water, the better for development of aquatic and marsh plants that support invertebrates. Stable water levels provide favorable growing conditions for submerged, floating, and emergent plants. Areas with shallow as well as stable water levels produce valuable marshes for early breeding activities of wood ducks, for later brood development, and still later for the wing molt.

The value of shoreline cover often relates to the water level of an impoundment. When the impoundment is full, shoreline vegetation usually provides cover and a source of food for wood ducks. In impoundments such as those used for flood control, however, managed water levels often result in bare shorelines for most of the year. Water levels in flood-control impoundments often fluctuate greatly depending on the volume of the flowage, and seasonal levels are seldom predictable.

Standard procedure in constructing most impoundments is to clear the basins of timber. Depending on the size of the impoundment, from several to many thousands of acres of bottomland and other hardwoods are removed. The seriousness of this loss depends on the remaining availability of similar woods; where sufficient natural cavities remain and mast production is adequate, the loss of timber may affect wood duck production only minimally.

Impoundments for Wildlife

Impoundments created specifically for waterfowl consist of three basic types: lake and marsh; moist-soil; and green-tree reservoir. Lake and marsh wetlands are developed primarily for breeding waterfowl and secondarily for migrating and wintering birds. Moist-soil impoundments provide seeds and invertebrates for migrating and wintering waterfowl. Green-tree reservoirs offer mast, weed seeds, and invertebrates primarily during the winter and secondarily for autumn and early spring migrants.

Freshwater marsh wetlands. The littoral zone of rivers, lakes, and ponds supports herbaceous plant communities that provide diverse habitats for wood ducks. A canopy or overstory is created by deep-marsh emergents such as bulrush, duck potato, cowlily, and American lotus. Nutritious seeds and tubers are produced by a variety of marsh plant species (Fredrickson and Taylor 1982), and the finely divided leaves of many submergent and floating plants are excellent substrates for invertebrate colonization (Krull 1970).

Wood ducks use marsh habitat extensively during stages of their annual cycle when dense cover and high-protein food are required. Protective cover, in close juxtaposition to an abundant invertebrate population, is especially important to young ducklings and later to adults during wing molt. Dense vegetation provides escape cover for flightless birds, and invertebrates provide the protein needed for growth and feather production. In addition, stands of herbaceous plants that create a spreading overstory commonly are used as nocturnal roost sites during summer and autumn (see Chapter 15).

Marsh management for wood ducks should encourage the production of plant species that provide either overhead cover or substrate for large invertebrate populations during brood-rearing and molting periods. On wetlands where conditions are favorable for aquatic plant growth, management goals often can be achieved simply by maintaining stable water levels during the growing season. Although actual depths vary with topography, turbidity, and plant species, plant growth in 0.3–0.9 meter (1–3 ft) of water is most beneficial to wood ducks and other wetland birds that feed on or near the surface.

Shallow-water impoundments that are held at stable levels for too long, however, often become less productive and may eventually shift toward monocultures. Periodic yearly drawdowns frequently are used to maintain and improve production and plant diversity. Many nutrients that are bound up in undecayed plant materials are released through decomposition when exposed to aerobic conditions and reflooding. Yoakum et al. (1980) reported that late spring and early summer drawdowns improved subsequent submergent plant production.

On impoundments where American lotus and other emergents form monocultures that inhibit the development of a variety of vegetation, control measures may be required to reestablish plant diversity. Drawdowns permit the control of many emergents by drying the wetland. Heavy emergent growth can be destroyed by mowing, crushing, or burning; disking and desiccation are required to kill roots (Green et al. 1964). Disking may not control American lotus, however, because new shoots often develop from the cut rhizomes (Fredrickson and Taylor 1982).

In the South, succession in marsh habitats generally results in the dominance of water-tolerant trees and shrubs. Woody growth may begin to encroach on marsh wetlands within one to three years after flooding (Fredrickson and Taylor 1982). Many types of wetland shrubs and trees provide valuable habitat for wood ducks, and the production of such vegetation should be considered in long-term management programs. In cases where managers want to maintain wetlands at an earlier successional stage, woody growth can be controlled by intensive water management. Mowing followed by shallow flooding during the growing season destroys woody vegetation at northern latitudes. In the South, however, shallow flooding stimulates the growth of many woody plants; consequently, disking (up to three times during the growing season) may be needed to set back succession (Fredrickson and Taylor 1982).

Moist-soil impoundments and agricultural crops. One of the most common water-management techniques for improving food resources for migrant and wintering ducks is the development of moist-soil impoundments. Water levels must be lowered to expose mud flats and reflooded later to make the seeds of moist-soil plants available as food. Such manipulation is particularly valuable where a fluctuating water level or high turbidity curtails the development of aquatic and marsh plants. For this technique to be effective, extensive mud flats must be exposed for 70–120 days, depending on latitude. During this period of little or no water, the impoundment is of minimum value for wood duck broods. Therefore, a satisfactory water level must be retained as long as possible when broods are present. A better alternative, however, would be to create auxiliary impoundments where stable water levels could be maintained.

For central Illinois, we advocate an exposure of impoundment basins no earlier than July 15 and no later than August 1. These dates ensure the survival of a large proportion of wood duck broods. This schedule also retards the development of willows, cottonwoods, and soft maple trees, the seeds of which germinate in profusion earlier in the season. These drawdown dates allow ample time for moist-soil plants to reach maturity before frost in mid-October. By regulating the frequency, timing, and length of drawdown, wetland managers can stimulate development of specific moist-soil plant communities. Japanese millet is sown extensively in the Midwest, as is water millet (barnyardgrass) in California.

Probably because of their bill structure—which is more adapted for picking and grasping than for sieving—wood ducks make extensive use of large seeds and usually eschew relatively small ones. Consequently, some moist-soil impoundments receive little use by wood ducks, especially where quality scrub/shrub and bottomland oaks are flooded (Taylor 1977, Reinecke et al. 1989, Heitmeyer and Fredrickson 1990).

Wood ducks characteristically confine their feeding to marsh habitats and wooded wetlands when an adequate food supply is available there (Drobney and Fredrickson 1979). In areas where natural foods are scarce or unavailable, wood ducks regularly feed in agricultural fields that have been harvested, knocked down, or flooded (see Chapter 16).

Management plans that incorporate millet, corn, or rice into moist-soil impoundments often provide food for large numbers of migrating and wintering wood ducks. In southern Louisiana, Nassar et al. (1988) found more wood ducks feeding in rice, Japanese millet, and browntop millet beds than in areas of natural vegetation. They observed approximately 5,000 wood ducks using 10.9 hectares (27 ac) of rice impoundments, November through mid-December. Bartonek et al. (1990) also reported that rice was an important food resource for wood ducks in the Sacramento Valley of California.

At Anderson Lake Fish and Wildlife Area in central Illinois, Japanese millet and corn regularly are planted in a 32.4-hectare (80 ac) moist-soil impoundment. Wood ducks begin feeding on the millet seeds soon after flooding begins in early October, according to site manager Roger Cox. Corn is planted on slightly higher ground around the perimeter of the impoundment and generally is not flooded until much of the millet has been consumed. As the corn becomes inundated, wood ducks readily leave millet beds to feed on the more easily consumed corn kernels.

Row crops often are planted on public waterfowl management areas to provide food primarily for mallards and geese, but wood ducks also take advantage of this bonanza. Approximately 66,000 hectares (163,086 ac) of agricultural crops are planted annually on national wildlife refuges alone (U.S. Fish and Wildlife Service 1976). Although farm crops are high-energy food, most lack one or more essential nutrients, provide limited habitat diversity, and generally are more expensive to produce than natural foods (Fredrickson and Taylor 1982, Reinecke et al. 1989). Thus, whenever possible, wetland managers should try to meet food production objectives from moist-soil impoundments and inundated forested wetlands.

The use of agricultural crops is most beneficial, however, when integrated with moist-soil management. The planting of sections of moist-soil impoundments with row crops on a one- to three-year rotation provides high-energy food, promotes production of moist-soil plants, and controls woody growth (Fredrickson and Taylor 1982, Reinecke et al. 1989).

Green-tree reservoirs. Green-tree reservoirs are bottomland hardwoods shallowly flooded to provide feeding, resting, and roosting habitat for waterfowl (Rudolph and Hunter 1964). Guidelines for green-tree reservoir development and management were presented by Mitchell and Newling (1986) and Reinecke et al. (1989). Wigley and Filer (1989) summarized general characteristics, management practices, and problems associated with 179 green-tree reservoirs scattered throughout the Mississippi and Atlantic flyways.

Areas with desirable characteristics for the establishment of green-tree reservoirs generally are found along low-gradient river systems in the southcentral and southeastern United States. Low levees usually are built around sections of floodplain forests with mast-bearing oak timber. The seeds of elm, ash, and maple also provide a valuable and reliable source of nutrition for wood ducks during spring (Sweet 1976, Drobney 1977), and these trees should be included in green-tree impoundments whenever possible. To avoid harming trees, flooding needs to take place in autumn after growth has stopped, and water should be removed before growth resumes in spring. Flooding can be initiated safely after leaves begin to show autumn coloration, and water should be removed in spring before new leaves start to develop (Rudolph and Hunter 1964).

Green-tree reservoirs provide critical nutrients for migrating, wintering, and breeding wood ducks. Shallow flooding—less than 30 centimeters (12 in)—in autumn increases the availability of high-energy acorns and seeds of such understory plants as wild millet and smartweed. The life cycles of wetland invertebrates that live in floodplain habitats allow those invertebrates to respond quickly to increasing water levels and nutrient inputs from leaf litter.

Green-tree impoundments normally are flooded before autumn and winter rains cause streams and rivers to overflow their banks, and water usually is held at a constant level until drained in spring. A major advantage of green-tree management is the ability to provide quality forested wetland habitat at a time when the floodplain normally is dry. Some concern has been expressed, however, that regular flooding patterns and holding water at constant levels may, in time, alter the structure or function of these intensively managed bottomlands. Fredrickson (1978) noted that the composition of plant species in green-tree reservoirs often shifts toward communities more tolerant of flooding. Trees such as pin oak and Nuttall oak gradually are replaced by more water-tolerant species such as overcup oak, red maple, bald-

cypress, and water tupelo. Batema (1987) reported that many nutrients in green-tree reservoirs can become bound in the litter, making them largely unavailable to plants and animals. He also found that regular flooding patterns on green-tree sites may cause a shift in aquatic invertebrate communities and result in reduced productivity.

Fredrickson and Heitmeyer (1988) emphasized that water management on green-tree impoundments should simulate natural flooding patterns whenever possible. Flooding should occur gradually in autumn to a maximum depth of 30 centimeters (12 in). Drainage in spring also should be gradual so as to reduce nutrient loss from the system, and it should be as late as feasible so that wood ducks have access to invertebrates over a longer time period when protein demands are high.

Scrub/shrub wetlands. Freshwater wetlands dominated by woody vegetation less than 6.1 meters (20 ft) tall are classified as scrub/shrub wetlands. Although peat bogs and pocosins are included in this category, scrub/shrub wetlands of value to wood ducks support buttonbush, willow, swamp privet, and other woody perennials that form dense stands with interspersions of open water and overhanging branches several feet above the surface (see Chapter 3).

Scrub/shrub wetlands are an important component of quality wood duck habitat. They provide a valuable cover resource that is used throughout the year. In floodplain forest habitats, scrub/shrub wetlands are especially important for wood duck brood rearing (Fredrickson and Heitmeyer 1988).

Although shrubs produce relatively few seeds of value to waterfowl, they contribute an important source of nutrients to wetlands when they shed leaves. Leaf litter serves as an organic substrate from which energy is transferred through microbial bacteria and fungi to aquatic macroinvertebrate communities.

Magee (1989) studied litter decomposition, nutrient cycling, and invertebrate response to flooding in willow wetlands on the Ted Shanks Wildlife Area in northeastern Missouri. Flooding occurred in November, and invertebrate populations remained low until the following spring. In two years of study, peak invertebrate densities of 1,500–4,500 per square meter (139.35–418.05/ft^2) were recorded seven to eight months following flooding. Highest density and greatest biomass occurred at water depths that ranged from 1 to 30 centimeters (0.4–12 in), the wood duck's preferred feeding zone. Magee (1989) found that the invertebrate production of willow wetlands provided an important source of protein for migrating, breeding, brood-rearing, and molting waterfowl; however, flooding to depths greater than 30 centimeters (12 in) after leaf fall or flooding for short periods reduced invertebrate populations in willow wetlands.

Willow, cottonwood, and buttonbush occur along river drainages throughout much of the wood duck's range. These hardy plants are adapted to seasonal flooding and seasonal drought. In areas where they invade moist-soil impoundments or form extensive stands, they often are viewed as undesirable. Despite this attitude, however, maintenance or improvement of scrub/shrub wetlands should be an important consideration in the management of wetland complexes for wood ducks.

Because the value of scrub/shrub wetlands is reduced when extensive monocultures develop, management strategy should include the establishment of a mixture of woody species to increase cover and food diversity. Fredrickson and Reid (1988) reported that extensive stands of willows and cottonwoods can be made more attractive to wetland wildlife by creating openings or edge. Disturbance of soil through disking is an effective and economical means of controlling young woody plant growth.

Scrub/shrub wetlands usually have insufficient nest sites compared with the quality food base they provide breeding wood ducks. Therefore, the use of nest houses where this habitat occurs may prove highly rewarding.

Beaver Ponds

Other than natural geologic events, the beaver is the sole natural creator of impoundments. Beavers create desirable habitat for wood ducks by constructing dams on small woodland streams (see Chapter 3). The impoundments that result change the nature of stream channels by reducing current velocity, stabilizing water levels, flooding riparian timber, and retaining larger amounts of sediments and organic matter. These modifications to woodland streams often result in the development of the aquatic plant communities and abundant invertebrate populations required by wood ducks (Naiman et al. 1988).

Beavers occasionally build dams that flood agricultural lands, roads, and commercial timber, but such damage often can be controlled without harvesting the animals or destroying the dams. Bailey (1922), Boettger and Smart (1968), and Laramie (1978) developed methods to restrict water levels in beaver impoundments. Control structures made of pipe are installed through the dam and allow the water level to be lowered to the desired height. If flood damage to valuable lands is prevented, many beaver ponds that would otherwise be destroyed can be preserved.

Another consideration in prolonging the life of beaver impoundments is the management of beaver populations. The average life span of a beaver pond is influenced by food supply and beaver density (Yoakum et al. 1980). After beavers remove preferred food trees, they generally move to another location. Soon after a beaver colony abandons a site, the dam begins to deteriorate and water levels gradually return to former levels. Maintaining colonies at low numbers (two or three beavers) through harvest or by live-trapping and translocation generally prolongs the life of impoundments (Arner et al. 1966, Yoakum et al. 1980, Hill 1987).

An extension of developing artificial impoundments for moist-soil food production is the modification of beaver ponds to meet that goal. Techniques for managing beaver ponds in the southeastern United States were reviewed by Arner and Hepp (1989). They discussed the manipulation of water levels to encourage plant communities that produce palatable seeds, support invertebrate populations, and provide cover.

Impoundments by beavers produce important year-round habitat for wood ducks and enhance habitat conditions for other wildlife. Recovery of beaver populations, by translocation programs and the species' colonizing tendency, may create local problems for landowners. Beaver numbers can be controlled, however, and the benefits of their ponds, from the standpoint of natural communities and wildlife diversity and abundance, far outweigh their costs. *Photo by Dan Holm; courtesy of the Illinois Natural History Survey.*

Arner (1963) designed a three-log drain that is placed through a beaver dam to allow partial dewatering of the impounded area. After dewatering accomplished its objective, Arner (1963) found that beavers repaired the major breaks in the dam within one week after the drain was removed. In central Alabama, however, one of every three partially dewatered beaver ponds developed moist-soil plant communities that provided little food for waterfowl (Arner 1963).

Traditional methods of controlling undesirable marsh vegetation—water level manipulation, burning, mechanical disturbance, or herbicides—also are effective in beaver pond wetlands (Arner and Hepp 1989). On areas where the seed bank is poor and few desirable plants grow, Arner and Hepp (1989) suggested planting half to two-thirds of the dewatered area to Japanese millet.

Because wood ducks use food and cover resources in beaver ponds throughout the year (see Chapter 3), drawdown programs designed to provide cover and food during winter should be scheduled so that habitat loss to breeding and brood-rearing birds is minimized (Arner and Hepp 1989).

Timber Management

Forest management for waterfowl often is directed toward maintaining or improving the mast-producing oak component of bottomland hardwood forests. Reinecke et al. (1989) presented guidelines for harvesting bottomland timber in a manner that promotes acorn production and encourages regeneration of desirable oak trees. They recommended using small clearcuts (<0.5 hectare: 1.2 ac) to create openings in stands of undesirable trees when oak seedlings are established in the understory. Initially, partial cuts may be used to provide openings for seedling development. In addition to increasing mast production, small clearcuts enhance the quality and value of commercial timber stands. Acorns and other woodland foods also can be made available to waterfowl by shallowly flooding bottomland forests, as noted earlier in the discussion of green-tree reservoirs.

Elms, red ash, and red maple often are removed from bottomland forests to provide openings for oak development (Reinecke at al. 1989). However, the seeds of these trees provide an important and dependable source of nutrition for breeding wood ducks. To promote seasonal diversity of food, an interspersion of tree species is beneficial.

Seeds from annual plants are another source of food for waterfowl in forested wetlands. Annual plants generally germinate and produce seeds on sites that become dry during the growing season and where sufficient sunlight reaches the forest floor. Harrison and Chabreck (1988) reported that artificial openings in forested wetlands allow annual plant growth in areas where natural food production is especially poor. They recommended that openings be at least 0.1 hectare (0.25 ac). Areas prone to frequent flooding and that support water hyacinth should not be cleared because annual plants will seldom become established. In addition, management of natural or artificial openings in forested wetlands for annual plants requires yearly mowing and/or disking to discourage encroachment by trees and shrubs.

Although bottomland forests can be managed through selective harvest strategies to increase the production of waterfowl foods, tree cutting must be conducted judiciously so that the wood duck's need for nest cavities is met. Wood ducks prefer to nest near water and high in trees where their nests are least accessible to predators. Old-growth hardwood timber stands (about 80 to 100+ years) are needed to produce suitable wood duck nest cavities in primary and secondary branches high in the canopy (see Chapter 7). Unfortunately, old-growth timber stands have been almost totally eliminated on private lands (see Chapter 3). Moreover, commercial harvest schedules generally are set on a short rotation basis in order to maximize profits. As a result, trees seldom attain the size needed to produce the best cavities for wood ducks on tracts managed for timber production.

Gilmer et al. (1978) suggested how northern hardwood forests might be managed to provide cavities for wood ducks. The production and preservation of old-growth hardwood stands within 0.8 kilometer (0.5 mi) of adequate brood habitat should be encouraged, and timber harvest in stands 0.8–1.6 kilometers (0.5–1.0 mi) from water should be scheduled beyond the normal rotation age in order to promote cavity development. On the Chippewa National Forest in Minnesota, Gilmer et al. (1978) found that wood duck nests (n = 31) usually were located within 200 meters (656 ft; mean = 35 meters: 115 ft) of the nearest canopy opening. Because wood duck females prefer to nest near forest openings that are larger than 0.1 hectare (0.25 ac), occasional openings of that size can be created in expanses of mature forest near wetlands to improve nesting habitat for woodies (Gilmer et al. 1978).

Age of trees. The time required by various trees to reach diameters conducive to providing cavities suitable for wood ducks is shown in Figure 129. For fast-growing species, such as black willow and cottonwood, it would take 20–40 years to reach the minimum diameter capable of developing large

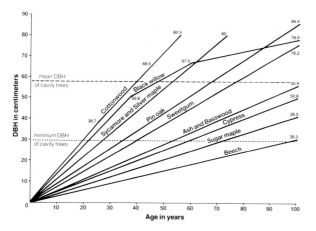

Figure 129. Diameter (dbh) of various tree species in relation to the age at which their minimum and mean sizes have potential for providing cavities for nesting wood ducks. Minimum diameter necessary for cavity development based on data in Table 65. Mean diameter for cavity development from Robb (1986). Growth rate of tree species from Graber and Graber (1976).

cavities. It would take slower-growing species such as sycamore and silver maple 30–55 years, pin oak 35–70 years, sweet gum 40–80 years, black oak 50–100 years, ash and basswood 55–105 years, bald-cypress 60–115 years, sugar maple 80–100 + years, and American beech 100 + years.

Because the incidence of cavity development increases with tree diameter (MacTeels 1975, Robb 1986), the older a tree the more likely it is to develop a cavity suitable for wood ducks. It is therefore essential in wood duck habitats to leave groves of mature trees 5–10 hectares (12.4–24.7 ac) in extent every 1.6 kilometers (1 mi) of stream bank or comparable linear length of wetland.

Cavity formation is normally a long process (see Chapter 7), and extensive woodlands are necessary to provide adequate numbers of sites. Mechanical modification of individual trees to produce cavities requires a large investment of time, and many of those cavities may last for only a short period. Placing nest houses in areas where few natural cavities occur and where immediate nest sites are desired provides a more practical means of increasing the availability of sites.

Additional Considerations about Cover

Single wetland sites with limited habitat diversity may not provide adequate cover and food to support a substantial local population of wood ducks. For maximum populations, several habitat types in close proximity must be available, and optimum requirements are best met by wetland complexes that supply a variety of cover and food

resources—for example, areas with overflow hardwoods and scrub/shrub and emergent wetlands.

Typical breeding cover consists of shallowly flooded trees and partially inundated shrubs that allow free movement beneath a canopy of lateral and overhead cover. In areas where desirable woody vegetation is unavailable, wood ducks rely on such residual herbaceous cover as cattail, bulrush, and burreed that remains standing in spring. McGilvrey (1968) reported that breeding wood ducks prefer wetlands where the ratio of cover to open water is at least 50:50.

In addition to locating wetlands that provide sufficient cover and food, wood ducks must find acceptable nest cavities within 1.6 kilometers (1 mi) of water to breed successfully. Characteristics of suitable cavities are presented in Chapter 7.

Researchers generally agree that denser cover and herbaceous emergents are of greater importance to broods than to breeding wood ducks (McGilvrey 1968). Nonetheless, the woody cover desirable for breeding wood ducks may suffice for early brood cover. In southeastern Missouri, Fredrickson and Heitmeyer (1988) found that females often moved recently hatched broods into shallowly flooded forests and remained there for several weeks. Because of declining water levels, however, broods eventually moved to more permanently flooded wetlands with dense vegetation. Streams are an important component of wood duck brood habitat because they allow woodies relatively safe movements between wetlands, in comparison with overland travel (see Chapter 3).

McGilvrey (1968) suggested that optimum brood-rearing habitat should contain a ratio of 75-percent cover to 25-percent open water. He proposed that quality brood-rearing habitat be made up of 30–50-percent shrubs, 40–70-percent herbaceous emergents, and 0–10-percent trees. Upland cover associated with stands of grasses and forbs that occur as far as 15 meters (49 ft) from the shoreline may be used by wood duck broods as daytime loafing and nocturnal roosting areas.

Scrub/shrub and emergent wetlands are extensively used by molting wood ducks. Dense cover associated with abundant food is particularly important because wood ducks are incapable of flight during the three weeks required to grow new flight feathers. Additionally, postbreeding wood ducks prefer dense stands of shrubs and herbaceous emergents that provide overhead cover 0.5–1.0 meter (1.6–3.3 ft) above the surface for night roosting (see Chapter 15). In the Lower Mississippi Alluvial Plain, wood ducks use scrub/shrub and forested wetlands throughout autumn and winter (Fredrickson and Heitmeyer 1988, Reinecke et al. 1989).

Where wooded cover is lacking along streams, ponds, and marshes, shoreline trees may be felled in locations where their canopies and trunks would provide cover for breeding adults and broods. Near Anoka, Minnesota, Lyle Bradley found an increased occupancy of wood duck nest houses after he increased the number of loafing sites and the quality of cover by cutting down trees along the margin of a 4-hectare (10 ac) pond (Hawkins et al. 1990).

As a result of the frequency with which Minser (1993) observed broods concentrated where fallen trees provided stream-side cover, he suggested the felling of suitable trees where cover was lacking.

Food Requirements in Summary

Structural, behavioral, and physiological adaptations impose constraints on the types and amounts of food that wood ducks ingest (see Chapter 16). Because bill morphology precludes efficient straining of food from the water column and bottom mud, wood ducks generally feed by pecking at individual items. They seldom obtain food more than 30 centimeters (12 in) below the surface. However, wood ducks do commonly feed on deeper water. For example, they often consume vegetation and invertebrates associated with submerged plant beds or fallen trees, or pursue aquatic insects that emerge or swarm near the surface. They also dive for corn and acorns.

Wood ducks meet their nutritional requirements by consuming both plant and animal food throughout the year. Although physiological demands influence what proportion of the diet is made up of plants and what proportion is comprised of animals, wood ducks consume both in order to meet energy, protein, and mineral needs. With the exception of females during the egg-laying period, the wood duck's spring, summer, and autumn diet is about one-third animal foods (Drobney and Fredrickson 1979). An abundant and diverse invertebrate food base is essential to laying females because of high daily protein requirements. Drobney and Fredrickson (1985) determined that a female wood duck probably ingests 5,000–9,000 invertebrates each day in order to acquire enough protein to produce a single egg.

A high-quality invertebrate food base also is an invaluable component of wood duck brood habitat. Young ducklings require a high-protein diet during their first month of life to promote tissue growth (see Chapter 13). Like breeding females, however, ducklings also require nutrients that are provided by plant foods. Hocutt and Dimmick (1971) found that the diet of one-week-old wood ducks was made up of about 70-percent animal food. In contrast, animal food formed only 28 percent of the diet of two- to three-week-old ducklings.

Wetlands without high-protein food sources typically support few breeding wood ducks and have poor brood survival. In chapters 10 and 18, we noted how changes in brood habitat quality negatively influenced wood duck production on our study areas in the Illinois River Valley. Aquatic plants were extremely abundant in backwater lakes along the Illinois River at the turn of the century (Kofoid 1903) and into the 1940s (Bellrose et al. 1979), but the plants gradually disappeared, and by 1976 only a few remnant stands of the most tolerant species remained. Bellrose et al. (1979, 1983) determined that sedimentation was primarily responsible for the disappearance of aquatic vegetation. Macroinvertebrate communities that relied on aquatic plants for food, shelter, and substrate also were lost. Although nest success on our study areas remained high (see Chapter 10), breeding populations diminished because of poor aquatic and marsh brood habitat.

Wood ducks consume a wide variety of plant and animal food throughout the year. The latter—specifically invertebrates—is essential to brood production and woodie population recruitment. Not only must food resources be abundant, they also must be where woodies are willing and able to utilize them to meet seasonal nutritional requirements. *Photo by Stephen Kirkpatrick.*

POPULATION MANAGEMENT

The most important single factor in the come-back of the wood duck was the reduction in its kill (Bellrose 1990). A closed season was initiated in 1916 and continued to 1941. After 1941, a relaxation in regulations and, in some states, a special early season were responsible for substantially increasing the kill. Thriving populations during recent decades suggest that current regulations have adequately restrained the hunter harvest and permitted numbers to increase in most regions of the United States.

According to some, an important objective of waterfowl management is to permit the greatest possible harvest of a species without jeopardizing its future. This philosophy was expressed by Gottschalk (1967: 7), who urged waterfowl managers to "continue to seek under-harvested populations of waterfowl, and try to find ways of devising more recreation through regulations that permit greater pressure on those populations." In the case of the wood duck, however, meeting this objective through the precise definition of hunter regulations is fraught with problems and pitfalls.

Determining Annual Status

One problem for those who manage the wood duck harvest is how to determine the species' annual status. The status of most game ducks is based on population estimates derived from counts on aerial transects across their breeding grounds. However, no satisfactory method has been devised for wood ducks. At best, the previous annual harvest and band recovery rates provide a window on trends in numbers (see Chapter 5).

Probably no other species of game duck has more fragmented breeding subpopulations than does the wood duck. Its many subpopulations stem from the diversity of its breeding habitat and the strong homing (philopatry) exhibited by each subpopulation. The quality and distribution of wetlands are more uniform in the range of prairie-breeding ducks than in the range of wood ducks, and pioneering is more evident among prairie ducks than among woodies.

Breeding woodies occupy more diverse habitat types than do other ducks (see Chapter 3). Their most extensive habitats are riverine and therefore linear. Other habitats, such as beaver ponds, lakes, swamps, and marshes, generally are dispersed in the eastern United States. These pockets of breeding habitat, combined with the precision homing of adults and a large proportion of yearlings, result in

numerous subpopulations that reflect local conditions. Thus, the extrapolation of data on provincial abundance—acquired, for example, through nest house use, brood counts, and nocturnal roost counts—to a more extensive area can be misleading because such data are likely to be indicative of only a specific subpopulation. Because of strong homing, each local breeding population of wood ducks becomes a cohesive unit, the productivity of which is determined by habitat quality, predator pressure, and yearly weather conditions.

Inadequate means of determining the annual and regional status of wood duck numbers make for difficulty in fine-tuning regulations to permit a maximum harvest without temporarily, at least, imperiling the future of some population elements.

Effect of Hunting Mortality

The sensitivity of wood duck populations to hunting losses (see Chapter 18) requires that the harvest be kept within carefully prescribed bounds. Mallard populations compensate with varying degrees of natural mortality to annual changes in hunting mortality. Thus, large kills of mallards and kindred species can be minimized by lowered natural losses and a stable population of adults can be maintained (Anderson 1975). (Mallard populations vary from year to year largely because of changes in recruitment.) In the wood duck, on the other hand, hunting mortality tends to be additive to natural mortality (Trost 1990, see also Chapter 18). Unfortunately, despite our banding analyses, we are unable to determine the added mortality caused by a given rate of hunting mortality. However, because wood duck populations exhibit particular sensitivity to hunting losses, changes in regulations that permit a higher harvest should be made with caution.

We gain further insight into the effect of hunting on wood duck populations from their catastrophic decline in the early twentieth century and the species' partial recovery by midcentury. Marginal populations were wiped out and other populations were greatly reduced, but some—those in secure, extensive habitats—were little affected (see Chapter 5). For example, most wood duck populations west of the 96th meridian were either extirpated or barely existing by 1920. Yet since the early 1970s, they have reoccupied much riverine habitat in the Great Plains. Since the 1950s, marginal habitat well within the traditional breeding range of the wood duck has slowly been reoccupied (see Chapter 5). Little by little, wood ducks have established new nesting "colonies" in habitats once considered unfavorable to the species because of its absence.

We deduce from the fall and rise of woodie populations in marginal habitats that the ranks of these birds were initially depleted by excessive harvest. Because a large proportion of the wood duck harvest is taken in close proximity to where the ducks are hatched, a local population is especially vulnerable to excessive hunting (see Chapter 4). Because of strong homing, wood ducks were slow to pioneer vacant or underpopulated habitats. Low recruitment rates in habitats with poor food bases or a paucity of nest sites further delayed expansion.

Thompson and Baldassarre (1989) pointed out the affinity of postbreeding wood ducks for their breeding areas in northern Alabama. Radio-marked ducks remained on the area until a mean date of November 9; only 6.5 percent left before November 1. Of 89 direct recoveries of standard leg bands, 55 percent were reported within 30 kilometers (18.6 mi) of their banding sites, and 73 percent of the female recoveries the following year were made within the same 30 kilometers. Gilmer et al. (1977) reported that 59 percent of the females radio-marked in spring in northern Minnesota remained on the study area at least until the hunting season. Because of their attachment to breeding areas, female wood ducks are especially vulnerable when and where early-season and heavy hunting pressures prevail.

A case in point is the Holston River in eastern Tennessee. Minser et al. (1990) found that the number of broods declined an average of 52 percent after a special September season was inaugurated, 1981–1989. Prior to the special season, broods averaged 2.9 per kilometer (4.67/mi), 1973–1975; broods averaged only 1.35 per kilometer (2.17/mi), 1985–1990. Because habitat conditions were similar during the two periods, the lower number of broods appears attributable to a reduction in breeding females caused by overharvest. Minser et al. (1990) cited bag records that recorded the kill of 223 wood ducks in Tennessee during September, 1981–1989; 101 of these were on the Holston River. Sixty-eight percent of those bagged on the Holston River were females, as were 64 percent of the 122 killed elsewhere in Tennessee. As was pointed out earlier, females are more likely than males to become victims during September seasons because of their greater propensity to remain on or near their breeding grounds. Because hunting mortality appears to be additive for wood ducks, the decline in breeding numbers on the Holston River seems attributable to an overharvest of local females.

In studying the effect of early September seasons on wood duck populations in Kentucky, Anderson (1984) pointed out the abnormally high proportion (58.2 percent) of adult females harvested,

1982–1983, compared with the percentage (50.8) of adult females in the banded sample; chi-square showed a strong significant difference.

Effect of Hunting Regulations

Harvest of wood ducks is controlled through promulgation and enforcement of opening season date, length of season, bag limits, shooting hours, point system, and special seasons. Special seasons, point system, and bag limits have been defined with specific reference to the woodie. Open dates, length of season, and shooting hours have been established mainly in consideration of the statuses of other species, largely the mallard and northern pintail. Thus, to some extent, annual degree of hunting pressure on the wood duck varies with the hunting regulations set primarily for other species.

Because wood ducks migrate south moderately early from the northern two-thirds of their range in eastern North America, the opening of the regular duck season has an impact on the harvest of wood ducks—the earlier the opening, the larger the wood duck kill. The closing date is important largely in the southern third of the wood duck's range, because farther north most wood ducks have left their range prior to the closing date.

Shooting hours. Over the several decades prior to 1989, shooting hours extended from one-half hour before sunrise to sunset. Because of their exceptional presunrise and postsunset activity (see Chapter 15), wood ducks are more vulnerable to hunting pressure at these periods than are other species of ducks. In 1989, shooting hours were changed to begin at sunrise. This change in regulations should reduce the harvest of wood ducks during the period when they are especially vulnerable to shooting.

Tabberer et al. (1973) pointed out that shooting at the roost site decreased the opportunity to harvest wood ducks legally, because such shooting caused the number of ducks using the roost to decline and the proportion returning to the roost after sunset to increase. They observed a high crippling loss and a low percentage of dead ducks retrieved because of darkness. Beshears (1974) noted that shooting at roosts accounted for a large proportion of the wood duck kill on inland areas of Alabama. Luckett and Hair (1979) concluded that hunting wood ducks on their evening roost flights resulted in many being shot illegally; in addition, intensifying darkness made finding downed crippled and dead birds increasingly difficult. They suggested a midafternoon closing to reduce the loss of wood ducks associated with late shooting.

In an Iowa study in 1963 and 1964 (Bishop 1966), 46.4 percent of 1,427 wood ducks were harvested prior to 8:00 a.m. CST, an additional 23.5 percent by 12:00 noon, 16.1 percent more by 3:00 p.m., and another 14.0 percent by legal closing time. Thus, more than two-thirds of the legal kill had been achieved by midday. Where wood ducks are hunted intensively, we propose a 4:00 p.m. closing time to reduce crippling losses and illegal late shooting.

Bag limits. Although shortening the hunting season is the most effective way to reduce the seasonal kill of ducks (Bellrose 1944), restricting the daily bag is the second most effective tactic. As the daily bag limit increases, however, the number of hunters achieving it decreases.

Beginning in 1941, with the very first regulations permitting the hunting of wood ducks, either a restricted daily bag limit or a point system has been used to keep a cap on the kill. Most states in the Atlantic Flyway changed from one in the bag or possession limit to two in the bag or possession limit for the 1959–1960 season. All states in the Mississippi Flyway changed from one to two for the 1962–1963 season. In the Pacific Flyway, one in the bag or possession was permitted until 1962–1963, when two in the bag or possession prevailed until five (six in two states) were permitted in the 1968–1969 season and seven in the 1975–1976 season.

States in all three flyways began to change to the point system for restricting wood duck kill in the 1970–1971 season. At first, 90 of 100 points for the daily wood duck allotment were selected by eight states. In the 1973–1974 season, three states in the Atlantic Flyway used 70 points—a precedent followed by six states the next year and generally thereafter. All states in the Mississippi Flyway (with the exception of Minnesota) changed to 70 points for wood ducks in the 1976–1977 season. With few exceptions, 70 points remained unchanged in the states of the Mississippi Flyway up to the 1988–1989 season, when a limit of two in the bag or possession was reinstituted and continued in 1989–1992. During special September seasons in three states of the Mississippi Flyway and special early October seasons in four states of the Atlantic Flyway, bag limits of four or five were permitted; this number was dropped to two in Kentucky and Tennessee in 1988 and 1989.

The effect of daily bag limits on the potential kill of wood ducks is suggested by data in Table 222. Based on receipt of duck wings of all species in relation to hunters killing various number of ducks, Carney and Smart (1964) projected increases of 10 to 66 percent in the number of ducks killed per day

Table 222. Estimated percentage increase in duck kill with increase in bag limit, based on response to wing collection surveys, 1960–63.[a]

Flyway	Bag limit		
	1–2	2–3	3–4
Atlantic	65.4	21.4	9.5
Mississippi	64.7	20.9	9.5
Pacific	61.2	22.8	9.6

[a] Data from Carney and Smart (1964).

as bag limits increased. Heusmann (1990) reported that in three states with a five-duck limit during a special October season in the Atlantic Flyway, 40.7 percent of the wood ducks killed were represented by one bird, 27.1 percent by two, 17.0 percent by three, 10.5 percent by four, and 4.7 percent by five birds. Although the total kill escalated with each duck added to the bag limit, the total kill was one-third to one-half below a successive legal increase in the bag limit.

Special seasons. The U.S. Fish and Wildlife Service granted an early five-day season for wood ducks within the overall season-length framework in Virginia and North Carolina in 1977, South Carolina in 1981, Georgia in 1980, and Iowa in 1979. These early openings were discontinued after the 1987 season. A five-day addition prior to the regular season was granted in Florida, Kentucky, and Tennessee in 1981 and continued through the 1989 season; its future remains uncertain. The five-day addition occurred between October 1 and 15 in Florida and in early September in Kentucky and Tennessee.

The early October season greatly increased the wood duck kill in Virginia and North Carolina but resulted in only a slight increase in South Carolina, Georgia, and Iowa (Table 223). The wood duck harvest resulting from extension of the season in Florida, Kentucky, and Tennessee was substantial (Table 224). From 31 to 88 percent of the total seasonal wood duck harvest occurred during those five days.

Sauer et al. (1990) reported that direct recovery rates for bandings in Kentucky and Tennessee increased during years with five-day extensions, but rates in other states did not increase. In Iowa, where the increased harvest from the early season was minimal, Kienzler and Hansen (1990) detected no difference in direct recovery rates. According to Heusmann (1990), direct recovery rates increased 25 percent in North Carolina, 31 percent in South Carolina, and 124 percent in Georgia during the years of the early October season. In those states and Virginia, 44.7 percent of all wings received from hunters were from early October.

Table 223. Mean yearly harvest of wood ducks for a comparable number of years prior to and during special early hunting seasons that were part of the regular seasons.

States	Years of special season	Harvest in years before special season	Harvest in years during special season	Percentage difference	t-test
Virginia	1976–87	6,900	29,800	331.9	8.71 P<0.001
North Carolina	1978–87	28,900	68,000	135.3	5.29 P<0.001
South Carolina	1981–84	63,700	68,400	7.4	0.49 P>0.10
Georgia	1980–87	44,500	51,300	15.3	0.93 P>0.10
Iowa	1979–87	48,900	49,900	2.04	0.31 P>0.10

Early hunting seasons in southern states may result in the harvest of an unusually large proportion of adult females (Anderson 1984, Minser et al. 1990). Large harvests in some states and the vulnerability of adult female wood ducks early in the season justify caution in changing regulations to increase local harvests.

Wildlife managers should be keenly aware of the overharvest that may occur within a particular subpopulation. Because a large proportion of wood ducks are killed in the vicinity of their breeding areas, local populations are at risk. Where recruitment is minimal, subpopulation numbers may diminish to the point that a particular element is depleted or eliminated as a viable breeding unit. The high degree of homing by adults and yearlings reduces the likelihood of pioneering into new areas; therefore, if local hunting pressure seriously reduces a fragmented population, a vacant habitat may remain unoccupied for some years or an underpopulated habitat may fail to reach its carrying capacity.

The 750,000 or more wood ducks taken annually by waterfowl hunters in the United States since the late 1970s makes the woodie second only to the mallard in importance among hunted duck species east of the Mississippi River. Conservative bag limits set by the U.S. Fish and Wildlife Service and hunter compliance with harvest regulations have prevented overharvest and not jeopardized the species' overall increase in that time. Continued scrutiny of woodie indices, concerted habitat management investments, and conservative harvest will help ensure that wood ducks will continue to be an attraction to hunters and nonhunters alike. *Photo by F. Eugene Hester.*

Table 224. Mean increase in harvest of wood ducks in three states accruing from a special five-day early extension to the regular season, 1981–88.[a]

State	Harvest during five-day additive period	Harvest during regular season	Total harvest for entire season	Percentage harvest of five-day season
Florida	7,000	15,800	22,800	30.7
Kentucky	14,900	2,000	16,900	88.2
Tennessee	17,000	8,800	25,800	65.9

[a] Data from K. Gambel (1989, personal communication 1990).

In deliberating regulations that affect the status of wood ducks, waterfowl administrators need to consider the sources of the harvest. Because of postbreeding movements prior to the autumn migration, an early geographic mixture of woodies occurs. Even in the most northern regions of the wood duck range—Quebec, Ontario, and Minnesota—the regular-season harvest contains birds from other political units (tables 225 and 226). Lateral movements are prevalent among postbreeding wood ducks (see Chapter 14), which results in a regional harvest from diverse sources during regular seasons.

As autumn passage progresses southward (see Chapter 4), local wood duck populations are increasingly augmented by birds from other states (Figure 130). Perhaps because Atlantic Flyway states are smaller than states in the Mississippi Flyway, band recoveries from other states increase more rapidly in the Atlantic Flyway as latitude decreases than is the case in the Mississippi Flyway. Regardless of the explanation, out-of-state direct band recoveries of adult wood ducks increased during seasons of regular length in both flyways—4.04 percent for each degree southward in the Atlantic Flyway and 3.6 percent for each degree southward in the Mississippi Flyway. Thus, the question for managers is whether a higher kill can be permitted in southern states without adversely affecting the population of wood ducks in more northern states. Earlier openings of hunting seasons in southern states permit a higher kill of local woodies, but the

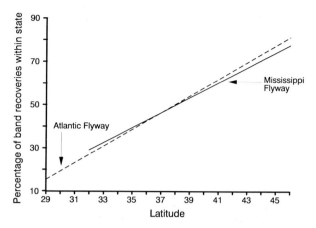

Figure 130. Percentage of wood duck band recoveries within state of banding compared with recoveries from out of state, arranged by degrees of latitude. The regression equations for the Mississippi and Atlantic flyways are: $r = 0.62$, $P < 0.05$, $y = -81.41 + 3.46x$; and $r = 0.71$, $P < 0.001$, $y = -96.6 + 3.87x$, respectively.

specific dates for early seasons are difficult to set because of the lack of exact information on early autumn migration.

Data on autumn migration of wood ducks in the Atlantic Flyway, based on estimated numbers at national wildlife refuges, suggested that northern birds do not begin to augment populations on the southeast coast and in Florida until mid-October (see Figure 10). Band recoveries in the northern region showed a rapid decline after October 15 (see Figure 11), indicating a major exodus to more southern latitudes by the end of that month.

Table 225. Harvest of wood ducks in provinces/states of the Mississippi Flyway from in-state and out-of-state breeding sources, 1981-85. Based on the proportion of direct adult recoveries between bandings in an indigenous state or province and other regions.

Province/state	Mean harvest[a]	Proportion of recoveries from other states	Estimated harvest	
			From other states/provinces	From local state/province
Ontario	23,770	36.74	8,733	15,037
Minnesota	129,920	51.44	66,831	63,089
Wisconsin	79,540	30.61	24,347	55,193
Michigan	36,900	23.03	8,498	28,402
Iowa	48,120	30.98	14,908	33,212
Illinois	50,760	63.81	32,390	18,370
Indiana	11,980	24.20	2,899	9,081
Ohio	25,080	18.47	4,632	20,448
Missouri	25,960	39.68	10,301	15,659
Kentucky	2,600	8.08	210	2,390
Arkansas	42,940	82.30	35,340	7,600
Tennessee	9,680	41.05	3,974	5,706
Louisiana	185,120	81.27	150,447	34,673
Mississippi	51,820	86.89	45,026	6,794
Alabama	18,060	77.18	13,939	4,121
Total	742,250		422,475	319,775

[a]Data from Gambel (1989) and Canadian Wildlife Progress Notes: "Migratory Birds Killed in Canada."

Table 226. Harvest of wood ducks in provinces/states of the Atlantic Flyway from in-state and out-of-state breeding sources, 1981-85. Based on the proportion of direct adult recoveries between bandings in an indigenous state or province and other regions.

Province/state[a]	Mean harvest[b]	Proportion of recoveries from other states	Estimated harvest	
			From other states/provinces	From local state/province
Quebec	23,450	12.14	2,847	20,603
Ontario	71,300	36.74	26,196	45,104
Maine	11,240	42.69	4,798	6,442
Vermont	5,720	33.63	1,924	3,796
New Hampshire	7,100	6.96	494	6,606
Massachusetts	5,420	44.27	2,399	3,021
Connecticut	5,080	14.68	746	4,334
New York	30,900	42.19	13,037	17,863
Pennsylvania	29,860	47.03	14,043	15,817
West Virginia	3,520	5.50	194	3,326
New Jersey	13,580	40.51	5,501	8,079
Delaware	3,040	11.69	355	2,685
Maryland	7,260	49.94	3,626	3,634
Virginia	33,840	65.93	22,311	11,529
North Carolina	74,740	78.76	58,865	15,875
South Carolina	75,160	82.88	62,293	12,867
Georgia	54,820	80.44	44,097	10,723
Florida	19,620	75.75	14,862	4,758
Total	475,650		278,588	197,062

[a]Rhode Island omitted because of limited data.
[b]Data from Gambel (1989) and Canadian Wildlife Progress Notes: "Migratory Birds Killed in Canada."

Southward departures appear to occur earlier in the Mississippi Flyway than in the Atlantic Flyway (see figures 10 and 12). Census data suggest that numbers decline in the northern regions of both flyways as early as mid-September; in the Midwest, populations dropped conspicuously after mid-October. Band recoveries also indicate that most wood ducks depart the northern zones of both flyways between October 10 and 30 (see figures 11 and 12). Thus, there appears to be little ingress of wood ducks into southern states in the Atlantic Flyway before October 15 and in the Mississippi Flyway before October 10.

A temporal analysis of band recoveries in Alabama, from bandings made out-of-state, showed similar seasonal distributions for wood ducks banded in the northern and southern regions of the Atlantic and Mississippi flyways (Hayden and Pollock 1990). Recoveries rose rapidly after November 25 and remained high through January 15. Because of late openings in the waterfowl season in Alabama, differences in the regional origin of harvested wood ducks were minimal. Earlier seasons would be required to reduce hunting losses to northern-reared wood ducks.

Future studies may be able to refine data on postbreeding and migration movements to clarify the composition of wood duck populations in southern states prior to the obvious influx of northern migrants. One approach, taken by Thul and O'Brien (1990), was to use blood parasites as biological tags to estimate the temporal pattern of northern wood ducks in southern harvests.

Propagation of Wood Ducks

Scores of aviculturists raise wood ducks for pleasure and profit. Eggs collected from birds retained as breeders are incubated in a number of ways: by the parental hen; by a foster bantam hen or other domestic poultry; or with an electric incubator. In some instances, a combination of these methods is employed, beginning with a laying hen or a foster mother and ending with an incubator.

We raised wood ducks on three occasions and, over a period of five years, have obtained valuable data from Bernard and Peter Van Norman of Hanna City, Illinois, who have raised scores of wood ducks for many years. They consider that the best way to incubate wood duck eggs is with a broody bantam hen; their second and third choices are a broody female wood duck and an electric incubator, respectively.

Even aviary-reared wood duck females are excitable and make poor mothers compared with the more complacent bantam foster mothers. Because of female woodies' flighty behavior, the Van Normans remove eggs from these incubating hens after 10–14 days and place them under foster bantams for hatching and rearing, thus providing time for the female wood ducks to lay second clutches.

For unknown reasons electric incubators fail to hatch the same proportion of eggs hatched by maternal wood ducks, bantams, and other broody poultry. Doty (1972) recorded a 67-percent hatch of wood duck eggs by electric incubation and a 93-percent hatch with broody foster mallards—success rates typical of other aviculturists. Electric incubators are convenient, however, and remain the preferred method when large numbers of eggs are to be hatched. Several types of electric incubators are marketed: forced-air and still-air, those that turn eggs automatically and those that require eggs to be turned manually.

Incubation temperature. Temperatures for incubating wood duck eggs range from 37.5 degrees Celsius (99.5° F) to 38.3 degrees Celsius (101° F) for forced-air incubators; 38.9 degrees Celsius (102° F) is the ideal temperature for still-air incubators.

Humidity during incubation. Humidity control is as important as temperature control. Development of the air cell at the rounded end of the egg is largely controlled by humidity. If the humidity is too low, the air cell will be too large and the duckling too small; if the humidity is too high, the air cell will be too small and the duckling too large (Mason 1988). The air cell must be sufficiently large for the duckling to use its beak to cut a 360-degree cap through which to extricate itself. When the humidity is too high, space is insufficient for the duckling to apply its egg tooth to excise the cap completely. When the humidity is too low, the air cell is larger than normal and the egg membrane may be too tough for the egg tooth to excise the egg cap.

Bernard Van Norman candles his woodie eggs weekly to cull dead embryos and observe air cell development. These observations enable him to adjust the humidity level if it is too high or too low. Figure 131 shows air cell developments at the blunt end of the egg under normal incubation: 8 percent of volume by day 7, 14 percent by day 14, 19 percent by day 21, and 25 percent by day 28.

Relative humidity should be maintained at 70 percent (wet bulb—30–31 degrees Celsius: 86–88° F) until the last few days of incubation, when it is raised to 80 percent, thereby increasing the pliability of the egg membrane at the time when the egg tooth must cut the escape window. In addition to maintaining the humidity within tolerances, daily fine-spraying of the eggs with warm water until the last few days of incubation is recommended.

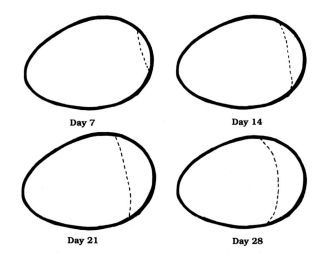

Figure 131. Development of the air cell in the wood duck egg under normal incubation. About 30 percent of the blunt end of the egg ultimately should be occupied by the air cell.

Attitude and turning of eggs. Eggs should be placed in an incubator with the pointed end down and rotated about every four hours to ensure normal development of the embryo. The longer the turning interval, the weaker the ducklings at hatching and the greater the likelihood of physical deformities. When the eggs start to pip, two to three days prior to hatching, turning should cease. At this time, many aviculturists place the eggs in a hatcher compartment in a position identical to that of the egg when removed from the incubator. The recommended hatcher temperature is 38 degrees Celsius (100° F), with a relative humidity of 80 percent.

The ducklings should be left in the incubator or hatcher for 24 hours to dry and gather strength. When they become lively, they are placed in a brooder.

Brooding. Woodie ducklings can be brooded by their mother or by a foster mother such as a bantam, other chicken, or domestic mallard, or they may be placed in a homemade or conventional brooder. Because of the flighty behavior of female wood ducks, Bernard Van Norman prefers to use a bantam as a surrogate mother as well as for incubation.

Brooder temperature should start about 32 degrees Celsius (90°F) and decrease about 3–5 degrees Celsius per week until the young are largely covered by contour feathers—a stage that is achieved in five to six weeks.

Food. Starter feed should contain 19–22 percent protein and be used for the first two to three weeks; the protein content should then be reduced to 12–14 percent for normal growth. Abnormally rapid growth from a diet too high in protein may lead to wing deformity and other skeletal problems.

Some aviculturists have experienced difficulty getting ducklings that were hatched in electric incubators to start feeding. When placed with ducklings of other species, however, woodie ducklings soon learn to fend for themselves. Bernard Van Norman found that sprinkling duckweed plants over dry starter feed enticed day-old ducklings to feed. Duckweeds are tiny floating plants high in protein that develop in sloughs, swamps, ditches, and marshes where organic matter is abundant. They can readily be skimmed off the surface of the water to supplement commercial crumbles. Lawton L. Shurtleff found that by chopping earthworms into segments or using meal worms to sprinkle over commercial crumbles, wood duck ducklings could be induced to initiate feeding. Otherwise, Shurtleff observed considerable duckling mortality during the first few days of life.

Yeagley (1953) reported that dropping 24-hour-old ducklings into a pan of water from a height of 1.2 meters (4 ft) or more appeared to release them from their escape fixation—the urge to flee from any confinement—whereupon they began to drink and feed with zest. Dropping them on land may accomplish the same result. Some aviculturists, however, claim that these actions do not help.

Water. Until ducklings are several weeks old, they should be kept from water deep enough for swimming. For the first three or four weeks, only drinking water should be furnished. Without the guidance of a mother, ducklings have a penchant for remaining in the water too long, becoming soaked and chilled and frequently dying from hypothermia or drowning.

Establishing New Breeding Colonies

We believe that artificial propagation should play a very limited role in wood duck management. However, suitable wetland areas, especially new ones, devoid of breeding woodies may provide opportunities to establish breeding groups of birds through the release of flightless and flighted young. At this stage of population growth in the eastern United States, the establishment of new birds in vacant habitats is unlikely to succeed. The absence of breeding wood ducks usually indicates that the habitat is limited in one or more aspects: the food base or cover may be inadequate; predator populations affecting nest success or brood survival may be too high; or a paucity of nest sites may limit nesting opportunities. Nest houses may provide a means of remedying the deficiency in natural cavities and improving nest success to some extent, but

other limitations in the habitat may be more difficult to overcome.

Strong homing by young wood ducks provides the means by which females return to the point of release. We demonstrated this fundamental behavior of young wood ducks in 1942–1943 (McCabe 1947, Bellrose 1958). Wood ducks artificially hatched and reared for three to six weeks at Havana, Illinois, were transported to and released in Madison, Wisconsin, Medaryville, Indiana, and Wheaton, Illinois. Small numbers of females returned the following spring to nest near their respective release sites, but none returned to the area where they had been reared. Three of 45 female wood ducks (6.7 percent) released in 1953 near their rearing site on Quiver Creek at Havana, Illinois, were captured as incubating birds the following year.

Prior to 1969, wood ducks had never been known to nest at the Arrowwood National Wildlife Refuge in eastcentral North Dakota. A release of 253 (132 females) hand-reared wood ducks during the summer of 1968 resulted in the return of at least 15 females to nest in houses in 1969 (Doty and Kruse 1972). The number of wood duck nests steadily increased from 16 in 1969 to 121 in 1975, but it declined to 30 in 1982 (Doty et al. 1984). From 1983

Aviculturists have found that bantam hens, other chickens, and domestic mallard hens can be used to incubate and brood pen-raised woodie ducklings. These foster mothers tend to be less flighty and more attentive than are captive woodie hens. Artificial propagation of wood ducks (exclusive of nest house programs) should play a minor role in wood duck management. Efforts and resources to enhance woodie populations should focus instead on improving habitat conditions for wild birds. *Photo courtesy of Bernard Van Norman.*

to 1989 an average of 43 nest attempts were made each year, according to Paul Van Ningen. Thus, the wood duck population at Arrowwood National Wildlife Refuge was established by releasing hand-reared birds and providing nest sites. The large number of wood ducks currently breeding in nest houses along the James and Sheyenne rivers in North Dakota may owe their origin to the pioneering of yearlings from the initial release of woodies at Arrowwood.

Numerous breeding colonies of wood ducks on the Great Plains appear to have originated from intentional and unintentional releases of wood ducks from aviaries. Details on these events have not been documented but have been brought to our attention on several occasions.

McGilvrey (1971) made spring releases of small numbers of pen-reared wood ducks over a three-year period at the Patuxent Wildlife Research Center in Laurel, Maryland. His goal was to augment the wild population already breeding there, and he was eminently successful: the number of hens using nest houses increased from 22 in 1966 to 111 in 1970. McGilvrey concluded that under favorable habitat conditions, small numbers of spring-released wood ducks could appreciably increase sparse breeding populations in underpopulated habitats.

Lane et al. (1968) raised 780 young wood ducks that were released on six national wildlife refuges: Savannah, Harris Neck, and Blackbeard Island in coastal Georgia; Piedmont in central Georgia; St. Marks in northern Florida; and the Carolina Sandhills in northcentral South Carolina. They stated that wood ducks had not been known to occupy nest houses previously at Savannah, Harris Neck, and Blackbeard Island. At St. Marks, Piedmont, and the Carolina Sandhills, only limited use of nest houses was made.

Following the release of hand-reared birds at the three coastal Georgia refuges, the use of nest houses increased from 0 to 81.1 percent. Adding hand-reared ducks to the breeding population at Piedmont National Wildlife Refuge appeared to increase numbers, but little change ensued in use of nest houses at St. Marks and Carolina Sandhills National Wildlife Refuges. Lane et al. (1968) believed that holding the birds near the release site for four to five months prior to their release in January helped to keep them in the vicinity as breeders; it also increased survival.

Capen et al. (1974) tried a different approach to establish new breeding colonies of wood ducks in Maine. They captured wild wood duck hens and broods in nest houses, clipped the wings of the hens, and released the females and ducklings on water areas where none were known to nest.

Twenty-two of 25 hens (88 percent) remained with their ducklings on the new areas, which averaged 71 kilometers (44 mi) from their original nesting sites. Eight of 87 female ducklings (11 percent) returned to nest in the areas where they had achieved flight maturity.

Summer releases at Havana, Illinois, at Arrowwood National Wildlife Refuge, and in Maine suggest that about 10 percent of hens returned to nest in houses—lower than the 37- to 64-percent return rates calculated for wild yearling females. Hence, either there is higher mortality among artificially reared and released hens than among wild females, or there is less homing and therefore more pioneering among artificially displaced wood ducks.

Releases, therefore, must be of sufficient size to overcome losses to annual mortality and pioneering to a different area. If birds are released shortly before the nesting season, as suggested by Lane et al. (1968), a much larger proportion of released birds is available for local breeding.

The addition of predator-resistant nest houses should enhance the productivity of introduced females. The second requirement is an adequate food base and cover for ducklings. Survival to maturity needs to be more than 50 percent to compensate for annual adult losses and provide a yearly increment to the breeding population.

When the annual recruitment of young falls below the annual survival rate of 46–49 percent (see Table 198), an established breeding population usually will decline. If a yearly debit persists, the local population may eventually disappear unless there is pioneering by ducks from outside the project area. In most instances, such a decline appears more attributable to loss of broods than to loss of nests. As discussed in Chapter 18, a reduced food base brought about a decline in breeding populations at the Chautauqua National Wildlife Refuge and elsewhere in Mason County, Illinois. Doty et al. (1984) suggested that at Arrowwood National Wildlife Refuge the decline in breeding wood ducks—after robust growth for six years from startup—may have been related to reduced brood survival rates caused by increased predation or increased habitat deficiencies.

It is our contention that the establishment of new colonies of wood ducks by artificial releases on anything but a temporary basis is destined to long-term failure unless habitat quality is also addressed.

THE FUTURE

Adaptability is the key to animal survival. Aside from the mallard, the wood duck probably is the most adaptable duck in North America. Of all environmental factors that affect waterfowl populations, the food base is most important. Fortunately, the wood duck has shown great adaptiveness in utilizing a broad variety of plants and animals to meet its nutritional needs.

Wood ducks exploit waste grain—including corn, wheat, rice, and soybeans—left in fields after harvest. They feed on some of the largest and hardest seeds in nature: acorns, pecans, lotus, and arrowarum. They fly to upland groves of oaks and to pecan and filbert orchards to scour the ground for fallen nuts. In season, they eagerly consume grapes, mulberries, black cherries, and blackberries. They dabble on any small freshwater area for insects, aquatic plants and their seeds, dropped tree seeds, and other plant and animal flotsam. They feed in flooded fields on weed seeds, including smartweeds, millet, foxtail grass, and many others. They are more likely to feed on terrestrial insects than is any other duck species. Even small fish and frogs are relished.

Their adaptability to foods was illustrated by changes in food items when mast failed in South Carolina in 1974. Landers et al. (1977) reported that as a result of an acorn shortage, wood ducks shifted their diet to a variety of moist-soil plant species that had been previously ignored.

Wood ducks walk or run through grain fields, oak groves, and nut orchards; they dabble on the water surface; and they feed with immersed heads, tipping up and even diving when necessary to secure such choice items as acorns and corn. Because of their diverse methods of feeding and their gastrointestinal ability to digest and assimilate a broad spectrum of foods, wood ducks are able to exploit a variety of wetlands and to enhance their survival potential by reducing interspecific competition.

By utilizing riverine habitats through much of the year, wood ducks minimize competition with other species of waterfowl. In such habitats, only scant numbers of hooded mergansers and common goldeneyes compete for nest sites, and neither of these species competes for food. The mallard is the wood duck's principal food competitor during autumn and winter. Both species have remarkably similar food habits, which are centered on mast and grain. To avoid competition with the larger, more dominant mallards, wood ducks utilize riverine habitats and small water areas to a greater degree than mallards do. Geographically, the respective wintering grounds of the two species are partially distinct—wood ducks occupy the rivers and swamps of the Southeast on a much larger scale than do mallards. In the Mississippi Delta, woodies tend to winter in the more southern regions and

mallards in the more northern. In severe winters, mallards and wood ducks are forced into similar habitats. When circumstances confine them to the same wetland, wood ducks more frequently feed in the shallow margins where overhead cover is dense, while mallards are likely to feed in the more open, marginal areas.

Because of their southern distribution, wood ducks are less likely to migrate long distances than are other major species of ducks. Reduced migration conserves energy for reproduction and a longer breeding season, thereby enabling them to renest more often and, in the mid- to Deep South, to raise two broods. The net result is a reproductive potential unmatched by other species, though partly lost through unusually large brood mortality.

The Achilles' heel of populations of mature wood ducks is their vulnerability to shooting on the evening flight to roosts. Although wood ducks partially adjust after several shooting experiences, the evening flight exposes them to high kill and cripple losses. Although they are not in the class of mallards and northern pintails in their wariness of blinds, wood ducks appear to learn to avoid blinds more readily than do teal or northern shovelers. A characteristic of wood ducks is their tendency to ignore decoys completely or to decoy without inspection.

Now that the wood duck has become the second most important duck in the bag of hunters in the eastern United States, with an annual harvest of about 981,500 (1978–1990), waterfowl administrators should strive to maintain this level of harvest to compensate partially for the reduced population of other species. To overharvest for long, however, would bring the wood duck into a decline that likely would be precipitous and certainly would be highly unpopular among hunters and bird watchers alike. Careful husbandry is in order.

The wood duck has biological means that bode well for its future. Habitat acquisition and improved management of the water levels of overflow bottomland hardwoods can help maintain the current population levels in the Mississippi Flyway.

In the wood duck, nature has provided a unique and adaptable bird. It lives more intimately with humans than does any other wild duck. But like other birds, its adaptability is limited, and it requires time to adjust to changing environments. Human activities can change conditions in relatively little time; wood ducks adjust in the long term. How well wood ducks survive into the future will depend on human population growth and the effects of increasing numbers of people on the environment, including the intensity of land use and of land and water pollution.

Epilogue

In the wood duck, evolution has crafted a species uniquely adapted to a niche in wetlands unoccupied by other waterfowl. By changing its nest site from the ground to tree cavities, the wood duck increased nest success, thereby permitting survival in habitats subject to fluctuating water levels and heavy predator populations. Even today, however, there is an occasional reversal from the wood duck's proclivity to use tree sites to its probable primordial trait of nesting on the ground.

The body size and shape of the female wood duck may have evolved to permit use of abandoned nest cavities of the pileated woodpecker, a species abundant in mature forests before the Civil War. In any event, the wood duck's size—within the habitat niche it occupies—is a compromise between costs of survival and costs of reproduction.

The woodie's unusually large eye fits into the scheme of its evolutionary development by providing high resolution and light enhancement necessary for rapid flight through a matrix of branches, where contact could lead to a debilitating injury or death. The wood duck's broad wings and large tail (compared with those of other species of ducks) are further examples of evolutionary adaptation to twisting flight in heavily wooded habitat.

The digestive system of the wood duck has evolved to utilize plants and invertebrates of swamps, overflow bottomlands, streams, and similar wooded wetlands. The grinding activity of the gizzard and its enzymes have the capability to dissolve hard seed coats of acorns, pecans, American lotus, and other nutlike seeds, enabling the wood duck to exploit food resources of swamps and overflow bottomland hardwoods to a degree unequaled by other waterfowl species.

Sexual dimorphism and a biased sex ratio in favor of males provide a female wood duck with a varying choice of mates as well as an available mate for renesting purposes. Eons ago, both sexes probably were of similar coloration, but genetic mutations produced color patterns that proved attractive to females. The result of thousands of years of mutational changes in plumage, bill, and eye is the resplendent male color pattern that many naturalists have considered to be the most beautiful among all ducks. Yet for all its color, the wood duck male had to acquire a plumage that permitted a degree of predator oversight to sustain adequate survival. This seems to have been accomplished by segmenting color blocks—a dark-colored back in concert with shadows from overhead cover and with the reflectiveness of dark water—that permit drakes to blend successfully into the background of murky wooded habitats. Females, on the other hand, had to develop a species-specific plumage to reduce chances for hybridization with other species. The white tear-shaped mark posterior to the eye may be a key plumage character in distinguishing it from the similar female mandarin duck.

In subjecting competing males to rigorous testing by complex courtship signals, the female wood duck is able to select for a mate that, among the suitors present, is the most fit. This instinctive determination also serves to expedite transfer of the hen's genetic characteristics into the next generation. Almost invariably, the oldest, most aggressive, persistent, and energetic male will be selected, with the consequence that his advantageous genes also will be perpetuated.

It appears that many yearling males and some females become sexually mature late in their first

breeding season. This may explain the frequent courtship activities that were in evidence during April and May at Nauvoo Slough, Illinois. Because yearling males are more inept at courtship than are older males, they are less likely to be selected the first year. Those that do mate are into the chronology of pair formation later than are older birds. Thus, both older male and female wood ducks have a better opportunity to mate than do yearlings. The older the bird, the more likely its genes are beneficial to the next generation. (Older birds, by mere virtue of survival, demonstrate more fitness than younger birds do.)

Wood duck pairs remain together longer into the incubation period than do other ducks that mate on an annual basis. This longer attachment period by males may have evolved to permit rapid resumption of nesting when nests are destroyed during early stages of incubation. By nature of their indigenous nesting habitat (tree cavities), wood ducks are more dispersed during the breeding season than are prairie-nesting ducks. It follows, therefore, that a renesting wood duck would have more difficulty in finding a new mate than do females of other species. Male wood ducks that stay with their mates the longest are most likely to place their genes in the offspring of that particular female. That advantage, of course, is at odds with the prospect of further disseminating a particular male's genes by breaking the pair bond and mating with another female. Individual males vary in this strategy, which may relate to their opportunity to mate with more than one female.

Over the long term, intraspecific parasitic egg laying (dump nesting) has had to be advantageous to the wood duck. The individual female that utilizes this strategy is able to lay more eggs than are conventional females and thereby minimizes the risk of complete failure of perpetuating her genes. Almost three of four nests in natural cavities fail to hatch. Therefore, the spreading of eggs to as many different nests as feasible would enhance the prospect of gene survival.

The grouping of nest houses has added a dimension to the wood duck's nesting dynamics. Interestingly, it still has resulted in a greater production of young in most instances. A slightly larger proportion of dump nests hatch, and despite a larger proportion of eggs that fail to hatch, more ducklings usually leave a dump nest. Exceptions occur where unusually high nest concentrations result in abnormal intraspecific strife.

Adaptation by the wood duck to the deciduous forest biome has provided it with a breeding range distinctively south of that utilized by other major species of waterfowl. Because of this southern distribution, the wood duck either does not migrate or migrates comparatively short distances. This allows more time and energy for reproduction, often resulting in production of two broods in the southern half of the species' breeding range. In other instances, it provides an extensive period for renesting to compensate for failed clutches.

Riverine breeding habitats are best for woodie use during spring, when water levels are high. Water levels decline to subnormal stages by midsummer, thereby degrading habitat quality. Segments of most wood duck populations respond—through genetic programming—by emigrating to new areas, often hundreds of miles distant, to locate food resources that have seasonally developed on other wetlands. Wood ducks thereby maximize the seasonal availability of wetland resources within their range.

Woodies also maximize breeding habitat by nesting in towns and cities located near or adjacent to streams and other wetlands. They are in relatively close proximal relationship with people at this time in their breeding cycle, because the natural cavities that occur in mature shade trees generally provide safer nest sites than do cavities in the wild. The nest cavities in human communities experience relatively few visitations by raccoons and rat snakes, the two greatest nemeses of nesting wood ducks.

The wood duck's adaptability and the widespread human interest in its welfare augur well for the species' future prosperity.

Common and Scientific Names of Animals and Plants Cited in the Text

Animals

alligator (American): *Alligator mississippiensis*
ani, smooth-billed: *Crotophaga ani*
ant: Family Formicidae

bass: *Micropterus*
bass, largemouth: *M. salmoides*
beaver: *Castor canadensis*
bee: Order Hymenoptera
bee, honey: *Apis mellifera*
beetle: Order Coleoptera
beetle, ground: Family Carabidae
beetle, leaf: Family Chrysomelidae
beetle, predacious diving: Family Dytiscidae
beetle, snout: Family Curculionidae
beetle, water scavenger: Family Hydrophilidae
beetle, whirligig: Family Gyrinidae
bird: Class Aves
bird, passerine: Order Passeriformes
birdfly (hippoboscid): Family Hippoboscidae
blackbird, red-winged: *Agelaius phoeniceus*
bluebird: *Sialia sialis*
boatman, water-: Family Corixidae
bobcat: *Lynx rufus*
bowfin: *Amia calva*
bufflehead: *Bucephala albeola*
bug, plant: Family Miridae
bug, spittle: Family Cercopidae
bug, squash: Family Coreidae
bug, stink: Family Pentatomidae
bug, true: Order Heteroptera
bug, water (leaf): Order Heteroptera
bullfrog: *Rana catesbeiana*

cankerworm: Family Geometridae
canvasback: *Aythya valisineria*
cat, house: *Felis silvestris*
cattle (domestic): *Bos taurus*
chickadee: *Parus atricapillus*

chicken (domestic): *Gallus gallus*
chigger: Order Acarina
clam, Asiatic: *Corbicula fluminea*
cottonmouth: *Agkistrodon piscivorus*
crayfish: Order Decapoda
cricket: Family Gryllidae
cutworm: Family Noctuidae

damselfly: Suborder Zygoptera
deer, white-tailed: *Odocoileus virginianus*
dog, domestic: *Canis familiaris*
dragonfly: Suborder Anisoptera
duck: Family Anatidae
duck, African black: *Anas sparsa*
duck, American black: *A. rubripes*
duck, Australian wood: *Chenonetta jubata*
duck, black-bellied whistling: *Dendrocygna autumnalis*
duck, fulvous whistling: *D. bicolor*
duck, harlequin: *Histrionicus histrionicus*
duck, mandarin: *Aix galericulata*
duck, mottled: *Anas fulvigula*
duck, Muscovy: *Cairina moschata*
duck, ruddy: *Oxyura jamaicensis*
duck, sea: Tribe Mergini
duck, whistling: *Dendrocygna*
duck, wood: *Aix sponsa*

earthworm: Class Oligochaeta
eider: *Somateria mollisima*
eider, Steller's: *Polysticta stelleri*

falcon, peregrine: *Falco peregrinus*
fish, bony: Class Osteichthyes
flatworm: Phylum Platyhelminthes
flea: Order Siphonaptera
flicker (northern): *Colaptes auratus*
fluke: Class Trematoda
fluke, blood (schistosome): *Schistosoma*
fly: Order Diptera
fly, black: Family Simuliidae

fly, caddis: Family Trichoptera
fly, crane: Family Tipulidae
fly, flesh: Family Sarcophagidae
fly, horse: Family Tabanidae
fly, stable: Family Muscidae
flycatcher, great crested: *Myiarchus crinitus*
fox: Family Canidae
frog: Family Ranidae

gadwall: *Anas strepera*
goldeneye, Barrow's: *Bucephala islandica*
goldeneye, common: *B. clangula*
goose, cackling: *Branta canadensis minima*
goose, Canada: *B. canadensis*
goose, lesser snow: *Chen caerulescens*
goose, Ross': *C. rossii*
grackle: *Quiscalus*
grackle, common: *Q. quiscula*
grasshopper: Family Locustidae
grouse, ruffed: *Bonasa umbellus*

hawk: Family Accipitridae
hawk, marsh (harrier, northern): *Circus cyaneus*
hawk, red-shouldered: *Buteo lineatus*
hawk, red-tailed: *B. jamaicensis*
heron, black-crowned night: *Nycticorax nycticorax*
hopper, leaf: Class Jassoidea
hopper, tree: Family Membracidae

insect: Class Insecta
isopod (sow-bugs): Order Isopoda

jay, blue: *Cyanocitta cristata*

kestrel (American): *Falco sparverius*

lacewing: Order Neuroptera
leech: Class Hirudinea
lice, bird: Order Mallophaga

maggot (larvae): Order Diptera
maggot, rat-tailed (fly, flower): *Eristalis tenax*
mallard: *Anas platyrhynchos*
mammal: Class Mammalia
mayfly: Order Ephemeroptera
mayfly, burrowing: *Hexagenia bilineata*
merganser, common: *Mergus merganser*
merganser, hooded: *Lophodytes cucullatus*
midge: Family Chironomidae
midge, biting: *Culicoides*
mink: *Mustela vison*
minnow, top (fish, mosquito): *Gambusia affinis*
mite, feather: Order Acarina
mosquito: Family Culicidae
moth: Order Lepidoptera
mouse, deer: *Peromyscus maniculatus*
mouse, white-footed: *P. leucopus*
murre, thick-billed: *Uria lomvia*
muskrat: *Ondatra zibethicus*

oldsquaw: *Clangula hyemalis*

opossum (Virginia): *Didelphis virginiana*
owl, barred: *Strix varia*
owl, great horned: *Bubo virginianus*
owl, screech-: *Otus asio*

petrel, snow: *Pagodroma nivea*
pheasant, ring-necked: *Phasianus colchicus*
pickerel, chain: *Esox niger*
pigeon, rock (domestic): *Columba livia*
pike, northern: *Esox lucius*
pintail, northern: *Anas acuta*
pronghorn: *Antilocapra americana*

quail, (northern) bobwhite: *Colinus virginianus*

raccoon: *Procyon lotor*
redhead: *Aythya americana*
roundworm: Phylum Nematoda

salamander: Order Caudata
salmon: *Oncorhynchus*
scaup, lesser: *Aythya affinis*
shoveler, northern: *Anas clypeata*
snail: Class Gastropoda
snake, bull: *Pituophis melanoleucus*
snake, rat, black: *Elaphe obsoleta obsoleta*
snake, rat, gray: *Elaphe obsoleta spiloides*
snake, water, blotched: *Nerodia erythrogaster transversa*
sparrow, white-throated: *Zonotrichia querula*
spider: Class Arachnidea
squirrel, flying: *Glaucomys*
squirrel, fox: *Sciurus niger*
squirrel, gray: *S. carolinensis*
squirrel, red (pine): *Tamiasciurus hudsonicus*
starling (European): *Sturnus vulgaris*
steelhead: *Oncorhynchus mykiss*
stonefly: Order Plecoptera
stork, white: *Ciconia ciconia*
strider, water: Family Gerridae
swallow, tree: *Tachycineta bicolor*
swan: *Cygnus*

tapeworm: Class Cestoda
teal, blue-winged: *Anas discors*
teal, cinnamon: *A. cyanoptera*
teal, green-winged: *A. crecca*
tern, black: *Chlidonias niger*
tick: Order Acarina
treader, water: Family Mesoveliidae
trout: Family Salmonidae
turkey, wild: *Meleagris gallopavo*
turtle, snapping: *Chelydra serpentina*

warbler, European blackcap (blackcap): *Sylvia atricapilla*
wasp: Order Hymenoptera
weasel: *Mustela*
wigeon, American: *Anas americana*
woodcock (American): *Scolopax minor*
woodpecker: Subfamily Picinae
woodpecker, ivory-billed: *Campephilus principalis*
woodpecker, pileated: *Dryocopus pileatus*

woodpecker, red-bellied: *Melanerpes carolinus*
woodpecker, red-cockaded: *Picoides borealis*
woodpecker, red-headed: *M. erythrocephalus*
worm, meal: *Tenebrio molitor*
worm, thorny-headed: *Polymorphus minutus*
wren, house: *Troglodytes aedon*

Plants

acorn: *Quercus*
alder: *Alnus*
alder, black (holly, winterberry): *Ilex verticillata*
almond: *Prunus amygdalus*
apple: *Malus*
arrowarum (Virginia): *Peltandra virginica*
arrowhead (common): *Sagittaria latifolia*
ash: *Fraxinus*
ash, black: *F. nigra*
ash, green: *F. pennsylvanica* var. *subintegerrima*
ash, red: *F. pennsylvanica*
aspen: *Populus*
aspen, bigtooth: *P. grandidentata*
aspen, quaking: *P. tremuloides*
avens: *Geum*
azolla, Atlantic (water fern): *Azolla carolinina*

baldcypress (common): *Taxodium distichum*
barnyardgrass: *Echinochloa crusgalli*
basswood (linden), American: *Tilia americana*
bay, sweet (magnolia, sweetbay): *Magnolia virginiana*
bayberry (waxmyrtle): *Myrica pensylvanica*
beakrush: *Rhynchospora*
beech, American: *Fagus grandifolia*
beech, blue (hornbeam, American): *Carpinus caroliniana*
beechnut: *Fagus grandifolia*
beggarticks: *Bidens*
birch, river: *Betula nigra*
blackberry: *Rubus*
bogrosemary dwarf: *Andromeda glaucophylla*
buckwheat: *Fagopyrum*
bulrush: *Scirpus*
bulrush, river: *S. fluviatilis*
bulrush, softstem: *S. validus*
burreed: *Sparganium*
burreed, greater (giant): *S. eurycarpum*
buttercup: *Ranunculus*
buttonbush (common): *Cephalanthus occidentalis*

canarygrass, reed: *Phalaris arundinacea*
cattail: *Typha*
cedar, northern white (arborvitae, eastern): *Thuja occidentalis*
cherry, bird, wild: *Prunus*
cherry, black: *P. serotina*
chufa (flatsedge): *Cyperus esculentus*
coontail (hornwort, common): *Ceratophyllum demersum*
corn (Indian): *Zea mays*
cottonwood: *Populus*
cowlily: *Nuphar advena*
cranberry: *Vaccinium*

cutgrass, rice: *Leersia oryzoides*
cypress: *Taxodium*

dayflower, Asiatic (aneilema, Keisak): *Murdannia keisak*
dock: *Rumex*
dogwood: *Cornus*
dogwood, gray: *C. racemosa*
ducksmeat, common: *Spirodela polyrhiza*
duckweed: *Lemna*
duckweed, common: *L. minor*
duckweed, star: *L. trisulca*

elm, American: *Ulmus americana*
elm, slippery: *U. rubra*

fetterbush (lyonia): *Lyonia lucida*
filbert: *Corylus*
fir: *Abies*
fir, balsam: *A. balsamea*
foxtail, giant (bristlegrass, Faber): *Setaria faberi*
frogbit: *Limnobium spongia*

gale, sweet (waxmyrtle, sweetgale): *Myrica gale*
grape, wild: *Vitis*
grass, foxtail: *Alopecurus*
grass, meadow: *Panicularia nervata*
grass, panic (panicum): *Panicum*
grass, slough (razorsedge, netted): *Scleria reticularis*
gum, black (tupelo, blackgum): *Nyssa sylvatica*
gum, sweet (sweetgum, American): *Liquidambar styraciflua*
gum, tupelo (tupelo, water): *Nyssa aquatica*

hackberry: *Celtis occidentalis*
hawthorn, green: *Crataegus viridis*
hazelnut: *Corylus*
hickory: *Carya*
hickory, bitternut: *C. cordiformis*
hickory, water: *C. aquatica*

inkberry (holly): *Ilex glabra*

labrador-tea (ledum, Labrador-tea): *Ledum groenlandicum*
larch: *Larix*
laurel (kalmia), bog: *Kalmia polifolia*
leatherleaf, Cassandra: *Chamaedaphne calyculata*
lizardtail: *Saururus cernuus*
loosestrife, swamp: *Decodon verticillatus*
lotus, American: *Nelumbo lutea*

mannagrass: *Glyceria*
maple: *Acer*
maple, boxelder: *A. negundo*
maple, red: *A. rubrum*
maple, silver, soft: *A. accharinum*
maple, sugar, hard: *A. saccharum*
mermaidweed, marsh: *Proserpinaca palustris*
millet: *Echinochloa*
millet, browntop (panicum, branched): *Panicum ramosum*
millet, Japanese: *Echinochloa crusgalli* var. *frumentacea*

millet, water, wild (barnyardgrass): *E. crusgalli*
mulberry: *Morus*
mulberry, red: *M. rubra*

nightshade: *Solanum*

oak: *Quercus*
oak, black: *Q. velutina*
oak, blackjack: *Q. marilandica*
oak, California white (valley): *Q. lobata*
oak, cherrybark: *Q. falcata* var. *pagodaefolia*
oak, chestnut: *Q. prinus*
oak, laurel: *Q. laurifolia*
oak, (common) live: *Q. virginiana*
oak, Nuttall: *Q. nuttallii*
oak, Oregon white: *Q. garryana*
oak, pin: *Q. palustris*
oak, post: *Q. stellata*
oak, (northern) red: *Q. rubra*
oak, scarlet: *Q. coccinea*
oak, swamp chestnut: *Q. michauxii*
oak, swamp white: *Q. bicolor* (northern range)
oak, swamp white (overcup): *Q. lyrata* (southern range)
oak, water: *Q. nigra*
oak, white: *Q. alba*
oak, willow: *Q. phellos*
oat, domestic: *Avena*
oat, wild: *A. fatua*
olive, Russian-: *Elaeagnus angustifolia*

pecan, bitter (hickory, water): *Carya aquatica*
pecan, commercial, sweet (hickory, pecan): *C. illinoensis*
pickerelweed (common): *Pontederia cordata*
pine: *Pinus*
pine, loblolly: *P. taeda*
pine, pond: *P. serotina*
pine, slash: *P. elliottii*
pine, white: *P. strobus*
planer tree (waterelm): *Planera aquatica*
plum, wild: *Prunus*
pondweed: *Potamogeton*
pondweed, curlyleaf: *P. crispus*
pondweed, longleaf (floatingleaf): *P. natans*
pondweed, sago (fennelleaf): *P. pectinatus*
poplar: *Populus*
poplar, tulip (tuliptree, North American): *Liriodendron tulipifera*
potato, duck (arrowhead): *Sagittaria latifolia*
privet (forestiera), swamp (narrowleaf): *Forestiera angustifolia*

reed (common): *Phragmites australis*
reedgrass, bluejoint: *Calamagrostis canadensis*
rice: *Oryza*
rice, wild (wildrice, annual): *Zizania aquatica*
rose, swamp: *Rosa palustris*
rose, wild: *Rosa*
rush: *Juncus*
rush, soft (common): *J. effusus*

sassafras: *Sassafras*

sedge, clump: *Carex*
sedge, hammock: *C. joorii*
skunkcabbage: *Symplocarpus foetidus*
smartweed: *Polygonum*
smartweed (knotweed), marsh: *P. coccineum*
snowbell: *Styrax*
sorghum: *Sorghum*
soybean: *Glycine*
spatterdock (cowlily): *Nuphar advena*
spikerush: *Eleocharis*
spruce: *Picea*
spruce, black: *P. mariana*
stargrass, water (mudplantain, waterstar): *Heteranthera dubia*
sweetgum: *Liquidambar styraciflua*
sycamore, American: *Platanus occidentalis*

titi (cyrilla, swamp): *Cyrilla racemiflora*
tupelo, blackgum: *Nyssa sylvatica*
tupelo, water: *N. aquatica*

viburnum: *Viburnum*

walnut, black: *Juglans nigra*
waterelm: *Planera aquatica*
waterhemp: *Acnida*
waterhyacinth: *Eichhornia crassipes*
waterlily: *Nymphaea*
waterlily, white: *N. tuberosa*
waterlily, yellow (banana): *N. mexicana*
waterpepper, wild (smartweed, swamp): *Polygonum hydropiperoides*
waterprimrose: *Ludvigia*
watershield, Schreber: *Brasenia schreberi*
wheat: *Triticum*
whitetop: *Cardaria pubescens*
wildcelery, American: *Vallisneria americana*
willow: *Salix*
willow, black: *S. nigra*
winterberry (holly): *Ilex verticillata*

Glossary

Addle = To become rotten.

Allopreening = Preening of another bird by its mate.

Bag limit = Maximum allowable daily kill (harvest) by a hunter, according to regulations set annually by the U.S. Fish and Wildlife Service.

Basal metabolic rate (BMR) = Rate at which ingested substances are energetically processed by a bird at rest.

Basic (eclipse) plumage = A plumage worn by wood ducks during the summer and in which adults are flightless for about one month. In males, the plumage is relatively dull and femalelike. Definite alternate (nuptial) plumage replaces basic in 100–120 days from its initial appearance and is worn until the following summer.

Bergman's rule = Among forms of a particular species, body size tends to be larger in the cooler regions of its range and smaller in the warmer regions.

Carrying capacity = Optimal number of an animal population that can be supported and sustained by a particular habitat in relation to temporal and spatial parameters.

Circadian = Designating a biological period of about 24 hours.

Clutch = Eggs laid and incubated by one female per nesting.

Compound clutch = Eggs deposited by more than one female in a single nest (see also **Dump nest**).

Conspecifics = Individuals of the same species.

Crepuscular = Active at twilight.

Crest = A tuft of long feathers on the head capable of being raised.

Culmen = A ridge running lengthwise down the middle of the upper mandible.

Dabbling ducks (dabblers) = Duck species that principally feed in shallow water by "tipping up" or dabbling on the surface.

Density dependent = Limited by density of breeding population (as in recruitment of young).

Diameter at breast height (dbh) = The standard diameter of a tree trunk; taken at breast height to avoid unusual diameters prone to occur closer to the base.

Diving ducks (divers) = Duck species that feed principally by diving below the surface of water areas.

Dump nest = A compound clutch, or nest containing eggs deposited by more than one female.

Endogenous rhythm = Behavioral pattern originating within the body principally as a result of genetic makeup (heredity).

Environmental resistance = Sum of all factors (predators, weather, food, cover) adversely influencing recruitment.

Exogenous rhythm = Behavioral pattern originating outside the body and synchronized by some environmental factor, usually the result of imprinting.

Fecundity = The inherent ability of a species to multiply; the number of eggs capable of being produced by a species.

Fen or bog = Plant community occupying a wet peat-based site.

Food base = The available food resource at a particular time and place necessary to meet the metabolic requirements of a species or discrete population.

Foot-candle = Intensity of light as measured by the amount cast by an international candle 0.3 meter (1 ft) away.

Forced copulation = Copulation by a male with an unreceptive female.

Gonadogenesis = Formation of sex cells.

Harvest = Number or proportion of a wildlife population brought to bag by hunters.

Heating-degree day = The number of degrees of heat required to raise the daily temperature to 18.3 degrees Celsius (65° F).

Homeostasis (homeothermy) = Ability to maintain normal internal stability by coordinated response of organ system to environmental changes.

Homing = Return each year to the same breeding, migration, or wintering area.

House-years = The number of nest houses occupied by wood ducks times the number of years of observation;

e.g., 10 houses occupied for 10 years equals 100 house-years.

Imprinting = Fixing in the brain an external source of information that results in a particular behavioral association and/or pattern.

Inciting = Ritualized courtship behavior and calls by female wood ducks to attract males and maintain pair bonds by stimulating their mates to thwart advances of other drakes.

Interspecific = Between species or individuals of different species.

Intraspecific = Within the framework of a species; between individuals of the same species.

Kill = Number or proportion of a population removed by hunting, consisting of harvest and cripple loss; usually considered an additive 20 percent to the calculated harvest.

Kilocalorie = The heat required to raise the temperature of one kilogram of water one degree Celsius (in contrast to a calorie, which is measured by raising the temperature of one gram of water one degree Celsius). Kilocalories generally are used when measuring the energy produced by food oxidized in animal metabolism.

Lamellae = Minute toothlike ridges on the inside edges of both upper and lower mandible that function as a sieve, enhancing waterfowl feeding. The strainers formed when the bill is closed retain solid food particles while the water is expelled by the tongue.

Littoral zone = A zone of shallow water adjacent to shore where light penetrates sufficiently to permit photosynthesis in rooted plants.

Natality = Inherent ability of a population to increase; reproductive rate.

Nesting efficiency = The proportion of young leaving a nest as compared to the number of eggs laid.

Niche = That part of a habitat particularly suited to the requirements of a given species, or the ecological role of a particular organism, population, or species.

Onomatopoeia = Word or words imitative of the natural sound associated with a particular call.

Patagial tag = A straplike mark attached to the patagium, a membranous fold of skin (possessing flexor muscles and tendons) along the anterior margin of the wing between shoulder and carpal joint.

Philopatry = Annual homing to the same nesting area and often the same nest site.

Phylogenesis = Evolutionary development of a species.

Pioneering = Breeding of females, usually yearlings, in a different area than where they were hatched/reared, the rate depending on the proportion that emigrate as opposed to those that return to their natal area.

Polyandry = The mating of a female with more than one male; not known to result in more than one current pair bond in the wood duck. Renesting females may have a different mate.

Polygyny = The mating of a male with more than one female; in the wood duck a bond is maintained for several weeks to several months depending on season, age, and physiological state.

Population dynamics = Factors regulating population levels, consisting of productivity (the recruitment of flying young) and mortality (the loss of adults and immatures).

Population saturation = Population at maximum levels commensurate with habitat quantity/quality.

Precocial = Hatched at a relatively advanced state (in contrast to altricial birds, which are naked and helpless at hatching).

Recruitment = Addition of a number or proportion of fledged young to an adult population of breeding birds.

Remiges (singular remex) = Large flight feathers, composing the primaries and secondaries of the wing.

Roost = A shallow water area used by wood ducks over much of the year to congregate in communal association for the night. Overhead cover—usually of a woody nature, but often herbaceous in summer or early autumn—is an important prerequisite of a roost site.

Schizogony = Part of a complex life cycle exhibited by some parasite protozoans; asexual replication occurs in the wood duck.

Serotype = A subpopulation of species of microorganisms that have the same antigenic properties.

Spatial = Space requirements; relating to the utilization of a given area.

Spermatogenesis = Forming sperm.

Sporogony = Part of a complex life cycle exhibited by some parasitic protozoans; sexual replication occurs in an intermediate host (e.g. mosquito, biting midge, black fly).

Supracoracoides = The muscle employed to raise the wing, in contrast to the pectoral muscle used to depress the wing.

Temporal = Relating to time, to the duration of an activity.

Wing aspect ratio = Wing area divided into the square of the span.

Wing loading = Body weight divided by wing area (more precisely, the square root of wing area by the cube root of body weight).

Wing span = Length measurement from wing tip to wing tip with the wings fully extended.

Zugunruhe = From the German language, implying the restlessness that precedes migratory departure of birds.

Statistical Symbols and Definitions

Analysis of variance (ANOVA) = Statistical technique to evaluate differences in the mean value of a random variable for two or more populations. "One-way," "two-way," or "n-way ANOVA" refers to the number of ways populations are grouped or classified.

C.L. = confidence limits = The interval within which a specified proportion of mean values of many repeated samples is included.

C.V. = coefficient of variation = An estimate of dispersion within a sample defined as s divided by X; useful when samples with different units of measurement are being compared.

Degrees of freedom (df) = Typically, sample size (n) minus the number of parameters estimated. More degrees of freedom permit more powerful tests.

F-statistic = Test statistic often used in parametric ANOVA. Based on the F-distribution, this statistic is a ratio of variances.

Intercept = In linear regression, where the regression line crosses the ordinate or Y axis.

Kruskal-Wallis test = Nonparametric, one-way ANOVA based on ranks.

Linear regression = A technique used to estimate the relationship between an independent or predictor variable (y) and a dependent or response variable (x).

Mann-Whitney test = Nonparametric test based on ranks for differences between two independent samples.

n = Number of independent observations in a sample.

Nonparametric statistics = A general term for techniques that make few or no assumptions about the distributions of sampled populations or equality of population parameters.

P = alpha probability = The probability that a test statistic could have occurred by random chance alone rather than by some true difference between, for example, two sampled populations.

Parametric statistics = A general term for techniques that involve estimates of population parameters such as variance about a mean value.

Pearson moment correlation = Parametric test statistic that estimates the strength of association between two random variables; ranges from −1 to 1.

r = correlation coefficient = An estimate of the degree of association between two variables. The coefficient can range from −1 (perfect negative association) to 1 (perfect positive association). A 0 would indicate no association.

R^2 = coefficient of determination = In regression, an estimate of how much percentage of variation in the dependent variable is explained by variation in the independent variable.

S.D. or s = standard deviation = The square root of the sample variance. Used as an estimate of dispersion within a sample. In a population with a normal distribution, about 68 percent of the items are included within one S.D. about the mean.

S.E. = standard error of the mean = Defined as s divided by n, this estimates the standard deviation of the sampling distribution or sample means.

Slope = In linear regression, an estimate of how the dependent variable (x) affects the independent variable (y). Graphically, the slope is the change in y units/change in x units.

t-statistic = Parametric technique for evaluating between two sample means.

Variance = Estimate of dispersion about a mean in a sample or population.

X = mean = The sum of observations (scores or measured values) divided by the number of observations.

X^2 = chi-square = A test statistic used to estimate the magnitude of deviations between observed and expected distributions.

Appendices D and E

D. Data used to determine wood duck populations for states and provinces within the Atlantic Flyway, 1961–70.

State or province	Data[a]					
	1	2	3	4	5	6
Maine	5,000	0.4076	2,038	0.02364	0.01761	0.4269
Vermont	4,210	0.2784	1,172	0.02933	0.01486	0.3363
New Hampshire	4,570	0.3682	1,683	0.02899	0.00217	0.0696
Massachusetts	5,360	0.3667	1,966	0.01999	0.01588	0.4427
Connecticut	2,390	0.3537	845	0.02273	0.00391	0.1468
New York	33,140	0.3027	10,031	0.02044	0.01492	0.4219
Pennsylvania	19,320	0.3243	6,265	0.02899	0.02574	0.4703
West Virginia	1,520	0.3641	553	0.01357	0.00079	0.0550
New Jersey	5,800	0.3987	2,312	0.01285	0.00875	0.4051
Delaware	650	0.4563	297	0.01556	0.00206	0.1169
Maryland	1,860	0.4164	775	0.00404	0.00403	0.4994
Virginia	6,260	0.4346	2,721	0.01533	0.02967	0.6593
North Carolina	22,040	0.3955	8,717	0.02657	0.09850	0.7876
South Carolina	31,410	0.4398	13,814	0.02401	0.11626	0.8288
Georgia	17,280	0.4410	7,620	0.02510	0.10320	0.8044
Florida	26,030	0.4287	11,159	0.02251	0.07032	0.7575
Quebec	16,948	0.4076	6,908	0.05017	0.00693	0.1214
Ontario[b]	32,189	0.4076	13,120	0.02223	0.01291	0.3674

[a]1 Total harvest (both sexes and age classes) based on a yearly average for the period 1961–70 in the selected state or province.

2 Percentage adults in the harvest of the selected state or province based on age ratios from "wing bee" findings for the period 1961–70.

3 Average harvest of adults for the selected state or province (#1 x #2).

4 Percentage recovery of adults banded and harvested in the selected state or province.

5 Percentage recovery of adults banded in states or provinces other than the state or province in which the birds were harvested.

6 Proportion of recoveries of adults banded in states or provinces other than the state or province in which they were harvested, compared with the total harvest of banded birds in that state or province (#5 ÷ (#4 + #5)).

7 Proportion of birds banded in the selected state or province compared with the total harvest of banded birds in that state or province (1.0 - #6).

8 Harvest of adult wood ducks in the selected state or province that were produced in that state or province (#3 x #7).

9 Band recovery rate in the selected state or province corrected for unreported bands (#4 x 3.28). Updating to 3.32 (Nichols et al. 1991) would lower population estimates by 1.22 percent.

10 Estimated breeding population for the selected state or province (#8 ÷ #9).

[b] Represents 75 percent of the kill from Ontario for the period 1974–78; zone 3 excluded.

E. Data used to determine wood duck populations for states and provinces within the Mississippi Flyway, 1961–70.

State or province	Data[a]					
	1	2	3	4	5	6
Minnesota	67,330	0.3099	20,866	0.01580	0.01674	0.5144
Wisconsin	55,729	0.3780	21,062	0.02713	0.01197	0.3061
Michigan	22,650	0.3700	8,381	0.01821	0.00545	0.2303
Iowa	21,450	0.2957	6,343	0.03023	0.01357	0.3098
Illinois	25,460	0.3479	8,858	0.01267	0.02234	0.6381
Indiana	7,900	0.3459	2,733	0.01109	0.00354	0.2420
Ohio	22,720	0.3420	7,770	0.01735	0.00393	0.1847
Missouri	10,290	0.3387	3,485	0.01485	0.00977	0.3968
Kentucky	410	0.3750	154	0.02138	0.00188	0.0808
Arkansas	22,470	0.4915	11,044	0.00796	0.03702	0.8230
Tennessee	6,470	0.4515	2,921	0.01241	0.00864	0.4105
Louisiana	71,810	0.4415	31,704	0.02972	0.12892	0.8127
Mississippi	20,330	0.4656	9,466	0.00978	0.06480	0.8689
Alabama	11,600	0.4637	5,379	0.01225	0.04143	0.7718
Ontario[b]	10,730	0.4076	4,374	0.02223	0.01291	0.3674

[a]See footnote[a] of Appendix D.

[b]Represents 25 percent of the kill from Ontario for the period 1974–78; zone 3 excluded.

Appendix D. (continued)

	Data[a]		
7	8	9	10
0.5731	1,168	0.07754	15,063
0.6637	778	0.09620	8,087
0.9304	1,566	0.09509	16,469
0.5573	1,096	0.06557	16,715
0.8532	721	0.07455	9,671
0.5781	5,799	0.06704	86,501
0.5297	3,319	0.09509	34,904
0.9450	523	0.04451	11,750
0.5949	1,375	0.04215	32,622
0.8831	262	0.05104	5,133
0.5006	388	0.01325	29,283
0.3407	927	0.05028	18,437
0.2124	1,851	0.08715	21,239
0.1712	2,365	0.07875	30,032
0.1956	1,490	0.08233	18,098
0.2425	2,706	0.07383	36,652
0.8786	6,069	0.16456	36,880
0.6326	8,300	0.07291	113,839

Appendix E. (continued)

	Data[a]		
7	8	9	10
0.4856	10,133	0.05182	195,542
0.6939	14,615	0.08899	164,232
0.7697	6,451	0.05973	108,003
0.6902	4,378	0.09915	44,155
0.3691	3,269	0.04156	78,657
0.7580	2,072	0.03638	56,954
0.8153	6,335	0.05691	111,316
0.6032	2,102	0.04871	43,153
0.9192	142	0.07013	2,025
0.1770	1,955	0.02611	74,876
0.5895	1,722	0.04070	42,310
0.1873	5,938	0.09748	60,915
0.1311	1,241	0.03208	38,685
0.2282	1,227	0.04018	30,538
0.6326	2,767	0.07291	37,951

Appendices F and G

F. Data used to determine wood duck populations for states and provinces within the Atlantic Flyway, 1981–85.

State or province	Data[a]					
	1	2	3	4	5	6
Maine	11,240	0.3734	4,197	0.02364	0.01761	0.4269
Vermont	5,720	0.2604	1,489	0.02933	0.01486	0.3363
New Hampshire	7,100	0.3443	2,445	0.02899	0.00217	0.0696
Massachusetts	5,420	0.3614	1,959	0.01999	0.01588	0.4427
Connecticut	5,080	0.3265	1,659	0.02273	0.00391	0.1468
New York	30,900	0.3265	10,089	0.02044	0.01492	0.4219
Pennsylvania	29,860	0.2711	8,095	0.02899	0.02574	0.4703
West Virginia	3,520	0.3667	1,291	0.01357	0.00079	0.0550
New Jersey	13,580	0.4014	5,451	0.01285	0.00875	0.4051
Delaware	3,040	0.3871	1,177	0.01556	0.00206	0.1169
Maryland	7,260	0.3778	2,743	0.00404	0.00403	0.4994
Virginia	33,840	0.3956	13,387	0.01533	0.02967	0.6593
North Carolina	74,740	0.4622	34,545	0.02657	0.09850	0.7876
South Carolina	75,160	0.4407	33,123	0.02401	0.11626	0.8288
Georgia	54,820	0.4229	23,183	0.02510	0.10320	0.8044
Florida	19,620	0.5086	9,979	0.02251	0.07032	0.7575
Quebec	23,454	0.3734	8,758	0.05017	0.00693	0.1214
Ontario[b]	71,300	0.3734	26,623	0.02223	0.01291	0.3674

[a]See footnote[a] of Appendix D, except data in columns 1 and 2 are for the period 1981–85.
[b]Represents 75 percent of the kill from Ontario for the period 1981–85; zone 3 excluded.

G. Data used to determine wood duck populations for states and provinces within the Mississippi Flyway, 1981–85.

State or province	Data[a]					
	1	2	3	4	5	6
Minnesota	129,920	0.2813	36,546	0.01580	0.01674	0.5144
Wisconsin	79,540	0.3821	30,392	0.02713	0.01197	0.3061
Michigan	36,900	0.2931	10,815	0.01821	0.00545	0.2303
Iowa	48,120	0.2407	11,582	0.03023	0.01357	0.3098
Illinois	50,760	0.2073	10,523	0.01267	0.02234	0.6381
Indiana	11,980	0.2655	3,181	0.01109	0.00354	0.2420
Ohio	25,080	0.2872	7,203	0.01735	0.00393	0.1847
Missouri	25,960	0.2701	7,012	0.01485	0.00977	0.3968
Kentucky	2,600	0.2064	537	0.02138	0.00188	0.0808
Arkansas	42,940	0.4036	17,331	0.00796	0.03702	0.8230
Tennessee	9,680	0.3250	3,146	0.01241	0.00864	0.4105
Louisiana	185,120	0.3777	69,920	0.02972	0.12892	0.8127
Mississippi	51,820	0.3871	20,060	0.00978	0.06480	0.8689
Alabama	18,060	0.4085	7,378	0.01225	0.04143	0.7718
Ontario[b]	23,767	0.3734	8,875	0.02223	0.01291	0.3674

[a]See footnote[a] of Appendix D, except data in columns 1 and 2 are for the period 1981–85.
[b]Represents 25 percent of the kill from Ontario for the period 1981–85; zone 3 excluded.

Appendix F. (continued)

	Data[a]		
7	8	9	10
0.5731	2,405	0.07754	31,016
0.6637	988	0.09620	10,270
0.9304	2,275	0.09509	23,925
0.5573	1,092	0.06557	16,654
0.8532	1,415	0.07455	18,981
0.5781	5,832	0.06704	86,993
0.5297	4,288	0.09509	45,094
0.9450	1,220	0.04451	27,410
0.5949	3,243	0.04215	76,940
0.8831	1,039	0.05104	20,357
0.5006	1,373	0.01325	103,623
0.3407	4,561	0.05028	90,712
0.2124	7,337	0.08715	84,188
0.1712	5,671	0.07875	72,013
0.1956	4,535	0.08233	55,083
0.2425	2,420	0.07383	32,778
0.8786	7,695	0.16456	46,761
0.6326	16,842	0.07291	230,997

Appendix G. (continued)

	Data[a]		
7	8	9	10
0.4856	17,747	0.05182	342,474
0.6939	21,089	0.08899	236,982
0.7697	8,324	0.05973	139,360
0.6902	7,994	0.09915	80,625
0.3691	3,884	0.04156	93,455
0.7580	2,411	0.03638	66,273
0.8153	5,873	0.05691	103,198
0.6032	4,230	0.04871	86,840
0.9192	494	0.07013	7,044
0.1770	3,068	0.02611	117,503
0.5895	1,855	0.04070	45,577
0.1873	13,096	0.09748	134,346
0.1311	2,630	0.03208	81,983
0.2282	1,684	0.04018	41,911
0.6326	5,614	0.07291	76,999

Appendix H

H. Wood duck nest house information from national wildlife refuges assigned to refuge wetland habitat types.

Habitat[a]	Refuge[b] (state)	Flyway[c]	(region[d])	Period	House-years	Nest starts	Percentage of wood duck use	Percentage of nest success
S	(1) Lake Woodruff (FL)	A	(S)	1978–80	80	10	12.5	60.0
S	(2) Pungo (NC)	A	(S)	1979	146	42	28.8	86.0
S	(3) St. Marks (FL)	A	(S)	1979	55	36	65.5	88.9
S	(4) Erie (PA)	A	(C)	1977–79	402	201	50.0	72.0
S	(5) Great Swamp (NJ)	A	(C)	1979	499	424	85.0	20.0
S	(6) Catahoula (LA)	M	(S)	1979	52			
S	(7) Felsenthal (AR)	M	(S)	1980	20			
S	(8) Big Lake (AR)	M	(S)	1980–81	764	606	79.3	
S	(9) Yazoo (MS)	M	(S)	1966–68	392	496	126.5	65.3
S	(10) Wapanocca (AR)	M	(S)	1979	240	173	72.1	90.8
S	(11) Wapanocca (AR)	M	(S)	1982–83	509	365	71.7	76.0
S	(12) White River (AR)	M	(S)	1970–80	4,000	2,400	60.0	40.0
S	(13) Reelfoot (TN)	M	(S)	1974–79	2,106	2,001	95.0	90.0
S	(14) Hillside (MS)	M	(S)	1979	147	6	4.1	96.0
S	(15) Noxubee (MS)	M	(S)	1968–69	309	126	40.8	77.8
R,S	(16) Hatchie (TN)	M	(S)	1967–79	3,795	2,759	72.7	73.7
S	(17) Mingo (MO)	M	(C)	1975–81	685	409	59.7	68.9
S	(18) Muscatatuck (IN)	M	(C)	1978–79	30	3	10.0	30.0
R,S	(19) Upper Mississippi (IL)	M	(C)	1975–78	547	97	17.7	68.8
				Total	14,778	10,154		
				Mean			56.0	69.0
				Standard deviation			33.5	22.1
				Weighted mean by sum			68.7	66.1

R,M	(20) Missisquoi (VT)	A	(N)	1957–79	2,622	621	23.7	
R,I	(21) Tennessee (TN)	M	(S)	1979	5	0	0.0	
R,I	(22) Cross Creek (TN)	M	(S)	1979	113	35	31.0	55.0
R,I	(23) Wheeler (AL)	M	(S)	1979	534	328	61.4	61.5
R	(24) Mark Twain (IL)	M	(C)	1969–79	638	22	3.4	50.0
R	(25) Mark Twain (IA)[g]	M	(C)	1950–79	310	214	69.0	61.0
R	(26) DeSoto (IA)	M	(C)	1975–80	308	249	80.8	
R	(27) Meredosia (IL)	M	(C)	1978–79	52	2	3.8	100.0
R	(28) Chautauqua (IL)	M	(C)	1958–79	3,768	1,436	38.1	76.8
R	(29) Stillwater (NV)	P	(S)	1968–70	15	2	13.3	100.0
R	(30) Columbia White-tailed deer (WA)	P	(N)	1977–80	90	30	33.0	
R	(31) Lee Metcalf (MT)	P	(N)	1978–79	52	7	13.5	71.4
R	(32) Toppenish (WA)	P	(N)	1979	43	16	37.2	75.0
R	(33) Kootenai (ID)	P	(N)	1978	97	2	2.1	50.0
R,M	(34) Nisqually (WA)	P	(N)	1977–79	42	0	0.0	
				Total	8,689	2,964		
				Mean			27.4	70.1
				Standard deviation			26.3	18.4
				Weighted mean by sum			34.1	72.1

M,S	(35) Okefenokee (GA)	A	(S)	1983	116	88	75.9	70.0
M,S	(36) Montezuma (NY)	A	(N)	1978–79	145	54	37.2	81.5
M,S	(37) Iroquois (NY)	A	(N)	1979	360	288	80.0	61.5
M,S	(38) Presquille (VA)	A	(C)	1979	60	35	58.3	85.7

Appendix H. (continued)

	Major predators[e]	Major competitors[e]	House designs				Source
			Wood	Protected wood	Metal	Other[f]	
(1)		FLK,SCO,BAT,ANT		X			R. Blacker
(2)	STR,RSN	STR		X			G. Fringeli
(3)	GRS	GSQ	X	X			C. Gidden
(4)		STR,GKL			X		D. Lons
(5)	STR	STR		X			T. Gutzke
(6)			X			FT	S. Joyner
(7)							M. Kaehny
(8)							Refuge staff
(9)	WP,FLK,BWS			X			Cunningham (1968)
(10)	RSN		X	X	X		J. Oliveros
(11)							R. Lloyd
(12)	RSN	HOM	X	X			J. Johnson
(13)	RAC,BRS	FLK		X			W. Crews
(14)		STR		X			H. Bell
(15)	GRS,FLK	HOM,STR,GCF		X	X		Baker (1971)
(16)	UNB	RAC,HBE,SCO	X	X			J. Bryant
(17)	RAC	HOM	X		X		G. Clawson
(18)	RAC	STR		X	X		C. Scheffe
(19)		SQR			X		S. Stenquist
(20)		GCF			X		T. Mountain
(21)				X			V. Childs
(22)		SCO,WSP	X				A. Schriver
(23)	RSN	SCO		X		RFB	T. Atkeson
(24)		SCO,STR			X		M. Austin
(25)	RAC	SQR,SCO			X		O. Fears
(26)			X	X	X		Robinson (1981)
(27)		STR			X		K. Kenow
(28)	UNB,RAC	STR			X		K. Kenow
(29)		AKS,STR,SCO	X				L. Napier
(30)		STR	X				A. Clark
(31)	STR	STR,AKS	X				R. Twist
(32)		SCO	X				H. Hill
(33)	RAC,MNK	GDU,STR,AKS	X				L. Napier
(34)					X		W. Hesselbart
(35)			X	X			J. Schnoer
(36)	GKL,STR	STR	X	X			S. Flanders, V. Dewey
(37)		HOM,GKL		X			J. Morse
(38)	STR	STR		X	X		H. Olson

Appendix H. (continued)

Habitat[a]	Refuge[b] (state)	Flyway[c] (region[d])		Period	House-years	Nest starts	Percentage of wood duck use	Percentage of nest success
M,S	(39) Seney (MI)	M	(N)	1974–79	492	15	3.0	66.0
M,S	(40) Tamarac (MN)	M	(N)	1979	115	26	22.6	86.0
				Total	1,288	506		
				Mean			46.2	75.1
				Standard deviation			30.6	10.6
				Weighted mean by sum			39.3	68.2
M	(41) Carolina Sandhills (SC)	A	(S)	1965–79	1,775	847	47.7	86.3
M	(42) Pee Dee (NC)	A	(S)	1977–83	121	53	43.8	71.7
M	(43) Piedmont (GA)	A	(S)	1979	227	75	33.0	79.0
M	(44) Savannah (GA)	A	(S)	1977–78	131	124	94.7	91.9
M,I	(45) Santee (SC)	A	(S)	1979	311	236	75.9	97.0
M,I	(46) Eufaula (AL)	A	(S)	1975–76	351	327	93.2	67.7
M	(47) Truston Pond (RI)	A	(N)	1979	15	0	0.0	
M	(48) Morton (NY)	A	(N)	1979	7	1	14.3	100.0
M	(49) Great Meadows (MA)	A	(N)	1979–80	165	74	44.8	
M	(50) Tinicum (PA)	A	(C)	1978–79	26	4	15.4	75.0
M	(51) Bombay Hook (DE)	A	(C)	1979	74	61	82.4	64.0
M	(52) Mason Neck (VA)	A	(C)	1976–80	6	0	0.0	
M	(53) Eastern Neck (MD)	A	(C)	1970–75	426	124	29.1	60.5
M	(54) Arrowhead (ND)	C	(N)	1969–70	153	50	32.7	80.0
M	(55) Lacassine (LA)	M	(S)	1976–80	104			
M	(56) Big Stone (MN)	M	(N)	1973–78	284	34	12.0	100.0
M	(57) Fergus Falls (MN)	M	(N)	1978–80	210	1	0.5	
M	(58) Detroit Lakes (MN)	M	(N)	1979	4	0	0.0	
M	(59) Necedah (WI)	M	(N)	1979	51	18	35.3	38.9
M	(60) Ottawa (OH)	M	(C)	1979	64	4	6.3	75.0
M	(61) Union Slough (IA)	M	(C)	1980–85	1,005	737	73.3	82.1
M	(62) Klamath Basin (CA)	P	(S)	1963–79	28	22	78.6	60.0
M	(63) Sacramento (CA)[h]	P	(S)	1978	229	116	50.7	
M	(64) Grays Lake (ID)	P	(N)	1979	31	0	0.0	
M	(65) Ridgefield (WA)	P	(N)	1979	29	24	82.8	55.0
M	(66) Conboy Lake (WA)	P	(N)	1979	20	5	25.0	60.0
				Total	5,847	2,937		
				Mean			38.9	74.7
				Standard deviation			32.4	16.8
				Weighted mean by sum			50.2	81.1
MB	(67) Wertheim (NY)	A	(N)	1985	35	8	22.9	87.5
MB	(68) Mackay Island (VA)	A	(C)	1970–78	437	179	41.0	41.0
MB	(69) Back Bay (VA)	A	(C)	1979	5	2	40.0	100.0
MB	(70) Merritt Island (FL)	A	(S)	1977–80	75	0	0.0	
MB	(71) San Bernard (TX)	C	(S)	1979	2			
				Total	554	189		
				Mean			26.0	76.2
				Standard deviation			19.2	31.1
				Weighted mean by sum			34.1	43.4
IB,I	(72) Cape Romain (SC)	A	(S)	1979	28	18	64.3	76.0
I	(73) Ninigret (RI)	A	(N)	1977–80	45	0	0.0	
I	(74) Parker River (MA)	A	(N)	1979	26	4	15.4	25.0
I	(75) Chincoteague (VA)	A	(C)	1979	78	13	16.7	38.5
M,I	(76) Blackwater (MD)	A	(C)	1971–79	180	63	35.0	30.0

Appendix H. (continued)

	Major predators[e]	Major competitors[e]	Wood	Protected wood	Metal	Other[f]	Source
(39)		RSQ	X				S. Kallin
(40)	RAC	RSQ	X	X			T. Atkins
(41)	RAC		X	X		P	M. Hurdle
(42)	STR	STR,WSP		X			J. Holloman
(43)		WSP,SCO		X			R. Shell
(44)	STR	STR		X			J. Davis
(45)		SCO,GCF				FG	P. Ferguson
(46)	STR	STR		X		ST	R. Lloyd
(47)				X			J. Wood
(48)	RAC	STR	X	X			T. Schreiner
(49)		SCO		X			T. Goettel
(50)	HUM	STR		X			P. Caldwell
(51)	RAC	STR		X	X		M. Garner
(52)				X			D. Ciccone
(53)	RAC	STR			X		P. Feiger
(54)				X	X		Doty and Kruse (1972)
(55)				X		PVC, PL,CBD	S. Klett
(56)		SCO			X	TT	Refuge Staff
(57)		AKS,STR	X			TT	C. Vukonich
(58)		AKS		X			L. Hanson
(59)		STR	X				R. Nord
(60)		STR			X		L. Wargowsky
(61)					X	FC	J. Guthrie
(62)	STR	HOM	X				E. O'Neill
(63)	RAC,GOS	FLK,SCO,AKS,RAC	X				L. Schultz
(64)		GDU,AKS,FLK	X	X			E. Loth
(65)	HUM	STR	X				D. Gahimer
(66)		STR	X				H. Hill
(67)			X				R. Secatore
(68)		GSQ		X			G. Bond
(69)		STR,SCO		X			G. Bond
(70)		SCO				ST	H. Poiterint
(71)				X			E. Possardt
(72)				X			J. Munoz
(73)				X			D. Tiller
(74)	STR	STR		X			M. Bauer
(75)	BRS,UNB	STR			X		E. Poulson
(76)		STR		X			W. Giese

Appendix H. (continued)

Habitat[a]	Refuge[b] (state)	Flyway[c] (region[d])		Period	House-years	Nest starts	Percentage of wood duck use	Percentage of nest success
I	(77) Hagerman (TX)	C	(S)	1978–79	6			
I	(78) Tishomingo (OK)	C	(S)	1965–79	975	98	10.1	
I	(79) Salt Plains (OK)	C	(C)	1978–79	23	10	43.5	90.0
I	(80) Ankenny (OR)	P	(N)	1974–82	275	55	20.0	65.5
I	(81) Finley (OR)	P	(N)	1968–79	1,008	504	50.0	40.0
I	(82) Cold Springs (WA)	P	(N)	1969–72	62	19	30.6	80.0
I	(83) Willapa (WA)	P	(N)	1979	14	8	57.1	50.0
				Mean			31.2	55.0
				Standard deviation			20.7	23.6
				Weighted mean by sum			29.1	43.9

[a] S = swamp; R = riverine; M = marsh; MB = brackish marsh; I = impoundments or ponds; and IB = brackish impoundment.

[b] National wildlife refuges not listed had no nest house programs at the time of the inquiry. (Number) = horizontal reference.

[c] A = Atlantic; M = Mississippi; and P = Pacific.

[d] N = Northern; C = Central; and S = Southern.

[e] STR = starling; RSN = rat snake; GRS = gray rat snake; RAC = raccoon; WP = woodpecker; FLK = flicker; GSQ = gray squirrel; SCO = screech-owl; BAT = bat; ANT = ant; GKL = common grackle; BWS = blotched watersnake; BRS = black rat snake; UNB = unknown bird; HOM = hooded merganser; GCF = great crested flycatcher; HBE = honey bee; SQR = squirrel; WSP = wasp; AKS = American kestrel; MNK = mink; GDU = common goldeneye; RSQ = red squirrel; HUM = human; and GOS = gopher snake.

[f] FT = fiber tube; RFB = round fiber board; ST = Sunoco tube; P = paper; FG = fiberglass; PVC = PVC pipe; PL = plastic; CBD = cardboard; TT = Tom Tubbs®; and FC = freon cans.

[g] Includes Louisa, Big Timber, and Keithsburg.

[h] Includes Colusa, Sacramento, Delevan, and Sutter.

Appendix H. (continued)

	Major predators[e]	Major competitors[e]	House designs				Source
			Wood	Protected wood	Metal	Other[f]	
(77)				X			J. Williams
(78)		SCO	X				J. Harman
(79)				X		FG	R. Sullivan
(80)		STR	X				J. Annear
(81)		SCO	X				J. Annear
(82)		STR	X			FG	B. Weldon
(83)		STR, AKS		X			J. Wilih

Appendix I

I. Wood duck nest house information from publications.[a]

Location*	Flyway[b] (region[c])		Period	House-years	Nest start	Percentage of wood duck use	Percentage of nest success	Major predators[d]
(1) NC Florida	A	(S)	1978–79	90	59	65.6	44.1	
(2) C North Carolina	A	(S)	1954–68	921	822	89.3	55.3	RAC
(3) South Carolina	A	(S)	1983	392	255	65.1		
(4) South Carolina	A	(S)	1982–86	21,076	5,553	26.3		
(5) South Carolina	A	(S)	1989	3,817	2,367	62.0	77.7	GRS,FLK,RAC
(6) C Georgia	A	(S)	1969	194	67	34.5	68.7	GRS
(7) NE Tennessee	A	(S)	1971–75	129	43	33.3		
(8) NE Tennessee	A	(S)	1971–75	164	54	32.9		
(9) NE Tennessee	A	(S)	1971–75	133	15	11.3		
(10) NE Louisiana	A	(S)	1978–79	168	68	40.5	75.0	BRS,RAC
(11) NW South Carolina	A	(S)	1974–75	150	50	33.3		HUM
(12) NW South Carolina	A	(S)	1978	20	20	100.0		UNB,BRS,RAC
(13) NW South Carolina	A	(S)	1978	35	33	94.3		UNB,BRS,RAC
(14) E North Carolina	A	(S)	1966–75	1,227	412	33.6		
(15) C Georgia	A	(S)	1964	282	6	2.1	50.0	
			Total	28,798	9,824			
			Mean			48.3	61.8	
			Standard deviation			29.7	13.9	
			Weighted mean by sum			34.1	71.4	
(16) SC Maine	A	(N)	1980–81	2,081	831	39.9		
(17) SC Maine	A	(N)	1978–79	1,707	763	44.7		
(18) NW Vermont	A	(N)	1949–51	242	183	75.6	80.3	RAC
(19) Massachusetts	A	(N)	1949–51	3,203	1,427	44.6	64.3	RAC
(20) New Hampshire	A	(N)	1956	265	50	18.9	83.1	RAC
(21) New Hampshire	A	(N)	1955	353	87	24.6	56.0	RAC
(22) New Hampshire	A	(N)	1954	229	80	34.9	64.3	
(23) New Hampshire	A	(N)	1953	239	83	34.7	62.7	
(24) New Hampshire	A	(N)	1958	345	52	15.1	71.2	RAC
(25) New Hampshire	A	(N)	1957	250	48	19.2	60.9	RAC
(26) W and C New York	A	(N)	1953	135	30	22.2	80.0	RAC
(27) Massachusetts	A	(N)	1970–75	1,108	537	48.5	77.1	
(28) Massachusetts	A	(N)	1970–75	297	94	31.6	73.4	
(29) Massachusetts	A	(N)	1979–82	2,186	676	30.9	84.0	
(30) C New York	A	(N)	1973–79	439	320	72.9	62.5	FLK
(31) W Massachusetts	A	(N)	1950–56	483	415	85.9	65.8	RAC,NRT
(32) W Connecticut	A	(N)	1941–46	274	12	4.4		
(33) Rhode Island	A	(N)	1955–56	92	66	71.7		
(34) Rhode Island	A	(N)	1955–56	95	50	52.6		
(35) NW New York	A	(N)	1952	24	0	0.0		
(36) Connecticut	A	(N)	1953–62	6,225	4,102	65.9	90.0	RAC
			Total	20,272	9,906			
			Mean			39.9	71.7	
			Standard deviation			24.0	10.2	
			Weighted mean by sum			48.9	80.2	
(37) NC New Jersey	A	(C)	1971–76	2,750	3,011	109.5	48.8	RAC
(38) C Maryland	A	(C)	1963–64	70	27	38.6		
(39) C Maryland	A	(C)	1963–70	944	315	33.4		
(40) E Massachusetts	A	(C)	1952–66	509	317	62.3	73.5	
(41) NW Pennsylvania	A	(C)	1953–54	141	71	50.4	32.4	
(42) NW Pennsylvania	A	(C)	1955–56	78	24	30.8	66.7	RAC
(43) NE Ohio	A	(C)	1968–74	5,174	918	17.8		

Appendix I. (continued)

	Major competitors[d]	House designs Wood	Protected wood	Metal	Other[e]	Reference
(1)	X	X				Wenner and Marion (1981)
(2)		X	X	X		Stephenson (1970)
(3)	SCO,FLK,STR,WSP	X	X		AB,B,ST	Prevost (1983)
(4)			X			Prevost et al. (1990)
(5)	STR,BLB,GCF		X			Harrigal (1990)
(6)			X			Odom (1970)
(7)	STR,SCO	X	X			Muncy and Burbank (1975)
(8)	STR			X		Muncy and Burbank (1975)
(9)				X[f]		Muncy and Burbank (1975)
(10)					AT	Moore (1981)
(11)	SCO,STR,FLK		X			Luckett (1977)
(12)					B	Griffith and Fendley (1981)
(13)		X				Griffith and Fendley (1981)
(14)	STR		X			Grabill (1977)
(15)	RWP,GSQ,FLSQ				WAB	Almand (1965)
(16)		X				Spencer et al. (1980)
(17)		X				Spencer et al. (1979)
(18)		X				Miller (1952)
(19)			X			McLaughlin and Grice (1952)
(20)	RAC,HOM	X				Lee (1956)
(21)	RAC,HOM	X				Lee (1955)
(22)	RAC,HOM,GDU	X				Lee (1954)
(23)	RAC,HOM,GDU,WSP	X				Lee (1953)
(24)	HOM	X				Lacaillade (1959)
(25)	RAC,HOM,WSP	X				Lacaillade (1958)
(26)	STR,SCO	X	X		NK	Klein (1955)
(27)	STR	X				Heusmann et al. (1977)
(28)	GKL,HOM			X[f]		Heusmann et al. (1977)
(29)		X	X			Heusmann (1984)
(30)			X			Haramis and Thompson (1984,1985)
(31)	STR,GSQ	X	X			Grice and Rogers (1965)
(32)	GSQ,RSQ	X				Frank (1948)
(33)		X				Cronan (1957)
(34)			X			Cronan (1957)
(35)					NK	Carpenter (1953)
(36)		X	X			Beckley (1965)
(37)	STR	X	X			Zipko (1979)
(38)	STR			X		McGilvrey and Uhler (1971)
(39)				X[f]		McGilvrey and Uhler (1971)
(40)			X			Heusmann (1972)
(41)	HOM	X				Decker (1959)
(42)	HOM		X			Decker (1959)
(43)				X		Bednarik et al. (1974)

Appendix I. (continued)

Location*	Flyway[b] (region[c])		Period	House-years	Nest start	Percentage of wood duck use	Percentage of nest success	Major predators[d]
(44) SE Ohio	A	(C)	1968–74	1,554	171	11.0		
(45) NE Ohio	A	(C)	1976–84	9,979	3,672	36.8	44.0	
(46) SE Ohio	A	(C)	1976–84	5,853	1,779	30.4	68.5	
			Total	27,052	10,305			
			Mean			42.1	55.7	
			Standard deviation			27.8	16.3	
			Weighted mean by sum			38.1	51.6	
Atlantic Flyway			Total	76,122	30,035			
			Mean			43.1	65.9	
			Standard deviation			26.4	13.9	
			Weighted mean by sum			39.5	66.3	
(47) Mississippi	M	(S)	1969–73	2,475	1,747	70.6	67.9	UNB,RAC,RSN
(48) WC Mississippi	M	(S)	1966–69	283	247	87.3		FLK,RAC,BRS
(49) S Louisiana	M	(S)	1976–77	58	57	98.3	66.7	HUM
(50) NW Tennessee	M	(S)	1981–82	19	11	57.9		
(51) NW Tennessee	M	(S)	1981–82	102	54	52.9		
(52) NW Tennessee	M	(S)	1981–82	69	36	52.2		
(53) Louisiana	M	(S)	1951–61	1,229	416	33.8	72.8	GRS,UNB
(54) NE Louisiana	M	(S)	1978–79	146	274	187.7	59.1	WP,BRS
(55) NE Louisiana	M	(S)	1978–79	44	59	134.1	69.5	BRS
(56) NE Louisiana	M	(S)	1978–79	540	360	66.7	32.5	
(57) N Louisiana	M	(S)	1970–72	130	79	60.8	75.9	BRS
(58) C Mississippi	M	(S)	1976–77	200	252	126.0	42.1	FLK,RAC,GRS
(59) W Tennessee	M	(S)	1977	34	9	26.5	84.0	
(60) W Tennessee	M	(S)	1977	33	5	15.2	73.4	
(61) W Tennessee	M	(S)	1977	7	0	0.0		
(62) E Louisiana	M	(S)	1976–77	80	17	21.3	94.1	
(63) NE Louisiana	M	(S)	1976–77	128	214	167.2	61.7	BRS
(64) NE Louisiana	M	(S)	1976–77	48	57	118.8	45.6	
(65) NE Louisiana	M	(S)	1976–77	23	16	69.6	93.8	
(66) NE Louisiana	M	(S)	1976–77	270	130	48.1	24.6	BRS
(67) NE Louisiana	M	(S)	1976–77	97	2	2.1	100.0	
(68) WC Mississippi	M	(S)	1967	135	161	119.3	77.6	RAC,FLK
(69) NC Alabama	M	(S)	1941	98	9	9.2		
(70) NE Arkansas	M	(S)	1970–71	254	341	134.3	89.5	
(71) C Louisiana	M	(S)	1972	16	34	212.5	12.7	HUM,RSN
(72) C Alabama	M	(S)	1961–69	657	326	49.6		
(73) C Alabama	M	(S)	1961–69	476	207	43.5		
			Total	7,651	5,120			
			Mean			76.5	65.4	
			Standard deviation			56.8	24.3	
			Weighted mean by sum			66.9	63.4	
(74) SE Minnesota	M	(N)	1967–68	110	5	4.5	60.0	FSQ
(75) C Wisconsin	M	(N)	1982–84	759	75	9.9	68.0	RAC
(76) N Minnesota	M	(N)	1965–66	612	68	11.1		
(77) C Minnesota	M	(N)	1964–75	668	278	41.6	77.3	RAC,HUM,FLK
(78) SC Michigan	M	(N)	1972–73	54	6	11.1		
(79) SC Michigan	M	(N)	1979	74	20	27.0	85.0	
			Total	2,277	452			
			Mean			17.5	72.6	
			Standard deviation			14.0	10.9	
			Weighted mean by sum			19.9	75.7	
(80) C Ohio	M	(C)	1956	501	44	8.8	75.0	
(81) C Illinois	M	(C)	1964–65	565	413	73.1	62.6	STR
(82) C Illinois	M	(C)	1963–65	140	36	25.7	19.4	STR

Appendix I. (continued)

	Major competitors[d]	House designs				Reference
		Wood	Protected wood	Metal	Other[e]	
(44)				X		Bednarik et al. (1974)
(45)				X	FG	Bednarik (1984)
(46)				X	FG	Bednarik (1984)
(47)			X			Strong (1973)
(48)		X	X			Strange (1970)
(49)			X			Strader (1978)
(50)					PB	Spero et al. (1983)
(51)	GKL				AB	Spero et al. (1983)
(52)		X				Spero et al. (1983)
(53)		X				Smith, M. M. (1961)
(54)			X			Moore (1981)
(55)					PVC	Moore (1981)
(56)					MW18-72	Moore (1981)
(57)			X			LA Tech. Wildl. Club (1972)
(58)			X			Landin (1977)
(59)	SCO			X		Goetz and Sharp (1981)
(60)	SCO,WSP		X			Goetz and Sharp (1981)
(61)				X[f]		Goetz and Sharp (1981)
(62)			X			DiGiulio and Hamilton (1979)
(63)			X			Davis (1978)
(64)					MW12	Davis (1978)
(65)					PVC	Davis (1978)
(66)					MW18-72	Davis (1978)
(67)	WSP				AT	Davis (1978)
(68)			X			Cunningham (1967)
(69)	GRS	X				Bryan (1945)
(70)			X	X		Brown (1972a)
(71)			X			Britt (1972)
(72)	WSP	X				Beshears (1970)
(73)	WSP			X		Beshears (1970)
(74)	HOM			X		Strom (1969)
(75)	STR,HOM	X	X	X	B,TT	Soulliere (1985)
(76)	GDU	X				L.L. Johnson (1970)
(77)	GSQ,STR,HOM	X	X			Fiedler (1967)
(78)	STR	X				Boyer (1975b)
(79)		X				Aldrich and Bronner (1979)
(80)	STR	X	X		AC,GD	Stewart (1957)
(81)	STR			X		Shake (1967)
(82)	STR			X		Shake (1967)

Appendix I. (continued)

Location*	Flyway[b] (region[c])		Period	House-years	Nest start	Percentage of wood duck use	Percentage of nest success	Major predators[d]
(83) C Illinois	M	(C)	1975–81	421	237	56.3	75.5	
(84) NE Illinois	M	(C)	1967–81	78	68	87.2	79.4	
(85) NE Illinois	M	(C)	1967–81	7	6	85.7	66.7	
(86) NE Illinois	M	(C)	1967–81	21	14	66.7	71.4	
(87) NE Illinois	M	(C)	1967–81	632	421	66.6	66.5	
(88) NE Illinois	M	(C)	1967–81	108	52	48.2	65.4	
(89) NE Illinois	M	(C)	1967–81	52	15	28.8	73.3	
(90) NW Indiana	M	(C)	1954	65	6	9.2		FSQ
(91) SE Iowa	M	(C)	1943–65	398	281	70.6	94.0	RAC,GSQ,GRS
(92) SE Missouri	M	(C)	1961–62	144	68	47.2	39.7	RAC,RHW,BRS
(93) SE Missouri	M	(C)	1966–70	1,035	438	42.3	51.1	BRS,RAC,STR
(94) SC Illinois	M	(C)	1974–77	89	35	39.3		
(95) SC Illinois	M	(C)	1974–77	192	32	16.7		
(96) SE Iowa	M	(C)	1951	36	9	25.0	66.7	WSP,HOM,FSQ
(97) NE Illinois	M	(C)	1967–70	133	89	66.9	85.4	
(98) SE Missouri	M	(C)	1966–74	825	1,058	128.2	53.4	STR
(99) C Illinois	M	(C)	1939–45	3,218	1,579	49.1	36.4	FSQ,RAC,BLS
(100) C Illinois	M	(C)	1958–62	1,427	574	40.2	72.6	RAC,STR
(101) NW Ohio	M	(C)	1968–74	11,797	4,653	39.4		
(102) SW Ohio	M	(C)	1968–74	7,532	2,099	27.9		
(103) NW Ohio	M	(C)	1976–84	10,700	3,152	29.5	65.4	
(104) SW Ohio	M	(C)	1976–84	1,948	409	21.0	80.4	
(105) W Kentucky	M	(C)	1970–71	57	8	14.0	62.5	RAC
(106) W Indiana	M	(C)	1958–60	79	10	12.7	90.0	
(107) W Indiana	M	(C)	1958–60	307	34	11.1	67.6	
(108) W Indiana	M	(C)	1958–60	137	9	6.6	88.9	
(109) W Indiana	M	(C)	1956–57	179	12	6.7	100.0	
(110) W Indiana	M	(C)	1956–57	121	8	6.6	100.0	
			Total	42,944	15,869			
			Mean			40.6	69.6	
			Standard deviation			29.4	19.0	
			Weighted mean by sum			37.0	60.6	
Mississippi Flyway			Total	52,872	21,441			
			Mean			53.6	68.2	
			Standard deviation			46.8	20.6	
			Weighted mean by sum			40.6	61.9	
(111) C California	P	(S)	1954	39	14	35.9	92.9	
(112) C California	P	(S)	1952–56	388	164	42.3	76.2	HUM
(113) C California	P	(S)	1989	230	200	87.0	67.5	
(114) NC California	P	(S)	1957–65	89	86	96.6	51.2	FLK
			Total	746	464			
			Mean			65.5	72.0	
			Standard deviation			30.8	17.4	
			Weighted mean by sum			62.2	68.3	
(115) WC Oregon	P	(N)	1965–67	319	202	63.3	73.8	RAC
(116) WC Oregon	P	(N)	1967–68	256	110	43.0		
(117) WC Oregon	P	(N)	1965–66	171	131	76.6	68.7	
(118) WC Oregon	P	(N)	1965–67	115	47	40.9	74.5	
(119) WC Washington	P	(N)	1984	63	52	82.5	61.5	
(120) WC Washington	P	(N)	1984	138	83	60.1	47.0	RAC
(121) WC Washington	P	(N)	1974–84	723	388	53.7	61.1	
(122) WC Washington	P	(N)	1984	29	7	24.1	85.7	
			Total	1,814	1,020			
			Mean			55.5	67.5	
			Standard deviation			19.3	12.4	
			Weighted mean by sum			56.2	64.6	

Appendix I. (continued)

	Major competitors[d]	House designs				Reference
		Wood	Protected wood	Metal	Other[e]	
(83)	STR	X				Nault (1981)
(84)					WB	Montgomery et al. (1982)
(85)					TT	Montgomery et al. (1982)
(86)					CBD	Montgomery et al. (1982)
(87)				X		Montgomery et al. (1982)
(88)				X[f]		Montgomery et al. (1982)
(89)			X			Montgomery et al. (1982)
(90)	FSQ,STR	X				McCall (1954)
(91)		X				Leopold (1966)
(92)		X	X	X		Hartowicz (1963)
(93)	HOM,STR	X		X		Hansen (1971)
(94)		X				Gore (1978)
(95)				X		Gore (1978)
(96)		X				Dreis and Hendrickson (1952)
(97)				X	WB	Dillon (1970)
(98)	HOM,STR	X	X	X		Clawson (1975a)
(99)		X				Bellrose et al. (1964)
(100)				X		Bellrose et al. (1964)
(101)				X		Bednarik et al. (1974)
(102)				X		Bednarik et al. (1974)
(103)				X	FG	Bednarik (1984)
(104)				X	FG	Bednarik (1984)
(105)			X			Allen (1972)
(106)				X[f]		Richardson (1959,1960)
(107)				X		Richardson (1959,1960)
(108)		X				Richardson (1959,1960)
(109)				X		Martin (1957,1958)
(110)		X				Martin (1957,1958)
(111)		X				Robinson (1958)
(112)	AKS,HBE,SCO		X			Naylor (1960)
(113)						Krammerer (1990)
(114)		X			NK	Jones and Leopold (1967), Jones (1964)
(115)	HOM			X		Morse and Wight (1969)
(116)		X				Morse (1969)
(117)	HOM	X				Morse (1966)
(118)	HOM	X				Finley (1968)
(119)				X		Beall et al. (1984)
(120)		X				Beall et al. (1984)
(121)		X	X			Beall et al. (1984)
(122)					TT	Beall et al. (1984)

Appendix I. (continued)

Location*	Flyway[b] (region[c])		Period	House-years	Nest start	Percentage of wood duck use	Percentage of nest success	Major predators[d]
Pacific Flyway			Total	2,560	1,484			
			Mean			56.3	69.1	
			Standard deviation			26.8	13.7	
			Weighted mean by sum			58.0	65.9	
(123) EC Texas	C	(S)	1970–75	158	31	19.6	61.3	
(124) EC Texas	C	(S)	1977–79	96	67	69.8	62.7	RSN
Central Flyway			Total	254	98			
			Mean			44.7	62.0	
			Standard deviation			35.5	1.0	
			Weighted mean by sum			38.6	62.2	
Publications (United States)			Total	131,808	53,058			
			Mean			50.1	67.5	
			Standard deviation			38.3	17.7	
			Weighted mean by sum			40.3	64.6	

[a] Some reports were subdivided when separate time periods, locations, or house designs were defined in the text.

[b] A = Atlantic; M = Mississippi; C = Central; and P = Pacific.

[c] N = Northern; C = Central; and S = Southern.

[d] RAC = raccoon; SCO = screech-owl; FLK = flicker; STR = starling; WSP = wasp; GRS = gray rat snake; BRS = black rat snake; HUM = human; UNB = unknown bird; RWP = red wasp; GSQ = gray squirrel; HOM = hooded merganser; GDU = common goldeneye; GKL = common grackle; RSQ = red squirrel; RSN = rat snake; WP = woodpecker; FSQ = fox squirrel; AKS = American kestrel; HBE = honey bee; BLB = bluebird; GCF = great crested flycatcher; FLSQ = flying squirrel; NRT = Norway rat; BLS = bull snake; and RHW = red-headed woodpecker.

[e] AB = ammo box; B = bucket; ST = Sunoco tube; AT = auto tire; WAB = wood ammo box; NK = nail keg; FG = fiberglass; PB = plastic bucket; PVC = PVC pipe; TT = Tom Tubbs®; AC = aluminum ammunition cannister; GD = grease drum; WB = wastebasket; CBD = cardboard; and MW12 and MW18-72 = modified wood houses (12 and 18-72 = number erected together as colonial houses).

[f] Horizontal metal design.

* (Number) = horizontal reference.

Appendix I. (continued)

Major competitors[d]	House designs				Reference
	Wood	Protected wood	Metal	Other[e]	
(123)		X			Labuda (1977)
(124)		X			Ridlehuber (1980)

Appendix J

J. Wood duck nest house information from survey responses of national wildlife refuge personnel; arranged by regions of flyways.

Refuge[a] (state)	Flyway[b] (region[c])		Period	House-years	Nest starts	Percentage of wood duck use	Percentage of nest success
(1) St. Marks (FL)	A	(S)	1979	55	36	65.5	88.9
(2) Pungo (NC)	A	(S)	1979	146	42	28.8	86.0
(3) Lake Woodruff (FL)	A	(S)	1978–80	80	10	12.5	60.0
(4) Okefenokee (GA)	A	(S)	1983	116	88	75.9	70.0
(5) Eufaula (AL)	A	(S)	1975–76	351	327	93.2	67.7
(6) Santee (SC)	A	(S)	1979	311	236	75.9	97.0
(7) Carolina Sandhills (SC)	A	(S)	1965–79	1,775	847	47.7	86.3
(8) Pee Dee (NC)	A	(S)	1977–83	121	53	43.8	71.7
(9) Piedmont (GA)	A	(S)	1979	227	75	33.0	79.0
(10) Merritt Island (FL)	A	(S)	1977–80	75	0	0.0	
(11) Savannah (GA)	A	(S)	1977–78	131	124	94.7	91.9
(12) Cape Romain (SC)	A	(S)	1979	28	18	64.3	76.0
			Total	3,416	1,856		
			Mean by item			52.9	79.5
			Standard deviation			30.5	11.5
			Weighted mean by sum			54.3	83.1
(13) Missisquoi (VT)	A	(N)	1957–79	2,622	621	23.7	
(14) Wertheim (NY)	A	(N)	1985	35	8	22.9	87.5
(15) Iroquois (NY)	A	(N)	1979	360	288	80.0	61.5
(16) Montezuma (NY)	A	(N)	1978–79	145	54	37.2	81.5
(17) Great Meadows (MA)	A	(N)	1979–80	165	74	44.8	
(18) Morton (NY)	A	(N)	1979	7	1	14.3	100.0
(19) Truston Pond (RI)	A	(N)	1979	15	0	0.0	
(20) Parker River (MA)	A	(N)	1979	26	4	15.4	25.0
(21) Ninigret (RI)	A	(N)	1977–80	45	0	0.0	
			Total	3,420	1,050		
			Mean by item			26.5	71.1
			Standard deviation			25.0	29.3
			Weighted mean by sum			30.7	64.8
(22) Great Swamp (NJ)	A	(C)	1979	499	424	85.0	20.0
(23) Erie (PA)	A	(C)	1977–79	402	201	50.0	72.0
(24) Eastern Neck (MD)	A	(C)	1970–75	426	124	29.1	60.5
(25) Mackay Island (VA)	A	(C)	1970–78	437	179	41.0	41.0
(26) Back Bay (VA)	A	(C)	1979	5	2	40.0	100.0
(27) Presquile (VA)	A	(C)	1979	60	35	58.3	85.7
(28) Bombay Hook (DE)	A	(C)	1979	74	61	82.4	64.0
(29) Tinicum (PA)	A	(C)	1978–79	26	4	15.4	75.0
(30) Mason Neck (VA)	A	(C)	1976–80	6	0	0.0	
(31) Blackwater (MD)	A	(C)	1971–79	180	63	35.0	30.0
(32) Chincoteague (VA)	A	(C)	1979	78	13	16.7	38.5
			Total	2,193	1,106		
			Mean by item			41.2	58.7
			Standard deviation			26.7	25.7
			Weighted mean by sum			50.4	43.0
Atlantic Flyway			Total	9,029	4,012		
			Mean by item			41.5	69.9
			Standard deviation			29.0	22.8
			Weighted mean by sum			44.4	67.8

Appendix J. (continued)

	Major predators[d]	Major competitors[d]	House designs			
			Wood	Protected wood	Metal	Other
(1)	GRS	GSQ	X	X		
(2)	STR,RSN	STR		X		
(3)		FLK,SCO,BAT,ANT		X		
(4)			X	X		
(5)	STR	STR		X		ST
(6)		SCO,GCF				FG
(7)	RAC		X	X		P
(8)	STR	STR,WSP		X		
(9)		WSP,SCO		X		
(10)		SCO				ST
(11)	STR	STR		X		
(12)				X		
(13)		GCF			X	
(14)			X			
(15)		HOM,GKL		X		
(16)	GKL,STR	STR	X	X		
(17)		SCO		X		
(18)	RAC	STR	X	X		
(19)				X		
(20)	STR	STR		X		
(21)				X		
(22)	STR	STR		X		
(23)		STR,GKL			X	
(24)	RAC	STR			X	
(25)		GSQ		X		
(26)		STR,SCO		X		
(27)	STR	STR		X	X	
(28)	RAC	STR		X	X	
(29)	HUM	STR		X		
(30)				X		
(31)		STR		X		
(32)	BRS,UNB	STR			X	

Appendix J. (continued)

Refuge[a] (state)	Flyway[b] (region[c])		Period	House-years	Nest starts	Percentage of wood duck use	Percentage of nest success
(33) Yazoo (MS)	M	(S)	1966–68	392	496	126.5	65.3
(34) Reelfoot (TN)	M	(S)	1974–79	2,106	2,001	95.0	90.0
(35) Big Lake (AR)	M	(S)	1980–81	764	606	79.3	
(36) Wapanocca (AR)	M	(S)	1979	240	173	72.1	90.8
(37) Wapanocca (AR)	M	(S)	1982–83	509	365	76.7	76.0
(38) White River (AR)	M	(S)	1970–80	4,000	2,400	60.0	40.0
(39) Noxubee (MS)	M	(S)	1968–69	309	126	40.8	77.8
(40) Hillside (MS)	M	(S)	1979	147	6	4.1	96.0
(41) Catahoula (LA)	M	(S)	1979	52			
(42) Hatchie (TN)	M	(S)	1967–79	3,795	2,759	72.7	73.7
(43) Wheeler (AL)	M	(S)	1979	534	328	61.4	61.5
(44) Cross Creek (TN)	M	(S)	1979	113	35	31.0	55.0
(45) Tennessee (TN)	M	(S)	1979	5	0	0.0	
(46) Lacassine (LA)	M	(S)	1976–80	104			
(47) Felsenthal (AR)	M	(S)	1980	20			
			Total	13,090	9,295		
			Mean by item			60.0	72.6
			Standard deviation			36.4	17.5
			Weighted mean by sum			71.0	67.6
(48) Tamarac (MN)	M	(N)	1979	115	26	22.6	86.0
(49) Seney (MI)	M	(N)	1974–79	492	15	3.0	66.0
(50) Necedah (WI)	M	(N)	1979	51	18	35.3	38.9
(51) Big Stone (MN)	M	(N)	1973–78	284	34	12.0	100.0
(52) Fergus Falls (MN)	M	(N)	1978–80	210	1	0.5	
(53) Detroit Lakes (MN)	M	(N)	1979	4	0	0.0	
			Total	1,156	94		
			Mean by item			12.2	72.7
			Standard deviation			14.2	26.5
			Weighted mean by sum			8.1	78.5
(54) Mingo (MO)	M	(C)	1975–81	685	409	59.7	68.9
(55) Muscatatuck (IN)	M	(C)	1978–79	30	3	10.0	30.0
(56) Upper Mississippi (IL)	M	(C)	1975–78	547	97	17.7	68.8
(57) DeSoto (IA)	M	(C)	1975–80	308	249	80.8	
(58) Mark Twain (IA)[f]	M	(C)	1950–79	310	214	69.0	61.0
(59) Chautauqua (IL)	M	(C)	1958–79	3,768	1,436	38.1	76.8
(60) Meredosia (IL)	M	(C)	1978–79	52	2	3.8	100.0
(61) Mark Twain (Gardner) (IL)	M	(C)	1969–79	638	22	3.4	50.0
(62) Union Slough (IA)	M	(C)	1980–85	1,005	737	73.3	82.1
(63) Ottawa (OH)	M	(C)	1979	64	4	6.3	75.0
			Total	7,407	3,173		
			Mean by item			36.2	68.1
			Standard deviation			31.7	19.9
			Weighted mean by sum			42.8	75.4
Mississippi Flyway			Total	21,653	12,562		
			Mean by item			41.3	70.9
			Standard deviation			35.5	19.3
			Weighted mean by sum			58.0	69.7
(64) Stillwater (NV)	P	(S)	1968–70	15	2	13.3	100.0
(65) Klamath Basin (CA)	P	(S)	1963–79	28	22	78.6	60.0
(66) Sacramento (CA)[g]	P	(S)	1978	229	116	50.7	
			Total	272	140		
			Mean by item			47.5	80.0
			Standard deviation			32.8	28.3
			Weighted mean by sum			51.5	62.5

Appendix J. (continued)

	Major predators[d]	Major competitors[d]	House designs			
			Wood	Protected wood	Metal	Other
(33)	WP,FLK,BWS			X		
(34)	RAC,BRS	FLK		X		
(35)						
(36)	RSN		X	X	X	
(37)						
(38)	RSN	HOM	X	X		
(39)	GRS,FLK	HOM,STR,GCF		X	X	
(40)		STR		X		
(41)			X			FT
(42)	UNB	RAC,HBE,SCO	X	X		
(43)	RSN	SCO		X		RFB
(44)		SCO,WSP	X			
(45)				X		
(46)				X		PVC,P,CBD
(47)						
(48)	RAC	RSQ	X	X		
(49)		RSQ	X			
(50)		STR	X			
(51)		SCO			X	TT
(52)		AKS,STR	X			TT
(53)		AKS		X		
(54)	RAC	HOM	X		X	
(55)	RAC	STR		X	X	
(56)		SQR			X	
(57)			X	X	X	
(58)	RAC	SQR,SCO			X	
(59)	UNB,RAC	STR			X	
(60)		STR			X	
(61)		SCO,STR			X	
(62)					X	FC
(63)		STR			X	
(64)		AKS,STR,SCO	X			
(65)	STR	HOM	X			
(66)	RAC,GOS	FLK,SCO,AKS,RAC	X			

Appendix J. (continued)

Refuge[a] (state)	Flyway[b] (region[c])		Period	House-years	Nest starts	Percentage of wood duck use	Percentage of nest success
(67) Nisqually (WA)	P	(N)	1977–79	42	0	0.0	
(68) Toppenish (WA)	P	(N)	1979	43	16	37.2	75.0
(69) Columbia White-tailed deer (WA)	P	(N)	1977–80	90	30	33.0	
(70) Ankenny (OR)	P	(N)	1974–82	275	55	20.0	65.5
(71) Lee Metcalf (MT)	P	(N)	1978–79	52	7	13.5	71.4
(72) Kootenai (ID)	P	(N)	1978	97	2	2.1	50.0
(73) Ridgefield (WA)	P	(N)	1979	29	24	82.8	55.0
(74) Conboy Lake (WA)	P	(N)	1979	20	5	25.0	60.0
(75) Grays Lake (ID)	P	(N)	1979	31	0	0.0	
(76) Willapa (WA)	P	(N)	1979	14	8	57.1	50.0
(77) Finley (OR)	P	(N)	1968–79	1,008	504	50.0	40.0
(78) Cold Springs (WA)	P	(N)	1969–72	62	19	30.6	80.0
			Total	1,763	670		
			Mean by item			29.3	60.8
			Standard deviation			25.1	13.3
			Weighted mean by sum			38.0	45.5
Pacific Flyway			Total	2,035	810		
			Mean by item			32.9	64.3
			Standard deviation			26.6	16.8
			Weighted mean by sum			39.8	46.1
(79) San Bernard (TX)	C	(S)	1979	2			
(80) Arrowhead (ND)	C	(N)	1969–70	153	50	32.7	80.0
(81) Salt Plains (OK)	C	(C)	1978–79	23	10	43.5	90.0
(82) Tishomingo (OK)	C	(S)	1965–79	975	98	10.1	
(83) Hagerman (TX)	C	(S)	1978–79	6			
Central Flyway			Total	1,159	158		
			Mean by item			28.8	85.0
			Standard deviation			17.0	7.1
			Weighted mean by sum			13.6	81.7
National wildlife refuges			Total	33,876	17,542		
			Mean by item			39.3	69.7
			Standard deviation			30.5	20.2
			Weighted mean by sum			51.8	68.3

[a] Refuges not listed had no nest house programs. Refuge respondents listed in Appendix H. (Number) = horizontal reference.
[b] A = Atlantic; M = Mississippi; C = Central; and P = Pacific.
[c] N = Northern; C = Central; and S = Southern.
[d] GRS = gray rat snake; GSQ = gray squirrel; STR = starling; RSN = rat snake; FLK = flicker; SCO = screech-owl; BAT = bat; ANT = ant; GCF = great crested flycatcher; RAC = raccoon; WSP = wasp; HOM = hooded merganser; GKL = common grackle; HUM = human; BRS = black rat snake; UNB = unknown bird; WP = woodpecker; HBE = honey bee; AKS = American kestrel; SQR = squirrel; GOS = gopher snake; MNK = mink; and GDU = common goldeneye; BWS = blotched water snake.
[e] ST = Sunoco tube; FG = fiberglass; P = paper; FT = fiber tube; RFB = round fiber board; PVC = PVC pipe; PL = plastic; CBD = cardboard; TT = Tom Tubbs®; and FC = freon cans.
[f] Includes Louisa, Big Timber, and Keithsburg.
[g] Includes Colusa, Sacramento, Delevan, and Sutter.

Appendix J. (continued)

	Major predators[d]	Major competitors[d]	House designs			
			Wood	Protected wood	Metal	Other
(67)						X
(68)		SCO	X			
(69)		STR	X			
(70)		STR	X			
(71)	STR	STR,AKS	X			
(72)	RAC,MNK	GDU,STR,AKS	X			
(73)	HUM	STR	X			
(74)		STR	X			
(75)		GDU,AKS,FLK	X	X		
(76)		STR,AKS		X		
(77)		SCO	X			
(78)		STR	X			FG
(79)				X		
(80)				X	X	
(81)				X		FG
(82)		SCO	X			
(83)				X		

Appendix K

K. Wood duck nest house information from unpublished reports.[a]

Location*	Flyway[b]	(region[c])	Period	House-years	Nest starts	Percentage of wood duck use	Percentage of nest success
(1) SC South Carolina	A	(S)	1983–85	70	33	47.1	
(2) Vermont	A	(N)	1981–82	1,110	430	38.7	
(3) Vermont	A	(N)	1950–52	564	248	44.0	69.4
(4) NC Mississippi	M	(S)	1979–82	910	586	64.4	
(5) SE Minnesota	M	(N)	1980–82	1,331	259	19.5	
(6) SW Wisconsin	M	(N)	1982	38	11	28.9	
(7) SW Wisconsin	M	(N)	1982	58	23	39.7	
(8) Wisconsin	M	(N)	1981–83	3,546	517	14.6	
(9) NE Minnesota	M	(N)	1980–82	2,113	204	9.7	
(10) NC Minnesota	M	(N)	1980	19	1	5.3	
(11) S Wisconsin	M	(N)	1983	687	246	35.8	
(12) N Wisconsin	M	(N)	1983	1,062	178	16.8	
(13) N Wisconsin	M	(N)	1982	330	130	39.4	
(14) W Minnesota	M	(N)	1980–82	1,362	187	13.7	
	Northern Mississippi	total		10,546	1,756		
		Mean				22.3	
		Standard deviation				12.6	
		Weighted mean by sum				16.7	
(15) NC Iowa	M	(C)	1975–80	903	486	53.8	80.0
(16) SW Iowa	M	(C)	1950–58	365	104	28.5	
(17) NE Indiana	M	(C)	1982	276	79	28.6	
(18) Illinois	M	(C)	1984	1,872	521	27.8	
(19) NW Indiana	M	(C)	1983	50	0	0.0	
(20) NE Illinois	M	(C)	1976–84	403	258	64.0	
(21) W Ohio	M	(C)	1983	1,804	629	34.9	
	Central Mississippi	total		5,673	2,077		
		Mean				33.9	
		Standard deviation				20.6	
		Weighted mean by sum				36.6	
(22) C California	P	(S)	1974–88	2,274	2,521	110.9	65.7
(23) NC California	P	(S)	1970–78	230	115	50.0	
(24) NC California	P	(S)	1971–78	126	35	27.8	
(25) NC California	P	(S)	1971–78	272	134	49.3	
(26) NW California	P	(S)	1983–90	238	170	71.4	
	Southern Pacific	total		3,140	2,975		
		Mean				61.9	67.1
		Standard deviation				31.4	1.9
		Weighted mean by sum				94.7	65.8
(27) SW Washington	P	(N)	1974–84	723	388	53.7	61.1
(28) WC Oregon	P	(N)	1977–81	104	10	9.6	
(29) NW Oregon	P	(N)	1951–57	1,097	881	80.3	
(30) C British Columbia	P	(N)	1973	899	194	21.6	61.3
(31) NW Idaho	P	(N)	1976–80	951	406	42.7	73.4
	Northern Pacific	total		3,774	1,879		
		Mean				41.6	65.3
		Standard deviation				27.7	7.0
		Weighted mean by sum				49.8	66.2
(32) Manitoba	Winnipeg		1975–82	462	175	37.9	

Appendix K. (continued)

	Major predators[d]	Major competitors[d]	House designs				Source/date
			Wood	Protected wood	Metal	Other[e]	
(1)	RSN		X				N. Brunswick/1986
(2)							W. Crenshaw/1983
(3)							
(4)							F. Walker/1983
(5)			X				M. Zicus/1983
(6)					X		K. Mello/1983
(7)			X				K. Mello/1983
(8)			X		X	PB	J. Wetzel/1989
(9)			X				M. Zicus/1983
(10)		GDU,HOM	X		X		M. Barquist/1980
(11)			X	X			J. Wetzel/1984
(12)			X	X	X	PB	J. Wetzel/1984
(13)			X				J. Wetzel/1985
(14)			X	X		TT	M. Zicus/1983
(15)			X	X			G. Welp
(16)			X		X		
(17)							T. Spoore
(18)							D. Thornberg/1984
(19)					X[f]		T. Spoore
(20)			X	X	X		J. Laskowski/1985
(21)							K. Bednarik/1982
(22)							S. Simmons/1988
(23)		STR					Delevan National Wildlife Refuge
(24)		AKS					Sacramento National Wildlife Refuge
(25)		HBE					Colusa National Wildlife Refuge
(26)			X				R. Goss/1990
(27)	RAC,FLK		X	X			J. Beall/1983
(28)		SQR					
(29)							C. Kebbe/1974
(30)							T. Glew and R. Cerenzia/1973
(31)							E. Bizeau/1981
(32)							E. Roger/1983

Appendix K. (continued)

Location*	Flyway[b] (region[c])	Period	House-years	Nest starts	Percentage of wood duck use	Percentage of nest success
Unpublished reports		Total	26,244	10,159		
		Mean			37.8	68.5
		Standard deviation			23.6	6.7
		Weighted mean by sum			38.7	67.7

[a] Data were subdivided when separate time periods, locations, or house designs were defined in the report.
[b] A = Atlantic; M—ississippi; and P = Pacific.
[c] N = Northern; C = Central; and S = Southern.
[d] RSN = rat snake; HOM = hooded merganser; STR = starling; AKS = American kestrel; HBE = honey bee; RAC = raccoon; FLK = flicker; SQR = squirrel; and GDU = common goldeneye.
[e] PB = plastic bucket and TT = Tom Tubbs®.
[f] Horizontal metal design.
*(Number) = horizontal reference.

References

Abbott, C. C. 1895. The birds about us. J. B. Lippincott Co., Philadelphia. 288 pp.

Abernethy, Y. and R. E. Turner. 1987. U.S. forested wetlands: 1940–1980. BioScience 37: 721–727.

Abraham, R. L. 1974. Vocalizations of the mallard *(Anas platyrhynchos)*. Condor 76: 401–420.

Afton, A. D. 1979. Time budget of breeding northern shovelers. Wilson Bull. 91: 42–49.

———. 1985. Forced copulation as a reproductive strategy of male lesser scaup: A field test of some predictions. Behavior 92: 146–167.

Agersborg, G. S. 1885. The birds of southeastern Dakota. Auk 2: 276–289.

Aldrich, J. W. and W. N. Bronner. 1979. Gratiot-Saginaw and Maple River state game areas wood duck nest box summary. Wildl. Div. Rept. No. 2,844. Michigan Dept. Natur. Resour., Lansing. 10 pp.

Alexander, C. P. 1915. Field report–Kinloch Gun Club, South Carolina, 5 September. Unpubl. rept. on file with the Kinloch Gun Club, South Carolina. Unpaginated. On file at the Patuxent Wildlife Research Center, Laurel, Maryland.

Alexander, M. M. 1943. Food habits of the snapping turtle in Connecticut. J. Wildl. Manage. 7: 278–282.

Allen, C. E. 1980. Feeding habits of ducks in a green-tree reservoir in eastern Texas. J. Wildl. Manage. 44: 232–236.

Allen, D. L. 1943. Michigan fox squirrel management. Game Div. Publ. 100. Michigan Dept. Conserv., Lansing. 404 pp.

Allen, J. A. 1872. Notes on ornithological reconnaissance of portions of Kansas, Colorado, Wyoming, and Utah. Bull. Mus. Comp. Zool. 3: 113–183.

Allen, J. W. 1972. Comments on a two-year wood duck survey. Kentucky Warbler 48: 3–6.

Allen, R. B., P. O. Corr, and J. A. Dorso. 1990. Nesting success and efficiency of waterfowl using nest boxes in central Maine: A management perspective. Pages 291–296 *in* L. H. Fredrickson, G. V. Burger, S. P. Havera, D. A. Graber, R. E. Kirby, and T. S. Taylor, eds., Proc. 1988 N. Am. Wood Duck Symp., St. Louis. 390 pp.

Allen, W. R. 1971. The eastern valley waterfowl resource: Its history, management, and future development. Div. For., Fish. and Wildl., TVA, Norris, Tennessee. Mimeo. 76 pp.

Almand, J. D. 1965. A contribution to the management requirements of the wood duck, *Aix sponsa*, in the Piedmont of Georgia. M.S. thesis, Univ. Georgia, Athens. 58 pp.

Altmann, J. 1974. Observational study of behavior: Sampling methods. Behavior 49: 227–267.

American Ornithologists' Union. 1886. The code of nomenclature and check-list of North American birds. New York. 392 pp.

———. 1895. Check-list of North American birds. New York. 372 pp.

———. 1910. Check-list of North American birds. New York. 430 pp.

———. 1931. Check-list of North American birds. Lancaster, Pennsylvania. 526 pp.

———. 1957. Check-list of North American birds. The Lord Baltimore Press, Inc., Baltimore. 691 pp.

———. 1983. Check-list of North American birds. Allen Press, Inc., Lawrence, Kansas. 877 pp.

Ammann, G. A. 1937. Number of contour feathers in *Cygnus* and *Xanthocephalus*. Auk 54: 201–202.

Anderson, D. R. 1975. Population ecology of the mallard V. Temporal and geographic estimates of survival, recovery, and harvest rates. Resour. Publ. 125. U.S. Fish and Wildl. Serv., Washington, D.C. 110 pp.

Anderson, D. R. and K. P. Burnham. 1976. Population ecology of the mallard VI. The effect of exploitation on survival. Resour. Publ. 128. U.S. Fish and Wildl. Serv., Washington, D.C. 66 pp.

Anderson, H. G. 1959. Food habits of migratory ducks in Illinois. Illinois Natur. Hist. Surv. Bull. 27: 289–344.

Anderson, R. C. 1954. *Ornithofilaria fallisensis* n. sp. (Nematoda: Filarioidea) from the domestic duck with descriptions of microfilariae in waterfowl. Can. J. Zool. 32: 125–137.

Anderson, R. M. 1907. The birds of Iowa. Proc. Davenport Acad. Sci. 11: 125–417.

Anderson, V. R. 1984. Final report on Kentucky's three year experimental teal-wood duck season. Kentucky Dept. Fish and Wildl. Resour., Frankfort. 21 pp.

Andrews, R. and J. Judson. 1987. Unveiling the secrets of the masked marauder. Iowa Conserv. 46: 23–25.

Ankney, C. D. 1974. The importance of nutrient reserves to breeding blue geese *(Anser caerulescens)*. Ph.D. thesis, Univ. West. Ontario, London. 212 pp.

———. 1979. Does the wing molt cause nutritional stress in lesser snow geese? Auk 96: 68–72.

———. 1982. Annual cycle of body weight in lesser snow geese. Wildl. Soc. Bull. 10: 60–64.

Anthony, A. W. 1886. Field notes on the birds of Washington County, Oregon. Auk 3: 161–172.

Armbruster, J. S. 1982. Wood duck displays and pairing chronology. Auk 99: 116–122.

Arner, D. H. 1963. Production of duck food in beaver ponds. J. Wildl. Manage. 27: 76–81.

Arner, D. H. and G. H. Hepp. 1989. Beaver pond wetlands: A southern perspective. Pages 117–128 in L. M. Smith, R. L. Pederson, and R. M. Kaminski, eds., Habitat management for migrating and wintering waterfowl in North America. Texas Tech Univ. Press, Lubbock. 560 pp.

Arner, D. H., J. Baker, and D. Wesley. 1966. The management of beaver and beaver ponds in the southeastern United States. Dept. Zoology and Water Resour. Res. Inst., Mississippi St. Univ., State College. 17 pp.

Askins, Capt. C. 1931. Game bird shooting. The MacMillan Co., New York. 321 pp.

Attwater, H. P. 1892. List of birds observed in the vicinity of San Antonio, Bexor County, Texas. Auk 9: 229–238, 337–345.

Audubon Christmas Bird Counts. 1983–1987. Amer. Birds Vol. 37–41(4).

Audubon, J. J. 1827–38. The birds of America; from original drawings. 4 vols. orig. publ. in 87 parts without text. Published by the author. London.

———. 1840–44. The birds of America. 7 vols. John James Audubon and J. B. Chevalier, New York.

Austin, G. T. 1970. The occurrence and status of certain anatids in southern Nevada. Condor 72: 474.

Bailey, F. M. 1928. Birds of New Mexico. New Mexico Dept. Game and Fish, Santa Fe. 807 pp.

Bailey, H. B. 1912. Notes on birds breeding in the mountains of Virginia. Auk 29: 79–84.

Bailey, R. G. 1978. Description of the ecoregions of the United States. Misc. Publ. IR-1391. USDA For. Serv., Ogden, Utah. 77 pp.

Bailey, R. O., N. R. Seymour, and G. R. Stewart. 1978. Rape behavior in blue-winged teal. Auk 95: 188–190.

Bailey, V. 1922. Beaver habitats, beaver control and possibilities in beaver farming. Bull. No. 1,078. U.S. Dept. Agric., Washington, D.C. 29 pp.

Baima, S. 1971. The effects of habitat on starling (*Sturnus vulgaris*) breeding behavior. M.S. thesis, West. Illinois Univ., Macomb. 45 pp.

Baird, S. F. 1858. Birds: Exploration and surveys for a railroad route from the Mississippi River to the Pacific Ocean. Smithson. Inst., Washington, D.C. 1,005 pp.

Baker, J. L. 1971. Wood duck (*Aix sponsa*) production from nest boxes and brood studies on the Noxubee National Wildlife Refuge. Ph.D. thesis, Mississippi St. Univ., State College. 48 pp.

Baker, J. R. 1939. The relation between latitude and breeding seasons in birds. Proc. Zool. Soc. London 109: 557–582.

Baldassarre, G. A., R. J. Whyte, E. E. Quinlan, and E. G. Bolen. 1983. Dynamics and quality of waste corn available to postbreeding waterfowl in Texas. Wildl. Soc. Bull. 11: 25–31.

Baldwin, S. P. and S. C. Kendeigh. 1938. Variations in the weight of birds. Auk 55: 416–467.

Ball, I. J., Jr. 1971. Movements, habitat use and behavior of wood duck (*Aix sponsa*) broods in north-central Minnesota as determined by radio tracking. M.S. thesis, Univ. Minnesota, St. Paul. 56 pp.

———. 1973. Ecology of duck broods in a forested region of north-central Minnesota. Ph.D. thesis, Univ. Minnesota, St. Paul. 67 pp.

Ball, I. J., Jr., D. S. Gilmer, L. M. Cowardin, and J. H. Riechmann. 1975. Survival of wood duck and mallard broods in north-central Minnesota. J. Wildl. Manage. 39: 776–780.

Bang, B. G. 1971. Functional anatomy of the olfactory system in 23 orders of birds. S. Karger, Basel, New York. 76 pp. (Acta anatomica. Supplementum, 58.)

Barbour, T. 1943. Cuban ornithology. Memoirs of the Nuttall Ornithological Club, No. IX. The Club, Cambridge, Massachusetts. 144 pp.

Barclay, J. S. 1970. Ecological aspects of defensive behavior in breeding mallards and black ducks. Ph.D. thesis, Ohio St. Univ., Columbus. 176 pp.

Barden, L. S. 1968. A population analysis of Maine-banded wood ducks. M.S. thesis, Univ. Maine, Orono. 109 pp.

Barrett, J. 1973. Breeding behavior of captive mallards. M.S. thesis, Univ. Minnesota, St. Paul. 71 pp.

Barrow, J. H., Jr., N. Kelker, and H. Miller. 1968. The transmission of *Leucocytozoon simondi* to birds by *Simulium rugglesi* in northern Michigan. Am. Midl. Natur. 79: 197–204.

Barrows, W. B. 1912. Michigan bird life. Michigan Agric. Coll. Spec. Bull., Dept. Zool. Physiol., Ann Arbor. 822 pp.

Barry, S. C. 1992. Evaluation of a wood duck nest box program at Yazoo National Wildlife Refuge, Mississippi, 1987–1991. M.S. thesis. Mississippi St. Univ., Starkville. 84 pp.

Bartelt, G. A. and R. E. Trost. 1990. Populations, harvest, and survival of wood ducks in Wisconsin, Minnesota, and Michigan, 1961–87. Pages 341–348 in L. H. Fredrickson, G. V. Burger, S. P. Havera, D. A. Graber, R. E. Kirby, and T. S. Taylor, eds., Proc. 1988 N. Am. Wood Duck Symp., St. Louis. 390 pp.

Barton, B. S. 1799. Fragments (which are intended to illustrate to some degree, the natural history of a country extremely interesting to philosophers, and hitherto very imperfectly explored). The Linnaean Soc., Philadelphia. xviii+24 pp. (Reprinted in 1974 by Arno Press, New York.)

Bartonek, J. C. and J. J. Hickey. 1969. Selective feeding by juvenile diving ducks in summer. Auk 86: 443–457.

Bartonek, J. C., J. T. Beall, and J. E. Cornely. 1990. Distribution, status, and harvests of wood ducks in the Pacific Flyway. Pages 127–134 *in* L. H. Fredrickson, G. V. Burger, S. P. Havera, D. A. Graber, R. E. Kirby, and T. S. Taylor, eds., Proc. 1988 N. Am. Wood Duck Symp., St. Louis. 390 pp.

Bartram, W. 1791. Travels through North and South Carolina. James & Johnson, Philadelphia. 522 pp. (Reprinted in 1980, Peregrine Smith, Inc., Salt Lake City.)

Batema, D. L. 1987. Relations among wetland invertebrate abundance, litter decomposition and nutrient dynamics in a bottomland hardwood ecosystem. M.S. thesis, Univ. Missouri, Columbia. 191 pp.

Bateman, H. A. 1977. The wood duck in Louisiana. Louisiana Dept. Wildl. and Fish., Baton Rouge. 31 pp.

Bateson, P. 1982. Preference for cousins in Japanese quail. Nature 295: 236–237.

Batt, B. D. J. and H. H. Prince. 1979. Laying dates, clutch size and egg weight of captive mallards. Condor 81: 35–41.

Baumgartner, F. M. 1942. An analysis of waterfowl hunting at Lake Carl Blackwell, Payne County, Oklahoma, for 1940. J. Wildl. Manage. 6: 83–91.

Baumgartner, L. L. 1940. The fox squirrel: Its life history, habits and management. Ph.D. thesis, Ohio St. Univ., Columbus. 257 pp.

Beacham, E. D. 1957. A breeding record for the wood duck in Alberta. Can. Field-Natur. 71: 35.

Beall, J., D. Clouse, and J. Stephenson. 1984. Expansion of a local breeding wood duck population on Fort Lewis, Washington. Presented at the Natl. Military Fish and Wildl. Assoc. Meeting, 17–21 November, 1984, New Orleans, Louisiana. Held in conjunction with the 38th Annu. Conf. Southeast. Assoc. Fish and Wildl. Agencies. Mimeo. rept. 6 pp.

Beard, E. B. 1953. The importance of beaver in waterfowl management at the Seney National Wildlife Refuge. J. Wildl. Manage. 17: 398–436.

———. 1964. Duck brood behavior at the Seney National Wildlife Refuge. J. Wildl. Manage. 28: 492–521.

Beckley, O. E. 1965. Wood duck nesting box program: Ten year report. Connecticut Conserv. Bull. 11 (January–February): 1, 6.

Beckman, L. A. 1909. Field report—Santee Club, South Carolina. Unpubl. rept. on file with the Santee Coastal Reserve, McClellanville, South Carolina. Unpaginated.

Bednarik, K. E. 1984. Wood duck nest box inventory and utilization, 1984. Div. Wildl., In-service Note 527. Ohio Dept. Natur. Resour., Columbus. 10 pp.

Bednarik, K. E., J. L. Weeks, and R. A. Warhurst. 1974. Wood duck production on Ohio streams, 1974. Div. Wildl., In-service Note 263. Ohio Dept. Natur. Resour., Columbus. 4 pp.

Beer, R. E. 1970. Ectoparasites of birds: A brief review. Pages 507–514 in O. S. Pettingill, Jr. Ornithology in laboratory and field. 4th ed. Burgess Publishing Co., Minneapolis. 524 pp.

Belles-Isles, J. C. and J. Picman. 1986. House wren nest-destroying behavior. Condor 88: 190–193.

Belles-Isles, J. C. and J. Picman. 1987. Suspected adult intraspecific killing by house wrens. Wilson Bull. 99: 497–498.

Bellrose, F. C. 1943. Two wood ducks incubating in the same nesting box. Auk 60: 446–447.

———. 1944. Duck populations and kill: An evaluation of some waterfowl regulations in Illinois. Illinois Natur. Hist. Surv. Circ. 45, Champaign. 48 pp.

———. 1951. Waterfowl flight. Illinois Wildl. 6: 10–11.

———. 1953 (revised 1955). Housing for wood ducks. Illinois Natur. Hist. Surv. Circ. 45, Champaign. 48 pp.

———. 1955. The status of the wood duck in the Mississippi Flyway, 1955. Mississippi Flyway Tech. Comm. Newsletter No. 31. 7 pp.

———. 1958. The orientation of displaced waterfowl in migration. Wilson Bull. 70: 20–40.

———. 1959. Lead poisoning as a mortality factor in waterfowl populations. Illinois Natur. Hist. Surv. Bull. 27: 235–288.

———. 1964a. Spent shot and lead poisoning. Pages 479–485 in J. P. Linduska, ed., Waterfowl tomorrow. U.S. Fish and Wildl. Serv., Washington, D.C. 770 pp.

———. 1964b. Radar studies of waterfowl migration. Trans. N. Am. Wildl. and Natur. Resour. Conf. 29: 128–142.

———. 1975. Impact of ingested lead pellets on waterfowl. Pages 163–167 in Proc. First Intern. Waterfowl Symp., St. Louis. Ducks Unlimited, Inc., Chicago. 224 pp.

———. 1976. Ducks, geese and swans of North America. Stackpole Books, Harrisburg, Pennsylvania. 544 pp.

———. 1988. The adaptability of the mallard leads to its future. Pages 5–10 in M. A. Johnson, ed., Proc. Mallard Symp., Bismarck, North Dakota. 147 pp.

———. 1990. The history of wood duck management. Pages 13–20 in L. H. Fredrickson, G. V. Burger, S. P. Havera, D. A. Graber, R. E. Kirby, and T. S. Taylor, eds., Proc. 1988 N. Am. Wood Duck Symp., St. Louis. 390 pp.

Bellrose, F. C. and R. D. Crompton. 1970. Migrational behavior of mallards and black ducks as determined from banding. Illinois Natur. Hist. Surv. Bull. 30: 167–234.

Bellrose, F. C. and R. D. Crompton. 1972. Nest houses for wood ducks. Illinois Dept. Conserv. and Illinois Natur. Hist. Surv., Champaign. 4 pp.

Bellrose, F. C. and N. M. Trudeau. 1988. Wetlands and their relationship to migrating and winter populations of waterfowl. Pages 183–194 in D. D. Hook, W. H. McKee, Jr., H. K. Smith, J. Gregory, V. G. Burrell, Jr., M. R. DeVoe, R. E. Sojka, S. Gilbert, R. Banks, L. H. Stolzy, C. Brooks, T. D. Matthews, and T. H. Shear, eds., The ecology and management of wetlands. Vol. I: Ecology of wetlands. 592 pp.

Bellrose, F. C., H. C. Hanson, and P. D. Beamer. 1945. Aspergillosis in wood ducks. J. Wildl. Manage. 9: 325–326.

Bellrose, F. C., T. G. Scott, A. S. Hawkins, and J. B. Low. 1961. Sex ratios and age ratios in North American ducks. Illinois Natur. Hist. Surv. Bull. 27: 391–474.

Bellrose, F. C., K. L. Johnson, and T. U. Meyers. 1964. Relative value of natural cavities and nesting houses for wood ducks. J. Wildl. Manage. 28: 661–676.

Bellrose, F. C., F. L. Paveglio, Jr., and D. W. Steffeck. 1979. Waterfowl populations and the changing environment of the Illinois River Valley. Illinois Natur. Hist. Surv. Bull. 32: 1–54.

Bellrose, F. C., S. P. Havera, F. L. Paveglio, Jr., and D. W. Steffeck. 1983. The fate of lakes in the Illinois River Valley. Biol. Notes 119. Illinois Natur. Hist. Surv., Champaign. 27 pp.

Bellrose, F. C., R. P. Larkin, and K. Archer–Belcher. 1990. The flight of waterfowl: Body size, wing dimensions, and aerodynamics. Unpubl. manuscript on file at Forbes Laboratory, Illinois Natur. Hist. Surv., Havana. 37 pp.

Benfield, D. H. 1970. Changes in weight and primary feather length of immature wood ducks (*Aix sponsa*). M.S. thesis, North Carolina St. Univ., Raleigh. 32 pp.

Bennett, G. F., W. Blandin, H W Heusmann, and A. G. Campbell. 1974. Hematozoa of the Anatidae of the Atlantic Flyway. I. Massachusetts. J. Wildl. Dis. 10: 442–451.

Bennett, G. F., A. D. Smith, W. Whitman, and M. Cameron. 1975. Hematozoa of the Anatidae of the Atlantic Flyway. II. The Maritime provinces of Canada. J. Wildl. Dis. 11: 280–289.

Bent, A. C. 1923. Life histories of North American wild fowl. Order: Anseres (Part I). U.S. Natl. Mus. Bull. 126. Washington, D.C. 244 pp.

———. 1925. Life histories of North American wild fowl. Order: Anseres (Part II). U.S. Natl. Mus. Bull. 130. Washington, D.C. 396 pp.

———. 1939. Life histories of North American woodpeckers. Smithson. Inst. Bull. 174: 164–194.

Benton, A. H. and V. Shatrau. 1965. The bird fleas of eastern North America. Wilson Bull. 77: 76–81.

Bergman, R. 1970. Trout. Alfred A. Knopf, New York. 428 pp.

Berthold, P. 1975. Migratory fattening endogenous control and interaction with migratory activity. Naturwissenschaften 62: 399.

———. 1990. Genetics of migration. Pages 269–280 *in* E. Gwinner, ed., Bird migration: Physiology and ecophysiology. 435 pp.

Beshears, W. W., Jr. 1969. Wood duck studies, trapping and banding. Fed. Aid Rept. W-35-R. Alabama Dept. Conserv., Montgomery. 31 pp.

———. 1970. Wood duck studies, inspection of nest houses. Fed. Aid Rept. W-35-R. Alabama Dept. Conserv., Montgomery. 31 pp.

———. 1974. Wood ducks in Alabama. Natur. Resour. Spec. Rept. 4. Alabama Dept. Conserv., Montgomery. 45 pp.

Beyer, G. E., A. Allison, and H. H. Kopman. 1907. List of the birds of Louisiana, Part III. Auk 24: 314–321.

Billard, R. S. and P. S. Humphrey. 1972. Molts and plumages in the greater scaup. J. Wildl. Manage. 36: 765–774.

Birkhead, T. R., L. Atkin, and A. P. Moller. 1987. Copulation behaviour of birds. Behaviour 101: 101–133.

Bishop, R. 1966. Evaluation of Iowa's duck wing survey. Iowa St. Conserv. Commiss. Fish and Game Div., Quart. Biol. Rept. 19: 38–46.

Blanchan, N. 1898. Birds that hunt and are hunted: Life histories of 170 birds of prey, gamebirds and waterfowls. Doubleday, McClure Co., New York. xii + 359 pp.

Blohm, R. J. 1978. Migrational homing of male gadwalls to breeding grounds. Auk 95: 763–766.

———. 1979. The breeding ecology of the gadwall in southern Manitoba. Ph.D. thesis, Univ. Wisconsin, Madison. 177 pp.

———. 1982. Differential occurrence of yearling and adult male gadwalls in pair bonds. Auk 99: 378–379.

Blue Ribbon Panel for the Bottomland Hardwoods. 1984. Panel report. DOA, DOI, USDA, DOC, EPA, Vicksburg, Mississippi. 51 pp.

Boettger, R. W. and M. Smart. 1968. Beaver flowages converted from liabilities to assets. Maine Fish and Game 10: 5–7.

Boie, F. 1828. Bemerkungen über mehrere neue Vogelgattungen. Isis von Oken XXI: col. 312–329.

Bolen, E. G. and B. W. Cain. 1968. Mixed wood duck-tree duck clutch in Texas. Condor 70: 389–390.

Bolen, E. G. and C. Cottam. 1967. Wood duck nesting record from South Texas. Southwest. Natur. 12: 198–199.

Bond, J. 1961. Birds of the West Indies. Houghton Mifflin, Boston. 256 pp.

Borden, R. and H. A. Hochbaum. 1966. Gadwall seeding in New England. Trans. N. Am. Wildl. and Natur. Resour. Conf. 31: 79–88.

Borell, A. E. 1948. The wood duck in New Mexico. Wilson Bull. 60: 117.

Bouvier, J. M. 1974. Breeding biology of the hooded merganser in southwestern Quebec, including interactions with common goldeneyes and wood ducks. Can. Field-Natur. 88: 323–330.

Bowers, E. F. 1977. Population dynamics and distribution of the wood duck (*Aix sponsa*) in eastern North America. Ph.D. thesis, Louisiana St. Univ., Baton Rouge. 273 pp.

Bowers, E. F. and J. S. Atkins. 1990. Nest box height preference of the wood duck. Pages 245–248 *in* L. H. Fredrickson, G. V. Burger, S. P. Havera, D. A. Graber, R. E. Kirby, and T. S. Taylor, eds., Proc. 1988 N. Am. Wood Duck Symp., St. Louis. 390 pp.

Bowers, E. F. and F. W. Martin. 1975. Managing wood ducks by population units. Trans. N. Am. Wildl. and Natur. Resour. Conf. 40: 300–324.

Boyd, E. M. 1951. The external parasites of birds: A review. Wilson Bull. 63: 363–369.

Boyer, R. L. 1974. A survey of wood duck (*Aix sponsa* L.) nest sites and brood rearing habitat on the Shiawassee National Wildlife Refuge. M.S. thesis, C. Michigan Univ., Mount Pleasant. 65 pp.

———. 1975a. Wildlife occupying potential wood duck tree nest sites. Wilson Bull. 87: 558–559.

————. 1975b. The wood duck (*Aix sponsa*) on Shiawassee National Wildlife Refuge. Jack-Pine Warbler 53: 126–130.

Brabander, J. J., R. E. Masters, and R. M. Short. 1985. Bottomland hardwoods of eastern Oklahoma: A special study of their status, trends, and values. U.S. Fish and Wildl. Serv., Div. Ecol. Serv., Tulsa, Oklahoma. 143 pp.

Brakhage, G. K. 1966. Management of mast crops for wood ducks. Pages 75–80 *in* J. B. Trefethen, ed., Wood duck management and research: A symposium. Wildl. Manage. Inst., Washington, D.C. 212 pp.

Breckenridge, W. J. 1947. Wood ducks versus squirrels. Auk 64: 621.

————. 1956. Nesting study of wood ducks. J. Wildl. Manage. 20: 16–21.

Brewster, W. 1924. The birds of the Lake Umbagog region of Maine. Bull. Mus. Comp. Zool. 66: 209.

Brewster, W. G., J. M. Gates, and L. D. Flake. 1976. Breeding waterfowl populations and their distribution in South Dakota. J. Wildl. Manage. 40: 50–59.

Briggs, R. L. 1978. Wood ducks gathering acorns. N. Am. Bird Bander 3: 102.

Brisbin, I. L., Jr., G. C. White, P. B. Bush, and L. A. Mayack. 1986. Sigmoid growth analyses of wood ducks: The effects of sex, dietary protein and cadmium on parameters of the Richards model. Growth 50: 41–50.

Brisbin, I. L., Jr., R. A. Kennamer, G. C. White, P. B. Bush, and L. A. Mayack. 1987. Growth characteristics of wood ducks from two southeastern breeding locations. Wilson Bull. 99: 91–94.

Britt, T. E. 1972. Wood duck nest house use in Louisiana. Fed. Aid Rept., Louisiana Wildl. and Fish. Commiss., Baton Rouge.

Brodkorb, P. 1951. The number of feathers in some birds. J. Florida Acad. Sci. 12: 241–245.

Brooks, A. 1918. Brief notes on the prevalence of certain birds in British Columbia. Ottawa Natur. 31: 139–141.

Brown, B. W. 1972a. The Big Lake wood duck: A two-year study of its preflight mortality, nesting population growth and migration, 1970–71. Proc. Annu. Conf. Southeast. Assoc. Game and Fish Commiss. 26: 195–202.

————. 1972b. A boat-mounted ladder-stand for inspecting duck nest boxes. Proc. Annu. Conf. Southeast. Assoc. Game and Fish Commiss. 26: 207–209.

Brown, D. E. 1985. Arizona wetlands and waterfowl. Univ. Arizona Press, Tucson. 169 pp.

Brown, J. L. 1964. The evolution of diversity in avian territorial systems. Wilson Bull. 76: 160–169.

————. 1975. The evolution of behavior. W. W. Norton and Co., Inc., New York. 761 pp.

Brown, L. G. and F. C. Bellrose. 1943. Use of nesting boxes for wood ducks by other wildlife. J. Wildl. Manage. 7: 298–306.

Brownie, C., D. R. Anderson, K. P. Burnham, and D. S. Robson. 1985. Statistical inference from band recovery data: A handbook. 2nd ed. Resour. Publ. 156. U.S. Fish and Wildl. Serv., Washington, D.C. 305 pp.

Bryan, P. 1945. Use of wood duck nesting boxes in Wheeler Wildlife Refuge, Alabama. J. Tennessee Acad. Sci. 20: 35–40.

————. 1946. Further use of wood duck nesting boxes in Wheeler Wildlife Refuge. J. Tennessee Acad. Sci. 21: 76–77.

Buffon, G. L. L., Compte de. 1783. Histoire naturelle des oiseaux. 9 vols. De L'Impremeris Royale. Paris.

Bull, E. L. and E. C. Meslow. 1977. Habitat requirements of the pileated woodpecker in northeastern Oregon. J. For. 75:335–337.

Bull, J. 1964. Birds of the New York area. Harper & Row, New York. 540 pp.

Bump, G. 1939 [1940]. Pathological examination of game. New York St. Conserv. Dept. Annu. Rept. 29: 236–242.

Bump, G., R. W. Darrow, F. C. Edminster, and W. F. Crissey. 1947. The ruffed grouse. The Holling Press, Inc., Buffalo, New York. 915 pp.

Burgess, E. C., J. Ossa, and T. M. Yuill. 1979. Duck plague–a carrier state in waterfowl. Avian Dis. 24: 940–949.

Burke, C. J., S. M. Byers, R. A. Montgomery. 1978. A field guide to the aging of wood duck embryos. J. Wildl. Manage. 42: 432–437.

Burleigh, T. D. 1958. Georgia birds. Univ. Oklahoma Press, Norman. 746 pp.

Buscher, H. N. 1965. Dynamics of the intestinal helminth fauna in three species of ducks. J. Wildl. Manage. 29: 772–781.

Butler, A. W. 1898. The birds of Indiana: A descriptive catalogue of the birds that have been observed within the state, with an account of their habits. Report of the State Geologist of Indiana, 1897. 1,197 pp.

California Department of Fish and Game. 1930. Wood duck–how to distinguish them. California Fish and Game 16: 342.

Cameron, A. W. 1967. Birds of the St. Pierre and Miquelon Archipelago. Natur. Can. 94: 389–420.

Campbell, L. 1968. Birds of the Toledo area. The Blade, Toledo, Ohio. 330 pp.

Campbell, R. W., N. K. Dawe, I. McTaggart-Cowan, J. M. Cooper, G. W. Kaiser, and M. C. E. McNall. 1990. The birds of British Columbia. Vol. I. Royal Mus. of British Columbia, Victoria. 514 pp.

Capen, D. E., W. J. Crenshaw, and M. W. Coulter. 1974. Establishing breeding populations of wood ducks by relocating wild broods. J. Wildl. Manage. 38: 253–256.

Carey, C., H. Rahn, and P. Parisi. 1980. Calories, water, lipid and yolk in avian eggs. Condor 82: 335–343.

Carleton, G. 1971. Wood duck presumed nesting in cliff. Kingbird 21: 212.

Carney, S. M. 1964. Preliminary keys to waterfowl age and sex identification by means of wing plumage. Spec. Sci. Rept., Wildl. 82. U.S. Fish and Wildl. Serv., Washington, D.C. 47 pp.

Carney, S. M. and G. Smart. 1964. Increases in the duck kill that might be anticipated due to increases in the daily bag limit as derived from wing collection data. Admin. Rept. No. 56, U.S. Fish and Wildl. Serv., Washington, D.C. 2 pp. + 2 tables.

Carney, S. M., M. F. Sorensen, and E. M. Martin. 1975. Distribution in states and counties of waterfowl species harvested during 1961–70 hunting seasons. Spec. Sci. Rept., Wildl. No. 187. U.S. Fish and Wildl. Serv., Washington, D.C. 132 pp.

Carney, S. M., M. F. Sorensen, and E. M. Martin. 1978. Average harvest of each duck species in states and counties during 1966–75 hunting seasons. Admin. Rept., U.S. Fish and Wildl. Serv., Off. Migr. Bird Manage., Laurel, Maryland. 99 pp.

Carney, S. M., M. F. Sorensen, and E. M. Martin. 1983. Distribution of waterfowl species harvested in states and counties during 1971–80 hunting seasons. Spec. Sci. Rept., Wildl. No. 254. U.S. Fish and Wildl. Serv., Washington, D.C. 114 pp.

Carney, S. M., M. F. Sorensen, and E. M. Martin. 1984. Waterfowl harvest and hunter activity in the United States during the 1983 hunting season. Admin. Rept., June 27, 1984. U.S. Fish and Wildl. Serv., Washington, D.C. 27 pp.

Carney, S. M., M. F. Sorensen, and E. M. Martin. 1985. Waterfowl and hunter activity in the United States during the 1984 hunting season. Admin. Rept., June 26, 1985. U.S. Fish and Wildl. Serv., Washington, D.C. 27 pp.

Carney, S. M., M. F. Sorensen, and E. M. Martin. 1986. Waterfowl harvest and hunter activity in the United States during the 1985 hunting season. Admin. Rept., July 8, 1986. U.S. Fish and Wildl. Serv., Washington, D.C. 27 pp.

Carpenter, M. M. 1953. Wood duck production and life history on the Montezuma Wildlife Refuge, New York, 1952. M.S. thesis, Cornell Univ., Ithaca, New York. 63 pp.

Catesby, M. 1731–1743. The natural history of Carolina, Florida and the Bahama Islands. . . . 2 vols. M. Catesby, London.

Cheatum, E. L. 1952. Disease and parasite investigations. Final Rept., Pittman-Robertson Proj. 1-R, Supplement E. New York St. Conserv. Dept., Albany. 75 pp.

Cheng, K. M., J. T. Burns, and F. McKinney. 1983. Forced copulation in captive mallards. III. Sperm competition. Auk 100: 302–310.

Cink, C. L. 1977. Wood duck production in the Salt Creek watershed of eastern Nebraska. Trans. Nebraska Acad. Sci. 4: 53–56.

Clark, C. 1955. Waterfowl of Lake St. Marys, Ohio, and vicinity. Div. Wildl., Tech. Bull. No. 2. Ohio Dept. Natur. Resour., Columbus. 29 pp.

Clawson, R. L. 1975a. The ecology of dump nesting in wood ducks. M.S. thesis, Univ. Missouri, Columbia. 122 pp.

———. 1975b. Wood ducks trapped by predator guards. J. Wildl. Manage. 39: 220.

Clawson, R. L., G. W. Hartman, and L. H. Fredrickson. 1979. Dump nesting in a Missouri wood duck population. J. Wildl. Manage. 43: 347–355.

Clay, D. L., I. L. Brisbin, Jr., and K. A. Youngstrom. 1979. Age-specific changes in the major body components and caloric values of growing wood ducks. Auk 96: 296–305.

Clutton-Brock, T. H., F. E. Guinness, and S. D. Albon. 1982. Red deer: Behaviour and ecology of two sexes. Edinburgh Univ. Press, Edinburgh. 378 pp.

Collias, N. E. and E. C. Collias. 1963. Selective feeding by wild ducklings of different species. Wilson Bull. 75: 6–14.

Conlin, M. 1976. Stream channelization in Illinois—1976 update. Unpubl. rept. on file at Illinois Dept. Conserv., Springfield. 17 pp.

Conrad, W. B., Jr. 1965a. A study of the food habits of ducks wintering on the lower Pee Dee and Waccamaw rivers, Georgetown, South Carolina. M.S. thesis, Auburn Univ., Auburn, Alabama. 100 pp.

———. 1965b. A food habits study of ducks wintering on the lower Pee Dee and Waccamaw rivers, Georgetown, South Carolina. Proc. Annu. Conf. Southeast. Assoc. Game and Fish Commiss. 19: 93–98.

Conroy, M. J. and R. T. Eberhardt. 1983. Variation in survival and recovery rates of ring-necked ducks. J. Wildl. Manage. 47: 127–137.

Cook, R. S. 1971. *Leucocytozoon:* Danilewsky 1890. Pages 291–299 in J. W. Davis, R. C. Anderson, L. Karstad, and D. O. Trainer, eds., Infectious and parasitic diseases. Iowa St. Univ. Press, Ames. 344 pp.

Cooke, W. W. 1906. Distribution and migration of North American ducks, geese, and swans. Biol. Surv. Bull. No. 26. U.S. Dept. Agric., Washington, D.C. 90 pp.

Cornwell, G. W. 1963. New waterfowl host records for *Sarcocystis rileyi* and a review of Sarcosporidiosis in birds. Avian Dis. 7: 212–216.

Cornwell, G. W. and A. B. Cowan. 1963. Helminth populations of the canvasback (*Aythya valisineria*) and host-parasite-environmental interrelationships. Trans. N. Am. Wildl. and Natur. Resour. Conf. 28: 173–199.

Cory, C. B. 1909. The birds of Illinois and Wisconsin. Field Mus. Natur. Hist. Zool. Serv. Publ. 9. 764 pp.

Costanzo, G. R., T. T. Fendley, and J. R. Sweeney. 1983. Winter movements and habitat use by wood ducks in South Carolina. Proc. Annu. Conf. Southeast. Assoc. Fish and Wildl. Agencies 37: 67–78.

Cottrell, S. D. 1979a. Wood duck brood use of an east Tennessee riverine habitat. M.S. thesis, Michigan St. Univ., East Lansing. 52 pp.

———. 1979b. Waterfowl—wetlands resources of the upper French Broad River, North Carolina. Tennessee Valley Auth., Div. Land For. Resour., Norris, Tennessee. 21 pp. Mimeo.

Cottrell, S. D. and H. H. Prince. 1990. Comparison of wood duck survey techniques on the Holston River in east Tennessee. Pages 219–224 in L. H. Fredrickson, G. V. Burger, S. P. Havera, D. A. Graber, R. E. Kirby, and T. S. Taylor, eds., Proc. 1988 N. Am. Wood Duck Symp., St. Louis. 390 pp.

Cottrell, S. D., H. H. Prince, and P. I. Padding. 1990. Nest success, duckling survival, and brood habitat selection of wood ducks in a Tennessee riverine system. Pages 191–197 *in* L. H. Fredrickson, G. V. Burger, S. P. Havera, D. A. Graber, R. E. Kirby, and T. S. Taylor, eds., Proc. 1988 N. Am. Wood Duck Symp., St. Louis. 390 pp.

Coues, E. 1871. Notes on the natural history of Fort Macon, North Carolina and vicinity (No. 1). Pages 12–49 *in* Proc. Acad. Natur. Sci. Philadelphia. 372 pp.

———, ed. 1893. The history of the Lewis and Clark Expedition. Francis P. Harper, New York. 4 vols. (Reprinted by Dover Publications, New York.)

Coulter, M. W. 1955. Spring food habits of surface-feeding ducks in Maine. J. Wildl. Manage. 19: 263–267.

———. 1957a. Food of wood ducks in Maine. J. Wildl. Manage. 21: 235–236.

———. 1957b. Predation by snapping turtles upon aquatic birds in Maine marshes. J. Wildl. Manage. 21: 17–21.

Coulter, M. W. and W. R. Miller. 1968. Nesting biology of black ducks and mallards in northern New England. Bull. 68-2. Vermont Fish and Game Dept., Montpelier. 74 pp.

Cowardin, L. M., V. Carter, F. C. Golet, and E. T. LaRoe. 1979. Classification of wetlands and deepwater habitats of the United States. U.S. Fish and Wildl. Serv., Washington, D.C. 103 pp.

Cowardin, L. M., D. S. Gilmer, and C. W. Schaiffer. 1985. Mallard recruitment in the agricultural environment of North Dakota. Wildl. Monogr. 92. The Wildl. Soc., Washington, D.C. 37 pp.

Crichton, U. F. J. and H. E. Welch. 1972. Helminths from the digestive tracts of mallards and pintails in the Delta Marsh, Manitoba. Can. J. Zool. 50: 633–637.

Cringan, A. T. 1971. Status of the wood duck in Ontario. Trans. N. Am. Wildl. Natur. Resour. Conf. 36: 296–312.

Cristy, B. H. 1931. A fifty-year comparison. Auk 48: 365–378.

Cronan, J. M., Jr. 1957. Effects of predator guards on wood duck box usage. J. Wildl. Manage. 21: 468.

———. 1958. Rhode Island's waterfowl program. Wildl. Pamphlet 5. Rhode Island Dept. Agric. Conserv., Div. Fish and Game, Providence. 40 pp.

Cronan, J. M., Jr. and B. F. Halla. 1968. Fall and winter foods of Rhode Island waterfowl. Wildl. Pamphlet 7. Rhode Island Dept. Natur. Resour., Providence. 40 pp.

Cunningham, E. R. 1967. Wood duck nest box program progress report, 1967. Yazoo National Wildlife Refuge, Hollandale, Mississippi. 7 pp.

———. 1968. A three-year study of the wood duck on the Yazoo National Wildlife Refuge. Proc. Annu. Conf. Southeast. Assoc. Game and Fish Commiss. 22: 145–155.

Currier, P. J. 1982. The floodplain vegetation of the Platte River: Phytosociology, forest development, and seedling establishment. Ph.D. thesis, Iowa St. Univ., Ames. 177 pp.

Curtis, J. T. 1959. The vegetation of Wisconsin. Univ. Wisconsin Press, Madison. 657 pp.

Dane, C. W. 1965. The influence of age on the development and reproductive capability of the blue-winged teal (*Anas discors* Linnaeus). Ph.D. thesis, Purdue Univ., Lafayette, Indiana. 171 pp.

David, P. 1986. Survival and movements of wood duck broods in northern Illinois. M.S. thesis, Univ. Wisconsin, Madison. 63 pp.

Davidson, W. R. and V. F. Nettles. 1977. Rhinosporidiosis in a wood duck. J. Am. Vet. Med. Assoc. 171: 989–990.

Davis, D. J. 1978. The utilization of artificial nest cavities by wood ducks. M.S. thesis, Louisiana St. Univ., Baton Rouge. 215 pp.

Dawson, W. L. 1903. The birds of Ohio. Wheaton Publishing Co., Columbus, Ohio. 2 vols. 671 pp.

———. 1923. The birds of California. Vol. 4: 1797–1800. South Moulton Co., San Diego. Pages 549–2,121.

Dawson, W. L. and J. H. Bowles. 1909. The birds of Washington. The Occidental Publishing Co., Seattle. 2 vols. 997 pp.

Day, A. M. 1949. North American waterfowl. The Stackpole Co., Harrisburg, Pennsylvania. 363 pp.

———. 1959. North American waterfowl. 2nd. ed. The Stackpole Co., Harrisburg, Pennsylvania. 363 pp.

Decker, E. 1959. A four-year study of wood ducks on a Pennsylvania marsh. J. Wildl. Manage. 23: 310–315.

Delnicki, D. and K. J. Reinecke. 1986. Mid-winter food use and body weights of mallards and wood ducks in Mississippi. J. Wildl. Manage. 50: 43–51.

Dennis, D. G. 1990. Status of wood ducks in Canada. Pages 135–137 *in* L. H. Fredrickson, G. V. Burger, S. P. Havera, D. A. Graber, R. E. Kirby, and T. S. Taylor, eds., Proc. 1988 N. Am. Wood Duck Symp., St. Louis. 390 pp.

Derrickson, S. R. 1977. Aspects of breeding behavior in the pintail (*Anas acuta*). Ph.D. thesis, Univ. Minnesota, St. Paul. 122 pp.

DiGiulio, R. T. 1978. Wood duck (*Aix sponsa*) brood-usage of agricultural field wetlands in Concordia Parish, Louisiana. M.S. thesis, Louisiana St. Univ., Baton Rouge. 131 pp.

DiGiulio, R. T. and R. B. Hamilton. 1979. Utilization of agricultural wetlands in a Mississippi River bottomland by wood duck and hooded merganser broods. Proc. Annu. Conf. Southeast. Assoc. Game and Fish Commiss. 33: 81–87.

Dillery, D. G. 1965. Post-mortem digestion of stomach contents in the savannah sparrow. Auk 82: 281.

Dillon, S. T. 1970. Response of wood ducks to nest boxes at Max McGraw Wildlife Foundation. Presented at 32nd Midwest Wildl. Conf., Winnipeg, Manitoba. Mimeo. 10 pp.

Dirschl, H. J. 1969. Foods of lesser scaup and blue-winged teal in the Saskatchewan River Delta. J. Wildl. Manage. 33: 77–87.

Dixon, J. 1924. Nesting of the wood duck in California. Condor 26: 41–66.

Dockstader, F. J. 1961. Indian art in America. New York Graphic Soc., Greenwich, Connecticut. 224 pp.

Doty, H. A. 1972. Hatchability tests with eggs from captive wood ducks. Poultry Sci. 51: 849–853.

Doty, H. A. and A. D. Kruse. 1972. Techniques for establishing local breeding populations of wood ducks. J. Wildl. Manage. 36: 428–435.

Doty, H. A. and F. B. Lee. 1974. Homing to nest baskets by wild female mallards. J. Wildl. Manage. 38: 714–719.

Doty, H. A., F. B. Lee, A. D. Kruse, J. W. Matthews, J. R. Foster, and P. M. Arnold. 1984. Wood duck and hooded merganser nesting on Arrowwood NWR, North Dakota. J. Wildl. Manage. 48: 577–580.

Dreis, R. E. 1951. Productivity of the wood duck, *Aix sponsa* (L.), in eastern Louisa County, Iowa, 1951. M.S. thesis, Iowa St. Univ., Ames. 63 pp.

———. 1954. A field observation method of aging broods of wood ducks. J. Wildl. Manage. 18: 280–281.

Dreis, R. E. and G. O. Hendrickson. 1952. Wood duck production from nest-boxes and natural cavities on the Lake Odessa area, Iowa, in 1951. Iowa Bird Life 22: 18–22.

Dresser, H. E. 1866. On the birds of southern Texas (conclusion). Ibis Series 2, 2: 23–46.

Drobney, R. D. 1977. The feeding ecology, nutrition, and reproductive bioenergetics of wood ducks. Ph.D. thesis, Univ. Missouri, Columbia. 170 pp.

———. 1980. Reproductive bioenergetics of wood ducks. Auk 97: 480–490.

———. 1982. Body weight and composition changes and adaptations for breeding in wood ducks. Condor 84: 300–305.

———. 1984. Effect of diet on visceral morphology of breeding wood ducks. Auk 101: 93–98.

Drobney, R. D. and L. H. Fredrickson. 1979. Food selection by wood ducks in relation to breeding status. J. Wildl. Manage. 43: 109–120.

Drobney, R. D. and L. H. Fredrickson. 1985. Protein acquisition: A possible proximate factor limiting clutch size in wood ducks. Wildfowl 36: 122–128.

Drobney, R. D., C. T. Train, and L. H. Fredrickson. 1983. Dynamics of the platyhelminth fauna of wood ducks in relation to food habits and reproductive state. J. Parasitol. 69: 375–380.

Du Pratz, M. Le-Page. 1763. History of Louisiana, or of the western part of Virginia and Carolina. 2 vols. T. Becket and P. A. De Hondt, London.

Dwyer, T. J. 1974. Social behavior of breeding gadwalls in North Dakota. Auk 91: 375–386.

———. 1975. Time budget of breeding gadwalls. Wilson Bull. 87: 335–343.

Dwyer, T. J., S. R. Derrickson, and D. S. Gilmer. 1973. Migrational homing by a pair of mallards. Auk 90: 687.

Dwyer, T. J., G. L. Krapu, and D. M. Janke. 1979. Use of prairie pothole habitat by breeding mallards. J. Wildl. Manage. 43: 528–531.

Eaton, E. H. 1910. Birds of New York. Part I: water birds and game birds. Memoir 12. New York St. Mus., Albany. 501 pp.

Edson, J. M. 1908. Birds of the Bellingham Bay region (Washington). Auk 25: 425–439.

Edwards, G. 1743–1751. A natural history of uncommon birds. College of Physicians in Warwick-Lane, London. 4 vols.

Edwards, J. L. 1931–1932. Young wood ducks use wings under water. Abstract Proc. Linnean Soc. of New York. Nos. 43–44.

Eifrig, G. 1904. Birds of Allegany and Garrett counties, western Maryland. Auk 21: 234–250.

Elder, W. H. and M. W. Weller. 1954. Duration of fertility in the domestic mallard hen after isolation from the drake. J. Wildl. Manage. 18: 495–502.

Enquist, M. and O. Leimar. 1990. The evolution of fatal fighting. Anim. Behav. 39: 1–9.

Errington, P. L. 1937. A wood-duck marsh in northwestern Iowa. Auk 54: 533–534.

Erskine, A. J. 1961. Nest-site tenacity and homing in the bufflehead. Auk 78: 389–396.

Evans, C. D., A. S. Hawkins, and W. H. Marshall. 1952. Movement of waterfowl broods in Manitoba. Spec. Sci. Rept. Wildl. No. 16. U.S. Fish and Wildl. Serv., Washington, D.C. 47 pp. + 19 plates.

Evenden, F. G., Jr. 1952a. Notes on Mexican bird distribution. Wilson Bull. 64: 112–113.

———. 1952b. Waterfowl sex ratios observed in the western United States. J. Wildl. Manage. 16: 391–393.

Faanes, C. A. and J. M. Andrew. 1983. Avian use of forest habitats in the Pembina Hills of northeastern North Dakota. Resour. Publ. 151. U.S. Fish and Wildl. Serv., Washington, D.C. 24 pp.

Fallis, A. M. and G. F. Bennett. 1966. On the epizootiology of infections caused by *Leucocytozoon simondi* in Algonquin Park, Canada. Can. J. Zool. 44: 101–112.

Fallis, A. M. and D. M. Wood. 1957. Biting midges (Diptera: Ceratopogonidae) as intermediate hosts for *Haemoproteus* of ducks. Can. J. Zool. 35: 425–435.

Fallis, A. M., R. C. Anderson, and G. F. Bennett. 1956. Further observations on the transmission and development of *Leucocytozoon simondi*. Can. J. Zool. 34: 389–404.

Farmer, A. H., Jr. 1970. Wood duck brood movements as determined by radio-tracking. M.S. thesis, North Carolina St. Univ., Raleigh. 48 pp.

Farrar, J. 1985. Partners on the Platte. Nature Conserv. News 35: 13–18.

Feduccia, A., ed. 1985. Catesby's birds of colonial America. Univ. North Carolina Press, Chapel Hill. 176 pp.

Fendley, T. T. 1978. The ecology of wood ducks (*Aix sponsa*) utilizing a nuclear production reactor effluent stream. Ph.D. thesis, Utah St. Univ., Logan. 158 pp.

———. 1980. Incubating wood duck and hooded merganser hens killed by black rat snakes. Wilson Bull. 92: 526–527.

Fendley, T. T. and I. L. Brisbin, Jr. 1977. Growth curve analyses: A potential measure of the effects of environmental stress upon wildlife populations. Proc. Intern. Congr. Game Biol. 37: 337–350.

Fiedler, D. J. 1966. Results of wood duck usage of artificial nesting boxes during the 1966 nesting season in the study area in Morrison County in central Minnesota — A progress report. Mimeo. rept., Saint Cloud St. Univ., Saint Cloud, Minnesota. 12 pp.

————. 1967. The ecology of the wood duck in central Minnesota. M.A. thesis, Saint Cloud St. Univ., Saint Cloud, Minnesota. 56 pp.

Fiedler, P. C., B. G. Keesee, and P. A. Lopushinsky. 1990. Wood duck use of nesting structures in central Washington. Pages 265-267 *in* L. H. Fredrickson, G. V. Burger, S. P. Havera, D. A. Graber, R. E. Kirby, and T. S. Taylor, eds., Proc. 1988 N. Am. Wood Duck Symp., St. Louis. 390 pp.

Finley, W. L. 1968. Three year summary of wood duck nest box investigations at the William L. Finley Refuge. Unpubl. rept. in refuge files of William L. Finley Refuge, Corvallis, Oregon. 11 pp.

Fisher, A. K. 1902. Two vanishing game birds: The woodcock and the wood duck. Pages 447-458 *in* 1901 Yearbook. U.S. Dept. Agric., Washington, D.C. 846 pp.

Fleskes, J. P., J. A. Guthrie, and G. L. Welp. 1990. Raising wood ducks on a prairie marsh: The story of Union Slough. Pages 275-278 *in* L. H. Fredrickson, G. V. Burger, S. P. Havera, D. A. Graber, R. E. Kirby, and T. S. Taylor, eds., Proc. 1988 N. Am. Wood Duck Symp., St. Louis. 390 pp.

Foley, D. D. and W. R. Taber. 1951. Lower Hudson waterfowl investigation. Final Rept., Proj. 47-R. New York Conserv. Dept., Albany. 796 pp.

Folk, L., K. Hudec, and J. Toufar. 1966. The weight of the mallard and its changes in the course of the year. Zoologicke Listy 15: 249-260.

Folley, B. 1979. Analysis of Wisconsin wood duck banding data 1959-75. M.S. thesis, Univ. Wisconsin, Stevens Point. 113 pp.

Forbush, E. H. 1912. A history of the game birds, wildfowl and shore birds of Massachusetts and adjacent states. Massachusetts St. Board Agric., Boston. 622 pp.

————. 1925. Birds of Massachusetts and other New England states. Vol. I. Water birds, marsh birds and shore birds. Massachusetts Dept. Agric., Boston. 481 pp.

Ford, A., ed. 1957. Bird biographies. Macmillan, New York, New York. 295 pp.

Forrester, D. J., K. C. Wenner, F. H. White, E. C. Greiner, W. R. Marion, J. E. Thul, and G. A. Berkhoff. 1980. An epizootic of avian botulism in a phosphate mine settling pond in northern Florida. J. Wildl. Dis. 16: 323-327.

Forsythe, S. W. 1985. The protection of bottomland hardwood wetlands of the lower Mississippi Valley. Trans. N. Am. Wildl. and Natur. Resour. Conf. 50: 566-572.

Frank, W. J. 1948. Wood duck nesting box usage in Connecticut. J. Wildl. Manage. 12: 128-136.

Frayer, W. E., T. J. Monahan, D. C. Bowden, and F. A. Graybill. 1983. Status and trends of wetlands and deepwater habitats in the conterminous United States, 1950's to 1970's. Dept. For. and Wood Serv., Colorado St. Univ., Fort Collins. 32 pp.

Fredrickson, L. H. 1978. Lowland hardwood wetlands: Current status and habitat values for wildlife. Pages 296-306 *in* P. E. Greeson, J. R. Clark, and J. E. Clark, eds., Wetland functions and values: The state of our understanding. Am. Water Resour. Assoc. 674 pp.

Fredrickson, L. H. and J. L. Hansen. 1983. Second broods in wood ducks. J. Wildl. Manage. 47: 320-326.

Fredrickson, L. H. and M. E. Heitmeyer. 1988. Waterfowl use of forested wetlands of the southern United States: An overview. Pages 307-323 *in* M. W. Weller, ed., Waterfowl in winter. Univ. Minnesota Press, Minneapolis. 624 pp.

Fredrickson, L. H. and F. A. Reid. 1988. Control of willow and cottonwood seedlings in herbaceous wetlands. Fish and Wildl. Leaflet 13, 4-10. U.S. Fish and Wildl. Serv., Washington, D.C. 4 pp.

Fredrickson, L. H. and T. S. Taylor. 1982. Management of seasonally flooded impoundments for wildlife. Resour. Publ. 148. U.S. Fish and Wildl. Serv., Fort Collins, Colorado. 29 pp.

Friend, M., ed. 1987. Field guide to wildlife diseases. Resour. Publ. 167. U.S. Fish and Wildl. Serv., Washington, D.C. 225 pp.

Friend, M. and G. L. Pearson. 1973. Duck plague (duck virus enteritis) in wild waterfowl. U.S. Bur. Sport Fish. and Wildl., Washington, D.C. 16 pp.

Frye, R. G. 1986. Bottomland hardwoods — current supply, status, habitat quality, and future impact from reservoirs. Pages 24-28 *in* C. A. McMahan and R. G. Frye, eds., Bottomland hardwoods in Texas. PWD-RP-7100-133-3/87. Texas Parks and Wildl. Dept., Austin. 170 pp.

Fuller, R. W. and E. Bolen. 1963. Dual wood duck occupancy of a nesting box. Wilson Bull. 75: 94-95.

Gabrielson, I. N. and S. G. Jewett. 1970. Birds of the Pacific Northwest. Dover Publications, Inc., New York. 650 pp.

Gambel, K. 1990. Waterfowl harvest and population survey data. U.S. Fish and Wildl. Serv., Columbia, Missouri. 78 pp.

Ganier, A. F. 1933. A distributional list of the birds of Tennessee. Avifauna, No. 1. Tennessee Ornithol. Soc., Nashville. 64 pp.

Gates, J. M. 1962. Breeding biology of the gadwall in northern Utah. Wilson Bull. 74: 43-67.

Gatti, R. 1983. Incubation weight loss in the mallard. Can. J. Zool. 61: 565-569.

Gauthier, G. 1987. Further evidence of long-term pair bonds in ducks of the genus *Bucephala*. Auk 104: 521-522.

Gayle, C. 1986. Cavity formation and accelerating cavity development. Submitted as best management practices for creating and maintaining wood duck habitat on national wildlife refuges in Region 3: A workshop. Necedah, Wisconsin. Unpubl. manuscript. Branch of Refuges, U.S. Fish and Wildl. Serv., Fort Snelling, Minnesota. 6 pp.

Geis, A. D. and E. L. Atwood. 1961. Proportion of recovered waterfowl bands reported. J. Wildl. Manage. 25: 154–159.

Geist, V. 1966. The evolution of horn-like organs. Behaviour 27: 175–214.

———. 1971. Mountain sheep. Univ. Chicago Press, Chicago. 383 pp.

Gibbs, M. 1879. Annotated list of the birds of Michigan. Bull. U.S. Geol. and Geogr. Surv. Territ. 5: 481–497.

Gigstead, G. 1938. Wood ducks in the Illinois River bottoms. Trans. N. Am. Wildl. Conf. 3: 603–609.

Gilmer, D. S. 1971. Home range and habitat use of breeding mallards (*Anas platyrhynchos*) and wood ducks (*Aix sponsa*) in north-central Minnesota as determined by radio-tracking. Ph.D. thesis, Univ. Minnesota, St. Paul. 142 pp.

Gilmer, D. S., R. E. Kirby, I. J. Ball, and J. H. Reichmann. 1977. Post-breeding activities of mallards and wood ducks in north-central Minnesota. J. Wildl. Manage. 41: 345–359.

Gilmer, D. S., I. J. Ball, L. M. Cowardin, J. E. Mathisen, and J. H. Reichmann. 1978. Natural cavities used by wood ducks in north-central Minnesota. J. Wildl. Manage. 42: 288–298.

Godfrey, W. E. 1966. The birds of Canada. Queen's Printer, Ottawa. 428 pp.

Goetz, R. C. and D. W. Sharp. 1981. The effect of orientation and light intensity on utilization of artificial wood duck nest boxes. Proc. Annu. Conf. Southeast. Assoc. Fish and Wildl. Agencies 43: 591–597.

Goldstein, H., D. Eisikovitz, and Y. Yom-Tov. 1986. Infanticide in the palestine sunbird. Condor 88: 528–529.

Gollop, J. B. and W. H. Marshall. 1954. A guide for aging duck broods in the field. Mississippi Flyway Counc. Tech. Sect. 14 pp.

Gore, J. R. 1978. Wood duck response to nesting boxes placed in low quality habitat. Trans. Illinois St. Acad. Sci. 71: 295–301.

Goss, N. S. 1891. History of the birds of Kansas. G. W. Crane & Co., Topeka, Kansas. 693 pp.

Gottlieb, G. 1963. A naturalistic study of imprinting in wood ducklings. J. Comp. Physiol. Psychol. 56: 86–91.

———. 1965. Imprinting in relation to parental and species identification by avian neonates. J. Comp. Physiol. Psychol. 59: 345–356.

———. 1974. On the acoustic basis of species identification in wood ducklings (*Aix sponsa*). J. Comp. Physiol. Psychol. 87: 1,038–1,048.

———. 1977. The call of the duck. Natur. Hist. 86: 40, 44, 46.

———. 1980. Development of species identification in ducklings: VII. Highly specific early experience fosters species-specific perception in wood ducklings. J. Comp. Physiol. Psychol. 94: 1,019–1,027.

Gottschalk, J. S. 1967. To have—or to have not. Remarks given at opening of the 1967 Waterfowl Advisory Committee Meeting, August 8, Washington, D.C. Unpubl. rept. 8 pp.

Graber, J. W. and R. R. Graber. 1976. Environmental evaluations using birds and their habitats. Biol. Notes No. 97. Illinois Natur. Hist. Survey. 39 pp.

Grabill, B. A. 1977. Reducing starling use of wood duck boxes. Wildl. Soc. Bull. 5: 69–70.

Graham, B. J. 1980. Nest hole competition between wood ducks and hooded mergansers. Jack-Pine Warbler 58: 36.

Graham, J. M., G. R. Smith, E. D. Borland, and J. W. MacDonald. 1978. Avian botulism in winter and spring and the stability of *Clostridium botulinum* type C toxin. Vet. Record 102: 40–41.

Gray, A. P. 1958. Bird hybrids, a check-list with bibliography. Tech. Comm. No. 13, Commonwealth Agri. Bur., Farnham Royal, Bucks, England. 390 pp.

Green, W. E., L. G. MacNamara, and F. M. Uhler. 1964. Water off and on. Pages 557–568 in J. P. Linduska, ed., Waterfowl tomorrow. U.S. Fish and Wildl. Serv., Washington, D.C. 770 pp.

Greenewalt, C. H. 1975. The flight of birds. Trans. Am. Philosoph. Soc., New Series 65: 1–67.

Grice, D. 1963. The need for a renewed wood duck study in Massachusetts. Massachusetts Div. Fish and Game, Boston. 12 pp. Mimeo.

Grice, D. and J. P. Rogers. 1965. The wood duck in Massachusetts. Fed. Aid Proj. W-19-R. Final rept. Massachusetts Div. Fish and Game, Boston. 96 pp.

Griffith, M. A. and T. T. Fendley. 1981. Five-gallon plastic bucket: An inexpensive wood duck nesting structure. J. Wildl. Manage. 45: 281–284.

Grinnell, G. B. 1901. American duck shooting. For. and Stream Publ. Co., New York. 623 pp.

Grinnell, J. and H. C. Bryant. 1915. The wood duck in California. California Fish and Game 1: 1–14.

Grinnell, J., H. C. Bryant, and T. I. Storer. 1918. Wood duck. Pages 140–146 in The game birds of California. Univ. California Press, Berkeley. 642 pp.

Griscom, L. 1948. The present status of New England waterfowl. Proc. Northeast Wildl. Conf.: 79–85.

Gromme, O. J. 1930. Egrets and little blue herons in Wisconsin. Auk 47: 559.

Gwinner, E. 1986. Internal rhythms in bird migration. Sci. Am. 254: 84–92.

———. 1990. Circannual rhythms in bird migration: Control of temporal patterns and interactions with photoperiod. Pages 257–268 in E. Gwinner, ed., Bird migration: Physiology and ecophysiology. Springer-Verlag, Berlin. 435 pp.

Gysel, L. W. 1961. An ecological study of tree cavities and ground burrows in forest stands. J. Wildl. Manage. 25: 12–20.

Hall, D. L. 1962. Food utilization by waterfowl in green timber reservoirs at Noxubee National Wildlife Refuge. Proc. Annu. Conf. Southeast. Assoc. Game and Fish Commiss. 16: 184–199.

Hall, M. S. 1969. Unusual site for a wood duck nest. New York Fish and Game J. 16: 127.

Hammond, M. C. and G. E. Mann. 1956. Waterfowl nesting islands. J. Wildl. Manage. 20: 345–352.

Handley, D. E. 1955. Ducks of Ohio's farm ponds. Ohio Conserv. Bull. 19: 6–7.

————. 1962. Wood duck nest box checks, 1960. Game Res. in Ohio 1: 76–79.

Hankla, D. J. and V. E. Carter. 1966. Impact of forest management and other human activities on wood duck habitat in the southeast. Pages 29–36 *in* J. B. Trefethen, ed., Wood duck management and research: A symposium. Wildl. Manage. Inst., Washington, D.C. 212 pp.

Hankla, D. J. and P. B. Smith. 1963. Wood duck trapping techniques. Proc. Annu. Conf. Southeast. Assoc. Game and Fish Commiss. 17: 79–85.

Hansen, H. L. 1966. Silvical characteristics of tree species and decay processes as related to cavity production. Pages 65–69 *in* J. B. Trefethen, ed., Wood duck management and research: A symposium. Wildl. Manage. Inst., Washington, D.C. 212 pp.

Hansen, J. L. 1968. Predation, homing by black rat snakes on a wood duck nesting area—Mingo Refuge. Proc. Midwest Wildl. Conf. 12 pp.

————. 1971. The role of nest boxes in management of the wood duck on Mingo National Wildlife Refuge. M.A. thesis, Univ. Missouri, Columbia. 159 pp.

Hansen, J. L. and L. H. Fredrickson. 1990. Black rat snake predation on box nesting wood ducks. Pages 251–254 *in* L. H. Fredrickson, G. V. Burger, S. P. Havera, D. A. Graber, R. E. Kirby, and T. S. Taylor, eds., Proc. 1988 N. Am. Wood Duck Symp., St. Louis. 390 pp.

Hanson, H. C. 1954. Criteria of age of incubated mallard, wood duck, and bob-white quail eggs. Auk 71: 267–272.

————. 1962. The dynamics of condition factors in Canada geese and their relation to seasonal stresses. Arct. Inst. N. Am. Tech. Publ. 12: 1–68.

Haramis, G. M. 1975. Wood duck (*Aix sponsa*) ecology and management within the green-timber impoundments at Montezuma National Wildlife Refuge. M.S. thesis, Cornell Univ., Ithaca, New York. 153 pp.

————. 1990. Breeding ecology of the wood duck: A review. Pages 45–60 *in* L. H. Fredrickson, G. V. Burger, S. P. Havera, D. A. Graber, R. E. Kirby, and T. S. Taylor, eds., Proc. 1988 N. Am. Wood Duck Symp., St. Louis. 390 pp.

Haramis, G. M. and D. Q. Thompson. 1984. Survival of juvenile wood ducks in a northern greentree impoundment. J. Wildl. Manage. 48: 1,364–1,369.

Haramis, G. M. and D. Q. Thompson. 1985. Density-production characteristics of box-nesting wood ducks in a northern greentree impoundment. J. Wildl. Manage. 49: 429–436.

Haramis, G. M., W. G. Alliston, and M. E. Richmond. 1983. Dump nesting in the wood duck traced by tetracycline. Auk 100: 729–730.

Hardister, J. P., Jr., F. E. Hester, and T. L. Quay. 1962. Movements of juvenile wood ducks as measured by web-tagging. Proc. Annu. Conf. Southeast. Assoc. Game and Fish Commiss. 16: 70–75.

Harlow, R. C. 1918. Notes on the breeding birds of Pennsylvania and New Jersey. Auk 35: 18–29, 136–147.

Harrigal, D. 1990. Statewide wood duck box project, 1989 annual report. South Carolina Wildl. and Marine Resour. Dept., Columbia. 28 pp.

Harrison, A. J., Jr. and R. H. Chabreck. 1988. Duck food production in openings in forested wetlands. Pages 339–351 *in* M. W. Weller, ed., Waterfowl in winter. Univ. Minnesota Press, Minneapolis.

Hartley, D. R. and E. P. Hill. 1990. Effect of heat in plastic nest boxes for wood ducks. Pages 249–250 *in* L. H. Fredrickson, G. V. Burger, S. P. Havera, D. A. Graber, R. E. Kirby, and T. S. Taylor, eds., Proc. 1988 N. Am. Wood Duck Symp., St. Louis. 390 pp.

Hartman, G. W. 1972. The biology of dump nesting in wood ducks. M.A. thesis, Univ. Missouri, Columbia. 66 pp.

Hartmann, J. R. 1988. The impact of federal programs on the conversion and conservation of wetlands in thirteen selected study areas. Vol. II of a report to Congress. Final rept. U.S. Dept. Int., Off. Policy Anal. and Fish and Wildl. Serv. Contract No. 14-01-0001-898-C-05. Washington, D.C. 105 pp.

Hartowicz, E. 1963. Nesting of the wood duck (*Aix sponsa*) in southeast Missouri. M.A. thesis, Univ. Missouri, Columbia. 64 pp.

————. 1965. Evening roosting habits of wood ducks in southeast Missouri. J. Wildl. Manage. 29: 399–401.

Harvey, W. F., IV, G. R. Hepp, and R. A. Kennamer. 1989a. Age determination of female wood ducks during the breeding season. Wildl. Soc. Bull. 17: 254–258.

Harvey, W. F., IV, G. R. Hepp, and R. A. Kennamer. 1989b. Body mass dynamics of wood ducks during incubation: Individual variation. Can. J. Zool. 67: 570–574.

Hatch, P. L. 1892. *Aix sponsa* (L.). Pages 51–55 *in* Notes on the birds of Minnesota. First report of the State Zoologist. Harrison & Smith, Minneapolis. 487 pp.

Hathcock, R. 1976. Effigy forms: Birds. Pages 285–333 *in* Ancient Indian pottery of the Mississippi Valley. Hurley Press, Inc., Camden, Arkansas. 232 pp.

Havera, S. P. 1985. Cooperative waterfowl research. Federal Aid Project W-88-R-1-5. Final rept. Illinois Natur. Hist. Surv., Champaign. 752 pp.

Hawkins, A. S. 1940. A wildlife history of Faville Grove, Wisconsin. Trans. Wisconsin Acad. Sci. Arts and Lett. 32: 26–65.

————. 1945. Bird life in the Texas Panhandle. Panhandle Plains Hist. Rev.: 110–150.

Hawkins, A. S. and C. E. Addy. 1966. Problems in flyway-wide appraisal of wood duck habitat. Pages 45–51 *in* J. B. Trefethen, ed., Wood duck management and research: A symposium. Wildl. Manage. Inst., Washington, D.C. 212 pp.

Hawkins, A. S. and F. C. Bellrose. 1940. Wood duck habitat management in Illinois. Trans. N. Am. Wildl. Conf. 5: 392–395.

Hawkins, A. S., L. R. Bradley, and R. H. Cunningham. 1990. Producing urban and suburban wood ducks. Pages 255–257 *in* L. H. Fredrickson, G. V. Burger, S. P. Havera, D. A. Graber, R. E. Kirby, and T. S. Taylor, eds., Proc. 1988 N. Am. Wood Duck Symp., St. Louis. 390 pp.

Hayden, D. C. and K. H. Pollock. 1990. Analysis of Alabama wood duck banding and recovery records, 1970–86. Pages 361–366 *in* L. H. Fredrickson, G. V. Burger, S. P. Havera, D. A. Graber, R. E. Kirby, and T. S. Taylor, eds., Proc. 1988 N. Am. Wood Duck Symp., St. Louis. 390 pp.

Hein, D. 1961. Wood duck roosting flights at Paint Creek, Iowa. Proc. Iowa Acad. Sci. 68: 264–270.

———. 1965. Wood duck roosting flight phenomena. Ph.D. thesis, Iowa St. Univ., Ames. 203 pp.

———. 1966. Float counts vs. flight counts as indices to abundance of nesting wood ducks. J. Wildl. Manage. 30: 13–16.

Hein, D. and A. O. Haugen. 1966a. Autumn roosting flight counts as an index to wood duck abundance. J. Wildl. Manage. 30: 657–668.

Hein, D. and A. O. Haugen. 1966b. Illumination and wood duck roosting flights. Wilson Bull. 78: 301–308.

Heinroth, O. 1910. Beobachtungen bei einem Einburgerungsversuch mit der Brautente (*Lampronessa sponsa* L.). J. für Ornithol. 58: 101–156.

Heinz, G. H. and L. W. Gysel. 1970. Vocalization behavior of the ring-necked pheasant. Auk 87: 279–295.

Heitmeyer, M. E. 1985. Wintering strategies of female mallards related to dynamics of lowland hardwood wetlands in the Upper Mississippi Delta. Ph.D. thesis, Univ. Missouri, Columbia. 378 pp.

———. 1987. The prebasic moult and basic plumage of female mallards (*Anas platyrhynchos*). Can. J. Zool. 65: 2,249–2,261.

———. 1988. Protein costs of the prebasic molt of female mallards. Condor 90: 263–266.

Heitmeyer, M. E. and L. H. Fredrickson. 1990. Abundance and habitat use of wood ducks in the Mingo Swamp of southeastern Missouri. Pages 141–151 *in* L. H. Fredrickson, G. V. Burger, S. P. Havera, D. A. Graber, R. E. Kirby, and T. S. Taylor, eds., Proc. 1988 N. Am. Wood Duck Symp., St. Louis. 390 pp.

Helvie, J. 1983. Butte Sink land protection plan. Unpublished paper on file with the U.S. Fish and Wildl. Serv., Sacramento National Wildlife Refuge, Willows, California. 34 pp.

Henne, J. L. 1989. Factors affecting hatchability of wood duck eggs on Yazoo National Wildlife Refuge. M.S. thesis, Mississippi St. Univ., State College. 94 pp.

Hepp, G. R. 1977. Ecology of wood duck (*Aix sponsa*) broods in the Piedmont region of South Carolina. M.S. thesis, Clemson Univ., Clemson, South Carolina. 113 pp.

Hepp, G. R. and J. D. Hair. 1977. Wood duck brood mobility and utilization of beaver pond habitats. Proc. Annu. Conf. Southeast. Assoc. Fish and Wildl. Agencies 31: 216–225.

Hepp, G. R., D. J. Stangohr, L. A. Baker, and R. A. Kennamer. 1987. Factors affecting variation in the egg and duckling components of wood ducks. Auk 104: 435–443.

Hepp, G. R., R. A. Kennamer, and W. F. Harvey IV. 1989. Recruitment and natal philopatry of wood ducks. Ecology 70: 897–903.

Hepp, G. R., R. A. Kennamer, and W. F. Harvey IV. 1990. Incubation as a reproductive cost in female wood ducks. Auk 107: 756–764.

Hepp, G. R., P. Connolly, R. A. Kennamer, and W. F. Harvey IV. 1991. Wood duck hatch date: Relationship to pairing chronology, plasma luteinizing hormone and steroid hormones during autumn and winter. Hormones and Behavior 25: 242–257.

Herman, C. M. 1963. The occurrence of protozoan blood parasites in the Anatidae. Trans. Congr. Intern. Union Game Biol. 6: 341–349.

———. 1968. Blood parasites of North American waterfowl. Trans. N. Am. Wildl. and Natur. Resour. Conf. 33: 348–359.

Herman, C. M., J. O. Knisley, Jr., and G. D. Knipling. 1971. Blood parasites of wood ducks. J. Wildl. Manage. 35: 119–122.

Hester, F. E. 1962. Survival, renesting, and return of adult wood ducks to previously used nest boxes. Proc. Annu. Conf. Southeast. Assoc. Game and Fish Commiss. 16: 67–70.

———. 1966. The value of roost counts as a population index for wood ducks. Pages 159–162 *in* J. B. Trefethen, ed., Wood duck management and research: A symposium. Wildl. Manage. Inst., Washington, D.C. 212 pp.

Hester, F. E. and J. Dermid. 1973. The world of the wood duck. J. B. Lippincott Co., Philadelphia. 160 pp.

Hester, F. E. and T. L. Quay. 1961. A three-year study of the fall migration and roosting-flight habits of the wood duck in east-central North Carolina. Proc. Annu. Conf. Southeast. Assoc. Game and Fish Commiss. 15: 55–60.

Heusmann, H W. 1972. Survival of wood duck broods from dump nests. J. Wildl. Manage. 36: 620–624.

———. 1975. Several aspects of the nesting biology of yearling wood ducks. J. Wildl. Manage. 39: 503–507.

———. 1984. The effects of weather on local wood duck production. J. Wildl. Manage. 48: 573–577.

———. 1990. Effect of October bag liberalization on southeast wood duck harvests. Pages 317–321 *in* L. H. Fredrickson, G. V. Burger, S. P. Havera, D. A. Graber, R. E. Kirby, and T. S. Taylor, eds., Proc. 1988 N. Am. Wood Duck Symp., St. Louis. 390 pp.

Heusmann, H W and R. H. Bellville. 1978. Effects of nest removal on starling populations. Wilson Bull. 90: 287–290.

Heusmann, H W and R. H. Bellville. 1982. Wood duck research in Massachusetts 1970–1980. Res. Bull. No. 19. Massachusetts Div. Fish and Wildl., Westborough. 67 pp.

Heusmann, H W and R. G. Burrell. 1990. Impact of opening dates on local wood duck populations. Pages 311–315 *in* L. H. Fredrickson, G. V. Burger, S. P. Havera, D. A. Graber, R. E. Kirby, and T. S. Taylor, eds., Proc. 1988 N. Am. Wood Duck Symp., St. Louis. 390 pp.

Heusmann, H W and T. Early. 1988. A comparison of wooden boxes and plastic buckets as waterfowl nest structures. Wildl. Soc. Bull. 16: 45–48.

Heusmann, H W and P. R. Pekkala. 1976. Wood duck incubates eggless clutch. Wilson Bull. 88: 148–149.

Heusmann, H W, W. W. Blandin, and R. E. Turner. 1977. Starling-deterrent nesting cylinders in wood duck management. Wildl. Soc. Bull. 5: 14–18.

Heusmann, H W, R. Bellville, and R. G. Burrell. 1980. Further observations on dump nesting by wood ducks. J. Wildl. Manage. 44: 908–915.

Hickey, J. J. 1952. Survival studies of banded birds. Spec. Sci. Rept., Wildl. 15. U.S. Fish and Wildl. Serv., Washington, D.C. 177 pp.

Higgins, J. W. 1979. Waterfowl habitat selection on an east Texas bottomland impoundment. M.S. thesis, Stephen F. Austin St. Univ., 93 pp.

Hill, E. P. 1987. Beaver restoration. Pages 281–285 *in* Restoring America's wildlife 1937–1987. U.S. Fish and Wildl. Serv., Washington, D.C. 394 pp.

Hochbaum, H. A. 1942. Sex and age determination of waterfowl by cloacal examination. Trans. N. Am. Wildl. Conf. 7: 299–307.

———. 1944. The canvasback on a prairie marsh. Am. Wildl. Inst., Washington, D.C. 201 pp.

Hocutt, G. E. and R. W. Dimmick. 1971. Summer food habits of juvenile wood ducks in east Tennessee. J. Wildl. Manage. 35: 286–292.

Holloman, J. L. 1967. Return of yearling female wood ducks, *Aix sponsa*, to their natal areas to nest. M.S. thesis, North Carolina St. Univ., Raleigh. 58 pp.

Holm, E. R. and M. L. Scott. 1954. Studies on the nutrition of wild waterfowl. New York Fish and Game J. 1: 171–187.

Hoppe, D. M. 1976. Prevalence of macroscopically detectable *Sarcocystis* in North Dakota ducks. J. Wildl. Dis. 12: 27–29.

Houston, C. S., ed. 1974. To the Arctic by canoe, 1819–1821. Arctic Inst. N. Am., McGill-Queen's Univ. Press, Montreal. 217 pp.

———. 1984. Arctic ordeal. The journal of John Richardson, surgeon-naturalist with Franklin. McGill-Queen's Univ. Press, Montreal. 349 pp.

Howe, H. F. 1976. Egg size, hatchling asynchrony, sex, and brood reduction in the common grackle. Ecology 57: 1,195–1,207.

Howell, A. H. 1910. Notes on the birds of the sunken lands of southeastern Missouri. Auk 27: 381–384.

———. 1924. Birds of Alabama. Brown Printing Co., Montgomery, Alabama. 384 pp.

Hoyt, S. F. 1957. The ecology of the pileated woodpecker. Ecology 38: 246–256.

Hubbard, J. P. 1978. Revised check-list of the birds of New Mexico. Publ. No. 6. New Mexico Ornith. Soc. 110 pp.

Hubert, W. A. and J. N. Krull. 1973. Seasonal fluctuations of aquatic macroinvertebrates in Oakwood Bottoms Greentree Reservoir. Am. Midl. Natur. 90: 177–185.

Humphrey, P. S. and G. A. Clark, Jr. 1964. The anatomy of waterfowl. Vol. 4. Pages 167–232 *in* J. Delacour, The waterfowl of the world. Country Life Ltd., London. 364 pp.

Humphrey, P. S. and K. C. Parkes. 1959. An approach to the study of molts and plumages. Auk 76: 1–31.

Hunt, R. A. and C. F. Smith. 1966. An evaluation of hand-reared wood ducks at Goose Island, Mississippi River, Wisconsin. Pages 132–140 *in* J. B. Trefethen, ed., Wood duck management and research: A symposium. Wildl. Manage. Inst., Washington, D.C. 212 pp.

Hunter, B. F., W. E. Clark, P. J. Perkins, and P. R. Coleman. 1970. Applied botulism research including management recommendations. Wildl. Manage. Prog. Rept. California Dept. Fish and Game, Sacramento. 87 pp.

Huntingford, F. and A. Turner. 1987. Animal conflict. Chapman and Hall, London. 448 pp.

Huntingford, F. and A. Turner. 1988. 1987 inventory of Illinois surface water resources. Div. Fish., Springfield. 38 pp.

Imhof, T. A. 1976. Alabama birds. Univ. Alabama Press, Birmingham. 445 pp.

Ingalls, C. E. 1881. The pine grosbeak. Forest and Stream (April 14): 206.

Irving, W. 1835. A tour on the prairies. John Murray, London. 335 pp.

Jackson, J. A. 1974. Gray rat snake versus red-cockaded woodpeckers: Predator-prey adaptations. Auk 91: 342–347.

James, D. A. and J. C. Neal. 1986. Arkansas birds: Their distribution and abundance. Univ. Arkansas Press, Fayetteville. 402 pp.

James, R. D., P. L. McLaren, and J. C. Barlow. 1976. Annotated checklist of the birds of Ontario. Life Sci. Misc. Publ. Royal Ontario Mus., Ottawa, Ontario. 75 pp.

Jobanek, G. A. and D. B. Marshall. 1992. John K. Townsend's 1836 report of the birds of the lower Columbia River region, Oregon and Washington. Northwestern Natur. 73: 1–14.

Jobes, C. R., R. Tangen, and J. Cooper. 1976. Egg laying and incubation behavior in wood ducks *(Aix sponsa)*. Unpubl. rept. submitted to Dr. James Cooper, Univ. of Minnesota, St. Paul. 14 pp.

Johnsgard, P. A. 1961. Tracheal anatomy of the Anatidae and its taxonomic significance. Wildfowl 12: 58–69.

———. 1965. Handbook of waterfowl behavior. Cornell Univ. Press, Ithaca, New York. 378 pp.

———. 1978. Ducks, geese, and swans of the world. Univ. Nebraska Press, Lincoln. 404 pp.

Johnson, A. S. 1970a. Biology of the raccoon *(Procyon lotor varius)* in Alabama. Exp. Sta. Bull. No. 402. Auburn Univ., Auburn, Alabama. 148 pp.

Johnson, C. D. 1976. Wetland use in Wisconsin: Historical perspective and present picture. Wisconsin Dept. Natur. Resour., Water Qual. Plan. Sect., Madison. 48 pp.

Johnson, D. H., J. D. Nichols, and M. D. Schwartz. 1992. Population dynamics of breeding waterfowl. Pages 446–485 *in* B. D. J. Batt, A. D. Afton, M. G. Anderson, C. D. Ankney, D. H. Johnson, J. A. Kadlec, and G. L. Krapu, eds., Ecology and management of breeding waterfowl. Univ. Minnesota Press, Minneapolis. 635 pp.

Johnson, F. A., J. E. Hines, F. Montalbano III, and J. D. Nichols. 1986. Effects of liberalized harvest regulations on wood ducks in the Atlantic Flyway. Wildl. Soc. Bull. 14: 383–388.

Johnson, K. L. 1959. A study of wood duck nesting habits and nesting success in Mason County, Illinois. M.S. thesis, Western Illinois Univ., Macomb. 60 pp.

Johnson, L. L. 1970b. A study of the goldeneye, mallard, and other forest nesting species. Minnesota Dept. Natur. Resour., Game Res. Quart. 30: 129–134.

Johnson, N. F. 1971. Effects of levels of dietary protein on wood duck growth. J. Wildl. Manage. 35: 798–802.

Johnson, R. H. 1947. A new method of erecting wood duck nesting boxes. Pennsylvania Game News 18: 9.

Johnston, D. E. and J. B. Kethley. 1973. A numerical phenetic study of the quill mites of the family Syringophilidae (Acari). J. Parasitol. 59: 520–530.

Johnston, R. F. 1965. A directory to the birds of Kansas. Mus. Natur. Hist., Univ. Kansas, Lawrence. 67 pp.

Jolly, G. M. 1965. Explicit estimates from capture-recapture data with both death and immigration—stochastic model. Biometrika 52: 225–247.

Jones, R. E. 1964. Reproduction of the wood duck, *Aix sponsa*, in the Sacramento Valley, California. M.S. thesis, Univ. California, Berkeley. 137 pp.

Jones, R. E. and A. S. Leopold. 1967. Nesting interference in a dense population of wood ducks. J. Wildl. Manage. 31: 221–228.

Judd, S. D. 1900. Food of nestling birds. Pages 411–436 *in* U.S. Dept. Agric., Yearbook 1900. Washington, D.C. 888 pp.

Kalmbach, E. R. and W. L. McAtee. 1930. Homes for birds. Farmers' Bull. No. 1,456. U.S. Dept. Agric., Washington, D.C. 21 pp.

Kaminski, R. M. and H. H. Prince. 1981. Dabbling duck activity and foraging response to aquatic macroinvertebrates. Auk 98: 115–126.

Kear, J. 1965. The internal food reserves of hatching mallard ducklings. J. Wildl. Manage. 29: 523–528.

———. 1968. The calls of very young Anatidae. Vogelwelt 1: 93–113.

Kear, J. and P. A. Johnsgard. 1968. Foraging dives by surface-feeding ducks. Wilson Bull. 80: 231.

Kebbe, C. E. 1956. Nesting record of the wood duck in southeastern Oregon. The Murrelet 37: 3.

Keefe, J. 1953. Knee deep in coons. Missouri Conserv. 14: 10–11.

Keirans, J. E. 1967. Some avian ectoparasites in New England. Entomol. News 78: 40–42.

Keller, C. E., S. A. Keller, and T. C. Keller. 1979. Indiana birds and their haunts. Indiana Univ. Press, Bloomington. 214 pp.

Kennamer, R. A. and G. R. Hepp. 1987. Frequency and timing of second broods in wood ducks. Wilson Bull. 99: 655–662.

Kennamer, R. A., W. F. Harvey IV, and G. R. Hepp. 1990. Embryonic development and nest attentiveness of wood ducks during laying. Condor 92: 587–592.

Kennard, F. H. 1915. The Okaloacoochee Slough. Auk 32: 154–166.

Kent, F. W. and T. H. Kent. 1975. Birding in eastern Iowa: Twenty-five years of observations from Iowa City (1949–1973). Kent, Iowa City, Iowa. 150 pp.

Keran, D. C. 1978. Site selection for wood duck nest boxes. Loon 50: 191–194.

Kerwin, J. A. and L. G. Webb. 1971. Foods of ducks wintering in coastal South Carolina, 1965–1967. Proc. Annu. Conf. Southeast. Assoc. Game and Fish Commiss. 25: 223–245.

Kessel, B. 1957. A study of the breeding biology of the European starling (*Sturnus vulgaris* L.) in North America. Am. Midl. Natur. 58: 257–331.

Kessel, B. and D. D. Gibson. 1976. Status and distribution of Alaska birds. Cooper Ornithol. Soc., Stud. Avian Biol. 1: 1–100.

Kienzler, J. M. and J. L. Hansen. 1990. Effects of Iowa's September duck season on wood ducks. Pages 349–356 *in* L. H. Fredrickson, G. V. Burger, S. P. Havera, D. A. Graber, R. E. Kirby, and T. S. Taylor, eds., Proc. 1988 N. Am. Wood Duck Symp., St. Louis. 390 pp.

King, F. H. 1883. Economic relations of Wisconsin birds. Pages 441–610 *in* Geology of Wisconsin: Survey of 1873–1879. Vol. I. Part II. Natural history. Commissioners of Public Printing, Madison, Wisconsin. 725 pp.

King, J. R. 1973. Energetics of reproduction in birds. Pages 78–107 *in* D. S. Farner, ed., Breeding biology of birds. Natl. Acad. Sci., Washington, D.C. 515 pp.

King, W. R. 1866. The sportsman and naturalist in Canada. Hurst and Blackett, London. 334 pp.

Kirby, R. E. 1973. Utilization of beaver flowages by waterfowl on the Chippewa National Forest, Minnesota. M.A. thesis, S. Illinois Univ., Carbondale. 264 pp.

———. 1976. Fall movements, behavior and habitat use of young waterfowl in north-central Minnesota. Ph.D. thesis, Univ. Minnesota, St. Paul. 189 pp.

———. 1990a. Wood duck nonbreeding ecology: Fledging to spring migration. Pages 61–76 *in* L. H. Fredrickson, G. V. Burger, S. P. Havera, D. A. Graber, R. E. Kirby, and T. S. Taylor, eds., Proc. 1988 N. Am. Wood Duck Symp., St. Louis. 390 pp.

———. 1990b. Survival of postfledging wood ducks in northcentral Minnesota. Pages 185–189 *in* L. H. Fredrickson, G. V. Burger, S. P. Havera, D. A. Graber, R. E. Kirby, and T. S. Taylor, eds., Proc. 1988 N. Am. Wood Duck Symp., St. Louis. 390 pp.

Kirby, R. E. and L. H. Fredrickson. 1990. Molts and plumages of the wood duck. Pages 29–33 *in* L. H. Fredrickson, G. V. Burger, S. P. Havera, D. A. Graber, R. E. Kirby, and T. S. Taylor, eds., Proc. 1988 N. Am. Wood Duck Symp., St. Louis. 390 pp.

Kirby, R. E., J. H. Reichmann, and M. E. Shough. 1976. A preliminary report on Minnesota's innovative 1973 waterfowl season. Wildl. Soc. Bull. 4: 55–63.

Kirby, R. E., L. M. Cowardin, and J. R. Tester. 1988. Premigrational movements and behavior of young mallards and wood ducks in north-central Minnesota. Fish and Wildl. Res. 5, U.S. Fish and Wildl. Serv., Washington, D.C. 25 pp.

Kistler, J. W. 1939. The rainbow of our waterfowl. North Carolina Wildl. Conserv. 3: 8–11.

Kittredge, J. and A. K. Chittenden. 1929. Oak forest of northern Michigan. U.S. Dept. Agric., Agric. Exp. Sta. Michigan St. Coll. and Lake States For. Exp. Sta., Tech. Bull. No. 190. East Lansing, Michigan. 47 pp.

Klein, H. G. 1955. Wood duck production and use of nest boxes on some small marshes in New York. New York Fish and Game J. 2: 68–83.

Klett, A. T., T. L. Shaffer, and D. H. Johnson. 1988. Duck nest success in the prairies pothole region. J. Wildl. Manage. 52: 431–440.

Klopateck, J. M., R. J. Olson, C. J. Emerson, and J. L. Jones. 1979. Land use conflicts with natural vegetation in the United States. Environ. Conserv. 6: 192–200.

Knappen, P. 1932. Number of feathers on a duck. Auk 49: 461.

Knopf, F. L. 1986. Changing landscapes and the cosmopolitanism of the eastern Colorado avifauna. Wildl. Soc. Bull. 14: 132–142.

Knopf, F. L. and T. E. Olson. 1984. Naturalization of Russian-olive: Implications to Rocky Mountain wildlife. Wildl. Soc. Bull. 12: 289–298.

Kodric-Brown, A. and J. H. Brown. 1984. Truth in advertising: The kinds of traits favored by sexual selection. Am. Natur. 124: 309–323.

Kofoid, C. A. 1903. Plankton studies. IV. The plankton of the Illinois River, 1894–1899, with introductory notes upon the hydrography of the Illinois River and its basin. Part I. Quantitative investigations and general results. Illinois St. Lab. Natur. Hist. Bull. 6: 95–629.

Korschgen, C. E. 1972. Behavior of the wood duck. M.A. thesis, Univ. Missouri, Columbia. 77 pp.

———. 1976. Breeding stress of female American eiders (*Somateria mollissima dresseri* Sharpe). Ph.D. thesis, Univ. of Maine, Orono. 110 pp.

Korschgen, C. E. and L. H. Fredrickson. 1976. Comparative displays of yearling and adult male wood ducks. Auk 93: 793–807.

Korschgen, L. J. 1955. Fall foods of waterfowl in Missouri. Fed. Aid Proj. 13-R Rept. No. 14. Missouri Fish and Game Div., Columbia. 41 pp.

Kortright, F. H. 1942. The ducks, geese and swans of North America. The Stackpole Co., Harrisburg, Pennsylvania. 476 pp.

Krammerer, G. 1990. Members' efforts hatch several thousand wood ducks. California Waterfowl Summer: 5–8.

Krapu, G. L. and H. A. Doty. 1979. Age-related aspects of mallard reproduction. Wildfowl 30: 35–39.

Krapu, G. L. and G. A. Swanson. 1975. Some nutritional aspects of reproduction in prairie nesting pintails. J. Wildl. Manage. 39: 156–162.

Krementz, D. G., M. J. Conroy, J. E. Hines, and H. F. Percival. 1987. Sources of variation in survival and recovery rates of American black ducks. J. Wildl. Manage. 51: 689–700.

Krull, J. N. 1970. Aquatic plant macroinvertebrate associations and waterfowl. J. Wildl. Manage. 34: 707–718.

Kumlien, L. and N. Hollister. 1903. The birds of Wisconsin. Bull. Wisconsin Natur. Hist. Soc., Vol. 3. Madison. 143 pp.

Labuda, S. E., Jr. 1977. Utilization of artificial nesting cavities by wood ducks (*Aix sponsa*) in central Texas. M.S. thesis, Texas A&M Univ., College Station. 43 pp.

Lacaillade, H. C., Jr. 1958. Investigations of waterfowl habitat improvement possibilities in New Hampshire: Wood duck breeding studies. Fed. Aid Proj. W-7-R-13, Job No. I-D, Compl. Rept. New Hampshire Fish and Game Dept., Concord. 8 pp. + 3 figures.

———. 1959. Investigations of waterfowl habitat improvement possibilities in New Hampshire: Wood duck breeding studies. Fed. Aid Proj. W-7-R-14, Job No. I-D, Compl. Rept. New Hampshire Fish and Game Dept., Concord. 16 pp.

Lack, D. 1954. The natural regulation of animal numbers. Oxford. 343 pp.

Ladd, W. N., Jr. 1990. Status of wood ducks in the Central Flyway. Pages 121–126 in L. H. Fredrickson, G. V. Burger, S. P. Havera, D. A. Graber, R. E. Kirby, and T. S. Taylor, eds., Proc. 1988 N. Am. Wood Duck Symp., St. Louis. 390 pp.

Landers, J. L., A. S. Johnson, P. H. Morgan, and W. P. Baldwin. 1976. Duck foods in managed tidal impoundments in South Carolina. J. Wildl. Manage. 40: 721–728.

Landers, J. L., T. T. Fendley, and A. S. Johnson. 1977. Feeding ecology of wood ducks in South Carolina. J. Wildl. Manage. 41: 118–127.

Landin, M. C. 1977. The effects of supplemental feeding on wood duck (*Aix sponsa*) productivity. M.S. thesis, Mississippi St. Univ., State College. 75 pp.

Lane, P. W., G. W. Bond, Jr., and W. H. Julian, Jr. 1968. Wood duck production and transplants on National Wildlife Refuges in the south Atlantic states. Proc. Annu. Conf. Southeast. Assoc. Game and Fish Commiss. 22: 202–208.

Lapage, G. 1961. A list of the parasitic protozoa, helminths and arthropoda recorded from species of the family Anatidae (ducks, geese and swans). Parasitol. 51: 1–6.

Laramie, H. A. 1978. Water level control in beaver ponds and culverts. New Hampshire Fish and Game Dept., Concord. 5 pp.

Laughlin, S. B. and D. P. Kibbe, eds. 1985. The atlas of breeding birds of Vermont. Univ. Press of New England, Hanover, Vermont. 456 pp.

Lawson, J. [1709] 1967. A new voyage to Carolina. H. T. Lefler, ed. Univ. North Carolina Press, Chapel Hill. 305 pp.

Lawyer, G. A. 1919. Federal protection of migratory birds. Pages 303–316 in U.S. Dept. Agric., Yearbook 1918. Washington, D.C. 760 pp.

Le Clercq, Fr. C. 1691. Nouvelle relation de la Gaspesie. Chez Amable Auroy, Paris. 572 pp.

Lee, J. A. 1953. Waterfowl breeding studies: Wood duck nesting box inspection. Fed. Aid Proj. W-7-R-9, Job No. I-C, Compl. Rept., New Hampshire Fish and Game Dept., Concord. 7 pp.

————. 1954. Wood duck breeding studies. Fed. Aid Proj. W-7-R-10, Job No. II-B, Compl. Rept., New Hampshire Fish and Game Dept., Concord. 8 pp.

————. 1955. Wood duck breeding studies. Fed. Aid Proj. W-7-R-11, Job No. II-B, Compl. Rept., New Hampshire Fish and Game Dept., Concord. 7 pp.

————. 1956. Investigation of waterfowl habitat improvement possibilities in New Hampshire: Wood duck breeding studies. Fed. Aid Proj. W-7-R-12, Job No. I-D, Compl. Rept., New Hampshire Fish and Game Dept., Concord. 7 pp. + 3 figures.

Leopold, F. 1951. A study of nesting wood ducks in Iowa. Condor 53: 209–220.

————. 1966. Experiences with home-grown wood ducks. Pages 113–123 in J. B. Trefethen, ed., Wood duck management and research: A symposium. Wildl. Manage. Inst., Washington, D.C. 212 pp.

Lett, W. P. 1883. The ducks of this locality [Ottawa, Canada]. Trans. Ottawa Field Natur. Club 4: 52–64.

Levine, N. D. and R. Graham. 1942. Paratyphoid in baby wood ducks. J. Am. Vet. Med. Assoc. 100: 240–241.

Lightbody, J. P. 1985. Growth rates and development of redhead ducklings. Wilson Bull. 97: 554–559.

Lincoln, F. C. 1934. The operation of homing instinct. Bird Banding 5: 149–155.

Lingle, G. R. 1978. Factors influencing autumn dispersal and night roosting of the wood duck in central Michigan. Jack-Pine Warbler 56: 122–127.

Linnaeus, C. 1758. Systema naturae: Regnum animale. Vol. 1, 10th ed. Photographic facsimile reprinted by the British Museum (Natural History), London. 824 pp.

Locke, L. N., V. Stotts, and G. Wolfhard. 1970. An outbreak of fowl cholera on the Chesapeake Bay. J. Wildl. Dis. 6: 404–407.

Loflin, R. K. 1982. Ani male apparently killed by other anis while attempting to parasitize nest. Auk 99: 787–788.

Loisel, G. 1912. Histoire des menageries de l'Antiquite a nos jours. 3 vols., Paris.

Lokemoen, J. T. 1967. Flight speed of the wood duck. Wilson Bull. 79: 238–239.

Lokemoen, J. T., H. F. Duebbert, and D. E. Sharp. 1990. Homing and reproductive habits of mallards, gadwalls, and blue-winged teal. Wildl. Monogr. 106. The Wildl. Soc., Bethesda, Maryland. 28 pp.

Lombardo, M. P. 1986. A possible case of adult intraspecific killing in the tree swallow. Condor 88: 112.

Lombardo, M. P., L. C. Romagnano, P. C. Stouffer, A. S. Hoffenberg, and H. W. Power. 1989. The use of nest boxes as night roosts during the nonbreeding season by European starlings in New Jersey. Condor 91: 744–747.

Long, J. W. 1879. American waterfowl shooting. O. Judd Co., New York. 330 pp.

Lorenz, K. Z. 1941. Comparative studies on the behaviour of Anatinae. J. Ornithol. 84: 194–294.

————. 1951–1953. Comparative studies on the behavior of the Anatinae. Avic. Mag. 57: 157–182; 58: 8–17, 61–72, 86–94, 172–184; 59: 24–34, 80–91.

Louisiana Department of Wildlife and Fisheries. 1981. Pesticide residue analysis of breast muscle tissue and a food habit study of wood ducks collected in Louisiana. Proj. W-29-R, Study II, Job 6. Louisiana Dept. Wildl. and Fish, New Orleans. 23 pp.

Louisiana Technical Wildlife Club. 1972. Study of wood duck acceptance of artificial box nests in four north Louisiana habitats. Mimeo. rept., Northeast Louisiana St. Coll., Monroe. 20 pp.

Lovvorn, J. R. and J. A. Barzen. 1988. Molt in the annual cycle of the canvasback. Auk 105: 543–552.

Lowney, M. S. 1987. Availability and use of natural cavities for wood duck production in bottomland hardwood forests in the Lower Mississippi Flyway. M.S. thesis, Mississippi St. Univ., State College. 52 pp. + append.

Luckett, L. M. 1977. Ecology and management of the wood duck, Aix sponsa, in the Piedmont region of South Carolina. M.S. thesis, Clemson Univ., Clemson, South Carolina. 99 pp.

Luckett, L. M. and J. D. Hair. 1979. Analysis of wood duck roost counts in northwest South Carolina. Proc. Annu. Conf. Southeast. Assoc. Fish and Wildl. Agencies 33: 96–103.

Lumpkin, J. W. 1972. Certain aspects of wood duck nest box production on Kentucky Lake Reservoir, Tennessee. M.S. thesis, Tennessee Tech. Univ., Cookeville. 32 pp.

Lumsden, H. G. 1976. Choice of nest boxes by starlings. Wilson Bull. 88: 665–666.

Mabbott, D. C. 1920. Food habits of seven species of American shoal-water ducks. U.S. Dept. Agric. Bull. 862. Washington, D.C. 67 pp.

MacDonald, P. O., W. E. Frayer, and J. K. Clauser. 1979. Documentation, chronology, and future projections of bottomland hardwood habitat loss in the Lower Mississippi Alluvial Plain. 2 vols. U.S. Fish and Wildl. Serv., Ecol. Serv., Washington, D.C. 133 pp.

MacFarlane, R. R. 1908. List of birds and eggs observed and collected in the Northwest Territories of Canada, between 1880 and 1894. Pages 285–470 in Charles Mair, Through the Mackenzie Basin. A narrative of the Athabasca and Peace River Treaty Expedition of 1889, Toronto. 308 pp.

MacInnes, C. D., R. A. Davis, R. N. Jones, B. C. Lieff, and A. J. Pakulak. 1974. Reproductive efficiency of McConnell River small Canada geese. J. Wildl. Manage. 38: 686–707.

Macoun, J. and J. M. Macoun. 1909. Catalogue of Canadian birds. Rept. No. 973. Canada Dept. Mines, Geol. Surv. Branch, Ottawa. 761 pp.

MacTeels, B. 1975. Waterfowl production and utilization along the proposed route of the Tennessee-Tombigbee Waterway. Ph.D. thesis, Mississippi St. Univ., State College. 84 pp.

Magee, P. A. 1989. Aquatic macroinvertebrate association with willow wetlands in northeastern Missouri. M.S. thesis, Univ. Missouri, Columbia. 50 pp.

Malcomson, R. O. 1960. Mallophaga from birds of North America. Wilson Bull. 72: 182–197.

Martin, A. C., R. H. Gensch, and C. P. Brown. 1946. Alternative methods in upland gamebird food analysis. J. Wildl. Manage. 10: 8–12.

Martin, A. C., H. S. Zim, and A. L. Nelson. 1951. American wildlife and plants—a guide to wildlife food habits. McGraw-Hill, New York. 500 pp.

Martin, D. N. 1957. Wood duck nest box survey. Pittman-Robertson Proj. W-2-R-17. Quarterly Progress Rept. 17(4), 18(3). Indiana Dept. Conserv., Indianapolis. 6 pp.

———. 1958. Evaluation of predator resistant wood duck houses. Pittman-Robertson Proj. W-2-R-17. Quarterly Progress Rept. 19(1). Indiana Dept. Conserv., Indianapolis. 6 pp.

Martin, E. M. and A. O. Haugen. 1960. Seasonal changes in wood duck roosting flight habits. Wilson Bull. 72: 238–243.

Martin, T. E. 1988. On the advantage of being different: Nest predation and the coexistence of bird species. Proc. Natl. Acad. Sci. 85: 2,196–2,199.

Martinson, R. K. and A. S. Hawkins. 1968. Lack of association among duck broodmates during migration and wintering. Auk 85: 684–686.

Mason, B. E. 1988. Humidity control—friend or foe? Gamebird Breeders, Aviculturists, Zoologists and Conservationists' Gazette [Salt Lake City] May–June: 9–13.

Mason, P. J. and J. L. Dusi. 1983. A ground nesting wood duck. Auk 100: 506.

Mathisen, J. E. 1972. A plan for the maintenance and development of forest openings. U.S. For. Serv., Chippewa National For., Cass Lake, Minnesota. 22 pp. Mimeo.

Mattocks, J. G. 1971. Goose feeding and cellulose digestion. Wildfowl 22: 107–113.

May, M. E. 1986. Wood duck nest site selection in east Texas. M.S. thesis, Stephen F. Austin St. Univ., Austin, Texas. 141 pp.

McAtee, W. L. 1908. Unpublished field report. On file at Patuxent Wildl. Res. Ctr., Laurel, Maryland.

———. 1915. Eleven important wild-duck foods. U.S. Dept. Agric. Bull. 205: 1–25.

———. 1923. Local names of migratory birds. Misc. Circ. U.S. Dept. Agric. 13: 1–95.

McCabe, R. A. 1947. The homing of transplanted young wood ducks. Wilson Bull. 59: 104–109.

McCall, J. D. 1954. Waterfowl breeding ground survey. Pittman-Robertson Wildl. Res. Proj. W-Z-R, Quarterly Prog. Rept. 15. Indiana Dept. Conserv., Indianapolis. 6 pp.

McClane, A. J. 1965. McClane's standard fishing encyclopedia. Holt, Rinehart, and Winston, New York. 1,057 pp.

McDonald, M. E. 1969. Catalogue of helminths of waterfowl (Anatidae). Spec. Sci. Rept. Wildl. 126. U.S. Fish and Wildl. Serv., Washington, D.C. 692 pp.

McEneaney, T. 1988. Birds of Yellowstone. Roberts Rinehart, Boulder, Colorado. 171 pp.

McGilvrey, F. B. 1966a. Fall food habits of wood ducks from Lake Marion, South Carolina. J. Wildl. Manage. 30: 193–195.

———. 1966b. Fall food habits of wood ducks from Santee Refuge, South Carolina. J. Wildl. Manage. 30: 577–580.

———. 1966c. Second nestings of the wood duck. Auk 83: 303.

———. 1968. A guide to wood duck production habitat requirements. Res. Publ. 60. U.S. Fish Wildl. Serv. 32 pp.

———. 1969. Survival in wood duck broods. J. Wildl. Manage. 33: 73–76.

———. 1971. Increasing a wood duck nesting population by releases of pen-reared birds. Proc. Annu. Conf. Southeast. Assoc. Game and Fish Commiss. 25: 202–206.

———. 1975. Methods to increase waterfowl production and use of low quality wetlands. Unpubl. rept. U.S. Fish and Wildl. Serv., Laurel, Maryland. 79 pp.

McGilvrey, F. B. and F. M. Uhler. 1968. Imprinting ducks to artificial nesting structures. Annu. Prog. Rept., February 15, 1967–January 1, 1968. U.S. Fish and Wildl. Serv., Laurel, Maryland. 3 pp.

McGilvrey, F. B. and F. M. Uhler. 1971. A starling-deterrent wood duck nest box. J. Wildl. Manage. 31: 793–797.

McHenry, M. G. 1971. Breeding and post-breeding movement of blue-winged teal (Anas discors) in southwestern Manitoba. Ph.D. thesis, Univ. Oklahoma, Norman. 67 pp.

McIlhenny, E. A. 1897. A list of the species of Anseres, Paludicolae, and Limicolae occurring in the state of Louisiana. Auk 14: 285–289.

McIlquham, C. J. and B. R. Bacon. 1989. Wood duck nest on a muskrat house. J. Field Ornithol. 60: 84–85.

McKinney, F. 1967. Breeding behaviour of captive shovelers. Wildfowl 18: 108–121.

———. 1973. Ecoethological aspects of reproduction. Pages 6–21 in D. S. Farner, ed., Breeding biology of birds. Natl. Acad. Sci., Washington, D.C. 515 pp.

———. 1975. The evolution of duck displays. Pages 331–357 in G. Baerends, C. Beer, and A. Manning, eds., Function and evolution in behaviour. Oxford Univ. Press, London. 393 pp.

———. 1986. Ecological factors influencing the social systems of migratory dabbling ducks. Pages 153–177 in D. I. Rubenstein and R. W. Wrangham, eds., Ecological aspects of social evolution—birds and mammals. Princeton Univ. Press, Princeton, New Jersey. 551 pp.

McKinney, F. and P. Stolen. 1982. Extra-pair-bond courtship and forced copulation among captive green-winged teal (Anas crecca carolinensis). Anim. Behav. 30: 461–474.

McKinney, F., S. R. Derrickson, and P. Mineau. 1983. Forced copulation in waterfowl. Behavior 86: 250–294.

McLaughlin, C. L. and D. Grice. 1952. The effectiveness of large-scale erection of wood duck boxes as a management procedure. Trans. N. Am. Wildl. Conf. 17: 242–259.

McLaughlin, J. D. and M. D. B. Burt. 1973. Changes in the cestode fauna of the black duck, *Anas rubripes* (Brewster). Can. J. Zool. 51: 1,001–1,006.

McLaughlin, J. D. and M. D. B. Burt. 1979. A survey of the intestinal helminths of waterfowl from New Brunswick, Canada. Can. J. Zool. 57: 801–807.

Meier, A. H. 1973. Daily hormone rhythms in the white-throated sparrow. Am. Sci. 61: 184–187.

Meier, A. H. and K. B. Davis. 1967. Diurnal variations of the fattening response to prolactin in the white-throated sparrow, *Zonotrichia albicollis*. Gen. Comp. Endocrinol. 8: 110–114.

Meier, W. S. 1983. Plastic-pail condos for wood ducks. Wisconsin. Natur. Resour. 7: 4–6.

Mendall, H. L. 1958. The ring-necked duck in the Northeast. Univ. Maine Bull. 60: 1–317.

Mendall, H. L. and J. S. Gashwiler. 1940. Water bulrush as a food of waterfowl. Auk 57: 245–246.

Mengel, R. M. 1965. The birds of Kentucky. Ornithol. Monogr. No. 3. Am. Ornithol. Union, Anchorage, Kentucky. 581 pp.

Merrill, J. C. 1888. Notes on the birds of Fort Klamath, Oregon. Auk 5: 139–146, 251–262, 357–366.

Métras, L. 1984. Migratory birds killed in Canada during the 1982 season [also lists 1981]. Prog. Notes 143. Can. Wildl. Serv., Ottawa, Ontario. 39 pp.

———. 1986. Migratory birds killed in Canada during the 1985 season [also lists 1982, 1983, 1984]. Prog. Notes 166. Can. Wildl. Serv., Ottawa, Ontario. 42 pp.

Meyer, C. L., G. F. Bennett, and C. M. Herman. 1974. Mosquito transmission of *Plasmodium* (Giovannolaia) *circumflexum* Kikuth, 1931, to waterfowl in the Tantramar Marshes, New Brunswick. J. Parasitol. 60: 905–906.

Meyers, T. U. 1962. A wood duck nesting study in Mason County, Illinois. M.S. thesis, West. Illinois Univ., Macomb. 68 pp.

Michigan Department of Natural Resources. 1982. Michigan's wetlands. Michigan Dept. Natur. Resour., Lansing. 47 pp.

Mielcarek, J. E. 1954. The occurrence of *Plasmodium relictum* in the wood duck (*Aix sponsa*). J. Parasitol. 40: 232.

Milbert, D. 1984. I sketch wood ducks in the wild. Minnesota Volunteer 47: 44–47.

Miller, D. B. 1977a. Social displays of mallard ducks (*Anas platyrhynchos*): Effects of domestication. J. Comp. Physiol. Psychol. 91: 221–232.

———. 1977b. Two-voice phenomenon in birds: Further evidence. Auk 94: 567–572.

Miller, D. B. and G. Gottlieb. 1976. Acoustic features of wood duck (*Aix sponsa*) maternal calls. Behavior 57: 260–280.

Miller, M. R. 1974. Digestive capabilities, gut morphology, and cecal fermentation in wild waterfowl (genus *Anas*) fed various diets. M.S. thesis, Univ. California, Davis. 87 pp.

———. 1986. Molt chronology of northern pintails in California. J. Wildl. Manage. 50: 57–64.

Miller, W. De W. 1925. The secondary remiges and coverts in the Mandarin and wood ducks. Auk 42: 41–50.

Miller, W. R. 1950. Wood duck nesting studies—1950. Pittman-Robertson Proj. W-8-R-4. Vermont Fish and Game Serv., Montpelier. 7 pp.

———. 1951. Wood duck nesting studies—1951. Pittman-Robertson Proj. W-8-R-5. Vermont Fish and Game Serv., Montpelier. 5 pp.

———. 1952. Aspects of wood duck nesting box management. Proc. Annu. Northeast. Fish and Wildl. Conf. 8: 41–50.

Minser, W. G. III. 1968. Seasonal abundance and distribution of the wood duck (*Aix sponsa*) on the upper Holston River in east Tennessee. M.S. thesis, Univ. Tennessee, Knoxville. 80 pp.

———. 1993. The relationship of wood duck brood density to river habitat factors. Proc. Annu. Conf. Southeast Assoc. Fish and Wildl. Agencies 47.

Minser, W. G. III and J. C. Cole. 1991. The feasibility of nightlighting for monitoring brood productivity for wood ducks on rivers. Proc. Annu. Conf. Southeast. Assoc. Fish and Wildl. Agencies 45: 167–174.

Minser, W. G. III and J. M. Dabney. 1973. A comparison of day and night float counts for wood duck broods on the Holston River in east Tennessee. Proc. Annu. Conf. Southeast. Assoc. Fish and Game Commiss. 27: 311–315.

Minser, W. G. III, J. M. Dabney, and W. H. Schacher. 1990. Implications of September hunting on wood duck brood production on the Holston River in Tennessee. Proc. Annu. Conf. Southeast. Assoc. Fish and Wildl. Agencies 44: 206–214.

Mitchell, W. A. and C. J. Newling. 1986. Greentree reservoirs. Section 5.5.3 *in* C. O. Martin, ed., Wildlife resources management manual. U.S. Army Corps Engin. Waterways Exp. Sta. Tech. Rept. EL-86-9. Vicksburg, Mississippi. 22 pp.

Mock, D. W. 1984. Infanticide, siblicide, and avian nestling mortality. Pages 3–30 *in* G. Hausfater and S. B. Hardy, eds., Infanticide: Comparative and evolutionary perspectives. Aldine Publ. Co., New York. 598 pp.

Mohr, C. O. 1943. Illinois furbearer: Distribution and income. Illinois Natur. Hist. Surv. Bull. 22: 505–537.

Mollhagen, T. R. 1976. A study of the systematics and hosts of the parasitic nematode genus *Tetrameres* (Habronematoidea: Tetrameridae). Ph.D. thesis, Texas Tech. Univ., Lubbock. 545 pp.

Montgomery, R. A., S. T. Dillon, and S. M. Byers. 1982. Uses of various styles of wood duck nesting structures. Unpubl. rept. Max McGraw Wildl. Foundation, Dundee, Illinois. 21 pp.

Moore, W. P. III. 1981. Utilization of colonial structures and other artificial nest cavities by wood ducks. M.S. thesis, Louisiana St. Univ., Baton Rouge. 131 pp.

Moorman, T. E. 1987. Second brood production by wood ducks in eastern central Alabama and western central Georgia. M.S. thesis, Auburn Univ., Auburn, Alabama. 20 pp.

Morse, T. E. 1966. 1966 Benton County wood duck nest box investigations report. Unpubl. rept. Oregon St. Univ., Dept. Fish and Wildl., Corvallis. 9 pp.

————. 1969. Nest box selection of wood ducks as influenced by color and site factors. M.S. thesis, Oregon St. Univ., Corvallis. 48 pp.

Morse, T. E. and H. M. Wight. 1969. Dump nesting and its effect on production in wood ducks. J. Wildl. Manage. 33: 284–293.

Morse, T. E., J. L. Jakabosky, and V. P. McCrow. 1969. Some aspects of the breeding biology of the hooded merganser. J. Wildl. Manage. 33: 596–604.

Mumford, R. E. 1952. A study of wood duck populations on Indiana streams. M.S. thesis, Purdue Univ., West Lafayette, Indiana. 47 pp.

Muncy, J. A. and J. H. Burbank. 1975. Comparative use of three types of wood duck nest boxes. Proc. Annu. Conf. Southeast. Assoc. Game and Fish Commiss. 29: 493–500.

Murphy, M. E. and J. R. King. 1982. Amino acid composition of the plumage of the white-crowned sparrow. Condor 84: 435–438.

Murphy, M. E. and J. R. King. 1986. Composition and quantity of feather sheaths produced by white-crowned sparrows during postnuptial molt. Auk 105: 822–825.

Musselman, T. E. 1948. A changing nesting habitat of the wood duck. Auk 65: 197–203.

Nagel, R. E. 1969. Predation on eggs in simulated nests and tree cavity abundance in wood duck nesting habitat. M.S. thesis, Iowa St. Univ., Ames. 94 pp.

Naiman, R. J., J. M. Melillo, and J. E. Hobbie. 1986. Ecosystem alteration of boreal forest streams by beaver *(Castor canadensis)*. Ecology 67: 1,254–1,269.

Naiman, R. J., C. A. Johnston, and J. C. Kelley. 1988. Alteration of North American streams by beaver: The structure and dynamics of streams are changing as beaver recolonize their historic habitat. BioSci. 38: 753–762.

Nassar, J. R., R. H. Chabreck, and D. C. Hayden. 1988. Experimental plantings for management of crayfish and waterfowl. Pages 427–439 *in* M. W. Weller, ed., Waterfowl in winter. Univ. Minnesota Press, Minneapolis. 624 pp.

National Research Council. 1982. Impacts of emerging agricultural trends on fish and wildlife habitat. Natl. Acad. Press, Washington, D.C. 244 pp.

Nault, J. M. 1981. Selectivity of wood duck box use by wood ducks and starlings using several independent variables. Unpubl. rept. Chautauqua Natl. Wildl. Refuge, Havana, Illinois. 40 pp.

Naylor, A. E. 1960. The wood duck in California with special reference to the use of nest boxes. California Fish and Game 46: 241–269.

Nelson, A. L. 1944. A mouse eaten by a wood duck. Wilson Bull. 56: 170.

Nelson, E. C. and J. S. Gashwiler. 1941. Blood parasites of some Maine waterfowl. J. Wildl. Manage. 5: 199–205.

Nelson, E. W. 1876. Birds of north-eastern Illinois. Bull. Essex Inst. 8: 90–155.

Nero, R. W. 1957. Bronzed grackle nesting in bird house. Blue Jay 15: 63–64.

Nichols, J. D. and F. A. Johnson. 1990. Wood duck population dynamics: A review. Pages 83–105 *in* L. H. Fredrickson, G. V. Burger, S. P. Havera, D. A. Graber, R. E. Kirby, and T. S. Taylor, eds., Proc. 1988 N. Am. Wood Duck Symp., St. Louis. 390 pp.

Nichols, J. D., K. J. Reinecke, and J. E. Hines. 1983. Factors affecting the distribution of mallards wintering in the Mississippi Alluvial Valley. Auk 100: 932–946.

Nichols, J. D., M. J. Conroy, D. R. Anderson, and K. P. Burnham. 1984. Compensatory mortality in waterfowl populations: A review of the evidence and implications for research and management. Trans. N. Am. Wildl. and Natur. Resour. Conf. 49: 535–554.

Nichols, J. D., R. J. Blohm, R. E. Reynolds, R. E. Trost, J. E. Hines, and J. P. Bladen. 1991. Band reporting rates for mallards with reward bands of different dollar values. J. Wildl. Manage. 55: 119–126.

Nixon, C. M., S. P. Havera, and J. A. Ellis. 1978. Squirrel hunting in Illinois. Illinois Dept. Conserv., Springfield. 37 pp.

Norton, A. H. 1909. The food of several Maine waterbirds. Auk 26: 438–440.

Novak, M. 1987. Beaver. Pages 283–312 *in* M. Novak, J. A. Baker, M. E. Obbard, and B. Malloch, eds., Wild furbearer management and conservation in North America. Ontario Ministry Natur. Resour., Toronto. 1,150 pp.

Novak, M., M. E. Obbard, J. G. Jones, R. Newman, A. Booth, A. J. Satterthwaite, and G. Linscombe. 1988. Furbearer harvests in North America, 1600–1984. Supplement to: Wild furbearer management and conservation in North America. Ontario Ministry Natur. Resour., Toronto. 270 pp.

Odom, R. R. 1970. Nest box production and brood survival of wood ducks on the Piedmont National Wildlife Refuge 1969. Proc. Annu. Conf. Southeast. Assoc. Game and Fish Commiss. 24: 108–117.

Ogburn-Cahoon, H. 1979. A survey of parasitic helminths of the wood duck *(Aix sponsa)* in Louisiana. M.S. thesis, Univ. Georgia, Athens. 128 pp.

O'Meara, D. C. 1956. Blood parasites of some Maine waterfowl. J. Wildl. Manage. 20: 207–209.

Oring, L. W. 1968. Growth, molts, and plumages of the gadwall. Auk 85: 355–380.

O'Roke, E. C. 1934. A malaria-like disease of ducks caused by *Leucocytozoon anatis* Wickware. Univ. Michigan Sch. For. Conserv. Bull. 4. 44 pp.

Owen, R. B., Jr. 1968. Premigratory behavior and orientation in blue-winged teal *(Anas discors)*. Auk 85: 617–632.

Owen, R. B., Jr. and K. J. Reinecke. 1979. Bioenergetics of breeding dabbling ducks. Pages 71–93 *in* T. A. Bookhout, ed., Waterfowl and wetlands—an integrated review. Proc. 1977 Symp. Northcentral Sec. The Wildl. Soc., Madison, Wisconsin. 147 pp.

Pace, J. L. 1971. Starling (*Sturnus vulgaris* L.) nesting in natural cavities and in two types of wood duck metal nest houses. M.S. thesis, Western Illinois Univ., Macomb. 30 pp.

Palmer, R. S. 1949. Maine birds. Bull. Mus. Comp. Zool. at Harvard College 102: 90–93.

———. 1972. Patterns of molting. Pages 65–102 *in* D. S. Farner and J. R. King, eds., Avian biology, Vol. II. Academic Press, New York. 612 pp.

———, ed. 1976. Handbook of North American birds. Vol. 3. Waterfowl. Part 2. Yale Univ. Press, New Haven, Connecticut. 560 pp.

Palmieri, J. R. 1973. New definitive and intermediate hosts and host localities for *Apetamon gracilis* (Rud., 1819) Szidat, 1928. J. Parasitol. 59: 1,063.

Papadopoulas, M. C., A. R. El Bousky, A. E. Roodbeen, and E. H. Ketelaars. 1986. Effect of processing time and moisture content on amino acid composition and nitrogen characteristics of feather meal. Animal Feed Sci. and Tech. 14: 279–290.

Parmalee, P. W. 1957. Vertebrate remains from the Cahokia Site, Illinois. Illinois St. Acad. Sci. 50: 235–242.

Parr, D. E. and M. D. Scott. 1978. Analysis of roosting counts as an index to wood duck population size. Wilson Bull. 90: 423–437.

Parr, D. E., M. D. Scott, and D. D. Kennedy. 1979. Autumn movements and habitat use by wood ducks in southern Illinois. J. Wildl. Manage. 43: 102–108.

Paulus, S. L. 1984. Molts and plumages of gadwalls in winter. Auk 101: 887–889.

Peabody, Rev. W. O. B. 1838. Ornithological report. Pages 31–33 *in* E. Hitchcock, ed., Report on a re-examination of the economical geology of Massachussets. Dutton and Wentworth, Boston. 139 pp.

Pearson, T. G., C. S. Brimley, and H. H. Brimley. 1919. Birds of North Carolina. North Carolina Geological and Economic Survey Rept. Vol. 4. Edwards and Broughton, Raleigh. 380 pp.

Pearson, T. G., C. S. Brimley, and H. H. Brimley. 1942. Birds of North Carolina. North Carolina Dept. Agric., St. Mus. Div., Raleigh. 416 pp.

Pehrsson, O. 1987. Effect of body condition on molting in mallards. Condor 89: 329–339.

Pence, D. B. 1972. The nasal mites of birds from Louisiana. I. Dermanyssids (Rhinonyssinae) from shore and marsh birds. J. Parasitol. 58: 152–168.

Perret, N. G. 1962. The spring and summer foods of the common mallard (*Anas platyrhynchos platyrhynchos* L.) in south central Manitoba. M.S. thesis, Univ. British Columbia, Vancouver. 82 pp.

Perry, H. R., Jr. 1977. Wood duck roost utilization of northeastern North Carolina swamps. Proc. Annu. Conf. Southeast. Assoc. Fish and Wildl. Agencies 31: 307–311.

Perry, M. C. and F. M. Uhler. 1981. Asiatic clam (*Corbicula manilensis*) and other foods used by waterfowl in the James River, Virginia. Estuaries 4: 229–233.

Peters, H. S. 1936. A list of external parasites from birds of the eastern part of the United States. Bird-Banding 7: 9–27.

Peters, H. S. and T. D. Burleigh. 1951. The birds of Newfoundland. Dept. Natur. Resour., Province of Newfoundland, St. John's. 431 pp.

Pettingill, O. S., Jr. 1935. Ducks in chimneys. Auk 52: 303.

Pettingill, O. S., Jr. and N. R. Whitney, Jr. 1965. Birds of the Black Hills. Lab. Ornithol. Spec. Publ. No. 1. Cornell Univ., Ithaca, New York. 28 pp.

Phillips, J. C. 1925. A natural history of the ducks. Houghton Mifflin Co., Boston. Vol. 3. (Reprinted 1986, Dover Publications, Inc., New York.) 383 pp.

Phillips, J. C. and F. C. Lincoln. 1930. American waterfowl: Their present situation and the outlook for their future. Houghton Mifflin Co., Boston. 312 pp.

Piest, L. A. and L. K. Sowls. 1985. Breeding duck use of a sewage marsh in Arizona. J. Wildl. Manage. 49: 580–585.

Pindar, L. O. 1889. List of the birds of Fulton County, Kentucky. Auk 6: 310–316.

Pirnie, M. D. 1935. Michigan waterfowl management. Franklin DeKleine Co., Lansing, Michigan. 328 pp.

Poston, H. J. 1974. Home range and breeding biology of the shoveler. Rept. Ser. No. 25. Can. Wildl. Serv., Ottawa. 49 pp.

Premachandra, B. N., G. W. Pipes, and C. W. Turner. 1959. Study of growth in New Hampshire chickens with varying thyroid status. Poultry Sci. 38: 795–798.

Prevost, M. B. 1983. 1983 statewide wood duck box production report. South Carolina Wildl. and Marine Resour. Dept., Columbia. 11 pp.

Prevost, M. B., T. H. Strange, and R. D. Perry. 1990. Management of a large-scale wood duck nest box project in South Carolina. Pages 297–302 *in* L. H. Fredrickson, G. V. Burger, S. P. Havera, D. A. Graber, R. E. Kirby, and T. S. Taylor, eds., Proc. 1988 N. Am. Wood Duck Symp., St. Louis. 390 pp.

Prince, H. H. 1965. The breeding ecology of wood duck (*Aix sponsa* L.) and common goldeneye (*Bucephala clangula* L.) in central New Brunswick. M.S. thesis, Univ. New Brunswick, Fredericton. 109 pp.

———. 1968. Nest sites used by wood ducks and common goldeneyes in New Brunswick. J. Wildl. Manage. 32: 489–500.

Prokop, R. J. 1981. Wood duck distribution and production in Oklahoma. M.S. thesis, Oklahoma St. Univ., Stillwater. 71 pp.

Rahn, H. and A. Ar. 1974. The avian egg: Incubation time, water loss and nest humidity. Condor 76: 147–152.

Rahn, H., C. V. Paganelli, and A. Ar. 1975. Relation of avian egg weight to body weight. Auk 92: 750–765.

Rapp, W. F., Jr. 1941. Red-shouldered hawk eating a wood duck. Auk 58: 572–573.

Rapp, W. F., Jr., J. L. C. Rapp, H. E. Baumgarten, and R. A. Moser. 1958. Revised check-list of Nebraska birds. Occas. Pap. No. 5. Nebraska Ornithol. Union., Crete. 35 pp.

Rawls, C. K., Jr. 1954. Reelfoot Lake waterfowl research. Tennessee Game and Fish Commiss., Nashville. 80 pp.

Reed, A. 1975. Reproductive output of black ducks in the St. Lawrence estuary. J. Wildl. Manage. 39: 243–255.

Reeves, H. M. 1966. Influence of hunting regulations on wood duck population levels. Pages 163–178 *in* J. B. Trefethen, ed., Wood duck management and research: A symposium. Wildl. Manage. Inst., Washington, D.C. 212 pp.

———. 1990. The wood duck: Some historical and cultural aspects. Pages 3–12 *in* L. H. Fredrickson, G. V. Burger, S. P. Havera, D. A. Graber, R. E. Kirby, and T. S. Taylor, eds., Proc. 1988 N. Am. Wood Duck Symp., St. Louis. 390 pp.

Reinecke, K. J. and R. B. Owen, Jr. 1980. Food use and nutrition of black ducks nesting in Maine. J. Wildl. Manage. 44: 549–558.

Reinecke, K. J., R. M. Kaminski, D. J. Moorhead, J. D. Hodges, and J. R. Nassar. 1989. Mississippi Alluvial Valley. Pages 203–247 *in* L. M. Smith, R. L. Pederson, and R. M. Kaminski, eds., Habitat management for migrating and wintering waterfowl in North America. Texas Tech Univ. Press, Lubbock. 560 pp.

Reinecker, W. C. 1987. Migration and distribution of northern pintails banded in California. California Fish and Game 73: 139–155.

Reynolds, R. E. 1987. Breeding duck population production and habitat surveys, 1979–85. Trans. N. Am. Wildl. Natur. Resour. Conf. 52: 186–205.

Richardson, D. M. 1989. Winter weights and prebasic molt of captive mallards fed diets differing in quantity and quality. M.S. thesis, Mississippi St. Univ., State College. 104 pp.

Richardson, E. L. 1959. Evaluation of predator resistant wood duck houses. Pittman-Robertson Proj. W-2-R-19. Quart. Prog. Rept. 20(1). Indiana Dept. Conserv., Indianapolis. 1 p.

———. 1960. Evaluation of predator resistant wood duck houses. Pittman-Robertson Proj. W-2-R-20. Quart. Prog. Rept. 21(1), 21(3). Indiana Dept. Conserv., Indianapolis. 1 p.

Ricklefs, R. E. 1966. The temporal component of diversity among species of birds. Evolution 20: 235–242.

———. 1967. A graphical method of fitting equations to growth curves. Ecology 48: 978–983.

———. 1974. Energetics of reproduction in birds. Pages 152–292 *in* R. A. Paynter, Jr., ed., Avian energetics. Nuttall Ornithol. Club, Cambridge, Massachusetts. 334 pp.

———. 1977. Composition of eggs of several bird species. Auk 94: 350–356.

Ridgway, R. 1881. Nomenclature of North American birds. Smithson. Inst., Washington, D.C. 94 pp.

Ridlehuber, K. T. 1980. Wood duck production and habitat use. Ph.D. thesis, Texas A&M Univ., College Station. 44 pp.

Ringelman, J. K. and J. R. Longcore. 1982. Survival of juvenile black ducks during brood rearing. J. Wildl. Manage. 46: 622–628.

Robb, J. R. 1986. The importance of nesting cavities and brood habitat to wood duck production. M.S. thesis, Ohio St. Univ., Columbus. 135 pp.

Robb, J. R. and T. A. Bookhout. 1990. Female and juvenile wood duck survival and movements in Indiana. Pages 179–184 *in* L. H. Fredrickson, G. V. Burger, S. P. Havera, D. A. Graber, R. E. Kirby, and T. S. Taylor, eds., Proc. 1988 N. Am. Wood Duck Symp., St. Louis. 390 pp.

Robbins, C. S. and J. W. Aldrich. 1966. Principal historical breeding and wintering range of the wood duck, based on records through 1938. Page viii *in* J. B. Trefethen, ed., Wood duck management and research: A symposium. Wildl. Manage. Inst., Washington, D.C. 212 pp.

Roberts, T. S. 1932. The birds of Minnesota. 2 vols. Univ. Minnesota Press, Minneapolis. 821 pp.

Robinson, J. C. 1981. A study of the wood duck nesting success at DeSoto Refuge. Unpubl. rept. U.S. Fish and Wildl. Serv., Missouri Valley, Iowa. 21 pp.

Robinson, R. H. 1958. Use of nest boxes by wood ducks in the San Joaquin Valley, California. Condor 60: 256–257.

Robson, D. S. and W. D. Youngs. 1971. Statistical analysis of reported tag-recaptures in the harvest from an exploited population. Biom. Unit Rept. BU-369-M. Cornell Univ., Ithaca, New York. 15 pp.

Roe, H. B. and Q. C. Ayres. 1954. Engineering for agricultural drainage. McGraw-Hill Book Co., New York. 501 pp.

Rogers, J. P. and J. L. Hansen. 1967. Second broods in the wood duck. Bird-Banding 38: 234–235.

Rogers, R. 1955. Snake in the box. Louisiana Conserv. 7: 10–11.

Rogers-Price, V. 1983. John Abbott in Georgia: The visions of a naturalist artist (1751–ca. 1840). Madison-Morgan Cult. Ctr., Madison, Georgia. 149 pp.

Rollin, N. 1957. Incubation by drake wood duck in eclipse plumage. Condor 59: 263–265.

Romagnano, L., M. P. Lombardo, P. C. Stouffer, and H. W. Power. 1986. Suspected infanticide in the starling. Condor 88: 530–531.

Romanoff, A. L. and A. J. Romanoff. 1949. The avian egg. John Wiley and Sons, New York. 918 pp.

Roosevelt, R. B. 1884. Florida and the game water birds of the Atlantic Coast and the lakes of the U.S. Orange Judd Co., New York. 443 pp.

Rosen, M. N. 1969. Species susceptibility to avian cholera. Bull. Wildl. Dis. Assoc. 5: 195–200.

———. 1971. Botulism. Pages 100–117 *in* J. W. Davis, R. C. Anderson, L. Karstad, and D. O. Trainer, eds., Infectious and parasitic diseases of wild birds. Iowa St. Univ. Press, Ames. 344 pp.

Roslien, D. J. and A. O. Haugen. 1964. Occurrence of *Haemoproteus nettionis* in wood ducks (*Aix sponsa* L.). Proc. Iowa Acad. Sci. 71: 235–240.

Rothbart, P. 1979. Survival, habitat use, and movements of wood duck broods in northern Louisiana. M.S. thesis, Louisiana St. Univ., Baton Rouge. 165 pp.

Rothschild, M. and T. Clay. 1957. Fleas, flukes, and cuckous: A study of bird parasites. 3rd ed. Collins, London. 305 pp.

Rudolph, D. C., H. Kyle, and R. N. Conner. 1990. Redcockaded woodpeckers vs. rat snakes: The effectiveness of the resin barrier. Wilson Bull. 102: 14–22.

Rudolph, R. R. and C. G. Hunter. 1964. Green trees and greenheads. Pages 611–618 *in* J. P. Linduska, ed., Waterfowl tomorrow. U.S. Fish and Wildl. Serv., Washington, D.C. 770 pp.

Ryder, J. P. 1970. A possible factor in the evolution of clutch size in Ross' goose. Wilson Bull. 82: 5–13.

Ryser, F. A. 1985. Birds of the Great Basin. Univ. Nevada Press, Reno. 604 pp.

Sadler, T. S. and M. T. Myers. 1976. Alberta birds, 1961–1970, with particular reference to migration. Occas. Pap. No. 1. Provincial Mus. Alberta Natur. Hist., Edmonton. 314 pp.

Salyer, J. C. 1946. The Carolina beaver: A vanishing species? J. Mammal. 27: 331–335.

Sanderson, G. C. 1951a. Breeding habits and a history of the Missouri raccoon population from 1941 to 1948. Trans. N. Am. Wildl. Conf. 16: 445–461.

———. 1951b. The status of the raccoon in Iowa for the past twenty years as revealed by fur reports. Proc. Iowa Acad. Sci. 58: 527–531.

———. 1987a. Harvest information for the raccoon in the U.S., 1933 through 1964–65. Unpubl. harvest information. Illinois Natur. Hist. Surv., Champaign. 9 pp.

———. 1987b. Raccoon. Pages 486–499 *in* M. Novak, J. A. Baker, M. E. Obbard, and B. Malloch, eds., Wild furbearer management and conservation in North America. Ontario Ministry Natur. Resour., Toronto. 1,150 pp.

Sanderson, G. C. and F. C. Bellrose. 1986. A review of the problem of lead poisoning in waterfowl. Spec. Publ. 4. Illinois Natur. Hist. Surv., Champaign. 34 pp.

Sanderson, G. C. and G. F. Hubert, Jr. 1981. Selected demographic characteristics of Illinois (U.S.A.) raccoons (*Procyon lotor*). Pages 487–513 *in* J. A. Champman and D. Pursley, eds., Worldwide Furbearer Conf. Proc. Vol. 1., Frostburg, Maryland. 652 pp.

Sanderson, G. C. and A. V. Nalbandov. 1973. The reproductive cycle of the raccoon in Illinois. Illinois Natur. Hist. Surv. Bull. 31: 29–85.

Sargeant, A. B., S. H. Allen, and R. T. Eberhardt. 1984. Red fox predation on breeding ducks in midcontinent North America. Wildl. Monogr. 89. 41 pp.

Sather-Blair, S. 1986. Western riparian wetland losses and degradation: Status and trends of the influence of federal water and private hydroelectric projects. Draft background document. U.S. Dept. Inter., Off. Policy Anal., Washington, D.C. 56 pp.

Sauer, J. R., J. S. Lawrence, E. L. Warr, G. W. Cook, and V. R. Anderson. 1990. Experimental September duck hunting seasons and the survival of wood ducks in Kentucky and Tennessee. Pages 357–360 *in* L. H. Fredrickson, G. V. Burger, S. P. Havera, D. A. Graber, R. E. Kirby, and T. S. Taylor, eds., Proc. 1988 N. Am. Wood Duck Symp., St. Louis. 390 pp.

Saunders, A. A. 1937. Injury feigning by a wood duck. Auk 54: 202–203.

———. 1959. Forty years of spring migration in southern Connecticut. Wilson Bull. 71: 208–219.

Savard, J. P. 1985. Evidence of long-term pair bonds in Barrow's goldeneye (*Bucephala islandica*). Auk 102: 389–391.

Schacher, W. H. and W. G. Minser. 1988. An evaluation of a wood duck nesting box program in eastern Tennessee. Proc. Annu. Conf. Southeast. Assoc. Fish and Wildl. Agencies 42: 337–342.

Schamel, D. L. 1974. The breeding biology of the Pacific eider (*Somateria mollissima v-nigra* Bonaparte) on a barrier island in the Beaufort Sea, Alaska. M.S. thesis, Univ. Alaska, Fairbanks. 95 pp.

Scheffer, T. C., G. H. Englerth, and C. G. Duncan. 1949. Decay resistance of seven native oaks. J. Agric. Res. 78: 129–152.

Scheider, F. 1957. Wood duck diving for fish. Kingbird 7: 14.

Scherpelz, J. A. 1979. Chronology of pair formation and breeding biology in the wood duck. M.S. thesis, Univ. Missouri, Columbia. 58 pp.

Schiller, E. L. 1951. The cestoda of Anseriformes of the north central states. Am. Midl. Natur. 46: 444–461.

Schneberger, E. and J. L. Funk, eds. 1971. Stream channelization: A symposium. North Central Div., Special Publ. No 2. Am. Fish. Soc. Held in conjunction with the 33rd Midwest Fish and Wildl. Conf. Omaha, Nebraska. 83 pp.

Schoffman, R. J. 1946. A preliminary report on the food of ducks at Reelfoot Lake, Tennessee. J. Tenn. Acad. Sci. 21: 10–13.

Schreiner, K. M. and G. O. Hendrickson. 1951. Wood duck production aided by nesting boxes, Lake Odessa, Iowa, in 1950. Iowa Bird Life 21: 6–10.

Schroeder, C. H. 1960. Occurrence of breeding wood ducks and ring-necked ducks in North Dakota. Pittman-Robertson Proj. W-38-R-7. North Dakota Game and Fish Dept., Bismarck. 11 pp.

Scott, M. D. and D. E. Parr. 1978. Environmental factors affecting wood duck roosting flights in southern Illinois. Trans. Illinois St. Acad. Sci. 71: 72–80.

Scott, M. L. 1973. Nutrition in reproduction: Direct effects and predictive functions. Pages 46–59 *in* D. S. Farner, ed., Breeding biology of birds. Natl. Acad. Sci., Washington, D.C. 515 pp.

Seber, G. A. F. 1973. The estimation of animal abundance and related parameters. Charles Griffen and Co., Ltd., London. 506 pp.

Seegar, W. S., E. L. Schiller, W. J. L. Sladen, and M. Trpis. 1976. A Mallophaga, *Trinoton anserinum*, as a cyclodevelopmental vector for a heartworm parasite of waterfowl. Science 194: 739–740.

Semel, B. and P. W. Sherman. 1986. Dynamics of nest parasitism in wood ducks. Auk 103: 813–816.

Semel, B., P. W. Sherman, and S. M. Byers. 1988. Effects of brood parasitism and nest box placement on wood duck breeding ecology. Condor 90: 920–930.

Semel, B., P. W. Sherman, and S. M. Byers. 1990. Nest boxes and brood parasitism in wood ducks: A management dilemma. Pages 163–170 *in* L. H. Fredrickson, G. V. Burger, S. P. Havera, D. A. Graber, R. E. Kirby, and T. S. Taylor, eds., Proc. 1988 N. Am. Wood Duck Symp., St. Louis. 390 pp.

Seton, E. T. 1929. Lives of game animals. Vol. 4, Part 2. Doubleday, Doran, Garden City, New York. 506 pp.

Seymour, N. R. 1974. Aerial pursuit flights in the shoveler. Can. J. Zool. 52: 1,473–1,480.

Seymour, N. R. and R. D. Titman. 1978. Changes in activity patterns, agonistic behavior and territoriality of black ducks during the breeding season in a Nova Scotia tidal marsh. Can. J. Zool. 56: 1,773–1,785.

Seymour, N. R. and R. D. Titman. 1979. Behavior of unpaired black ducks *(Anas rubripes)* during the breeding season in a Nova Scotia tidal marsh. Can. J. Zool. 57: 2,421–2,428.

Shake, W. F. 1967. Starling-wood duck relationships. M.S. thesis, West. Illinois Univ., Macomb. 46 pp.

Shaw, S. P. and C. G. Fredine. 1956. Wetlands of the United States: Their extent and their value to waterfowl and other wildlife. Circ. No. 39. U.S. Fish and Wildl. Serv., Washington, D.C. 37 pp.

Shirley, H. L. 1936. Will pine or aspen dominate Minnesota forests? Proc. Minnesota Acad. Sci. 4: 25–28.

Short, H. L. and E. A. Epps. 1976. Nutrient quality and digestibility of seeds and fruits from southern forests. J. Wildl. Manage. 40: 283–289.

Siegfried, W. R. 1974. Climbing ability of ducklings of some cavity-nesting waterfowl. Wildfowl 25: 74–80.

Siegler, H. R. 1950. Food habits of waterfowl in New Hampshire. Unpubl. rept. New Hampshire Fish and Game Dept., Concord. 7 pp.

Sieh, J. C. 1957. The status of the wood duck in Iowa in 1957. Iowa Conserv. Commiss. Quart. Biol. Repts. 9: 36–37.

Slemons, R. D. and B. C. Easterday. 1975. The natural history of type-A influenza viruses and wild waterfowl. Pages 215–224 *in* L. A. Page, ed., Wildlife diseases. Plenum Press, New York. 686 pp.

Smart, G. 1965. Development and maturation of primary feathers of redhead ducklings. J. Wildl. Manage. 29: 533–536.

Smith, A. G. 1971. Ecological factors affecting waterfowl production in the Alberta parklands. Resour. Publ. 98. U.S. Fish and Wildl. Serv., Washington, D.C. 49 pp.

Smith, G. W. and R. E. Reynolds. 1992. Hunting and mallard survival, 1979–1988. J. Wildl. Manage. 56: 303–316.

Smith, M. M. 1958. Louisiana wood duck roost counts. Louisiana Wildl. and Fish. Commiss., New Orleans. 3 pp.

———. 1961. Louisiana waterfowl population study. Final report, June 1949–June 1961. Louisiana Wildl. and Fish. Commiss., New Orleans. 49 pp.

———. 1966. Distribution and density of wood ducks in eastern Canada. Pages 151–158 *in* J. B. Trefethen, ed., Wood duck management and research: A symposium. Wildl. Manage. Inst., Washington, D.C. 212 pp.

Smith, P. W. 1961. The amphibians and reptiles of Illinois. Illinois Natur. Hist. Surv. Bull. 28: 1–298.

Smith, R. I. 1968. The social aspects of reproductive behavior in the pintail. Auk 85: 381–396.

Smith, R. L. and L. D. Flake. 1985. Movements and habitats of brood-rearing wood ducks on a prairie river. J. Wildl. Manage. 49: 437–442.

Snow, F. H. 1875. A catalogue of the birds of Kansas. Kansas Acad. Sci. No. 8. 3: 14.

Sokal, R. R. and F. J. Rohlf. 1981. Biometry. W. H. Freeman and Co., San Francisco. 859 pp.

Soulliere, G. J. 1985. Wood duck production and management in central Wisconsin. M.S. thesis, Univ. Wisconsin, Stevens Point. 60 pp.

———. 1986. Cost and significance of a wood duck nesthouse program in Wisconsin: An evaluation. Wildl. Soc. Bull. 14: 391–395.

———. 1987. Distinguishing hooded merganser and wood duck nests by eggshell thickness. J. Wildl. Manage. 51: 534.

———. 1988. Density of suitable wood duck nest cavities in a northern hardwood forest. J. Wildl. Manage. 52: 86–89.

Sousa, P. J. and A. H. Farmer. 1983. Habitat suitability index models: Wood duck. FWS/OBS-82/10.43. U.S. Fish and Wildl. Serv., Fort Collins, Colorado. 27 pp.

Sowls, L. K. 1955. Prairie ducks. A study of their behavior, ecology, and management. The Stackpole Co., Harrisburg, Pennsylvania. 193 pp.

Spencer, H. E., Jr., P. O. Corr, and A. E. Hutchinson. 1979. 1978–79 migratory bird project report. Maine Dept. Inland Fish. and Wildl., Wildl. Div. Leafl. Series 11: 1–21.

Spencer, H. E., Jr., P. O. Corr, and A. E. Hutchinson. 1980. 1979–80 migratory bird project report. Maine Dept. Inland Fish. and Wildl., Wildl. Div. Leafl. Series 12: 1–28.

Spero, V. M. and T. D. Pitts. 1984. Use of wood duck nest boxes by common grackles. J. Field Ornithol. 55: 482–483.

Spero, V. M., F. G. Dallmeier, R. M. Wheat, and T. D. Pitts. 1983. A nesting study of wood ducks on Kentucky Lake, Tennessee. Migrant 54: 69–75.

Spieker, J. O. 1978. Virulence assay and other studies of six North American strains of duck plague virus tested in wild and domestic waterfowl. Ph.D. thesis, Univ. Wisconsin, Madison. 110 pp.

Spiker, C. J. 1931. A biological reconnaissance of the Peterboro Swamp and the Labrador Pond areas. Roosevelt Wild Life Bull. 6: 1–151.

Stahl, P., G. W. Pipes, and C. W. Turner. 1961. Time required for low temperature to influence thyroxine secretion rate in fowls. Poultry Sci. 40: 646–650.

Stanek, R. F. 1970. Observations on the testing of methods to reduce rat snake predation on wood duck nesting boxes in Louisiana. M.S. thesis, Louisiana St. Univ., Baton Rouge. 51 pp.

Stearns, F. 1966. Present and future status of forests of the north central states. Pages 5–22 *in* J. B. Trefethen, ed., Wood duck management and research: A symposium. Wildl. Manage. Inst., Washington, D.C. 212 pp.

Steele, J. H. and M. M. Galton. 1971. Salmonellosis. Pages 51–58 *in* J. W. Davis, R. C. Anderson, L. Karstad, and D. O. Trainer, eds., Infectious and parasitic diseases of wild birds. Iowa St. Univ. Press, Ames. 344 pp.

Stephenson, D. W. 1970. Nest losses in artificial breeding colonies of wood ducks. M.S. thesis, North Carolina St. Univ., Raleigh. 53 pp.

Stewart, P. A. 1957. The wood duck, *Aix sponsa* (Linnaeus), and its management. Ph.D. thesis, Ohio St. Univ., Columbus. 352 pp.

———. 1958. Local movements of wood ducks *(Aix sponsa)*. Auk 75: 157–168.

———. 1962. Nesting attentiveness and incubation period of a wood duck. Bird-Banding 33: 85–89.

———. 1967a. Disgorging of food by wood ducks. Wilson Bull. 79: 339–340.

———. 1967b. Diving wood duck ducklings entangled in filamentous algae. Condor 69: 531.

———. 1967c. Wood duck ducklings captured by bullfrogs. Wilson Bull. 79: 237–238.

———. 1971a. Egg turning by an incubating wood duck. Wilson Bull. 83: 97–99.

———. 1971b. Wood ducks nesting in chimneys. Auk 88: 425.

———. 1974. Mother wood ducks feeding away from their broods. Bird-Banding 45: 58.

———. 1977a. Radial dispersal and southward migration of wood ducks banded in Iowa. Iowa Bird Life 47: 48–50.

———. 1977b. Radial dispersal and southward migration of wood ducks banded in New York. N. Am. Bird Bander 2: 159–160.

———. 1977c. Radial dispersal and southward migration of wood ducks banded in Vermont. Bird-Banding 48: 333–336.

———. 1979. Radial dispersal of wood ducks after the nesting season and before fall migration. N. Am. Bird Bander 4: 1–3.

———. 1981. Female wood duck apparently killed by black rat snake. Chat 45: 97.

Stewart, R. E. and C. S. Robbins. 1958. Birds of Maryland and the District of Columbia. N. Am. Fauna 62: 85–87.

Stoddard, H. L. 1942. The bobwhite quail: Its habits, preservation and increase. Charles Scribner's Sons, New York. 559 pp.

Stollberg, B. P. 1950. Food habits of shoal-water ducks on Horicon Marsh, Wisconsin. J. Wildl. Manage. 14: 214–217.

Stone, W. 1909. The birds of New Jersey. Annu. rept. New Jersey St. Mus. 1908: 11–347.

Stoner, D. 1932. Ornithology of the Oneida Lake region. Pages 268–765 *in* Roosevelt Wildl. Annal vol. 2. Roosevelt Wildl. Forest Exper. Sta., Syracuse Univ., New York.

Stotts, V. D. and D. E. Davis. 1960. The black duck in the Chesapeake Bay of Maryland: Breeding behavior and biology. Chesapeake Sci. 1: 127–154.

Stoudt, J. H. 1944. Food preferences of mallards on the Chippewa National Forest, Minnesota. J. Wildl. Manage. 8: 100–112.

Stout, I. J. and G. W. Cornwell. 1976. Nonhunting mortality of fledged North American waterfowl. J. Wildl. Manage. 40: 681–693.

Strader, R. W. 1978. Wood duck nesting behavior and productivity in a south Louisiana beaver pond. M.S. thesis, Louisiana St. Univ., Baton Rouge. 108 pp.

———. 1990. Wood duck duckling production and survival from a south Louisiana beaver pond. Pages 279–284 *in* L. H. Fredrickson, G. V. Burger, S. P. Havera, D. A. Graber, R. E. Kirby, and T. S. Taylor, eds., Proc. 1988 N. Am. Wood Duck Symp., St. Louis. 390 pp.

Strader, R. W., R. T. DiGiulio, and R. B. Hamilton. 1978a. Egg carrying by wood duck. Wilson Bull. 90: 131–132.

Strader, R. W., R. E. Murry, Sr., H. R. Perry, Jr., and R. B. Hamilton. 1978b. Hen wood duck calls brood from neighboring nest box. J. Wildl. Manage. 42: 919–920.

Strange, T. H., Jr. 1970. A comparison of wood duck *(Aix sponsa)* nesting in natural cavities and artificial nest boxes. M.S. thesis, Louisiana Polytech. Inst., Ruston. 53 pp.

Strange, T. H., Jr., E. R. Cunningham, and J. W. Goertz. 1971. Use of nest boxes by wood ducks in Mississippi. J. Wildl. Manage. 35: 786–793.

Strom, D. W. 1969. A determination and evaluation of what constitutes wood duck brood habitat in the Nelson-Trevino Bottoms of the Upper Mississippi Refuge. Final rept., Div. Wildl. Refuges, Region 3, U.S. Fish and Wildl. Serv., St. Paul. 36+ pp.

Strong, L. 1973. Studies of wood duck nesting in artificial structures. Pages 5–25 *in* Statewide Wildl. Invest., Final rept. Mississippi Game and Fish Commiss., Jackson.

Stuewer, F. W. 1943a. Raccoons: Their habits and management in Michigan. Ecol. Monogr. 13: 203–257.

———. 1943b. Small entrance to a wood duck nest. J. Wildl. Manage. 7: 236.

Stullken, D. E. and C. M. Kirkpatrick. 1953. A determination of hole sizes which exclude certain predatory animals. J. Wildl. Manage. 17: 124–128.

Stupka, A. 1963. Notes on the birds of Great Smoky Mountains National Park. Univ. Tennessee Press, Knoxville. 242 pp.

Sturkie, P. D. 1965. Avian physiology. 2nd ed. Comstock Publishing Associates, Ithaca, New York. 766 pp.

Stutzenbaker, C. D. 1988. The mottled duck: Its life history, ecology, and management. Texas Parks and Wildl. Dept., Austin. 209 pp.

Sutherland, D. E. 1971. A 1965 waterfowl population model. Rept. No. 4, Flyway Habitat Unit Project, U.S. Bur. Sport Fish. and Wildl., Div. Wildl. Refuges, Washington, D.C. 11 pp.

Sutton, G. M. 1967. Oklahoma birds: Their ecology and distribution, with comments on the avifauna of the southern Great Plains. Univ. Oklahoma Press, Norman. 674 pp.

Swanberg, P. O. 1950. On the concept of the incubation period. Var Fagalvarld 9: 63–80.

Swanson, G. A. and J. C. Bartonek. 1970. Bias associated with food analysis in gizzards of blue-winged teal. J. Wildl. Manage. 34: 739–746.

Swanson, G. A. and H. K. Nelson. 1970. Potential influence of fish rearing programs on waterfowl breeding habitat. Pages 65–71 *in* E. Schneberger, ed., A symposium on the management of midwestern winter-kill lakes. Northcentral Div. of Am. Fish. Soc., Bethesda, Maryland. 75 pp.

Swanson, G. A. and A. B. Sargeant. 1972. Observation of nighttime feeding behavior of ducks. J. Wildl. Manage. 36: 959–961.

Swanton, J. R. 1946. The Indians of the southeastern United States. Bur. Am. Ethnol. Bull. 137. Smithson. Inst., Washington, D.C. 943 pp. + 107 plates.

Sweet, M. J. 1976. Mallard and wood duck utilization of Oakwood Bottoms Greentree Reservoir. M.A. thesis, S. Illinois Univ., Carbondale. 110 pp.

Tabberer, D. K. 1971. The wood duck roost count as an index to wood duck abundance in Louisiana. M.S. thesis, Louisiana St. Univ., Baton Rouge. 77 pp.

Tabberer, D. K., J. D. Newsom, P. E. Schilling, and H. A. Bateman. 1971. The wood duck roost count as an index to wood duck abundance in Louisiana. Proc. Annu. Conf. Southeast. Assoc. Game and Fish Commiss. 25: 254–261.

Tabberer, D. K., J. D. Newsom, and P. E. Schilling. 1973. Law enforcement implications of wood duck roost study in Louisiana. Proc. Annu. Conf. Southeast. Assoc. Game and Fish Commiss. 27: 318–324.

Talent, L. G., R. L. Jarvis, and G. L. Krapu. 1983. Survival of mallard broods in south-central North Dakota. Condor 85: 74–78.

Taylor, T. S. 1977. Avian use of moist soil impoundments in southeastern Missouri. M.S. thesis, Univ. Missouri, Columbia. 98 pp.

Teague, R. D. 1971. Wildlife homes from old tires. One-Sheet Answers, OSA #17. Agric. Ext. Serv., Univ. California, Davis. 2 pp.

Teels, B. M. 1975. Waterfowl production and utilization along the proposed route of the Tennessee-Tombigbee Waterway. Ph.D. thesis, Mississippi St. Univ., Starkville. 84 pp.

Terres, J. K. 1980. The Audubon Society encyclopedia of North American birds. Alfred A. Knopf, Inc., New York. 1,109 pp.

Thompson, J. D. and G. A. Baldassarre. 1988. Postbreeding habitat preference of wood ducks in northern Alabama. J. Wildl. Manage. 52: 80–85.

Thompson, J. D. and G. A. Baldassarre. 1989. Postbreeding dispersal by wood ducks in northern Alabama with reference to early hunting seasons. Wildl. Soc. Bull. 17: 142–146.

Thompson, S. C. and S. B. Simmons. 1990. Characteristics of second clutches in California wood ducks. Pages 171–177 *in* L. H. Fredrickson, G. V. Burger, S. P. Havera, D. A. Graber, R. E. Kirby, and T. S. Taylor, eds., Proc. 1988 N. Am. Wood Duck Symp., St. Louis. 390 pp.

Thruston, G. P. 1890. The antiquities of Tennessee and the adjacent states. Robert Clarke and Co., Cincinnati, Ohio. 369 pp.

Thul, J. E. 1979. A morphological and parasitological study of wood ducks in the Atlantic Flyway. M.S. thesis, Univ. Florida, Gainesville. 279 pp.

———. 1985. Parasitic arthropods of wood ducks, *Aix sponsa* L., in the Atlantic Flyway. J. Wildl. Dis. 21: 316–318.

Thul, J. E. and T. O'Brien. 1990. Wood duck hematozoan parasites as biological tags: Development of a population assessment model. Pages 323–334 *in* L. H. Fredrickson, G. V. Burger, S. P. Havera, D. A. Graber, R. E. Kirby, and T. S. Taylor, eds., Proc. 1988 N. Am. Wood Duck Symp., St. Louis. 390 pp.

Thul, J. E., D. J. Forrester, and E. C. Greiner. 1980. Hematozoa of wood ducks (*Aix sponsa*) in the Atlantic Flyway. J. Wildl. Dis. 16: 383–390.

Thul, J. E., D. J. Forrester, and C. L. Abercrombie. 1985. Ecology of parasitic helminths of wood ducks, *Aix sponsa*, in the Atlantic Flyway. Proc. Helminthol. Soc. Washington 52: 297–310.

Thwaites, R. G., ed. 1906. Maximilian, Prince of Wied's, travels in the interior of North America, 1832–1834. Vol. XXII. Early western travels 1748–1846. Part I. A. H. Clarke Co., Cleveland. 393 pp.

Tiner, R. W., Jr. 1984. Wetlands of the United States: Current status and recent trends. National wetlands inventory. U.S. Fish and Wildl. Serv., Washington, D.C. 59 pp.

———. 1987. Mid-Atlantic wetlands: A disappearing natural treasure. U.S. Fish and Wildl. Serv. and U.S. Environ. Prot. Agency, Washington, D.C. 28 pp.

Titman, R. D. 1983. Spacing and three-bird flights of mallards breeding in pothole habitat. Can. J. Zool. 61: 839–847.

Titman, R. D. and G. A. Seaman. 1978. Quebec banded wood duck recovered in Saba, Netherlands Antilles. Bird-Banding 49: 77.

Titman, R. D. and N. R. Seymour. 1981. A comparison of pursuit flights by six North American ducks of the genus *Anas*. Wildfowl 32: 11–18.

Todd, F. S. 1979. Waterfowl. Ducks, geese and swans of the world. Sea World Press, Inc., San Diego. 399 pp.

Todd, W. E. C. 1940. Birds of western Pennsylvania. Univ. Pittsburgh Press, Pittsburgh. 710 pp.

———. 1963. Birds of the Labrador Peninsula and adjacent areas. Univ. Toronto Press, Toronto. 819 pp.

Tolle, D. A. 1973. Fall movements of wood ducks in northeastern Ohio. M.S. thesis, Ohio St. Univ., Columbus. 123 pp.

Trainer, D. O., C. S. Schildt, R. A. Hunt, and L. R. Jahn. 1962. Prevalence of *Leucocytozoon simondi* among some Wisconsin waterfowl. J. Wildl. Manage. 26: 137–143.

Trautman, M. B. 1940. The birds of Buckeye Lake, Ohio. Univ. Michigan Mus. Zool. Misc. Publ. No. 44. Univ. Michigan Press, Ann Arbor. 466 pp.

———. 1977. The Ohio country from 1750 to 1977—a naturalist's view. Biol. Notes No. 10. Ohio Biol. Surv. Ohio St. Univ., Columbus. 25 pp.

Trost, R. E. 1987. Mallard survival and harvest rates: A reexamination of relationships. Trans. N. Am. Wildl. and Natur. Resour. Conf. 52: 264–284.

———. 1990. Relationship between harvest and survival rates of wood ducks in eastern North America, 1966–84. Pages 367–370 *in* L. H. Fredrickson, G. V. Burger, S. P. Havera, D. A. Graber, R. E. Kirby, and T. S. Taylor, eds., Proc. 1988 N. Am. Wood Duck Symp., St. Louis. 390 pp.

Tuck, L. M. 1960. The murres: their distribution, populations and biology. Canadian Wildl. Serv. Rept. Series, No. 1. Ottawa, Ontario. 260 pp.

Tufts, R. W. 1961. The birds of Nova Scotia. Nova Scotia Mus., Halifax. 481 pp.

Turček, F. J. 1966. On plumage quantity in birds. Ekologia Polska-Seria A. Nr. 32. 18 pp.

Turner, E. C., Jr. 1971. Fleas and lice. Pages 175–184 *in* J. W. Davis, R. C. Anderson, L. Karstad, and D. O. Trainer, eds., Infectious and parasitic diseases of wild birds. Iowa St. Univ. Press, Ames. 344 pp.

Turner, R. E. and N. J. Craig. 1980. Recent areal changes in Louisiana's forested wetland habitat. Proc. Louisiana Acad. Sci. XLIII: 61–68.

Turner, R. E., S. W. Forsythe, and N. J. Craig. 1981. Bottomland hardwood forest land resources of the southeastern United States. Pages 13–28 *in* J. R. Clark and J. Benforado, eds., Wetlands of bottomland hardwood forests. Elsevier Scientific Publishers Co., New York. 401 pp.

Uhler, F. M. 1964. Bonus from waste places. Pages 643–653 *in* J. P. Linduska, ed., Waterfowl tomorrow. U.S. Bur. Sport Fish. and Wildl., Washington, D.C. 770 pp.

Uhler, F. M. and F. B. McGilvrey. 1967. Improvement of artificial nesting structures for waterfowl. Annu. Prog. Rept. Feb. 1, 1966–Jan. 31, 1967. U.S. Bur. Sport Fish. and Wildl., Patuxent Wildl. Res. Ctr., Laurel, Maryland. 16 pp.

University of Minnesota, Center for Urban and Regional Affairs. 1981. Presettlement wetlands of Minnesota. The Center, St. Paul, Minnesota. 1 map.

U.S. Bureau of the Census. 1950. Drainage of agricultural lands. U.S. Census Agric. 4: 1–307.

———. 1959. Drainage of agricultural lands. U.S. Census Agric. General Rept., vol. 4. Washington, D.C. 364 pp.

———. 1964. Irrigation, land improvement practices, and use of agricultural chemicals. Pages 909–955 *in* U.S. Census Agric. General Rept., vol. 2. Washington, D.C. 1,213 pp.

U.S. Fish and Wildlife Service. 1976. Operation of the National Wildlife Refuge System. Final Environ. Impact Statement, U.S. Fish and Wildl. Serv., Washington, D.C.

———. 1977. Concept plan for waterfowl wintering habitat preservation. Central Valley California. Region 1. Portland, Oregon. 116 pp. + appendices.

———. 1988. The impact of federal programs on wetlands. Volume I: The lower Mississippi Alluvial Plain and the Prairie Pothole Region. A report to Congress by the Secretary of the Interior, October 1988. U.S. Fish and Wildl. Serv., Washington, D.C. 114 pp.

U.S. Forest Service. 1978. Forest statistics of the United States, 1977. USDA For. Serv., Washington, D.C. 133 pp.

U.S. Geological Survey. 1970. The national atlas of the United States. U.S. Dept. Inter., Washington, D.C. 417 pp.

Vance, J. M. 1986. Two faces of the river. Missouri Conserv. 47: 16–23.

Van Tyne, J. and A. J. Berger. 1959. Fundamentals of ornithology. John Wiley and Sons, Inc., New York. 624 pp.

Vaught, R. W., H. C. McDougle, and H. H. Burgess. 1967. Fowl cholera in waterfowl at Squaw Creek National Wildlife Refuge, Missouri. J. Wildl. Manage. 31: 248–253.

Vince, M. A. 1969. Embryonic communication, respiration and the synchronization of hatching. Pages 233–260 *in* R. A. Hinde, ed., Bird vocalizations. Cambridge Univ. Press, London. 394 pp.

Visher, S. S. 1913. An annotated list of the birds of Sanborn County, southeast-central South Dakota. Auk 30: 561–573.

Vorhies, C. T. 1947. More records of the wood duck in Arizona. Condor 49: 245.

Warren, B. H. 1890. Report on birds of Pennsylvania. 2nd ed. E. K. Meyers, Harrisburg, Pennsylvania. 434 pp.

Warren, D. S. 1969. Utilization and durability of wood duck nesting boxes. M.S. thesis, Louisiana St. Univ., Baton Rouge. 40 pp.

Wauer, R. H. 1969. Recent bird records from the Virgin River Valley of Utah, Arizona, and Nevada. Condor 71: 331–335.

Wayne, A. T. 1910. Birds of South Carolina. [Contributions from Charleston Museum No. 1.] The Daggett Printing Co., Charleston, South Carolina. 254 pp.

Webster, C. G. 1958. Better nest boxes for wood ducks. Wildl. Leafl. 393. U.S. Bur. Sport Fish. and Wildl., Washington, D.C. 18 pp.

Webster, C. G. and F. B. McGilvrey. 1966. Providing brood habitat for wood ducks. Pages 70–75 *in* J. B. Trefethen, ed., Wood duck management and research: A symposium. Wildl. Manage. Inst., Washington, D.C. 212 pp.

Webster, C. G. and F. M. Uhler. 1964. Improved nest structures for wood ducks. Wildl. Leafl. 458. U.S. Bur. Sport Fish. and Wildl., Washington, D.C. 20 pp.

Webster, C. G. and F. M. Uhler. 1967. Improved nest structures for wood ducks. Mod. Game Breed. 3: 28–36.

Webster, R. G., M. Morita, C. Pridgen, and B. Tumova. 1976. Ortho- and paramyxoviruses from migrating feral ducks: Characterization of a new group of influenza A viruses. J. Gen. Virol. 32: 217–225.

Weier, R. W. 1966. A survey of wood duck nest sites on Mingo National Wildlife Refuge in southeast Missouri. M.A. thesis, Univ. Missouri, Columbia. 78 pp.

Weller, M. W. 1965. Chronology of pair formation in some of the Nearctic *Aythya* (Anatidae). Auk 82: 227–235.

———. 1976. Molts and plumages of waterfowl. Pages 34–38 *in* F. C. Bellrose, Ducks, geese and swans of North America. Stackpole Books, Harrisburg, Pennsylvania. 544 pp.

Welty, J. C. 1979. The life of birds. Saunders College Publishing, Philadelphia. 623 pp.

Wenner, K. C. and W. R. Marion. 1981. Wood duck production on a northern Florida phosphate mine. J. Wildl. Manage. 45: 1,037–1,042.

Wesche, T. A. 1985. Stream channel modifications and reclamation structures to enhance fish habitat. Pages 103–163 *in* J. A. Gore, ed., The restoration of rivers and streams: Theories and experience. Butterworth Publishers, Stoneham, Maine. 280 pp.

Wetmore, A. 1936. The number of contour feathers in passeriform and related birds. Auk 53: 159–169.

Weydemeyer, W. 1975. Half-century record of the breeding birds of the Fortine area, Montana: Nesting data and population status. Condor 77: 281–287.

Widmann, O. 1907. A preliminary catalog of the birds of Missouri. Trans. Missouri Acad. Sci. XVII: 1–288.

Wielicki, D. J. 1987. Aspects of mallard nutrition during molt. M.S. thesis, Univ. Manitoba, Winnipeg.

Wigley, T. B., Jr. and T. H. Filer, Jr. 1989. Characteristics of greentree reservoirs: A survey of managers. Wildl. Soc. Bull. 17: 136–142.

Wigley, T. B., Jr. and M. E. Garner. 1987. Impact of beavers in the Arkansas Ozarks. Arkansas Agric. Exp. Sta., Div. Agric., Rept. Series 298. Monticello, Arkansas. 12 pp.

Wilkins, T. M., A. L. Bowman, and J. T. Fulton. 1990. Management of wood ducks at Yazoo National Wildlife Refuge. Pages 269–273 *in* L. H. Fredrickson, G. V. Burger, S. P. Havera, D. A. Graber, R. E. Kirby, and T. S. Taylor, eds., Proc. 1988 N. Am. Wood Duck Symp., St. Louis. 390 pp.

Williams, C. M., C. G. Lee, J. D. Garlich, and J. C. H. Shih. 1991. Evaluation of a bacterial feather fermentation product, feather-lysate, as a feed protein. Poultry Sci. 70: 85–94.

Williams, L. E. 1984. The voice and vocabulary of the wild turkey. Real Turkeys, Gainesville, Florida. 85 pp.

Williams, S. O. III. 1987. The changing status of the wood duck *(Aix sponsa)* in Mexico. Am. Birds 41: 372–375.

Wilson, A. 1828. American ornithology; or the natural history of the birds of the United States (text 3 vols.). Collins and Co., Philadelphia.

Wilson, A. and C. L. Bonaparte. 1831. American ornithology; or the natural history of the birds of the United States. 4 vols. Constable and Co., Edinburgh. 1,287 pp.

Wingfield, B. and J. B. Low. 1955. Waterfowl productivity in Knudson Marsh, Salt Lake Valley, Utah. Proc. Utah Acad. Sci. 32: 45–49.

Wisconsin Department of Natural Resources. 1976. Wetland use in Wisconsin: Historical perspective and present picture. Division of environmental water quality planning section. Wisconsin Dept. Natur. Resour., Madison. 48 pp.

Wishart, R. A. 1983. Pairing chronology and mate selection in the American wigeon *(Anas americana)*. Can. J. Zool. 61: 1,733–1,743.

———. 1985. Moult chronology of American wigeon, *Anas americana*, in relation to reproduction. Can. Field-Natur. 99: 172–178.

Wobeser, G. A. 1981. Diseases of wild waterfowl. Plenum Press, New York. 300 pp.

Woehler, E. E. 1957. How about raccoon stocking? Wisconsin Conserv. Bull. 22: 12–14.

Wood Duck Committee. 1964. Wood duck committee report, 1964 spring meeting. Unpubl. rept. on file with the U.S. Fish and Wildl. Serv., Mississippi Flyway Tech. Comm., Columbia, Missouri. 12 pp.

———. 1986a. Trends in harvest and the population status of wood ducks in the Mississippi Flyway 1961–1984. Preliminary rept. on file with the U.S. Fish and Wildl. Serv., Mississippi Flyway Tech. Comm., Columbia, Missouri. 33 pp.

———. 1986b. Trends in harvest and the population status of wood ducks in the Mississippi Flyway 1961–1985. Rept. on file with the U.S. Fish and Wildl. Serv., Mississippi Flyway Tech. Comm., Columbia, Missouri. 16 pp.

Wood, J. E. 1964. A preliminary study of wood duck habitat and production on Noxubee National Wildlife Refuge. M.S. thesis, Mississippi St. Univ., State College. 31 pp.

Wood, M. 1973. Birds of Pennsylvania: When and where to find them. Pennsylvania St. Univ. Agric., University Park. 103 pp.

Woodward, D. K., R. B. Hazel, and B. P. Gaffney. 1985. Economic and environmental impacts of beaver in North Carolina. Pages 89–96 *in* P. T. Bromley, ed., Proc. Second Eastern Wildlife Damage Control Conference, Raleigh, North Carolina. 281 pp.

Woolfenden, G. E. 1961. Postcranial osteology of the waterfowl. Bull. Florida St. Mus. Biol. Sci. 6: 1–129.

Woolfenden, G. E. and J. W. Fitzpatrick. 1984. The Florida scrub jay: Demography of a cooperative breeding bird. Princeton Univ. Press, Princeton, New Jersey. 406 pp.

Wright, B. S. 1954. High tide and east wind. The Stackpole Co., Harrisburg, Pennsylvania. 162 pp.

Wyndham, E. 1986. Length of birds' breeding seasons. Am. Natur. 128: 155–164.

Wynne-Edwards, V. C. 1962. Animal dispersion in relation to social behaviour. Oliver and Boyd, Edinburgh. 653 pp.

Yamashina, Y. 1952. Classification of the Anatidae based on cyto-genetics. Papers from the coordinating committee on research genetics. Tokyo, Japan. 3: 1–34.

Yeagley, H. L. 1953. Some surprises in research. Audubon Mag. 55: 158–161.

Yoakum, J., W. P. Dasmann, H. R. Sanderson, C. M. Nixon, and H. S. Crawford. 1980. Habitat improvement techniques. Pages 329–403 *in* S. D. Schemnitz, ed., Wildlife management techniques manual. 4th ed. The Wildl. Soc., Washington, D.C. 686 pp.

Young, R. C. and W. M. Dennis. 1983. Productivity of the aquatic macrophyte community of the Holston River: Implications to hypolimnetic oxygen depletions on Cherokee Reservoir. Tennessee Valley Authority, Div. Air Water Resour. Rept., Muscle Shoals, Alabama. 34 pp.

Zahm, G., E. S. Jemison, and R. E. Kirby. 1987. Behavior and capture of wood ducks in pecan groves. J. Field Ornithol. 58: 474–479.

Zicus, M. C. 1982. Age determination of female wood ducks in spring. Minnesota Wildl. Res. Quart. 42: 12–17.

Zicus, M. C. and S. K. Hennes. 1988. Cavity nesting waterfowl in Minnesota. Wildfowl 39: 115–123.

Zipko, S. J. 1979. Effects of dump nests and habitat on reproductive ecology of wood ducks, *Aix sponsa* (Linnaeus). Ph.D. thesis, Rutgers Univ., Newark, New Jersey. 169 pp.

Zipko, S. J. and J. Kennington. 1977. A ground-nesting wood duck. Auk 94: 159.

Index

A Natural History of the Ducks (Phillips),
    xiii
A New Voyage to Carolina, 8
Abbott, Charles C., 9
Acanthocephalans (thorny-headed
    worms), 432
Age:
    determining, 344–46
    differences in migration, 89–90
    effects on breeding, 204–8
    effects on helminth infestation, 433
    embryo, 230
    ratios, 442–43
    recovery rates by, 447
    related changes in body composition,
        326–27
    survival rates by, 446–47
Alabama, 25
    autumn migration in, 86
    stream habitats in, 45, 49
    winter distribution, 33
Alaska, 29
Alberta, 27–28
Alligators, 298
American black duck, 11, 79
American Ornithologists' Union
    (AOU), 5
American Ornithology (Wilson), xiii
Anderson, Vernon, 24
Arizona, 31
    winter distribution, 35
Arkansas, 24–25
    autumn migration in, 86
    stream habitats in, 45, 49
    winter distribution, 33
Arthur, George, 267, 497
Aspergillosis, 423–24
Atlantic Flyway, 17, 18–22
    annual harvest of beaver in, 70
    autumn migration along, 83–86
    bag limits in, 510
    bottomland wetlands along, 57
    botulism outbreaks in, 422–23
    Connecticut, 20
    Cuba, 22
    effect of latitude on breeding along,
        203, 204–5
    farm pond habitats along, 59
    Florida, 21–22
    Georgia, 21
    harvest and band recoveries along,
        85, 86, 113–18, 120
    Maine, 19
    Maryland, 20
    Massachusetts, 20
    migration corridors along, 93–94
    nest house occupancy rate in, 489–90
    nest houses along, 270–71
    New Hampshire, 19–20
    New Jersey, 20
    New York, 20
    Newfoundland, 18
    nonmigratory wood ducks in, 79

North Carolina, 21
Nova Scotia, 18–19
Ontario, 19
Pennsylvania, 20
Quebec, 19
Rhode Island, 20
South Carolina, 21
    spring migration along, 91–92
    states and provinces within, 16
Vermont, 20
Virginia, 20–21
West Virginia, 20
Western Indies, 22
    wetland types along, 55, 56, 58
    winter distribution, 32–33
Audubon, John James, 2, 9–10, 240
Australian wood duck, 5
Avian cholera, 423

Bacterial infections, 420–23
Baird, John C., 18
Band recoveries, 90, 364–67, 446–56
    by age classes, 447
    Atlantic Flyway, 85, 86
    data, 113–18
    effect of special seasons on, 452–56
    geographic variation in, 451–52
    local development, 367–68
    Mississippi Flyway, 86–87
    by sex classes, 447
    temporal/spatial relationship, 87–89
    see also Harvest
Banding, 90
    juveniles with web tags, 97
    in late summer and autumn, 90
    traps, 85
    with leg bands, 97
Barber, S. R., 26
Barras, Scott C., 334, 412
Barrow's goldeneyes duck, 1
Barton, Benjamin Smith, 9
Bartram, John, 9
Bartram, William, 9
Bateman, Hugh, 25, 119, 214, 272
Bauer, Richard D., 396
Baxter, Ace, 480
Beaver, annual harvest of, 70
Beaver ponds, 68–70, 504–5
    management of, 496
Behavior characteristics, 1–2
Bellrose, Frank, vii–xii, 238, 461,
    472, 490
Bendarik, Karl, 24, 481
Bent, Arthur Cleveland, xiii
*Birds of Massachusetts and Other New
    England States* (Forbush), xiii
Black-bellied whistling duck, 1
Bobcats, 294
Bond, Glen W., Jr., 272
Botulism, 420–23
Bradley, Homer, 30
Bradley, Lyle, 490

Breckenridge, Walter J., 256
Breeding, 185
    body mass change, 209–14
    chronology of nesting during, 202–9
    comfort activity, 187–88
    diet during, 402–4
    effect of age on, 204–8
    effect of temperature on, 208–9
    egg-laying activities, 192–96
    habitat needs for, 70–71
    home range, 197–99
    incubation activities, 196
    individual response, 209
    nest site selection, 189–92
    physiology of, 201–15
    populations, 16–32
    postbreeding habitat needs, 75–76
    prelaying activities, 185–92
    protein requirements during, 212
    ranges, 15–16
    reproduction, physiology of, 214–15
    sexual maturity, 202
    see also Broods and brooding; Dump
        nesting; Mating; Nesting;
        Postbreeding
Breeding populations, 16–32
    Atlantic Flyway, 16, 18–22
    Great Plains Flyway, 17
    Mississippi Flyway, 17
    Pacific Flyway, 18
British Columbia, 29
    winter distribution, 34
Brood parasitism. *See* Dump nesting
Broods and brooding, 301–4
    clutch sizes, 217–18, 219, 224–27, 244
    daily movement patterns in, 307
    displaced ducklings, 310–11, 312
    escape behaviors of flightless young,
        312–13
    female absence from, 307
    habitat needs for, 73–74
    hen feigning behavior, 313
    hen tolerance, 307–8
    hen/brood bond, 308–11
    hens accepting displaced ducklings,
        311
    home ranges, 306–7
    motherless, 318
    movement, 304–6
    survival of flightless young, 313–21
    survival rates, 315–18
Brown, Stephen, 20
Brunswig, Norman L., 482
Bufflehead duck, 1
Buffon, G. L. L., 8
Burgess, Harold, 394
Byrns, James, 476

California, 31
    autumn migration in, 87
    spring migration in, 93
    winter distribution, 35
Catesby, Mark, xiii, 8–9

Central Flyway. *See* Great Plains Flyway
Cestodes (tapeworms), 432
Chickadee, 2
Childress, Don, 28, 30
Clark, William, 10
Classification, duck, 5–6
Clutch sizes, 217–18, 219, 224–27
  for normal and dump nests, 244
Cole, J. C., 51
Colorado, 28
  winter distribution, 34
Comfort activity, 187–88
Common duck, 1
Common mergansers, 1
Compound nesting. *See* Dump nesting
Connecticut, 20
  spring migration in, 92
Connelley, Daniel P., 31
Copulation, 134–36
  forced, 161–63
Courtship. *See* Mating
Cox, Roger, 502
Cuba, 22
Cullerton, Richard C., 285, 475, 480
Cunningham, Ray, 101, 104, 256, 272,
  275, 276, 287, 369, 490

Dabbling, 389
Darby, William R., 19
Davis, Brian, 31
Denny, Ralph, 30
Dewberry, Oscar, 21
Dibblee, Randy L., 18
Dick, Don, 316
Diet, 387–88, 396–99
  autumn, 407–12
  breeding season, 402–4
  ducklings, 413–17
  effect of season on, 401–12
  historical accounts of diversity in,
    387–88
  late summer, 405–7
  spring, 402–4
  studies concerning, 400–1
  winter, 407–12
  see also Feeding; Nutrition
Diseases, 419–20, 434–35
  aspergillosis, 423–24
  avian cholera, 423
  botulism, 420–23
  duck virus enteritis, 420
  epizootic, 419
  Newcastle, 420
  rhinosporidiosis, 424
  salmonellosis, 423
  see also Metallic poisoning; Parasitic
    infestations
Displays, 124–25, 126
  courtship, 127–34
  postcopulatory, 135
Distribution:
  autumn, 32
  breeding populations, 16–32
  breeding ranges, 15–16
  winter, 32–35
Diving, for food, 389
Dixon, Joseph, xiii
Donnelley, Jack A., 21
Duck plague. *See* Duck virus enteritis
Duck stamps:
  Federal, 11
  postage, 12
  state, 12
Duck virus enteritis, 420

Ducklings:
  age of, determining, 344–46
  diet, 413–17
  displaced, 310–11, 312
  downy to juvenile, change from,
    335–36
  escape behaviors of flightless, 312–13
  feeding behavior of, 413–17
  growth, 323–28
  juvenile to alternate plumage, 361
  motherless, 318
  nest exodus, 235–40
  nutritional requirements, 415–17
  sex of, determining, 344
  stranded, 251–53
  survival of flightless, 313–21
  survival rates, 315–18
  vocalizations, 140–41, 152–53, 154,
    235–38
Ducks, Geese and Swans of North America
  (Bellrose), vii, x
Due, Lem, 27
Dump nesting, 243–62
  altercations between females, 255–62
  chronology of, 247–48
  clutch sizes, 244
  and conspecific injuries and fatalities,
    256–62
  density of breeders, 244–45
  effect of on production of young,
    248–51
  factors affecting, 244–48
  and infertility, 251–53
  intraspecific strife, 255–56
  nest destruction, 246
  and nonterm embryos, 251–53
  parasitic laying during incubation,
    253–54
  scarcity of nest sites, 245–46
  and stranded ducklings, 251–53
  by yearlings and older birds, 246–47
  see also Nesting

Ectoparasites, 427–29
Edwards, George, 9
Eggs, 222–24
  age of embryo, determining, 230
  composition, 223–24
  loss in weight, 224
  pipping and hatching, 234
  propagation of, 513–15
  size, 222–23, 224
  see also Embryos
Ellebrecht, Louis, 468
Embryos:
  age of, determining, 230
  developmental stages, 231
  nonterm, 251–53
Eng, Robert L., 28
Epizootic diseases, 419
Esophagus, importance of, 392–93
Evolutionary development, 519–20
Eyes, 3, 4

Farm ponds:
  habitats, 59, 67–68
  management of, 496
Feeding:
  behavior of ducklings, 413–17
  and consumption of grit, 400
  dabbling during, 389
  diving during, 389
  habits, 2
  importance of esophagus in, 392–93
  manner of, 389–93

nutrition and food selection, 396–99
  sites, 393–96
  see also Diet; Nutrition
Feigning behavior, 313
Females:
  altercations between, 255–62
  brood hen tolerance, 307–8
  brood hens feigning behavior, 313
  courtship displays, 133–34
  daily energy requirements for
    reproduction, 215
  dispersal of ducklings, 99–104
  double-brooded, 220–21
  hen/brood bond, 308–11
  homing of, 94–99
  homing of juvenile, 97–99
  influence on nest site selection of
    yearlings, 102–4
  postbreeding molts, 360
  seasonal weight changes, 209–14
  selecting other nest sites, 95–97
  vocalizations, 137–38, 147–52, 235–38
Ferrigno, Fred, 20
Filarial worms, 427
*First Check-List of North American
  Birds*, 5
Fisher, David, 44, 45
Flake, Lester D., 27
Flickers. *See* Woodpeckers
Flies, wet and dry, 11
Flightless period, weights during, 214
Flights, roosting, 378–83
  autumn, 379–80
  influence of weather on, 381–82
  spring, 380–81
  winter, 380
  see also Migration
Flock:
  formation, 355–59
  sizes, 382–83
Florida, 21–22
  autumn migration in, 85
  winter distribution, 33
Forbush, Edward Howe, xiii
Franklin, John, Sir, 11
Fredrickson, Leigh, 104
French Broad River (western North
  Carolina), 48–49
Fulton, John, 368
Fungal infections, 423–24
Funk, Howard D., 27, 28

Game ducks, 11
Geese, 5
Geiger, A. E., 475
Georgi, Michelle, 241
Georgia, 21
  autumn migration in, 85
  spring migration in, 91–92
  winter distribution, 33
Gigstead, Gill, 461
Gilchrist, Charles P., Jr., 20
Graber, David, 24
Great Plains Flyway, 17, 26–29
  Alberta, 27–28
  autumn distribution, 32
  Colorado, 28
  harvest and band recoveries along,
    113, 119
  Kansas, 26, 27
  Manitoba, 26
  migration corridors along, 94
  Montana, 28
  Nebraska, 26, 27
  nest houses along, 270–71

New Mexico, 29
North Dakota, 26–27
Oklahoma, 26, 27
Saskatchewan, 26
South Dakota, 26, 27
states and provinces within, 17
Texas, 26, 27
wetland types along, 56–57
winter distribution, 34
Wyoming, 28
Green-winged teal duck, 2
Grice, David, 323
Grinnell, George Bird, 109
Grit, consumption of, 400
Growth, 323–28
age-related changes in body composition, 326–27
characteristics, 326
culmen, 327–28
tarsus, 327–28
wing, 327–28
Gunkel, Neil, 241

Habitat management, 495–507
beaver ponds, 496, 504–5
brood-rearing habitats, 506–7
farm ponds, 496
food base, 497–98
food requirements, 507
fundamentals of, 496
impoundments for human purposes, 500–1
impoundments for wildlife, 501–5
overflow hardwood flats, 499–500
riverine, 496, 498–99
timber, 505–6
wetlands, 496
Habitats, 37
beaver ponds, 68–70
channels, 67–68
deepwater, 37
farm ponds, 59, 67–68
impoundments, 67–68
losses, 60–67
preferences for, 41–53
seasonal needs, 70–76
second-growth forests, 67
streams, 41–52
trends in, 59–70
types of, 37–41
wetlands, 37–41, 54–59
wetlands and productivity, 76–77
Haemoproteus, 424, 426
Hansen, James L., 24, 45
Hardwoods:
bottomland, 63–67
flats, 499–500
Harlequin duck, 5
Hart, Mark, 23
Hartman, Fred E., 20
Harvest:
in Atlantic Flyway, 120
and band recovery data, 113–18
in Great Plains Flyway, 119
in Mississippi Flyway, 120
see also Band recoveries
Havera, Stephen, 168
Hawkins, Arthur, 92, 158, 390, 461, 490
Hawks, 295
Helmeke, Don, 190, 238, 463, 487, 490
Helminths, 429–34
acanthocephalans, 432
cestodes, 432
effects of age and sex on, 433
effects of season on, 433

nematodes, 430, 431–32
trematodes, 431
Helvie, Jack, 31, 35
Hematozoas, 424–27
haemoproteus, 424, 426
leucocytozoon, 424, 426
plasmodium, 424, 426–27
Heusmann, H. W., 20, 101
Hindman, Larry J., 20
Histoire Naturelle (Buffon), 8
History, 7–13
contemporary appreciation, 11–13
Indian culture, 7–8
vanguards, 8–11
Hoehn, Tom, 20
Holm, Dan, 472
Holston River (eastern Tennessee), 48
food base in, 497
Home ranges, 306–7
daily movement patterns in, 307
and female absence from broods, 307
size of, 306
Homing:
of females, 94–99
of juvenile females, 97–99
of males, 104–5
Hood, Robert, 26
Hooded merganser, 1, 2, 3
Hooey, D. F., 26
Hopps, Eric, 79, 83, 124, 125, 132, 133, 134, 141, 142, 143, 145, 147, 148, 153, 331, 351, 376, 377, 380, 383
Humburg, Dale D., 24
Hunt, R. A., 23
Hunting regulations, 509–13
bag limits, 510
shooting hours, 509–10
special seasons, 510–13

Idaho, 29–30
winter distribution, 34
Illinois, 24
autumn migration in, 86
spring migration in, 92–93
stream habitats in, 45, 46–47
winter distribution, 33
Incubation, 228–34
age of embryo, determining, 230
daily recess patterns, 231–33
developmental stages, 231
pair-bond duration, 233–34
parasitic laying during, 253–54
periods, 228–29
propagation, 513–15
Indian culture, 7–8
Indiana, 24
autumn migration in, 86
stream habitats in, 45, 47
Infertility, 251–53
Ingstad, Robert E., 363
Invertebrate consumption rates, 212
Iowa, 24
autumn migration in, 86
spring migration in, 92
stream habitats in, 45, 46
winter distribution, 33
Irving, Washington, 10

Jeffrey, Robert, 29
Jessen, Robert L., 23
Johnson, Fred, 22
Johnson, Kenneth L., 27
Johnson, Mike, 26, 27
Jones, Robert E., 26, 158
Jones, Tom, 276, 487

Kaminski, Richard M., 241, 334
Kansas, 26, 27
stream habitats in, 50
winter distribution, 34
Keim, William, 285, 475, 480
Kelmeke, Don, 290
Kentucky, 24
spring migration in, 92
stream habitats in, 45, 47
winter distribution, 33
Kirsch, Leo, 363
Koke, Delbert, 142, 150, 192, 195, 196, 211, 228, 232, 233, 235, 238, 287
Kraft, Marvin J., 27
Kuck, Tom, 27

Lacaillade, Harold C., 19
Lake Chautauqua National Wildlife Refuge, Illinois, nest houses in, 269–70
Lakowski, John, 470
Lawson, John, 8
Laying activity, 217–21
Le Clercq, C., Friar, 8
Lehmann, V. W., 22
Leopold, Frederic, 218, 228, 233, 242, 243, 484, 490
Leucocytozoon, 424, 426
Lewis, Meriwether, 10
Lice, 428
Life Histories of North American Wild Fowl (Bent), xiii
Lincoln/Peterson mark/recapture sampling, 315
Long, William H., 214
Louis XIV, King of France, 8
Louisiana, 25
autumn migration in, 86
winter distribution, 33
Lumsden, Harry, 19

McEneaney, Terry, 30
Maine, 19
autumn migration in, 84
spring migration in, 92
Male, Mike, 79, 235
Males, 1–2
courtship displays, 129–33
homing of, 104–5
postbreeding molts, 359–60
seasonal weight changes, 209–14
vocalizations, 139–40, 143–47
Mallard duck, 2, 5, 11
Mandarin duck, 5
and wood duck similarities, 6
Manitoba, 26
spring migration in, 92
Martz, Jerry, 23
Maryland, 20
autumn migration in, 85
winter distribution, 32
Mason County complex, Illinois, nest houses in, 264–67
Massachusetts, 20
autumn migration in, 84
spring migration in, 92
winter distribution, 32
Mating, 123
aerial courtship flights, 127
aerial pursuits, 158–61
behavior of courting parties, 124–27
behaviors associated with copulation, 134–36
and confrontations between males, 125–26

courtship displays, 124–25, 126, 127–34
  forced copulation, 161–63
  pairing chronology, 153–56
  renesting courtship, 164–65
  reproductive maturity, 123–24
  reproductive strategy, 156–65
  trios, 163–64
  and value of autumn roosts to pair formation, 156
  vocalizations, 136–53
  see also Breeding; Postbreeding
Maximilian, Alexander Philip, Prince, 10
Merganser duck, 2
Metallic poisoning, 434
Mexico, winter distribution, 35
Michigan, 23
  autumn migration in, 86
  stream habitats in, 50
  winter distribution, 33
Microfilarial, 425, 427
Migration, 79–81
  autumn, 83–90
  chronology of, 83
  corridors, 93–94
  dispersal of female ducklings, 99–104
  flight characteristics, 81–82
  homing of females during, 94–99
  homing of males during, 104–5
  northward postbreeding, 363–67
  by sex and age classes, 89–90
  spring, 90–93
  weights during, 214
  see also Roosts and roosting
Migratory Bird Treaty Act, 110
Minks, 293–94
Minnesota, 23
  autumn migration in, 86
  spring migration in, 92
  stream habitats in, 50
  winter distribution, 33
Minser, William G., 48, 51, 497
Mississippi, 25
  autumn migration in, 86
  winter distribution, 33
Mississippi Delta, 52
Mississippi Flyway, 17, 23–25
  Alabama, 25
  annual harvest of beaver in, 70
  Arkansas, 24–25
  autumn distribution, 32
  autumn migration along, 84, 86–87
  bag limits in, 510
  bottomland wetlands along, 57
  botulism outbreaks in, 422
  effect of latitude on breeding along, 203, 204–5
  farm pond habitats along, 58
  harvest and band recoveries along, 86–87, 113–18, 120
  Illinois, 24
  Indiana, 24
  Iowa, 24
  Kentucky, 24
  Louisiana, 25
  Michigan, 23
  migration corridors along, 93–94
  Minnesota, 23
  Mississippi, 25
  Missouri, 24
  nest house occupancy rate in, 488–89
  nest houses along, 270–71
  nonmigratory wood ducks in, 79
  Ohio, 24

Ontario, 23
  spring migration along, 91, 92–93
  states and provinces within, 17
  stream habitats along, 44–49
  Tennessee, 24
  wetland types along, 54, 55–56
  winter distribution, 32, 33–34
  Wisconsin, 23
Missouri, 24
  autumn migration in, 86
  spring migration in, 92
  stream habitats in, 45, 47
  winter distribution, 33
Mitchusson, Tim, 29
Mites, 428
Molts, 329–33
  adult, 346–50
  back, 350
  nutrition and, 351–53
  postbreeding, 359–62
  rump, 349
  scapulars, 349–50
  sequential, 333–35
  tail coverts and tail, 349
  wing, 350, 361
  winter, 352–53
  see also Plumages
Montalbano, Frank, III, 21, 22
Montana, 28, 30
Montgomery, Robert, 104
Mortality factors:
  diseases, 314
  drowning, 314
  predation, 314, 315
Mortality rates, 446–56
  annual, 419
  natural versus hunting, 456–58
Moser, Tim, 50
Mowbray, Elmer E., Jr., 363
Munro, W. T., 29
Muscovy duck, 5
Myers, James E., 20

Natural History of Carolina, Florida, and the Bahama Islands (Catesby), xiii
Nault, Julia, 470
Nauvoo Slough (backwater area of Mississippi River), food base in, 497–98
Nebraska, 26, 27
  winter distribution, 34
Nelson, Harvey, 485, 490
Nematodes (roundworms), 430, 431–32
Nest cavities, 167, 263
  availability of, 171–73
  basal area, 177
  competition for, 275–77
  density, 177–79
  depth, 176
  entrance, 174–75
  formation, 167–69
  height, 175–76
  location, 171–72
  longevity, 173
  selection of, 173–77, 189–92
  tree size, 172–73
  tree species, 179–83
  types of, 169–71
  volume, 177
Nest houses, 263–70, 461
  along Atlantic Flyway, 270–71
  along Great Plains Flyway, 270–71
  along Mississippi Flyway, 270–71
  along Pacific Flyway, 270–71

basic management principles for, 492–93
  board, 462–67
  colonial, 472–73
  companion, 474–75
  competition for, 277–86
  construction plan for board, 464
  construction plan for metal, 468
  duplex, 472
  estimates of numbers of, 487
  histories in board and metal, 266–67
  histories in nest houses on posts, 268
  histories in sheet metal, 268–69
  horizontal, 474–75
  impact of on local populations, 490–91
  maintaining, 486
  metal, 264, 468–72
  occupancy trends, 488–90
  placement of, 480–86
  plastic, 476–77
  programs, 480–86, 487
  slab, 461–62
  starlings site preference, 284–86
  unconventional designs for, 478
Nest predators. *See* Predators
Nesting, 217
  and addition of down to nests, 218–19
  behavior, 1
  chronology of, 202–9
  clutch sizes, 217–18, 219, 224–27, 244
  double-brooded females, 220–21
  eggs, 222–24
  habit of, 1
  at high latitudes, 202–3
  incubation, 228–34
  laying activity, 217–21
  natural cavities, 263
  and nest exodus, 235–40
  in nest houses, 263–70
  periods of peak, 203
  pipping and hatching, 234
  ranges, 1
  renesting, 219–20
  sites, 95–97, 189–92
  sites, unconventional, 272–73
  starling chronology of, 283–84
  success, 263–71
  trek to water, 241–42
  see also Breeding; Dump nesting
Nesting of the Wood Duck in California (Dixon), xiii
Nevada, 31
  winter distribution, 35
New Hampshire, 19–20
New Jersey, 20
New Mexico, 29
  winter distribution, 34, 35
New York, 20
  autumn migration in, 85, 86
  migration corridors in, 93
  winter distribution, 32
Newcastle disease, 420
Newfoundland, 18
Nichols, Edward, 295
Nocturnal roosts. *See* Roosts and roosting
Norell, Dick, 29
North Carolina, 21
  autumn migration in, 85
  stream habitats in, 48
  winter distribution, 32
North Dakota, 26–27
Northern pintail duck, 11
Nova Scotia, 18–19

autumn migration in, 84
spring migration in, 92
Nutrition, 396–99
  duckling requirements, 415–17
  molts and, 351–53
  protein requirements, 212
  see also Diet; Feeding

Odor-sensing organs, 2
Ohio, 24
  autumn migration in, 86
  spring migration in, 92
  stream habitats in, 45, 47
  winter distribution, 33
Oklahoma, 26, 27
  stream habitats in, 46, 50
  winter distribution, 34
Older, Phil, 26
Oldsquaw duck, 5
Olfactory bulb ratio, 2
On a Tour of the Prairies (Irving), 10
Ontario, 19, 23
  winter distribution, 32
Opossums, 294
Oregon, 30–31
  autumn migration in, 87
  winter distribution, 34
Owls, 275

Pacific Flyway, 17, 29–32
  Alaska, 29
  Arizona, 31
  autumn migration along, 84, 87
  bag limits in, 510
  botulism outbreaks in, 422
  British Columbia, 29
  California, 31
  effect of latitude on breeding along,
    203, 204–5
  harvest and band recoveries
    along, 113
  Idaho, 29–30
  migration corridors along, 94
  Montana, 30
  nest house occupancy rate in, 490
  nest houses along, 270–71
  Nevada, 31
  nonmigratory wood ducks in, 79
  Oregon, 30–31
  spring migration along, 91, 93
  Washington, 29
  wetland types along, 56
  winter distribution, 34–35
  Wyoming, 31
Parasitic infestations, 419–20, 424–35
  ectoparasites, 427–29
  external, 427–29
  filarial worms, 427
  helminths, 429–34
  hematozoas, 424–27
  sarcosporidiosis, 427
Payne, Fred J., 18, 19
Pearson, Gary, 422
Pedley, Fred, 31
Pennsylvania, 20
  autumn migration in, 84
  spring migration in, 92
Phillips, John C., xiii
Photoperiod, 201–2
Plasmodium, 424, 426–27
Plumages, 329–33
  age by wing, determining, 345–46
  body, 338–40
  downy to juvenile, 335–36

feather characteristics of plumage
    tracts, 330–33
  head, 336–38
  juvenile to alternate, 336–43, 361
  tail, 341
  wing coverts, 342–43
  wing feather development, 341–42
  see also Molts
Poisoning. *See* Metallic poisoning
Population, 107–8, 437
  breeding, 16–32
  early twentieth century, 107–8
  effect of reproductive rates, 437–41
  habitats of secondary quality, 119–21
  harvest and band recovery, 113–18,
    446–56
  measurement of production, 441–45
  natural mortality versus hunting
    mortality, 456–58
  period of decline in, 109–10
  recruitment versus survival, 458–59
  responses to decline in, 110–12
  species comparison, 456
  survival rates, 446–56
Population management, 495, 508–16
  determining annual status, 508
  effect of hunting mortality, 508–9
  effect of hunting regulations, 509–13
  establishing new breeding colonies,
    515–16
  future of, 516–17
  propagation, 513–15
Postbreeding, 355
  autumn nest house inspection, 369
  flock formation, 355–59
  local development, 367–68
  molting, 359–62
  nocturnal roosts, 368–69
  northward movements, 363–67
  survival, 367–68
Predators, 286–98, 314, 315
  bobcats, 294
  hawks, 295
  minks, 293–94
  opossums, 294
  potential, 298–99
  principal, 299
  raccoons, 287–91
  snakes, 295–98
  squirrels, 292–93
  starlings, 295
  woodpeckers, 294–95
Preening, 187
  mutual, 132–33
Propagation, 513–15
  attitude and turning of eggs, 514
  brooding, 514
  food requirements, 514–15
  humidity during incubation, 514
  incubation temperature, 514
  water requirements, 515

Quebec, 19
  spring migration in, 92
Quiver Creek complex, Mason County,
    Illinois, nest houses in, 267–69

Raccoons, 275, 276, 277, 299
  intrusion versus wood duck
    flushing, 290
  as nest predators, 287–91
  population trends, 290–91
  raiding nest houses, 471
Rauber, Ernest L., 295

Recovery rates. *See* Band recoveries
Reed, Austin, 19
Reproduction. *See* Breeding; Mating
Rhode Island, 20
Rhonosporidiosis, 424
Riverine habitats, 498–99
  management of, 496
Rodger, N. E., 92
Roosts and roosting, 368–69, 371
  abandonment, 376
  autumn, 156
  behavior, 383–85
  flight characteristics, 378–83
  flock sizes, 382–83
  probable functions of, 372–73
  reasons for, 384–85
  seasonal pattern of roost formation,
    376–78
  sites, 1, 373–76
  see also Migration
Ruckel, James M., 20
Running habits, 2

Salmonellosis, 423
Sanderson, Glen C., 27, 289
Sarcosporidiosis, 427
Saskatchewan, 26
Serduik, Leonard, 28
Sex:
  determining, 344
  differences in migration, 89–90
  effects on helminth infestation, 433
  ratios, 443–45
  recovery rates by, 447
  survival rates by, 447
Shurtleff, Lawton L., 305, 515
Simmons, Stephen, 31, 97, 99, 101, 102,
    202, 293, 294, 487, 490
Size, 2–4
Smith, Milford, 461
Snakes, 295–98
  bull, 298
  rat, 295–97, 299
Snowy petrel, 2
South Carolina, 21
  autumn migration in, 85
  winter distribution, 33
South Dakota, 26, 27
  winter distribution, 34
Spencer, Howard E., Jr., 19
Sporre, Tom, 24
Squirrels, 275–76, 277
  as nest predators, 292–93
Squirrels, flying, 275
Staab, John, 227
Starlings, 276–77, 278–79, 281–83, 299
  nest house site preference, 284–86
  as nest predators, 295
  nesting chronology, 283–84
Steller's elder duck, 5
Strange, Tommy, 21
Streams, 41–52
  overflow bottomland, 52–53
  riverine habitat qualities, 51–52
  width, 50–51
Stutzenbaker, Charles, 27
Summer ducks. *See* Wood ducks
Survival rates, 446–56
  by age classes, 446–47
  brood, 315–18
  effect of special seasons on, 452–56
  geographic variation in, 451–52
  postbreeding, 367–78
  by sex classes, 447
Swans, 5

Swimming habits, 2

Tail, length of, 3
Taylor, Basil, 272
Taylor, John P., 29
Tennessee, 24
  stream habitats in, 42–44, 45, 47–48
  winter distribution, 33
Texas, 26, 27
  wetlands in, 54, 57
  winter distribution, 33, 34
Thornburg, Dennis, 24, 209
Timber management, 505–6
Townsend, John, 107
Trautman, Milton B., 272
Trematodes (flukes), 431, 432
Turtles, snapping, 298

Union Slough (northcentral Iowa), food
  base in, 498
Utah, winter distribution, 34–35

Van Norman, Bernard, 132, 513,
  514, 515
Van Norman, Peter, 513
Vanguards, 8–11
Vermont, 20
  spring migration in, 92
Viral infections, 420
Virginia, 20–21
  winter distribution, 32
Vocalizations, 136–53

duckling, 140–41, 152–53, 154
during nest exodus, 235–38
female, 137–38, 147–52
male, 139–40, 143–47

Washington, 29
  autumn migration in, 87
  winter distribution, 34
Weights:
  flightless period, 214
  incubation, 212–13
  migration and winter, 214
  posthatching period, 213–14
  prelaying and laying, 209–12
  seasonal changes in, 209–14
Wellenkotter, George, 478
Wells, Richard K., 25
Welp, Glen L., 208, 478, 498
Wenner, Karl C., 229
West Virginia, 20
Western Indies, 22
Wetlands, 37–41
  bottomland hardwoods, 63–67
  breeding habitats, 1
  coastal, 38
  drainage and channelization, 61–63
  emergent, 39–40
  forested, 40–41
  management of, 496
  palustrine, 38–39, 59
  and productivity, 76–77
  types of, 54–59

Whistling ducks, 5
Will, G. C., 29
Wilson, Alexander, xiii, 9, 240
Wing bees, 437, 438
Wing parameters, 3
Wintering:
  habitat needs for, 75–76
  physiology of, 201–15
Wisconsin, 23
  autumn migration in, 86
  migration corridors in, 93
  spring migration in, 92
  winter distribution, 33
Wood ducks, 1
  Australian, 5
  behavior, 1–2
  classification of, 5–6
  common names of, 5
  evolutionary development, 519–20
  history, 7–13
  and Mandarin duck similarities, 6
  physical aspects of, 2–4
  unique attributes of, 1–2
Woodpeckers:
  as nest predators, 294–95
  pileated, 167
Woolington, Dennis, 31
Wyoming, 28, 31

Zimmerman, John L., 241